Scott Foresman
Reading
Grade 5

Teacher's
Resource Book

Scott Foresman

Editorial Offices: Glenview, Illinois • Parsippany, New Jersey • New York, New York
Sales Offices: Parsippany, New Jersey • Duluth, Georgia • Glenview, Illinois
Coppell, Texas • Ontario, California

Credits

Illustrations

Teresa Anderko: pp. 178, 569, 586; **Patti Corcoran:** pp. 21, 63, 85, 109, 129, 158, 178 left, 253, 256, 264, 288, 292, 293 right, 301, 360, 362, 428 right, 448, 456 right, 515, 545, 583, 606, 608, 610 left, 652, 654, 655, 674; **Nelle Davis:** pp. 151, 202 left, 470, 630; **Waldo Dunn:** pp. 16, 18, 40, 45, 60, 75, 131, 155, 227 left, 228 right, 249 left, 274, 348, 387, 414, 493, 549, 606, 657, 661; **Morissa Geller:** pp. 214, 281, 293, 456 left, 475 left, 508; **Vickie Learner:** p. 248; **Laurie O'Keefe:** pp. 126, 180, 362, 608; **Mapping Specialists:** pp. 249, 269, 475; **Joel Snyder:** pp. 1, 26, 114, 136 right, 170, 192, 238, 271, 315, 323, 324, 330, 384, 406, 453 right, 475 right, 497, 500, 519, 588, 632; **TSI Graphics:** pp. 70, 92, 107, 136, 140, 381, 399, 409, 428 right, 544, 560, 586, 635; **N. Jo Tufts:** pp. 62, 190, 191, 199, 214, 264, 304, 355, 399, 409, 443, 456, 591, 596, 662; **Jessica Wolk-Stanley:** pp. 4, 38, 67, 70, 89, 104, 183, 195, 217, 230, 296, 318, 340, 365, 428 left, 618; **Lisa Zucker:** pp. 23 right, 249 right, 340 left.

ISBN 0-328-02234-9
ISBN 0-328-04061-4

4 5 6 7 8 9 10 - V004 - 10 09 08 07 06 05 04 03
  5 6 7 8 9 10 - V004 - 10 09 08 07 06 05 04

Table of Contents

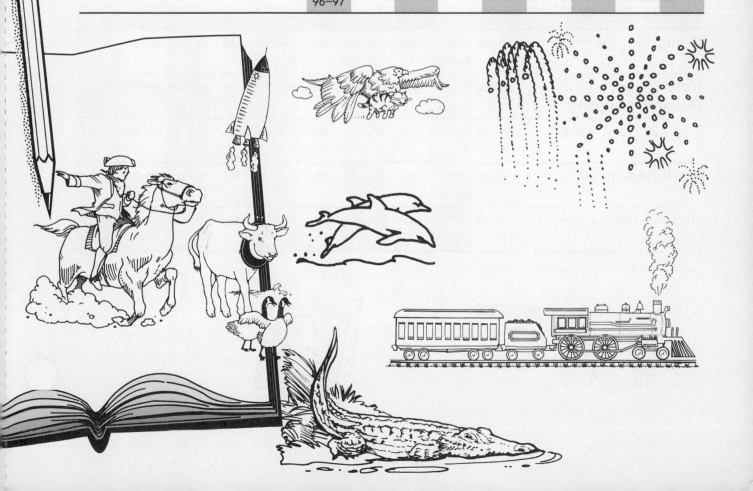

Unit 1

Relating to Others	Family Times	Comprehension	Vocabulary	Selection Test	Writing Across Texts	Grammar	Phonics/ Word Study	Spelling	Research and Study Skills	Writing Process
From the Diary of Leigh Botts	1–2	3, 5, 8–9	4	6–7	10	11–15	16	17–20	21–22	
Faith and Eddie	23–24	25, 27 30–31	26	28–29	32	33–37	38	39–42	43–44	
Looking for a Home	45–46	47, 49, 52–53	48	50–51	54	55–59	60	61–64	65–66	
Meeting Mr. Henry	67–68	69, 71, 74–75	70	72–73	76	77–81	82	83–86	87–88	
Eloise Greenfield	89–90	91, 93, 96–97	92	94–95	98	99–103	104	105–108	109–110	111–113

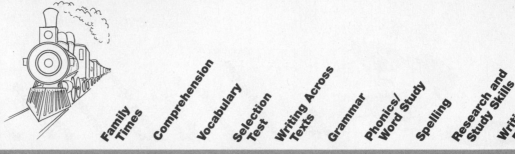

Unit 4

Time and Time Again	Family Times	Comprehension	Vocabulary	Selection Test	Writing Across Texts	Grammar	Phonics/ Word Study	Spelling	Research and Study Skills	Writing Process
The Yangs' First Thanksgiving	340–341	342, 344, 347–348	343	345–346	349	350–354	355	356–359	360–361	
The Jr. Iditarod Race	362–363	364, 366, 369–370	365	367–368	371	372–376	377	378–381	382–383	
The Night Alone	384–385	386, 388, 391–392	387	389–390	393	394–398	399	400–403	404–405	
The Heart of a Runner	406–407	408, 410, 413–414	409	411–412	415	416–420	421	422–425	426–427	
The Memory Box	428–429	430, 432, 435–436	431	433–434	437	438–442	443	444–447	448–449	450–452

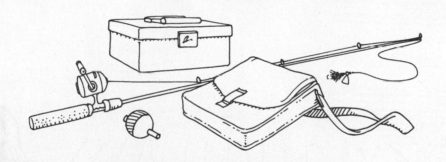

Unit 5

Traveling On	Family Times	Comprehension	Vocabulary	Selection Test	Writing Across Texts	Grammar	Phonics/ Word Study	Spelling	Research and Study Skills	Writing Process
I Want to Vote!	453–454	455, 457, 460–461	456	458–459	462	463–467	468	469–472	473–474	
The Long Path to Freedom	475–476	477, 479, 482–483	478	480–481	484	485–489	490	491–494	495–496	
from Chester Cricket's Pigeon Ride	497–498	499, 501, 504–505	500	502–503	506	507–511	512	513–516	517–518	
Passage to Freedom: The Sugihara Story	519–520	521, 523, 526–527	522	524–525	528	529–533	534	535–538	539–540	
Paul Revere's Ride	541–542	543, 545, 548–549	544	546–547	550	551–555	556	557–560	561–562	563–565

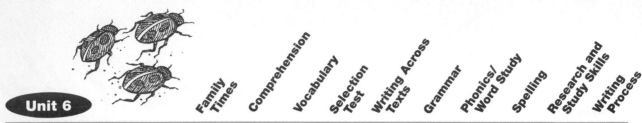

Unit 6

Think of It!	Family Times	Comprehension	Vocabulary	Selection Test	Writing Across Texts	Grammar	Phonics/ Word Study	Spelling	Research and Study Skills	Writing Process
The Baker's Neighbor	566–567	568, 570, 573–574	569	571–572	575	576–580	581	582–585	586–587	
Andy's Secret Ingredient	588–589	590, 592, 595–596	591	593–594	597	598–602	603	604–607	608–609	
In the Days of King Adobe	610–611	612, 614, 617–618	613	615–616	619	620–624	625	626–629	630–631	
Just Telling the Truth	632–633	634, 636, 639–640	635	637–638	641	642–646	647	648–651	652–653	
Is It Real?	654–655	656, 658, 661–662	657	659–660	663	664–668	669	670–673	674–675	676–678

Family Times

Name_____

Summary

Leigh Botts Invents an "Alarming" New Lunchbox!

Leigh Botts is growing more and more annoyed because someone in school keeps stealing food from his lunchbag. He rigs a lunchbox with a hidden alarm. It will ring loudly if the thief ever strikes again. Leigh's invention is a big hit in school! Leigh records what happens in his diary, which his favorite author, Mr. Henshaw, suggested that he keep. Write on, Leigh!

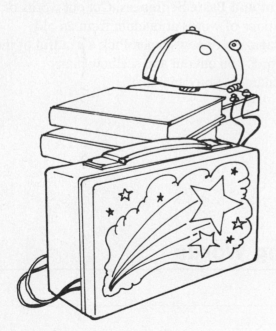

Activity

Read All About It! Summarize a key scene from Leigh's diary as a radio drama. Assign parts and read your drama as if you were doing a radio play together. You may even add sound effects.

Reading Skills

Sequence

Sequence is the order in which things happen. For example: First, Leigh buys a special lunchbox. Then he reads library books on electricity. Next he rigs his lunchbox with a battery and doorbell. Finally, he tests his invention.

Words such as *then* and *after* are often clues to a sequence. In the above example, did you notice four words that help you understand the order of events? (They are *first, then, next,* and *finally*.)

Activity

Make Cartoon Puzzles. Cut out the panels of a newspaper comic strip. Mix up their order. Then challenge someone to arrange the comic strip panels in their correct sequence.

Family Times

Tested Vocabulary

Words to Know

Knowing the meanings of these words is important to reading "From the Diary of Leigh Botts." Practice using these words to learn their meanings.

cafeteria a self-service food retail area in a school or business

demonstration a hands-on show or display

diary a book used to record private thoughts and feelings

racket a loud noise

switch a device that controls the flow of an electric current

triggered caused to begin

Grammar

Sentences

A **sentence** is a group of words that makes a statement, a question, a command, a request, or an exclamation. You can tell if a group is a sentence by checking whether it expresses a complete thought.

Not a Sentence: This great invention.
Sentence: This great invention will save people a lot of time.

Not a Sentence: Wondering where he went.
Sentence: I have been wondering where he went.

Activity
Cut and Paste Sentences. Cut out words or groups of words at random from an old magazine or newspaper. Pick a handful of the words you cut out and see how many sentences you can make.

Tested Spelling Words

Sequence

- **Sequence** is the order in which things happen. Keeping track of the sequence of events will help you better understand what you read.

- Words such as *then* and *after* are often clues to a sequence. Words such as *meanwhile* and *during* show that several events can happen at once.

- By arranging events in sequence, you can see how one thing leads to another.

Directions: Reread the excerpt from *Homer Price*. On the lines below, write the steps from the box in the order that Mr. Murphy follows them to build a musical mousetrap.

Steps

Make a bargain with the town mayor.
Finally, let the mice go.
Drive up and down the streets.
First, build an organ out of reeds.
Fasten the mousetrap to the car.
Then, compose a tune the mice like.
Let the mice run into the trap.
Next, drive the car to a town.
Then, start the musical mousetrap.
Drive the mice to the city limits.

How to Remove Mice with a Musical Mousetrap

1. _____

2. _____

3. _____

4. _____

5. _____

6. _____

7. _____

8. _____

9. _____

10. _____

Notes for Home: Your child read a story and identified the order in which events occurred.
Home Activity: Choose a task that your child performs, such as making the bed, and work together to create a list of steps that are required to complete the task.

Vocabulary

Directions: Choose the word from the box that best matches each clue. Write the word on the line.

_____ 1. This might keep you from sleeping.

_____ 2. You might go here if you're hungry.

_____ 3. You may not want anyone to read this.

_____ 4. You flip this to turn on a light.

_____ 5. You might do this at a science fair.

Check the Words You Know
__ cafeteria
__ demonstration
__ diary
__ racket
__ switch
__ triggered

Directions: Write the word from the box that belongs in each group.

6. sparked, began, _____

7. restaurant, diner, _____

8. explosion, noise, _____

9. journal, log, _____

10. show, display, _____

Directions: Choose the word from the box that best replaces the underlined words. Write the word on the line.

_____ 11. There will be a science fair tomorrow in the place where people eat lunch.

_____ 12. I will give a hands-on show of my new invention.

_____ 13. When you flip the device that controls the flow of an electric current, this turns a series of flashing lights.

_____ 14. Once these flashing lights have been caused to begin, the machine's sound system will give off a series of bell whistles and dog barks.

_____ 15. If this loud noise can't wake my brother Michael each morning, I don't know what will!

Write a News Article

Imagine you are a news reporter. On a separate sheet of paper, write an article about a demonstration you have seen. It could be a cooking show, a science fair, a karate class, and so on. Use as many vocabulary words as you can.

Notes for Home: Your child identified vocabulary words in "From the Diary of Leigh Botts." *Home Activity:* Give your child clues to words he or she knows. For example: *Heavy feet on the stairs make this.* Have your child guess the word you are describing. *(racket)*

© Scott Foresman 5

Sequence

- **Sequence** is the order in which things happen.
- Words such as *then* and *after* are often clues to a sequence. Words such as *meanwhile* and *during* show that two or more things happen at the same time.

Directions: Reread what happens in "From the Diary of Leigh Botts" when Leigh builds a burglar alarm for his lunchbox. Then answer the questions below. Think about the sequence in which things happen in the story.

I tore home with all the things I bought. First I made a sign for my door that said

KEEP OUT

MOM

THAT MEANS YOU

Then I went to work fastening one wire from the battery to the switch and from the other side of the switch to the doorbell. Then I fastened a second wire from the battery to the doorbell. It took me a while to get it right. Then I taped the battery in one corner of the lunchbox and the doorbell in another. I stood the switch up at the back of the box and taped that in place, too.

Text excerpt from DEAR MR. HENSHAW by Beverly Cleary. Text copyright ©1983 by Beverly Cleary. By permission of Morrow Junior Books, a division of William Morrow & Company, Inc.

1. What clue words help you understand the order in which Leigh does things?

_____

2. What does Leigh do first?

_____

_____

3. What does Leigh do last?

_____

_____

4. What does Leigh do right after fastening both wires to the doorbell?

_____

_____

5. What might happen if Leigh were to leave out or skip a step in building his lunchbox alarm? On a separate sheet of paper, explain your answer.

Notes for Home: Your child read a story and used story details to identify the order in which things happened. ***Home Activity:*** Invite your child to name all the important things he or she did today, in the order that they occurred.

Selection Test

Directions: Choose the best answer to each item. Mark the letter for the answer you have chosen.

Part 1: Vocabulary

Find the answer choice that means about the same as the underlined word in each sentence.

1. We met in the <u>cafeteria</u>.
   A. place to buy and eat meals
   B. storage area
   C. small theater or stage area
   D. entrance hall

2. The <u>demonstration</u> was very helpful.
   F. act of criticizing or judging something
   G. act of repairing something
   H. act of showing or explaining something
   J. act of designing something

3. For her invention, she needed a <u>switch</u>.
   A. the engine that makes a machine go
   B. a source of power
   C. a thin, metal wire
   D. a device to turn power on and off

4. Someone <u>triggered</u> the alarm.
   F. stopped
   G. repaired
   H. set off
   J. disabled

5. He opened the <u>diary</u>.
   A. a book of poetry or verse
   B. a book for writing down each day's thoughts or happenings
   C. a book of instructions for using something
   D. a book in which pictures or clippings are pasted

6. They were making a <u>racket</u>.
   F. loud noise
   G. strange sight
   H. terrible mess
   J. cage or trap

Part 2: Comprehension

Use what you know about the story to answer each item.

7. What had happened to Leigh at school before this story begins?
   A. Kids made fun of his lunchbox.
   B. Someone took his notebook.
   C. He got into trouble with the teacher.
   D. Someone took his lunch.

8. Leigh went to the hardware store to buy the things he needed to make a—
   F. new lunchbox.
   G. burglar alarm.
   H. doorbell.
   J. flashlight.

9. To make his invention, what did Leigh do first?
   A. He bought wire and a bell.
   B. He made a cardboard shelf inside his lunchbox.
   C. He went to the library for books about batteries.
   D. He connected a battery to a switch.

10. Leigh was smiling when he got to school on Monday because he—
   F. always smiled at school.
   G. was eager to show Mr. Fridley his invention.
   H. had a new lunchbox.
   J. was thinking about catching the lunch thief.

GO ON

11. Why was Leigh expecting to hear his alarm go off during class on Monday morning?
    A. Someone usually stole his food before lunchtime.
    B. He had set the alarm to go off before lunch.
    C. He had agreed to show his teacher how the alarm worked.
    D. His mom had packed his lunch carefully.

12. Which of these statements from the story is a generalization?
    F. "The kids were surprised, but nobody made fun of me."
    G. "My little slices of salami rolled around cream cheese were gone, but I expected that."
    H. "Boys my age always get watched when they go into stores."
    J. "I tore home with all the things I bought."

13. At lunchtime, Leigh began to realize he had a problem just after he—
    A. set his lunchbox on the table.
    B. showed his invention to the principal.
    C. set off the alarm.
    D. opened the lunchbox lid.

14. What was the most important result of Leigh's invention?
    F. No one stole his lunch.
    G. Leigh felt like some sort of hero.
    H. It made a lot of noise.
    J. Mr. Fridley was grinning.

15. The author of this selection probably wanted to—
    A. give information about electrical circuits.
    B. teach a lesson about being a thief.
    C. explain how to make a lunchbox alarm.
    D. tell a story about a boy and how he solves his problem.

STOP

Sequence

- **Sequence** is the order in which things happen.
- Words such as *then* and *after* are often clues to a sequence. Words such as *meanwhile* and *during* show that two or more things happen at the same time.

Directions: Read the following story.

Dear Diary,

I had a great time today washing cars! It was to raise money for my class. First I put on some old clothes that Mom said I could get wet and dirty. Then I reported to the parking lot where the car wash was being held. I filled my buckets with soap and warm water. As each car drove up, I washed it with soapy water and a large sponge. Next I hosed off the soapy water. Then I applied a wax with a soft towel. Afterward I shined the car with another towel. Pretty soon, it looked like new! It was really fun! At the end of the day, I gave Ms. Miller all the money I collected.

Directions: Read the steps in the box below. Write them in the chart in the order that they occurred in the story.

> He shined the car with a towel.
> He handed over all the money he collected.
> He put on old clothes.
> He applied wax with a soft towel.
> He washed the car with soapy water.

1.

2.

3.

4.

5.

Notes for Home: Your child read a story and used story details to identify the order in which things happened. ***Home Activity:*** Invite your child to tell what happened in an episode of a favorite television show. Make sure he or she relates the events of the show in their proper order.

Making Judgments

Directions: Read the story. Then read each question about the story. Choose the best answer to each question. Mark the letter for the answer you have chosen.

Wanted: More Vacation

So much work and too little play is not good for anybody, especially school students. That's what we have—too much work and too little play. Getting more vacation is a way to correct that problem.

I think that we students should be given much more vacation time than we get right now. Currently in our school, we're off only one week in winter, one week in spring, two months in summer, and all national holidays. It's not enough. We work hard in school, and we need time to relax. We need more time than we get now. Actually, we need a lot more time.

Students should get more vacation time because I feel we go to school too much during the year. I've only checked with my best friend Matt, but I think the whole school would agree with me on this. They all understand the importance of time away from books and homework. They would agree that more time for ballgames and television would be a good idea.

Adults who work in business get vacation, so why shouldn't kids? Yes, school is important, but so is vacation. It's something that all kids deserve. Now is the time to see that we get what we deserve.

1. The writer's opinion is that students should—
   A. vacation all year.
   B. keep the same vacation days.
   C. get more school time.
   D. have more vacation time.

2. In the third paragraph, the arguments—
   F. are wrong because the facts are wrong.
   G. contain no supporting facts.
   H. will convince everyone who reads it.
   J. are supported clearly with facts.

3. What does the author use to support his argument in the third paragraph?
   A. many details
   B. statistics
   C. his and one other person's opinion
   D. true stories

4. In the fourth paragraph, the writer gives the impression that—
   F. students have no vacation.
   G. adults never work.
   H. vacations are costly.
   J. students don't want vacations.

5. In general, the writer supports his opinion—
   A. very well.
   B. poorly.
   C. convincingly.
   D. fairly.

Notes for Home: Your child read a story and made judgments about the author's ideas. *Home Activity:* Read a letter to the editor in a newspaper or magazine with your child. Encourage your child to evaluate the writer's opinion and supporting arguments.

Writing Across Texts

Directions: Complete the table with information from the selections "From the Diary of Leigh Botts" and "The Rampanion."

Leigh	Alison
Problem: Someone has been stealing Leigh's lunch.	**Problem:** 3.
How Leigh tries to solve it: 1.	**How Alison tries to solve it:** 4.
Degree of success: 2.	**Degree of success:** 5.

Write an Essay

What problems do Leigh Botts and Alison DeSmyter try to solve in these selections? Do they succeed? What do you think they learn in the process? Write a brief essay in which you compare and contrast Alison's and Leigh's approaches to problem-solving. Use the information from the table above and write your essay on a separate sheet of paper.

Notes for Home: Your child used information from different sources to write an essay. *Home Activity:* As you read stories and articles with your child, talk about how the ideas or characters connect to other reading he or she has done.

Grammar: Sentences

Directions: Read each group of words. Write **S** if it is a sentence. Write **NS** if it is not a sentence.

_____ 1. Anthony has had his dog, Buddy, for six years.

_____ 2. Came home from school one day.

_____ 3. The dog was gone.

_____ 4. His treasured friend and playmate.

_____ 5. He looked for his dog immediately.

_____ 6. First he checked all of Buddy's favorite places.

_____ 7. Every yard and hiding place in the neighborhood.

_____ 8. Called his friends and asked for their help.

_____ 9. Someone came to the door.

_____ 10. A neighbor had found Buddy.

Directions: Add a word or group of words to complete each sentence. Write the complete sentence on the line. Remember to start each sentence with a capital letter.

11. Eva's pet parrot, Scratch, _____.

_____

12. _____ was very excited and upset.

_____

13. The bird _____.

_____

14. The neighbors _____.

_____

_____

15. _____ flew down to sit on Eva's shoulder.

_____

_____

Notes for Home: Your child identified and wrote complete sentences. ***Home Activity:*** Look at a favorite magazine. Together read the titles of some articles and the captions under the pictures. Have your child identify which groups of words are sentences and which are not.

Practice

Grammar: Sentences

A **sentence** is a group of words that makes a statement, a question, a command, a request, or an exclamation. You can tell if a group of words is a sentence by checking whether it expresses a complete thought. Each sentence begins with a capital letter and ends with a punctuation mark.

Sentence: The computer has many uses.
Not a sentence: Has many uses.

Directions: Read each group of words. Write **S** if it is a sentence. Write **NS** if it is not a sentence.

_____ 1. The computer is a remarkable invention.

_____ 2. The first computer.

_____ 3. Do you have a computer?

_____ 4. Some computers are very expensive.

_____ 5. A computer in my house.

Directions: Choose the group of words in ( ) that will complete each sentence. Write the complete sentence on the line.

6. _____ was also an important invention.(The electric light/Provided light for the house)

_____

7. The lightbulb _____. (helped people in many ways/a bright light)

_____

8. Electric light _____. (in the house/helped people work at night)

_____

9. _____ replaced candles. (To light the house/The lightbulb)

_____

10. Mr. Edison _____. (was a great inventor/the inventor)

_____

Notes for Home: Your child identified groups of words that make a sentence. *Home Activity:* Ask your child to talk about inventions that save time or have made life easier. Encourage your child to use complete sentences to tell about the invention.

© Scott Foresman 5

Grammar: Sentences

Directions: Match each word group on the left with a word group on the right to make a sentence that makes the most sense. Draw a line between the word groups that go together.

1. A good invention begins   provides power for a flashlight.

2. Many inventions   can help you see at night.

3. A computer   often sells her inventions.

4. A lamp   are helpful to people.

5. A battery   with a good idea.

6. The inventor   can help you search the Internet.

Directions: Add a word or group of words to complete each sentence. Write the complete sentence on the line.

7. The first computers _____.

8. A computer _____.

9. _____ send e-mail messages.

10. _____ contains keys used for typing.

11. Most computers need _____.

12. _____ play video games.

13. While I was playing a video game _____.

14. _____ that we have computers at school.

15. If computers had not been invented, _____.

Write a Description

Think about the different inventions you use every day. Choose one invention that you feel is especially important. On a separate sheet of paper, describe the invention and tell why it is important. Use complete sentences in your writing.

Notes for Home: Your child formed sentences by matching groups of words and by supplying missing words. **Home Activity:** Open a book. Read aloud only part of a sentence. See if your child can make a complete sentence that includes the words you read.

Grammar: Sentences

RETEACHING

Mark the word group that best describes the picture. The best description tells a complete thought. It is a complete sentence.

1. The children   _____

2. Are planting a tree.   _____

3. The children are planting a tree.   _____

A **sentence** is a group of words that makes a statement, a question, a command, a request, or an exclamation.

Directions: Write **sentence** after each complete sentence. If the word group is not a sentence, write **not a sentence.**

1. Some trees produce fruit.   _____

2. Apples and pears.   _____

3. Very beautiful to see.   _____

4. The fruit gets ripe on the tree.   _____

5. Fruit growers protect the trees.   _____

6. Plenty of sun and water.   _____

7. We pick apples every fall.   _____

Directions: Circle each word group that is a sentence. Draw a line through each word group that is not a sentence.

8. Trees do not eat food.

9. Food from water, air, and light.

10. Roots get food from the ground.

11. Carries the food all the way to the trunk.

12. Deep below the surface of the ground.

13. Water travels up the trunk to the branches.

14. The green leaves.

15. Some leaves stay green all year.

Notes for Home: Your child identified groups of words that make sentences. *Home Activity:* Talk with your child about plants in your home or outside. Encourage your child to use complete sentences in your conversation.

© Scott Foresman   5

Grammar: Sentences

Directions: Draw a line through each word group that is not a sentence. On the lines, write the word groups that are sentences.

1.–9. Fish are found in fresh water and salt water. All over the world. Many different shapes, sizes, and colors. Most fish are covered with scales. These flat, bony structures protect the body of the fish. Also have fins. Fins are on the body of the fish. Move through the water. All fish can breathe under water.

_____

_____

_____

_____

_____

_____

Directions: Write complete sentences. Add words to each group below.

10. A major source of food.

_____

11. With hooks, lines, and poles.

_____

12. Large nets.

_____

13. Caught in the nets.

_____

14. Schools of fish.

_____

Write an Underwater Adventure Journal Entry

On a separate sheet of paper, write a journal entry about an underwater adventure. Be sure each sentence is complete.

 Notes for Home: Your child identified and wrote complete sentences. *Home Activity:* Write a list of words or phrases that relate to marine life. Let your child say complete sentences that each word suggests to him or her.

Phonics: *r*-Controlled Vowels

Directions: Read the words in the box. Say the words to yourself. Listen for the vowel sounds that the letters **ar, er, or, ur,** and **ir** represent. Some sound like **her.** Some sound like **car.** Some sound like **for.** Sort the words by sound. Write each word in the correct column.

garbage	morning	worry
portable	story	parked
first	surf	alarm

her

1. _____

2. _____

3. _____

car

4. _____

5. _____

6. _____

for

7. _____

8. _____

9. _____

Directions: Read the following "to-do" list. Each item has a word with a missing letter. Write the word on the line with the correct letter filled in.

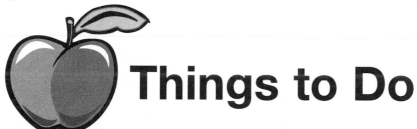

Things to Do

_____ **10.** Go to the h_rdware store.

_____ **11.** Buy stuff for my b_rglar alarm.

_____ **12.** W_rk on my new invention.

_____ **13.** Take a sh_rt nap.

_____ **14.** Clean any d_rt from my invention.

_____ **15.** T_rn it on and test it.

Notes for Home: Your child sorted and wrote words with *r*-controlled vowels, like *first, car,* and *short.* **Home Activity:** Read some ads in newspapers and magazines to help your child recognize other words with these vowel sounds and spellings.

Spelling: Vowel Sounds with *r*

Pretest Directions: Fold back the page along the dotted line. On the blanks, write the spelling words as they are dictated. When you have finished the test, unfold the page and check your words.

1._____

2._____

3._____

4._____

5._____

6._____

7._____

8._____

9._____

10._____

11._____

12._____

13._____

14._____

15._____

16._____

17._____

18._____

19._____

20._____

1. His brother joined the **army**.
2. We must eat or **starve**.
3. The cut left a small **scar**.
4. The **garbage** can is full.
5. I do not want to **argue**.
6. Their **apartment** was large.
7. Jess plays songs on her **guitar**.
8. King River is in **Arkansas**.
9. Thea eats well-done **hamburger**.
10. **Return** your library books.
11. He did it on **purpose**.
12. The **surface** of the water is clear.
13. A cat will **curl** up to sleep.
14. What is in the woman's **purse**?
15. The **furniture** was very old.
16. A lion tamer has **courage**.
17. I write in my **journal** every day.
18. Show **courtesy** toward others.
19. I **nourish** myself with good food.
20. Lylia is going on a long **journey**.

Notes for Home: Your child took a pretest on words that have vowel sounds with the letter *r*. *Home Activity:* Help your child learn misspelled words before the final test. Your child should look at the word, say it, spell it aloud, and then spell it with eyes shut.

Think and Practice

Spelling: Vowel Sounds with *r*

Word List

army	apartment	purpose	courage
starve	guitar	surface	journal
scar	Arkansas	curl	courtesy
garbage	hamburger	purse	nourish
argue	return	furniture	journey

Directions: Choose the words from the box that have the vowel sound with **r** that you hear in **hurt.** Write each word in the correct column.

Vowel-r sound spelled ur

1. _____

2. _____

3. _____

4. _____

5. _____

6. _____

7. _____

Vowel-r sound spelled our

8. _____

9. _____

10. _____

11. _____

12. _____

Directions: Decide where to add the letters **ar** in each letter group to spell a word from the box. Write the word on the line.

13. guit _____

14. sc _____

15. my _____

16. kansas _____

17. stve _____

18. gue _____

19. gbage _____

20. aptment _____

Notes for Home: Your child spelled words where the letter *r* changes the vowel sound. *Home Activity:* Read a magazine article with your child. Together, see how many words you can find that have the same vowel sounds and spellings as *scar, curl,* and *journal.*

© Scott Foresman 5

Name _____

Spelling: Vowel Sounds with *r*

Directions: Proofread this journal entry. Find five spelling mistakes. Use the proofreading marks to correct each mistake.

June 13—I have been writing in my

jurnal since March. Since then I

have been working on our apertment.

First, I rearranged the furniture.

Then I painted. I had to aregue with

Dad about painting the serface of

the kitchen counter. It took courage

to paint it purple! Now, though, I've

decided to retern to the original

color, and both Dad and I are happy.

Maybe I'll even put the furniture back.

≡	Make a capital.
/	Make a small letter.
∧	Add something.
ꝰ	Take out something.
⊙	Add a period.
¶	Begin a new paragraph.

Spelling Tip
return

How can you remember that **return** has a **u** in the middle? Think of this hint: Make a "U" **turn** to re**turn**. Check the journal entry to see if this word is spelled correctly.

Word List
army	purpose
starve	surface
scar	curl
garbage	purse
argue	furniture
apartment	courage
guitar	journal
Arkansas	courtesy
hamburger	nourish
return	journey

Write a Journal Entry

Imagine you have a problem you need to solve. On a separate sheet of paper, write a journal entry that describes your problem plus an idea for solving it. Try to use at least five of your spelling words.

Notes for Home: Your child spelled words where the letter *r* changes the vowel sound, such as in *scar, curl,* and *journal*. **Home Activity:** Write each spelling word with the letters scrambled. See if your child can unscramble each word and spell it correctly.

Name _____

REVIEW

Spelling: Vowel Sounds with *r*

Word List				
army	argue	hamburger	curl	journal
starve	apartment	return	purse	courtesy
scar	guitar	purpose	furniture	nourish
garbage	Arkansas	surface	courage	journey

Directions: Choose the word from the box that best completes each statement. Write the word on the line to the left. Look at the pairs of words that are being compared. See the example below.

Crawl is to *baby* as *walk* is to *adult*.

_____ 1. *City* is to *Little Rock* as *state* is to _____.

_____ 2. *Blow* is to *horn* as *strum* is to _____.

_____ 3. *Sailors* are to *navy* as *soldiers* are to _____.

_____ 4. *Groceries* are to *food* as *trash* is to _____.

_____ 5. *Car* is to *bicycle* as *palace* is to _____.

_____ 6. *Friends* are to *agree* as *enemies* are to _____.

_____ 7. *Metal* is to *scratch* as *skin* is to _____.

_____ 8. *Air* is to *suffocate* as *food* is to _____.

_____ 9. *Pig* is to *sausage* as *cow* is to _____.

_____ 10. *Laundry* is to *basket* as *money* is to _____.

_____ 11. *Coat* is to *clothing* as *table* is to _____.

_____ 12. *Coward* is to *fear* as *hero* is to _____.

_____ 13. *Begin* is to *finish* as *leave* is to _____.

_____ 14. *Intentionally* is to *intention* as *purposely* is to _____.

Directions: Choose the word from the box that has the same or nearly the same meaning as the word or words below. Write the word on the line.

15. politeness _____   18. daily record _____

16. feed _____   19. roll up _____

17. trip _____   20. face or side _____

Notes for Home: Your child spelled words in which the letter *r* changes the vowel sound. *Home Activity:* Look around the room with your child. Together, see how many items you can find whose names have the same vowel sounds and spellings as in *scar*, *curl*, and *journal*.

Locate/Collect Information

You can **locate and collect information** from many different sources, such as books, magazines, newspapers, audiotapes, videotapes, CD-ROMs, and web sites on the Internet. You can also talk to people who are experts on the subject you are researching. When doing research, you need to pick the reference source that best suits the purposes of your project.

Directions: Use the following resource list from a library media center to answer the questions on the next page.

Library Media Center: Inventors/Inventions

Audiotapes

- *The Genius of Thomas Edison,* narrated by Maria Walsh. Recorded Sound Productions, 1997. (30 min.)
- *Great Inventions of the Nineteenth Century,* narrated by Joseph Smith. Educational Tapes, Inc., 1993. (30 min.)
- *Meet the Inventors: Interviews with 26 Real Kid Inventors,* narrated by Charles Osborne. Facts on Tape, 1998. (45 min.)

Videotapes

- *The Art and Science of Computers.* Documentary. Edu-films, Inc., 1994. (45 min.)
- *Computers, Computers, Computers!* Documentary. Millennium Technology Films, 1998. (60 min.)
- *The Life and Times of Thomas Alva Edison.* Documentary. Insight Productions, 1994. (58 min.)

Pictures and Print

- Smithson, Stephen. *Picture This: A Photo Collection of Great Inventions.* Chicago: AllStar Books, 1992.
- See librarian at desk for access to our photo archives of local inventors and inventions.

Internet Web Sites

- information on Alexander Graham Bell
  http://www.agbell.com/Inventions.html
- information on child inventors (under 18 years old)
  http://www.KidsInvent.org

Resource People: Inventors

- Becker, Cassandra. 43 Maple Drive, Hollistown. 555-5487.
- Danbury, Robert. 2356 Norfolk Street, Oakdale. 555-6110.
- Foxworthy, Nancy. 99200 Central Avenue, Hollistown. 555-0002.

Resource People: Experts on Specific Topics

- Lederer, David. 9 Kenosha Drive, Oakdale. 555-7360. Expert on Alexander Graham Bell.
- Prager, Benjamin, Ph.D. 1334 Rainbow Hill, Hollistown. 555-0741. Expert on Thomas Edison (published author).

Name _____

1. If you were doing a report on Thomas Edison, which audiotape and videotape resources would be best to use?

_____

_____

2. What would be the best web site to use to find out about Alexander Graham Bell?

_____

3. Why are photographs useful for researching inventions? _____

_____

4. Name an inventor you could interview. _____

_____

5. Which resource person would be the best source for information about Thomas Edison?

_____

6. If you were doing a report on inventions made by children, which two resources would be best to use?

_____

_____

7. For a report on computers, which two resources would be best to use? _____

_____

8. For information about a recent invention, why might it be more useful to interview a person familiar with the invention than to use only books?

_____

_____

9. How are the two groups of resource people different from each other?

_____

_____

10. Why might you want to use different sources when researching?

_____

_____

© Scott Foresman 5

Notes for Home: Your child chose resources to fit specific research purposes. *Home Activity:* With your child, list the resources he or she might use to do a report on the history of your family.

Name_____

Summary

Eddie Proves a Dog Can Be a Girl's Best Friend!

Faith has just moved from California to Mexico. Learning Spanish isn't easy for her. She often feels lost and out of place in her new surroundings. But there's one friend she can always depend on—her faithful dog Eddie. Eddie isn't just caring. He's also smart. He knows many languages, including English and Spanish, and he even narrates the story. Good dog!

Reading Skills

Character

Characters are the people or animals in stories. In "Faith and Eddie," the two main characters are the girl and her dog. Other characters include Faith's mother and a Spanish language tutor.

You can learn about characters from the things they think, say, and do, and from the way other characters treat them. Eddie treats Faith with such loyalty and compassion that readers feel great affection for the dog.

My brother Tony is a great athlete and a good sport. He never cheats. He scores many goals for his team.

Activity

Be a Friend. Have your child describe some of Faith's problems. Then imagine you were her friend or neighbor. Talk about tips you would give her for coping in her new home. Describe experiences you've had where you've had to learn something new.

Activity

Make a Family Album. Draw pictures of various members of your family. Beneath each picture, write a short description of each person. Give examples of things that person often does, says, or thinks that reveal something about that person.

Family Times

Words to Know

Knowing the meaning of these words is important to reading "Faith and Eddie." Practice using these words to learn their meanings.

alternating happening by turns

anticipation state of looking forward to something

cemetery a graveyard or burial place

darted moved suddenly and quickly

faith belief without proof

retraced went back over one's steps

scent a distinct smell or odor

withdrew took out or took away

Grammar

Subjects and Predicates

A sentence must have both a subject and a predicate. The **subject** is the word or words about which something is said. The **predicate** is the word or words that tell something about the subject. In the sentences below, the complete subject is underlined once. The complete predicate is underlined twice.

The lonely girl played with Eddie.

Eddie was a faithful companion.

Activity
Make Friendly Statements. Pair up family members and make up sentences that tell about friends or other relatives. Take turns having one person give a subject and the other person complete the sentence by giving a predicate. Keep a list of the sentences you created and mark the subjects and predicates.

Tested Spelling Words

© Scott Foresman 5

24 Faith and Eddie

Name _____

Character

- **Characters** are the people or animals in a story.

- You can learn about characters from the things they think, say, and do.

- You can also learn about characters from the way that other characters in the story treat them and what they say about them.

Directions: Reread "No Friends." Then complete the table. Use the examples of things that characters do and say to tell what it shows about Lucy.

	Example	What It Shows About Lucy
What Lucy Does	She leans on the window and blinks back tears.	1.
	She makes a face when asked to go to the store.	2.
What Lucy Says	"I wish we still lived in Guelph."	3.
	"There's nothing to do here."	4.
What Mrs. Bell Says	"We only got here yesterday."	5.

Notes for Home: Your child analyzed characters—the people or animals in a story. *Home Activity:* Play "Guess Who?" Think of someone you both know. Describe the way that person acts and talks, and challenge your child to guess who it is. Switch roles and play again.

Vocabulary

Directions: Choose the word from the box that best replaces the underlined word or words. Write the word on the line.

_____ 1. Billy and Carla had <u>belief without proof</u> that they would find the golden key and win the game.

_____ 2. They <u>went back over</u> their steps to make sure they had followed all the clues.

_____ 3. The last clue took them to a large stone statue in a <u>graveyard</u>.

_____ 4. Carla reached up to the statue's hand and <u>took out</u> the golden key.

_____ 5. Then Carla and Billy <u>moved quickly</u> to home base to claim their prize!

Check the Words You Know
__ alternating
__ anticipation
__ cemetery
__ darted
— faith
__ retraced
— scent
__ withdrew

Directions: Choose the word from the box that best matches each clue. Write the letters of the word on the blanks. The boxed letters spell something that you should have in yourself.

6. belief without proof

7. happening by turns

8. state of looking forward to something

9. a smell or odor

10. took out

6. ☐ __ __ __ __

7. __ __ __ __ __ ☐ __ __ __

8. __ __ __ __ ☐ __ __ __

9. __ __ __ ☐ __

10. __ __ __ ☐ __ __ __ __

What you should have in yourself: __ __ __ __ __

Write a Report

Imagine you are a dog trainer. On a separate sheet of paper, write a report about a dog that you have been training. What methods do you use to get the dog to behave? How does the dog respond to your directions? Use as many vocabulary words as you can.

© Scott Foresman 5

Notes for Home: Your child identified and used vocabulary words from "Faith and Eddie." *Home Activity:* Using a dictionary, find simple definitions for a variety of words and read them aloud to your child. See if your child can guess each word. Keep a list of "Words I Know."

Name _____

Character

- **Characters** are the people or animals in a story.
- You can learn about characters from what they think, say, and do.
- You can also learn about characters from the way other characters in the story treat them or talk about them.

Directions: Reread what happens in "Faith and Eddie" when Faith comes home from school one day. Then answer the questions below. Think about what you learn about the characters of Faith and Eddie.

> That afternoon, Faith rushed through the door, her eyes all red and swollen. She sank to her knees and hugged me and sobbed.
>
> "Oh, Eddie," she said. "I hate it. I just hate it."
>
> I pressed my muzzle up into her face and licked her cheek. It tasted salty.
>
> "The kids at school hate me," she said. "The teacher hates me. I can't understand a thing anyone says and they can't understand me, either." She sniffled. "Diego keeps making fishy faces at me."
>
> At that she buried her face into my neck and cried.
>
> From FAITH AND THE ELECTRIC DOGS by Patrick Jennings. Copyright © 1996 by Patrick Jennings. Reprinted by permission of Scholastic Inc.

1. What does Faith do when she gets home?

_____

2. Why does Faith think her teacher and classmates hate her?

_____

_____

3. How does Eddie react to Faith's behavior?

_____

4. What does Faith's behavior tell you about the type of person she is?

_____

5. What do you learn about Eddie's character from the rest of the story? On a separate sheet of paper, write your answer and give examples to support it.

Notes for Home: Your child read a story and used story details to analyze its characters. *Home Activity:* Name a family member or friend. Talk with your child about the type of person that individual is, based on the way he or she thinks, talks, and behaves.

Selection Test

Directions: Choose the best answer to each item. Mark the letter for the answer you have chosen.

Part 1: Vocabulary

Find the answer choice that means about the same as the underlined word in each sentence.

1. She had <u>faith</u> in the plan.
   - A. a position of leadership
   - B. lack of confidence
   - C. belief without proof
   - D. strong interest

2. We <u>retraced</u> the journey.
   - F. plotted on a map or chart
   - G. went back over
   - H. took a new route
   - J. told about again

3. They walked through a <u>cemetery</u>.
   - A. graveyard
   - B. meadow
   - C. narrow street
   - D. city square

4. A mouse <u>darted</u> under the leaves.
   - F. made tunnels
   - G. sat silently without stirring
   - H. crept quietly
   - J. moved suddenly and quickly

5. His shirt had <u>alternating</u> stripes.
   - A. forming a smooth wavy pattern
   - B. arranged in an unexpected or disorganized manner
   - C. blending together to create a single color
   - D. first one and then the other, by turns

6. The children looked up in <u>anticipation</u>.
   - F. state of being amazed
   - G. state of looking forward to something
   - H. state of being disappointed
   - J. state of avoiding something

7. This plant is known for its <u>scent</u>.
   - A. color
   - B. size
   - C. smell
   - D. shape

8. She opened the drawer and <u>withdrew</u> a small package.
   - F. took out
   - G. discovered
   - H. hid
   - J. returned

Part 2: Comprehension

Use what you know about the story to answer each item.

9. Which character is the narrator of the story?
   - A. Faith
   - B. Hector
   - C. Bernice
   - D. Eddie

10. Who is Coco?
    - F. a household servant
    - G. Faith's tutor
    - H. a family friend
    - J. Faith's mother

11. In what way is Eddie an unusual dog?
    - A. He comforts Faith when she is sad.
    - B. He plays Fetch and Tug-of-war.
    - C. He understands everything people say.
    - D. He talks to Faith just as a person would.

12. From the story you can tell that Faith
    - F. loves to go on adventures.
    - G. is very unhappy about living in Mexico.
    - H. is trying hard to succeed in school.
    - J. makes friends with almost everyone she meets.

GO ON →

13. Why does Eddie rush through the city without paying much attention to his old street-dog chums?

    A.   He is worried about Faith.

    B.   He no longer needs dog friends now that he has a home.

    C.   He does not like other dogs.

    D.   He no longer recognizes the dogs he once knew.

14. Which detail tells you what time of year the story takes place?

    F.   Eddie learned to play Fetch.

    G.   Faith and Eddie went outside after dinner.

    H.   Graves were still decorated from the Days of the Dead.

    J.   A crescent moon glimmered behind the wispy fog.

15. Eddie wants to help Faith. Which of his actions has an effect that is different from what he intended?

    A.   howling by the front gate until Milagros opens it

    B.   hurrying to the school and looking through the window

    C.   following his nose across a stream and a pasture

    D.   howling in the graveyard so that Faith will hear him

STOP

Character

- **Characters** are the people or animals in a story.

- You can learn about characters from the things they think, say, and do.

- You can also learn about characters from the way other characters in the story treat them or talk about them.

Directions: Read the story below.

Tory wasn't very happy when her brother Joey received a new puppy. She thought it was a nicer gift than any their parents had ever given her.

"How come he gets a great pet and I don't?" Tory whined.

That night, Tory took the dog's bone and hid it. The next morning, Mother asked, "Tory? Have you seen the puppy's bone?"

Tory just shook her head and walked away.

That afternoon, Father said, "Tory, we know you're a loving girl. And here's a present just for you." He handed her a new pet gerbil in a cage.

"Thanks!" Tory cried. Later she brought back the dog's bone, apologized to her family, and happily played with her gerbil until bedtime.

Directions: Complete the table. Think about what you learned about Tory's character from the things she thinks, says, and does, and from what others say about her.

Tory's Character	Examples
Tory is jealous.	**1.** What Tory thinks:
	2. What Tory says:
	3. What Tory does:
Tory is loving.	**4.** What Father says:
	5. What Tory does:

 Notes for Home: Your child read a story and used story details to analyze a character. *Home Activity:* Invite your child to describe his or her own personality, based on things he or she often does, says, or thinks. Then describe your own personality to your child.

© Scott Foresman 5

Setting

Directions: Read the story. Then read each question about the story. Choose the best answer to each question. Mark the letter for the answer you have chosen.

A Sore Vacation

Alex looked around at the neat, clean room. He sat carefully on the edge of the chair. He was careful not to let his back touch anything. This was a nice chair. He would like to settle back into it. If he just felt better, he would like this chair. On the other hand, if he felt better, he wouldn't be here.

Everything about the room would be comfortable if only he felt better. He looked up as the doctor came into the room.

"Take off your shirt and sit down," ordered the doctor.

Alex could barely sit. His whole body was sore from the sunburn. He was glad to have his shirt off, although it hurt getting it off. He was sure the room got brighter in the glow of his red skin.

Alex tried to relax as the doctor applied lotion to his body. He jerked every time he felt the doctor's fingers. At the same time, he was glad to feel the cool, soft lotion. He wished he could just get into a bathtub full of it.

This vacation had seemed like such a good idea. The travel poster showed clear water and beautiful sand. That was just what Alex wanted.

As soon as he arrived, he was out on the beach in front of the hotel. After a long plane ride, he had been glad to relax in the sun.

"Nobody told me Mexico could be this hot," Alex said. "I should have come here for winter vacation instead of in July."

"Take my advice. Next time, try not to fall asleep in the sun," the doctor said.

1. The setting of the story is—
   A. Alex's hotel lobby.
   B. beside a pool.
   C. a doctor's office.
   D. at the beach.

2. A clue to the setting is—
   F. the hot sun.
   G. Alex's vacation.
   H. the neat, clean room.
   J. the travel poster.

3. The time of year is—
   A. summer.
   B. autumn.
   C. winter.
   D. spring.

4. The best word to describe Mexico in July is—
   F. cool.
   G. warm.
   H. chilly.
   J. hot.

5. Alex wouldn't have burned if he had—
   A. gone to the beach.
   B. sat in the shade.
   C. gone out at noontime.
   D. worn sunglasses.

Notes for Home: Your child read a story and used details to answer questions about the setting. *Home Activity:* Have your child look around the room and describe the setting in detail.

Writing Across Texts

Directions: The left column shows a list of difficult times that Faith experiences in the story "Faith and Eddie." On the right side, write how Eddie seems to make things better in these difficult situations.

What Faith Does	How Eddie Makes It Better
Faith moves to a new country where she does not speak the language.	She gets a new dog.
Faith has a bad day in school.	1.
Faith draws her family tree during her Spanish lesson.	2.
Faith leaves school by herself and gets lost.	3.
Faith thinks Eddie is a strange dog and runs away from him.	4.
Faith realizes the dog is Eddie.	5.

Write a Paragraph

The stories you read in this unit are linked by a common theme: how relating to others teaches us about the important things in life. On a separate sheet of paper, write a paragraph explaining why having a good friend like Eddie is important. How would Faith's life be different if she hadn't had a friend like Eddie? Compare Faith's situation to Leigh Botts's. How might Leigh Botts's situation have been different if he had a friend to confide in?

Notes for Home: Your child used information from a reading selection to write about how a friend makes a girl's life better. ***Home Activity:*** Discuss with your child any stories you both know that reflect this unit's theme.

Grammar: Sentences and End Punctuation

Directions: Add the correct end mark to each sentence.

1. Making new friends can be hard _____

2. Sometimes friends will disagree with one another _____

3. Have you ever disagreed with a friend _____

4. You should talk about your feelings with a good friend _____

5. Sandra is my best friend _____

6. A good friend respects your decisions _____

7. Even best friends can have different feelings and values _____

8. Each person is, after all, different _____

9. Don't you agree _____

10. Of course, you must be a good friend too _____

Directions: Use the end mark in ( ) to write five sentences about friendship. Remember to begin each sentence with a capital letter.

11. (period)

_____

_____

12. (period)

_____

_____

13. (exclamation point)

_____

_____

14. (period)

_____

_____

15. (question mark)

_____

_____

 Notes for Home: Your child identified the correct end mark for sentences and wrote complete sentences. *Home Activity:* With your child, look through a paragraph in one of his or her favorite books. Ask your child to explain why the particular end mark is used.

Practice

Grammar: Subjects and Predicates

A **sentence** must have both a **subject** and a **predicate.**

The **complete subject** is made up of all the words that tell whom or what the sentence is about. A complete subject may have several words or only one word.

The **complete predicate** is made up of all the words in the predicate. The complete predicate tells what the subject is or does. It may have several words or only one word.

Mexico is south of the U.S. border.

Nearly all Mexicans speak Spanish.

complete subject   complete predicate

The most important word in the complete subject is called the **simple subject.** It usually is a noun or a pronoun. Some simple subjects, such as *Mexico City*, have more than one word.

The most important word in the complete predicate is the verb. It is called the **simple predicate.** Some simple predicates can have more than one word, such as *have attracted.*

The beautiful sights of Mexico City have attracted many tourists.

Directions: For each sentence, underline the complete subject once. Underline the complete predicate twice.

1. Many English words come from Spanish.

2. These words include *canyon, patio,* and *rodeo.*

3. Many Americans and Canadians use these words often.

4. Most native people in Mexico speak two languages.

5. They know Spanish and their native language.

Directions: For each sentence, underline the simple subject once and the simple predicate twice.

6. The official language of Mexico is Spanish.

7. People speak Spanish all over Latin America.

8. Many Americans use Spanish too.

9. Some American states have Spanish names.

10. Such places include California and Florida.

Notes for Home: Your child identified subjects and predicates in sentences. ***Home Activity:*** Have your child write sentences that tell what happened in school this week. Ask him or her to identify the complete and simple subjects and predicates in each sentence.

Grammar: Subjects and Predicates

Directions: Tell what is underlined in each sentence. Write **S** for subject or **P** for predicate.

_____ 1. <u>Most people in Mexico</u> live in cities and towns.

_____ 2. The largest Mexican city <u>is Mexico City</u>.

_____ 3. Many Mexican towns <u>are hundreds of years old</u>.

_____ 4. <u>A typical town or village</u> includes a plaza.

_____ 5. <u>The older buildings</u> are made of stone or adobe.

Directions: Use the nouns and verbs shown below to write complete sentences. Then, underline the complete subject of each sentence once and the complete predicate twice. Finally, circle the simple subject and the simple predicate in each sentence.

6. farmers   live

_____

7. roads   curve

_____

8. rain   falls

_____

9. people   wear

_____

10. merchants   sell

_____

Write a Description

Think of a place you would like to visit. On a separate sheet of paper, write a description of the place. Tell what things you see and what people do there. In each sentence, underline the complete subject once and the complete predicate twice.

Notes for Home: Your child identified and wrote subjects and predicates in sentences. **Home Activity:** Pick out easy sentences from a newspaper. Ask your child to identify the subject and predicate in each one.

Extra Practice

Grammar: Subjects and Predicates

Imagine that you are a detective. Read the sentence to find out who did what.

The young boy walked quietly into the room.

Who walked quietly into the room? Write all the words in the subject of the sentence.

_____

What did the young boy do? Write all the words in the predicate of the sentence.

_____

The **complete subject** is made up of all the words that tell whom or what the sentence is about. The subject names someone or something. It may have one word or many words. The **complete predicate** is made up of all the words in the predicate of a sentence. The predicate tells what the subject is or does. It may have one word or many words.

Directions: Circle the complete subject in each sentence. Write each complete subject under the heading **Who Did It?**

Who Did It?

1. Sherlock Holmes solved many mysteries. _____

2. People asked him to solve many mysteries. _____

3. The police came to him for help. _____

4. Doctor Watson helped Holmes with his work. _____

5. Holmes had many adventures. _____

Directions: Circle the complete predicate in each sentence. Write each complete predicate under the heading **What Did They Do?**

What Did They Do?

6. The crime victims counted on Holmes. _____

7. Two men looked for clues. _____

8. The criminals hid from Holmes. _____

9. Criminals could not trick him. _____

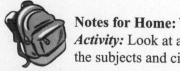

Notes for Home: Your child identified and wrote subjects and predicates of sentences. *Home Activity:* Look at a magazine or newspaper article with your child. Have him or her underline the subjects and circle the predicates of five sentences.

Grammar: Subjects and Predicates

Directions: Decide if the underlined part is the complete subject or the complete predicate. Circle the correct answer.

1. <u>Pearl oysters</u> are different from clams.   subject   predicate

2. People <u>may find a small pearl in an ordinary oyster</u>.   subject   predicate

3. <u>These pearls</u> are not worth very much.   subject   predicate

4. Pearl oysters <u>grow in warm southern seas</u>.   subject   predicate

5. Pearl divers <u>look for pearls under water</u>.   subject   predicate

6. <u>People all over the world</u> prize pearls.   subject   predicate

Directions: Underline the complete subject and circle the complete predicate.

7. Oysters are useful creatures.

8. Fishermen grow oysters as a sea crop.

9. Most oysters live in the quiet, shallow waters of bays.

10. Hole-boring snails are enemies of oysters.

11. Oysters live in many parts of the world.

12. Many oysters make pearls.

13. The shells are very beautiful.

14. Some people eat raw oysters.

15. Oysters breathe with gills.

16. Some oysters live more than twenty years.

Write a Newscast

On a separate sheet of paper, write a newscast about the things that live in the sea. Be sure to use a complete subject and complete predicate in each sentence.

Notes for Home: Your child identified complete subjects and predicates of sentences. *Home Activity:* Write two subjects. (For example: *Black pearls* and *Oyster shells*) Have your child make up predicates to go with the subjects and write the complete sentences.

Phonics: Vowel Digraphs

Directions: Read each sentence. Say the underlined word to yourself. Listen for the vowel sounds that the letters **ee, ai,** and **oa** represent. Circle the word in ( ) that has the same **vowel sound** as the underlined word.

1. My dog howled, then sat to <u>wait</u> for me.   (fate/fat)

2. I rubbed my <u>cheek</u> against his warm fur.   (weak/wreck)

3. I took him for a quick walk in the wet <u>rain</u>.   (plane/plan)

4. We walked along the sand near the <u>coast</u>.   (most/moss)

5. We watched the fishing <u>boats</u> come in.   (robe/rob)

Directions: Read the postcard below. Say the underlined words to yourself. Match each underlined word with a word below that rhymes. Write the word on the correct line.

Dear Mom,

Camp is great! Guess what? My friend, Liza, has a seeing eye dog named Kip. Kip is very calm. He never jumps on my <u>knees</u>. He is patient while Liza <u>feeds</u> him. It's <u>plain</u> that he loves her. He goes <u>straight</u> to her when she calls. They swim together each day. When he shakes himself off, we all get <u>soaked</u>! I wish I had a dog like Kip.

Love,

Terri

6. ate   _____

7. cane   _____

8. ease   _____

9. joked   _____

10. reads   _____

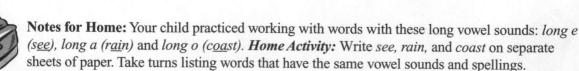

Notes for Home: Your child practiced working with words with these long vowel sounds: *long e (see), long a (rain)* and *long o (coast).* **Home Activity:** Write *see, rain,* and *coast* on separate sheets of paper. Take turns listing words that have the same vowel sounds and spellings.

Name _____

Spelling: Short e and Long e

Pretest Directions: Fold back the page along the dotted line. On the blanks, write the spelling words as they are dictated. When you have finished the test, unfold the page and check your words.

1._____
2._____
3._____
4._____
5._____
6._____
7._____
8._____
9._____
10._____
11._____
12._____
13._____
14._____
15._____
16._____
17._____
18._____
19._____
20._____

1. The weight is **heavy**.
2. Let's plan **ahead**.
3. **Measure** the triangle.
4. The bus **already** came.
5. She is not **jealous** of others.
6. Flowers grow in the **meadow**.
7. The soldier held his **weapon**.
8. Did you hear what I **said**?
9. Let's play **again**.
10. Lean **against** the wall.
11. Juan earned a college **degree**.
12. Say **cheese** for the camera!
13. Sara is determined to **succeed**.
14. The principal gave a **speech**.
15. The **breeze** cooled us off.
16. Our **goalie** blocked the point.
17. Please, cut a **piece** of pizza.
18. I **believe** it is true.
19. The **thief** took it.
20. Hail to the **chief**.

Notes for Home: Your child took a pretest on words that have the short *e* and long *e* sounds. *Home Activity:* Help your child learn misspelled words before the final test. Your child can underline the word parts that caused the problems and concentrate on those parts.

© Scott Foresman 5

Spelling: Short *e* and Long *e* 39

Spelling: Short e and Long e

Word List			
heavy	meadow	degree	goalie
ahead	weapon	cheese	piece
measure	said	succeed	believe
already	again	speech	thief
jealous	against	breeze	chief

Directions: Choose the words from the box that have the **long e** sound. Write each word in the correct column.

Long e spelled ee

1. _____
2. _____
3. _____
4. _____
5. _____

Long e spelled ie

6. _____
7. _____
8. _____
9. _____
10. _____

Directions: Write the **short e** word from the box that begins and ends with the same letters as each word below.

11. mellow _____
12. accident _____
13. hay _____
14. action _____
15. spend _____

16. jobs _____
17. accepted _____
18. anybody _____
19. woman _____
20. mile _____

HEAVY CHEESE

Notes for Home: Your child spelled words with the short *e* sound spelled *ea* and *ai (ahead, said)* and the long *e* sound spelled *ee* and *ie (cheese, piece)*. **Home Activity:** Read a brief newspaper article with your child. Together, find all the short *e* and long *e* words you can.

Spelling: Short *e* and Long *e*

Directions: Proofread this description. Find five spelling mistakes.
Use the proofreading marks to correct each mistake.

> What are my best friends like? For one thing, they are never jelous of me. They like to see me succead and to get ahead. My best friends would never turn agianst me. Also, they trust me and always beleeve what I have said to them. They don't mind if I give them a peace of advice. If you have friends like that, you are already a very lucky person indeed!

≡	Make a capital.
/	Make a small letter.
∧	Add something.
⌐	Take out something.
⊙	Add a period.
¶	Begin a new paragraph.

Spelling Tip
piece
Don't confuse the word
piece with **peace**.
Remember this hint: I
want a **piece** of **pie**.

Word List
heavy
ahead
measure
already
jealous
meadow
weapon
said
again
against
degree
cheese
succeed
speech
breeze
goalie
piece
believe
thief
chief

Write a Description

Think about a good friend. How does your friend act?
What does your friend look like? What sorts of
activities do you both enjoy? What makes this person
a good friend? On a separate sheet of paper, write a
description of your friend. Try to use at least five of
your spelling words.

© Scott Foresman 5

Notes for Home: Your child spelled words with the short *e* sound spelled *ea* and *ai* (ah*ea*d, s*ai*d) and the long *e* sound spelled *ee* and *ie* (ch*ee*se, p*ie*ce). ***Home Activity:*** Together, look at pictures in a magazine to find items whose names have the short *e* and long *e* sounds.

Name _____

Spelling: Short e and Long e

REVIEW

Word List			
heavy	meadow	degree	goalie
ahead	weapon	cheese	piece
measure	said	succeed	believe
already	again	speech	thief
jealous	against	breeze	chief

Directions: Choose the word from the box that best matches each clue. Write the letters of the word on the blanks. The boxed letters tell what you'll find in each word.

1. think to be true

2. a position on the soccer team

3. one more time

4. a college title

5. a gun, for example

6. a cool wind

7. spoke

8. a formal talk

9. a grassy field

10. use a ruler

11. opposed to

12. a dairy product

1. __ __ ☐ __ __ __ __

2. __ __ ☐ __ __ __

3. __ __ __ ☐ __

4. __ __ __ ☐ __ __

5. __ __ __ ☐ __ __

6. __ __ __ ☐ __ __

7. __ __ ☐ __ __

8. __ __ __ ☐

9. __ __ __ ☐ __

10. __ __ __ ☐ __ __

11. __ __ __ ☐ __ __

12. __ __ __ ☐ __ __

What you'll find in each word: _____

Directions: Choose the word from the box that is most opposite in meaning for each word or words below. Write the word on the line.

13. light _____

14. fail _____

15. whole _____

16. behind _____

17. not yet _____

18. donor _____

19. follower _____

20. content _____

Notes for Home: Your child spelled words with the short *e* sound spelled *ea* and *ai (ahead, said)* and the long *e* sound spelled *ee* and *ie (cheese, piece)*. **Home Activity:** Have your child spell each spelling word and tell whether it has a short *e* or long *e* sound.

42 Spelling: Short *e* and Long *e*

Dictionary/Glossary

A **dictionary** is a book of words and their meanings. A **glossary** is a short
dictionary in the back of some books. It includes definitions of words used in
the book. Words are listed in alphabetical order. **Guide words** appear at the top
of each page and show the first and last entry word for that page.

Directions: Use this section of a dictionary page to answer the questions that follow.

245 fretful/frogman

fret•ful (fret′fəl), cross, discontented, or worried; ready
to fret: *My baby brother is fretful because his ear hurts.*
adjective.

fric•tion (frik′shən), **1** a rubbing of one thing against
another, such as skates on ice, hand against hand, or a
brush on shoes: *Matches are lighted by friction.* **2** the
resistance to motion of surfaces that touch: *Oil reduces
friction.* **3** a conflict of differing ideas and opinions;
disagreement; clash: *Constant friction between the two
nations brought them dangerously close to war. noun.*

Fri•day (frī′dā), the sixth day of the week; the day after
Thursday. *noun.*

a hat	i it	oi oil	ch child	a in *about*
ā age	ī ice	ou out	ng long	e in *taken*
ä far	o hot	u cup	sh she	ə = i in *pencil*
e let	ō open	u̇ put	th thin	o in *lemon*
ē equal	ô order	ü rule	ŦH then	u in *circus*
ėr term	ȯ author		zh measure	

fried (frīd), **1** cooked in hot fat: *fried eggs.* **2** See **fry.**
I fried the ham. The potatoes had been fried. **1** *adjective,*
2 *verb.*

friend (frend), **1** a person who knows and likes another.
2 a person who favors and supports: *He was a generous
friend of the art museum.* **3** a person who belongs to the
same side or group: *Are you a friend or an enemy? noun.*

From SCOTT FORESMAN BEGINNING DICTIONARY by E.L. Thorndike and Clarence L. Barnhart. Copyright © 1997 by Scott Foresman and Company.

1. Using the guide words, list two other words that might appear on this page.

   _____

2. According to the pronunciation key at the top right side of the page, the vowel sound in *fried*
   sounds like the long *i* sound in what other word?

   _____

3. Which definition of *friend* is used in the following sentence?
   Tyrell has been my best friend for years.

   _____

   _____

4. How many syllables do the words *Friday* and *friend* each have? _____

   _____

5. Write a sentence using the third meaning of *friction*. _____

   _____

6. Which word on the dictionary page can be used as a verb? _____

Name _____

Directions: Use this section of a glossary from a textbook to answer the questions that follow.

---

eyelid/glutton

eye•lid (ī′lid′), the movable cover of skin, upper or lower, by means of which we can shut and open our eyes. *noun.*

fam•i•ly (fam′əlē), **1** a father, mother, and their children: *A new family moved to our block.* **2** all of a person's relatives: *a family reunion. noun, plural* **fam•i•lies.**

fife (fīf), a small, shrill musical instrument like a flute, played by blowing. Fifes are used with drums to make music for marching. *noun.* [*Fife* comes from German *Pfeife,* meaning "pipe."]

gar•lic (gär′lik), the bulb of a plant related to the onion, used in cooking. Its flavor is stronger than that of an onion. *noun.*

ges•ture (jes′chər), **1** a movement of the hands, arms, or any part of the body, used instead of words or with words to help express an idea or feeling: *Speakers often make gestures with their hands to stress something they are saying.* **2** to make gestures; use gestures. 1 *noun,* 2 *verb.* **ges•tures, ges•tured, ges•tur•ing.**

gla•cier (glā′shər), a large mass of ice formed from the snow on high ground and moving very slowly down a mountain or along a valley. *noun.* [*Glacier* comes from the French *glace,* which comes from the Latin *glacies,* meaning "ice."]

---

7. Which definition of *gesture* is used in the following sentence? How can you tell?
   The coach gestured secretly to the player.

   _____

8. Which entry word on the glossary page has the most syllables? How many syllables does the word have?

   _____

9. Which word comes from a German word? What does the German word mean?

   _____

   _____

10. In what ways is a glossary similar to a dictionary? How is a glossary different from a dictionary?

    _____

    _____

    _____

    _____

    _____

Notes for Home: Your child used a dictionary and a glossary to find information about words. *Home Activity:* With your child, select various words from a dictionary or glossary. Discuss all the information you find about that word.

Family Times

Name_____

Summary

Orphan Children Ride Trains to New Homes

Between 1854 and 1930, more than 200,000 children—most of them orphans—were placed in homes by the Children's Aid Society. They boarded trains in large eastern U.S. cities and rode to other parts of the country, where families met them and chose the children they wanted. Three brothers—Lee, Leo, and Gerald—were among the orphan train riders. Lee tried to keep his brothers together once they left the train.

Reading Skills

Generalizing

Generalizing is making a statement about what several people or things have in common. When you read about several things or people, you make a generalization about what they have in common. A clue word such as *many* or *most* may appear in your statement. For example: **Most of the orphan children came from large eastern cities.**

A valid generalization is supported by facts and logic. A faulty generalization is not. The sample generalization above is valid, since the author of the article provided facts to support it.

Activity

Finish the Story. The story about Lee and his brothers is true. Have your child tell you the rest of "Looking for a Home," including what happens to the three brothers after leaving the train. Discuss how you would feel if you were Lee riding on the train.

Activity

Look and Generalize. Look around the rooms of your home. Try to make generalizations about the different items or people you see. Use clue words such as *most, all, few, always, usually,* or *seldom.* For example: **Most of the pictures on my bedroom wall are posters.**

Family Times

Words to Know

Knowing the meaning of these vocabulary words is important to reading "Looking for a Home." Practice using these words to learn their meanings.

awe a feeling of wonder

bitter showing pain or grief

determined set or fixed in one's mind

horrified filled with shock or horror

panicked acted as if it were an emergency without having real cause

select choose

suspicious doubtful

Grammar

Four Kinds of Sentences

There are four kinds of sentences. Each begins with a capital letter and ends with a special end mark.

❖ A **declarative sentence** makes a statement. It ends with a period. **Many children were orphans.**
❖ An **interrogative sentence** asks a question. It ends with a question mark. **How many went on trains?**
❖ An **imperative sentence** makes a command or request. The subject *(you)* is not shown, but it is understood. It ends with a period. **Give me a rough estimate.**
❖ An **exclamatory sentence** shows strong feeling. It ends with an exclamation mark. **That's a lot of riders!**

Activity
Listen and Tell. Listen carefully to a radio or TV show. Make a list of some of the different types of sentences you hear. Tell whether each sentence is declarative, interrogative, imperative, or exclamatory.

Tested Spelling Words

_____ _____ _____ _____

_____ _____ _____ _____

_____ _____ _____ _____

_____ _____ _____ _____

_____ _____ _____ _____

Generalizing

- **Generalizing** is making a statement that tells what several people or things have in common.
- Sometimes a clue word such as *most, all, sometimes, always,* or *never* signals that a generalization is being made.
- A valid generalization is supported by facts and logic. A faulty generalization is not.

Directions: Reread "A Special Family." Then complete the table. Tell whether each statement is a generalization. Explain your reasons for all answers.

Statement	Generalization (Yes or No?)	Reason
Joshua has a few memories of his Korean foster family.	1.	2.
Most Asians in the Levins' school have Asian parents.	3.	4.
Eric Levin is an adopted child.	5.	6.

Directions: Complete the table. Tell whether each generalization is **valid** or **faulty.** Explain your reasons for all answers.

Statement	Generalization (Valid or Faulty?)	Reason
All the Levin children have musical talent.	7.	8.
The Levins do many things together as a family.	9.	10.

Notes for Home: Your child identified generalizations. *Home Activity:* Ask your child to look around a room in your home and make a generalization about it, such as *All the walls are painted white.* Then talk about whether you agree with the generalization.

Name _____

Vocabulary

Directions: Choose a word from the box that best matches each definition. Write the word on the line.

_____ 1. shocked; terrified

_____ 2. acted as if there was an emergency without having real cause

_____ 3. miserable; angry

_____ 4. a feeling of wonder

_____ 5. doubtful

Check the Words You Know
__ awe
__ bitter
__ determined
__ horrified
__ panicked
__ select
__ suspicious

Directions: Choose the word from the box that best completes each statement. Write the word on the line to the left.

_____ 6. The boys looked in _____ at the huge train.

_____ 7. They began to _____ their seats.

_____ 8. Each boy was _____ to find a good seat.

_____ 9. However, no one _____ in the rush to sit down.

_____ 10. None felt angry or _____ about the seats they found.

Directions: Choose the word from the box that best completes each statement. Write the word on the line to the left.

_____ 11. *Respect* is to *respectful* as *suspicion* is to _____.

_____ 12. *Terrify* is to *terrified* as *horrify* is to _____.

_____ 13. *Sleepy* is to *alert* as *happy* is to _____.

_____ 14. *Toss* is to *throw* as *choose* is to _____.

_____ 15. *Hopeful* is to *hope* as *awesome* is to _____.

Write a Description

On a separate sheet of paper, describe a real or imaginary trip by train, boat, or airplane. Include vivid sensory details to tell what you see, hear, smell, touch, or taste. Use as many vocabulary words as you can.

Notes for Home: Your child identified and used vocabulary words from "Looking for a Home." *Home Activity:* Ask your child to describe events that would cause a person to feel *awe, bitter, determined, horrified, panicked,* and *suspicious.*

Generalizing

- **Generalizing** is making a statement that tells what several people or things have in common.

- Sometimes a clue word such as *most, always,* or *never* signals that a generalization is being made.

- A valid generalization is supported by facts and logic. A faulty generalization is not.

Directions: Read this passage from "Looking for a Home" that tells about the placement of orphan train riders. Then answer the questions below. Think about ways that the author makes generalizations in her writing.

> Most placements were successful, and the program grew. During the first 20 years an average of 3,000 children rode the orphan trains each year. Brace continued to raise the needed money through his speeches and his writing. Railroads gave discount fares to the children, and wealthy people sometimes paid for whole trainloads of children.
>
> Unfortunately, many children who needed homes were not allowed to go on the trains. It was always difficult to find homes for older children, and while some teenagers as old as 17 were successfully placed, 14 was usually the oldest a rider could be. It was always easiest to find homes for babies.

From ORPHAN TRAIN RIDER: ONE BOY'S TRUE STORY by Andrea Warren. Copyright ©1996 by Andrea Warren. Reprinted by permission of Houghton Mifflin Company. All rights reserved.

1. What clue words can you find in the passage that signal a generalization?

_____

2. What facts does the author offer to support her generalizations?

_____

_____

3. Explain why the sentence about Charles Loring Brace is or is not a generalization.

_____

_____

4. Explain why this generalization is valid or faulty: *Most orphans as old as 17 were easily placed.*

_____

_____

5. What generalizations can you make about Lee and his two brothers from "Looking for Home"? Explain your thinking on a separate sheet of paper.

Notes for Home: Your child read a nonfiction article and identified generalizations that the author made. *Home Activity:* Talk with your child about members in your family. Encourage him or her to make general statements about ways that some of the members are alike.

Selection Test

Directions: Choose the best answer to each item. Mark the letter for the answer you have chosen.

Part 1: Vocabulary

Find the answer choice that means about the same as the underlined word in each sentence.

1. Eduardo panicked when he saw the house.
   A. felt a great and sudden fear
   B. felt a loss of confidence
   C. felt a sense of relief
   D. felt wild and silly

2. Anna wanted to select one.
   F. send
   G. complete
   H. choose
   J. try

3. Gillian was determined.
   A. sent for punishment
   B. firm; with her mind made up
   C. making the best of it
   D. very respectful

4. The sight horrified us.
   F. amused
   G. filled with anger
   H. made sad
   J. shocked very much

5. The stars filled him with awe.
   A. shame
   B. anger
   C. wonder
   D. joy

6. It was a bitter experience.
   F. causing pain or grief
   G. exhausting
   H. causing delight or joy
   J. surprising

7. The girl's actions made him suspicious.
   A. unsafe
   B. embarrassed or shy
   C. curious
   D. unwilling to trust

Part 2: Comprehension

Use what you know about the selection to answer each item.

8. Where did Lee and his brothers come from?
   F. Texas
   G. New Jersey
   H. Iowa
   J. New York

9. Children on the orphan trains were taken to other parts of the country to—
   A. make money.
   B. find new homes.
   C. go to school.
   D. make new friends.

10. Why did Lee feel a sense of dread when he got back on the train after the first children were chosen?
    F. He was afraid no one would ever choose him.
    G. He was tired of the train food.
    H. He felt sure he would be separated from his brothers.
    J. He wanted to stay in that town.

11. What happened to Lee at the Rodgerses' house?
    A. He got a haircut.
    B. He got separated from Leo.
    C. He got his own bedroom.
    D. He felt welcome in his new home.

12. Which of these events happened last?
    F. Lee spoke rudely to Ben Nailling.
    G. The Rodgerses decided to keep only Leo.
    H. A man and woman took Gerald.
    J. Lee accidentally killed some chicks.

© Scott Foresman 5

GO ON

13. What was the most important difference between Lee's experience at the Naillings' and his other experiences?

 A. The bedroom was sunny.
 B. He was firmly disciplined.
 C. He felt wanted.
 D. There was lots of food.

14. Which statement is a valid generalization based on the facts in this selection?

 F. Children on the orphan trains often fought with each other.
 G. The oldest orphan train riders were always chosen first.
 H. The matrons on the orphan trains treated the children kindly.
 J. Most brothers and sisters traveling together ended up in different homes.

15. The author of this selection most likely thinks that—

 A. orphans enjoy long train rides.
 B. every child needs love and a good home.
 C. the orphan trains were a useful experience for the children.
 D. Lee Nailling was not a nice boy.

STOP

Generalizing

- **Generalizing** is making a statement that tells what several people or things have in common.

- Sometimes a clue word such as *most, always,* or *never* signals that a generalization is being made.

- A valid generalization is supported by facts and logic. A faulty generalization is not.

Directions: Read the following passage.

Railroad trains are an important means of transportation. Every day, thousands of passenger trains carry people to work, home, and other places. Other trains carry products such as coal, grain, and lumber. Trains are the fastest means of transportation except for airplanes. Some passenger trains travel over 200 miles an hour. Trains can also carry heavier loads than any other means of transport except ships. A freight train can haul thousands of tons across a country. Nearly every country has at least one railroad line running through it.

Directions: Complete the table. Tell if the first three statements are generalizations or not. Tell if the last two statements are valid or faulty generalizations. Give reasons for your answers.

Statement	Generalization	Valid or Faulty?	Reason
Railroad trains are an important means of transportation.	1.		2.
One freight train carried grain to Iowa last week.	3.		4.
Some passenger trains travel over 200 miles per hour.	5.		6.
Most freight trains cannot carry more than 1,000 pounds.	Yes	7.	8.
Nearly every country has at least one railroad line.	Yes	9.	10.

Notes for Home: Your child identified generalizations in a nonfiction article. *Home Activity:* Choose a category of food, such as fruits, vegetables, or meats. Encourage your child to make general statements about ways that foods in that category are alike.

Sequence

Directions: Read the passage. Then read each question about the passage. Choose the best answer to each question. Mark the letter for the answer you have chosen.

How to Adopt

Deciding to adopt a child is a big decision for any couple. It is also a big decision for those who are currently caring for the child. There are many parts involved in giving a child a happy home.

The couple wishing to adopt a child first must apply to an adoption agency. The adoption agency will take steps to find out whether it is a good idea for this couple to adopt a child.

After the couple applies, the adoption agency assigns a caseworker to investigate. The caseworker needs to know the couple's background. The caseworker also checks the couple's health and their finances.

If the agency feels that the couple will be good parents and the child will be safe and happy with them, the agency has the child live in the couple's home for 6 to 12 months. This is an important time for deciding whether or not the adoption can become legal.

If the child and the couple still want the adoption, a lawyer then prepares an adoption request. The request is given to a court. If the court approves, the adoption becomes legal and the child and parents become a family.

1. The first step in the process to adopt a child is—
   A. telling the child.
   B. finding a lawyer.
   C. applying to an agency.
   D. writing to the judge.

2. The first thing that an adoption agency does is—
   F. contact the judge.
   G. find the child.
   H. contact a lawyer.
   J. investigate the people who want to adopt a child.

3. Before a child can be adopted, he or she must—
   A. apply to the judge.
   B. get lawyer approval.
   C. live with the people who want to adopt him or her.
   D. investigate the people who want to adopt him or her.

4. After a lawyer prepares an adoption request, it is given to the—
   F. parents.
   G. court.
   H. child.
   J. adoption agency.

5. The final step in making an adoption legal is—
   A. the court's approval.
   B. the child's approval.
   C. the parents' approval.
   D. the lawyer's approval.

Notes for Home: Your child read a nonfiction article and then identified the order in which steps were presented. **Home Activity:** Review with your child the important things that have happened in his or her life so far. Have your child name the events in the order that they occurred.

Writing Across Texts

Directions: Review "Looking for a Home" and "What Were Orphan Trains?"
Trace the experiences Lee Nailling and Claretta Carman Miller had from leaving
their families to coming to live with the families who would eventually adopt
them. Add a brief description of each experience to the table below.

	Lee	**Claretta**
Birth Families:	Father sent him to an orphanage after his mother died. Lee was often punished and didn't have enough to eat.	3.
First families they went to from orphan train:	1.	4.
Families who finally adopted them:	2.	5.

Write a Compare/Contrast Paragraph

Before finding successful placements with new families, many orphans on the
trains had unpleasant experiences. Trace the experiences of Lee Nailling and
Claretta Carman Miller. What did they probably learn about people when they
met the families who finally adopted them? Use the information from the table
above to write a paragraph comparing and contrasting the children's experiences.
Write your paragraph on a separate sheet of paper.

Notes for Home: Your child used information from different texts to write a compare/contrast
paragraph. *Home Activity:* As you read stories and articles with your child, talk about how the
ideas or experiences described connect to other reading they have done.

© Scott Foresman 5

Grammar: Subjects and Predicates ⟶ REVIEW

Directions: For each sentence, underline the complete subject once and the complete predicate twice.

1. Families have changed in unexpected ways!

2. Many different groups make a family today.

3. Often, one adult in the family has to work outside of the home.

4. Many mothers are working today.

5. Very young children sometimes go to day care centers.

6. Sometimes an older relative will help care for younger children.

7. Some families have only one parent in the house.

8. Some children live with one parent and one step-parent.

9. Grandparents are the only adults at home in other families.

10. Some young people live with foster parents.

Directions: Write sentences that include the following simple subjects and predicates. Remember to begin each sentence with a capital letter and end each one with the correct punctuation mark.

11. brothers and sisters   make

_____

_____

12. grandparents   tell

_____

_____

13. Mom   works

_____

_____

14. parents   spend

_____

_____

15. family   is

_____

_____

Notes for Home: Your child identified complete and simple subjects and predicates and wrote sentences with subjects and predicates. *Home Activity:* Give your child several different words. Ask him or her to use each of those words as the simple subject in a sentence.

Grammar: Four Kinds of Sentences

Practice

There are four kinds of sentences. Each begins with a capital letter and has a special end mark.

A **declarative sentence** makes a statement. It ends with a period.

Many children live with foster parents.

An **interrogative sentence** asks a question. It ends with a question mark.

What are foster parents?

An **imperative sentence** gives a command or makes a request. It ends with a period. The subject *(you)* is not shown, but it is understood.

Please tell me what foster parents do.

An **exclamatory sentence** shows strong feeling. It ends with an exclamation mark.

How interesting that is!

Directions: Write whether each sentence is **declarative, interrogative, imperative,** or **exclamatory.**

_____ 1. What jobs does a foster parent do?

_____ 2. Many foster parents open their homes to children.

_____ 3. Can anyone become a foster parent?

_____ 4. Call a state agency for more information.

_____ 5. What a helpful suggestion you made!

_____ 6. I'm glad I could help.

Directions: Read each sentence. Rewrite and correct each incorrect sentence.

7. foster parents are licensed by the state.

_____

8. I have heard that some foster children stay until they are adults?

_____

9. What happens after that!

_____

10. What a good question that is!

_____

Notes for Home: Your child identified sentences that make a statement, ask a question, give a command or make a request, or show strong feeling. *Home Activity:* Ask your child to write sentences about a topic and to identify each type of sentence.

Name _____

Grammar: Four Kinds of Sentences

Directions: Write whether each sentence is **declarative, interrogative, imperative,** or **exclamatory.**

_____ 1. Can foster parents adopt a foster child?

_____ 2. Many foster parents do adopt their foster children.

_____ 3. Fostering and adopting both mean taking care of children.

_____ 4. Tell me more about it later.

_____ 5. I like taking care of babies.

_____ 6. How I would love to bring up a family!

Directions: Rewrite each sentence. Add the correct capitalization and end punctuation.

7. what must a family do to adopt a child

_____

_____

8. read this book about adoption

_____

_____

9. what a huge number of laws there are

_____

_____

10. approval for adoption may take a year or more

_____

_____

Write a Conversation

On a separate sheet of paper, write several sentences that you might hear spoken between two relatives—a brother and sister, a mother and child, or an aunt and uncle. Supply one example of each type of sentence: declarative, interrogative, exclamatory, and imperative.

Notes for Home: Your child identified sentences that make a statement, ask a question, give a command or make a request, or show strong feeling. *Home Activity:* Take turns creating different kinds of sentences.

Grammar: Four Kinds of Sentences

Read the sentences below. Circle the end punctuation in each one.

1. There are two lions in the cage.

2. Do only lions and horses have manes?

3. How fierce that lion looks!

4. Stay back from the wall.

A **declarative sentence** makes a statement. It ends with a period. An **interrogative sentence** asks a question. It ends with a question mark. An **imperative sentence** gives a command or makes a request. It ends with a period. An **exclamatory sentence** expresses strong feeling. It ends with an exclamation mark. All sentences begin with a capital letter.

Directions: Circle the end punctuation in each sentence. Then write **declarative, interrogative, imperative,** or **exclamatory.**

1. Zoos are fun places to visit. _____

2. I have a wonderful idea. _____

3. Meet me at the bus stop. _____

4. Isn't this a perfect day for a trip? _____

5. How smart you are to bring a camera! _____

Directions: Write the correct punctuation mark at the end of each sentence. Circle any letter that should be capitalized. Then write each sentence correctly.

6. please hand me the camera _____

_____

7. how exciting it is to see a baby panda _____

_____

8. in which countries are pandas found _____

_____

9. the pandas are eating bamboo stalks _____

_____

10. please take some pictures of the pandas _____

_____

Notes for Home: Your child identified and wrote four kinds of sentences. *Home Activity:* Point to sentences in a magazine or newspaper and have your child identify whether they are declarative, interrogative, imperative, or exclamatory.

Grammar: Four Kinds of Sentences

Directions: Write the correct punctuation mark at the end of each sentence. Then identify each sentence as **declarative, interrogative, imperative,** or **exclamatory.**

1. How many different kinds of birds are there _____   _____

2. Find out if all birds can fly _____   _____

3. Flying birds have light bodies and strong wings _____   _____

4. Is an ostrich light enough to fly _____   _____

5. Look at this picture of an ostrich _____   _____

6. What a funny-looking bird it is _____   _____

7. An ostrich is often heavier than an adult human _____   _____

Directions: Write each sentence. Use capital letters and end punctuation correctly.

8. a bird's wing feathers are used for flying

_____

9. are birds' tail feathers important for flying

_____

10. read this article for more information about birds

_____

11. how important those tail feathers are for steering and balance

_____

12. feathers also keep birds warm

_____

13. i enjoy collecting feathers that have fallen on the ground

_____

14. how many feathers have you collected

_____

Notes for Home: Your child identified and wrote the correct punctuation for four kinds of sentences. *Home Activity:* Write declarative, interrogative, imperative, and exclamatory sentences and have your child add the correct punctuation at the end.

© Scott Foresman 5

Phonics: Diphthongs

Directions: Read each sentence. Look at the words in ( ). Both words make sense, but only one word has a vowel sound like **cow.** Circle the correct word.

1. The (crew/crowd) was waiting for the train.

2. Someone (shouted/shushed) his name.

3. The steam drifted (about/above) him.

4. In the distance, he saw a (horse/house).

5. When he arrived, the boy (found/thought) he liked his new home.

Directions: Read the clue in ( ). Choose the letters **ou** or **ow** to complete each word. It's tricky! These letters stand for the same sound. Write the correct letters on the blanks.

6. ar _____ _____ nd   (in a circle)

7. br _____ _____ n   (the color of toast)

8. all _____ _____ ed   (let someone do something)

9. gr _____ _____ nd   (the land under our feet)

10. m _____ _____ th   (the place on a face to eat and speak)

11. fr _____ _____ n   (look unhappy)

Directions: Complete each sentence with a word that has the same vowel sound as **crowd** and **mouth.** Write the word on the line to the left.

_____   12. The train traveled _____, not north.

_____   13. It took the children _____ of the city and into the country.

_____   14. After a long journey, the train stopped in a small _____, very different from the big city.

_____   15. The conductor helped the children _____ the steps and onto the platform.

Notes for Home: Your child practiced reading and writing words with letters *ou* and *ow* that represent the same vowel sound, such as *mouth* and *crowd.* **Home Activity:** Together, make a list of words with these spellings and this vowel sound. Make up rhymes that use pairs of these words.

Spelling: Vowel Sounds in *boy* and *out*

Pretest Directions: Fold back the page along the dotted line. On the blanks, write the spelling words as they are dictated. When you have finished the test, unfold the page and check your words.

1. _____
2. _____
3. _____
4. _____
5. _____
6. _____
7. _____
8. _____
9. _____
10. _____
11. _____
12. _____
13. _____
14. _____
15. _____
16. _____
17. _____
18. _____
19. _____
20. _____

1. You have to make a **choice**.
2. Drums can be very **noisy**.
3. Old fruit will **spoil**.
4. On the bottle it said **poison**.
5. Chicago is a big city in **Illinois**.
6. Good friends are always **loyal**.
7. Rain will **destroy** the drawing.
8. Wasps **annoy** me.
9. The **oyster** made a pearl.
10. He went on a long **voyage**.
11. The recipe needs baking **powder**.
12. Bring your **towel** to the pool.
13. I like to shop **downtown**.
14. You must swim or **drown**.
15. The dog will **growl**.
16. They paid the wrong **amount**.
17. This is **our** house.
18. Let's play **outside**.
19. Please sit on the **couch**.
20. Ants **surround** the ice cream.

Notes for Home: Your child took a pretest on words that have the vowel sounds heard in *boy* and *out*. **Home Activity:** Help your child learn misspelled words before the final test. Dictate the word and have your child spell the word aloud for you or write it on paper.

© Scott Foresman 5

Spelling: Vowel Sounds in *boy* and *out*

Think and Practice

Word List

choice	loyal	powder	amount
noisy	destroy	towel	our
spoil	annoy	downtown	outside
poison	oyster	drown	couch
Illinois	voyage	growl	surround

Directions: Choose the words from the box that have the vowel sound in **boy.**
Write each word in the correct column.

Vowel sound spelled oy

1. _____
2. _____
3. _____
4. _____
5. _____

Vowel sound spelled oi

6. _____
7. _____
8. _____
9. _____
10. _____

Directions: Write the word from the box that belongs in each group
of words. Hint: The word will have the vowel sound in **out.**

11. inside, between, _____

12. oink, moo, _____

13. chair, table, _____

14. uptown, midtown, _____

15. napkin, cloth, _____

16. circle, enclose, _____

17. liquid, paste, _____

18. swim, sink, _____

19. your, their, _____

20. cost, price, _____

© Scott Foresman 5

Notes for Home: Your child spelled words that have the vowel sounds heard in *boy* spelled *oi*
and *oy* and *out* spelled *ow* and *ou*. **Home Activity:** Together, write the spelling words on slips
of paper. Take turns choosing words and saying them aloud for the other person to spell.

Spelling: Vowel Sounds in *boy* and *out*

Directions: Proofread this letter. Find five spelling mistakes. Use the proofreading marks to correct each mistake.

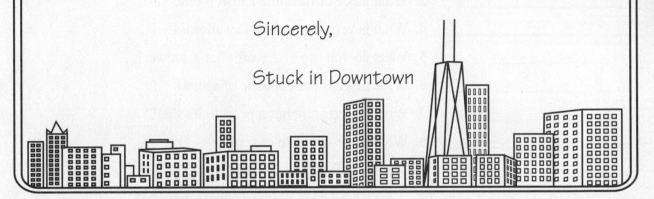

Dear Advice Giver,

Owr family lives in Illinoy. We just moved to a new home dountown. I should be glad, but it's starting to annoy me. It always seems very noisy outside. Strangers surrownd me. I'm afraid this move will destroy my life. Tell me what to do. Do I have another choyce?

Sincerely,

Stuck in Downtown

	Make a capital.
/	Make a small letter.
∧	Add something.
℘	Take out something.
⊙	Add a period.
¶	Begin a new paragraph.

Word List

choice	loyal	powder	amount
noisy	destroy	towel	our
spoil	annoy	downtown	outside
poison	oyster	drown	couch
Illinois	voyage	growl	surround

Spelling Tip
Illinois
Don't forget the final **-s** in **Illinois.** Always remember to add the final **-s**, even though the final **-s** is silent.

Write a Reply

Imagine you are the "Advice Giver" who received the letter above. On a separate sheet of paper, write a reply that tells "Stuck in Downtown" what to do. Try to use at least five of your spelling words.

Notes for Home: Your child spelled words with the vowel sounds heard in *boy* spelled *oi* and *oy* and *out* spelled *ow* and *ou*. **Home Activity:** Spell each spelling word slowly, one letter at a time. When your child knows the word, have him or her complete its spelling.

Spelling: Vowel Sounds in *boy* and *out*

Word List

choice	loyal	powder	amount
noisy	destroy	towel	our
spoil	annoy	downtown	outside
poison	oyster	drown	couch
Illinois	voyage	growl	surround

Directions: Choose the word from the box that best answers each question. Write the word on the line.

_____ **1.** What state is west of Indiana?

_____ **2.** What do you call a trip across the ocean?

_____ **3.** What piece of furniture can you relax on?

_____ **4.** What is very dangerous if swallowed?

_____ **5.** What do you use to dry off after a shower?

_____ **6.** What place is the opposite of *uptown?*

_____ **7.** What sea creature has a pearl in its shell?

_____ **8.** What is the opposite of *inside?*

_____ **9.** What is soft, dry, and dusty?

_____ **10.** What sound does a hungry stomach make?

Directions: Choose the word from the box that has the same or nearly the same meaning as each word or words below. Write the word on the line.

11. loud _____   **16.** owned together _____

12. enclose _____   **17.** ruin _____

13. selection _____   **18.** decay _____

14. sink _____   **19.** sum _____

15. bother _____   **20.** faithful _____

Notes for Home: Your child spelled words that have the vowel sounds heard in *boy* spelled *oi* and *oy (choice, loyal)* and *out* spelled *ow* and *ou (towel, couch)*. **Home Activity:** Read a short story with your child. Look for words that have the vowel sounds heard in *boy* and *out*.

Poster/Announcement

An **announcement** gives specific facts about an event. Like a news article, an announcement should answer the questions: *who?, what?, when?, where?,* and *why?* A **poster** is a type of announcement printed on a large sheet of paper and posted for the public to view.

Directions: Use the information on the poster to answer the questions on the next page.

Public Notice

Centerville Foster Care Agency
1592 Boulevard West, Room 507
Centerville, NY 10129

Anyone wishing to foster or adopt a child or children should schedule an appointment with the Centerville Foster Care Agency for an interview between the hours of 9:30 A.M. and 4:45 P.M. on Friday, October 15.

• Please bring documents showing who you are, where you live, and what kind of work you do.
• You will also need to bring a <u>completed</u> foster application or adoption application form. Forms are available from Centerville Foster Care Agency at the address above, Monday through Friday, 8:30 A.M.–5:00 P.M. You can also call our offices, and an application will be mailed to your home.
• This first interview will take approximately 45 minutes. Follow-up interviews will be scheduled as needed.
• Anyone unable to interview on the date and time assigned above may call our offices to schedule an interview at 555-1214, Monday through Friday, 8:30 A.M.–5:00 P.M.

We look forward to meeting you!

Name _____

1. What event does this poster announce? _____

_____

_____

2. Where should people go if they want an interview with the Centerville Foster Care Agency?

_____

_____

3. On what day and at what time will the interviews be held? _____

_____

4. What should people bring with them to the interview?

_____

_____

5. During what times may people call for an application to be mailed to them?

_____

6. What should applicants do if they cannot be at the agency for an interview during the time specified in the poster?

_____

7. If an applicant arrives at 10:30 A.M. for an interview, about what time can he or she expect the interview be done?

_____

8. Would a person have to have more than one interview before he or she could foster or adopt a child? Explain.

_____

_____

_____

9. What are two ways a person can get an application form? _____

_____

_____

10. What 5 "W" questions should an announcement answer?

_____

Notes for Home: Your child answered questions about information on a poster. *Home Activity:* Find an announcement in the newspaper, such as a wedding announcement. With your child, discuss all the information the announcement provides.

© Scott Foresman 5

Family Times

Summary

Jason Meets Mr. Henry and Gains a Whole New Attitude

Poor Jason! He is feeling sad after being cut from his school baseball team. But a heart-to-heart talk with the school custodian, Mr. Henry, sets him back on the right track. Mr. Henry tells Jason about some great baseball players who suffered setbacks in their careers. He also gives Jason some valuable tips for improving his baseball skills. With luck, Jason will soon be back on base!

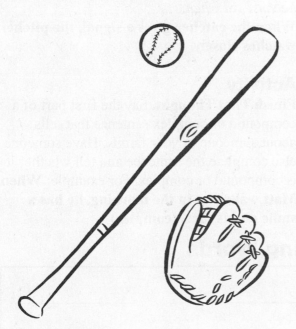

Activity

Summarize the Dialogue. Have your child summarize what Mr. Henry told Jason in "Meeting Mr. Henry," including which famous ballplayers had setbacks. Then act out the dialogue together.

Reading Skills

Cause and Effect

A **cause** is why something happens. An **effect** is what happens. For example: **The baseball player was thrown out at first base because he didn't run fast enough.**

The effect is the runner being thrown out. The cause is his slow running.

Sometimes a word or phrase such as *because, since,* or *as a result* signals a cause-effect relationship. Can you find a signal word in the example above? *(because)*

Activity

Be a Picture Detective. Find magazine or newspaper pictures that show something that happened. Point to the effect and describe it. Can you also find the cause in the picture? If not, tell what the cause may have been. For example, if you see players on a team jumping up and down and cheering (effect), you can infer that this team probably just won a game.

Family Times

Tested Vocabulary

Words to Know

Knowing the meanings of these words is important to reading "Meeting Mr. Henry." Practice using these words to learn their meanings.

challenging calling in question

corridors long hallways

custodian a janitor

cut dismissed, as from a team

valuable worth something

Grammar

Compound and Complex Sentences

A **simple sentence** expresses one complete thought.
Baseball is an exciting game.

A **compound sentence** contains two simple sentences joined by a comma and a conjunction such as *and, but,* or *or*.
Jason wanted to play baseball, but he got cut from the team.

A **complex sentence** contains a simple sentence plus a sentence part that cannot stand by itself. The sentence part is joined to the simple sentence with a word such as *if, because,* or *when*.
When the catcher gives a signal, the pitcher watches closely.

Activity
Finish That Thought. Say the first part of a compound or complex sentence that tells about someone in your family. Have someone else complete the sentence and tell whether it is compound or complex. For example: **When Matt wakes up in the morning, he has a smile on his face. (complex)**

Tested Spelling Words

© Scott Foresman 5

Cause and Effect

- A **cause** is why something happens. An **effect** is what happens.

- A cause may have more than one effect. An effect may have more than one cause.

- Sometimes a clue word such as *because* or *since* signals a cause-effect relationship. Sometimes there is no clue word, and you need to think about why something happened.

Cause	→	Effect

Directions: Reread "Baseball and Brothers." Then complete the table. Provide each missing cause or effect.

Cause (Why did it happen?)	Effect (What happened?)
1.	Meg says she hates baseball and thinks about giving it up.
2.	Mrs. O'Malley still plays baseball.
Mrs. O'Malley wants Meg to stop thinking about her problems, and she wants Charles to eat more peas.	3.
4.	Singing "Yankee Doodle" is very easy for Meg.
5.	Meg finds it difficult to walk away from baseball.

Notes for Home: Your child read a story and identified causes and effects. *Home Activity:* Help your child relate causes and effects by starting a sentence, such as *You eat breakfast because* _____. Ask your child to complete the sentence by giving a cause, or reason.

© Scott Foresman 5

Vocabulary

Directions: Read the want ad. Choose the word from the box that best completes each sentence. Write the word on the matching numbered line to the right.

JOB AVAILABLE

We have a position open for a school **1.** _____.

Job involves keeping classrooms and **2.** _____

clean. Not easy work! The principal will be

3. _____ you regularly to prove your worth.

Do a good job and be a **4.** _____ part of our

team. Do a poor job and get **5.** _____

immediately. Call 555–1234.

1. _____

2. _____

3. _____

4. _____

5. _____

Check the Words You Know
__ challenging
__ corridors
__ custodian
__ cut
__ valuable

Directions: Choose the word from the box that best matches each clue. Write the word in the puzzle.

Down

  6. calling in question
  7. long hallways
  8. worth something
  9. dismissed; let go

Across

10. a janitor

Write a Diary Entry

Imagine you are a school janitor. On a separate sheet of paper, write a diary entry that tells about your day. Use as many vocabulary words as you can.

Notes for Home: Your child identified and used vocabulary words from "Meeting Mr. Henry." *Home Activity:* Take turns using each vocabulary word in a sentence.

Cause and Effect

- A **cause** is why something happens. An **effect** is what happens.

- A cause may have more than one effect. An effect may have more than one cause.

- Sometimes a clue word such as *because* or *since* signals a cause-effect relationship. Sometimes there is no clue word and you need to think about why something happens.

Directions: Reread what happens in "Meeting Mr. Henry" when Jason plays imaginary baseball with Mr. Henry. Then answer the questions below. Think about each thing that happens and why it happens.

> And then right there in the middle of Eberwoods School, old, gray-haired Mr. Henry, the school custodian, went into a full windup.
>
> And as he did, something strange happened. He didn't look so old. He looked tall and young and powerful as he kicked high and came down over his head with a smooth motion and fired the imaginary ball. I swung.
>
> "Run!" he yelled.
>
> I ran. I didn't look down the other corridor where the imaginary ball went. I lifted my feet and ran hard and hit first base with my left shoe. The base slid far down the smooth, waxed floor.
>
> Mr. Henry laughed and slapped me on the back. "Now, if you'd moved like that when you hit that ground ball, you'd still be on your team. You run like that and you'll be getting your share of hits and then some."
>
> From FINDING BUCK MC HENRY by Alfred Slote. Copyright © 1991 by Alfred Slote. Used by permission of HarperCollins Publishers.

1. What causes Mr. Henry to seem younger to Jason?

_____

_____

2. Why is Jason able to run faster now than he did in the game?

_____

3. According to Mr. Henry, what is the reason Jason was cut from the team?

_____

4. What effect does Mr. Henry's practice session have on Jason?

_____

5. How does Jason change by the end of the story? What causes that change? On a separate sheet of paper, explain your answer.

Notes for Home: Your child used details from a story to identify causes and effects. *Home Activity:* Talk with your child about things that have happened to him or her or to you recently. Invite your child to explain what caused each thing to happen.

Selection Test

Directions: Choose the best answer to each item. Mark the letter for the answer you have chosen.

Part 1: Vocabulary

Find the answer choice that means about the same as the underlined word in each sentence.

1. My parents were <u>challenging</u> my answer.
   A. finding difficult to understand
   B. adding details to
   C. demanding proof of
   D. restating in different words

2. We walked quickly down the <u>corridors</u>.
   F. long hallways
   G. flights of stairs
   H. long ramps
   J. narrow streets

3. Joe's father is a <u>custodian</u>.
   A. guard
   B. coach
   C. driver
   D. janitor

4. Of the six players, only Allie was <u>cut</u> from the team.
   F. hurt
   G. dismissed
   H. named
   J. chosen

5. He knew the old book was <u>valuable</u>.
   A. popular
   B. falling apart
   C. stolen
   D. worth money

Part 2: Comprehension

Use what you know about the story to answer each item.

6. Where was Jason's team playing ball?
   F. Eberwoods School
   G. Tiger Stadium
   H. The Grandstand
   J. Sampson Park School

7. Jason offered to carry the bases into the gym because he
   A. wanted to help Mr. Henry.
   B. enjoyed talking with Mr. Henry.
   C. wanted to avoid talking with his teammates.
   D. hoped to get some batting tips.

8. Which sentence best describes Mr. Henry?
   F. He's always joking and fooling around.
   G. He doesn't like his job much.
   H. He observes people carefully.
   J. He loves baseball cards.

9. In what way were Josh Gibson, Satchel Paige, and Cool Papa Bell alike?
   A. They were all great pitchers.
   B. They all played for the Pittsburgh Crawfords.
   C. They were all known for their speed.
   D. They all played center field.

10. Jason knows about famous baseball players from the past because he—
    F. collects baseball cards.
    G. has seen them play.
    H. plays baseball.
    J. has read books about them.

11. What was Jason's problem as a baseball player, according to Mr. Henry?
    A. He took his eye off the ball.
    B. He didn't wait for a good pitch.
    C. He stood watching the ball after he hit it.
    D He was too chubby to run fast.

12. What will Jason do when he gets to The Grandstand?
    F. sign up for a new team
    G. look for information about the players Mr. Henry knew
    H. sell some of his baseball cards
    J. find out about the newest baseball cards

13. Mr. Henry probably compares Jason with Willie Mays and Roy Campanella to—

    A. help him gain confidence in himself.
    B. convince him that he is bound for the major leagues.
    C. help him understand his mistakes.
    D. make him feel embarrassed.

14. What does Mr. Henry think about Jason?
    F. He could be a famous player some day.
    G. He is foolish to be so interested in baseball.
    H. He should play a position other than catcher.
    J. He will get to play on a team if he gets more hits.

15. What did Mr. Henry prove to Jason?
    A. Baseball is easy to play.
    B. He could see without looking.
    C. Willie Mays was born to play baseball.
    D. Keeping the school clean is more important than baseball.

STOP

Name _____

Cause and Effect

- A **cause** is why something happens. An **effect** is what happens.

- A cause may have more than one effect. An effect may have more than one cause.

- Sometimes a clue word such as *because* or *since* signals a cause-effect relationship. Sometimes there is no clue word, and you need to think about why something happens.

Directions: Read the following story.

Jessie was very excited when he awoke that morning. He had hardly been able to sleep all night. Today was a special day because Grandpa had tickets to take him to a baseball game that night.

Around five o'clock, Grandpa and Jessie drove to the ball park. The game was sold out, so finding a parking spot was hard. Their seats were high in the bleachers, and Jessie could hardly see what was happening on the field. But that didn't stop him from eating four hot dogs during the game.

Who won the game? Jessie doesn't remember because he fell asleep by the sixth inning. But he *does* remember the stomachache he had the next day!

Directions: Complete the table. Think about each thing that happened and why it happened. Fill in each missing cause or effect.

Cause (Why It Happens)	Effect (What Happens)
Because Jessie is so excited,	he is hardly able to sleep.
1.	today is a special day for Jessie.
Because the game is sold out,	2.
Because the seats are far back,	3.
4.	he gets a stomachache.
5.	he doesn't know who won the game.

Notes for Home: Your child read a story and used story details to identify causes and effects. *Home Activity:* Read a brief newspaper or magazine article with your child. Ask your child to identify events that are described in the article and tell the reason why each event happened.

Drawing Conclusions

REVIEW

Directions: Read the story. Then read each question about the story. Choose the best answer to each question. Mark the letter for the answer you have chosen.

The First Game

Today would be Amy's first game in the Little League. She had been awake since before the sun came up. She had dressed before breakfast. She wondered if her uniform still fit right. She brushed her teeth three times. She walked Champ twice.

At last, it was time to go to the ballpark. Amy was quiet in the car. She didn't even notice her favorite songs on the radio. She bit her nails as her mother drove her to the ballpark.

"Stop that," Mother said. "You're going to be just fine." Amy wanted to believe that. Mother was usually right. She tried to think of other things as she bent her glove back and forth.

At the park, Amy joined her teammates on their side of the field. They got together and started their team cheer. They started practicing swinging the bats. They practiced throwing the ball. They listened to their coach remind them of their plans for winning the game.

From the stands she could hear cries of, "Go, Amy! Go, Fireball!" Fireball was a nickname her cousins had given her when she was little. She liked the nickname and was glad her team and the fans used it.

During the game, Amy didn't have time to worry. She struck out twelve batters. She got a single at her first turn at bat. Then she got a double in her next turn. By the end of the game, Amy wore a smile that no one could remove.

1. Before the beginning of the game, Amy feels—
   A. hungry.
   B. tired.
   C. nervous.
   D. confused.

2. Amy tries to think of other things because she—
   F. is bored in the car.
   G. wants to relax.
   H. doesn't like baseball.
   J. doesn't like her glove.

3. Amy's position on the team is—
   A. catcher.
   B. outfield.
   C. first base.
   D. pitcher.

4. Amy's playing is—
   F. poor.
   G. average.
   H. good.
   J. uneven.

5. After the game, Amy feels—
   A. embarrassed.
   B. happy.
   C. nervous.
   D. angry.

Notes for Home: Your child read a story and drew conclusions based on its details. *Home Activity:* Read a story together with your child. Afterward, invite your child to tell you what conclusions he or she can draw about how a character feels or why an event happened.

© Scott Foresman 5

Writing Across Texts

Directions: Review "From the Diary of Leigh Botts" and "Meeting Mr. Henry."
In the table below, make notes about what happens at the beginning, middle, and
end of both stories. Think about what the boys learn from their experiences. Do
they solve their problems? How do they feel?

Leigh	Jason
Beginning	
He feels sorry for himself since someone has been stealing his lunch.	1.
Middle	
2.	3.
End	
4.	5.

Write a Compare/Contrast Paragraph

Like Leigh Botts, Jason finds himself with a problem. Trace what happens in the
beginning, middle, and end of both stories. Compare how the boys face their
problems and explain what both boys learn from their experiences. Use the
information in the table above to compare the two boys. Write your paragraph on
a separate sheet of paper.

© Scott Foresman 5

Notes for Home: Your child used information from stories to compare and contrast
characters and show what the characters learned. **Home Activity:** As you read stories with
your child, compare and contrast characters from different stories.

Name _____

Grammar: Declarative and Interrogative Sentences

Directions: Write the correct end mark at the end of each sentence. Then, write **D** on the line to the left if the sentence is declarative. Write **I** if it is an interrogative sentence.

_____ **1.** Did you know that the first World Series game was played in 1903 _____

_____ **2.** The Pittsburgh Pirates played the Boston Red Sox _____

_____ **3.** Would 100,000 fans be a big crowd today _____

_____ **4.** Pittsburgh won 5 to 3 _____

_____ **5.** What very famous person was on the Boston team _____

_____ **6.** His name was Cy Young _____

_____ **7.** Winners of the first World Series were each paid $1,182 _____

_____ **8.** Now a Cy Young Award is presented every year _____

_____ **9.** Who do you think receives the award _____

_____ **10.** It goes to the best pitcher in the American League and the National League _____

Directions: Rewrite each of these declarative sentences as interrogative sentences. Be sure to use the correct end punctuation.

11. The World Series games are the best games.

_____

12. I try to watch every minute of every single game.

_____

13. Tickets for the World Series games are hard to get.

_____

14. All the games are shown live on television.

_____

15. I think baseball players deserve the fame they get.

_____

Notes for Home: Your child punctuated and wrote declarative sentences (statements) and interrogative sentences (questions). **Home Activity:** Ask your child several questions. Have your child change each question into a statement.

Practice

Grammar: Compound and Complex Sentences

A **simple sentence** expresses one complete thought. A **compound sentence** contains two simple sentences joined by a comma and a word such as *and, but,* and *or.*

> **Simple sentences:** Baseball players run bases. Custodians sweep floors.
> **Compound sentence:** Baseball players run bases, and custodians sweep floors.

A **complex sentence** is made up of a simple sentence and another part. In a complex sentence, the other part cannot stand alone as a simple sentence. The other part is joined to the sentence with a word such as *if, because,* or *when.*

> **Complex sentence:** When a home run is hit, the crowd cheers.
>   not a sentence   simple sentence

Directions: Write whether each sentence is **compound** or **complex.**

_____ **1.** Babe Ruth hit many home runs, but it took much effort.

_____ **2.** If he struck out, he tried even harder the next time.

_____ **3.** He had many hits, but not all of them were home runs.

_____ **4.** When he became too old to play, he retired.

_____ **5.** Because of his talent, Babe Ruth became very famous.

_____ **6.** Fans loved to see home runs, and they loved the great hitter.

Directions: Choose the group of words that will complete each sentence and makes sense. Write the complete sentence on the line. Add a comma, if necessary.

7. You can hit the ball over the fence _____.
(because you need to practice first/but you need to practice first)

_____

8. The ball was pitched _____.
(after the game was over/and the batter struck out)

_____

9. Although many players hit the ball hard, _____.
(but they sometimes hit home runs/only a few can hit home runs)

_____

10. Many people play baseball _____.
(if the player is good/but only a few play professionally)

_____

Notes for Home: Your child identified compound and complex sentences. *Home Activity:* Say a simple sentence, such as *I went to work today.* Challenge your child to expand it by changing it into either a complex or a compound sentence.

Name _____

Grammar: Compound and Complex Sentences

Directions: Make a compound sentence by joining the simple sentences, using a comma and one of these words: *and, but,* or *or.*

1. It was early in the season. We were playing our first game.

_____

2. Our best player strolled to the plate. She hit a home run.

_____

3. The fans rose to their feet. The ball went over the fence.

_____

4. Both teams played their best. Only one team can win the game.

_____

5. Our team practiced every day. We still lost the game.

_____

Directions: For each complex sentence, tell whether the underlined part of the sentence could stand on its own as a simple sentence. Write **S** if it is a sentence. Write **NS** if it is not a sentence.

_____ 6. If baseball had not been invented, <u>our lives would be very different</u>.

_____ 7. <u>Because the runner was fast</u>, she made it to first base.

_____ 8. Few people are great players <u>when they first play the game</u>.

_____ 9. After practicing for many years, <u>he became a good player</u>.

_____ 10. <u>When fans cheer</u>, the players feel appreciated.

Write a Paragraph

Think of a baseball game or other sporting event that you have watched. On a separate sheet of paper, describe the game. Include compound and complex sentences in your description.

Notes for Home: Your child formed compound sentences and identified parts of a complex sentence. *Home Activity:* Look for examples of compound and complex sentences in a newspaper. Have your child underline the sentence parts that can stand alone as a sentence.

Grammar: Compound and Complex Sentences

Read the simple sentences. The subjects are underlined once and verbs are underlined twice.

1. <u>Ed</u> <u>collects</u> buttons.   **2.** <u>Jan</u> <u>saves</u> string.

Sentences **1** and **2** are joined by a comma and the conjunction *and* below. The comma and conjunction that join them in the following compound sentence are circled.

3. Ed collects buttons, and Jan saves string.

Read each group of words.

4. If it rains this afternoon   **5.** Margo will stay at the library.

The first group of words cannot stand alone as a complete sentence. The second group of words is a simple sentence. Both groups of words make up the following **complex sentence.**

6. If it rains this afternoon, Margo will stay at the library.

A **compound sentence** contains two or more simple sentences joined by a conjunction. A compound sentence contains at least two complete subjects and two complete predicates. A **complex sentence** is made up of a simple sentence and another part. The other part is joined to the sentence with a word such as *if, because,* or *when.*

Directions: Write **compound** or **complex** for each sentence.

1. Morris opened the sardine can, and Lee toasted the bread. _____

2. Mark sleeps late because today is Saturday. _____

3. Victor will do his homework, or he will draw a picture. _____

4. The light blinked quickly when she flipped the switch. _____

5. If the weather is nice, we will continue our walk. _____

6. Lee cooked dinner, and Linnea made dessert. _____

7. I mopped the floor, and my sister washed the dishes. _____

8. Maureen and Joe swept the stairs because their father asked them to do it. _____

9. Jan will feed the dog, or her brother will do it. _____

10. If you need help, I will walk your dog. _____

Notes for Home: Your child distinguished between compound and complex sentences. *Home Activity:* After a discussion of the topic, have your child write an article about housework. Be sure your child uses at least two compound and two complex sentences.

Grammar: Compound and Complex Sentences

Directions: Underline each compound sentence. Circle each complex sentence.

1. Canada is our northern neighbor, and Mexico is our southern neighbor.

2. Mexico has a population of over 100 million people, but Canada has fewer than 40 million.

3. Although you may see a bullfight in Mexico, you probably wouldn't see one in Canada.

4. The capital of Canada is Ottawa, and the capital of Mexico is Mexico City.

5. I think both countries are fascinating because of their unique cultures.

6. If I ever have the chance, I will visit both countries.

Directions: Write a compound sentence. Use the conjunction in ( ) and the two simple sentences.

7. The Aztecs ruled ancient Mexico. They built a city named Tenochtitlán. (and)

_____

_____

8. Cold chocolate was the Aztecs' favorite drink. Only the wealthy could buy it. (but)

_____

_____

Directions: Combine each pair of word groups to make complex sentences. Use the word in ( ). You may need to change some capital letters to lowercase.

9. You visit Toronto, Ontario   You may take a trip to Niagara Falls. (if)

_____

_____

10. Niagara Falls may be crowded when you visit it   It is such a popular place. (because)

_____

_____

Write a Story

On a separate sheet of paper, write a story about two cities or two countries. Use compound and complex sentences in your writing.

 Notes for Home: Your child created both compound and complex sentences. *Home Activity:* Listen for examples of compound and complex sentences in radio or TV commercials. Have your child tell how he or she knows which sentence is compound and which is complex.

Phonics: Common Word Patterns

Directions: Read each word below. Some words have the pattern **consonant-vowel-consonant-e** as in **game,** which forms a **long vowel** sound. Other words have the pattern **vowel-consonant-consonant-vowel** as in **number,** which has a **short vowel** sound for the first vowel. Sort the words according to their word patterns. Write each word in the correct column.

base	powder	bike	elbow	five
center	harder	lesson	home	mule

CVCe
game

1. _____

2. _____

3. _____

4. _____

5. _____

VCCV
number

6. _____

7. _____

8. _____

9. _____

10. _____

Directions: Circle all the words that have a pattern like **game.**

11. It was time for the game to start.

12. With a big swing, she made a great hit.

13. It was a race to first base.

14. She made it to first just in time.

15. I like to watch Lisa make such good plays.

Directions: Circle all the words that have a pattern like **number.**

16. One lesson we can learn from baseball is how to work as a team.

17. Mike puts all the bases in a big basket.

18. The player in center field hit a home run.

19. "Batter up!" shouted the coach.

20. There have been many great players in the history of baseball.

© Scott Foresman 5

Notes for Home: Your child learned to recognize some common word patterns such as *CVCe (home)* and *VCCV (basket).* **Home Activity:** Look for these patterns and vowel sounds in a variety of print material such as signs, food packages, billboards, and store names.

Spelling: Long Vowels *a, i, o*

Pretest Directions: Fold back the page along the dotted line. On the blanks, write the spelling words as they are dictated. When you have finished the test, unfold the page and check your words.

1. _____   1. Use your **brain** to think.

2. _____   2. I draw on **plain** paper.

3. _____   3. What seat did you **claim**?

4. _____   4. Don't **complain**, just fix it.

5. _____   5. Spring is my **favorite** season.

6. _____   6. Fact can be **stranger** than fiction.

7. _____   7. The **aliens** went home.

8. _____   8. I want to go on a **vacation**.

9. _____   9. We ran on the **sidewalk**.

10. _____   10. He slid down the **slide**.

11. _____   11. You need water to **survive**.

12. _____   12. Stealing is a **crime**.

13. _____   13. Lin is at the **bowling** alley.

14. _____   14. Who is the **owner** of this dog?

15. _____   15. The **arrow** points up.

16. _____   16. She threw a **snowball**.

17. _____   17. Lisa ate the **whole** pie.

18. _____   18. Spin the **globe**.

19. _____   19. The **antelope** plays on the range.

20. _____   20. The **slope** is steep.

 Notes for Home: Your child took a pretest on words that have the long vowels *a, i,* and *o.*
Home Activity: Help your child learn misspelled words before the final test. Your child can underline the word parts that caused the problems and concentrate on those parts.

Think and Practice

Spelling: Long Vowels *a, i, o*

Word List				
brain	favorite	sidewalk	bowling	whole
plain	stranger	slide	owner	globe
claim	aliens	survive	arrow	antelope
complain	vacation	crime	snowball	slope

Directions: Choose the words from the box that have the **long a** sound. Write each word in the correct column.

Long a spelled ai

1. _____
2. _____
3. _____
4. _____

Long a spelled a

5. _____
6. _____
7. _____
8. _____

Directions: Choose the word from the box that rhymes with the underlined word or words and completes the sentence. Write the word on the line to the left.

_____ 9. I certainly <u>hope</u> you don't fall down a _____.

_____ 10. If I were you, <u>I'd walk</u> on the _____.

_____ 11. A gift's <u>donor</u> is usually its _____.

_____ 12. You do some <u>strolling</u> in a game of _____.

_____ 13. There is <u>no ball</u> that stings like a _____.

_____ 14. Will you eat a <u>roll</u>, either half or _____?

_____ 15. It's fun to <u>ride</u> on a slippery _____.

_____ 16. If it's sharp and <u>narrow</u>, it might be an _____.

_____ 17. "Sorry, you <u>can't elope</u>," said the papa _____.

_____ 18. It's never a good <u>time</u> to commit a _____.

_____ 19. I bought a long <u>robe</u> and a brand-ncw _____.

_____ 20. If you're still <u>alive</u>, you've managed to _____.

Notes for Home: Your child spelled words that have the long *a, i,* or *o* sound (*brain, stranger, slide, arrow, slope*). **Home Activity:** Together with your child, name other words that have the long *a, i,* or *o* sound. See how many of these words your child can spell correctly.

Name _____

Spelling: Long Vowels *a, i, o*

Directions: Proofread this letter. Find five spelling mistakes. Use the proofreading marks to correct each mistake.

≡	Make a capital.
/	Make a small letter.
∧	Add something.
℘	Take out something.
⊙	Add a period.
¶	Begin a new paragraph.

Dear Aunt Esther,

    On vacaition, Dad took our whoal family to our first baseball game. Now it's my favorite sport—even more than boaling! It's so cool how players slide! After the game, we met the team oner and some players on the sidwalk. I can't complain about having this much fun!

                    Love,

                    Dave

Spelling Tip

whole   **owner**

Remember that **long o** can be spelled with **consonant-vowel-consonant-e,** as in **whole,** but it can also be spelled with **ow,** as in **owner.** Remember which spelling to use.

Word List

brain	survive
plain	crime
claim	bowling
complain	owner
favorite	arrow
stranger	snowball
aliens	whole
vacation	globe
sidewalk	antelope
slide	slope

Write a Letter

Imagine you are Dave's Aunt Esther. On a separate sheet of paper, write a friendly letter back to Dave. Try to use at least five of your spelling words.

Notes for Home: Your child spelled words that have the long *a, i,* or *o* sounds *(brain, stranger, slide, arrow, slope)*. **Home Activity:** Say each spelling word aloud. Have your child tell whether the word has a long *a, i,* or *o* sound. Then have your child spell the word.

Spelling: Long Vowels *a, i, o*   REVIEW

Word List				
brain	favorite	sidewalk	bowling	whole
plain	stranger	slide	owner	globe
claim	aliens	survive	arrow	antelope
complain	vacation	crime	snowball	slope

Directions: Choose the word from the box that best completes each sentence. Write the word on the line to the left.

_____   1. Baseball is a popular game all over the _____.

_____   2. It has often been called America's _____ pastime.

_____   3. Baseball is a more popular sport than _____.

_____   4. A _____ baseball game lasts nine innings.

_____   5. The pitcher stands on a small _____ called a mound.

_____   6. A good baseball pitcher can _____ an entire game.

_____   7. In baseball, it's not a _____ to steal bases.

_____   8. Runners _____ into bases and kick up dirt!

_____   9. A good runner moves as swiftly as a speeding _____.

_____   10. A good sport doesn't _____ if he or she loses.

Directions: Choose the word from the box that best matches each clue. Write the word on the line.

_____   11. It's a very fast animal.

_____   12. They're strangers from another planet!

_____   13. He's new in town.

_____   14. She's the one who bought it.

_____   15. It's round and cold.

_____   16. It lets you think.

_____   17. It's not fancy.

_____   18. It's a rest from work.

_____   19. It's made of cement and is often found in front of houses.

_____   20. It's something you make when you say, "I didn't do that."

Notes for Home: Your child spelled words that have the long *a, i,* or *o* sound *(br<u>ai</u>n, str<u>a</u>nger, sl<u>i</u>de, arr<u>ow</u>, sl<u>o</u>pe).* **Home Activity:** Pick a spelling word. Give a hint about the word. (Example: *It's a long* a *word. It's in your head.*) See if your child can guess the word. *(brain)*

Technology: Card Catalog/Library Database

Libraries list the materials in their collections using a **card catalog** or a **computer database.** You can search for materials by author, title, or subject. Be sure to type words carefully when using a database. If you are not sure exactly what you want, you can use key words in the title, author's name, or subject to search the database. Always use the last name of an author first. Each listing will have a special **call number.** Use the call number to locate the item in the library.

Directions: Look at the starting screen for searching the library database below. Tell what number and words you should type to get information about each book or group of books.

Search Our Public Library
1 Title (exact search)
2 Title (key words)
3 Author (exact name)
4 Author (key words)
5 Subject (exact search)
6 Subject (key words)
Type a number or press return for more choices.

1. books about the baseball player Babe Ruth _____

2. books written by the baseball player Joe DiMaggio _____

3. books about how to coach baseball _____

4. a book called *Learning How to Play Baseball* _____

_____

5. a book you heard about that you remember has the word *pitching* in the title

_____

If you search on a broad subject category, the computer may give you categories of choices. For example, the computer screen below shows that a library has 23 books or other items about the history of baseball.

Directions: Use the information on the computer screen to answer the questions that follow.

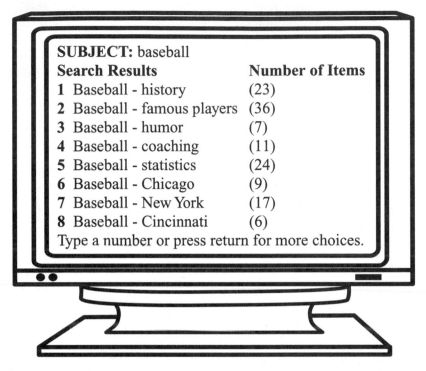

SUBJECT: baseball

Search Results	Number of Items
1 Baseball - history	(23)
2 Baseball - famous players	(36)
3 Baseball - humor	(7)
4 Baseball - coaching	(11)
5 Baseball - statistics	(24)
6 Baseball - Chicago	(9)
7 Baseball - New York	(17)
8 Baseball - Cincinnati	(6)

Type a number or press return for more choices.

6. What number should you type to find books about New York baseball teams? _____

7. What number should you type to find information about when baseball was invented? _____

8. What number should you type to find books about the baseball player Hank Aaron? _____

9. If you wanted to search for more books about baseball by Alfred Slote, the author of "Meeting Mr. Henry," would a subject search be the best way to search? Explain.

_____

_____

10. Do you think it is easier to use a library database or to look at cards in a card catalog? Explain.

_____

_____

_____

Notes for Home: Your child learned how to use an online card catalog at a library. **Home Activity:** Ask your child to make a list of five topics. At the library, work with your child to use the online catalog to find materials about these topics.

© Scott Foresman 5

Family Times

Name_____

Summary

Welcome to the World, Eloise Greenfield!

Over time, Eloise Greenfield's family has experienced many changes. Her story began with her own birth in the late 1920s in North Carolina, where her parents lived at the time. Later the family moved to Washington, D.C., so Eloise's father could find work during the Depression. In colorful detail, Eloise recalls her school days and her family's new home.

Activity

Create a Time Line. Have your child tell you about some of the highlights from Eloise's account of her life. On paper, create a time line that marks each significant event.

Reading Skills

Author's Purpose

Every writer has a reason for writing. The reason or reasons an author has for writing is the **author's purpose.**

The four most common purposes are to **entertain,** to **inform,** to **persuade,** or to **express.** In "Eloise Greenfield," the author is informing readers when she tells what childhood was like for her generation. She also expresses strong feelings about her memories.

Sometimes authors state their purpose directly. More often, however, readers need to infer the purpose based on the writing. The author of "Eloise Greenfield" leaves it up to readers to figure out her purpose.

Activity

Talk About Purpose. Talk together about your favorite radio programs, TV programs, and books. For each program or book mentioned, say what you think the author's purpose for writing is. Can you think of a program or book that reflects each of the common purposes?

Family Times

Tested Vocabulary

Words to Know

Knowing the meanings of these words is important to reading "Eloise Greenfield." Practice using these words to learn their meanings.

applied made a request

community a group of people living together in the same place who are subject to the same rules

council a group of people with the authority to make rules

in-between being at a middle place or stage

project a group of apartment buildings built and run as a unit

resident a person who lives someplace permanently

Grammar

Correcting Sentence Fragments and Run-ons

Two common errors in writing are sentence fragments and run-on sentences. A **sentence fragment** is a group of words that does not express a complete thought. A **run-on sentence** is two or more sentences joined incorrectly. For example, there may be no punctuation at all, or there may be just a comma without the necessary conjunction. See how the following fragment and run-on have been corrected.

Fragment: Eloise's mom and dad.
Sentence: Eloise's mom and dad moved North.

Run-on: The family moved to a project, Eloise began a new school.
Sentence: The family moved to a project, and Eloise began a new school.

Activity
Fix That Sentence. Write sentences about a good memory, but purposely write the sentences as fragments or run-ons. Then challenge another person to correct each error. Switch roles and repeat.

Tested Spelling Words

© Scott Foresman 5

90 Eloise Greenfield

Author's Purpose

> • The **author's purpose** is the reason an author has for writing. The purpose is usually not stated directly in the writing. Sometimes an author has more than one purpose for writing.
>
> • Four common purposes for writing are to persuade (convince), to inform (explain something), to entertain (amuse), or to express (describe something to help you see or feel a scene).

Directions: Reread "First Steps." Then complete the chart. For each passage given, write the author's purpose or purposes for writing. Choose from these purposes: to persuade, to inform, to express strong feeling, to entertain. You may use a purpose more than once.

Passage	Author's Purpose
I remember the very first time I walked by myself. My sister Alexis was in high school then.	1.
I was kind of scared, but I wanted to do it, so I pushed up off the arms of my wheelchair.	2.
I was so happy I'd made it that far. I looked up to heaven and said, "Thank you."	3.
Then I had to walk just a few more steps to get to the door—and I did it!	4.
She was so surprised. She burst out laughing and gave me a big hug.	5.

Notes for Home: Your child learned about the purposes an author may have for writing. *Home Activity:* Read the TV listings with your child. Pick out various television programs and discuss the purpose of each one.

Vocabulary

Directions: Read the announcement. Choose the word from the box that best
completes each sentence. Write the word on the matching numbered line to
the right.

■ **PUBLIC NOTICE** ■
A new apartment **1.** _____ is being built at 300 Main Street in our **2.** _____. The town **3.** _____ has ruled that any local **4.** _____ may apply for an apartment there. If you are interested and have not yet **5.** _____, please do so by December 31. Applications are available at City Hall.

1. _____

2. _____

3. _____

4. _____

5. _____

Check the Words You Know
__ applied
__ community
__ council
__ in-between
__ project
__ resident

Directions: Choose the word from the box that best matches each clue. Write
the letters of the word on the blanks. The boxed letters spell something that
many people in apartments pay.

6. a group of apartment buildings

7. being between

8. a group of people with power
to make rules

9. people living in the same
area

10. a person with a permanent
home

6. __ ☐ __ __ __ __ __

7. __ __ - __ ☐ __ __ __ __

8. __ __ __ ☐ __ __ __

9. __ __ __ __ ☐ __ __

10. __ __ ☐ __ __ __

What many people in apartments pay: __ __ __ __ __

Write a Set of Rules

On a separate sheet of paper, write a set of rules you'd like to see enforced in
your town. It could be rules about keeping the neighborhood clean or quiet or
about keeping dogs on leashes. Use as many vocabulary words as you can.

Notes for Home: Your child identified and used vocabulary words from "Eloise Greenfield."
Home Activity: Read an article with your child. Encourage him or her to figure out the
meanings of unfamiliar words using context clues—words surrounding the unfamiliar words.

Author's Purpose

- The **author's purpose** is the reason an author has for writing. Sometimes an author has more than one reason for writing. The author's purpose is usually not stated directly.

- Often an author's purpose is to persuade (convince), to inform (explain something), to entertain (amuse), or to express (describe something to help you see or feel a scene).

1. Reread "Eloise Greenfield." What is the author's purpose or purposes in telling the story?

_____

_____

Directions: Read each paragraph. For each one, identify the author's purpose.
Put an X on the line beside your choice or choices. Then explain your choice.

2. Everyone has the right to decent housing. Too many people in our community are living on the streets. Proposition 37 will solve this problem. It provides for low-income housing without new taxes. So vote *yes* on 37!

___ entertain   ___ persuade   ___ inform   ___ express

_____

3. If you can't finish your ice cream, my dog will gladly do it for you. Last night he ate my sundae while my back was turned. Can't finish that cone? Give my dog a call. He's got a beeper.

___ entertain   ___ persuade   ___ inform   ___ express

_____

4. I love my neighborhood. On summer evenings, a warm glow settles over the street. The old folks sit and rock on their porches. The little kids ride bikes in the street. The moms gossip on the sidewalk. It's the homiest, friendliest place you'll ever see.

___ entertain   ___ persuade   ___ inform   ___ express

_____

5. Beginning in the 1890s, many African Americans left their homes in the South and moved to northern cities. They moved to escape poverty and discrimination. Historians call this mass movement the Great Migration.

___ entertain   ___ persuade   ___ inform   ___ express

_____

 Notes for Home: Your child read a story and several paragraphs, and then determined each author's purpose for writing. **Home Activity:** Look through various parts of a magazine or newspaper with your child. Ask him or her to identify the purpose for writing each feature.

© Scott Foresman 5

Selection Test

Directions: Choose the best answer to each item. Mark the letter for the answer you have chosen.

Part 1: Vocabulary

Find the answer choice that means about the same as the underlined word in each sentence.

1. She applied for a job.
   - A. wished
   - B. had the skills
   - C. made a request
   - D. studied

2. He was the town's resident artist.
   - F. living in a place permanently
   - G. highly regarded
   - H. traveling from place to place
   - J. living alone

3. Mae is a member of the council.
   - A. a club for singers
   - B. a group of employees
   - C. a group of people who make rules
   - D. a club for checkers players

4. That summer was an in-between time.
   - F. having a quality of sadness
   - G. being or coming in the middle
   - H. not interesting; boring
   - J. showing strong feeling

5. They lived in a project.
   - A. a grid formed by several streets
   - B. a place where people live outdoors
   - C. an unfinished building or group of buildings
   - D. a group of apartment buildings built and run as a unit

6. He was a leader in the community.
   - F. a group of people living in one place
   - G. a group of people with the same last name
   - H. a band or company, especially a group of performers
   - J. a group of persons that has the duty to make laws

Part 2: Comprehension

Use what you know about the selection to answer each item.

7. Where was Eloise Greenfield's father when she was born?
   - A. at home helping out
   - B. working at Mr. Slim Gordon's store
   - C. downtown playing checkers
   - D. out of town

8. Langston Terrace was located in—
   - F. Parmele, North Carolina.
   - G. Washington, D.C.
   - H. Chicago.
   - J. Atlanta.

9. From her stories about school, you can tell that Eloise was a—
   - A. quiet child.
   - B. good student.
   - C. popular girl.
   - D. troublemaker.

10. Why did Eloise's parents want to move to Langston Terrace?
    - F. They had friends in the neighborhood.
    - G. It was named for a famous black congressman.
    - H. They needed more space.
    - J. The houses were very beautiful.

11. How was her home at Langston Terrace different from other places Eloise had lived?
    - A. It was in the city.
    - B. It had only one room.
    - C. Daddy's cousin Lillie was there.
    - D. Her family had a whole house to themselves.

GO ON ➤

12. Why was it difficult for families at Langston Terrace to save enough money to buy a house?

    F.   Whenever they earned more money, their rents increased.

    G.   They had to pay fees for the many social activities.

    H.   The rents there were higher than in other parts of the city.

    J.   They were too busy enjoying life to think about saving money.

13. What happened after Eloise's sister Vedie was born?

    A.   Eloise went to a new school.

    B.   The family moved to a three-bedroom house.

    C.   Eloise celebrated her ninth birthday.

    D.   The family moved to Washington.

14. The author tells about two events from when she was in grade school. She probably chose these particular events to help the reader understand—

    F.   what kind of schools she went to.

    G.   why she became famous.

    H.   what kind of child she was.

    J.   what life was like in olden times.

15. In this selection, the author's main purpose is to—

    A.   explain the difficulties of being poor.

    B.   share childhood memories.

    C.   give information about housing in the city.

    D.   entertain the reader with humor.

Author's Purpose

- The **author's purpose** is the reason an author has for writing. Sometimes an author has more than one reason for writing. The author's purpose is usually not stated directly.

- Often an author's purpose is to persuade (convince), to inform (explain something), to entertain (amuse), or to express (describe something to help you see or feel a scene).

Directions: Read each brief passage.

1. I was in my local bakery this morning and a duck walked in. He ordered a doughnut and told the owner, "Put it on my bill."

2. Students in this school want the right to plan the cafeteria menu. After all, it's the students who have to eat the food. We know best what we like. So let us choose the foods.

3. Last night I watched a great fireworks display in the neighborhood. Dozens of rockets shot up in the sky and exploded like crazy rainbows. The steady boom-boom of firecrackers sounded like beating drums.

4. Today our town council approved money to put up a stoplight at the corner of Broad and Main Streets. The corner has been the site of several accidents in recent years.

5. I visited our town library, and I think they should definitely order new books. Most of the books they have now are at least five to ten years old. We need new books to keep up with current times around here!

Directions: Complete the diagram. Think about the author's purpose in each passage above. Write whether the purpose is to persuade, inform, entertain, or express. Explain each answer.

Author's Purpose	Explanation
1.	
2.	
3.	
4.	
5.	

Notes for Home: Your child read paragraphs and determined the author's purpose for writing. *Home Activity:* Read a short story with your child. Have your child identify the author's purpose in writing the story.

Sequence

REVIEW

Directions: Read the story. Then read each question about the story. Choose the best answer to each question. Mark the letter for the answer you have chosen.

My New Home

As I think about living in Hicksville, I vividly remember the day we moved there. I hadn't known much about the town, and I didn't know anything at all about the neighborhood. Mom seemed to know I would like it. I was both scared and excited. Would I like the house? Would I make new friends?

I could hardly wait to see my new home. As soon as we got there, I raced from my parents' car and went straight into the house. It looked so much bigger than the old apartment.

"Where's my room?" I asked. Dad pointed to the long staircase.

"At the top of the stairs and to the right," Dad said.

I found my room right away because I recognized my boxes. My clothes, my music, and all my other things were in those boxes. As I began unpacking a box of school clothes, I heard a barking noise outside. I looked through my window.

I couldn't believe it. In the next yard were two dogs. I loved dogs, although I had none of my own. I went outside and looked over the backyard fence. A boy about my own age was feeding one of the dogs. The dog glanced at me and wagged its tail but kept eating. The boy came over to the fence.

"Hi," the boy said. "You must be the new neighbor."

1. The first thing the narrator does after getting to the new house is—
   A. go to the narrator's room.
   B. look out the window.
   C. leave the car.
   D. hear a dog bark.

2. In the room, the narrator first—
   F. starts to unpack.
   G. sees the window.
   H. hears dogs barking.
   J. meets the boy next door.

3. Just before looking out the window, the narrator—
   A. goes downstairs.
   B. hears the neighbors talking.
   C. hears barking.
   D. carries a box.

4. The narrator goes outside and looks over the fence because he or she—
   F. wants to meet a neighbor.
   G. is bored.
   H. hears voices.
   J. loves dogs.

5. The last thing the narrator does in the story is—
   A. return to the car.
   B. meet the neighbor.
   C. meet the dogs.
   D. unpack a box.

© Scott Foresman 5

Notes for Home: Your child read a story, and then identified the order in which events happened. *Home Activity:* With your child, read a magazine or newspaper article that tells about an event that took place. Then have your child describe the event to you, in his or her own words, in order.

Name _____

Writing Across Texts

Directions: A story you read recently was called "Looking for a Home." The same title might also fit Eloise Greenfield's autobiography. Complete the table below by listing details about each selection.

Questions	Eloise Greenfield	Looking for a Home
What is the setting for each selection?	Langston Terrace	farms in Texas
Who is the main character?	1.	2.
What genre, or type of writing, is each selection?	3.	4.
With whom did the main character of each selection live?	5.	6.
What was each main character looking for?	7.	8.
How did the main character feel about his or her experiences?	9.	10.

Write a Comparison/Contrast Paragraph

Compare and contrast the experiences of the main characters of the two selections. Write your paragraph on a separate sheet of paper.

Notes for Home: Your child used information from different texts to compare and contrast the experiences of two people. ***Home Activity:*** As you read stories and articles, encourage your child to compare and contrast characters.

Name _____

Grammar: Imperative and Exclamatory Sentences

REVIEW

Directions: Write the correct end mark at the end of each sentence. Write **I** on the line to the left if the sentence is an imperative sentence. Write **E** if it is an exclamatory sentence.

_____ 1. Look around your neighborhood _____

_____ 2. Take your time _____

_____ 3. What a big surprise you'll find _____

_____ 4. Stop and smell the sweet air _____

_____ 5. These flowers are beautiful _____

_____ 6. Look closely at the tall building across the street _____

_____ 7. It must have forty floors _____

_____ 8. Listen to the music coming from the band stand _____

_____ 9. Those musicians are really great _____

_____ 10. That trumpet player hits the highest notes _____

Directions: Write four imperative sentences that explain to someone else how to do something. Then write an exclamatory sentence. Remember to begin each sentence with a capital letter and end each one with the correct punctuation.

11. _____

_____

12. _____

_____

13. _____

_____

14. _____

_____

15. _____

_____

© Scott Foresman 5

Notes for Home: Your child identified sentences that gave commands and expressed strong feelings. *Home Activity:* Tone of voice is an important part of reading imperative and exclamatory sentences. Take turns creating and saying these types of sentences aloud.

Practice

Grammar: Correcting Sentence Fragments and Run-ons

A **sentence fragment** may begin with a capital letter and end with a period, but it does not express a complete thought. Some fragments can be corrected by adding words to them to make a complete sentence. Some fragments can be corrected by attaching them to a related sentence.

> **Sentence fragment:** Different kinds of neighborhoods.
> **Corrected sentence:** Children live in different kinds of neighborhoods.

> **Sentence and a fragment:** We live in the country. Where we can grow vegetables.
> **Corrected sentence:** We live in the country where we can grow vegetables.

A **run-on sentence** is two or more sentences combined with just a comma, or with no joining word or punctuation at all. Correct a run-on sentence by writing two separate sentences or by changing it to a compound sentence.

> **Run-on sentence:** Some young people live in the city others live in the country.
> **Separate sentences:** Some young people live in the city. Others live in the country.
> **Compound sentence:** Some young people live in the city, and others live in the country.

Dircctions: Read each group of words. Write **SF** if it is a sentence fragment. Write **S** if it is a complete sentence.

_____ 1. Neighborhoods in large cities.

_____ 2. Tall buildings stand on each block.

_____ 3. Noisy traffic all day long.

_____ 4. The quiet country with little noise.

_____ 5. Children walk along country roads.

_____ 6. Country life has its charms.

Directions: Correct each run-on sentence either by writing two sentences or by writing a compound sentence.

7. City children visit museums they also attend plays.

_____

8. City life is fast, there is much to do and see.

_____

9. The country is quiet some young people prefer that.

_____

10. They enjoy open fields, farm animals are near.

_____

Notes for Home: Your child identified sentence fragments and corrected run-on sentences. *Home Activity:* Write examples of sentence fragments and run-on sentences like those above for your child to correct. Then discuss the way your child has corrected each sentence.

Grammar: Correcting Sentence Fragments and Run-ons

Directions: Correct each fragment. Write the corrected sentence on the line.

1. Attended the block party.

_____

2. A group of happy neighbors.

_____

3. The mayor of the town.

_____

4. The glee club sang. A song about our block.

_____

5. Volunteers cleaned up. After everyone had left.

_____

Directions: Read each item. Write **S** if it is a correct sentence. Write **RS** if it is a run-on sentence, and rewrite the sentence correctly.

6. The neighborhood held a block party it was fun.

_____

7. People brought food, a band played all day.

_____

8. Neighbors chatted, and some people sang.

_____

9. Children played in the street no cars were allowed.

_____

10. We had a great time it didn't end until dark.

_____

Write About Your Neighborhood

On a separate sheet of paper, describe your neighborhood. Check and correct any fragments or run-ons.

Notes for Home: Your child corrected run-on sentences and sentence fragments. **Home Activity:** Have your child explain what run-on sentences and sentence fragments are and how to correct them.

© Scott Foresman 5

Extra Practice

Grammar: Correcting Sentence Fragments and Run-ons

RETEACHING

Read the run-on sentence. Then read the corrections of the run-on sentence.

Run-on Sentence	Corrected Sentences
Our team won the race we were happy.	1. Our team won the race. We were happy. 2. Our team won the race, and we were happy.

Read the sentence fragment. Then read the correction of the sentence fragment.

Sentence Fragment	Corrected Sentence
All of the leaves and the flower petals.	All of the leaves and the flower petals were brightly colored.

A **run-on sentence** is two or more sentences combined with just a comma or with no joining word or punctuation. A **sentence fragment** may begin with a capital letter and end with a period, but it does not express a complete thought.

Directions: Correct each run-on sentence. Write a compound sentence by adding a comma and the conjunction *and, but* or *or.*

1. Craig ran his first race last week Jay ran a race soon after.

_____

2. Lee's running shoes are badly worn mine are new.

_____

Directions: Add words to each sentence fragment and write each new sentence.

3. Marcella, Sophie, and Caroline in the park.

_____

4. Through the field and toward the pond.

_____

Notes for Home: Your child corrected sentence fragments and run-on sentences. *Home Activity:* Have your child write a list of rules for recognizing sentence fragments and run-ons. Then have him or her use the list to teach other family members.

Grammar: Correcting Sentence Fragments and Run-ons

Directions: Underline each sentence fragment. Make each fragment a complete sentence by adding words to it or by joining the fragment to another sentence. Rewrite the paragraph.

1.–7.   Jacob Riis was a photographer. And a journalist. Born in Denmark, Riis came to the United States in 1870. Started at the *New York Evening Sun* in 1890. Tried to improve housing and law enforcement. He also pushed for child-labor laws. His photographs showed that people needed better living conditions.

_____

_____

_____

_____

Directions: Rewrite each run-on sentence as a compound sentence.

8. Clouds are signs of rain fog is a low cloud.

_____

9. Some clouds are made of water drops others have ice crystals.

_____

10. A rainbow formed after the shower it disappeared quickly.

_____

11. The pond froze the stream did not.

_____

12. The clouds blew away the sun came out.

_____

Write About a Day

On a separate sheet of paper, write about a day when the weather changed your plans. Check to make sure there are no sentence fragments or run-ons in your writing.

Notes for Home: Your child corrected run-on sentences and added words to sentence fragments to make them complete sentences. *Home Activity:* Say sentence fragments about the weather. Have your child make a sentence from each sentence fragment.

Phonics: Complex Spelling Patterns

Directions: Words that end in **-ough** or **-ought** can be tricky. They don't all sound alike. Read the sentences. Then read the words in ( ). Circle the word that has the same vowel sound as the underlined word in the sentence.

1. They saved <u>enough</u> money to buy a house.   (though/tough)

2. They <u>brought</u> their belongings with them.   (thought/bough)

3. The new neighborhood was <u>rough</u>.   (though/tough)

4. People sometimes <u>fought</u> on his block.   (brought/found)

5. The police <u>ought</u> to do something about it.   (out/thought)

6. He never got in fights, <u>although</u> others did.   (loud/dough)

Directions: Read the poster below. The phrase in ( ) is a clue to the missing word. Choose the word from the box with the same vowel sound as the word in ( ). Make sure the words make sense in the sentence. Write the word on the line.

Hey everyone! We _____ (sounds like *fought*) you could use a party!

We _____ (sounds like *fought*) lots of food at the store.

Even _____ (sounds like *dough*) you have a lot of work to do, come join us!

It's a _____ (sounds like *tough*) job, but someone has to have fun!

though	thought	rough	bought

7. _____

8. _____

9. _____

10. _____

Notes for Home: Your child matched vowel sounds for words that end in *-ough* and *-ought* such as *though* and *thought*. **Home Activity:** Make up several short sentences that include words ending in *-ough* or *-ought*. Say the sentences aloud and have your child write them.

Name _____

Spelling: Vowel Sounds in *rule, use, off*

Pretest Directions: Fold back the page along the dotted line. On the blanks, write the spelling words as they are dictated. When you have finished the test, unfold the page and check your words.

1. _____
2. _____
3. _____
4. _____
5. _____
6. _____
7. _____
8. _____
9. _____
10. _____
11. _____
12. _____
13. _____
14. _____
15. _____
16. _____
17. _____
18. _____
19. _____
20. _____

1. **Choose** a shirt to wear.
2. It is time to go to **school**.
3. The **broom** is made of straw.
4. He uses a shovel to **scoop** sand.
5. There is a phone **booth** inside.
6. They **threw** away the garbage.
7. A work **crew** paved the road.
8. What a nice picture you **drew**!
9. I have found my lost **jewel**.
10. What will the **future** be like?
11. Tad likes all kinds of **music**.
12. I **usually** eat lunch outside.
13. His sense of **humor** is strange.
14. Have you ever been to **Utah**?
15. The teacher **taught** them to read.
16. It is **naughty** to be rude.
17. The couple has one **daughter**.
18. Put your **laundry** in the dryer.
19. **Sausage** is good at breakfast.
20. The ship will **launch** tomorrow.

Notes for Home: Your child took a pretest on words that have vowel sounds such as those in *rule, use,* and *off.* **Home Activity:** Help your child learn misspelled words before the final test. See if there are any similar errors and discuss a memory trick that could help.

Think and Practice

Spelling: Vowel Sounds in *rule*, *use*, *off*

Word List			
choose	threw	music	naughty
school	crew	usually	daughter
broom	drew	humor	laundry
scoop	jewel	Utah	sausage
booth	future	taught	launch

Directions: Choose the words from the box that have the vowel sound you hear in **off**. Write each word in the correct column.

Vowel sound spelled augh

1. _____

2. _____

3. _____

Vowel sound spelled au

4. _____

5. _____

6. _____

Directions: Complete each equation to spell a word from the box. Write the word on the line.

7. useful   –   eful   +   ually   =   _____

8. creep   –   eep   +   ew   =   _____

9. change   –   ange   +   oose   =   _____

10. Utopia   –   opia   +   ah   =   _____

11. fuel   –   el   +   ture   =   _____

12. brown   –   wn   +   om   =   _____

13. jest   –   st   +   wel   =   _____

14. scheme   –   eme   +   ool   =   _____

15. museum   –   eum   +   ic   =   _____

16. huge   –   ge   +   mor   =   _____

17. boat   –   at   +   oth   =   _____

18. scar   –   ar   +   oop   =   _____

19. thread   –   ad   +   w   =   _____

20. drive   –   ive   +   ew   =   _____

Notes for Home: Your child spelled words that have the vowel sounds heard in *rule* spelled *oo* and *ew (sch<u>oo</u>l, thr<u>ew</u>)*, *use* spelled *u (m<u>u</u>sic)*, and *off* spelled *augh* and *au (t<u>augh</u>t, l<u>au</u>ndry)*. **Home Activity:** Say each spelling word to your child. See if your child can spell it correctly.

Spelling: Vowel Sounds in *rule, use, off*

Directions: Proofread this description. Find five spelling mistakes. Use the proofreading marks to correct each mistake.

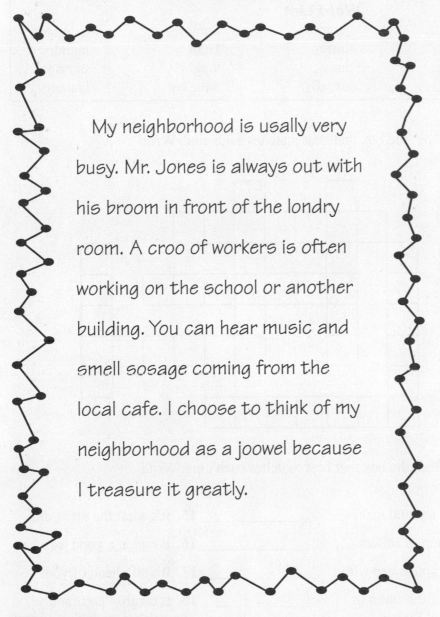

My neighborhood is usally very busy. Mr. Jones is always out with his broom in front of the londry room. A croo of workers is often working on the school or another building. You can hear music and smell sosage coming from the local cafe. I choose to think of my neighborhood as a joowel because I treasure it greatly.

Proofreading Marks	
≡	Make a capital.
/	Make a small letter.
∧	Add something.
℘	Take out something.
⊙	Add a period.
¶	Begin a new paragraph.

Spelling Tip

choose
Some people forget that **choose** has two **o**'s, not one. Remember: When you **cho͟o͟se**, you often pick between **two** things.

Word List
choose
school
broom
scoop
booth
threw
crew
drew
jewel
future
music
usually
humor
Utah
taught
naughty
daughter
laundry
sausage
launch

Write a Description

On a separate sheet of paper, write a description of your neighborhood or one you would like to live in. Try to use at least five of your spelling words.

Notes for Home: Your child spelled words that have the vowel sounds heard in *rule* spelled *oo* and *ew* (sch*oo*l, thr*ew*), *use* spelled *u* (m*u*sic), and *off* spelled *augh* and *au* (t*augh*t, l*au*ndry). **Home Activity:** Scramble the letters of each spelling word and have your child unscramble the words.

Name _____

Spelling: Vowel Sounds in *rule, use, off*

REVIEW

Word List				
choose	booth	jewel	humor	daughter
school	threw	future	Utah	laundry
broom	crew	music	taught	sausage
scoop	drew	usually	naughty	launch

Directions: Choose the word from the box that best matches each clue. Write the word in the puzzle.

Down

1. send up in the air
2. female child
4. learning place
5. small stall

Across

3. kind of meat
6. bad
7. instructed
8. dirty clothes

Directions: Choose the word from the box that best matches each clue. Write the word on the line.

_____ 9. It's what a piano makes.

_____ 10. It's a group of sailors.

_____ 11. It's what you sweep with.

_____ 12. It's one of the states in the United States.

_____ 13. It's a real gem.

_____ 14. It's how you get ice cream.

_____ 15. It's what the artist did.

_____ 16. It's what a good joke has.

_____ 17. It's all ahead of you.

_____ 18. It means "commonly."

_____ 19. It's what you do when you vote.

_____ 20. It's what the pitcher did.

Notes for Home: Your child spelled words that have the vowel sounds heard in *rule* spelled *oo* and *ew* (sch<u>oo</u>l, thr<u>ew</u>), *use* spelled *u* (m<u>u</u>sic), and *off* spelled *augh* and *au* (t<u>augh</u>t, l<u>au</u>ndry). **Home Activity:** Write the spelling words without the vowels. Ask your child to correct them.

Manual

A **manual** is a written set of directions that helps readers understand or use something. It usually comes in the form of a booklet or a book.

Directions: Use the pages from a manual for a refrigerator to answer the questions that follow.

Know Your Refrigerator

Table of Contents

Temperature Controls

There are two types of controls for your refrigerator. The fresh food control uses numbers. The freezer control uses letters. When installing, set the fresh food control at 5 and the freezer control at C as shown in the diagrams.

The fresh food control maintains the temperatures throughout the refrigerator. Setting the control to OFF will stop the cooling in both the fresh food area and the freezer area, but this will not shut off the power to the refrigerator.

The freezer control moves a damper that changes the amount of cold air that moves from the freezer to the fresh food compartment.

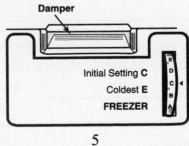

5

Name _____

1. What is the purpose of this manual? _____

_____

2. When might you use this manual? Give an example. _____

_____

_____

3. The table of contents is listed in alphabetical order. Why might this be helpful?

_____

_____

_____

4. On which page would you find information to clean the drawers? _____

5. What kinds of information would you expect to find on page 4? _____

_____

_____

6. What are the two types of temperature controls? _____

_____

7. At what settings should you put the two temperature controls when you are installing the refrigerator?

_____

_____

8. What is the coldest setting for each temperature control? _____

_____

9. Why are diagrams like the ones shown helpful in a manual?

_____

_____

10. If you were using this manual to help install a new refrigerator, why is it important to follow the directions for installation exactly as they are written?

_____

_____

_____

Notes for Home: Your child answered questions about a refrigerator manual. *Home Activity:* Together with your child, read part of a manual you have at home, such as a manual for operating your TV. Talk about the different kinds of information that the manual gives.

Name _____

Time Line

Directions: Write the main events of your personal narrative in time order on the slanted lines. Identify the date or time each event happened. Add more lines if you need them.

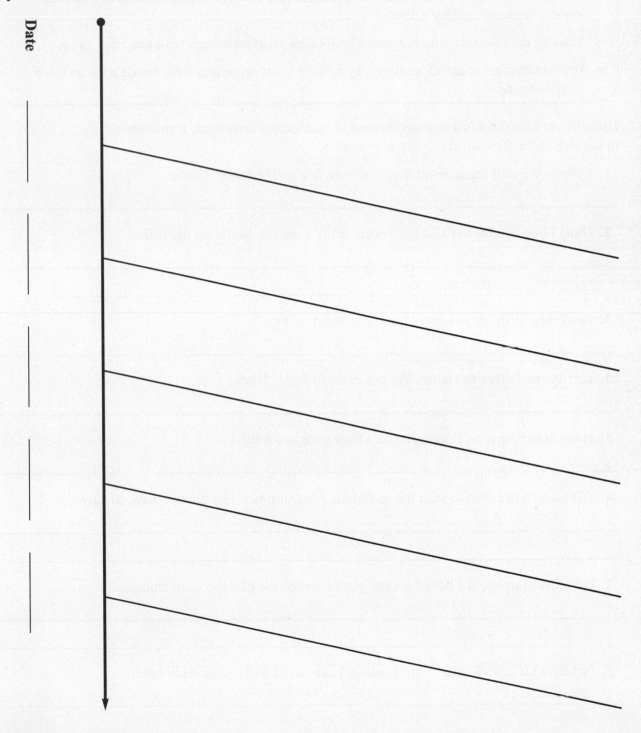

Date

Notes for Home: Your child used a time line to organize prewriting notes for a personal narrative. *Home Activity:* Work with your child to make a time line of important family dates.

Name _____

Elaboration
Combine Sentences

- When you write, you can elaborate by **combining short, choppy sentences** into one longer, more interesting sentence.
- You can make compound sentences by joining short sentences with *and, but,* or *or.*
- You can make a complex sentence by joining short sentences with words such as *when, if,* or *because.*

Directions: Use the word in parentheses to combine the sentences. Remember to capitalize the first word of your new sentence.

1. (when) We will learn about Texas history. We will visit the Alamo.

_____

2. (but) Lupe is a forward on her soccer team. I am the goalie on my team.

_____

_____

3. (and) My birthday is July 8. Lupe's birthday is July 9.

_____

4. (or) We can drive to Dallas. We can drive to Padre Island.

_____

5. (but) Some parts of Texas are flat. Other parts are hilly.

_____

6. (if) Lupe will come to visit me in Florida next summer. Her parents have to agree.

_____

_____

7. (because) Lupe and I have become good friends. We like the same things.

_____

_____

8. (when) Our schools are getting online. Lupe and I will e-mail each other.

_____

Notes for Home: Your child made compound and complex sentences by combining simple sentences. *Home Activity:* Ask your child to think of sentences beginning with the words *when, if,* and *because.*

© Scott Foresman 5

Name _____

Self-Evaluation Guide
Personal Narrative Checklist

Directions: Think about the final draft of your personal narrative. Then answer each question below.

	Yes	No	Not sure
1. Does my narrative flow smoothly from beginning to middle to end?			
2. Do I use enough details to let my audience know how I feel about the event?			
3. Did I keep my audience and purpose in mind?			
4. Did I use vivid words to express myself?			
5. Did I proofread and edit carefully to avoid errors?			

6. Which sentence of your personal narrative do you think is the most well-written? Explain.

_____

_____

_____

7. Was your topic a good one for a personal narrative, or should you have chosen a different topic? Explain.

_____

_____

_____

Notes for Home: Your child has just completed a self-evaluation of a personal narrative. *Home Activity:* Ask your child to tell you about the personal narrative he or she has just written.

Family Times

Name_____

Summary

Wayne Grover Rescues a Baby...Dolphin!

One day off the Florida coast, a family of three dolphins swam to diver Wayne Grover for help. The baby was tangled in fishing line and had a hook snagged in its back. Wayne knew that the baby's trail of blood could attract sharks. In a delicate operation, Wayne managed to remove the hook and cut the fishing line. When sharks approached, they were fought off by the protective dolphin parents. Talk about high drama at sea!

Activity

Supply the Dialogue. Wayne sensed that the dolphins wanted to speak to him. What might they have said to each other? Write a dialogue for Wayne and the dolphins. Then get family members to act out the scene.

Reading Skills

Steps in a Process

Sometimes a story or article describes how an action is taken or how something is made. The actions a person takes to make something or to reach a goal are the **steps in a process.** In "The Diver and the Dolphins," the author describes the steps he took to rescue an injured baby dolphin. First he cut away the finishing line. Then he stuck his hand deep inside the baby's wound. Finally, he pulled out the hook.

Sometimes there are clue words to help you understand the order of the steps. In the above example, did you find three such words? (They are *first, then*, and *finally*.)

Activity

Trace Your Steps. Think of a job or task done recently that had several steps to it. Draw pictures to show each step of the process in order. Then write a short caption for each picture.

Family Times

Tested Vocabulary

Words to Know

Knowing the meanings of these words is important to reading "The Diver and the Dolphins." Practice using these words to learn their meanings.

communicate exchange information

cooperate work together

desperate ready to run any risk

dolphins sea mammals

doomed headed for death or any terrible fate

hovered stayed in or near one place

injured hurt

Grammar

Nouns

A **noun** is a word that names a person, place, or thing. Some things may be things you can see and touch, such as *dolphin*. Other things are ideas that you cannot see or touch, such as *freedom*.

Nouns at School
Person: teacher
Place: library
Thing (can see): floor, map
Thing (cannot see): time, friendship

Activity

Go Noun-Spotting. Make a table like the one above called *Nouns at Home*. Then look around the rooms of your home. Together, identify the names of various people, places, and things that you see. Add your nouns to your table.

Tested Spelling Words

_____ _____ _____ _____

_____ _____ _____ _____

_____ _____ _____ _____

_____ _____ _____ _____

_____ _____ _____ _____

© Scott Foresman 5

The Diver and the Dolphins 115

Steps in a Process

- The actions you take to make something or to reach a goal are the **steps in a process.**

- When you read, look for clues that help you follow the steps. Clues may be numbers, illustrations, or words such as *first, next, then,* and *last.*

- If there are no clues, think of what you already know about how the process might be done.

Directions: Reread "First-Aid ABCs." Then complete the flowchart by listing in order the steps you should take if you suspect that someone is choking.

Step 1:

↓

Step 2:

↓

Step 3:

↓

Step 4:

↓

Step 5:

↓

Step 6: Repeat until the food or object comes out of the person's mouth.

Notes for Home: Your child read an article and showed the order of the steps for the Heimlich maneuver. **Home Activity:** Have your child describe the steps of the Heimlich maneuver in order. Then take turns acting out the Heimlich maneuver, without using any thrusting force.

© Scott Foresman 5

Vocabulary

Directions: Choose the word from the box that best completes each statement. Write the word on the line to the left.

_____ 1. *Bus* is to *travel* as *telephone* is to _____.

_____ 2. *Desert* is to *camels* as *ocean* is to _____.

_____ 3. *Enemy* is to *argue* as *friend* is to _____.

_____ 4. *Medal* is to *honored* as *bandage* is to _____.

_____ 5. *Separation* is to *separate* as *desperation* is to _____.

Check the Words You Know
__ communicate
__ cooperate
__ desperate
__ dolphins
__ doomed
__ hovered
__ injured

Directions: Choose the word from the box that best matches each clue. Write the word in the puzzle.

Down

6. stayed near
7. sea mammals

Across

8. headed for a terrible fate
9. work together
10. hurt

Write a Persuasive Paragraph

Think of a problem that an ocean creature has, such as polluted waters, lack of food, or safe resting places. On a separate sheet of paper, write a paragraph that persuades readers to help this ocean creature. Use as many vocabulary words as you can.

 Notes for Home: Your child identified and used vocabulary words from "The Diver and the Dolphins." *Home Activity:* Using a dictionary, find simple definitions for words and read them aloud to your child. See if your child can guess each word.

Steps in a Process

- The actions you take to make something or to reach a goal are the **steps in a process.**

- When you read, look for clues that help you follow the steps. Clues may be numbers, illustrations, or words such as *first, next, then,* and *last.*

- If there are no clues, think of what you already know about how the process might be done.

Directions: Reread what happens in "The Diver and the Dolphins" when Wayne frees the baby dolphin. Then answer the questions below. Think about the order of the steps.

I gently held the baby on the sea floor, then cut the trailing fishing line free until all that was left was the part embedded under the baby's tender skin. Getting it out with as little pain for the baby as possible was going to be the hard part.

Then, bit by bit, I started pulling the embedded line loose so I could cut it with my knife. As I pulled it up, more blood flowed out.

I looked around for sharks, not wanting to get in the way if the parent dolphins needed to protect their baby from attack.

Seeing no sharks, I gently continued to pull some line free.... Finally, all the line was cut free except for a short piece attached to the hook.

From DOLPHIN ADVENTURE by Wayne Grover. Copyright 1990 by Wayne Grover. By permission of Greenwillow Books, a division of William Morrow & Company, Inc.

1. What process is being described?

_____

2. Write all the steps Wayne took to get the line free. Number the steps in correct order.

_____

_____

3. What clue words does the writer use to indicate the order of the steps?

_____

4. Did Wayne work quickly or slowly? How do you know?

_____

_____

5. On a separate sheet of paper, write all the steps Wayne took to get the hook out of the dolphin's flesh. Number the steps in the correct order.

Notes for Home: Your child read a story and described the steps in a process. *Home Activity:* Work with your child to describe the steps in a simple process, such as making a sandwich or getting ready for school.

Selection Test

Directions: Choose the best answer to each item. Mark the letter for the answer you have chosen.

Part 1: Vocabulary

Find the answer choice that means about the same as the underlined word in each sentence.

1. He was <u>desperate</u>.
   A. ready to try anything
   B. totally out of control
   C. very sad
   D. greatly pleased

2. The dogs <u>hovered</u> as we ate.
   F. stayed in or near one place
   G. moved about in a secret way
   H. paid no attention
   J. gave long, sad cries

3. They were trying to <u>communicate</u>.
   A. blend in with others
   B. show sorrow for another's suffering
   C. help someone in need
   D. send and receive information

4. We watched the <u>dolphins</u>.
   F. kinds of seals
   G. fish that live in lakes
   H. kinds of sharks
   J. mammals that live in the sea

5. The king was <u>doomed</u>.
   A. weakened in spirit
   B. certain to have an unhappy end
   C. very excited
   D. having the most power

6. The children were learning to <u>cooperate</u>.
   F. speak clearly
   G. try hard to win
   H. work together with others
   J. find the way home

7. The horse was <u>injured</u>.
   A. hurt
   B. exhausted
   C. filled with anger
   D. tied down

Part 2: Comprehension

Use what you know about the selection to answer each item.

8. What noise were the dolphins making as they approached Wayne Grover?
   F. splashing
   G. clicking
   H. crying
   J. swishing

9. The baby dolphin's wound was caused by —
   A. a diver's knife.
   B. sharks.
   C. a fish hook.
   D. a boat.

10. What did Wayne Grover do first in the process of helping the baby dolphin?
    F. He went to the surface to breathe.
    G. He cut the fishing line.
    H. He tried to loosen the hook with his finger.
    J. He used his knife on the hook.

11. Grover stroked the baby dolphin to—
    A. find the wound.
    B. help it breathe.
    C. calm it.
    D. stop the bleeding.

GO ON

12. Why was Grover especially fearful of sharks while he worked to help the baby dolphin?
    F. Sharks are attracted to blood.
    G. Sharks often attack divers who stay in one place.
    H. Sharks often hunt for young dolphins.
    J. Sharks follow the sounds that dolphins make.

13. What was the last step Grover took before he let the baby dolphin go?
    A. He slipped the knife into the wound.
    B He took the hook out of the muscle.
    C. He held the dolphin down with his leg.
    D. He pressed hard on the wound to stop the flow of blood.

14. You can tell from reading this selection that the author—
    F. learned how to speak with dolphins.
    G. was frightened by this experience.
    H. was very moved by this experience.
    J. gained a new respect for sharks.

15. Which action by the father dolphin best supports the idea that the dolphin parents were asking Wayne Grover to help their baby?
    A. The father shot away when Grover reached out to touch him.
    B. After bringing the baby to Grover, the father lifted Grover's arm.
    C. The father raced off to attack a large bull shark.
    D. The father returned quickly when the mother clicked.

STOP

Steps in a Process

- The actions you take to make something or to reach a goal are the **steps in a process.**

- When you read, look for clues that help you follow the steps. Clues may be numbers, illustrations, or words such as *first, next, then,* and *last.*

- If there are no clues, think of what you already know about how the process might be done.

Directions: Read the story.

The best part of Dr. Lisa Carson's day is talking to the children who visit Sea View Park. Dr. Lisa, as the kids call her, is the aquarium director.

"What is your job?" the children always ask Dr. Lisa.

"I take care of the creatures at Sea View Park," she replies. "First thing every morning, I check all the tanks. I make sure nothing has fallen into the water. I make sure the water isn't too hot or too cold. Next, I feed all the fish, dolphins, and whales. Every creature has a different breakfast! Third, I check the fish to make sure they are healthy. I look at their scales and their eyes. I also see how well they are moving. Then, I check with the other animal workers. Finally, I make up the schedule of the day's events."

Directions: Complete the table. Think about what it says in the story to help you order the steps Dr. Lisa takes each morning. Give clue words for the steps given.

Dr. Lisa's Morning Routine	Clue Word
She checks all the tanks.	1.
2.	next
She checks the fish.	3.
4.	then
5.	finally

Notes for Home: Your child read a story, identified the steps in a process, and wrote the clue words that signal the order of each step. *Home Activity:* Have your child make a numbered list showing the steps necessary to make breakfast.

© Scott Foresman 5

Cause and Effect

Directions: Read the story. Then read each question about the story. Choose the best answer to each question. Mark the letter for the answer you have chosen.

Fun with Fins

"Let's go scuba diving, Nick!" Luis said on the phone.

"Great idea!" I answered. "I'll check with my parents and get back to you this afternoon."

My parents knew I was a good diver, so they gave me permission right away.

I called Luis back, and we made plans to dive at Crescent Reef in a week. Crescent Reef was one of our favorite spots.

Since I had not been scuba diving in a while, I spent the week rereading my safety manual. I studied the rules carefully. I reviewed how to use the breathing equipment and how to fasten the weight belt. I read about how long it is safe to stay in the deep water. I felt a lot more confident as a result.

On the day of the dive, Luis picked me up early. I loaded my diving equipment. Then I went back for the extras. Luis laughed when he saw my pack. On the four-hour drive to get to the reef, though, he was glad I had packed food and water bottles. On the four-hour drive back, he was glad I'd brought the extra dry towels too.

Thanks to my planning, the dive was a great success. We had the best time! I can't wait to do it again.

1. Nick asked his parents if he could go scuba diving because—
   A. he needed to get their permission first.
   B. he thought it was a great idea.
   C. Luis told him to ask.
   D. diving was his favorite sport.

2. One effect of Nick's not having dived for a while was that—
   F. he asked permission first.
   G. he packed a lot of food.
   H. he reread his safety manual to review the diving rules.
   J. he felt confident.

3. Rereading his safety manual caused Nick to—
   A. feel more confident.
   B. study the rules harder.
   C. pack more food.
   D. be a better friend.

4. Why did Nick pack food, water, and extra dry towels?
   F. Luis always forgot to pack.
   G. They had to drive four hours each way.
   H. They were leaving early.
   J. His parents told him to do it.

5. Why was Nick and Luis's diving trip a great success?
   A. Luis is a good friend.
   B. The weather was good.
   C. Nick planned the trip carefully.
   D. Nick wanted to go again.

Notes for Home: Your child read a story and identified causes and effects. *Home Activity:* Invite your child to explain the causes (why something happens) and effects (what happens) of playing a sport such as baseball or soccer.

Writing Across Texts

Directions: Consider what you learned about dolphins in "The Diver and the Dolphins" and "Dolphin Behavior." Add five more details to each side of the table below to show that dolphins are social animals.

The Diver and the Dolphins	Dolphin Behavior
The dolphin family circles the diver. The dolphin family makes clicking noises at the diver.	Dolphins feed, play, rest, touch, and resolve conflicts together. A baby stays close to its mother for six months.
1.	6.
2.	7.
3.	8.
4.	9.
5.	10.

Write Details to Support a Topic Sentence

Use supporting details from the table and the reading selections to write a paragraph that supports the following topic sentence: *Dolphins are social animals.*

Notes for Home: Your child has combined and used information from more than one source. *Home Activity:* As you read a story or an article with your child, discuss the details that authors use to support their topic sentences.

Grammar: Subjects

REVIEW

Directions: Underline the complete subject in each sentence. Then circle each simple subject.

1. Most people find dolphins to be very appealing creatures.

2. These friendly, intelligent mammals have even become film and TV stars.

3. A very popular movie in 1963 was called *Flipper*.

4. Flipper is a wounded dolphin in the movie.

5. A young boy and his family nurse Flipper back to health.

6. The devoted dolphin returns later to save the boy from sharks.

7. Many viewers were charmed by the dolphin movie star.

8. The movie's success led to an equally popular TV series.

9. Another film about Flipper was made more than thirty years later, in 1996.

10. A boy and a dolphin once again develop a special relationship.

Directions: Use each group of words as a complete subject in a sentence. Write your sentence on the line. Then circle the simple subject.

11. the intelligent dolphin

_____

_____

12. movies about animals

_____

_____

13. dolphins and dogs

_____

_____

14. trained seals

_____

_____

15. almost any animal

_____

_____

Notes for Home: Your child recognized and used subjects in sentences. *Home Activity:* Read part of a story about an animal with your child. Ask your child to identify the subjects of the sentences.

Grammar: Nouns

A **noun** is a word that names one or more persons, places, or things. Some nouns name things you cannot see, such as ideas or feelings.

 Person: doctor   **Place:** school   **Thing:** book   **Thing (Idea):** freedom

Nouns may be found in the subject of a sentence, in the predicate, or in both the subject and the predicate.

Directions: Write whether each noun names a person, place, or thing.

1. dolphin _____
2. ocean _____
3. protection _____
4. sailor _____
5. vacation _____

6. boat _____
7. island _____
8. fin _____
9. scientist _____
10. loyalty _____

Directions: Underline the noun or nouns in each sentence. Write **S** above the noun if it is the subject. Write **P** if it is in the predicate.

11. Scientists study the intelligence of animals.

12. Biologists carry out tests in laboratories.

13. Some workers observe dolphins in the sea.

14. Certain dolphins can live in fresh water.

15. Actually, dolphins are small whales, and they have beaks.

16. These mammals make many different special sounds.

17. Communication goes on among these fascinating creatures.

18. A young calf, or baby dolphin, will respond to a whistle from its mother.

19. Trained dolphins carry messages between people.

20. These remarkable mammals have rescued people in danger of being drowned.

Notes for Home: Your child identified nouns—words that name people, places, or things. *Home Activity:* Read a newspaper article together. Ask your child to point out each noun and tell whether it names a person, a place, or a thing.

Extra Practice

Grammar: Nouns

Directions: Underline the nouns in each sentence. Write **PER** above the noun if it names a person, **PL** if it names a place, or **T** if it names a thing. Remember, some nouns name things you cannot see, such as ideas.

1. Children visit the exhibits at the aquarium daily.

2. A guide shares facts about the fish and other creatures of the sea.

3. Two youngsters are quietly watching a tuna swim in the tank.

4. Many of the children in the room ask questions and talk about the answers.

5. The leader gives out booklets with information.

Directions: Add a noun that makes sense to complete each sentence. Write the noun on the line to the left.

_____ 6. The giant glass tank holds tropical _____.

_____ 7. The various fish have bright, beautiful _____.

_____ 8. A _____ feeds the fish at the same time each day.

_____ 9. A large turtle paddles steadily upward in another _____.

_____ 10. Children and adults are watching it closely through the _____.

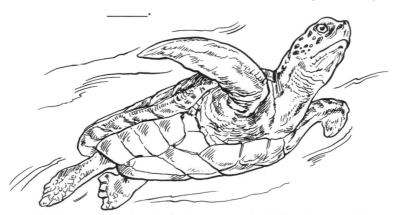

Write a Poem

On a separate sheet of paper, write a poem about an ocean creature's adventure. Include at least one noun that names a person, one that names a place, and two that each name a thing, including an idea. The poem does not have to rhyme.

© Scott Foresman 5

Notes for Home: Your child identified nouns—words that name people, places, and things. *Home Activity:* Say sentences to your child that tell about your day. After your child writes each sentence, ask him or her to identify the nouns it contains.

Name _____

Grammar: Nouns

Complete the sentence. Write one word for each picture.

The _____ rowed a _____ in the _____ .

    (noun)   (noun)   (noun)

A **noun** names a person, place, or thing. Nouns name things we can see or touch. Nouns also name ideas, such as *honesty, skill,* and *beauty.*

Directions: Circle the nouns in each sentence.

1. Emilio visited Newfoundland in Canada.

2. The island has an interesting history.

3. The Vikings were early explorers of the land.

4. One group built a settlement on the island in the tenth century.

5. The settlers stayed for only a few years.

Directions: Complete each sentence with a noun from the box. Use the noun that best fits the sentence. One noun will be used more than once.

coast	Canada	fish	John Cabot

6. _____ explored the eastern coast of Canada.

7. _____ claimed Newfoundland and other areas for England.

8. Cabot told stories about amazing numbers of fish off the _____ of Newfoundland.

9. Travelers to _____ found some of the best fishing banks in the world.

10. A fishing bank is a shallow part of the ocean that has many _____ .

 Notes for Home: Your child identified nouns in sentences. *Home Activity:* Together, think of categories such as *music* and *food.* Have your child write as many nouns as possible for each category.

© Scott Foresman 5

Grammar: Nouns

Directions: Circle the nouns in each sentence.

1. Canada is the northern neighbor of the United States.

2. The country has two official languages.

3. Both French and English are spoken there.

4. Many different people form the population.

5. Important products include wheat and iron.

6. Wheat is grown on the prairies.

7. The mountains are rich in minerals.

8. There are many rivers and lakes.

9. Waterfalls help produce electricity.

10. Montreal is a large city in Canada.

11. Montreal is named for a high mountain.

Directions: Find the nouns in the paragraph. List them below.

    Canada is the second largest country in the world. Only Russia is larger in area. The Pacific Ocean is on the west coast. The Atlantic Ocean is on the east coast. The United States shares the southern boundary. It is the longest border without posts for defense in the world.

12. _____ 17. _____ 22. _____

13. _____ 18. _____ 23. _____

14. _____ 19. _____ 24. _____

15. _____ 20. _____ 25. _____

16. _____ 21. _____ 26. _____

Write a Travel Guide

Write a travel guide that describes a place that interests you. Include details about places to visit and things to do. Use a separate sheet of paper.

© Scott Foresman 5

Notes for Home: Your child identified and wrote nouns in sentences. *Home Activity:* Have your child write, from memory, sentences that tell about what is in his or her bedroom. Make sure your child uses at least two nouns in each sentence.

Phonics: Consonant Sounds for *c* and *g*

Directions: Read the sentences below. Two words in each sentence have the letter **c**. One word has a **hard-c** sound as in **care**. The other word has a **soft-c** sound as in **face**. Circle the words with the **hard-c** sound. Underline the words with the **soft-c** sound.

1. I decided to try to call the dolphin.

2. My voice seemed to encourage the dolphin.

3. In fact, the dolphin surfaced immediately.

4. I carefully placed my hand on its skin.

5. The dolphin soon became peaceful.

Directions: Read the sentences below. Two words in each sentence have the letter **g**. One word has a **hard-g** sound as in **get**. The other word has the **soft-g** sound as in **giant**. Circle the word with the **hard-g.** Underline the word with the **soft-g.**

6. A large dolphin was snagged in the net.

7. It began to thrash its huge tail.

8. The situation grew dangerous.

9. One gentle tug released it.

10. I imagined the dolphin gave me a smile.

Directions: Find the word in each sentence that has both a **hard** and a **soft consonant sound.** Write the word on the line.

_____ 11. Dolphins can be very engaging and gentle creatures.

_____ 12. They speak their own language using signals.

_____ 13. I'm convinced they like me to come dive near them.

_____ 14. I see them circling around me in the water.

_____ 15. I encourage their playful behavior.

Notes for Home: Your child identified words with hard-*c* sounds *(care)*, soft-*c* sounds *(face)*, hard-*g* sounds *(get)*, and soft-*g* sounds *(giant)*. **Home Activity:** Read a book about sea animals with your child. Have your child to find and pronounce words with these letters and sounds.

Spelling: Consonant Sounds /j/ and /k/

Pretest

Pretest Directions: Fold back the page along the dotted line. On the blanks, write the spelling words as they are dictated. When you have finished the test, unfold the page and check your words.

1._____	1. Her father is an Army **major**.
2._____	2. Yolanda's best **subject** is math.
3._____	3. He is a **junior** camp counselor.
4._____	4. The **judge** banged her gavel.
5._____	5. We stayed at a mountain **lodge**.
6._____	6. The **ridge** is very high.
7._____	7. The window **ledge** is icy.
8._____	8. The **legend** was interesting.
9._____	9. A **general** commands troops.
10._____	10. Peaches are grown in **Georgia**.
11._____	11. A good **character** is important.
12._____	12. Rachel joined the **chorus**.
13._____	13. The **orchestra** plays today.
14._____	14. He is a good **mechanic**.
15._____	15. This is a hard **chord** to play.
16._____	16. A **raccoon** ate our food.
17._____	17. When did the accident **occur**?
18._____	18. This clock is not **accurate**.
19._____	19. Do you fish on **occasion**?
20._____	20. Did they **accuse** him?

© Scott Foresman 5

Notes for Home: Your child took a pretest on words that have the consonant sounds of /j/ and /k/. **Home Activity:** Help your child learn misspelled words before the final test. Your child should look at the word, say it, spell it aloud, and then spell it with eyes shut.

Spelling: Consonant Sounds /j/ and /k/

Word List

major	ridge	character	raccoon
subject	ledge	chorus	occur
junior	legend	orchestra	accurate
judge	general	mechanic	occasion
lodge	Georgia	chord	accuse

Directions: Choose the words from the box that have the consonant sound /k/ heard at the beginning of **car.** Write each word in the correct column.

Consonant /k/ spelled ch

1. _____

2. _____

3. _____

4. _____

5. _____

Consonant /k/ spelled cc

6. _____

7. _____

8. _____

9. _____

10. _____

Directions: Write the word from the box that belongs in each group of words. Hint: Each word has the consonant sound /j/ heard at the beginning of **jail.**

11. freshman, sophomore, _____

12. Alabama, Mississippi, _____

13. regular, common, _____

14. myth, story, _____

15. greater, important, _____

16. hill, mountain, _____

17. topic, theme, _____

18. inn, hotel, _____

19. lawyer, jury, _____

20. edge, cliff, _____

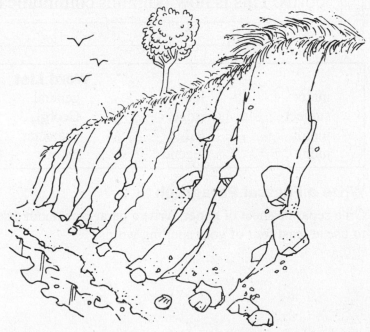

Notes for Home: Your child spelled words that have the consonant sounds /j/ *(junior, ridge, general)* or /k/ *(character, occur).* **Home Activity:** Help your child think of and spell additional words with these sounds and spellings. Then check the spellings in the dictionary.

Spelling: Consonant Sounds /j/ and /k/

Directions: Proofread this report. Find four spelling mistakes. Use the proofreading marks to correct each mistake.

Dolphins are the subjeck of my report. It is not acurate to call dolphins fish. They are actually mammals. Dolphins are warm-blooded and have lungs like other mammals. They are highly intelligent and in general are friendly and playful with humans. On one ocassion, I saw dolphins put on a show in the ocean. Several of them made clicking sounds together like a corus. This is how dolphins communicate.

≡	Make a capital.
/	Make a small letter.
∧	Add something.
℘	Take out something.
⊙	Add a period.
¶	Begin a new paragraph.

Spelling Tip

chorus   orchestra
The consonant sound /k/ can be spelled **ch, c,** or **cc.** Remember: You can **hear** the **chorus** and **orchestra.**

Word List

major	lodge	general	orchestra	occur
subject	ridge	Georgia	mechanic	accurate
junior	ledge	character	chord	occasion
judge	legend	chorus	raccoon	accuse

Write a Factual Paragraph

On a separate sheet of paper, write a paragraph about a sea animal or a fish. Try to use at least four of your spelling words.

Notes for Home: Your child spelled words that have the consonant sounds /j/ (*junior, ridge, general*) or /k/ (*character, occur*). **Home Activity:** Hold a spelling bee with your child, family, and friends using these spelling words.

Spelling: Consonant Sounds /j/ and /k/

Word List			
major	ridge	character	raccoon
subject	ledge	chorus	occur
junior	legend	orchestra	accurate
judge	general	mechanic	occasion
lodge	Georgia	chord	accuse

Directions: Choose the word from the box that answers each question. Write the word on the line.

_____ 1. In what state are peaches and peanuts grown?

_____ 2. Who decides who wins a contest?

_____ 3. What animal appears to wear a mask?

_____ 4. Which word can mean both "widespread" and "a commanding officer"?

_____ 5. What group plays music?

_____ 6. What would add to your name if you were named after your father?

_____ 7. What rhymes with *lord* and refers to something musical?

_____ 8. In what kind of building might you stay on a skiing vacation?

Directions: Choose the word from the box that contains each word below. Write the word on the line. Use each word only once.

9. rid _____

10. act _____

11. use _____

12. rate _____

13. sub _____

14. us _____

15. or _____

16. end _____

17. me _____

18. edge _____

19. as _____

20. cur _____

Notes for Home: Your child spelled words that have the consonant sounds /j/ *(junior, ridge, general)* or /k/ *(character, occur)*. **Home Activity:** Take turns picking a spelling word and giving clues about it like those above. Another person must guess the word and spell it.

Chart/Table

A **chart** organizes information in a visual way. It may include words, numbers, or both. A **table** is a type of chart that organizes information in rows and columns.

Directions: Use the table to answer the questions that follow.

Type of Whale	Scientific name	Where It Lives	Length
Dall porpoise	*Phocoenoides dalli*	Pacific Ocean	up to 6 feet (1.8 meters)
pilot whale	*Globicephala melaena*	Atlantic Ocean	up to 20 feet (6 meters)
white-sided dolphin	*Lagenorhynchus albirostris*	North Atlantic Ocean	up to 9 feet (2.7 meters)
killer whale	*Orcinus orca*	all oceans	up to 30 feet (9 meters)
bottle-nosed dolphin	*Tursiops truncatus*	all oceans	up to 9 feet (2.7 meters)
common porpoise	*Phocoena phocoena*	all oceans	up to 6 feet (1.8 meters)
common dolphin	*Delphinus delphis*	all oceans	up to 8 feet (2.4 meters)

1. What is the scientific name for the bottle-nosed dolphin? _____

_____

2. Where does the pilot whale live? _____

3. How long may a killer whale be? _____

4. What kind of dolphin has the scientific name *Phocoena phocoena?* _____

_____

5. Which type of whale may be the longest in length? _____

_____

6. Which types of dolphins may be the shortest in length? _____

_____

7. Which type of dolphin is found only in the Pacific Ocean? _____

_____

8. Which types of dolphins may be found in all oceans? _____

_____

_____

9. How much longer may a common dolphin be than a common porpoise? _____

_____

10. Where can the white-sided dolphin be found? _____

_____

11. Which dolphin has the scientific name *Lagenorhynchus albirostris?* _____

_____

12. Is every pilot whale 20 feet long? Explain. _____

_____

_____

_____

13. Which types of dolphins are found in only one ocean? _____

_____

14. Are most full-grown dolphins longer or shorter than most fifth graders? Explain.

_____

_____

_____

15. Are tables useful for comparing information? Explain. _____

_____

_____

_____

Notes for Home: Your child analyzed information in a table. ***Home Activity:*** Work with your child to create a table with information about different family members. Columns on the chart might list information such as each person's name, age, color of hair, color of eyes, and height.

Family Times

Name_____

Summary

Weather Bulletin: Watch Out for Hurricanes!

In "The Fury of a Hurricane," Patricia Lauber explains how hurricanes form and how hurricanes affect the land and wildlife. In 1992, Hurricane Andrew came ashore in southeastern Florida and damaged more than 100,000 homes and commercial areas. Mangrove swamps were shredded. It is still not known how much permanent damage was done to wildlife.

Activity

Conduct an Interview. Ask any questions you have about hurricanes. Let your child show off his or her knowledge by answering each question as a hurricane authority! If your child doesn't know the answer, visit your local library or search the Internet for the answer.

Reading Skills

Graphic Sources

Articles that give information often do so using both text and visuals. A **graphic source** is something that shows information visually, such as a picture, chart, graph, or map. For example, Patricia Lauber's article includes diagrams of hurricanes, photos of hurricane damage, and maps of places where hurricanes have struck.

Graphic sources can help you understand information, draw conclusions, and make predictions as you read. For example, Patricia Lauber's diagrams make it easier to understand how a hurricane forms.

Mon.	Tues.	Wed.	Thur.	Fri.	Sat.	Sun.

Activity

How's the Weather? Look together at graphic sources in newspapers, particularly in the section that focuses on the weather. What's the forecast for your part of the country? Talk about what each photo, illustration, chart, graph, map, or diagram shows. Take turns playing a weather forecaster, using the graphic sources as props to help you tell about the weather expected this week.

Family Times

Tested Vocabulary

Words to Know

Knowing the meaning of these words is important to reading "The Fury of a Hurricane." Practice using these words to learn their meanings.

damage harm or injury that lessens value

ecology relationships between living things and the environment

hurricane intense tropical storm

identify recognize as being a particular thing

mightiest strongest; most powerful

predict tell before an event happens

pressure the continued action of weight or other force

recovered got back something lost

Grammar

Proper Nouns

A **proper noun** names a particular person, place, or thing. The first word and each important word of a proper noun are capitalized.

Proper Nouns
Person: Sharon Jones, Dr. A. P. Smith
Place: Miami Beach, Florida
Thing: December (month) Fourth of July (holiday) *Hurricanes: Earth's Mightiest Storms*

Activity

Find that Proper Noun! Pair up family members, and set a time limit of three minutes to look through a newspaper or magazine. See how many proper nouns you can find in that time. Make a list of them. Who was able to find the most proper nouns? Then check that capital letters were used correctly in the lists.

Tested Spelling Words

_____ _____ _____ _____

_____ _____ _____ _____

_____ _____ _____ _____

_____ _____ _____ _____

© Scott Foresman 5

Graphic Sources

- A **graphic source** is something that shows information visually. Pictures, charts, graphs, and maps are graphic sources.

- Graphic sources can help you better understand what you read because they provide a lot of information that can be seen quickly.

Directions: Reread "Hurricane Seasons." Then use the bar graph and the text to answer the questions below.

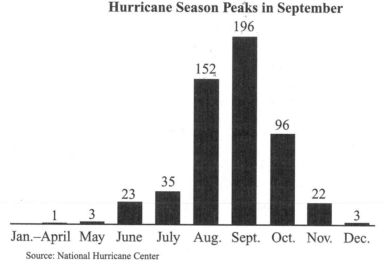

Hurricane Season Peaks in September

Source: National Hurricane Center

1. Read the labels on the bar graph and text. What does the bar graph show?

_____

_____

2. How do you know to which years the bar graph refers?

_____

_____

3. The text says that more than 80% of the hurricanes occur from August through October. How does the bar graph help show this information?

_____

_____

4. Would you use the text or the bar graph to compare different months?

_____

5. Which month has the second highest number of hurricanes? _____

Notes for Home: Your child read a short text and studied a related bar graph. *Home Activity:* Together with your child, read a weather report and study a weather map from a newspaper. Discuss what information each reveals and how the map can help you understand the text.

Vocabulary

Directions: Read the following weather bulletin. Choose the word from the box that best completes each sentence. Write the word on the matching numbered line to the right.

WEATHER BULLETIN

Our weather radar has managed to
1. _____ a dangerous **2.** _____ that is
blowing over the Atlantic Ocean. We
3. _____ that the **4.** _____ winds will
hit our area around noon tomorrow.
Since they could do heavy **5.** _____,
all residents are advised to board up
their windows.

1. _____
2. _____
3. _____
4. _____
5. _____

Check the Words You Know

__ damage
__ ecology
__ hurricane
__ identify
__ mightiest
__ predict
__ pressure
__ recovered

Directions: Choose the word from the box that best matches each clue. Write the word in the puzzle.

Down

6. the force per unit of area
7. relationship between living things and the environment
8. tell before an event happens
10. harm or injury

Across

9. got back something lost

Write a Weather Report

Imagine you witnessed a storm. On a separate sheet of paper, report what happened. Use as many vocabulary words as you can.

Notes for Home: Your child identified and used new vocabulary words from "The Fury of a Hurricane" *Home Activity:* Imagine you and your child are weather reporters. Use as many vocabulary words as possible to describe a terrible storm.

Graphic Sources

- A **graphic source** shows information, such as a picture, graph, or map, visually.
- As you read, compare the written words to the graphic sources for a better understanding of the main ideas.

Directions: Study the following maps from "The Fury of a Hurricane." Then use the maps to answer the questions below.

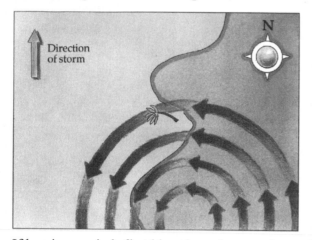
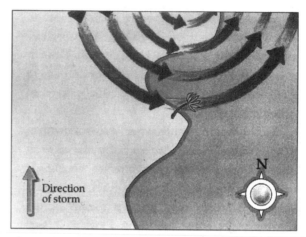

If hurricane winds first blow from the east, they will blow from the west after the eye has passed.

From HURRICANES: EARTH'S MIGHTIEST STORMS by Patricia Lauber. Copyright © 1996 by Patricia Lauber. Reprinted by permission of Scholastic Inc.

Directions: Refer to the graphics to answer the questions below.

1. According to the compass and the arrow, in which direction is the storm moving?

_____

2. What do the maps show?

_____

_____

_____

3. How does the caption help you interpret the maps?

_____

4. How do the maps help you understand what the text is saying about wind direction?

_____

5. Choose another graphic source from "The Fury of a Hurricane." On a separate piece of paper, tell how the graphic source helps you understand the information in the text.

Notes for Home: Your child analyzed two maps and a caption. ***Home Activity:*** Use newspapers to discuss with your child what is shown in a different graphic source, such as a schedule or a bar graph.

Selection Test

Directions: Choose the best answer to each item. Mark the letter for the answer you have chosen.

Part 1: Vocabulary

Find the answer choice that means about the same as the underlined word in each sentence.

1. These are the mightiest storms.
   - A. most frightening
   - B. longest lasting
   - C. most interesting
   - D. most powerful

2. The ecology of the area has changed.
   - F. population growth
   - G. physical features such as rocks
   - H. kinds of houses
   - J. relation between living things and their environment

3. They ran to take shelter from the hurricane.
   - A. a storm with violent winds that begins over tropical waters
   - B. a seasonal wind that brings rain from April to October
   - C. a cloud shaped like a funnel
   - D. a storm with heavy snow

4. People in the area soon recovered.
   - F. got help or support
   - G. became smaller
   - H. got back to normal
   - J. were hit again

5. The storm did not cause much damage.
   - A. loss of courage
   - B. harm or injury
   - C. change in how people live
   - D. feeling that nothing good can happen

6. Did you predict that this would happen?
   - F. tell ahead of time
   - G. make up one's mind
   - H. feel afraid
   - J. take for granted

7. The weather report shows an area of low pressure to the west.
   - A. amount of water in the air
   - B. wind speed
   - C. weight of the atmosphere on the earth's surface
   - D. calm area in the center of a storm

8. We wanted to identify each tree.
   - F. find a use for
   - G. give a name to
   - H. look at carefully
   - J. protect the life of

Part 2: Comprehension

Use what you know about the selection to answer each item.

9. Beginning in 1979, hurricanes for the first time were named after—
   - A. men.
   - B. women.
   - C. animals.
   - D. cities.

10. As a hurricane forms, the warm air—
    - F. becomes colder.
    - G. sinks into the water.
    - H. goes up.
    - J. becomes very dry.

11. On each side of a hurricane, the—
    - A. warm air sinks.
    - B. winds blow in different directions.
    - C. rain turns to snow.
    - D. water turns different colors.

GO ON

12. During Hurricane Andrew, the greatest damage was caused by—
    F. clouds.
    G. rain.
    H. thunder.
    J. wind.

13. When Hurricane Andrew hit Florida, help was slow to arrive because—
    A. the army was not prepared.
    B. too many people were using telephones at once.
    C. people did not realize how great the damage was.
    D. members of the government refused to spend money.

14. Which conclusion does this selection best support?
    F. Hurricanes and human activities have changed Florida's environment.
    G. Areas hit by hurricanes generally recover quickly.
    H. People should be doing more to stop hurricanes.
    J. Hurricanes have ruined most of Florida.

15. The author's main purpose in writing this selection is to—
    A. entertain with an exciting story.
    B. describe the towns of Homestead and Florida City.
    C. express strong opinions about hurricanes.
    D. give information about hurricanes.

STOP

© Scott Foresman 5

Graphic Sources

- A **graphic source** shows information, such as a picture, graph, or map, visually.
- As you read, compare the written words to the graphic sources for a better understanding of the main ideas.

Directions: Read the following passage and study the table. Then answer the questions below.

Hundreds of tropical storms are born every year in the world's oceans. Many never reach land and blow themselves out over the water. Only those that reach wind speeds of at least 74 miles per hour are classified as hurricanes. There are four more classes, or categories, of hurricanes above that. Of course, even a hurricane of the lowest category can cause a lot of damage. A hurricane like Hurricane Andrew, with wind speeds of up to 195 mi/hr, is truly a destructive force.

Category	Wind Speed	Force
1	74–95 mi/hr	weak
2	96–110 mi/hr	average
3	111–130 mi/hr	strong
4	131–155 mi/hr	very strong
5	more than 155 mi/hr	terrible

1. What does the table show?

_____

2. How does the table help you understand the text?

_____

_____

3. When does a tropical storm become a hurricane?

_____

4. Describe a hurricane of average force.

_____

_____

5. What category of hurricane was Hurricane Andrew? Explain.

_____

_____

Notes for Home: Your child read a nonfiction article and analyzed a table. ***Home Activity:*** Look through a newspaper and find a picture or chart. Help your child describe what this graphic source shows.

Author's Purpose and Text Structure

REVIEW

Directions: Read the passage. Then read each question about the passage. Choose the best answer to each question. Mark the letter for the answer you have chosen.

Fighting the Floodwaters

The city of New Orleans has always had a problem with flooding. The city's location is part of the reason. New Orleans lies between two great bodies of water, the Mississippi River on the south and Lake Pontchartrain on the north. When the Mississippi River rises from heavy rainfall to the north, the extra water naturally tries to spread out into the city. There is danger to the city from the river during heavy rains. Hurricanes traveling along the Gulf Coast also bring a threat of flooding in the city.

Another reason New Orleans often has water problems is that the city itself is like a saucer in a way. Its edges are higher than its middle. The middle dips below sea level. When a hurricane hits or when the river floods, there is always a chance that the city will fill with water.

The Orleans Levee Board was created to address the problem of flooding. The Levee Board taxes citizens and uses the money to build high banks along the river called *levees* and floodwalls.

Over the years, millions of dollars have been spent on hurricane and flood protection. Today the city is safeguarded by a complex system of levees, floodwalls, and floodgates. The longest of the levees and floodwalls are along the Mississippi River and Lake Pontchartrain.

1. This text is—
   A. fiction.
   B. nonfiction.
   C. poetry.
   D. drama.

2. This passage—
   F. describes a terrible flood.
   G. argues that levees are useful.
   H. provides flood statistics.
   J. describes a way to solve a flooding problem.

3. The organization of this text is best described as—
   A. cause and effect.
   B. problem and solution.
   C. comparison and contrast.
   D. sequence of events.

4. This passage is—
   F. funny.
   G. emotional.
   H. informative.
   J. persuasive.

5. What do you think is the author's purpose for writing?
   A. to entertain
   B. to express
   C. to persuade
   D. to inform

© Scott Foresman 5

 Notes for Home: Your child read a passage and identified the author's purpose and the organization of the text. **Home Activity:** Work with your child to analyze a newspaper article. Study the way the article is organized and evaluate the author's purpose.

Writing Across Texts

Directions: Consider what you learned in the selections "The Fury of a Hurricane" and "Flying into a Hurricane." Complete the web with details that show what you know about Earth's mightiest storms.

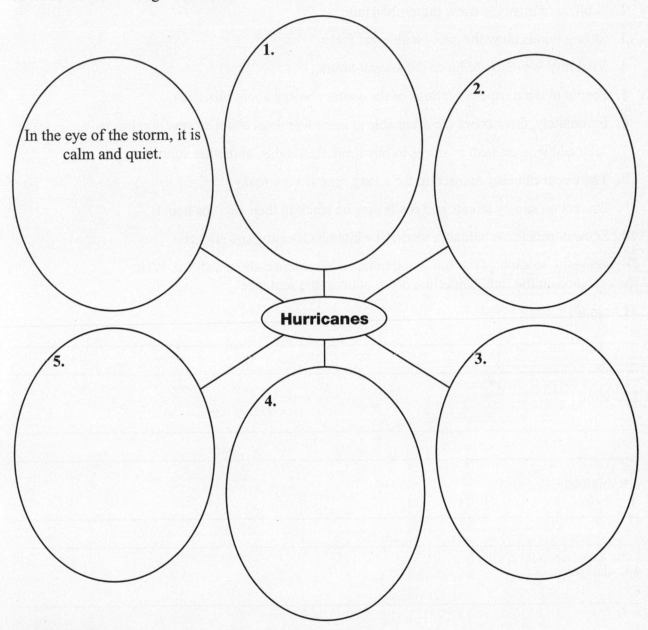

1.

2.

In the eye of the storm, it is calm and quiet.

Hurricanes

5.

4.

3.

Write a Diary

Imagine you lived in South Florida when Hurricane Andrew came ashore. Use descriptive, sensory details, as well as the facts that you listed above to create a diary about your feelings and experiences during the storm.

Notes for Home: Your child listed details about a hurricane gathered from different sources. *Home Activity:* Read and share news information, especially information about weather, with your child. Discuss the facts and experiences included in this information.

Grammar: Nouns

Directions: Circle each noun in the following sentences.

1. Do you know the difference between blizzards and other storms?

2. A blizzard involves snow rather than rain.

3. Strong winds blow the snow with great force.

4. Visibility is greatly reduced for several hours.

5. People in the northern sections of the country worry about blizzards.

6. Fortunately, forecasters are often able to issue warnings about stormy conditions.

7. Men and women rush to stores to buy food, flashlights, and other supplies.

8. The threat of being snowed in for a long time is very real.

9. Drivers on snowy streets and roads may be stuck in their cars for hours.

10. Snowstorms leave behind a world of whiteness, beauty, and silence.

Directions: Use each of the following nouns in a sentence about a storm. Write the sentence on the line. Underline every noun in the sentence.

11. clouds

_____

_____

12. wind

_____

_____

13. highway

_____

_____

14. danger

_____

_____

15. trees

_____

_____

Notes for Home: Your child identified and wrote sentences with nouns—words that name people, places, and things. ***Home Activity:*** Play a noun game. Give a prediction about the weather. Each time you use a noun, have your child raise his or her hand.

Grammar: Proper Nouns

A **proper noun** names a particular person, place, or thing. Begin the first word and every other important word in a proper noun with a capital letter. All other nouns are **common nouns**. Common nouns are not capitalized.

Common nouns: scientist, school, country
Proper nouns: Dr. Mark. E. Shen, Pace College, United States of America

Directions: Write whether each noun is **common** or **proper**.

1. hurricane _____

2. Hurricane Earl _____

3. Cape Cod _____

4. state _____

5. Mr. Taylor _____

6. California _____

7. peninsula _____

8. the District of Columbia _____

9. month _____

10. September _____

Directions: Rewrite each sentence. Capitalize proper nouns where necessary.

11. A class led by ms. miller learned about hurricanes.

_____

_____

12. Many hurricanes have formed over the ocean and hit the americas.

_____

_____

13. Hurricane david struck the dominican republic.

_____

_____

14. Did a hurricane named diane rip through rhode island?

_____

_____

15. Hurricanes usually hit between june and october.

_____

Notes for Home: Your child identified proper nouns—nouns that name particular persons, places, or things. **Home Activity:** Read a story or an article together. Invite your child to identify each proper noun.

© Scott Foresman 5

Grammar: Proper Nouns

Directions: Write **C** if the noun is common. Write **P** if the noun is proper. If it is a proper noun, write it correctly on the line.

1. rainstorm _____

2. university of texas _____

3. new york city _____

4. blizzard _____

5. dr. fernandez _____

6. weather reporter _____

7. channel 7 _____

8. newspaper _____

9. biologist _____

10. pacific ocean _____

Directions: Read the following journal entry. Replace each underlined word or phrase with a proper noun. Write the proper noun on the line with the matching number.

My class at **11.** <u>school</u> went on a very interesting field trip **12.** <u>yesterday</u>. We visited the **13.** <u>museum</u>, where we learned about different kinds of storms, especially tornadoes. Our guide told us that these whirling columns of wind are fairly frequent in the **14.** <u>nation</u>, especially between the months of March and June. **15.** <u>Our teacher</u> added that tornadoes can be more violent and destructive than hurricanes.

11. _____

12. _____

13. _____

14. _____

15. _____

Write a Weather Broadcast

Imagine you are a TV meteorologist. On a separate sheet of paper, write a weather report that tells about today's weather in your area. Use several proper nouns in your report.

Notes for Home: Your child identified and wrote proper nouns—words that name particular people, places, and things. **Home Activity:** Look at different labels on objects around your home. See how many proper nouns your child can find printed on them.

Grammar: Proper Nouns

> The proper nouns are underlined. Circle the capital letters in the proper nouns.
>
> Last <u>Thursday</u> <u>William</u> went with <u>Janet</u> to the <u>Museum</u>
> of <u>Natural</u> <u>History</u> in <u>New</u> <u>York</u> <u>City</u>.

> Use capital letters to begin the important words in proper nouns. Capitalize the names of people, pets, months, days, holidays, and particular places and things.

Directions: Circle the proper nouns in each sentence below.

1. Scientists scheduled the shuttle launch for August.

2. On Wednesday Jamie watched the shuttle launch.

3. He and his family arrived in Florida last June.

4. He attends Jefferson School near Orlando.

5. Next Friday he will show a film of the launch to Ms. Diaz.

6. The pilot could see the Atlantic Ocean below the shuttle.

7. The United States looked very small from the shuttle's window.

Directions: Write a proper noun to complete each sentence.

8. The day of the week I like best is _____.

9. I live with my family in the state of _____.

10. The name of the town I live in is _____.

11. My best friend's name is _____.

12. The school I attend is called _____.

13. My favorite holiday is _____.

14. I like the weather during the month of _____.

15. A famous place I would like to visit is _____.

16. My teacher's name is _____.

17. A good name for a dog is _____.

Notes for Home: Your child identified proper nouns. **Home Activity:** Make a list of familiar places and people, such as *doctor, bookstore, school, aunt,* and so forth. Have your child write a proper noun for each word on the list, such as *Doctor Marine.*

Name _____

Grammar: Proper Nouns

Directions: Write each sentence. Capitalize each proper noun.

1. In december of 1606, three ships set sail from london, england, for america.

   _____

   _____

2. The four-month voyage across the atlantic ocean ended in april, 1607.

   _____

3. The settlers named their colony for king james I of england.

   _____

4. On saturday aunt marta and I will visit Jamestown, virgina.

   _____

5. My dog, patches, will miss me until our return on sunday.

   _____

Directions: Write a proper noun for each common noun.

6. state _____

7. holiday _____

8. month _____

9. inventor _____

10. school _____

11. pet _____

12. lake _____

13. river _____

14. language _____

15. country _____

16. friend _____

17. ocean _____

18. day _____

19. town _____

Write an Itinerary

Plan a trip. Write a vacation itinerary describing where you would go, what you would see, and who would go with you. Use proper nouns. Write on a separate sheet of paper.

Notes for Home: Your child used correct capitalization to write proper nouns in sentences. *Home Activity:* Have your child fill in a calendar for the month, using capitals for proper nouns, such as *Uncle Ed's birthday* or *Memorial Day.*

Phonics: Silent Consonants

Directions: Silent consonants are letters you don't hear when you say a word.
Read the groups of words below. Say each word to yourself. Circle the word that
has the silent consonant. Underline the consonant that is silent.

1. kitten
   kite
   knocked
   keep

2. wrist
   ring
   rack
   rust

3. gate
   ghost
   gale
   gone

4. icing
   icicle
   igloo
   island

5. wrong
   won
   rang
   wind

6. baseball
   bomb
   burger
   basket

7. corridor
   careful
   charter
   column

8. forget
   forest
   foreign
   forgive

9. knife
   kissing
   kept
   kilometer

Directions: Read the weather report. Find six words with silent consonants.
Write each word on the line.

WEATHER BULLETIN

A large storm will hit our area sometime
today. Radar signs show us that it will
bring strong winds and heavy downpours.
If you live near the coast, take cover.
Listen for the warning whistle.
We know it will be hard, but
stay off the roads. Watch out
for fallen tree limbs. Fasten
all your shutters and doors
and stay inside.

10. _____

11. _____

12. _____

13. _____

14. _____

15. _____

Notes for Home: Your child identified words with silent consonants, such as the *g* in *design*.
Home Activity: Read or listen to a local weather report with your child. Ask your child to
point out any words with silent consonants.

Spelling: Words with *kn, mb, gh, st*

Pretest Directions: Fold back the page along the dotted line. On the blanks, write the spelling words as they are dictated. When you have finished the test, unfold the page and check your words.

Pretest

1. _____
2. _____
3. _____
4. _____
5. _____
6. _____
7. _____
8. _____
9. _____
10. _____
11. _____
12. _____
13. _____
14. _____
15. _____
16. _____
17. _____
18. _____
19. _____
20. _____

1. Her **knowledge** is very great.
2. I **know** many people.
3. No one **knew** how to do it.
4. He cracked his **knuckle**.
5. Grandmother is **knitting**.
6. This **knapsack** is very large.
7. My feet are cold and **numb**.
8. The team defused the **bomb**.
9. This **tomb** is ancient.
10. The **climber** scaled the cliff.
11. **Plumbing** is a hard job.
12. He thought he saw a **ghost**.
13. We ate **spaghetti** for lunch.
14. They were **aghast** at the idea.
15. The wet stones **glisten**.
16. Are you **listening** to me?
17. **Fasten** your seatbelts.
18. They **hustle** down the hall.
19. **Mistletoe** lives on trees.
20. Can you **whistle** a tune?

Notes for Home: Your child took a pretest on words that include the letters *kn, mb, gh,* and *st.*
Home Activity: Help your child learn misspelled words before the final test. Your child can underline the word parts that caused the problems and concentrate on those parts.

Name _____

Spelling: Words with *kn, mb, gh, st*

Word List				
knowledge	knitting	tomb	spaghetti	fasten
know	knapsack	climber	aghast	hustle
knew	numb	plumbing	glisten	mistletoe
knuckle	bomb	ghost	listening	whistle

Directions: Choose the words from the box that either begin or end with a silent consonant. Write each word in the correct column.

Begins with a Silent Consonant

1. _____

2. _____

3. _____

4. _____

5. _____

6. _____

Ends with a Silent Consonant

7. _____

8. _____

9. _____

Directions: Choose the word from the box that best completes each sentence. Write the word on the line to the left.

_____ 10. Always _____ your seat belt when riding in a car.

_____ 11. The _____ plant has small, waxy white berries and green leaves.

_____ 12. The _____ reached the snowy mountaintop.

_____ 13. We have leaky _____ in our house.

_____ 14. My favorite meal is _____ and meatballs.

_____ 15. We didn't have a _____ of a chance of winning.

_____ 16. They had to _____ to make the early train.

_____ 17. His parents were _____ at his bad grades.

_____ 18. "Are you _____ to me?" asked the teacher.

_____ 19. Sweat will _____ on your skin when you exercise.

_____ 20. Does your dog come when you _____?

Notes for Home: Your child spelled words with *kn, mb, gh,* and *st* in which the two letters together stand for only one sound. **Home Activity:** Help your child think of and spell additional words that have the letters *mb* and *st* where the *b* and *t* are silent, such as *comb, limb* and *wrestle.*

Spelling: Words with *kn, mb, gh, st*

Directions: Proofread this letter. Find five spelling mistakes. Use the proofreading marks to correct each mistake.

Dear Dan,

Last night a tornado hit our area. I knew something was wrong when I heard the wind whisle loudly. My mom was lissening to the radio. She stopped her nitting and told me to fastten the door. We spent the night in the cellar. I was num with fear.

Aren't you glad you live in another state?

Your friend,

Mark

≡	Make a capital.
/	Make a small letter.
∧	Add something.
ꙮ	Take out something.
⊙	Add a period.
¶	Begin a new paragraph.

Spelling Tip

Sometimes two consonants together stand for one sound. Remember to keep the **k** when spelling words with **kn**.

Word List

knowledge	plumbing
know	ghost
knew	spaghetti
knuckle	aghast
knitting	glisten
knapsack	listening
numb	fasten
bomb	hustle
tomb	mistletoe
climber	whistle

Write a Letter

On a separate sheet of paper, write a letter that Dan might send back to Mark. Describe a natural disaster that Dan experienced, such as a flood or blizzard. Try to use at least five of your spelling words.

Notes for Home: You child spelled words that have *kn, mb, gh,* or *st* in which the two letters together stand for only one sound. *Home Activity:* Say each word aloud. Have your child spell it and tell you which consonant is silent.

Proofread and Write

Spelling: Words with *kn, mb, gh, st*   REVIEW

Word List

knowledge	knitting	tomb	spaghetti	fasten
know	knapsack	climber	aghast	hustle
knew	numb	plumbing	glisten	mistletoe
knuckle	bomb	ghost	listening	whistle

Directions: Choose the word from the box that best matches each clue. Write the word on the line.

_____ 1. Anything that is dim, pale, or shadowy is like this.

_____ 2. This kind of noodle can be fun to eat.

_____ 3. If you like sewing, you might like this too.

_____ 4. This brings water to your kitchen sink.

_____ 5. This person is always going up or down.

_____ 6. Some students should do less talking and more of this.

_____ 7. An Egyptian pyramid is an example of this.

_____ 8. By studying, you get more of this every year.

Directions: Write the word from the box that belongs in each group.

9. sparkle, shine, _____

10. understand, think, _____

11. to flop, to fail, to _____

12. plant, white berries, _____

13. zip, button, _____

14. backpack, bookbag, _____

15. elbow, wrist, _____

16. cold, stiff, _____

17. hum, sing, _____

18. horrified, terrified, _____

19. realized, understood, _____

20. hurry, rush, _____

Notes for Home: Your child spelled words that have the letters *kn, mb, gh,* and *st* in which the two letters together stand for only one sound. ***Home Activity:*** Make a crossword puzzle with your child using words from the box. Decide where the words will intersect. Then write clues.

© Scott Foresman 5

Parts of a Book

Parts of a book include its cover, title page, copyright page, table of contents, chapter titles, captions, section heads, other text features, glossary, and index.

Directions: Use the parts of a book shown below to answer the questions on the next page.

Natural Disasters Since 1900

by Ronald O'Day

Chronicle Publication Society
New York, NY

Title Page

Copyright © 1985 Ronald O'Day

All rights reserved. No part of this book may be reproduced in any form without written permission of the publisher. Permission requests should be addressed to Chronicle Publishing Society, 100 Main Street, New York, NY, 10000.

O'Day, Ronald.
Natural Disasters Since 1900/by Ronald O'Day.
Includes index.
ISBN 1-33000-219-6
1. Earthquakes, Volcanoes, Floods, Storms.

Copyright Page

Table of Contents

Index

© Scott Foresman 5

Name _____

1. What is the title of this book? _____

2. Who wrote this book? _____

3. When was the book published? _____

4. If you were seeking information about the Johnstown flood of 1889, would this book be helpful to you? Explain.

   _____

   _____

5. If you were seeking information about the California earthquake of 1989, would this book be helpful? Why or why not?

   _____

   _____

6. How many chapters are there in this book? _____

7. What is the main topic of Chapter 3? _____

8. In which chapter would you learn about tornadoes? _____

9. In which chapter would you learn about causes of an earthquake? _____

10. On which page or pages are sandstorms discussed? _____

11. On which page or pages are blizzards discussed? _____

12. What is the meaning of the index entry **"Rivers,** see **Floods"?** _____

    _____

    _____

13. Which part of a book will help you decide how up-to-date its information is? Explain.

    _____

    _____

14. If you were seeking information on the volcanic eruption of Mt. St. Helens in Washington on May 18, 1980, would this book be helpful to you? Explain.

    _____

    _____

15. Which chapter might explain what the term *disaster* means? _____

Notes for Home: Your child used the parts of a book (the title page, copyright page, table of contents, and index) to find information. *Home Activity:* Choose a book. Have your child identify and talk about the different parts of the book.

© Scott Foresman 5

Family Times

Name_____

Summary

Hooray for Dwaina Brooks! She's Making a Difference!

Dwaina Brooks is an 11-year-old girl who cares about the homeless. After seeing homeless people cold and hungry in the Dallas streets each day, she decided to help. Dwaina and a few dozen friends turned her mother's kitchen into a food factory. With planning and cooperation, her group now makes and gives out some 300 sandwiches a night! Dwaina's good work is real food for thought!

Reading Skills

Fact and Opinion

As you read an article, you may find both statements of fact and opinion.

❖ A **fact** is something that can be proved true or false. For example, the author states that "the boxes were filled with more than three hundred sacks." You could prove that by counting the sacks.

❖ An **opinion** expresses ideas or feelings. It cannot be proved true or false, but may be supported or explained. "All of her children were generous, but Dwaina had always been a little different" is an opinion. It can't be proved, but it can be supported.

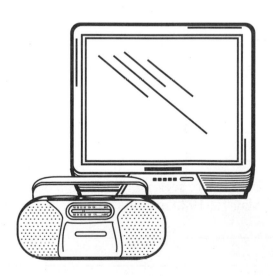

Activity

Sum It Up. Have your child summarize the story by relating its most important details. The summary should give a general idea of the steps Dwaina took to make her program successful.

Activity

Face the Facts . . . and Opinions. Listen to some TV or radio commercials. Call out "Fact!" or "Opinion!" when you hear one stated. If it is a fact, tell how you might go about proving it. See if others agree with you.

© Scott Foresman 5

Family Times

Tested Vocabulary

Words to Know

Knowing the meanings of these words is important to reading "Dwaina Brooks." Practice using these words to learn their meanings.

advised told how to do; gave advice

deliveries things that are carried and distributed

donate give money or help

organized got together and arranged

unfortunate not lucky

Grammar

Plural Nouns

Plural nouns name more than one person, place, or thing. Many plural nouns are formed by adding **-s** or **-es** to the singular form. But irregular nouns form the plural in unusual ways.

Regular	
Singular Noun	**Plural Noun**
girl	girls
glass	glasses
key	keys
baby	babies

Irregular	
Singular Noun	**Plural Noun**
man	men
foot	feet
deer	deer
wolf	wolves

Activity

See and Spell. Take turns pointing to items around your home. Challenge another person to spell the plural form of each item. Check a dictionary for the correct spelling.

Tested Spelling Words

Fact and Opinion

- A **fact** is something that can be proved true or false. Statements of fact can be proved by checking reference books, observing, measuring, and so on.

- An **opinion** tells a person's ideas or feelings. It cannot be proved true or false, but it can be supported or explained.

Directions: Reread "A Volunteer's Help." Then complete the table. Read each statement about Ellen's flood volunteer work, and answer the questions at the top of each column.

Statements	Does it state a fact or an opinion?	If an opinion, are there any clue words? If a fact, how could you try to prove it?
Ellen and her friends gathered 15 cartons of food and toys.	1.	2.
I felt really sad.	3.	4.
I thought there should be something we could do to help.	5.	6.
Lots of kids brought stuff in.	7.	8.
I felt good about it.	9.	10.

Notes for Home: Your child read a story and identified statements of fact and opinion. **Home Activity:** Read a movie or TV review with your child. Together, decide which statements are statements of fact and which are statements of opinion.

Vocabulary

Directions: Match each word on the left with its definition on the right. Write the letter of the definition next to the word.

_____	1. advised
_____	2. deliveries
_____	3. donate
_____	4. organized
_____	5. unfortunate

a. things sent and received

b. not lucky

c. arranged

d. told how to do

e. give money or help

Directions: Choose the word from the box that best completes each statement. Write the word on the line to the left.

_____ 6. *Pony* is to *ponies* as *delivery* is to _____.

_____ 7. *Happy* is to *sad* as *lucky* is to _____.

_____ 8. *Invent* is to *create* as *give* is to _____.

_____ 9. *Acted* is to *performed* as *counseled* is to _____.

_____ 10. *Long* is to *short* as *jumbled* is to _____.

Directions: Choose the word from the box that best completes each sentence. Write the word on the line.

_____ 11. Keitha and Matt _____ their time at the local food bank.

_____ 12. Last month the food bank _____ a drive to collect canned goods from the community.

_____ 13. Keitha and Matt designed flyers that _____ people on what kinds of goods were most needed and when donations could be dropped off at the food bank.

_____ 14. The food bank also provides meals to any _____ person who needs it.

_____ 15. Since Matt is old enough to drive, he makes _____ of hot meals to people who can't leave their homes.

Write a News Story

On a separate sheet of paper, write a news story about someone who did a good deed. Use as many vocabulary words as you can.

Notes for Home: Your child identified and used vocabulary words from "Dwaina Brooks." *Home Activity:* Discuss with your child ways people can help out others. Use the vocabulary words, such as: *You can <u>donate</u> your time to visiting someone in a nursing home.*

Fact and Opinion

- A **fact** is a statement that can be proved true or false. Even if it is false, it is still a statement of fact.

- An **opinion** is someone's ideas or feelings. Opinions cannot be proved true or false.

Directions: Reread this passage from "Dwaina Brooks" about Dwaina's accomplishments and goals. Then answer the questions below.

In a little more than two years, Dwaina Brooks, now in sixth grade, has organized several thousand meals for unfortunate people in the Dallas area. She and her mother and the classmates who sometimes still join in have perfected the art of helping others and having fun at the same time. They do it by doing something they already love to do: cooking and putting meals together.

Dwaina hopes to become a doctor and open her own clinic someday, but she thinks it's crazy to wait till then to start caring for others. "Kids should get going," she says. "There aren't enough jobs out there, especially for people without diplomas. Not even at McDonald's. We should try to help. If we don't act, there will be more and more homeless people. . . ."

From IT'S OUR WORLD TOO! by Phillip Hoose. Copyright ©1993 by Phillip Hoose. By permission of Little, Brown and Company.

1. Is the first sentence a statement of fact or a statement of opinion? Explain.

   _____

2. List two ways you could verify the statement made in the opening sentence.

   _____

   _____

3. Reread the quote from Dwaina. Is she stating facts or is she stating her opinion when she says, "Kids should get going."

   _____

   _____

4. How might you prove that there are not enough jobs for people without diplomas?

   _____

   _____

5. On a separate sheet of paper, write two statements of fact and two statements of opinion from the rest of the article.

Notes for Home: Your child read a nonfiction article and identified statements of fact and opinion. *Home Activity:* Work with your child to recognize statements of fact and opinion in a television or movie review.

Selection Test

Directions: Choose the best answer to each item. Mark the letter for the answer you have chosen.

Part 1: Vocabulary

Find the answer choice that means about the same as the underlined word in each sentence.

1. Leon agreed to <u>donate</u> his old bike.
   A. fix up
   B. give to a cause
   C. rent out
   D. set the value of

2. Alice made <u>deliveries</u> for her uncle.
   F. acts of carrying and giving out things
   G. requests or orders
   H. acts of collecting and organizing things
   J. reasons for doing something

3. The librarian <u>advised</u> me.
   A. refused to help
   B. gave an order to
   C. offered suggestions to
   D. tried to prevent

4. They <u>organized</u> the clothing.
   F. used again
   G. cleaned and repaired
   H. looked at carefully
   J. put together in order

5. He was an <u>unfortunate</u> man.
   A. not lucky
   B. not powerful
   C. not happy
   D. not interesting

Part 2: Comprehension

Use what you know about the selection to answer each item.

6. What grade was Dwaina in when she started making meals for the homeless?
   F. third
   G. fourth
   H. fifth
   J. sixth

7. Dwaina got the idea of making meals for the homeless when she—
   A. saw homeless people on the street.
   B. talked to a homeless man on the telephone.
   C. visited a homeless shelter.
   D. discussed the homeless with her class at school.

8. Which of these events happened first?
   F. A baker gave Dwaina twenty free boxes.
   G. Dwaina took 105 meals to the homeless center.
   H. Crystal and Stephanie helped make sandwiches.
   J. Two men helped carry the boxes into the homeless center.

9. Which word best describes Dwaina?
   A. nosy
   B. quiet
   C. wealthy
   D. caring

10. Dwaina and her mother decided to buy day-old bread instead of fresh bread because it—
    F. saved money.
    G. tasted better.
    H. lasted longer.
    J. was sold nearby.

GO ON

11. Which sentence states an opinion?
   A. Dwaina gave her lunch money to a homeless shelter.
   B. They spent three days shopping and preparing.
   C. Kids should pitch in to help the homeless.
   D. Dwaina and her classmates made more than 300 meals in one night.

12. Which statement is a valid generalization based on the facts in this selection?
   F. Most people who help the homeless were once homeless themselves.
   G. Many homeless people once had lives that were going along okay.
   H. Most homeless people need only one good meal.
   J. Many children are looking for ways to help homeless people.

13. Which sentence states a fact?
   A. We should all take care of other people.
   B. Dwaina Brooks will be a great doctor.
   C. Dwaina Brooks is the most generous girl in her school.
   D. There are hundreds of homeless people in Dallas.

14. What can you tell about the author of this selection?
   F. He is a lot like Dwaina.
   G. He is related to Dwaina.
   H. He has helped Dwaina.
   J. He admires Dwaina.

15. Which title below best fits this story?
   A. "Kids Can Make a Difference"
   B. "How to Make Hundreds of Sandwiches"
   C. "Coming Home on Fridays"
   D. "Life in a Homeless Shelter"

STOP

© Scott Foresman 5

Fact and Opinion

- A **fact** is a statement that can be proved true or false. Even if it is false, it is still a statement of fact.

- An **opinion** is someone's ideas or feelings. Opinions cannot be proved true or false.

Directions: Read the passage from a news article below.

1. Every morning, Bob Jackson and his mother walked past the empty lot. 2. "What a mess!" Bob said one day. 3. "We should do something about it."
4. "That's a great idea," his mom replied. 5. "The town owns this lot," she added. 6. "You have to call them first to get permission."

7. The next day, Bob spoke to his friends. 8. "The empty lot is the worst problem facing our town," he started. 9. "I spoke to the town clerk and she said we can clean it up. 10. I think we can make this lot the most beautiful place in town."

Directions: Imagine you are a fact checker for the local newspaper. For each sentence in the passage, tell whether it is a statement of fact or opinion. For each statement of fact, tell what you could do to prove it true or false.

Sentence	Fact or Opinion	How to Prove Facts
1.		Ask Bob or his mother.
2.		
3.		
4.		
5.		
6.		
7.		
8.		
9.		
10.		

Notes for Home: Your child read a passage and distinguished between statements of fact and opinion. **Home Activity:** Read a magazine article with your child. Work together to decide which statements are facts and which are opinions.

Dwaina Brooks

Steps in a Process

REVIEW

Directions: Read the passage. Then read each question about the passage. Choose the best answer to each question. Mark the letter for the answer you have chosen.

Working for the Homeless

Thursdays are one day of the week when Becky and her mother work together. They work as volunteers at a local soup kitchen. They cook and serve food to anyone who comes in.

There is a regular routine Becky, her mother, and the other volunteers always follow. They feed from 50 to 125 people every week, and they need to be well organized.

The first thing Becky does when she arrives is wash her hands. Then she puts on an apron. Then she goes to work on getting things ready for the next day. Next she scrubs and chops vegetables for the next day's meal. She puts the vegetables into several large pots on the stove.

Next it's time to work on the Thursday evening meal. Every Thursday the meal is chili. Chili is very popular at the soup kitchen. As each person files by a low counter, Becky dishes up a bowl of chili. She likes seeing the smiles as the smell of hot chili fills the room.

After everyone has been served, Becky helps clean up the kitchen. She washes the table tops and then wipes the trays.

At the end of the night, Becky is tired. She and her mother talk about the experience on the way home.

"Working in the soup kitchen is not always what people would call fun," Becky says, "but I really love doing it."

1. This article describes the process of—
   A. chopping vegetables.
   B. working in a soup kitchen.
   C. fighting homelessness.
   D. dishing up chili.

2. First, Becky—
   F. scrubs vegetables.
   G. washes counters.
   H. puts on her apron.
   J. washes her hands.

3. Right before she serves dinner, Becky always—
   A. cleans the kitchen.
   B. helps prepare the next day's meal.
   C. puts on her apron.
   D. washes her hands.

4. Last, Becky—
   F. helps clean up the kitchen.
   G. dishes up bowls of chili.
   H. puts on her apron.
   J. scrubs and chops vegetables.

5. What would happen if Becky forgot to put pots on the stove?
   A. She would be punished.
   B. The food would get burned.
   C. Dinner for the next day would not get cooked.
   D. The chili might taste spicy.

© Scott Foresman 5

Notes for Home: Your child read a story and identified steps in a process. *Home Activity:* Invite your child to list the steps necessary to brush his or her teeth.

Writing Across Texts

Directions: Dwaina Brooks and the diver in "The Diver and the Dolphins" were alike in some ways and different in other ways. In the table below, write your ideas about what made these two caring people so special.

Dwaina	The Diver
Dwaina was a generous and caring class leader.	He respected and protected all animals.
1.	He figured out the dolphins' problem.
2.	4.
3.	5.

Write a Poem

Write a poem of praise about these real-life, caring people. Use these lines to help you get started:

One works alone.
One works with others.

Notes for Home: Your child listed ideas from two selections about real-life heroes. ***Home Activity:*** Talk about the environment with your child. Discuss ways you and your family can show your concern for the world around you.

Grammar: Proper Nouns

REVIEW

Directions: Beside each noun, write **C** if it is common. If it is proper, write **P**, and then write the noun correctly.

1. shelter _____

2. california _____

3. grant park _____

4. kindergarten _____

5. street _____

6. los angeles _____

7. house _____

8. al smith _____

9. volunteer _____

10. church _____

11. saturday _____

12. boston celtics _____

13. mario _____

14. gomez trucking _____

Directions: Rewrite each sentence. Capitalize all proper nouns.

15. My brother mario was walking down fourth avenue one monday in june.

_____

_____

16. He noticed ms. katz, owner of hot hamburgers, throwing out boxes of food.

_____

_____

17. My brother volunteers at the drew shelter in amcstown, and he had a thought.

_____

_____

18. By july, mario and friends were collecting leftover food from ms. katz.

_____

_____

19. They borrowed a truck from mr. chan and drove the food to the fifth ave. food shelter.

_____

_____

20. From there, volunteers delivered it to the glendale shelter and othcr homeless shelters in the area.

_____

_____

Notes for Home: Your child distinguished common and proper nouns and spelled proper nouns with capital letters. **Home Activity:** Look through a magazine article with your child. Have your child list all the proper nouns she or he finds.

Grammar: Plural Nouns

Plural nouns name more than one person, place, or thing. Plural nouns are formed in different ways.

- Add **-s** to most singular nouns to form the plural.
  can/cans   bowl/bowls   house/houses   meal/meals   volunteer/volunteers

- Add **-es** to singular nouns ending in **ch, sh, x, z, s,** and **ss.**
  lunch/lunches   wish/wishes   box/boxes   gas/gases   glass/glasses

- If a noun ends in a **vowel** and **y,** add **-s.**
  donkey/donkeys   key/keys   journey/journeys

- If a noun ends in a **consonant** and **y,** change **y** to **i** and add **-es.**
  city/cities   county/counties   library/libraries   copy/copies

- Some nouns have **irregular plural** forms.
  You'll need to remember the spelling changes for nouns such as these. A dictionary can help you with irregular plurals too.
  ox/oxen   child/children   woman/women   tooth/teeth   mouse/mice

- For many nouns ending in **f** or **fe,** change **f** or **fe** to **v** and add **-es.**
  wolf/wolves   life/lives   leaf/leaves   knife/knives   shelf/shelves

- Some nouns have the same singular and plural forms.
  fish   sheep   deer   series   headquarters

Directions: Write the plural form of each singular noun. Use a dictionary if you need help.

1. watch _____
2. toy _____
3. foot _____
4. shelter _____
5. baby _____
6. fox _____
7. helper _____
8. moose _____
9. dish _____
10. man _____

11. boss _____
12. loaf _____
13. turkey _____
14. elk _____
15. bus _____
16. stripe _____
17. memory _____
18. task _____
19. zebra _____
20. half _____

Notes for Home: Your child formed plural nouns. **Home Activity:** Point out different singular items in your home. Have your child write the word that names each item, such as *floor, stove,* or *puppy.* Then have your child write the plural form of each noun.

Extra Practice

Grammar: Plural Nouns

Directions: Write the plural form of each singular noun.

1. check _____
2. woman _____
3. push _____
4. rose _____
5. sandwich _____
6. dress _____

7. tooth _____
8. monkey _____
9. tax _____
10. penny _____
11. knife _____
12. deer _____

Directions: Write the plural form of the noun in ( ) to complete each sentence.

_____ **13.** The (adult) on our street formed a special group.

_____ **14.** All the husbands and (wife) looked for ways to help others living in the neighborhood.

_____ **15.** The (child) contributed ideas also.

_____ **16.** Through the years, the group has helped many (person) in need.

_____ **17.** They ask supermarkets to donate (grocery).

_____ **18.** (Volunteer) collect and clean used clothing.

_____ **19.** Then they deliver the food and clothing in large (box).

_____ **20.** Today the group has many (branch) all over the city.

Write a Proposal

Make a plan for helping other people. On a separate sheet of paper, describe your plan. Use as many plural nouns as possible and underline them.

Notes for Home: Your child formed plural nouns—words that name more than one person, place, or thing. **Home Activity:** Look at magazine and newspaper advertisements together. Have your child identify several singular nouns. Then have him or her spell the plural forms.

© Scott Foresman 5

Name _____

Grammar: Plural Nouns

Follow the hint on each machine. Change each singular noun to a plural noun.

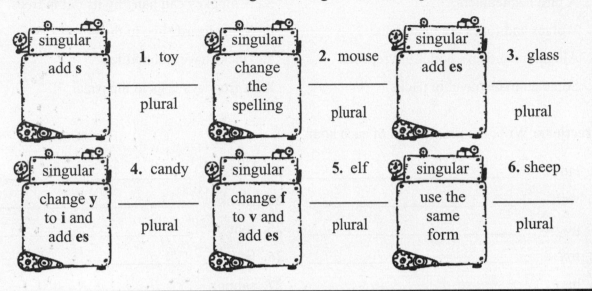

singular / add s	**1.** toy _____ plural
singular / change the spelling	**2.** mouse _____ plural
singular / add es	**3.** glass _____ plural

singular / change y to i and add es	**4.** candy _____ plural
singular / change f to v and add es	**5.** elf _____ plural
singular / use the same form	**6.** sheep _____ plural

A **plural noun** names more than one person, place, or thing. Most nouns add an ending in the plural form. Some nouns change their spelling in the plural form.

Directions: Write the plural form of each noun.

1. roof _____   **4.** tray _____   **7.** deer _____

2. thief _____   **5.** woman _____   **8.** spy _____

3. foot _____   **6.** bush _____   **9.** ax _____

Directions: Rewrite each sentence. Change the underlined singular noun to a plural noun.

10. Howard spotted the wild <u>strawberry</u>.

_____

11. The <u>leaf</u> hid some of them.

_____

12. We quickly filled the <u>box</u>.

_____

Notes for Home: Your child identified plural forms of nouns. *Home Activity:* Name objects in one room of your home. Have your child write the plural forms of the names of the objects.

Grammar: Plural Nouns

Directions: Underline each plural noun.

1. A bird has feathers.

2. Wolves and foxes are mammals.

3. Alligators and crocodiles are reptiles.

4. Some animals travel in packs.

5. A monkey can hang by its tail in trees.

6. Many lizards live in the desert.

7. Ducks have webbed feet.

8. A frog lays eggs in the water.

Directions: Write the plural form of each noun.

9. lady _____

10. wolf _____

11. goose _____

12. fox _____

13. hiss _____

14. birch _____

15. feather _____

16. ostrich _____

17. woman _____

18. puppy _____

19. boss _____

20. couch _____

21. man _____

22. ranch _____

23. branch _____

24. monkey _____

25. foot _____

26. baby _____

27. salmon _____

28. canary _____

29. bush _____

30. pouch _____

31. half _____

32. moose _____

33. class _____

34. summer _____

35. guppy _____

36. boot _____

Write a Funny Story

Write a funny story about animals. Include details about how they look and
what they do. Use plural nouns. Write on a separate sheet of paper.

Notes for Home: Your child wrote the plural forms of nouns. *Home Activity:* Read sentences
with plural nouns from a magazine or newspaper. Have your child identify the plural nouns
and write them in new sentences.

Word Study: Compound Words

Directions: Compound words are words formed from two other words, such as **something** and **bookshelf.** Combine a word from the left box with a word from the right box to form a compound word that makes sense. Write both words and the resulting compound word on the lines below.

mail	pop		head	ball
bread	night		body	stairs
fore	basket		out	doors
with	up		corn	stick
any	out		gown	box

	Left Box	**Right Box**	**Compound Word**
1.	_____	+ _____	= _____
2.	_____	+ _____	= _____
3.	_____	+ _____	= _____
4.	_____	+ _____	= _____
5.	_____	+ _____	= _____
6.	_____	+ _____	= _____
7.	_____	+ _____	= _____
8.	_____	+ _____	= _____
9.	_____	+ _____	= _____
10.	_____	+ _____	= _____

Directions: Read each sentence. Part of a compound word is missing. Choose the word that best completes the compound word and makes sense in the sentence. Write the whole compound word on the line to the left.

_____ 11. I was out_____ on my front porch.

_____ 12. Since it was summer_____, it was very hot.

_____ 13. I heard some_____ call out my name.

_____ 14. The sound came from _____where behind me.

_____ 15. It was my best friend Sue, who wanted me to play base_____ with her.

Notes for Home: Your child formed compound words, such as *something*. *Home Activity:* Experiment with common words children see around the house. Have your child put two words together to try to make a compound word. Check each word in a dictionary.

Spelling: Compound Words 1

Pretest Directions: Fold back the page along the dotted line. On the blanks, write the spelling words as they are dictated. When you have finished the test, unfold the page and check your words.

1._____

2._____

3._____

4._____

5._____

6._____

7._____

8._____

9._____

10._____

11._____

12._____

13._____

14._____

15._____

16._____

17._____

18._____

19._____

20._____

1. The **mailbox** is full.

2. There are many stores **nearby**.

3. We went **into** the library.

4. **Sometimes** I forget to be polite.

5. It was a beautiful **sunset**.

6. Is there **anything** I can do?

7. It was broad **daylight**.

8. Did you hear **something**?

9. Carl needs a **haircut**.

10. I lost my **notebook**.

11. The **earthquake** was scary.

12. The bandits have a **hideout**.

13. Read your history **textbook**.

14. We played **volleyball** today.

15. **Horseback** riding is fun.

16. Renaldo has neat **handwriting**.

17. My bike's **kickstand** broke.

18. The **rattlesnake** almost bit me.

19. This **fireplace** is made of stone.

20. **Housework** can be tiring.

Notes for Home: Your child took a pretest on compound words. *Home Activity:* Help your child learn misspelled words before the final test. Dictate the word and have your child spell the word aloud for you or write it on paper.

Name _____

Spelling: Compound Words 1

Word List				
mailbox	sunset	haircut	textbook	kickstand
nearby	anything	notebook	volleyball	rattlesnake
into	daylight	earthquake	horseback	fireplace
sometimes	something	hideout	handwriting	housework

Directions: Combine a word from each box below to form a compound word from the word list. Write the compound word on the line.

some	back
note	quake
some	out
hide	place
horse	thing
kick	stand
earth	times
rattle	book
fire	snake

1. _____

2. _____

3. _____

4. _____

5. _____

6. _____

7. _____

8. _____

9. _____

Directions: Find two words in each sentence that make up a compound word from the box at the top of the page. Write the word on the line.

_____ 10. Our house needs a lot of work done to it.

_____ 11. It took just a single volley for the ball to go out.

_____ 12. I looked in the cupboard to see what was left.

_____ 13. He dropped the piece of mail in the box.

_____ 14. Isn't there any way I can give this thing back?

_____ 15. We watched the sun as it set in the sky.

_____ 16. During the day, the light is very bright.

_____ 17. It is near the stream that runs by our house.

_____ 18. I wrote the text for the book, but I didn't illustrate it.

_____ 19. My hand is sore from writing.

_____ 20. My hair is long, and I need to get it cut.

Notes for Home: Your child spelled compound words, longer words formed by joining two or more shorter words. *Home Activity:* Together, see how many items you can find in your home that have names that are compound words. List them, and check a dictionary.

Dwaina Brooks

Spelling: Compound Words 1

Directions: Proofread this advertisement. Find four spelling mistakes. Use the proofreading marks to correct each mistake.

Volunteers Wanted!

Are you a young person looking for somethin to do this summer? Shady Rest Home is looking for young people who live nearbye to spend a few hours a week with our residents. We need volunteers to read, play voleyball and other games, or just visit and talk. Sometimes you might be needed to help in the kitchen or do some light housewerk. If interested, call 555-3725 or drop a note into a mailbox today.

| ≡ Make a capital. |
| ╱ Make a small letter. |
| ∧ Add something. |
| ⌒ Take out something. |
| ⊙ Add a period. |
| ¶ Begin a new paragraph. |

Spelling Tip

Remember to keep all the letters of the shorter words when spelling compound words. For example: **hide + out = hideout.**

Word List

mailbox	earthquake
nearby	hideout
into	textbook
sometimes	volleyball
sunset	horseback
anything	handwriting
daylight	kickstand
something	rattlesnake
haircut	fireplace
notebook	housework

Write an Advertisement

On a separate sheet of paper, write your own advertisement offering a service or selling a product. Try to use at least four of your spelling words.

Notes for Home: Your child spelled compound words, longer words formed by joining two or more shorter words. *Home Activity:* Look at the words in the box that your child didn't use in his or her writing exercise. Ask him or her to use several of these words in a sentence.

© Scott Foresman 5

Spelling: Compound Words 1

Word List

mailbox	anything	earthquake	handwriting
nearby	daylight	hideout	kickstand
into	something	textbook	rattlesnake
sometimes	haircut	volleyball	fireplace
sunset	notebook	horseback	housework

Directions: Write the word from the box that is associated with each place.

1. stationery store _____

2. barbershop _____

3. post office _____

4. school _____

5. stable _____

6. sports shop _____

7. bicycle shop _____

8. desert _____

Directions: Choose the word from the box that best completes each sentence. Write the word on the line to the left.

_____ 9. Many homes were destroyed by the _____.

_____ 10. All that was left standing of one house was the brick _____.

_____ 11. Rebecca wanted to do _____ to help the victims.

_____ 12. She filled out an application in her best _____.

_____ 13. She awoke at _____ to join the group of volunteers.

_____ 14. They scoured the disaster area looking for anyone concealed in a _____.

_____ 15. She shone her flashlight _____ dark spaces and holes.

_____ 16. She listened carefully but didn't hear _____.

_____ 17. _____ she felt like giving up.

_____ 18. Then several children were located in a _____ basement.

_____ 19. By _____ Rebecca was exhausted.

_____ 20. She couldn't even think of the _____ that would be needed to get these homes back in order.

© Scott Foresman 5

 Notes for Home: Your child spelled compound words, longer words formed by joining two or more shorter words, such as *housework* and *fireplace*. **Home Activity:** Challenge your child to make up a story using as many of the compound words listed above as possible.

Newspaper

A **newspaper** is a daily or weekly publication containing news, advertisements, features, editorials, and other useful information, such as TV listings. You can scan headlines to help you find articles you would like to read.

Directions: Scan the headlines from different parts of a newspaper. Then answer the questions that follow.

THE WORLD GAZETTE

President Signs
New Tax Bill ~~~~

~~~~~~~~~~~~~

Fire Destroys
Two Homes ~~~~

~~~~~~~~~~~

News Stories

Traffic Problems
Cause Headache

~~~~~~~~~~~~~~

To the Editor:

~~~~~~~~~~~~~

~~~~~~~~~~~~~

Editorial Page

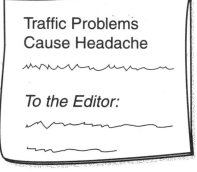

Stock Market
Listings

~~~~~~~~~~~~~

~~~~~~~~~~~~~

~~~~~~~~~~~~~

Business Section

Bulls Defeat Lakers

~~~~~~~~~~~~~

~~~~~~~~~~~~~

**Local Runner Sets
New Record**

~~~~~~~~~~~~~

~~~~~~~~~~~~~

Sports Section

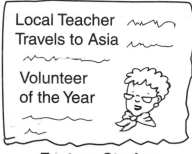

Local Teacher
Travels to Asia ~~~~

~~~~~~~~~~

Volunteer
of the Year

Feature Stories

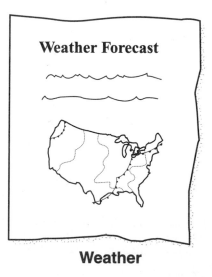

Weather Forecast

~~~~~~~~~~~~~

Weather

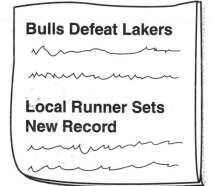

For Sale
Car for Sale

~~~~~~~~~~~~~

~~~~~~~~~~~~~

Help Wanted
Part-time
Cashier

~~~~~~~~~~~~~

Classified Ads

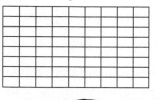

New
Play
Review
★ ★ ★

Movie Time
Shedule

~~~~~~~~~~

~~~~~~~~~~

~~~~~~~~~~

TV Listings

Entertainment Section

Name _____

1. Which part of the newspaper reports news about the U.S. President? What is the headline for an article on the President?

    _____

2. Which part of the paper has an article expressing the editor's opinion? What is the headline of that article?

    _____

3. Where would you look to find the latest stock market results? Give an example of another kind of article you might find in this section.

    _____

    _____

4. In which section would you find predictions about the high and low temperatures for the upcoming week?

    _____

5. Which part of the paper has an article on someone who volunteers time to help others? What is the headline for this article?

    _____

6. In which section would you look to find a job? What job is available? _____

    _____

7. In which section might you find information on an international peace treaty?

    _____

8. Which section includes a review of a new play? _____

9. Which section includes letters written to the editor? _____

10. When might a newspaper be a more useful resource than a nonfiction book? Explain.

    _____

    _____

    _____

    _____

    _____

    _____

    _____

    _____

© Scott Foresman 5

Notes for Home: Your child answered questions using information found in a newspaper. *Home Activity:* Look through your local newspaper with your child and find the different sections, such as News Stories, Editorial Page, Sports Section, and Entertainment.

Family Times

Name_____

Summary

The Everglades—Glorious Past, Uncertain Future

Deep in a watery glade, a storyteller brings Florida's Everglades to life for a group of children. He traces the Everglades' history, from its ancient past to its troubled present. He explains that human development has killed or driven out much of the Everglades' wildlife. But the storyteller predicts a brighter future for the Everglades if the children listening to his story go on to correct the mistakes others have made.

Activity

Get the Picture! Find out more about the Everglades and the creatures who live there. Draw a picture to illustrate one of these creatures, such as an alligator, a panther, or a pelican. Use markers, crayons, paints, or another drawing tool. When you are finished, display your illustration and tell how it reflects the story.

Reading Skills

Author's Viewpoint

The way an author thinks about the subject of his or her writing is the **author's viewpoint.** To learn an author's viewpoint, think about the author's opinion and choice of words. The storyteller in *Everglades* says "this river is like no other river on Earth." From this you know the author views the Everglades with great admiration.

When an author presents only one viewpoint, the result is unbalanced, or biased, writing. Balanced writing presents both sides of an issue equally. Because *Everglades* shows only the destructive effects of people, it can be considered biased writing.

Activity

What's the Viewpoint? Watch a TV news or documentary program about an issue that interests you. Try to figure out the viewpoint of the program based on the words and images presented. Is the program balanced or biased?

Family Times

Tested Vocabulary

Words to Know

Knowing the meanings of these words is important to reading *Everglades*. Practice using these words to learn their meanings.

brim edge bordering water

miraculous independent of the known laws of nature

pondered considered carefully

prospered flourished

quantities amounts or numbers of something

seeped leaked slowly

Grammar

Possessive Nouns

Nouns that show ownership are called **possessive nouns.** To form a **singular possessive noun,** add an **apostrophe (')** and **s** to a singular noun: **girl's, Chris's.**

To form a **plural possessive noun,** add an **apostrophe (')** to plural nouns that end in **s,** or add an **apostrophe (')** and **s** to plural nouns that do not end in **s: birds', children's.**

Activity

Whose Is It? Point to an object in the house and ask "Whose is it?" Have the other person answer the question by spelling the possessive noun and the object owned (**Chris's bike; the boys' toys).** Then switch roles and play again.

Tested Spelling Words

Author's Viewpoint

- **Author's viewpoint** is the way an author thinks about the subject of his or her writing.

- To learn an author's viewpoint, think about the author's opinion and choice of words. Sometimes you can figure out an author's viewpoint even when it is not stated directly.

- Unbalanced, or biased, writing happens when an author presents only one viewpoint. Balanced writing presents both sides of an issue equally.

Directions: Reread "Action Against Pollution." Then complete the table. Identify key words or phrases that reveal the viewpoint of the two authors. Then tell the authors' viewpoint.

Statement	What It Reveals
Young people realize that actions speak louder than words.	1.
. . . they're taking responsibility through a wide variety of actions that will help make the world a better place.	2.
When kids returned to class, they decided to do something about the problem.	3.
Thanks to their hard work and determination, it now has more than 2,500 chapters in 20 countries around the world.	4.
Authors' Viewpoint 5.	

Notes for Home: Your child read an article and identified the authors' viewpoint. *Home Activity:* Together with your child, read a column from the editorial page of a newspaper. Help your child figure out the author's viewpoint.

Vocabulary

Directions: Write the word from the box that belongs in each group.

1. leaked, drained, _____

2. amazing, unbelievable, _____

3. edge, border, _____

4. thought, considered, _____

5. amounts, numbers, _____

Directions: Choose the word from the box that best matches each clue. Write the word in the puzzle.

<table>
<tr><td>Check
the Words
You Know</td></tr>
<tr><td>__ brim</td></tr>
<tr><td>__ miraculous</td></tr>
<tr><td>__ pondered</td></tr>
<tr><td>__ prospered</td></tr>
<tr><td>__ quantities</td></tr>
<tr><td>__ seeped</td></tr>
</table>

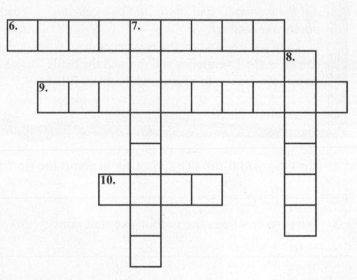

Across

6. It's what the rich person did.
9. Eggs by the dozen are these.
10. A cup can be filled to here.

Down

7. It's what the careful planner did.
8. It's what the leaky bag did.

Write a Description

Imagine a beautiful lake or pond and the animals and plants that live there. On a separate sheet of paper, describe the place. Use as many vocabulary words as you can.

 Notes for Home: Your child identified and used new vocabulary words from *Everglades*. *Home Activity:* Think of words your child knows. Give your child clues about each word. For example: *It's something that rings and is used for talking to others. (telephone)*

Author's Viewpoint

- An **author's viewpoint** is the way an author thinks about the subject of his or her writing. You can learn an author's viewpoint by looking at the words used and the opinions expressed.

- Balanced writing presents both sides of an issue. Unbalanced, or biased, writing presents one side more than another.

Directions: Reread what happens in *Everglades* as the storyteller completes his story. Then answer the questions below. Think about how the author reveals her viewpoint in the article.

> *Another child looked around. "And where did the mammals and snails and one-celled plants and animals go?"*
>
> They vanished when the engineers dug canals in the Everglades and drained the fresh water into the sea to make land. Farmers tilled the land; business people built towns and roads upon it. Pesticides and fertilizers flowed into the river waters and poisoned the one-celled animals and plants. The snails died, the fish died, the mammals and birds died.
>
> *"But this is a sad story," said a fifth child.*

Text Copyright ©1995 by Jean Craighead George. Used by permission of HarperCollins Publishers.

1. How do you think the author feels about the destruction of the Everglades?

_____

2. What words does the author use that convey this viewpoint?

_____

_____

3. Is the description of what happened to the creatures balanced or unbalanced? Explain.

_____

_____

4. State, in your own words, the viewpoint the author has about what happened to the creatures.

_____

_____

5. On a separate sheet of paper, identify the author's viewpoint as expressed in the article as a whole. Support your answer with examples.

Notes for Home: Your child read a passage, described the author's viewpoint, and identified whether the writing shows a bias. *Home Activity:* Work with your child to read a letter to the editor and identify the author's viewpoint and bias.

© Scott Foresman 5

Selection Test

Directions: Choose the best answer to each item. Mark the letter for the answer you have chosen.

Part 1: Vocabulary

Find the answer choice that means about the same as the underlined word in each sentence.

1. Dinah sat quietly and <u>pondered</u>.
   - A. thought carefully
   - B. worried
   - C. stared at closely
   - D. became sad

2. It was a <u>miraculous</u> day.
   - F. long and tiring
   - G. marvelous; wonderful
   - H. full of jokes and teasing
   - J. upsetting; disturbing

3. Water spilled over the <u>brim</u>.
   - A. a stone wall
   - B. a cover
   - C. a large pile
   - D. an edge

4. Water <u>seeped</u> into the basement.
   - F. ran through pipes
   - G. flowed quickly
   - H. fell steadily
   - J. leaked slowly

5. There were <u>quantities</u> of small fish.
   - A. small clusters
   - B. something hidden
   - C. large numbers
   - D. something dark

6. The wildlife <u>prospered</u>.
   - F. became fewer in number
   - G. spread out in different directions
   - H. grew or developed well
   - J. became too crowded

Part 2: Comprehension

Use what you know about the selection to answer each item.

7. What is the Everglades?
   - A. a round, deep lake
   - B. a shallow, warm river
   - C. a long, thin piece of land
   - D. an ocean bay

8. Limestone is made from—
   - F. water.
   - G. tiny one-celled animals.
   - H. seashells.
   - J. grass and trees.

9. Alligators can live in saw grass because of—
   - A. their leathery skin.
   - B. the abundance of birds.
   - C. their sharp teeth.
   - D. the blowing winds.

10. Which of these came to the Everglades first?
    - F. Spanish conquistadors
    - G. panthers
    - H. Calusa people
    - J. orchid hunters

11. Which sentence states an opinion?
    - A. Hunters shot tens of thousands of egrets.
    - B. *Seminole* means "runaway."
    - C. Alligators were hunted for their hides.
    - D. This is a sad story.

GO ON

12. What can you tell about the author of this selection?

    F.   She has a great love for the beauty of the natural world.

    G.   She would like to build a new home in the Everglades.

    H.   She sees no future for the creatures of the Everglades.

    J.   She thinks storytellers should tell happy stories, not sad ones.

13. Which sentence best describes this selection?

    A.   It is mostly make-believe, but some of it is based on facts.

    B.   It is mostly based on facts, but the author's choice of words expresses her point of view.

    C.   It is mostly based on old legends.

    D.   It is mostly opinions, with some facts to support the opinions.

14. Which of these human acts does the author think was harmful to the Everglades?

    F.   draining water from the Everglades to make land

    G.   catching fish in the Everglades

    H.   making tools out of seashells found in the Everglades

    J.   poling a dugout canoe through the Everglades

15. The author would most likely agree with which of these statements?

    A.   Some of the plants and animals of the Everglades should probably be restored, but only the ones people like.

    B.   People should continue to make money from the rich resources in the Everglades.

    C.   The wonders of nature in the Everglades can return only if people change their ways.

    D.   The Everglades was never a good environment for fishing.

STOP

Author's Viewpoint

- An **author's viewpoint** is the way an author thinks about the subject of his or her writing. You can learn an author's viewpoint by looking at the words used and the opinions expressed.

- Balanced writing presents both sides of an issue. Unbalanced, or biased, writing presents one side more than another.

Directions: Read the two passages below.

Passage 1

    The timber industry employs thousands of workers. Without trees to cut, many people would be out of work. Their families would go hungry. Some misguided people complain that by cutting down the forest, we are destroying the habitat of certain animals and birds. This is unlikely. Birds can always fly to a new home and animals can survive almost anything. What's important is to keep people working and make America strong.

Passage 2

    The world of many animals is very fragile. Cutting down a forest where these creatures have lived for generations is like a dcath sentence. They cannot adapt to the destruction of their environment and will die. These forests must be protected from greedy developers and lumber companies. They only want to get rich. New laws must be passed to end the killing of innocent creatures.

Directions: Complete the table. Think about the words used in the two passages and the opinions expressed that reveal each author's viewpoint.

Author's Viewpoint	Words Used	Opinions Expressed
Passage 1 Forests must be cut down to keep lumber workers employed.	1.	2.
Passage 2 3.	4.	5.

 Notes for Home: Your child read two passages and identified each author's viewpoint. *Home Activity:* Work with your child to read or listen to an advertisement. Talk about the words and the opinions that are used to try to convince people to buy the product.

Cause and Effect

Directions: Read the passage. Then read each question about the passage. Choose the best answer to each question. Mark the letter for the answer you have chosen.

Here Today—Gone Tomorrow?

Remember the dinosaurs? They are now extinct. They disappeared about 63 million years ago. Nobody knows exactly why. Remember the dodo? Remember the moa? Remember the passenger pigeon? The dodo, moa, and passenger pigeon are species of birds that are now extinct. They all disappeared within the last 200 years. Some of the mammals that have also become extinct in the last 200 years include a form of zebra called a quagga and a sea mammal called Steller's sea cow.

Over millions of years, many species have died out because natural conditions changed. However, the process of extinction may not be over. Many plants and animals *today* are in danger of becoming extinct. There are several reasons for this more recent pattern of extinction. Pollution, highway construction, overhunting, and wetland drainage all contribute to the extinction of plant and animal species. These reasons are all caused by humans.

Since the 1800s, the process of extinction has speeded up. This is a result of more people as well as more business and industry. Humans have changed the world more in the past 200 years than in all the previous centuries of human history. These changes are so rapid that many plants and animals cannot adapt. As a result of the changes, the plants and animals die out.

1. What has caused species to die out over millions of years?
   A. too much pollution
   B. too many people
   C. changing natural conditions
   D. growth of industry

2. What is the effect stated in the second paragraph?
   F. Many of today's plant and animal species are endangered.
   G. Wetlands are drained.
   H. Water is polluted.
   J. Highways are built.

3. The process of extinction has speeded up because of—
   A. more people on the earth.
   B. slowed industrial growth.
   C. clean air and water.
   D. animals' ability to adapt.

4. What is the effect of environmental changes that are too rapid?
   F. People now have more time for entertainment.
   G. Plants and animals adapt easily with changes.
   H. Plants and animals cannot adapt.
   J. Habitats stay the same.

5. What happens if plants and animals cannot adapt?
   A. They reproduce.
   B. They die out.
   C. They thrive.
   D. They get lost.

Notes for Home: Your child read a nonfiction article and identified causes and effects. *Home Activity:* Work with your child to identify causes and effects. Use "Because" statements such as *I hurt my arm because I tripped over the rock.*

Writing Across Texts

Directions: The Everglades have suffered many changes over the years—some natural and some caused by humans. In the left column, add five natural changes you read about in "The Fury of a Hurricane." In the right column, add five man-made changes you read about in *Everglades*.

Save Our National Park

The Fury of a Hurricane	Everglades
All the trees in Hurricane Andrew's path were felled.	Many areas of the Everglades were drained by engineers.
1.	6.
2.	7.
3.	8.
4.	9.
5.	10.

Write an Editorial

Using facts and details from "The Fury of a Hurricane" and *Everglades,* write an editorial to express your opinion on one of the following statements.

• Natural changes, such as those caused by hurricanes, pose the most serious threat to the Everglades.

• Changes caused by humans, such as chemical pollution, pose the most serious threat to the Everglades.

Write your editorial on a separate sheet of paper.

Notes for Home: Your child read and listed details about changes in the Florida Everglades. *Home Activity:* As you read a story or article, have your child express opinions about its topic.

© Scott Foresman 5

Grammar: Plural Nouns

Directions: Write the plural form of each singular noun.

1. swamp _____

2. bench _____

3. tooth _____

4. key _____

5. mouse _____

6. body _____

7. calf _____

8. deer _____

9. crocodile _____

10. tree _____

11. knife _____

12. ax _____

Directions: Use the plural form of the noun in ( ) to complete each sentence.
Write the plural noun on the line to the left.

_____ 13. Millions of _____ visit the Everglades. (tourist)

_____ 14. From all over the world, _____ come to see this tropical area. (family)

_____ 15. Adults and _____ are fascinated by its scenery and wildlife. (child)

_____ 16. Will these _____ join in helping to save the endangered area? (person)

_____ 17. Crocodiles are not as soft and cuddly as _____, but they are worth saving. (sheep)

_____ 18. Unusual plants and wildlife live in the Everglades' _____. (marsh)

_____ 19. _____ who are willing to clean up the area are always needed. (Volunteer)

_____ 20. Cleanup efforts may save the _____ of many plants and animals. (life)

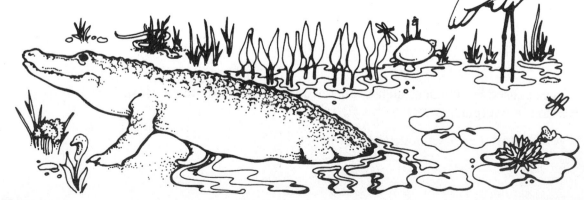

Notes for Home: Your child wrote the plural forms of both regular and irregular nouns.
Home Activity: Look through a magazine or catalog, and challenge your child to use singular nouns to name things in the pictures, then write the plural form of each noun.

Practice

Grammar: Possessive Nouns

A **singular possessive noun** shows that one person, place, or thing has or owns something.

- To make a singular noun show possession, add an **apostrophe (')** and **-s**

  the feathers of the bird   the bird's feathers

A **plural possessive noun** shows that more than one person, place or thing has or owns something.

- When a plural noun ends in **-s,** add just an **apostrophe (')** to make the noun show possession.

  the scales of the alligators   the alligators' scales

- When a plural noun does not end in **-s,** add an **apostrophe (')** and **-s** to show possession.

  the laughter of the people   the people's laughter

Directions: Circle the correct possessive noun in ( ) to complete each sentence.

1. The (library's/librarys') story hour will begin today at two o'clock.

2. The (children's/childrens') favorite storyteller will be there.

3. The (storyteller's/storytellers') name is Nina.

4. (Nina's/Ninas') voice is soft, but clear.

5. Nina tells different (culture's/cultures') stories.

Directions: Add an apostrophe to each underlined possessive noun. Rewrite the noun on the line.

_____ 6. I love the various <u>Native Americans</u> stories best.

_____ 7. These <u>stories</u> characters can be kind, wise, or tricky.

_____ 8. One <u>characters</u> name was Mother Earth.

_____ 9. <u>Mother Earths</u> children were the human race.

_____ 10. The <u>storys</u> message was that we should care for Earth as we would care for our own mother.

 Notes for Home: Your child learned how to use and punctuate possessive nouns. *Home Activity:* Ask your child to list items he or she owns, describing clothing, books, and so on. Help your child use possessive nouns to show ownership *(Al's skis, the twins' toys).*

© Scott Foresman 5

Grammar: Possessive Nouns

Directions: Rewrite each underlined phrase to show possession. Write the new phrase on the line to the left.

_____ 1. The <u>name of the alligator</u> comes from the Spanish word for lizard.

_____ 2. <u>Alligators of America</u> are found in the southeast.

_____ 3. <u>Alligators of China</u> live in the Yangtze River.

_____ 4. <u>The snouts of alligators</u> are broad and flat.

_____ 5. <u>The eggs of these creatures</u> hatch in the hot sun.

_____ 6. <u>Crocodiles of Florida</u> bury themselves in mud to hibernate.

_____ 7. <u>The teeth of crocodiles</u> can crush the bones of small animals.

_____ 8. <u>The snout of this reptile</u> is long and narrow.

_____ 9. <u>The skins of these animals</u> were used to make shoes and handbags.

_____ 10. Today, some people eat <u>the eggs of a crocodile</u>.

Write an Advertisement

Imagine you've been hired to help save an endangered species! On a separate sheet of paper, create an advertisement that teaches people ways to save creatures such as alligators and crocodiles. You may need to do some research first to learn more about a particular species. Use singular and plural possessive nouns in your advertisement.

Notes for Home: Your child learned how to use and punctuate possessive nouns. **Home Activity:** Take a walk with your child. Ask your child to use possessive nouns to show that one person, place, or thing owns something, such as *Mr. Wong's house.*

© Scott Foresman 5

Grammar: Possessive Nouns

Write the words that tell who owns the bicycles.

1. One girl's bicycle was pink. _____

2. The twins' bicycle has two seats. _____

3. The men's bicycles have large frames. _____

The words **girl's, twins',** and **men's** are possessive nouns. The possessive form of a noun shows ownership.

A **possessive noun** shows ownership. Possessive nouns are formed by adding an apostrophe (') and **-s** or only an apostrophe.

Directions: Write the possessive noun in each sentence.

1. The dog's tail wagged. _____

2. My grandfather's bicycle is in good condition. _____

3. James's bicycle needs a new set of brakes. _____

4. The workers' tools are at the repair shop. _____

5. One man's hammer has a broken handle. _____

6. The owner's daughter also works at the shop. _____

7. The customers' problems usually are simple. _____

Directions: Write the possessive form of each noun.

8. painter _____   15. pony _____

9. uncle _____   16. children _____

10. families _____   17. fox _____

11. goose _____   18. deer _____

12. woman _____   19. friends _____

13. sister _____   20. father _____

14. guest _____   21. ladies _____

© Scott Foresman 5

Notes for Home: Your child wrote the possessive forms of nouns. *Home Activity:* Have your child list characters from a favorite book or movie. Then have him or her write the possessive form of each name followed by the name of something the character owns. (*Tom's marbles*)

Grammar: Possessive Nouns

Directions: Circle each singular possessive noun. Underline each plural possessive noun. Then write each possessive noun.

1. The cook's knife was too dull to cut the meat._____

2. The dishwashers' gloves were made of rubber. _____

3. Ms. Santiago tasted the baker's cakes. _____

4. Then she shook the man's hand. _____

5. Other workers' smiles brightened the room. _____

6. The waitresses' dresses were long. _____

7. The owner's family ate at the center table. _____

8. The child's birthday cake was beautiful. _____

9. All of the children's eyes opened wide at the sight. _____

10. The family's birthday song filled the restaurant._____

11. Some customers' voices added volume to the song. _____

Directions: Write the possessive form of each underlined noun.

12. The ladies coats were left at the front rack._____

13. One guest sister arrived at the party very late. _____

14. The woman car was in a traffic jam. _____

15. Other drivers cars had blocked the entire street. _____

16. The traffic officers cars flashed their lights. _____

17. The men dogs waited in the front yard. _____

18. My friend birthday is tomorrow. _____

Write a Family Memoir

Write a family memoir, or personal record, that tells about things your family has that were saved from past generations. Use singular and plural possessive nouns. Write on a separate sheet of paper.

Notes for Home: Your child wrote possessive forms of nouns. *Home Activity:* Have your child make a list of jobs that people have in your community. Then have your child say the possessive forms of the job titles and a tool each person might use. *(The chef's spoon)*

Word Study: Base Words

Directions: Many words are formed by adding letters at the beginning or end of a word. The word you start with is called the **base word.** Read each sentence. Find the base word in the underlined word. Write the base word on the line.

_____   1. The water <u>sparkled</u> in the bright sun.

_____   2. Flowers once <u>bloomed</u> everywhere.

_____   3. The waters were <u>spilling</u> over with fish.

_____   4. Wild birds <u>gracefully</u> flew above the marshy waters.

_____   5. The sounds of insects <u>filled</u> the air.

_____   6. Some animals have all but <u>disappeared.</u>

_____   7. Other kinds of wildlife remain <u>unharmed.</u>

_____   8. Many people would like to <u>undo</u> the damage.

_____   9. Some <u>workers</u> help care for injured birds.

_____   10. The Everglades today are <u>unlike</u> the Everglades of long ago.

Directions: Combine each base word and ending to make a new word. You might need to add or take away letters to spell the word correctly. Write the word on the line.

11. leather   +   -y   =   _____

12. sun   +   -y   =   _____

13. cut   +   -ing =   _____

14. quick   +   -ly   =   _____

15. glitter   +   -ed   =   _____

Notes for Home: Your child identified base words in longer words, such as *appear* in *disappeared,* and used base words to form longer words. *Home Activity:* Read a magazine article with your child. Look for words made of base words and endings.

Spelling: Short Vowels *a, i, o, u*

Pretest Directions: Fold back the page along the dotted line. On the blanks, write the spelling words as they are dictated. When you have finished the test, unfold the page and check your words.

1._____

2._____

3._____

4._____

5._____

6._____

7._____

8._____

9._____

10._____

11._____

12._____

13._____

14._____

15._____

16._____

17._____

18._____

19._____

20._____

1. The pump **handle** is loose.

2. **Perhaps** they will not come.

3. Please control your **anger**.

4. There was an auto **accident**.

5. Traveling can be an **adventure**.

6. We will finish **before** them.

7. She cried **because** she was sad.

8. Have you **decided** what to do?

9. Let's **pretend** to be airplanes.

10. The clothes **belong** to Sue.

11. Is it really **possible**?

12. Detectives might **solve** the case.

13. This is a hard math **problem**.

14. Sarah likes to eat **lobster**.

15. The **python** is a large snake.

16. The monkey **swung** in the tree.

17. The **jungle** was full of noises.

18. The space **shuttle** took off.

19. I hate the sight of **blood**.

20. The **flood** caused damage.

Notes for Home: Your child took a pretest on words that have the short vowels *a, i, o,* and *u*. *Home Activity:* Help your child learn misspelled words before the final test. Have your child divide misspelled words into parts (such as syllables) and concentrate on each part.

Spelling: Short Vowels *a, i, o, u*

Word List			
handle	before	possible	swung
perhaps	because	solve	jungle
anger	decided	problem	shuttle
accident	pretend	lobster	blood
adventure	belong	python	flood

Directions: Choose the words from the box that have the **short u** sound heard in **sun** or the **short i** sound heard in **begin.** Write each word in the correct column.

Short u spelled u

1. _____

2. _____

3. _____

Short u spelled oo

4. _____

5. _____

Short i spelled e

6. _____

7. _____

8. _____

9. _____

10. _____

Directions: Choose the word from the box that best replaces the underlined word or words. Write the word on the line.

_____ **11.** We took in our new dog, Flash, purely by <u>chance</u>.

_____ **12.** Getting him home was an <u>exciting, dangerous experience</u>.

_____ **13.** My sister pinched him so hard putting on his collar, he must have thought she was a <u>hard-shelled sea animal</u>.

_____ **14.** She quickly learned to <u>control</u> the dog gently.

_____ **15.** My brother gave Flash a squeeze like a <u>big, thick snake</u>.

_____ **16.** Our cat, though, presents a serious <u>dilemma</u>.

_____ **17.** Fluff still has moments of <u>rage</u> about sharing our attention.

_____ **18.** <u>Maybe</u> Flash and Fluff will get along well soon.

_____ **19.** It's <u>not impossible</u> that a cat and dog can be friends.

_____ **20.** With a little training and separate rooms, we will <u>figure out</u> this difficulty.

Notes for Home: Your child spelled words that have the short vowel sounds *a, i, o,* or *u (handle, before, possible, swung, good).* **Home Activity:** Say these words with your child and look at how the vowel sounds are spelled. Add other words that have the same vowel sounds and spellings.

Proofread and Write

Spelling: Short Vowels *a, i, o, u*

Directions: Proofread this article. Find five spelling mistakes. Use the proofreading marks to correct each mistake.

For many years the Everglades were in danger of being destroyed. Then the people of Florida desided to solve the problum before it was too late.

Water that had been dammed up was allowed to flud into the area. Underpasses were built so wild animals could travel safely under highways. Exotic plants that didn't bilong there were removed bicuz they choked out native plants. These solutions helped save the Everglades.

Proofreading Marks	
≡	Make a capital.
/	Make a small letter.
∧	Add something.
ꝑ	Take out something.
⊙	Add a period.
¶	Begin a new paragraph.

Spelling Tip

blood   flood
The **short u** sound can be spelled **u** or **oo**. Remember to spell **blood** and **flood** with two **o**'s by remembering that liquids can **ooze**.

Word List

handle	possible
perhaps	solve
anger	problem
accident	lobster
adventure	python
before	swung
because	jungle
decided	shuttle
pretend	blood
belong	flood

Write a Science Article

On a separate sheet of paper, write a short article about how people in your community or state are protecting the environment. Try to use at least five of your spelling words.

Notes for Home: Your child spelled words that have the short vowel sounds *a, i, o,* or *u* (*handle, before, possible, swung, good*). **Home Activity:** Have your child find other verb forms of *decided, pretend,* and *swung,* such as *deciding, pretended,* and *swing.*

Spelling: Short Vowels *a, i, o, u*

Word List

handle	before	possible	swung
perhaps	because	solve	jungle
anger	decided	problem	shuttle
accident	pretend	lobster	blood
adventure	belong	python	flood

Directions: Choose the word from the box that is the most opposite in meaning for each word or words below. Write the word on the line.

1. impossible _____

2. solution _____

3. after _____

4. real _____

5. drought _____

6. undecided _____

7. joy _____

8. deliberate _____

Directions: Choose the word from the box that best matches each clue. Write the word on the line.

_____ 9. part of a teapot

_____ 10. a tasty shellfish

_____ 11. a fluid in the body

_____ 12. what members do to a club

_____ 13. the past tense of *swing*

_____ 14. a huge kind of snake

_____ 15. the same as *maybe*

_____ 16. found in a rainforest

_____ 17. a bus that runs back and forth

_____ 18. an exciting experience

_____ 19. what detectives do to crimes

_____ 20. why things happen

Notes for Home: Your children identified spelling words from opposites and clues. ***Home Activity:*** Challenge your child to write a paragraph using as many spelling words as possible.

Thesaurus

A **thesaurus** is a kind of dictionary in which synonyms (words that have the same or similar meanings), antonyms (words that have opposite meanings), and other related words are classified under headings. You can use a thesaurus to help you find new and interesting words when writing.

Directions: Use the thesaurus entry to answer the questions that follow.

Definition

Entry Word → **Friend** means someone you like and who likes you. *Colleen's friends gave her a surprise birthday party.* (noun) ← **Part of Speech**

Synonyms →

Comrade means a friend with whom you share things. *Gwen and her comrades in her Girl Scout troop are planning a trip to the zoo.*

Companion means a close friend who accompanies a person. *"Miss Hale and I take this trip every year," Miss Alexander explained, introducing her companion.*

Sidekick is an informal word for companion.

Pal means a friend and companion. *"Be a pal," Myron begged, "and ask her if she likes me."*

Buddy is an informal word for a close friend. *Ken and his buddy Yuji are almost like brothers.*

Cross References → See **familiar** and **friendly** for related words.

Antonyms → ANTONYMS: enemy, foe

From EVERYDAY SPELLING by James Breers, Ronald L. Cramer, W. Dorsey Hammond. © 1998 Addison-Wesley Educational Publishers Inc.

1. What entry word is shown? _____

2. Name the part of speech of the entry word. _____

3. What synonyms are given for the entry word? _____

_____

4. Rewrite this sentence using one of the synonyms from the entry: *My friend Marta and I went on a swamp tour in New Orleans.*

_____

_____

5. Rewrite this sentence by replacing the underlined words with a word from the entry: *The alligator is <u>no friend</u> to the birds who live in the swamp.*

_____

_____

6. Would you use *sidekick* when introducing a visiting friend to your school principal? Explain.

_____

_____

7. What would you do if you wanted to find additional words that have meanings similar to the entry word?

_____

_____

8. How does knowing the meaning of *friend* help you understand how to use *foe* in a sentence?

_____

_____

9. If you looked up the entry word *large* in a thesaurus, what synonyms might you find? What antonyms might you find?

_____

_____

10. Why might a thesaurus be a helpful reference source when you are writing a report for class?

_____

_____

Notes for Home: Your child answered questions about a thesaurus entry. *Home Activity:* If a thesaurus is available, challenge your child to look up five words and tell what information is shown. If not available, work together to write five thesaurus entries.

© Scott Foresman 5

Research and Study Skills: Thesaurus 201

Name_____

Summary

Sister and Brother Solve Jewelry Theft

While two young people were shopping for a tie for their dad, the store's sprinkler system went off. In the confusion that followed, someone broke into the jewelry case where the youngsters had stopped briefly. Amanda and Sherlock cleverly used a series of clues, such as the location of the sprinkler controls and the mysterious extra weight of a loaf of bread, to solve the crime. They realized that the baker and the jewelry clerk had planned the whole thing.

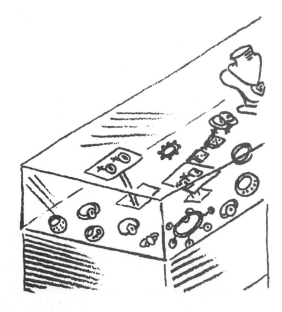

Activity

Finish the Story. Have your child tell you some of the clues used by Amanda and Sherlock to solve the crime mystery and why each clue helps them solve the crime. Talk with your child about other mysteries your child has read and some of the clues that are in each mystery.

Reading Skills

Drawing Conclusions

When you form opinions based on facts and details, you are **drawing conclusions.** To draw conclusions, use logic and clues from the reading. Also use your own knowledge and experience. For example, when the baker would not sell one of two similar loaves of bread to Amanda and Sherlock, the young people became suspicious. Using this information, logic, and what you know, you could conclude that the baker was hiding something important by not selling that loaf. To check your conclusion, ask yourself if it makes sense.

Activity

Look at Pictures. Look through a newspaper for photographs. Cover the caption and see what conclusions you can draw about the picture. Then read the caption to see how accurate you were.

Family Times

Tested Vocabulary

Words to Know

Knowing the meanings of these words is important to reading "Missing Links." Practice using these words to learn their meanings.

counter a long, flat, raised surface in a store, restaurant, bank, etc.

indicates points out; makes known; shows

jewelry ring, bracelet, or other ornament to be worn

sapphire clear, hard, usually blue precious stone

smudge a dirty mark; smear

Grammar

Commas with Nouns in Series and in Direct Address

When you list three or more items in a sentence, use commas to separate the items.

Nouns in Series: The bakery has cookies, pastries, and bread.

When you speak or write to someone, use commas to set off that person's name.

Direct Address: Come on, Sherlock, we need to hurry. I'm hurrying, Amanda.

Activity
Make a Shopping List. Write several nouns on slips of paper. Let your imagination go wild and list a variety of interesting or unusual objects. Take turns selecting three or more nouns and use them to write sentences that begin: **I'm going shopping to get. . . .** Use commas to separate items.

Tested Spelling Words

_____   _____   _____   _____

_____   _____   _____   _____

_____   _____   _____   _____

_____   _____   _____   _____

_____   _____   _____   _____

Drawing Conclusions

- When you form opinions based on facts and details, you are **drawing conclusions.**

- To draw a conclusion, use logic and clues from what you've read, as well as your own knowledge and experience.

- To check your conclusion, ask yourself if it makes sense. Are there other possible conclusions?

Directions: Reread "Granny's Missing Food." Then complete the table. Write a conclusion for each piece of evidence given. Write evidence that supports each conclusion drawn.

Evidence	Conclusions
Chicken, fruit, and cookies are missing from Granny's house.	1.
2.	The woman is the narrator's grandmother.
Clooz has only one business card.	3.
4.	The dog did not steal Granny's food.
Clooz and the narrator trade funny looks when Granny points to the newspapers she got from the checkout line at the supermarket.	5.

Notes for Home: Your child read a story and used story details, as well as logic, to draw conclusions. ***Home Activity:*** Offer clues about what you did today. Ask your child to draw conclusions about your activities.

© Scott Foresman 5

Vocabulary

Directions: Choose the word from the box that best matches each definition.
Write the word on the line.

_____   1. a long, flat, raised surface in a store,
                           restaurant, or a bank

_____   2. precious gem, brilliant blue in color

_____   3. ring, bracelet, necklace, or other
                           ornament to be worn

_____   4. smear of dirt or grease

_____   5. points out; shows; suggests

Directions: Choose the word from the box that best completes each sentence.
Write the word on the matching numbered line to the right.

I wanted to buy the perfect gift for my older sister's graduation. I went to the local **6.** _____ store to look at some necklaces. The sales clerk behind the large **7.** _____ where the jewelry was displayed was very helpful. While looking for a gift, I saw the most beautiful blue stone in a gold necklace. The sales clerk told me that the stone was a **8.** _____. The clerk told me the color and cut of the stone **9.** _____ that it is an excellent piece of jewelry. The necklace was so beautiful that I put my face close to the display case and made a big **10.** _____ on the glass. That was embarrassing! The necklace was too expensive, but I did find a very nice pair of earrings for my sister.

6. _____

7. _____

8. _____

9. _____

10. _____

Write a Story

Imagine that a robbery has taken place at a local jewelry store, and you are the detective in charge. On a separate sheet of paper, write a story about searching the crime scene for clues. What do you find? Use as many vocabulary words as you can.

Notes for Home: Your child identified and used new words from the story "Missing Links."
Home Activity: Act out a radio drama with your child about a jewelry robbery. Use the vocabulary words in your dialogue.

Drawing Conclusions

- When you form opinions based on facts and details, you are **drawing conclusions.**

- To draw a conclusion, use logic and clues from what you've read, as well as your own knowledge and experience. To check your conclusion, ask yourself if it makes sense. Are there other possible conclusions?

Directions: Reread what happens in "Missing Links" when Amanda and Sherlock inspect the smashed jewelry case. Then answer the questions below. Use story details to help you draw conclusions.

The case that Amanda had been looking into just a few minutes before was now smashed and almost empty. All the cuff links, the tie pins, and the beautiful ring were gone.

"What happened?" Amanda asked the salesman excitedly.

"I don't know, I don't know. I must have been putting some ladies' jewelry away in the next counter . . . there was so much confusion . . . I just didn't see . . . but I haven't been near the case. I know you're not supposed to touch anything. The police will probably want to check for fingerprints."

Sherlock, apparently, was already doing just that. He had his magnifying glass out and was peering intently into the shattered display case.

From FLUTE REVENGE by Andrew Bromberg.
Copyright © 1982 by William Morrow and Company, Inc. By permission of Greenwillow Books.

1. What has happened to the items from the jewelry case?

_____

2. What conclusion can you draw about the salesman from the way that he speaks?

_____

3. Why does the salesman say you're not supposed to touch anything?

_____

_____

4. Why does Sherlock study the case through his magnifying glass?

_____

5. What conclusions can you draw about Amanda and Sherlock from the whole story? On a separate sheet of paper, write your conclusions. Support them with evidence from the story.

© Scott Foresman 5

Notes for Home: Your child used story details to draw conclusions. *Home Activity:* Work with your child to draw conclusions about a movie you've seen or a book you've read together. Talk about why something happened or how the characters might feel in a certain situation.

Selection Test

Directions: Choose the best answer to each item. Mark the letter for the answer you have chosen.

Part 1: Vocabulary

Find the answer choice that means about the same as the underlined word in each sentence.

1. Miko put the box on the <u>counter</u>.
   - A. small container with a cover
   - B. large, square floor
   - C. display table or cabinet in a store
   - D. room where things are stored

2. Someone stole her <u>jewelry</u> case.
   - F. flat pouch for carrying paper money
   - G. belief or plan
   - H. rings, bracelets, or other ornaments to be worn
   - J. collection of coins

3. The clock <u>indicates</u> that it is two o'clock.
   - A. shows
   - B. pretends
   - C. discovers
   - D. hides

4. A <u>sapphire</u> ring was missing.
   - F. hard gray or pink rock
   - G. clear blue precious stone
   - H. gold band
   - J. deep red gem

5. He had a <u>smudge</u> on his chin.
   - A. short beard
   - B. healed cut
   - C. small dimple
   - D. dirty mark

Part 2: Comprehension

Use what you know about the story to answer each item.

6. Amanda and Sherlock went to the department store to—
   - F. play computer games.
   - G. look at men's jewelry.
   - H. solve a mystery.
   - J. buy a tie for their dad.

7. What happened while Sherlock and Amanda were in the department store?
   - A. A fire broke out in the store.
   - B. The sprinklers went off.
   - C. Amanda stole a sapphire ring.
   - D. The manager announced a big sale.

8. The salespeople were racing back and forth because they were trying to—
   - F. put out the fire.
   - G. keep the customers happy.
   - H. protect their merchandise.
   - J. catch a thief.

9. The sprinklers probably stopped suddenly because—
   - A. the store ran out of water.
   - B. they were not working properly.
   - C. someone turned them off.
   - D. someone opened the emergency exit.

10. Why was Sherlock studying the salesman's tie with his magnifying glass?
    - F. He was looking for clues.
    - G. He forgot his glasses at home.
    - H. Amanda suggested he should.
    - J. The spot was impossible to see otherwise.

GO ON

11. Amanda and Sherlock could not stay until the police arrived because they—
   A. would be in the way.
   B. would be late getting home.
   C. might become suspects.
   D. didn't know anything about solving mysteries.

12. The stolen jewelry was most likely hidden in—
   F. a loaf of bread.
   G. the baker's hat.
   H. the sprinklers.
   J. Sherlock's eclair.

13. You can tell that the baker is not very smart because he—
   A. could not bake a loaf of bread properly.
   B. didn't charge enough for the bread.
   C. didn't try to keep his bread dry.
   D. was wearing the stolen ring.

14. Which fact best supports the idea that Sherlock might make a good detective someday?
   F. He carries a magnifying glass with him wherever he goes.
   G. He has the same first name as the famous detective, Sherlock Holmes.
   H. He notices clues that help solve the mystery.
   J. He and his sister Amanda work well together.

15. The title of this story probably refers to the missing cuff links and to—
   A. loaves of bread.
   B. Sherlock and Amanda.
   C. the thieves.
   D. the clues needed to solve the mystery.

STOP

Drawing Conclusions

- When you form opinions based on facts and details, you are **drawing conclusions.**

- To draw a conclusion, use logic and clues from what you've read, as well as your own knowledge and experience. To check your conclusion, ask yourself if it makes sense. Are there other possible conclusions?

Directions: Read the story.

"How is the case going, Mom?" Amy asked her mother at dinner one night.

"We still don't have an answer," her mother replied, "but I think we're getting close."

"Is your theory the right one?" Amy asked.

"Well, dear," said her mother, "all we really know for sure is that the will isn't in any of the obvious places. We've looked in the safe-deposit box and searched every room in the mansion. Some of the other detectives agree with me that the grandfather hid the will because of the hints in the letter he left for his granddaughter. If we could decode that letter I'm sure we could find the will."

"I know you'll figure it out," said Amy, "I'm just glad you made it home in time for dinner for once!"

Directions: Complete the table. Write a conclusion for each set of evidence given. Write evidence that supports each conclusion given.

Conclusion	Evidence
Amy's mom is a detective.	**1.**
The grandfather hid the will.	**2.**
3.	The grandfather left his granddaughter a letter hinting where the will is hidden.
Detectives are like code-breakers.	**4.**
5.	Amy is glad her mom is home for dinner "for once."

Notes for Home: Your child used story details to draw conclusions. *Home Activity:* Watch a television show with your child and draw some conclusions about the characters—how they feel, what they are like, and why they act the way they do.

Predicting

Directions: Read the story. Then read each question about the story. Choose the best answer to each question. Mark the letter for the answer you have chosen.

Thrills and Chills

Suddenly, the lion moved! He stretched his neck, shook himself, yawned, and jumped from his pedestal. He then looked at the two girls and took a step toward them.

"Run for it!" Jill screamed.

Instead of moving, Tracy stared. "This is a mystery," she whispered. "How did that lion move?"

"I don't know. I just want to get out of here," Jill said, trembling.

The lion looked from Jill to Tracy, then turned away. He stalked away down the avenue, head high, looking straight ahead. As they watched, fascinated, he disappeared from sight.

Tracy and Jill stared at one another, then went to look at the empty pedestal. "Look!" cried Tracy. "There's a note here." She picked it up and read it aloud.

> **You have just witnessed an amazing sight.**
> **Tell all your friends to come to the museum for tomorrow night's grand opening of Laser Lights!**

"So that's how he moved," said Tracy. "What do you mean?" asked Jill.

"That was no lion! That was a laser show demonstration to promote a new museum exhibit."

The two girls heard a sound high above them. They turned and looked. A museum staff person was standing in a special projection booth. He waved and called out, "Hope to see you tomorrow night."

1. After reading the first paragraph, you would probably predict that—
   A. the girls are going to attack the lion.
   B. the lion is going to attack the girls.
   C. the girls will stand still.
   D. the girls will feed the lion.

2. What do you think about Tracy after she speaks for the first time?
   F. Tracy loves lions.
   G. Tracy is dreaming.
   H. Tracy is more surprised than scared.
   J. Tracy is more scared than Jill.

3. What clue word or words in the note would probably cause you to change your initial prediction?
   A. witnessed
   B. amazing
   C. laser lights
   D. friends

4. After listening to Tracy's explanation, Jill will likely feel—
   F. scared.
   G. relieved.
   H. angry.
   J. sad.

5. What do you predict Jill and Tracy will do next?
   A. They will agree never to go to the museum again.
   B. They will go searching for the lion.
   C. They will complain to museum security.
   D. They will go to the Laser Lights opening.

Notes for Home: Your child read a story and predicted events in the story. *Home Activity:* As you watch a movie with your child, make predictions about the characters and events. Make new predictions as needed as you continue watching.

Writing Across Texts

Directions: Think again about how the main characters in "Missing Links" and "Dwaina Brooks" use initiative to solve problems they see in the world around them. Fill in the rest of the problem-and-solution chart below.

Sherlock and Amanda	Dwaina
Problem: Sherlock and Amanda want to find out who stole the jewelry.	**Problem:** Dwaina wants to figure out how to feed the homeless in Dallas.
Attempts to solve the problem: 1.	**Attempts to solve the problem:** 6.
2.	7.
3.	8.
4.	9.
Solution: 5.	Solution: 10.

Write a Paragraph

On a separate sheet of paper, write one or two paragraphs to describe how Sherlock, Amanda, and Dwaina show initiative. Be sure to include specific examples from the selections.

Notes for Home: Your child compared fictional characters with a real-life person described in an article. *Home Activity:* As you read other stories or articles, have your child tell how characters' traits, such as initiative, bravery, intelligence, or determination, help them solve problems.

Grammar: Possessive Nouns

REVIEW

Directions: Circle the possessive noun in ( ) that correctly completes each sentence.

1. The (detective's/detectives') hat blew off as she ran for the bus.

2. She reached the corner just as the (buses/bus's) doors closed.

3. Was that the (criminal's/criminals') face smiling from the bus?

4. Detective (Moss'/Moss's) face certainly did not have a smile on it.

5. Her (life's/lives') work was solving mysteries.

6. She thought she had found this (mysterys'/mystery's) solution.

7. The (suspect's/suspects) escape on the bus was a terrible setback.

8. The passing (cars'/car's) loud horns sounded to her like cruel laughter.

9. She would rest at (Janes/Jane's) house and decide what to do next.

10. She had to find the thief who was stealing (womens'/women's) purses.

Directions: Add an apostrophe to make each underlined word or words possessive. Write the possessive noun on the line.

_____ 11. The door to the <u>companys</u> safe stood wide open.

_____ 12. Someone had smashed the cash <u>boxes</u> lids and stolen all the money.

_____ 13. Now it was the two <u>police officers</u> job to ask questions.

_____ 14. Had the door to the <u>secretaries</u> offices been locked or unlocked?

_____ 15. Why was one of the <u>workers</u> keys found on the floor?

_____ 16. Had the <u>bosss</u> wife really telephoned him at six o'clock?

_____ 17. Whose <u>childrens</u> toys were scattered around the room?

_____ 18. Why was a pile of <u>sheeps</u> wool lying next to the safe?

_____ 19. The <u>witnesses</u> statements did not agree.

_____ 20. The officers knew that <u>todays</u> mystery would not be easily solved.

© Scott Foresman 5

 Notes for Home: Your child formed possessive nouns—nouns that show that a person, place, or thing owns or has something. ***Home Activity:*** Point to things in your home or outside your window. Ask questions such as "Whose bike is that?" Have your child write the answers.

Grammar: Commas with Nouns in Series and in Direct Address

A list of three or more nouns forms a **series.** A **comma** is used after each word in a series except the last.

> Dinosaurs, snakes, lizards, and crocodiles were missing from the zoo.

When you speak or write to someone, you often use that person's name or title. This use of a noun is called **direct address.** One comma sets off the noun when it appears at the beginning or the end of a sentence. Two commas are used when it appears in the middle.

> Students, today we will learn about how to write a mystery.
> What do you know about mysteries, Anna?
> The mystery novel that you suggested, Josh, is excellent.

Directions: Write **C** if the sentence is punctuated correctly. Write **NC** if it is not correct. Then, write correctly any sentence marked **NC.**

1. Items such as jewelry, money, and appliances were taken from the house.

   _____

2. Chris do you know how the detective solved the mystery?

   _____

3. Footprints, fingerprints, and broken glass were all important clues.

   _____

4. How they know where to look for evidence is also a mystery, Leroy.

   _____

5. Detectives, Tina have found the criminal in hundreds of investigations.

   _____

Directions: Add commas to each sentence to set off nouns used in a series or in direct address.

6. The elusive thief was spotted in Europe the Americas and other continents.

7. Evidence to solve the case was found in Central Asia Mike.

8. The criminal Sophia was close to escaping.

9. While the thief was hiding in Florida he ate fish shellfish and plants.

10. Sarah some mysteries are never solved.

Notes for Home: Your child learned how to use commas with nouns in a series and in direct address. ***Home Activity:*** Ask your child to make a list of different kinds of dinosaurs. Then have your child write a sentence using commas to set off nouns in a series.

Name _____

Grammar: Commas with Nouns in Series and in Direct Address

Directions: Add commas to each sentence to set off nouns in a series or in direct address.

1. The items that the thief took from the store included rakes seeds and shovels.

2. Liz the thief might have enjoyed gardening.

3. The detective searched for clues in vacant lots gardens and fields.

4. This is the biggest mystery of the year Tim.

5. One of the clues Ashley was a freshly planted garden in the vacant lot.

Directions: Read the following paragraph. Add commas where necessary.

Class today we are going to read the first half of a mystery. I know that most of you enjoy solving mysteries. We will also spend time working on math spelling and science. Tonya Juan Kerry and Simon you will each lead a group. Remember class each group will try to solve the mystery after reading just half of the story.

Write a News Report

Imagine you have solved the mystery of the disappearance of a set of valuable jewels from a museum. On a separate sheet of paper, write a news report about your discovery. Tell how you solved the mystery. What clues did the thieves leave behind? Use commas to set off nouns in a series and in direct address.

Notes for Home: Your child learned how to use commas. *Home Activity:* With your child, write sentences describing things you see around you, such as books, clothes, and plants. Encourage your child to explain how to use commas to punctuate nouns in a series.

Grammar: Commas with Nouns in Series and in Direct Address

RETEACHING

Each sentence shows one way to use a comma. Circle each comma.

1. Tanya, go home please.
2. Then, Ray, you follow her.
3. We will go right now, Juan.
4. Dora, Amy, and Tony will come.

A **comma** can tell a reader where to pause. Use a comma to separate words in a series of three or more items. Use a comma to set off the name of someone directly spoken to in **direct address.**

Directions: Add commas where they are needed.

1. I hope to become an astronaut one day June.
2. Jenny tell me about Sally Ride.
3. She was the first American woman in space Maria.
4. An astronaut's life must be fascinating exciting and sometimes scary.
5. I would miss my family my friends and my cat on a space voyage.
6. You could use the communication system Ruby to relay messages.
7. How much food water and equipment can fit in a spacecraft?
8. Gina let's go to the library.
9. Let's find out more about space travel astronauts and moonwalks.

Directions: Write a sentence to answer each question.

10. What are the names of three of your classmates?

_____

11. What are three of your favorite sports?

_____

12. Which birds live in your town or city?

_____

© Scott Foresman 5

Notes for Home: Your child used commas in a series and in direct address. *Home Activity:* Have your child use newspapers or magazines to find and highlight examples of commas in a series and commas in direct address.

Grammar: Commas with Nouns in Series and in Direct Address

Directions: Add commas where they are needed.

1. John Glenn did not orbit the earth before Alan Shepard's space flight Danielle.

2. Kim who is your favorite hero?

3. I think Thomas Edison Martin Luther King, Jr. and Abraham Lincoln helped the most people.

4. I think Laurie someone like Charles Lindbergh is a true hero.

5. Pecos Bill Paul Bunyan and Calamity Jane are my favorite folk heroes.

6. John Henry was strong hardworking and brave.

7. Was he a real person Jill?

8. I think so Bonnie but I don't know for sure.

Directions: Write a complete sentence for each direction.

9. Name three states you would like to visit.

_____

10. Name three breakfast foods.

_____

11. Name the four seasons.

_____

12. Name three of your favorite vegetables.

_____

13. Name three kinds of transportation.

_____

14. Name three favorite story characters.

_____

Write a Restaurant Review

Write a restaurant review that includes descriptions of your three favorite foods in each food group. Use commas where they are needed. Write on a separate sheet of paper.

Notes for Home: Your child used commas in a series and in direct address. *Home Activity:* Have your child write a description of a favorite sports team or electronic game. Encourage your child to use words in a series in the description.

© Scott Foresrran 5

Word Study: Prefixes

Directions: Letters added to the beginnings of words are called **prefixes.**
Prefixes can change the meaning of the base word. Add the prefixes to each
word below to make a new word. Write each new word on the line.

1. re   +   heat   = _____
2. pre   +   occupied   = _____
3. un   +   believable   = _____
4. pre   +   school   = _____
5. re   +   turn   = _____
6. un   +   changed   = _____
7. pre   +   paid   = _____
8. re   +   view   = _____

Directions: Read the detective's report. Circle the words that contain the
prefixes *un-, re-,* and *pre-*. Write the prefix and the base word on the line
connected by a + sign. For example, **prepaid,** you would write **pre + paid.**

Detective's Report: Case No. 57

Submitted by Lydia Lookout, P. I.

    I was hired to investigate the disappearance of peanuts from
the local grocery store. Bob, the owner of the small
neighborhood store, was very unhappy about the missing
peanuts. He had suspected one or two people as thieves but
Bob felt that it would be unfair to prejudge his loyal
customers. Bob was unable to solve the mystery, so he hired
me to solve the case. I told Bob that I couldn't replace the
missing peanuts, but I could find the thief. After two days on
the case, I was still uncertain about the disappearing peanuts. I
decided to stay overnight in the store to catch the thieves in
action. Sometime after midnight, I heard a noise and turned on
the lights. The store was filled with happy squirrels eating
peanuts. The next day Bob called a roofer to repair the hole
where the squirrels had entered the store.

9. _____
10. _____
11. _____
12. _____
13. _____
14. _____
15. _____

© Scott Foresman 5

Notes for Home: Your child formed new words by adding the prefixes *un-, re-,* and *pre-*.
Home Activity: Read a newspaper story with your child. Help your child find words that have
these prefixes. Have your child write each word and circle its prefix.

Name_____

Spelling: Prefixes *dis-, un-, mid-, pre-*

Pretest Directions: Fold back the page along the dotted line. On the blanks, write the spelling words as they are dictated. When you have finished the test, unfold the page and check your words.

Pretest

1._____
2._____
3._____
4._____
5._____
6._____
7._____
8._____
9._____
10._____
11._____
12._____
13._____
14._____
15._____
16._____
17._____
18._____
19._____
20._____

1. We **discovered** it just in time.
2. The room was in total **disorder**.
3. I am sorry to **disappoint** you.
4. They **disobey** orders.
5. Does she **disapprove** of him?
6. The driver is **unsure** how to go.
7. The writing was too **unclear**.
8. Are you **unable** to help today?
9. You may **unbuckle** your seatbelt.
10. He has an **unlimited** supply.
11. The news came **midweek**.
12. It is time for a **midyear** review.
13. The games are on the **midway**.
14. The bell tower chimed **midnight**.
15. The deer stood in **midstream**.
16. We will have a **pretest** tomorrow.
17. They are too old for **preschool**.
18. The restaurants **precook** meals.
19. We **prepaid** for our tickets.
20. This program was **prerecorded**.

© Scott Foresman 5

Notes for Home: Your child took a pretest on words that begin with *dis-, un-, mid-,* and *pre-*. *Home Activity:* Help your child learn misspelled words before the final test. See if there are any similar errors and discuss a memory trick that could help.

Name _____

Spelling: Prefixes *dis-, un-, mid-, pre-*

Think and Practice

Word List

discovered	disapprove	unbuckle	midway	preschool
disorder	unsure	unlimited	midnight	precook
disappoint	unclear	midweek	midstream	prepaid
disobey	unable	midyear	pretest	prerecorded

Directions: Add the prefix **dis-, un-, mid-,** or **pre-** to each word below to form a word from the box. Write the word on the line.

1. covered _____
2. night _____
3. recorded _____
4. year _____
5. obey _____

6. stream _____
7. approve _____
8. sure _____
9. buckle _____
10. clear _____

Directions: Choose the word from the box that best matches each clue. Write the word in the puzzle.

Across
12. confusion or lack of order
13. fail to please
17. not able
18. half or part of the way through something
19. school for very young children
20. cook in advance

Down
11. short test before another exam
14. paid in advance
15. without limits
16. middle of the week

Notes for Home: Your child spelled words that begin with *dis-, un-, mid-,* and *pre-*. **Home Activity:** Read each word aloud from the box. Ask your child to identify and spell the base word. For example, *buckle* is the base word for *unbuckle*.

© Scott Foresman 5

Spelling: Prefixes *dis-, un-, mid-, pre-* **219**

Proofread and Write

Spelling: Prefixes *dis-, un-, mid-, pre-*

Directions: Proofread these rules. Find six spelling mistakes.
Use the proofreading marks to correct each mistake.

≡	Make a capital.
/	Make a small letter.
∧	Add something.
⤲	Take out something.
⊙	Add a period.
¶	Begin a new paragraph.

Rules for Our Trip to the Shopping Mall

We will be in a big crowd tomorrow at the shopping

mall, so everyone remember these rules!

1. Do not dissobey the instructions of the teacher or the group leader.

If you do, it will cause great disordar.

2. If you have diskovered that you are unnclear about which bus you

belong on, ask the teacher. Space on each bus is not unlimitted, so you

must go on the bus you were assigned.

3. We will eat middway through the day. The lunch is prepaid, so you

don't need to bring any money for food.

We want everyone to have fun, so please remember these rules and be

on time tomorrow!

Spelling Tip

discovered

How can you remember that **discovered** begins with **disc**, not **disk?** When something is **dis_c_overed,** you can see (**c**) it!

Word List

discovered	midweek
disorder	midyear
disappoint	midway
disobey	midnight
disapprove	midstream
unsure	pretest
unclear	preschool
unable	precook
unbucklc	prepaid
unlimited	prerecorded

Write Rules

Imagine you are in charge of a group that is visiting a shopping mall. On a separate sheet of paper, make a list of rules for the group to follow. Try to use at least five of your spelling words.

Notes for Home: Your child spelled words that begin with *dis-, un-, mid-,* and *pre-*. **Home Activity:** Read a magazine article with your child. See how many words you can find that start with the prefixes *dis-, un-, mid-,* or *pre-*.

Spelling: Prefixes *dis-*, *un-*, *mid-*, *pre-* REVIEW

Word List				
discovered	disapprove	unbuckle	midway	preschool
disorder	unsure	unlimited	midnight	precook
disappoint	unclear	midweek	midstream	prepaid
disobey	unable	midyear	pretest	prerecorded

Directions: Choose the word from the box that best completes each sentence.
Write the word on the line.

_____ 1. When I was in _____ I was too young to work at our family
store.

_____ 2. _____ through the fifth grade I began to help my parents at the
store.

_____ 3. I soon _____ that I enjoyed stocking the shelves.

_____ 4. After school I wanted to straighten the items that were in
_____.

_____ 5. I would never _____ when my parents asked me to complete a
task.

_____ 6. Mother was _____ to hide a smile at her delight in my
contribution to the store.

_____ 7. If I was _____ about how to do something, mother helped.

_____ 8. My love for helping at the store was endless and _____.

Directions: Choose the word from the box that has the same or nearly the same
meaning as each word or phrase below. Write the word on the line.

_____ 9. twelve o'clock A.M.   _____ 15. already paid

_____ 10. Wednesday   _____ 16. unfasten

_____ 11. June   _____ 17. taped

_____ 12. frown on   _____ 18. doubtful

_____ 13. quiz   _____ 19. let down

_____ 14. middle of the stream   _____ 20. preheat

© Scott Foresman 5

Notes for Home: Your child spelled words that begin with *dis-*, *un-*, *mid-*, and *pre-*. **Home
Activity:** Name one of these prefixes: *dis-*, *un-*, *mid-*, or *pre-*. Have your child identify the
spelling words that begin with that prefix, and have him or her write a sentence for each one.

Technology: Telephone Directory

A **telephone directory** is a book that lists entries that give the names, phone numbers, and addresses for individual people and businesses. The **white pages** list entries for individual people and businesses in alphabetical order. The **yellow pages** list entries and ads for businesses. Entries are grouped by category or type of business, such as *jewelry.* You can find this same information using a computer and the Internet. You can search online to find phone numbers for people and businesses in other cities, states, and even countries.

Directions: The computer screen shows you how to search a directory of online white pages. Use the computer screen to answer the questions that follow.

Enter the first and last name of the person and click Find!
For better results, enter the city and state also.
Last Name (required) [   ]
First Name [   ]
City [   ] State [   ]
Country [   ]
Find! If you need help, click here.

1. What entries will you get if you type "Gomez" in the box for Last Name, "Boston" in the box for City, and "MA" in the box for State?

_____

_____

_____

2. Would typing "Pamela" in the box for First Name and "USA" in the box for Country give you good search results? Explain.

_____

_____

3. You know Nan Worth lives in Florida. Tell how to find her phone number and address.

_____

_____

4. What should you do if you need help using this online telephone directory?

_____

Name _____

Directions: The computer screen shows you how to search a directory of online yellow pages. Use the computer screen to answer the questions that follow.

Enter a business category or name.
Then click Find!

City

State (required)

Find!   If you need help, click here.

5. What will you get if you enter the category "hotel" and "CA" for California?

_____

6. If you want information on Joe's Flower Shop in Dallas, Texas, what should you enter?

_____

_____

7. If you want to find a jewelry store in Albuquerque, New Mexico, what should you enter?

_____

_____

8. If you enter "bookstore" in the category box, will this produce good search results? Explain.

_____

_____

9. Do you have to type something in all three boxes? Explain. _____

_____

_____

10. Can you use an online telephone directory if you don't know how to spell someone's last name? Explain.

_____

_____

_____

Notes for Home: Your child answered questions about using an online telephone directory. *Home Activity:* Use your telephone books. Ask your child to find one person and a type of business to practice using both the white and yellow pages.

Research and Study Skills: Technology: Telephone Directory   223

© Scott Foresman 5

Name _____

Description Web

Directions: Write your topic (the thing you will describe) on the line in the Topic circle. Then organize details about the topic by writing them in the Details circles.

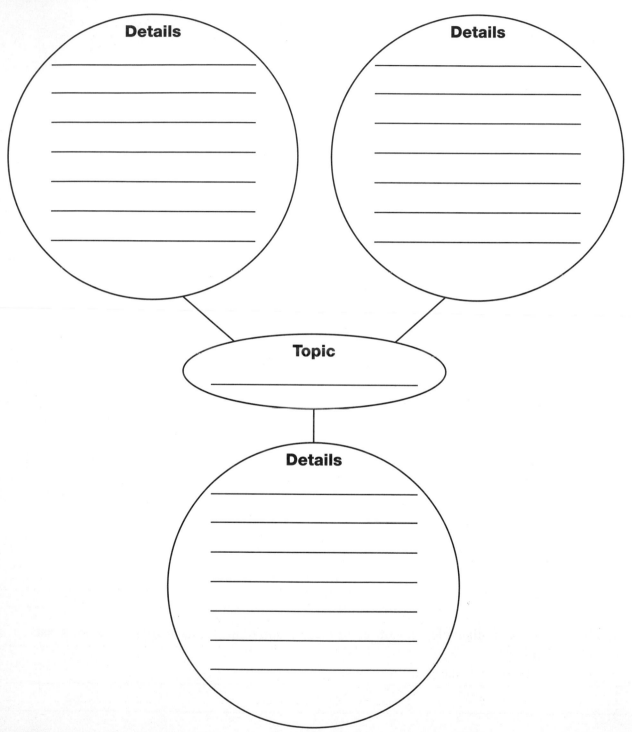

 Notes for Home: Your child used a web to organize information for writing a description. *Home Activity:* Ask your child to describe something at home by stating as many details as possible about the object.

Elaboration
Sense Words

- One way to elaborate is by adding **sense words** that help readers picture things clearly.
- You can provide vivid images by telling how things look, sound, feel, taste, and smell.

Directions: Substitute or add words from the box to the sentences below to make them more interesting. Write the new sentences using the words you picked.

snatch	dark	deadly
bumping	crashing	unsuspecting
damp	sharp	warm
special	squeaks	silently
unusual	high-pitched	slither
strike	fierce	pounce
crawl	dangerous	suddenly

1. Animals have ways of discovering food and danger.

_____

2. Bats fly through caves.

_____

3. They make sounds that echo off obstacles.

_____

4. These sounds prevent them from going into rocks.

_____

5. Big-eared rabbits listen for enemies.

_____

6. Rattlesnakes have pits that detect bodies.

_____

7. These snakes move toward prey.

_____

8. Suddenly they move and get their dinner.

_____

Notes for Home: Your child recently expanded sentences by adding sense words. *Home Activity:* Ask your child to describe an animal using sense words. For example: *The fluffy, spotted puppy chased the noisy bike.*

© Scott Foresman 5

Name _____

Self-Evaluation Guide
Descriptive Paragraph

Directions: Think about the final draft of your description. Then answer each question below.

	Yes	No	Not sure
1. Does my description tell about something in nature?			
2. Did I use descriptive words and images to give readers a good picture of this thing?			
3. Did I keep my audience and purpose in mind?			
4. Did I present my ideas in an organized way?			
5. Did I proofread and edit carefully to avoid errors?			

6. What part of your description do you think gives the best picture of your topic?

_____

_____

_____

7. Write one thing that you could change to make this description even better (a word, phrase, or sentence).

_____

_____

_____

_____

Notes for Home: Your child recently wrote a description. *Home Activity:* Encourage your child to tell you one way he or she tried to make this description vivid.

Family Times

Name_____

Summary

Deaf Student Faces Tough Time at New School

Mark is miserable. He's the first deaf student at his new school, and the other kids don't know how to act toward him. Their stares and laughter make him want to hide. Another student, Keith, is supposed to be helping Mark, but this only makes things worse. Then Mark and Keith find a common interest—basketball. Suddenly the new school doesn't seem so bad to Mark after all.

Reading Skills

Character

Characters are the people or animals in stories. You can learn about characters by:

❖ **what they think, say, and do.** Mark says "This is dumb!" He runs out of the classroom. Later he wonders, "Am I a freak?" We know from his words and thoughts that he's angry and unhappy.

❖ **the way other characters treat them or talk about them.** Keith says to Mark, "We need you." This shows that Keith wants Mark on his team. He likes Mark and respects his ability.

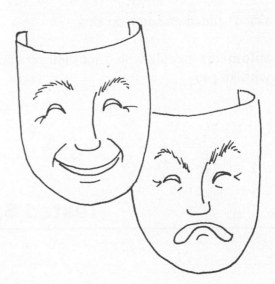

Activity

Act Out the Story. Have your child describe a scene from the story. Then, with other family members, act out the scenes described. For example, act out the scene between Mark and his dad when Mark wants to go back to live in Vermont, or the scene when Mark first decides to join in the basketball game with Keith.

Activity

Act Out Characters. With other members of your family, take turns impersonating a celebrity or public figure, such as a basketball star. See if your family can guess who you are impersonating from your words and actions.

© Scott Foresman 5

Family Times

Words to Know

Knowing the meanings of these words is important to reading *Going with the Flow*. Practice using these words to learn their meanings.

conversation talking informally together

dribbling moving a ball along by bouncing

gestured movements made with any part of the body to express oneself instead of using words

interpreter person who translates spoken language to a person who cannot hear

skied glided on snow on skis

volunteers people who offer their services without pay

Grammar

Verbs

Action verbs are verbs that tell what the subject of a sentence does or did. **Linking verbs** do not express actions. They link the verb to a word or words in the predicate. They show what the subject is or is like.

Action Verbs	Linking Verbs
throw	become
jump	am
run	will be
think	are
laugh	seem

Activity
Tell a Story. Make up a story using as many words from the table as you can. Just for fun, try making it a round robin story in which one family member leaves off and another continues until the story has concluded.

Tested Spelling Words

© Scott Foresman 5

Character

- **Characters** are the people or animals in a stories.

- You learn about characters from their words, actions, and the way other characters act toward them.

Directions: Reread "Jerome's Dream." Then complete the table. Give examples of things that characters think, say, and do to show what Jerome is like.

What the Characters Think, Do, and Say	Examples
What Jerome Thinks	1.
	2.
What Jerome Says	3.
What Jerome Does	4.
What Liza Says	5.

Notes for Home: Your child read a story and analyzed its main character. *Home Activity:* Think of a relative or neighbor. Describe things that the person frequently thinks, does, or says. Have your child guess who the person is, based on your clues. Switch roles and repeat the activity.

Vocabulary

Directions: Choose the word from the box that best completes each sentence.
Write the word on the line to the left.

_____ 1. Many _____ took part in the school games.

_____ 2. The principal raised her hands and _____ for the games to begin.

_____ 3. Some students _____ down nearby mountain slopes.

_____ 4. Others were good at _____ basketballs indoors.

_____ 5. All over school, people's _____ was about the games.

Check the Words You Know
__ conversation
__ dribbling
__ gestured
__ interpreter
__ skied
__ volunteers

Directions: Choose the word from the box that best matches each clue. Write
the word in the puzzle.

Down

6. people who offer their services
7. informal talk
8. signaled by hand
9. glided on skies

Across

10. one who translates

Write a Broadcast

Imagine you are a sportscaster. On a separate sheet of paper, write a broadcast
that describes a real or imaginary sports competition. Describe the action as if it
were happening right now in front of your eyes. Use as many vocabulary words
as you can.

Notes for Home: Your child identified vocabulary words in *Going with the Flow.* **Home
Activity:** Work with your child to write a sports article about a favorite sport or athlete, using
as many vocabulary words as you can.

Character

> • **Characters** are the people or animals in stories.
>
> • You learn about them from their words, actions, and the way other characters act toward them.

Directions: Reread what happens in *Going with the Flow* when Mark attends his new class for the first time. Think about what you've read, and then answer the questions below.

"Hi, Mark. How are you?" Mrs. LaVoie signed and mouthed the words silently to me across the room.

The whole fifth grade was watching us.

"This is dumb!" I signed back.

"They've never met a deaf kid before," she replied. "They..."

I didn't wait for her to finish. I had to get out of there. I raced down the center aisle, nearly tripped over the leg of some big, long-haired guy with a smirk on his face, and ran out the door.

Mrs. LaVoie found me in the gym under one of the bleachers. She put a hand on my arm.

From GOING WITH THE FLOW by Claire H. Blatchford. Copyright Text 1998 by Claire H. Blatchford, illustrations 1998 by Janice Lee Porter. Used by permission of Carolrhoda Books, Inc. All rights reserved.

1. What do the other students do when Mark signs with Mrs. LaVoie?

_____

_____

2. How does Mark feel about being in his new class? How do you know?

_____

_____

3. Why does Mark leave the room?

_____

_____

4. How does Mrs. LaVoie treat Mark?

_____

_____

5. How does Mark change by the end of the story? Write your answer on a separate sheet of paper. Give examples from the story to support your answers.

Notes for Home: Your child read a story and used story details to analyze a character. ***Home Activity:*** Watch a TV show or movie with your child, and then have your child describe his or her favorite character in the story.

Selection Test

Directions: Choose the best answer to each item. Mark the letter for the answer you have chosen.

Part 1: Vocabulary

Find the answer choice that means about the same as the underlined word in each sentence.

1. I didn't understand that <u>conversation</u>.
   A. a friendly talk
   B. a long book
   C. a math test
   D. a movie

2. A group of <u>volunteers</u> met at the town hall.
   F. people who have been elected to represent others
   G. teachers
   H. people who offer to work or help for free
   J. government workers

3. Nell works as an <u>interpreter</u>.
   A. person who helps others learn to study better
   B. person who translates one language into another
   C. writer for a newspaper
   D. coach who teaches others how to play a sport

4. Mike <u>gestured</u> excitedly.
   F. called out in a loud voice
   G. argued against something
   H. jumped up and down
   J. made hand movements

5. The girl <u>skied</u> very well.
   A. picked out skis
   B. explained how to ski
   C. waxed the skis
   D. glided on skis

6. All the players need to practice their <u>dribbling</u>.
   F. moving a ball by bouncing
   G. communicating without words
   H. throwing a ball into a basket
   J. passing a ball from one player to another

Part 2: Comprehension

Use what you know about the story to answer each item.

7. Who follows Mark into his classroom on the first day at his new school?
   A. his mother
   B. his fifth-grade teacher
   C. his interpreter
   D. the principal

8. Just after he rushes out of the classroom, Mark—
   F. takes a bus home.
   G. goes to eat in the cafeteria.
   H. hides in the gym.
   J. calls his friend Jamie.

9. After his first day at school, Mark feels—
   A. confident that he will succeed.
   B. ignored by his classmates.
   C. sure that he will make friends.
   D. sorry for himself.

10. Mark wants to move back to Vermont mainly because he wants to—
    F. play basketball.
    G. be with other deaf people.
    H. ski in races against Jamie.
    J. go to a better school.

© Scott Foresman 5

GO ON

11. You can tell that his father thinks Mark should—
    A. give the new school a chance before he gives up.
    B. forget the friends he had in Vermont.
    C. pretend he is not deaf so he will be accepted by others.
    D. move back to Vermont.

12. What is the first sign that Keith is a kind person?
    F. He smirks at Mark on Mark's first day in class.
    G. He laughs when Mark asks if his name is Teeth.
    H. He offers to take notes for Mark.
    J. He asks Mark to play basketball.

13. Keith trips Mark during the basketball game because he—
    A. knows that Mark is a better player than he is.
    B. is slower than Mark and cannot get out of his way.
    C. is trying to get Mark to give up and leave the basketball team.
    D. thinks Mark is playing without respect for him and the other players.

14. What makes the biggest difference in Mark's life?
    F. He joins the basketball team.
    G. Some of the boys laugh at him.
    H. Mrs. LaVoie helps him.
    J. He gets angry while playing basketball.

15. As a result of playing basketball with Keith, Mark learns to—
    A. try to fit in by working with others.
    B. look after himself first.
    C. realize that being deaf is not a problem.
    D. accept that he will always be left out.

STOP

Character

- **Characters** are the people or animals in stories.
- You learn about them from their words, actions, and the way other characters act toward them.

Directions: Read the story below.

Sharon's knees shook as she stood at the foul line. At that moment, she wondered why she had ever decided to play basketball.

"Don't worry, Sharon!" Coach Miller yelled. "You can make it!"

"I hope I can," Sharon said softly.

She took a deep breath and let the ball go.

It hit the basket rim and fell to the side. She had missed the first shot!

Sharon bounced the ball several times. Then she shot again. Whoosh! The ball sailed through the hoop! Sharon jumped up and down, flashing a victory sign with her fingers. Her team had won the game!

Directions: Complete the table. Think what you learn about Sharon's character from things she thinks, says, and does, and from what other characters say.

Sharon's Character	Examples
Sharon is nervous.	**1.** What she thinks:
	2. What she does:
	3. What she says:
	4. What Coach Miller says:
Sharon is happy.	**5.** What she does:

 Notes for Home: Your child read a story and used story details to analyze a character. ***Home Activity:*** Think of someone you and your child both know. Describe what that person often says, does, or thinks. Have your child guess who the person is. Reverse roles and repeat.

Drawing Conclusions and Predicting

Directions: Read the story. Then read each question about the story. Choose the best answer to each question. Mark the letter for the answer you have chosen.

Seeing the Problem

It was Tony's first day in his new school. As the newest student, Tony was seated in the back of the classroom.

Tony's new teacher, Mr. Brown, said they would start the day with a spelling lesson. Tony knew that the spelling book was blue, and he got it out of his book bag. Mr. Brown called on Tony. He asked Tony to read the spelling words which were written on the board.

Tony looked at the board. He squinted his eyes. He leaned his head forward and stared for a minute. When he didn't say anything, one or two children giggled.

Mr. Brown asked Tony if he would like to sit in the front of the room. Tony agreed. He picked up his book bag and spelling book and moved to a new seat at the very front of the class.

Mr. Brown then asked Tony once more to read the spelling words on the board. Tony squinted again and finally said, "I'm sorry, but I can't."

After class, Mr. Brown asked Tony to stay a few minutes. Tony hoped he hadn't done anything wrong on his first day.

Mr. Brown said, "Tony, I'd like you to visit the school doctor. She can give you an eye test."

1. Tony squints because he—
   A. dislikes being in the back of the classroom.
   B. has trouble seeing.
   C. can't hear the teacher.
   D. is in pain.

2. Tony doesn't read the words because he—
   F. dislikes Mr. Brown.
   G. dislikes reading.
   H. is embarrassed.
   J. can't see them clearly.

3. Mr. Brown changes Tony's seat to the front so that—
   A. he can talk to Tony.
   B. Tony is with his friends.
   C. Tony is closer to the chalkboard.
   D. Tony won't misbehave.

4. The eye doctor will probably tell Tony that he—
   F. needs glasses.
   G. is fine.
   H. should switch classes.
   J. should sit up front.

5. You could find out if your prediction is right by—
   A. rereading the passage.
   B. asking a friend.
   C. making another prediction.
   D. reading the rest of the story.

Notes for Home: Your child drew conclusions and made predictions based on story details. *Home Activity:* As you read with your child, pause often to let your child predict what will happen next. After reading, have your child draw conclusions about the characters and events.

Writing Across Texts

Directions: Think about Mark from *Going with the Flow* and what happened to
him when he moved to a new school. Then think back to the story "Faith and
Eddie." Remember what happened when Faith started school in Mexico. How
are the characters' experiences in a new school the same? How are they different?
Organize your thoughts in the Venn diagram below.

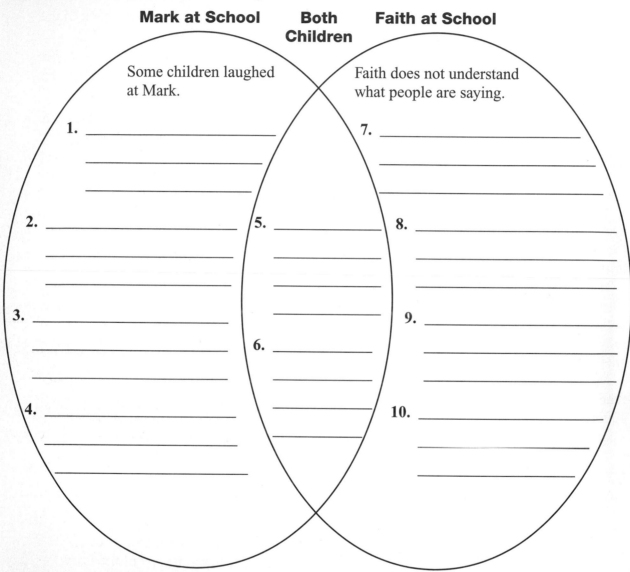

Mark at School   **Both Children**   **Faith at School**

Some children laughed at Mark.

Faith does not understand what people are saying.

1. _____

2. _____

3. _____

4. _____

5. _____

6. _____

7. _____

8. _____

9. _____

10. _____

Write a Paragraph

In *Going with the Flow,* you learned about a boy who struggles to fit in at his
new school. In "Faith and Eddie," you read about a girl who moves to a new
country. How was Mark's situation the same or different than Faith's? On a
separate sheet of paper, write a paragraph that tells which character's situation
would be more difficult, and why.

Notes for Home: Your child compared and contrasted the situations of two story characters to
make a judgment. *Home Activity:* Read a story to your child. Discuss how one character's life is
the same or different from another character's life. Ask your child: *Who* would you rather be?

Grammar: Predicates

Directions: Underline the complete predicate in each sentence. Then circle each simple predicate.

1. Joey's father took a new job in Tampa, Florida.

2. He told Joey about the move.

3. Joey thought about the meaning of a move to Florida.

4. He faced a new school, a new home, and new friends.

5. Tears came to his eyes.

6. Joey said good-bye to his friends one summer day.

7. Joey's room in the new house in Florida doubled the space of his old room.

8. A boy Joey's age lived right next door.

9. He took Joey to the nearby beach.

10. The nightmare of the move changed on that very first day!

Directions: Add a simple or complete predicate to each subject to form a sentence. Write the sentence on the line.

11. My friends at school _____.

_____

_____

12. My family's house _____.

_____

_____

13. New people and new places _____.

_____

_____

14. One advantage of a new school _____.

_____

_____

15. A home in Florida _____.

_____

_____

Notes for Home: Your child identified simple and complete predicates. *Home Activity:* Ask your child to find a paragraph he or she wrote at school. Have your child identify the complete and simple predicate in each sentence.

Grammar: Verbs

An **action verb** tells what action the subject of a sentence does.

    The players <u>shoot</u> the ball accurately.   They <u>ran</u> fast down the court.

Sometimes an action verb tells about an action that you cannot see, such as an action in someone's mind.

    The players <u>think</u> all the time.   They <u>surprised</u> us with their skill.

A **linking verb** does not show action. Instead, it links, or joins, the subject to a word in the predicate. That word helps to tell what the subject is or is like.

    The players <u>are</u> new.   They <u>seem</u> talented.

The most common linking verbs are *am, is, are, was,* and *were.* Other verbs often used as linking verbs are *become, seem, feel,* and *look.*

Directions: Underline the action verb in each sentence.

1. The ancient Aztecs played a form of basketball.

2. They threw a balled-up animal skin at a wooden hoop.

3. Dr. James Naismith invented modern basketball in 1891.

4. He nailed two empty peach baskets to the wall.

5. Next, he formed teams of eighteen players.

Directions: Underline the linking verb in each sentence.

6. Thirteen rules were part of the game.

7. The first basketballs looked uneven!

8. They felt squishy too.

9. Now, the balls are orange cowhide and nylon.

10. Basketball is an international sport.

Notes for Home: Your child identified action verbs and linking verbs. *Home Activity:* Ask your child to list ways he or she could help new classmates become part of the group. Guide your child to identify action verbs and linking verbs in the list.

Grammar: Verbs

Directions: Circle the verb in each sentence. Write **A** if the verb is an action verb. Write **L** if it is a linking verb.

_____ 1. Professional basketball began in 1896.

_____ 2. A group of players rented a hall in New Jersey.

_____ 3. They were very popular with the fans.

_____ 4. That night, each player earned fifteen dollars!

_____ 5. By the 1930s, basketball was a major sport.

Directions: Add a verb to complete each sentence. Try to use action verbs and linking verbs in your sentences. Write the verb on the line to the left.

_____ 6. The first NBA game _____ on November 1, 1946.

_____ 7. The Toronto Huskies _____ the New York Knicks.

_____ 8. Admission _____ free for fans taller than 6 feet, 8 inches.

_____ 9. The fans _____ loudly for their favorite players.

_____ 10. Today, basketball _____ popular with people of all ages.

_____ 11. The exercise _____ good for both amateur and professional players.

_____ 12. Good players _____ alert on the basketball court.

_____ 13. It also _____ if you have quick hands and feet.

_____ 14. Now, there _____ professional women's basketball teams.

_____ 15. Basketball _____ even an Olympic sport.

Write a Letter

How do you "go with the flow"? On a separate sheet of paper, write a letter telling a friend how you have learned to work with other people. Describe a problem you have faced and how you solved it. Use action and linking verbs.

Notes for Home: Your child identified and wrote action verbs and linking verbs. **Home Activity:** Invite your child to describe how to do something, such as how to make a sandwich or throw a basketball. Encourage your child to use both action and linking verbs.

Extra Practice

Grammar: Verbs

Underline each simple subject once. Underline each simple predicate twice.

1. The snail crawls.   **3.** The snake slithers.   **5.** He was certain.

2. The ants march.   **4.** I am sure.   **6.** They are positive.

Notice that the simple predicates in sentences 1–3 are verbs that show action. The action verbs tell what the simple subject does. The simple predicates in sentences 4–6 are linking verbs—verbs that link subjects to words in the predicates.

An **action verb** tells the action that the subject of a sentence does.
A **linking verb** helps to tell what the subject is or is like.

Directions: Underline the verb or verbs in each sentence.

1. My friend visits me on Saturdays.

2. My younger cousins are happy to watch television on the weekends.

3. They sometimes race from one room to another.

4. We laugh at their silly riddles, but we are glad to hear them.

5. I often cook lunch for them.

Directions: Write a verb to complete each sentence. Use a verb from the box below. One verb will be used more than once.

are	climb	drink	read	listen	is	chases

6. Each time the house _____ filled with much laughter.

7. My brother _____ our cousins out of his room.

8. They _____ their milk with long straws.

9. Karen and Bud never _____ to the rules of our games.

10. They _____ a little too young.

11. I _____ with them until their bedtime.

12. At that time they _____ very quiet.

13. Then I _____ into my own bed, tired from the long day.

Notes for Home: Your child identified and used verbs in sentences. *Home Activity:* Have your child listen to a favorite song and identify the verbs used in the lyrics.

Grammar: Verbs

Directions: Circle the verb in each sentence.

1. Mary Cassatt lived in Pittsburgh, Pennsylvania.

2. She traveled to France from America in 1868.

3. Cassatt studied the paintings of French artists.

4. Then she was a painter herself.

5. She painted pictures of mothers with their children.

6. Her paintings are in many museums today.

Directions: Write the scrambled words in the correct order. Circle the verbs.

7. Mandy a visited in museum Boston

_____

8. Mary Cassatt's an paintings she of exhibition saw

_____

9. Mandy her camera with pictures took

_____

10. guide facts told artist's the about life a

_____

11. paintings then Cassatt's were questions about there

_____

12. poster a bought at gift Mandy the shop

_____

13. were things new many to discover art about there

_____

Write a Description

Describe what it might be like to paint a picture. Use verbs. What might you think, feel, and do as you paint? Write on a separate sheet of paper.

 Notes for Home: Your child correctly reordered words in sentences and identified each verb. *Home Activity:* Have your child use a highlighter pen to identify verbs in newspaper articles or magazines. Ask whether each verb is an action verb or a linking verb.

Word Study: Regular Plurals

Directions: To form the plural of most nouns, add **-s.** For nouns that end in
x, s, ss, ch, or **sh,** add **-es.** For nouns that end in **consonant** and **y,** change the
y to **i** and add **-es.** Write the plural form for each noun below.

1. player _____
2. bleacher _____
3. basketball _____
4. box _____
5. lunch _____
6. turkey _____

7. enemy _____
8. glasses _____
9. teacher _____
10. photograph _____
11. signal _____
12. victory _____

Directions: Read the sports article. Make each word in ( ) plural. Write the
plural word on the line. You might need to change the spelling of a word to
make it plural.

We Are the Champions!

(Sign) for the game had been posted for
(month). When the night finally arrived,
you could see in the players' (eye) that
something special was going to happen.
(Word) can't do justice to how the team
played that night. Their (hand) wcrc
everywhere, shooting, dribbling, stealing.
The star made great (pass) and shot from
all corners of the court. No (speech) were
given that day, but the final score spoke for
itself. We will all have great (memory) of
this game for a long time to come.

13. _____
14. _____
15. _____
16. _____
17. _____
18. _____
19. _____
20. _____

Notes for Home: Your child practiced forming plural nouns, such as *steps* and *boxes.* **Home
Activity:** Read the labels on game boxes and food packages with your child. Help your child
notice plural words. Look to see whether *-s* or *-es* were added.

Spelling: Adding -s and -es

Pretest Directions: Fold back the page along the dotted line. On the blanks, write the spelling words as they are dictated. When you have finished the test, unfold the page and check your words.

1._____

2._____

3._____

4._____

5._____

6._____

7._____

8._____

9._____

10._____

11._____

12._____

13._____

14._____

15._____

16._____

17._____

18._____

19._____

20._____

1. It takes **months** to do this.

2. Wes will miss his old **friends**.

3. Study to improve your **grades**.

4. **Cowboys** ride horses.

5. The **valleys** are green and grassy.

6. **Donkeys** pulled the hay cart.

7. **Missiles** are dangerous.

8. Sew the **costumes** for the play.

9. These **pictures** are good.

10. Most **mornings**, he takes the bus.

11. Corey's tie **matches** his socks.

12. Daria hid in the **bushes**.

13. Fans watched from the **benches**.

14. Nobody listens to her **speeches**.

15. Did you check their hall **passes**?

16. His mom **kisses** him goodbye.

17. **Dresses** come in many colors.

18. My **batteries** are running low.

19. **Companies** give people jobs.

20. It's been done for **centuries**.

© Scott Foresman 5

Notes for Home: Your child took a pretest on adding -s and -es to nouns. *Home Activity:* Help your child learn misspelled words before the final test. Your child should look at the word, say it, spell it aloud, and then spell it with eyes shut.

Spelling: Adding -s and -es

Think and Practice

Word List				
months	valleys	pictures	benches	dresses
friends	donkeys	mornings	speeches	batteries
grades	missiles	matches	passes	companies
cowboys	costumes	bushes	kisses	centuries

Directions: Write the word from the box that is formed by adding **-es** to each base word. Hint: In some cases, you need to change the **y** to **i** before adding **-es**.

1. match _____

2. bench _____

3. kiss _____

4. dress _____

5. speech _____

6. pass _____

7. bush _____

8. century _____

9. company _____

10. battery _____

Directions: Choose the word from the box that is formed by adding **-s** to each base word. Write the letters of the word on the blanks. The boxed letters spell something you do to form plurals.

11. valley

12. grade

13. donkey

14. cowboy

15. month

16. friend

17. costume

18. morning

19. picture

20. missile

11. __ [ ] __ __ __ __ __

12. __ __ __ [ ] __

13. __ [ ] __ __ __ __ __

14. __ [ ] __ __ __ __

15. __ __ [ ] __ __ __

16. __ __ __ __ __ [ ]

17. __ [ ] __ __ __ __ __

18. __ __ [ ] __ __ __

19. __ __ __ __ __ [ ] __

20. __ __ [ ] __ __ __ __

Something you do to form plurals: __ __ __ __ __ __ __ __ __ __

Notes for Home: Your child spelled words that have -s and -es added to them to form plurals. *Home Activity:* Pick out items from the room whose names your child can spell. Then have your child spell the plural by adding -s or -es.

© Scott Foresman 5

Spelling: Adding -s and -es

Directions: Proofread this letter. Find five spelling mistakes. Use the proofreading marks to correct each mistake.

≡	Make a capital.
∕	Make a small letter.
∧	Add something.
⌿	Take out something.
⊙	Add a period.
¶	Begin a new paragraph.

Dear Jenna,

It's been two monthes since we moved here after Dad switched companys. I've made some new friends, and my grades are okay. I got two new dresess and hung new picturs on my wall. However, some mornings I wish I were back in my old home.

Hugs and kissess,

Tina

Word List

months	donkeys	matches	kisses
friends	missiles	bushes	dresses
grades	costumes	benches	batteries
cowboys	pictures	speeches	companies
valleys	mornings	passes	centuries

Write a Friendly Letter

Imagine you are Tina's friend Jenna. On a separate sheet of paper, write a friendly letter that tells what it is like when your best friend moves away. Try to use at least five of your spelling words.

Spelling Tip

Adding -es
Add **-es** to words that end in **sh, ch, s, ss,** or **x.** If the word ends in **consonant** and **y,** change **y** to **i** before adding **-es.**

Notes for Home: Your child spelled words that have *-s* and *-es* added to them to form plurals. *Home Activity:* Say each spelling word aloud, leaving off the final sound /s/. For example, say *picture,* not *pictures.* Have your child spell the plural form of the word.

Spelling: Adding -s and -es

Word List

months	valleys	pictures	benches	dresses
friends	donkeys	mornings	speeches	batteries
grades	missiles	matches	passes	companies
cowboys	costumes	bushes	kisses	centuries

Directions: Choose the word from the box that best completes each sentence.
Write the word on the line to the left.

_____ 1. Our _____ next door are leaving the neighborhood.

_____ 2. They've been planning to move for _____.

_____ 3. They've been waking early in the _____ to pack.

_____ 4. One of the moving _____ sent its van over today.

_____ 5. We stood near the rose _____ and watched the movers.

_____ 6. They carried out _____ that once hung on the walls.

_____ 7. They took girls' _____ that had hung in a closet.

_____ 8. They took wooden _____ from the backyard.

_____ 9. Some neighbors praised the family in brief _____.

_____ 10. After hugs and _____, the family drove away.

Directions: Write the word from the box that matches each clue.

_____ 11. sky rockets

_____ 12. similar to mules

_____ 13. actors' outfits

_____ 14. candle lighters

_____ 15. A and B+, for example

_____ 16. horse riders

_____ 17. hundreds of years

_____ 18. between hills

_____ 19. used in flashlights

_____ 20. thrown in football

Notes for Home: Your child spelled words that have -s and -es added to them to form plurals.
Home Activity: Spell a word that names one thing, such as *table* or *glass*. See if your child
can spell the plural by adding -s or -es.

Evaluate Information/Draw Conclusions

Directions: Read the article below and the advertisement on the next page.
Then answer the questions that follow the advertisement.

Ready? Get Set . . . Move!

Moving to a new home can be very challenging. It's not just all the packing and unpacking. If you're planning a move in the near future, here are some tips that will help you get where you're going.

Set Your Dates

It may sound obvious, but before you move, you must know exactly *when* you're moving. Whether you're leaving a house or an apartment, timing is everything. So check exactly when you're leaving your old home and arriving at your new home.

Notify All Services

Before you exit your old home, notify all important services. This includes utility companies, such as gas, electric, and telephone, and the bank. Most importantly, notify the U.S. post office of your change of address. The post office will forward your mail for up to six months. After that, letters may be returned.

Notify People

At least one month before you move, make a list of everyone you want to have your new address. This includes family, friends, neighbors, co-workers, doctors, dentists, and any other people with whom you communicate on a regular basis. The post office will supply you with cards that you can send to each person with your new address. If you already know your new telephone number, include that on the card as well.

Pack It Up

Perhaps the hardest part of any move is physically moving items from home to home. Plan ahead, and be sure to have plenty of boxes, tape, and other packing materials. Pack carefully. Mark your boxes to indicate the contents. Keep a list of what gets packed in each box and its condition. Double check to make sure you've left nothing behind.

Get Settled

Remember how you had to notify all your old services to discontinue? Well, now you've got the opposite task. Once in your new home, be sure all your new services have been activated. Is your telephone working? Do you have gas and electricity? Have you opened new bank accounts? Of course, in time you'll realize things you've forgotten. But the more that gets done immediately, the easier it will be to cope later!

Moving Day Checklist

Have I notified. . .

___ family	___ U.S. government (tax forms)	___ magazine subscriptions
___ friends	___ U.S. post office	___ newspaper subscriptions
___ neighbors	___ bank	___ clubs/organizations
___ co-workers	___ telephone company	___ others
___ doctors	___ gas/electric company	_____
___ dentists	___ landlord	_____

MOVING? WE CAN HELP!

Whether moving across the street or across the country, you need the services of a reliable mover. **Transport Movers** are the finest professional movers in the country.

- We are trustworthy, efficient, and economical.
- Other movers often break items in transport, but we almost never do. (And if we do, we'll reimburse you the full value of the item.)
- We require no more than three days' notice to be at your doorstep on the day you move.
- To find out more about **Transport Movers,** just call this toll free number: 1-800-555-MOVE.

Transport Movers
Moving Across America

1. What is the topic of the article in the pamphlet shown on the previous page?

_____

2. What are the five main points in the article? _____

_____

_____

_____

3. How reliable do you think the information is in the article? Explain.

_____

_____

4. What opinions are presented in the advertisement from Transport Movers?

_____

_____

5. Do you feel the information in the advertisement is as reliable as the information in the article? Explain.

_____

_____

_____

Notes for Home: Your child read an article and an advertisement, evaluated their information, and then drew conclusions about them. *Home Activity:* Read a newspaper or magazine article and advertisement with your child. Talk about the main ideas presented.

Family Times

Name_____

Summary

Farm Girl Braves Storm to Save Lives

Kate Shelley loved trains. She knew when every train was due to come roaring past her farm. One night she heard the Number Eleven crash as a bridge collapsed during a terrible storm. Kate rushed down to see if she could help and found two crewmen in the wreck. She made her way through the storm and darkness to the station. After reporting the accident, Kate led a rescue party to the wreck. She became a national hero. Kate Shelley even has a bridge named after her!

Activity

Create New Dialogue. Make up dialogue for the scene where Kate arrives at the train station to tell others about the train wreck. Write words for Kate, the station agent, and others at the station. Then act out the scene with your family.

Reading Skills

Graphic Sources

Some information is easier to understand when it is presented visually. A **graphic source,** such as a picture, graph, or map, is something that shows information visually. For example, *Kate Shelley: Bound for Legend* includes a map showing where the events of the story took place. The map makes it clear why Kate must cross the Des Moines River Bridge in order to get to the train station.

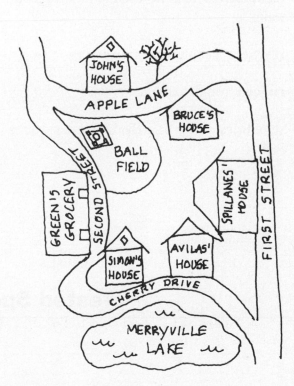

Activity

Make a Map. Make a map of your neighborhood. Include streets, houses, and other landmarks. Use the map to tell a story about an event in your life or to recount a day in the life of your family.

© Scott Foresman 5

Family Times

Tested Vocabulary

Words to Know

Knowing the meanings of these words is important to reading *Kate Shelley: Bound for Legend*. Practice using these words to learn their meanings.

dispatched sent off

downpour heavy rainfall

heroic very brave

locomotives engines used to pull railroad trains

rescuers people who save others

rugged rough and uneven

schedules times of arrivals and departures

Grammar

Subject-Verb Agreement

The subject and verb in a sentence must work together, or agree, in number. A singular noun subject needs a verb whose form agrees with singular nouns. A plural noun subject needs a verb whose form agrees with plural nouns.

Subject-Verb Agreement	
Singular:	Rover barks at the train. The train runs by our house. Its whistle is loud.
Plural:	Rover and Spot bark at the train. The trains run by our house. Their whistles are loud.

Activity

Sentence Starters. Play this game with a partner. One person starts a sentence with a singular or plural subject. The partner finishes the sentence with the proper verb agreement. Switch roles and play again.

Tested Spelling Words

© Scott Foresman 5

Graphic Sources

- A **graphic source,** such as a picture, graph, or map shows information visually.

- Before you read, look for graphic sources of information that could give you an idea of what the article or story is about.

- As you read, compare the written words to the graphic source for a better understanding of the main ideas.

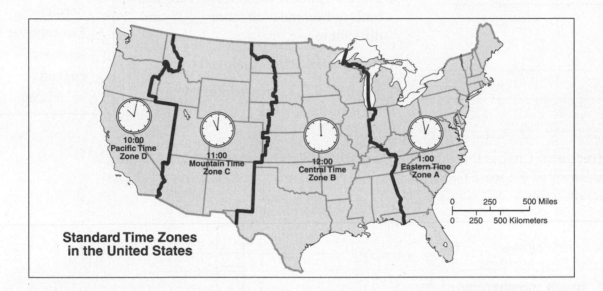

Standard Time Zones in the United States

Directions: Reread "Train Time." Use the text and map to answer each question.

1. What does the map show?

_____

2. What information does the map give that the article does not?

_____

3. How do you know that the map shows the United States after 1883, not before?

_____

4. How does the map help show the main idea in a different way than the text does?

_____

_____

5. If it were 3:00 Pacific Time, what time would it be Eastern Time? _____

Notes for Home: Your child read an article and got information from a related map. ***Home Activity:*** Together with your child, look at a map of your city, state, or country. Have your child describe locations of certain places, or the distances between two places on the map.

Vocabulary

Directions: Choose the word from the box that best completes each sentence. Write the word on the line.

_____

_____

_____

_____

_____

1. Last night's heavy _____ caused massive mud slides in our town.

2. The _____ for buses, trains, and postal service were all ruined.

3. The mud slides caused local roads and trails to become even more _____ and difficult to use.

4. People who came to help did a _____ job.

5. The mayor gave an award to the _____ for their brave work.

Check the Words You Know
__ dispatched
__ downpour
__ heroic
__ locomotives
__ rescuers
__ rugged
__ schedules

Directions: Choose the word from the box that best matches each clue. Write the letters of the word on the blanks. The boxed letters spell something you can take on trains.

6. train engines   **6.** __ __ __ __ __ __ ☐ __ __ __

7. rough and uneven   **7.** ☐ __ __ __ __ __

8. very brave   **8.** __ __ __ ☐ __

9. heavy rainfall   **9.** __ __ __ __ ☐ __ __ __

10. sent off   **10.** __ __ ☐ __ __ __ __ __ __ __

Something you take on trains: __ __ __ __ __

Write a Journal Entry

On a separate sheet of paper, write a journal entry about an imaginary train trip that runs into trouble. Describe the problem and how it was solved. Use as many vocabulary words as you can.

Notes for Home: Your child identified and used new vocabulary words from *Kate Shelley: Bound for Legend*. **Home Activity:** Make up a story with your child of a daring rescue, using the vocabulary words. When finished, share your story with others.

Graphic Sources

- A **graphic source,** such as a picture, graph, or map, shows information visually.

- Before you read, look for graphic sources of information that could give you an idea of what the article or story is about.

Directions: Look at the map of the vicinity of Kate Shelley's home from *Kate Shelley: Bound for Legend.* Then answer the questions below.

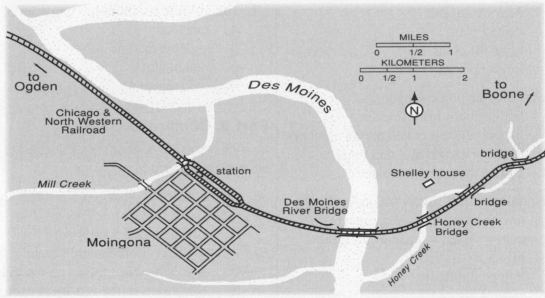

From KATE SHELLEY: BOUND FOR LEGEND by Robert D. San Souci, paintings by Max Ginsburg. Copyright © 1995 by Max Ginsburg, paintings. Used by permission of Dial Books for Young Readers, a division of Penguin Putnam Inc.

1. In which direction does a train travel from Moingona to the Honey Creek Bridge?

_____

2. Is the Shelley house closer to the Honey Creek Bridge or to the station at Moingona?

_____

3. If you traveled by train from Ogden to Boone, what bridges and stations would you travel past along the way?

_____

_____

4. Which bridge is closest to the Moingona station?

_____

5. How does the map help you better understand the story? Explain your answer on a separate sheet of paper.

Notes for Home: Your child answered questions about a map. *Home Activity:* Look at a map with your child. Talk about the information you can find by reading the map, such as distances between two locations.

Selection Test

Directions: Choose the best answer to each item. Mark the letter for the answer you have chosen.

Part 1: Vocabulary

Find the answer choice that means about the same as the underlined word in each sentence.

1. The newspaper included a report about the downpour.
   - A.   heavy rainfall
   - B.   ruined plan
   - C.   huge fountain
   - D.   falling prices

2. Please pick up some schedules.
   - F.   books about historic events
   - G.   lists of addresses and phone numbers
   - H.   times of arrival and departure
   - J.   guides to interesting places

3. That museum has some old locomotives.
   - A.   uniforms of railroad engineers
   - B.   engines used to push or pull trains
   - C.   oil lanterns
   - D.   letters and diaries

4. The rescuers looked into the cave.
   - F.   scientists
   - G.   people trying to save others
   - H.   artists
   - J.   people traveling to new places

5. We hiked across the rugged land.
   - A.   damp and muddy
   - B.   green and grassy
   - C.   dry and dusty
   - D.   rough and uneven

6. The mayor dispatched the rescue team.
   - F.   said good things about
   - G.   sent out
   - H.   gave instructions to
   - J.   welcomed

7. The girl told us about her heroic acts.
   - A.   unusual
   - B.   against the law
   - C.   unknown
   - D.   very brave

Part 2: Comprehension

Use what you know about the selection to answer each question.

8. How did fifteen-year-old Kate Shelley spend most of her time?
   - F.   She attended school with her younger brothers and sisters.
   - G.   She helped her father on the railroad.
   - H.   She swam in the nearby stream and played with her friends.
   - J.   She ran the family farm.

9. Which of these events happened first?
   - A.   Kate heard a pusher engine fall into Honey Creek.
   - B.   Kate moved the farm animals to higher ground.
   - C.   Kate decided to try to stop the midnight train bound for Chicago.
   - D.   Kate helped her mother bring in the laundry.

GO ON

10. When Kate decided that she had to go through the storm to the train station, her mother was—
   F. worried that she would be hurt.
   G. eager for Kate to face the danger.
   H. furious at Kate for disobeying her.
   J. confident that Kate would be safe.

11. According to the map in this selection, a train heading in a westerly direction as it passed the Shelley house was going toward—
   A. Boone.
   B. Ogden.
   C. Chicago.
   D. Ohio.

12. What was Kate's most terrifying moment while crossing the Des Moines River Bridge?
   F. realizing that the ties were two feet apart
   G. seeing the spot where her brother had died
   H. seeing the lights of the railway station in the distance
   J. seeing a huge tree rushing toward the bridge

13. Which sentence states an opinion?
   A. "She turned and headed for the Des Moines River Bridge."
   B. "As it headed for the fallen trestle, the engineer kept sounding the whistle."
   C. "The girl is crazy."
   D. "But the structure proved solid, and the storm was quieting at last."

14. Traveling east from Moingona, a train would first come to the—
   F. Des Moines River Bridge.
   G. Shelley House.
   H. Honey Creek Bridge.
   J. town of Boone.

15. Of all the honors Kate received, which did she think was the best?
   A. a medal from the state of Iowa
   B. whistles from trains that passed by
   C. a lifetime pass on the railroad
   D. greetings from passengers on the trains

STOP

Graphic Sources

- A **graphic source,** such as a picture, graph, or map, shows information visually.

- Before you read, look for graphic sources of information that could give you an idea of what the article or story is about.

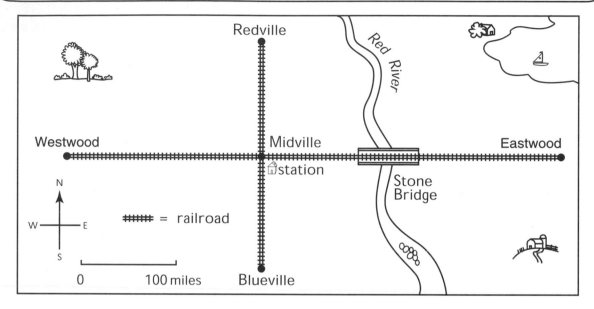

Directions: Look at the map. Use information from the map to answer the questions below.

1. About how many miles is it from Westwood to Eastwood?

_____

2. How could you get by train from Redville to Eastwood?

_____

3. In which direction do you travel from Redville to Blueville?

_____

4. About how many miles is it from Midville to Westwood?

_____

5. Why are maps like this used in stories?

_____

_____

Notes for Home: Your child answered questions about a map. *Home Activity:* With your child, draw a map of your neighborhood. Then talk about the information you can find by reading the map. Write a story about your neighborhood and include your map.

Text Structure

Directions: Read each passage. Then read each question about the passages. Choose the best answer to each question. Mark the letter for the answer you have chosen.

All About Trains

1. Trains can carry heavier cargo than airplanes. One locomotive engine can pull many cars full of freight. Planes, on the other hand, can carry only one cargo load of freight at a time. Planes travel faster than trains, though, which can mean that the cargo gets to its destination faster than it would by train.

2. At one time, Americans couldn't get from coast to coast by train. The train tracks did not go all the way across the United States. Then, in the early 1860s, the railroad companies decided to begin building a transcontinental railroad.

3. Some early trains carried large sums of money. Companies would send payrolls and other kinds of payments in cash by rail. As a result, the trains were often the targets of robbery.

4. In 1804, the steam locomotive was invented. This made it possible for a locomotive to pull cars along a train track. By 1831, there was steam-powered train service in the United States.

5. There are many kinds of railroad cars, and they have different purposes. A Pullman car is one with sleeping compartments in which passengers can sleep overnight. A hopper car hauls freight. A tank car carries oil and other liquids. A stock car holds cattle.

1. The text structure of the first passage is—
   A. cause and effect.
   B. problem and solution.
   C. chronological order.
   D. compare and contrast.

2. The text structure of the second passage is—
   F. cause and effect.
   G. problem and solution.
   H. chronological order.
   J. compare and contrast.

3. The text structure of the third passage is—
   A. cause and effect.
   B. problem and solution.
   C. chronological order.
   D. compare and contrast.

4. The text structure of the fourth passage is—
   F. cause and effect.
   G. problem and solution.
   H. chronological order.
   J. compare and contrast.

5. The text structure of the fifth passage is—
   A. cause and effect.
   B. problem and solution.
   C. chronological order.
   D. compare and contrast.

Notes for Home: Your child read individual passages and identified the way the information was organized in each one. **Home Activity:** Read a magazine or newspaper article with your child. Talk together about the way that the information is organized in the article.

Writing Across Texts

Directions: Consider what you know about frontier life and what you learned in *Kate Shelley: Bound for Legend* and "The Last Western Frontier." What do you think you would like about frontier life? What would you dislike? Add examples to each column to complete the table below.

What I Would Like About Frontier Life	What I Would Not Like About Frontier Life
I would get to work on a farm.	I would have lots of chores.
1.	6.
2.	7.
3.	8.
4.	9.
5.	10.

Write an Opinion

Imagine what it might have been like to be a pioneer in the westward expansion as described in both Kate Shelley's story and in "The Last Western Frontier." What are some reasons you would like frontier life? Why would you dislike it? Use information from each selection to write a paragraph that supports your feelings. Write your paragraph on a separate sheet of paper.

Notes for Home: Your child wrote an opinion about frontier life in the 1800s. ***Home Activity:*** Together with your child, discuss challenges faced by all families who move to a new place.

Grammar: Verbs

Directions: Circle the verb in each sentence. Write **A** if the verb is an action verb. Write **L** if the verb is a linking verb. Remember, an **action verb** tells what action the subject of a sentence is performing or does. A **linking verb** links, or joins, the subject to a word in the predicate. A linking verb helps to tell what the subject is or is like.

_____ 1. Rescuers usually are people.

_____ 2. However, every year animals save the lives of many people.

_____ 3. For example, a cat once was a brave hero.

_____ 4. Early one morning a lady's house filled with smoke.

_____ 5. The smoke looked thick and dangerous.

_____ 6. The cat jumped on the lady.

_____ 7. The cat's warning seemed useless.

_____ 8. Again and again the cat walked over her body and her head.

_____ 9. Just in time, the lady opened her eyes.

_____ 10. She and the cat raced outside to safety.

Directions: Use each of the following words as verbs in a sentence. Write the sentence on the line.

11. *looked* as an action verb

_____

12. *looked* as a linking verb

_____

13. *felt* as an action verb

_____

14. *felt* as a linking verb

_____

15. *seems*

_____

Notes for Home: Your child identified action and linking verbs. *Home Activity:* Identify some simple verbs such as *say, run,* and *hit*. Work with your child to see how many colorful verbs you can find to substitute for these verbs. Use a thesaurus if available.

Grammar: Subject-Verb Agreement

The subject and the verb in a sentence must **agree** in number. A **singular noun subject** needs a verb whose form agrees with singular nouns. A **plural noun subject** needs a verb that agrees with plural nouns. The word **singular** refers to "one"; **plural** means "more than one." Use the following rules for verbs that tell about present time.

- If the subject is a singular noun, add **-s** or **-es** to most verbs. If a verb ends in a **consonant** and **y**, change the **y** to **i** before adding **-es.**

> Thunder <u>scares</u> the cat.
> The animal <u>scurries</u> under the bed.

- If the subject is a plural noun, do not add **-s** or **-es** to the verb.

> Cats <u>react</u> to unexpected sounds or flashes of light.

- When two subjects combine to form a compound subject, use a plural verb form.

> Thunder and lightning <u>scare</u> the cat.
> Heavy rain and hailstones <u>are</u> not favorites of hers either.

Directions: Circle the correct form of the verb in ( ) to complete each sentence.

1. Legends (tells/tell) about people from the past.

2. Some legends (is/are) based on fact.

3. Other legends (stretches/stretch) the truth.

4. Stories about the past (thrill/thrills) me sometimes.

5. Every culture (has/have) its own legends.

6. My grandmother (knows/know) a legend about Sarah Winnemucca, a member of the Paiute tribe.

7. We (listens/listen) to my grandmother's stories eagerly.

8. Heroes (is/are) often the subjects of legends.

9. Davy Crockett and Daniel Boone (has/have) a role in many legends about pioneers settling in the West.

10. Legends and other tales (keeps/keep) history alive.

Notes for Home: Your child chose forms of verbs that agree with singular subjects and plural subjects. *Home Activity:* Invite your child to write a family legend about something good a family member has done. Remind your child to check for subject-verb agreement.

Grammar: Subject-Verb Agreement

Directions: Use the correct form of the verb in ( ) to complete each sentence.
Write the verb on the line.

_____ 1. My father (tell) many stories about Uncle Nick.

_____ 2. Uncle Nick always (demonstrate) great courage in his job as a firefighter.

_____ 3. Every day, Uncle Nick and the other firefighters (respond) to fire alarms.

_____ 4. Even at night, these guardians of our safety (fight) fierce blazes.

_____ 5. Sometimes the fires (burn) for days.

_____ 6. Uncle Nick (pull) people out of burning buildings.

_____ 7. These people always (express) their gratitude to him for saving their lives.

_____ 8. Uncle Nick now (possess) several medals for bravery.

_____ 9. In my view, Uncle Nick (deserve) a hero's honors.

_____ 10. Dad (think) that Uncle Nick may even become a legend some day.

Directions: Add a verb to complete each sentence. Be sure to use the correct
verb form. Write the verb on the line to the left.

_____ 11. Each day, the trains _____ along the railroad tracks.

_____ 12. During winter months, the passengers always _____ inside the station house.

_____ 13. The conductor _____ for anything that might block the tracks.

_____ 14. Sometimes, tree branches _____ on the tracks.

_____ 15. Workers _____ the tracks to make sure they are safe for the trains to travel.

Write a Song

What does "bravery" mean to you? On a separate sheet of paper, write a song
about a brave person in the news right now. Tell how the person is brave. Set
your words to a well-known tune. Be sure all the subjects and verbs in your
song agree.

Notes for Home: Your child wrote verbs that agree with singular subjects and plural subjects.
Home Activity: Read a news story with your child. Ask him or her to find all the subjects and
verbs and to explain how they agree, or match in number.

Grammar: Subject-Verb Agreement

Read each sentence. The simple subjects are underlined. Write the verbs.

1. Two <u>boys</u> build scenery. _____

2. A <u>girl</u> builds scenery. _____

The **subject** and the **verb** in a sentence must **agree** in number.

Directions: Write the verb that correctly completes each sentence.

1. Tony and his helper _____ the sets. (paint/paints)

2. Mary _____ her part. (study/studies)

3. Dan and a teacher _____ the rear curtains. (raise/raises)

4. The narrator _____ in a costume. (appear/appears)

5. Teachers and parents _____ with the scenery. (help/helps)

6. Parents and guests _____ on time. (arrive/arrives)

Directions: The verb in each sentence is incorrect. Rewrite each sentence with the correct form of the underlined verb.

7. Judy and Diego <u>moves</u> the scenery.

_____

8. Band members and the chorus <u>joins</u> in a song.

_____

9. Classmates and visitors <u>claps</u> loudly.

_____

10. The stage director <u>plan</u> a cast party.

_____

11. Scenery <u>are</u> put away.

_____

Notes for Home: Your child used verbs that agreed with the subjects of sentences. *Home Activity:* Write three subjects, such as *the plane, my friends,* and *the old car* and have your child write sentences using the subjects you wrote and verbs that agree.

Grammar: Subject-Verb Agreement

Directions: Edit the letter below to correct the eleven errors in subject-verb agreement. Cross out the incorrect verb form and write the correct form above it. Make sure subjects are used with the correct verb forms.

1315 West Main Street

Glenview, IL 60089

November 19, 2002

The Art Institute of Chicago

111 South Michigan Avenue

Chicago, IL 60603

Dear Sir or Madam:

My class have just read an article about Leo and Diane Dillon, two people who illustrates books. Our teacher, Mrs. Ford, always tell us we should take an interest in what we reads. I enjoys reading, but I really likes to draw. Mrs. Ford say that people draws many kinds of things and that some people, like Leo and Diane Dillon, has careers in art.

If other artists has jobs like Leo and Diane Dillon, I think a career in art sound interesting. I would like to find out more about art and artists in the United States. Would you please send me any information you have on American artists? Thank you for your help.

Sincerely,

Bob Smith

Bob Smith

Notes for Home: Your child corrected a letter with errors in subject-verb agreement. ***Home Activity:*** Write sentences with blanks for verbs. Then have your child fill in verbs. Make sure the verbs your child writes agree with the subjects in the sentences.

Word Study: Irregular Plurals

Directions: Most plural nouns are formed by adding **-s** or **-es.** Some plural nouns do not follow a regular spelling pattern. These are called **irregular plurals.** Read the paragraph. Find each irregular plural noun and write it on the line.

The children heard the whistle as the train neared the town. Suddenly they heard a crash, and then it was quiet. They raced to the edge of town. Men and women had already begun to arrive. What a scene it was! The train had been carrying a special load. Oxen were lumbering about, and geese ran honking everywhere. The mice that had been nesting in the hay were under everyone's feet. Thankfully, no one was hurt, and the animals were all rounded up safely.

1. _____
2. _____
3. _____
4. _____
5. _____
6. _____
7. _____

Directions: Look at the plural nouns you wrote above. Write the singular form of each noun on the line.

8. _____
9. _____
10. _____
11. _____
12. _____
13. _____
14. _____

Directions: Write another sentence for the story using the plural form of **foot.**

15. _____

_____

Notes for Home: Your child identified irregular plural nouns, such as *children (child)* and *men (man).* **Home Activity:** Use several of the irregular plural nouns from the paragraph above and write a new story with your child.

Spelling: Irregular Plurals

Pretest Directions: Fold back the page along the dotted line. On the blanks, write the spelling words as they are dictated. When you have finished the test, unfold the page and check your words.

1._____
2._____
3._____
4._____
5._____
6._____
7._____
8._____
9._____
10._____
11._____
12._____
13._____
14._____
15._____
16._____
17._____
18._____
19._____
20._____

1. Some **radios** run on batteries.
2. The store rents **videos**.
3. **Pianos** are very heavy.
4. Some houses have **patios**.
5. Bluegrass music uses **banjos**.
6. This book has stories of **heroes**.
7. Baked **potatoes** are tasty.
8. The cave is full of **echoes**.
9. **Tornadoes** cause damage.
10. These **tomatoes** are not ripe yet
11. The **cuffs** of his pants are dirty.
12. **Cliffs** rise high above the river.
13. We have the same **beliefs**.
14. Animal **hoofs** are hard.
15. All the **roofs** were full of snow.
16. They talked among **themselves**.
17. Paramedics save **lives**.
18. The **leaves** are turning red.
19. These **loaves** of bread are stale.
20. They cut the fruit into **halves**.

© Scott Foresman 5

 Notes for Home: Your child took a pretest on words that are irregular plurals. *Home Activity:* Help your child learn misspelled words before the final test. Your child can underline the word parts that caused the problems and concentrate on those parts.

Spelling: Irregular Plurals 265

Think and Practice

Spelling: Irregular Plurals

Word List				
radios	banjos	tornadoes	beliefs	lives
videos	heroes	tomatoes	hoofs	leaves
pianos	potatoes	cuffs	roofs	loaves
patios	echoes	cliffs	themselves	halves

Directions: Choose the words from the box that are formed by adding **-es** to a base word. Write each word in the correct column.

f changes to v before -es is added

1. _____
2. _____
3. _____
4. _____
5. _____

-es is added to words ending with o

6. _____
7. _____
8. _____
9. _____
10. _____

Directions: Add **-s** to each word in ( ) to form a word from the box and complete the sentence. Write the word on the line.

_____ 11. The horses' (hoof) loosened several rocks.

_____ 12. Rocks from the (cliff) fcll onto the land below.

_____ 13. Some rocks went through the (roof) of old buildings.

_____ 14. Other rocks crashed onto several (patio).

_____ 15. A rescue alert was heard on many (radio).

_____ 16. All differing customs and (belief) were set aside during the rescue.

_____ 17. One musician was able to rescue her two (piano).

_____ 18. But she wasn't able to save her damaged (banjo).

_____ 19. One man escaped with only minor tears to his shirt (cuff).

_____ 20. Newscasts showed home (video) of the damage shot by the homeowners.

Notes for Home: Your child spelled irregular plural nouns that have *-s* and *-es* added to them but that do not follow regular spelling patterns. *Home Activity:* Spell each spelling word aloud to your child. Have your child spell each word you say.

Spelling: Irregular Plurals

Directions: Proofread this news bulletin. Find five spelling mistakes. Use the proofreading marks to correct each mistake.

≡	Make a capital.
/	Make a small letter.
∧	Add something.
℘	Take out something.
⊙	Add a period.
¶	Begin a new paragraph.

News Bulletin!

Alert! Several tornados have been spotted near the cliffs. The rooves of some homes have been damaged. No lifes have been lost, and many have been rescued. People should shut themselfs safely in their basements and stay off their patios. Do not try to take home videoes. Stay tuned to your radios for updated reports.

Word List

radios	banjos	tornadoes	beliefs	lives
videos	heroes	tomatoes	hoofs	leaves
pianos	potatoes	cuffs	roofs	loaves
patios	echoes	cliffs	themselves	halves

Write a News Report

Imagine you are a news correspondent reporting the results of a storm. On a separate sheet of paper, write your news report. Try to use at least five of your spelling words.

Spelling Tip

potatoes

How can you remember to spell **potatoes,** not **potatos?** Think of this hint: **Pota<u>toes</u>** have both eyes and <u>**toes**</u>.

Notes for Home: Your child spelled irregular plural nouns that have -*s* and -*es* added to them but that do not follow regular spelling patterns. *Home Activity:* Make a list of the spelling words, but misspell several words. Have your child correct the list.

© Scott Foresman 5

Spelling: Irregular Plurals

REVIEW

Word List				
radios	banjos	tornadoes	beliefs	lives
videos	heroes	tomatoes	hoofs	leaves
pianos	potatoes	cuffs	roofs	loaves
patios	echoes	cliffs	themselves	halves

Directions: Choose the word from the box that best completes each statement. Write the word on the line to the left.

_____ **1.** *Strings* are to *violins* as *keys* are to ____.

_____ **2.** *People* are to *feet* as *horses* are to ____.

_____ **3.** *Below* is to *basements* as *above* is to ____.

_____ **4.** *Corn* is to *ears* as *bread* is to ____.

_____ **5.** *Talent* is to *artists* as *bravery* is to ____.

_____ **6.** *Head* is to *hair* as *tree* is to ____.

_____ **7.** *We* is to *ourselves* as *they* is to ____.

_____ **8.** *Green* is to *lettuce* as *red* is to ____.

_____ **9.** *Shake* is to *earthquakes* as *swirl* is to ____.

_____ **10.** *Bang* is to *drums* as *strum* is to ____.

_____ **11.** *Creamed* is to *spinach* as *mashed* is to ____.

_____ **12.** *Arms* is to *hands* as *sleeves* is to ____.

Directions: Choose the word from the box that answers each question. Write the word on the line.

_____ **13.** What might you rent for a double feature?

_____ **14.** Where would you not want to walk if you were afraid of heights?

_____ **15.** What might you hear when you shout in the Grand Canyon?

_____ **16.** What would you learn about if you read biographies?

_____ **17.** Where do people hold barbecues in the summer?

_____ **18.** What do teenagers usually play too loud?

_____ **19.** Into what would you cut a pie for two very big eaters?

_____ **20.** What do you call strong feelings or ideas?

© Scott Foresman 5

Notes for Home: Your child spelled irregular plural nouns that have *-s* and *-es* added to them but that do not follow regular spelling patterns. ***Home Activity:*** Give your child clues about each spelling word. See if your child can identify and spell each word.

Atlas/Map

An **atlas** is a book of maps. A **map** is a drawing of a place. A **map key** shows
what the symbols on a map mean. A **compass** shows the directions north, south,
east, and west.

Directions: Use the map below to answer the questions on the next page.

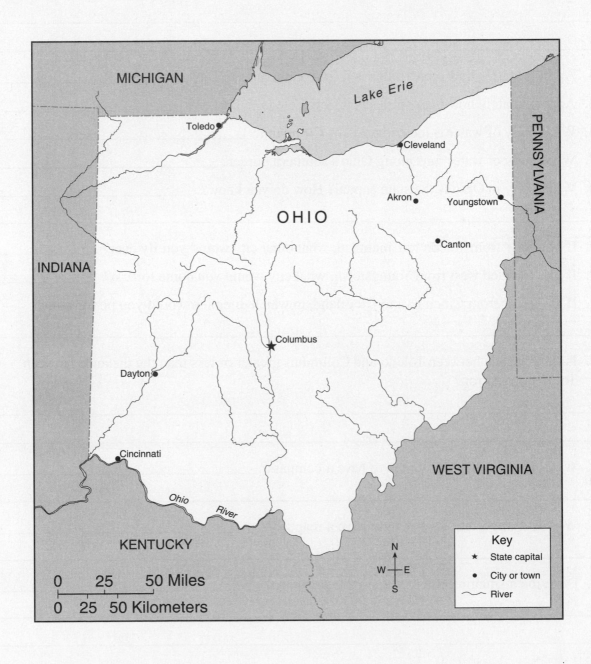

Name _____

1. What five states border Ohio? _____
_____

2. Which state is on Ohio's western border? _____

3. If you measured that the distance between two cities was two inches on the map, how many actual miles is this distance? How do you know?
_____
_____

4. Approximately how many miles is it from Columbus to Dayton? _____

5. Approximately how many miles is it from Toledo to Dayton? _____

6. What body of water is located north of Cleveland? _____

7. What body of water runs along Ohio's southern border? _____

8. Which city in Ohio is the state capital? How do you know? _____
_____

9. If you flew from Toledo to Cincinnati, what other city would you fly over? _____

10. If you traveled west from Youngstown, what city would you come to first? _____

11. If you went from Cincinnati to Cleveland, in which direction would you be traveling?
_____

12. Is the distance between Toledo and Columbus greater or less than the distance between Toledo and Akron?
_____
_____

13. Why is it important for a map to have a compass? _____
_____

14. Why is it important for a map to have a map key? _____
_____

15. Describe a situation where you might use a map. _____
_____
_____
_____

Notes for Home: Your child read a map and answered questions about it. *Home Activity:* Look at any map you have at home. Have your child point out information on it, such as the location of places or the direction and distance from one place to another.

Family Times

Name_____

Summary

Lupe Medrano Wins Big at Marble Championship

Lupe Medrano is the top student at her school. However, she is a failure at sports—until she tries her hand at marbles. She practices playing marbles day and night and exercises her poor thumb until it is sore and swollen. When Lupe enters the marble championship she wins one match after another. Then she takes on the top girl and boy and wins in both divisions. Now she is truly the marble champ!

Reading Skills

Plot

Every story has a **plot,** the important events that happen to the characters. A plot usually has these parts:

- ❖ **Conflict** is the story's main problem. Lupe's problem is that she wants to be good at a sport.
- ❖ **Rising action** includes the events that add interest and suspense. Lupe practices marbles and enters the championship.
- ❖ **Climax** is the high point of the story. Lupe plays in a difficult girls' division finals match and wins!
- ❖ **Outcome** is the story's ending. Lupe beats the boys' champion, and then goes out to dinner to celebrate her victory with her family.

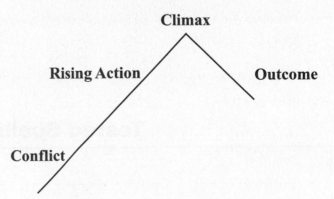

Activity

Find Out More. Look up the game of marbles in game books and encyclopedias. Learn what different marbles are called and the many kinds of marble games you can play. Write a set of directions for a marbles game you might like to try.

Activity

Summarize a Plot. Watch a TV program or movie together. Then sum up the plot. Describe the conflict, the rising action, climax, and outcome. Use the diagram above to help you think about the different parts of the plot.

Family Times

Tested Vocabulary

Words to Know

Knowing the meanings of these words is important to reading "The Marble Champ." Practice using these words to learn their meanings.

championship first place in a competition

opponent person one plays against in a game

strengthen make or grow stronger

swollen swelled; enlarged

trophy a statue or cup given as an award

Grammar

Verb Tenses: Present, Past, and Future

A verb in the **present tense** shows action that is happening now.

> She <u>plays</u> marbles.

A verb in the **past tense** shows action that has already happened. It often ends in *-ed*. Verbs that do not end in *-ed* are called **irregular verbs.**

> **Regular: She <u>played</u> marbles yesterday.**
> **Irregular: She <u>won</u> several times.**

A verb in the **future tense** shows action that will happen. It is usually preceded by the word *will*.

> She <u>will play</u> marbles tomorrow.

Activity

Role-playing. Role-play a person you admire, such as an athlete or actor. Say three sentences about what you do, each in a different tense. For example: **I <u>play</u> center for my basketball team. Last year I <u>played</u> in every game. This year I <u>will travel</u> to six other cities with the team.**

Tested Spelling Words

Plot

- The important events that happen in a story make up the **plot**.

- A plot has several parts. **Conflict** is the story's main problem. During the **rising action** one event follows another. Each event adds interest or suspense to the conflict. The **climax** is the high point when the main character faces the problem directly. The **outcome** is the ending of the story.

Directions: Reread "Anything You Set Your Mind To." Then complete the plot map by identifying each important part of the story.

Climax: When is Terry's problem finally solved?

4. _____

_____

_____

Rising Action: What does Terry do to try to solve his problem?

2. _____

_____

3. _____

_____

Outcome: How does the story end?

5. _____

_____

_____

_____

_____

_____

_____

_____

Conflict: What problem does Terry have?

1. _____

_____

_____

Notes for Home: Your child identified the main events in the plot of a story. *Home Activity:* Read a story with your child. Have your child identify the different plot elements described above.

Vocabulary

Directions: Choose the word from the box that best matches each clue.
Write the word on the line.

_____ 1. Healthy foods do this to you.

_____ 2. You might play in this.

_____ 3. You might win this.

_____ 4. It's someone to defeat.

_____ 5. A hurt finger might become this.

Directions: Write the word from the box that belongs in each group.

6. enemy, foe, _____

7. award, medal, _____

8. enlarged, puffy, _____

9. contest, competition, _____

10. toughen, harden, _____

Directions: Choose the word from the box that best completes each sentence.
Write the word on the line.

_____ 11. The big _____ wrestling match would be held this Saturday night.

_____ 12. My _____ was bigger than me, but I was faster.

_____ 13. I had worked hard to _____ my upper body muscles.

_____ 14. Although my wrist is a little _____, I believe I can win the match.

_____ 15. I already know where I want to display the _____ in my room.

Write a Pep Talk

Imagine you are a sports coach. On a separate sheet of paper, write a pep talk to
give to your players. Your pep talk should help make the team eager to win. Use
as many vocabulary words as you can.

Notes for Home: Your child identified and used vocabulary words from "The Marble
Champ." **Home Activity:** Choose items in the room where you and your child are sitting.
Describe each item. See if your child can guess what it is, based on the clues you offer.

Plot

- The important events that happen in a story make up the **plot.**

- These parts include the conflict that a character faces, the rising action, the climax, and resolution, or outcome.

Directions: Read the following plot summary of "The Marble Champ." Then answer the questions below.

Lupe was a straight-A student who had won many awards and contests, but she wasn't good at sports. She wanted desperately to win some kind of sports contest. She chose marbles.

For the next two weeks, Lupe practiced marbles so much that her thumb became swollen. She received tips from her brother on how to shoot.

At the playground championship, Lupe beat all her female opponents in marbles and won a trophy. She then defeated the winner of the boys' division and won a second trophy.

That night, Lupe went out with her family to celebrate. Later, she proudly placed the two trophies on her bedroom shelf. She felt good about finally winning a sports award.

1. Who is the main character of the story? How would you describe this character?

_____

_____

2. What conflict does Lupe face early in the story?

_____

_____

3. What is the rising action, the events that build to the climax?

_____

_____

4. What is the climax, or high point, of the story?

_____

_____

5. What is the resolution, or outcome, of the story? Write your answer on a separate sheet of paper.

Notes for Home: Your child read a plot summary of a story read in class, and then answered questions about its plot, or important parts of the story. *Home Activity:* Read a story with your child. Then talk together to identify the most important parts of the story.

Selection Test

Directions: Choose the best answer to each item. Mark the letter for the answer you have chosen.

Part 1: Vocabulary

Find the answer choice that means about the same as the underlined word in each sentence.

1. Maria watched her opponent.
   A. person who helps a player
   B. person who judges a game
   C. person who writes about sports
   D. person one plays against in a game

2. The championship is on Saturday.
   F. game to decide the first-place winner
   G. important test
   H. party held to honor a special person
   J. practice time

3. Sarah put the trophy on her dresser.
   A. book signed by the author
   B. award in the form of a figure or cup
   C. marble of three different colors
   D. woven string worn around the neck

4. I need to strengthen my legs.
   F. wash
   G. stretch
   H. make stronger
   J. cool off

5. My hand was swollen.
   A. cut
   B. larger than normal
   C. broken
   D. covered with spots

Part 2: Comprehension

Use what you know about the story to answer each item.

6. The beginning of this story is mostly about—
   F. what Lupe has done in the past.
   G. how Lupe plans to become the marble champ.
   H. where Lupe Medrano comes from.
   J. when Lupe learned to ride a bike.

7. Lupe's main problem in this story is that she—
   A. doesn't get along with her family.
   B. never gets enough attention for her achievements.
   C. is doing poorly in school.
   D. wants to be good at sports, but she isn't.

8. The first time Lupe tries to play marbles, what is her main problem?
   F. The marbles keep breaking.
   G. Her thumb is too weak.
   H. Her aim is not accurate.
   J. Her brother takes his marbles back.

9. Which word best describes Lupe?
   A. lazy
   B. determined
   C. complaining
   D. nervous

GO ON

10. How do the members of Lupe's family react to her plans to become the marble champ?
    F. They tell her to focus on schoolwork and give up on other activities.
    G. They are positive that she will win.
    H. They are surprised, but they support her.
    J. They pay no attention to her.

11. Lupe's hardest match is against—
    A. Rachel, her first opponent.
    B. Yolanda, her second opponent.
    C. the girl in the baseball cap.
    D. Alfonso, a boy from her neighborhood.

12. During the rising action in this story, Lupe is—
    F. practicing.
    G. beating the girls' champion.
    H. beating the boys' champion.
    J. receiving a trophy.

13. Why was Lupe's decision to play marbles a sensible one?
    A. She picked a sport that nobody else could play well.
    B. She picked a sport that fit her abilities.
    C. She picked a sport in which winning is a matter of luck rather than skill.
    D. She picked a sport that would make her stronger and healthier.

14. The author's main purpose in this selection is to—
    F. tell an amusing story about Lupe.
    G. explain how to play marbles.
    H. persuade kids to play marbles.
    J. describe the awards that Lupe has won before.

15. What does Lupe's treatment of the girls she defeats suggest about her?
    A. She wishes she had never won.
    B. She is a good sport.
    C. She wants to embarrass them.
    D. She is a mean person.

STOP

Name _____

Plot

- The important events that happen in a story make up the **plot.**
- These parts include the conflict that a character faces, the rising action, the climax, and the resolution, or outcome.

Directions: Read the story below.

Dave wanted to win the school spelling bee badly. Both his older brothers had won when they were his age. Now Dave wanted to prove that he was just as good!

A month before the contest, Dave began to prepare. He studied a long list of spelling words every day. His sister also read aloud words from the dictionary that Dave would then try to spell.

On the day of the spelling bee, Dave was ready. His first words to spell were *separate, rhythm,* and *judgment.* Dave got each one right.

In the final round, Dave faced only one other student. The word was *chrome.* The other student spelled it without the *h.* Now it was Dave's turn. He said, "Chrome. C-H-R-O-M-E." Dave won the contest! The crowd cheered.

Directions: Complete the diagram. Think about what happens in each part of the plot.

Climax

4. _____

_____

_____

Rising Action Events

3. _____

_____

_____

2. _____

_____

_____

Resolution

5. _____

_____

_____

Conflict

1. _____

_____

Notes for Home: Your child read a story and identified the plot, or important parts of the story. ***Home Activity:*** Make up a story with your child about someone who faces and overcomes a problem. Then talk with your child about the different parts of the story.

Theme

Directions: Read the story. Then read each question about the story. Choose the best answer to each question. Mark the letter for the answer you have chosen.

A Runner's Shortcut

Kevin really wanted to win the city runners' marathon. First prize was a hundred dollars in cash. Kevin needed the money badly. He had persuaded his brother to loan him money for a new stereo, and it was time to pay him back. His brother had already asked him twice about getting his money back.

Keven hadn't been running on a regular basis lately, but he really wanted a chance at the hundred dollars. He decided he would enter the race.

When the race began, Kevin ran hard. But he just couldn't keep up with the leaders. After two hours, his legs hurt and he was panting. He was also very far behind. He could see the hundred dollars slipping away, and he could hear his brother yelling at him about paying back the loan.

Then Kevin had a new thought. He decided to cheat. He remembered that the Number 10 bus came along the same route as the race. He left the running path and caught the bus. It drove him near the finish line where Kevin got off the bus and ran the rest of the race. He arrived feeling fresh and hardly out of breath. The judges awarded Kevin the cash prize.

Later, however, many people complained. They said they saw Kevin get on and off the bus. The judges had no choice but to take the prize away from Kevin. He felt embarrassed. He was sorry he had cheated and knew that no prize was worth his good name.

1. Kevin wanted to win the race because—
   A. he was a good runner.
   B. he was proud.
   C. he had won before.
   D. he needed money.

2. When Kevin saw he was behind, he decided to—
   F. ride the bus.
   G. quit the race.
   H. run faster.
   J. rest for a while.

3. In the end, Kevin—
   A. won the prize.
   B. lost the prize.
   C. split the prize with someone else.
   D. gave away the prize.

4. One theme of the story is that—
   F. cheaters sometimes win.
   G. cheaters never lose.
   H. cheating doesn't pay.
   J. cheating is okay.

5. Another theme of the story is that cheaters—
   A. should hide better.
   B. shouldn't need money.
   C. may end up embarrassed and sorry.
   D. may win big money.

Notes for Home: Your child read a story and identified its underlying meaning, or theme.
Home Activity: Watch a TV show or movie with your child. Later, discuss what the characters learned from their experiences, and what the story can teach you about real life.

Writing Across Texts

Directions: Think about Lupe from "The Marble Champ" and Kate Shelley from *Kate Shelley: Bound for Legend*. Each girl succeeded against difficult odds. What enabled them to succeed? Use the web below to organize what you would like to learn about the girls.

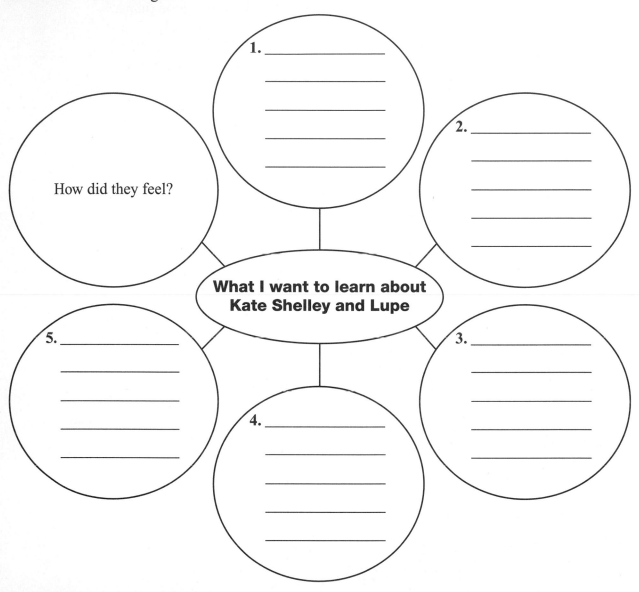

Write Interview Questions

Think about the personalities of Lupe from "The Marble Champ" and Kate Shelley from *Kate Shelley: Bound for Legend*. Suppose you could interview each girl to find out more about her as a person. Make a list of interview questions that would help you get to know each girl better.

Notes for Home: Your child prepared interview questions for a fictional story character and a real-life person. ***Home Activity:*** As you read stories with your child, discuss what else you would like to know about each main character and whether the characters are like people you know.

Grammar: Subject-Verb Agreement

Directions: Circle the action verb in ( ) that agrees with the subject in each sentence.

1. Athletes always (practices/practice) their particular sports many hours a day.

2. Practice (makes/make) perfect!

3. Lots of things, however, (improves/improve) with practice.

4. My older sister, for example, (bakes/bake) chocolate chip cookies.

5. The cookies (tastes/taste) good now, but at the beginning she always burned them.

6. My dad really (enjoys/enjoy) the computer.

7. His fingers (moves/move) fast on the keyboard now, but he started with one finger at a time.

8. Even my dog (gets/get) better every time he catches a ball.

9. My younger brother, however, (disproves/disprove) this theory.

10. His singing voice never (gets/get) better!

Directions: Circle the linking verb in ( ) that agrees with the subject in each sentence.

11. Practice (is/are) even important in arithmetic.

12. The multiplication tables (was/were) hard for me to learn.

13. My younger sister (has/have) the same problem.

14. Flash cards (was/were) a big help to me.

15. The answers (is/are) much easier after many tries.

Notes for Home: Your child identified verbs that agree with their subjects. *Home Activity:* Practice and oral repetition help children become familiar with the sound of correct agreement between subjects and verbs. Read aloud a short story with your child.

Grammar: Verb Tenses: Present, Past, and Future

Verbs in the **present tense** show actions happening now. Remember that in a sentence about present time, the verb that agrees with a singular noun subject usually ends in **-s** or **-es**.

> Karen <u>swings</u> the bat fast.   Jan <u>catches</u> the ball expertly.

Present tense verbs that agree with plural subjects usually do not end in **-s** or **-es.**

> Both girls <u>swing</u> at the ball swiftly.   They also <u>catch</u> expertly.

Verbs in the **past tense** show actions that have already happened. Add **-ed** to most verbs to show the past tense. The spelling of some regular verbs changes when you add **-ed.**

- For verbs ending in **e,** drop the **e** and add **-ed: hoped, loved.**

- For verbs ending in a **consonant** and **y,** change the **y** to **i** and add **-ed: tried, hurried.**

- For one-syllable verbs ending in one vowel followed by one consonant, double the consonant and add **-ed: flipped, planned.**

Verbs that do not add **-ed** in the past tense are called **irregular verbs.** Irregular verbs do *not* follow a regular pattern: **sang, went, caught.**

A verb in the **future tense** shows an action that will happen. Verbs in the future tense include the helping verb *will*.

> We <u>will play</u> marbles.   I <u>will win</u> the championship!

Directions: Write the correct tense for each verb below. Use the verb form that agrees with a singular subject.

Verb	Present	Past	Future
jump	1. _____	6. _____	11. _____
stop	2. _____	7. _____	12. _____
carry	3. _____	8. _____	13. _____
bake	4. _____	9. _____	14. _____
draw	5. _____	10. _____	15. _____

Notes for Home: Your child wrote verbs in the present, past, and future tenses. *Home Activity:* Ask your child to describe a time when he or she excelled at something: sports, academics, music, and so on. Check that your child uses the correct verb tense when speaking.

Grammar: Verb Tenses: Present, Past, and Future

Directions: Circle the verb in each sentence. Write **present, past,** or **future** to tell the tense of each verb.

_____ 1. Some people succeed mainly through hard work.

_____ 2. Others demonstrate natural talent.

_____ 3. Both types develop their skills through constant effort.

_____ 4. James Francis Thorpe possessed both talent and ambition.

_____ 5. Some sportswriters call Jim Thorpe the greatest American male athlete ever.

_____ 6. A Sac and Fox Native American, Jim Thorpe lived in Oklahoma as a child and as a teenager.

_____ 7. Jim Thorpe began his athletic career as a college football star.

_____ 8. If you know football history, you will recognize the name of Glenn "Pop" Warner, his first coach.

_____ 9. In 1912, Jim Thorpe earned two gold medals at the Olympic Games in Sweden.

_____ 10. Later, he played professional baseball and football.

_____ 11. Today's professional players enjoy salaries far higher than Jim Thorpe's.

_____ 12. Few athletes will equal this champion's record.

_____ 13. People admire great athletes like Jim Thorpe.

_____ 14. They will remember his accomplishments for a long time.

_____ 15. They even made a movie about his life.

Write a Recipe for Success

How can you become good at something? On a separate sheet of paper, write a recipe for success. Use all three verb tenses—present, past, and future—to explain how to succeed at sports, studying, or anything else worth doing.

Notes for Home: Your child identified verb tenses: present, past, and future. *Home Activity:* Say a simple sentence in the present tense. Then invite your child to say the sentence in the past tense and then in the future tense.

Grammar: Verb Tenses: Present, Past and Future

The verb in each sentence is underlined. Draw a line to match each sentence with the word that tells when the action takes place.

1. The team <u>practices</u> in the gym.   past

2. They <u>won</u> a game last night.   present

3. The coach <u>will discuss</u> it with them.   future

The **tense** of a verb shows the time of the action. Add **-ed** to most verbs to show the past tense. Past-tense verbs that do not end in **-ed** are called **irregular verbs.** They do not follow a regular pattern. The future tense usually is formed with the helping verb **will.**

Directions: A verb in each sentence is underlined. Circle its tense.

1. The players <u>tap</u> the ball back and forth.	present	past
2. One player <u>hits</u> the ball too hard.	present	future
3. The coach <u>will talk</u> to her about it later.	past	future
4. I hope she <u>learned</u> from her mistake.	past	future
5. Someone loudly <u>blows</u> a whistle.	future	present
6. The two captains of the teams <u>will shake</u> hands.	future	present
7. She <u>will toss</u> a coin in the air.	future	present
8. The spectators in the stands <u>cheer</u> for their teams.	present	past
9. The long game <u>ended</u> with the score tied.	past	present

Directions: Rewrite each sentence. Use the tense shown in ( ) to help you change the underlined verb.

10. Ivan <u>plays</u> a new position. (future tense)

_____

11. The coach <u>wants</u> him at third base. (past tense)

_____

12. He <u>watches</u> Ivan very carefully during the game. (future tense)

_____

 Notes for Home: Your child identified and wrote verbs in the present, past, and future tenses. *Home Activity:* Read aloud some poems with your child. Have your child point out verbs in the poems and tell whether each is in the present, past, or future tense.

Grammar: Verb Tenses: Present, Past and Future

Directions: Rewrite the paragraph. Change each verb to the past tense and underline it.

    The crew prepares the powerful car for the big race. One man rolls two new tires to another worker. They remove the old tires from the special wheels. Then they attach the new ones. Meanwhile, other crew members check the engine and brakes. A special team fills the large tank in the car with fuel. The crew chief times the car with a watch. He studies its movement. The car stops many laps later.

1.–9. _____

_____

_____

_____

_____

_____

Directions: Rewrite the paragraph in the future tense. Underline each verb.

10.–18. _____

_____

_____

_____

_____

_____

Write a Sportscast

On a separate sheet of paper, write a broadcast of a sports competition. Describe what happens before, during, and after the event. Use verbs in the present, past, and future tenses.

Notes for Home: Your child identified present-tense verbs and rewrote them in the past tense. *Home Activity:* Have your child write three sentences in which he or she tells about the weather yesterday and today and predicts it for tomorrow. Remind him or her to use correct verb tenses.

Name _____

Word Study: Contractions

Directions: A **contraction** is a word made by putting two words together. An **apostrophe** (') replaces the letter or letters that are left out. Combine each word pair to form a contraction. Write the contraction on the line.

1. I will _____

2. that is _____

3. was not _____

4. he is _____

5. should not _____

6. she will _____

7. is not _____

8. will not _____

9. we have _____

10. let us _____

11. that is _____

12. we would _____

Directions: Read the letter. Circle each contraction. Write the two words that make up each contraction on the line.

Dear Kelly,

I met this girl in school who's teaching me to play chess. It's a really interesting game. I didn't want to learn at first. The tricky part is remembering what each chess piece can do. I wasn't very good in the beginning, but she's been really patient. I'm getting the hang of it and, with practice, I'll get better. Maybe you'll play chess with me when I visit!

Your friend,
Malcolm

13. _____

14. _____

15. _____

16. _____

17. _____

18. _____

19. _____

20. _____

Notes for Home: Your child formed contractions such as *I'd (I had)* and *haven't (have not)*. **Home Activity:** Watch a favorite television show with your child and listen for contractions in the dialogue or narration. See who can be the first to say the two words that the contraction represents.

Spelling: Contractions

Pretest Directions: Fold back the page along the dotted line. On the blanks, write the spelling words as they are dictated. When you have finished the test, unfold the page and check your words.

1._____	1. Carrie **can't** sing very well.
2._____	2. I **wouldn't** know.
3._____	3. **Don't** you live nearby?
4._____	4. They **weren't** happy with him.
5._____	5. **I'm** writing a letter to a friend.
6._____	6. **I'll** tell you about it later.
7._____	7. **Let's** go to the movies tonight.
8._____	8. **That's** not what I meant.
9._____	9. **There's** someone at the door.
10._____	10. **What's** your favorite color?
11._____	11. **She's** trying to pay attention.
12._____	12. **You're** not crying, are you?
13._____	13. **They're** waiting for a ride home.
14._____	14. **Who's** coming to the party?
15._____	15. **We're** having a picnic tomorrow.
16._____	16. **I've** finished reading my book.
17._____	17. **You've** helped me a lot.
18._____	18. We **should've** taken the bus.
19._____	19. Tammy **could've** fixed anything.
20._____	20. **We've** only just arrived.

Notes for Home: Your child took a pretest on words that are contractions. *Home Activity:* Help your child learn misspelled words. Dictate the word and have your child spell the word aloud for you or write it on paper, making sure the apostrophe is in the correct place.

Spelling: Contractions

Think and Practice

Word List			
can't	I'll	she's	I've
wouldn't	let's	you're	you've
don't	that's	they're	should've
weren't	there's	who's	could've
I'm	what's	we're	we've

Directions: Choose the words from the box that contain the pronouns **I, you, she, we, they,** and **us.** Write the words in alphabetical order.

1. _____   6. _____

2. _____   7. _____

3. _____   8. _____

4. _____   9. _____

5. _____   10. _____

Directions: Write the word from the box that matches each clue.

_____ **11.** It rhymes with *could've* and means "should have."

_____ **12.** It rhymes with *burnt* and means "were not."

_____ **13.** It rhymes with *won't* and means "do not."

_____ **14.** It rhymes with *bats* and means "that is."

_____ **15.** It rhymes with *cuts* and means "what is."

_____ **16.** It rhymes with *shoes* and means "who is."

_____ **17.** It rhymes with *should've* and means "could have."

_____ **18.** It rhymes with *shouldn't* and means "would not."

_____ **19.** It rhymes with *bears* and means "there is."

_____ **20.** It rhymes with *ant* and means "cannot."

 Notes for Home: Your child spelled contractions. *Home Activity:* Read a story with your child. Have your child identify the contractions and explain which two words have been combined to form each contraction.

Spelling: Contractions

Directions: Proofread this speech. Find five spelling mistakes.
Use the proofreading marks to correct each mistake.

≡	Make a capital.
/	Make a small letter.
∧	Add something.
✐	Take out something.
⊙	Add a period.
¶	Begin a new paragraph.

As team captain, I'm telling you players that wev'e got to practice more if we're going to win games. We shouldv'e won yesterday, and we could've won. But we're making too many mistakes, and thats' hurting us. We ca'nt win if we don't practice. So let's work hard and show whose the best!

Word List

can't	I'll	she's	I've
wouldn't	let's	you're	you've
don't	that's	they're	should've
weren't	there's	who's	could've
I'm	what's	we're	we've

Write a Pep Talk

Imagine you were coach of the team addressed above. On a separate sheet of paper, write a pep talk to give to team members. Try to use at least five of your spelling words.

Spelling Tip

who's

Don't confuse **who's** with **whose**.
Use **who's** when it takes the place of the words **who is**.

Notes for Home: Your child spelled contractions—words made of two other words with an apostrophe representing the missing letters. **_Home Activity:_** Say the two words that each spelling word combines, such as _let us_ for _let's_. Have your child spell the contraction.

Spelling: Contractions

Word List

can't	I'll	she's	I've
wouldn't	let's	you're	you've
don't	that's	they're	should've
weren't	there's	who's	could've
I'm	what's	we're	we've

Directions: Choose the word from the box that can replace the underlined words in each sentence. Write the word on the line to the left.

_____ **1.** I hear <u>there is</u> band practice today.

_____ **2.** I <u>do not</u> know the exact time, however.

_____ **3.** I think <u>we are</u> practicing right after school.

_____ **4.** <u>I will</u> check the exact time.

_____ **5.** Do you know where <u>they are</u> holding it?

_____ **6.** <u>I am</u> pretty sure it is on the football field.

_____ **7.** They <u>should have</u> told us already.

_____ **8.** Do you know <u>who is</u> leading the practice?

_____ **9.** Ms. Davis told me that <u>she is</u> attending.

_____ **10.** However, she <u>would not</u> say if she is leading it.

_____ **11.** <u>I have</u> got to be home by six o'clock.

_____ **12.** <u>Let us</u> hope that practice is over by then.

Directions: Choose the word from the box that means the same as each word or words below. Write the word on the lines.

13. could have _____

14. what is _____

15. cannot _____

16. we have _____

17. you are_____

18. were not _____

19. you have _____

20. that is _____

© Scott Foresman 5

Notes for Home: Your child spelled contractions—words made of two other words with an apostrophe representing the missing letters. *Home Activity:* Spell each spelling word aloud, without saying "apostrophe." See if your child can tell you where the apostrophe (') belongs.

Technology: Diagram/Scale Drawing

The Internet is a great place to find information. To find your topic, use a search engine to look for web pages. The computer screen for a search engine might look like this:

Search the Web

Search Tip: Type in more than one word and put AND in between them. Enter your words, then click Find.

| Find! |

If you need help, click here.

If you wanted to find out about games played with marbles, you could enter "marbles AND games." Then you might get this list of web pages:

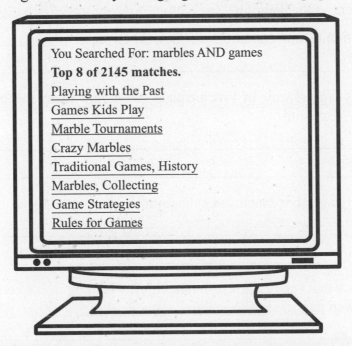

You Searched For: marbles AND games
Top 8 of 2145 matches.
Playing with the Past
Games Kids Play
Marble Tournaments
Crazy Marbles
Traditional Games, History
Marbles, Collecting
Game Strategies
Rules for Games

Web pages often include diagrams or scale drawings. A **diagram** is a special drawing with labels that usually show how something is made or done. A **scale drawing** is a diagram that uses a mathematical scale, such as 1 inch on the drawing equals 1 foot in real life.

© Scott Foresman 5

Name _____

Directions: The web page below explains how to play a game of marbles called Three Holes. It includes a diagram of the playing area. Use the instructions and the diagram to answer the questions that follow.

Three Holes

This is a game for several players. Dig three holes about 5 feet apart. Each hole is 3 inches in diameter. The holes are numbered 1, 2, and 3 and must be shot at in that order. Players shoot anywhere from behind a line 5 feet from the first hole. They take turns trying to shoot marbles into the holes. If a player misses, the marble is left in the field until it is his or her turn again. After a player has scored in the first hole, he or she may shoot to knock away opponents' marbles as well as shoot to get into the other two holes.

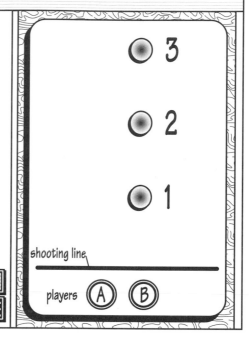

| Home | More Games |
| Marble Introduction | Tournaments |

1. What does the line represent in the diagram? _____

2. Is player B in a good position to shoot a marble into hole 3? Explain. _____

_____

3. If the diagram were drawn using a scale of 1 inch equals 1 foot, how many inches apart should the holes be drawn? Explain.

_____

_____

4. Why do you think the web page above included a diagram?

_____

_____

5. If you wanted to find games that senior citizens might enjoy, what key words could you type to search the Internet for web pages?

_____

Notes for Home: Your child read a diagram and answered questions about it. *Home Activity:* Help your child draw a scale drawing of the playing field for the marble game described above using a scale of 1 inch equals 1 foot.

Family Times

Name_____

Summary

Beekeeper Stays as Busy as His Bees

Beekeeping is a rewarding hobby for people like John Wetzler of Minnesota. He cares for his hives all year long. In the spring, worker bees collect nectar from flowers and turn it into honey. The queen bee lays eggs to make new workers. By the end of summer, the hives are full of honey, and John starts taking it out. He extracts the honey with a special machine. Then in the fall he wraps the hives to protect the bees during the long winter ahead. After a cold-weather rest, it's time to start all over again!

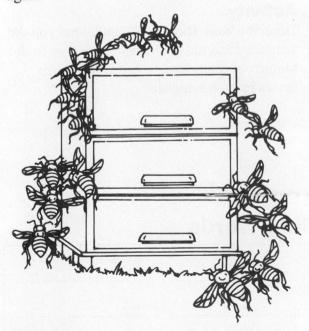

Reading Skills

Text Structure

The way a piece of writing is organized is called its **text structure.** Five common ways of organizing text are:

❖ chronological order.
❖ main ideas with supporting details.
❖ cause and effect.
❖ problem and solution.
❖ compare and contrast.

Fiction is usually structured chronologically. Events are told in the order in which they happen. Nonfiction can be organized in any of the above ways. "From Bees to Honey," for example, is organized chronologically. It follows the beekeeper in his tasks from early spring to late fall.

Activity

Summarize the Article. Have your child sum up the article for you, describing the beekeeper's year and explaining important terms. Together, draw pictures showing the bees and the beekeeper at work.

Activity

Show and Tell. Draw a picture of your favorite hobby or pastime. Then, in chronological order, explain how you have become more skilled at your hobby since the days when you were a beginner.

© Scott Foresman 5

Family Times

Tested Vocabulary

Words to Know

Knowing the meanings of these words is important to reading "From Bees to Honey." Practice using these words to learn their meanings.

colony a group of living things of the same kind that live together

condition state a person or thing is in

emerge come out

nectar sweet liquid found in many flowers

producers people who produce, or make, a product used by others

react act in response to something

storage condition of being saved for later use

venom poison made by insects, snakes, and other poisonous creatures

Grammar

Using Correct Verb Tenses

When you write, don't change from one verb tense to another in the same sentence unless the action shifts from one time to another.

Incorrect: John <u>collects</u> honey and <u>poured</u> it into jars.

Correct: John <u>collects</u> honey and <u>pours</u> it into jars.

Correct: John <u>collected</u> honey and <u>poured</u> it into jars.

Correct: John <u>collected</u> honey earlier and now <u>pours</u> it into jars.

Activity

Describe Your Days. Tell about what you did yesterday and today and what you plan to do tomorrow. Make sure to use correct verb tenses in each sentence.

Tested Spelling Words

© Scott Foresman 5

Text Structure

- **Text structure** is the way a piece of writing is organized. There are two main kinds of writing—fiction and nonfiction.

- Fiction tells stories of made-up people and events. Fiction is often organized in chronological order.

- Nonfiction tells stories of real people and events or gives real information. It can be organized in chronological order, by main ideas with supporting details, or as relationships such as cause and effect, problem and solution, and compare and contrast.

Directions: Reread "Bee Bodies." Then complete the table. Give two supporting details for each main idea in the article.

Main Ideas	Supporting Details
Body	1.
	2.
Eyes	3.
	4.
Mouth	5.
	6.
Wings	7.
	8.
Legs	9.
	10.

© Scott Foresman 5

Notes for Home: Your child used a table to help show how information in an article has been organized. *Home Activity:* Read a newspaper or magazine article with your child. Have him or her identify the way the information is organized.

Name _____

Vocabulary

Directions: Choose the word from the box that best completes each sentence.
Write the word on the line to the left.

_____ 1. Ants often live together in a _____.

_____ 2. See how they _____ from their anthill.

_____ 3. At a picnic, keep all your spare food in _____.

_____ 4. If food is left out, the ants _____ to it quickly.

_____ 5. What good _____ those ants are in! Watch them lift that cracker!

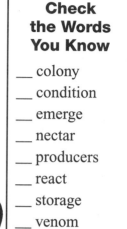

Check the Words You Know

__ colony
__ condition
__ emerge
__ nectar
__ producers
__ react
__ storage
__ venom

Directions: Choose the word from the box that best matches each clue.
Write the letters of the word on the blanks. The boxed letters spell something
that some ants in a colony might be.

6. sweet liquid

6. __ __ __ __ ☐ __

7. product makers

7. __ __ __ __ ☐ __ __ __ __

8. poison

8. __ __ ☐ __ __

9. state someone is in

9. __ __ __ __ ☐ __ __ __

10. state of being stored

10. ☐ __ __ __ __ __ __

What some ants in a colony might be: ___ ___ ___ ___ ___

Write a Description

Imagine you are a scientist who has discovered a new creature. On a separate
sheet of paper, describe the creature. Give vivid details that tell what the
creature looks like, how it moves, what sounds it makes, and what it likes to eat.
Use as many vocabulary words as you can.

Notes for Home: Your child identified and used vocabulary words from "From Bees to
Honey." **Home Activity:** Find out more about an insect that interests your child. Create an
encyclopedia entry of text and a picture that describes the insect.

Text Structure

- **Text structure** is the way a piece of writing is organized.

- Fiction tells stories of made-up people and events. Fiction is usually organized in chronological order. Nonfiction tells of real people and events. It can be organized in chronological order, by main idea and supporting details, or as relationships such as cause and effect, problem and solution, or compare and contrast.

Directions: Reread this passage from "From Bees to Honey" about the history of beekeeping. Then answer the questions below.

The relationship between humans and honeybees goes back thousands of years. In prehistoric times, people took honey from the hives of wild bees in hollow trees. About four thousand years ago, the Egyptians kept bees in cigar-shaped hives made of clay. During the Middle Ages, beekeepers used dome-shaped hives called skeps, which were woven of straw.

John Wetzler, like most modern beekeepers, uses hives made of wood. A hive consists of several boxes, or *hive bodies,* which are open at the top and bottom. Hanging inside each hive body are ten movable wooden *frames.* The frames hold sheets of wax called *foundation,* on which bees build the six-sided cells of their combs.

From A BEEKEEPER'S YEAR by Sylvia Johnson. Copyright © 1994 by Sylvia Johnson (Text), Illustrations © by E.M. Peterson Books. By permission of Little, Brown and Company.

1. What four time periods does the passage mention?

_____

_____

2. Which period is the earliest example of beekeeping?

_____

3. Which period is the most recent example of beekeeping?

_____

4. Is this passage an example of fiction or nonfiction writing? Explain. Which kind or kinds of organization does the author use: chronological order, main idea and supporting details, cause and effect, problem and solution, or compare and contrast?

_____

_____

5. What kinds of organization do you find in "From Bees to Honey"? Give examples. Write your answer on a separate sheet of paper.

Notes for Home: Your child read a passage and identified the ways that information is organized. *Home Activity:* Read a newspaper article together with your child. Invite him or her to describe how the information is organized.

Selection Test

Directions: Choose the best answer to each item. Mark the letter for the answer you have chosen.

Part 1: Vocabulary

Find the answer choice that means about the same as the underlined word in each sentence.

1. The teacher told us about <u>nectar</u>.
   A. the main bee in a hive
   B. a sheet of wax made by bees
   C. a mixture of sugar and water
   D. the sweet liquid found in flowers

2. When José teases you, don't <u>react</u>.
   F. listen carefully
   G. complain to someone
   H. respond to something
   J. disappear

3. Those ants live in a <u>colony</u>.
   A. group of living things
   B. barn for storing hay
   C. cage for birds
   D. underground cave

4. Scientists studied the <u>venom</u>.
   F. poison from an insect or animal
   G. communication between animals
   H. home for bees
   J. sticky substance

5. What is the <u>condition</u> of the animal?
   A. diet
   B. state
   C. age
   D. name

6. Who are the <u>producers</u> of that jelly?
   F. people who make
   G. people who sell
   H. people who use
   J. people who like

7. The proper <u>storage</u> of food is important.
   A. cooking to kill germs
   B. preparing to mix flavors
   C. selecting for good quality
   D. saving for a later date

8. When will the children <u>emerge</u>?
   F. stop playing
   G. pay attention
   H. come out
   J. work together

Part 2: Comprehension

Use what you know about the selection to answer each item.

9. John Wetzler produces honey mainly because he likes to—
   A. make money.
   B. eat lots of sweet foods.
   C. work with bees.
   D. hire his neighbors to work for him.

10. The information in this selection is presented as—
    F. a series of comparisons and contrasts.
    G. a series of causes and effects.
    H. problems and solutions.
    J. events in chronological order.

GO ON

11. John uses a smoker when opening the hive because he—
    A. wants some of the bees to die.
    B. has to melt the bee glue.
    C. does not want to be stung.
    D. wants to keep the bees warm.

12. What is the main difference between worker bees under 20 days old and worker bees over 20 days old?
    F. Young worker bees cannot lay eggs, but older ones can.
    G. Young worker bees work inside the hive, and older worker bees collect nectar.
    H. Older worker bees mostly guard the hive from wasps, but younger ones don't.
    J. Young worker bees forage for nectar and pollen while older ones stay inside the hive.

13. What does John do just before placing a frame in the honey extractor?
    A. puts plastic bags over the hives
    B. removes impurities from the honey
    C. removes the supers from the hives
    D. uncaps the frames

14. Which detail suggests that John is good at thinking of creative solutions to problems?
    F. his use of the brick code
    G. his use of the bee tool
    H. his use of the honey extractor
    J. his use of hive bodies

15. The text structure helps you understand the content of this selection mainly by—
    A. illustrating the dangers of beekeeping.
    B. describing the natural order of a beekeeper's activities.
    C. suggesting unusual solutions to problems.
    D. comparing wild bees and domesticated bees.

STOP

Text Structure

- **Text structure** is the way a piece of writing is organized..

- Fiction tells stories of made-up people and events. Fiction is usually organized in chronological order. Nonfiction tells of real people and events. It can be organized in chronological order, or as relationships such as cause and effect, as problem and solution, and compare and contrast.

Directions: Read each passage.

1. A serious danger that all beekeepers face is getting stung. They protect themselves by wearing a special bee suit and a hat with a heavy veil.

2. First, the worker bees are born. For their first twenty days, they do indoor jobs such as cleaning cells. After that, they collect pollen in the field.

3. Most bees in a colony are worker bees, who are all females. There is one queen bee. She is the only one in the colony who lays eggs. The male bees are drones, who mate with queens.

4. When bees take nectar from flowers, the enzymes in the their bodies react to it. As a result, a sweet substance—honey—is produced.

5. The beekeeper places small boxes in the hive. The bees then start to fill up the boxes with honey. Later, the boxes are removed.

Directions: Complete the table. Think about the text structure in each passage. Write whether it uses chronological order, cause and effect, problem and solution, or compare and contrast. Explain your answers.

Passage	Text Structure	Explanation
1		
2		
3		
4		
5		

Notes for Home: Your child read nonfiction passages and identified the way that each one was organized. **Home Activity:** Read a magazine article together with your child. Invite him or her to describe how the information is organized.

Steps in a Process

Directions: Read the passage. Then read each question about the passage. Choose the best answer to each question. Mark the letter for the answer you have chosen.

Baking a Honeycake

To bake a honeycake, you will need these ingredients: flour, baking powder, baking soda, cinnamon, brown sugar, eggs, honey, and oil. You will need two large bowls and a tube baking pan.

Start making the honeycake by mixing together these ingredients in a large bowl:

$2\frac{1}{2}$ cups of flour, 2 teaspoons of baking powder, 1 teaspoon of baking soda, and 2 teaspoons of cinnamon.

Then in a second large bowl, mix $\frac{3}{4}$ cup of brown sugar with 3 eggs.

Next, add a cup of honey and $\frac{3}{4}$ cup of oil to the second bowl.

Pour the contents of the first bowl into the second. Mix until blended.

Pour the batter into a 10-inch tube pan.

Bake at 325°F for 1 hour. After an hour, remove the pan from the oven and let it cool. Then remove the cake from the pan.

1. The first step in the process of making a honeycake involves—
   A. sugar.
   B. eggs.
   C. oil.
   D. cinnamon.

2. Just before adding honey and oil, you—
   F. mix the batter.
   G. mix sugar and eggs.
   H. mix flour and cinnamon.
   J. pour the contents of one bowl into another.

3. Right after mixing the batter, you—
   A. add eggs and sugar.
   B. add oil and honey.
   C. pour it in a pan.
   D. bake at 325° F.

4. The contents of the two bowls are combined—
   F. before honey is used.
   G. after honey is used.
   H. before oil is used.
   J. while honey is being added.

5. The final step in the process is to—
   A. remove the cake from the pan.
   B. let cool for 20 minutes.
   C. add oil and honey.
   D. remove the cake from the oven.

Notes for Home: Your child read an explanation of a process and identified the order of the steps. *Home Activity:* Read a set of directions, such as a cookbook recipe, with your child. Then have your child tell you the order of the steps.

Writing Across Texts

Directions: Think about what you learned in "From Bees to Honey" and what you learned in other selections in this unit. Use the web below to organize your thoughts about the lessons you or the characters learned in these selections.

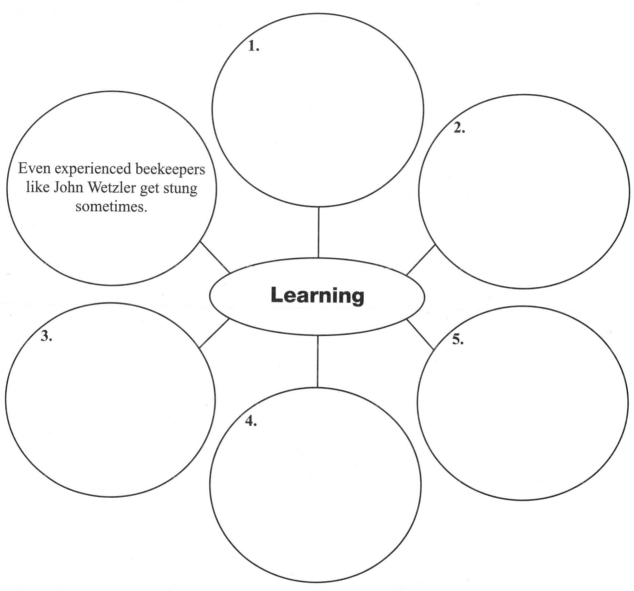

1.

2.

Even experienced beekeepers like John Wetzler get stung sometimes.

Learning

3.

5.

4.

Write a Paragraph

The selection "From Bees to Honey" shows that there is a lot to learn about bees before you can become a beekeeper. The first four selections in this unit relate to the theme of learning and working. On a separate sheet of paper, write a summary of the kinds of things characters learned in these four stories as well as what you learned by reading these selections.

Notes for Home: Your child wrote a summary about the things that were learned in the four selections read so far in this unit. ***Home Activity:*** As you read stories with your child, discuss the lessons that the characters learn or the things that your child learns from the stories.

Grammar: Verb Tenses: Present, Past, and Future

Directions: Circle the verb in each sentence. Write **present, past,** or **future** on the line to name the tense of each verb.

_____ 1. After college, Jill will train as a veterinarian.

_____ 2. She worked part-time for a veterinarian last year in high school.

_____ 3. She once helped a woman with a pet snake!

_____ 4. Jill likes all kinds of animals.

_____ 5. She goes to a woman veterinarian with her two dogs.

_____ 6. This animal doctor shows love and concern for all her patients.

_____ 7. Jill will follow her example.

_____ 8. Jill's uncle took care of circus animals all of his life.

_____ 9. Jill will spend most of her time as a veterinarian with house pets.

Directions: Write a sentence using the verb and verb tense given.

10. the present tense of *talk*

_____

11. the past tense of *talk*

_____

12. the future tense of *talk*

_____

13. the present tense of *play*

_____

14. the past tense of *play*

_____

15. the future tense of *play*

_____

Notes for Home: Your child identified the three main tenses of a verb. *Home Activity:* Ask your child to create sentences for all three tenses of the following verbs: (1) give, gave, will give; (2) make, made, will make; (3) run, ran, will run.

Grammar: Using Correct Verb Tenses

Use the correct verb tense to show action that is happening now **(present tense)**, action that happened in the past **(past tense)**, and action that will happen in the future **(future tense).**

    Present: Lara <u>helps</u> immigrant classmates with their English.

    Past: Yesterday, Steven <u>volunteered</u> at the hospital.

    Future: Next week, Reggie <u>will start</u> soccer practice.

Directions: Circle the correct verb form in ( ) to complete each sentence.

1. Last summer, Denise (visits/visited) her cousins in Minnesota for the first time.

2. Right away, she (noticed/will notice) several different crops on the cousins' farm.

3. For as long as she lives, Denise (remembers/will remember) the fun of hayrides and picnics.

4. On her very first day at the farm, she (will feed/fed) the chickens and milked a cow.

5. Denise was not afraid of bees, so she (helps/helped) workers gathering honey from the hives.

6. She was very careful, and she (will receive/received) no stings.

7. Every day during her visit, Denise and her cousins (swims/swam) in a pond.

8. On her last evening with her cousins, she (see/saw) a film with them at a drive-in movie theater.

9. Denise usually (cries/cried) a little when a pleasant vacation is over!

10. She writes to her cousins often, and she (visits/will visit) them again next summer.

Notes for Home: Your child identified verb tenses to show action that takes place in the past, present, and future. ***Home Activity:*** Ask your child to describe a hobby he or she enjoys. Encourage your child to use present, past, and future tenses.

Grammar: Using Correct Verb Tenses

Directions: Circle the correct verb form in ( ) to complete each sentence. Write **present, past,** or **future** to tell the tense of the verb.

_____   1. If you want to listen, I (tell/will tell) you about my hobby.

_____   2. My hobby is archery, and I (liked/like) it a lot.

_____   3. I (learn/learned) about archery when I went to camp.

_____   4. In the mornings I practice, and in the afternoons I (took/take) a break.

_____   5. I am sure that I (love/will love) my unusual hobby always.

Directions: Use the correct form of the verb in ( ) to complete each sentence. Write the verb on the line.

_____   6. My cousin's hobby is fishing, so last week I (decide) to go fishing with her.

_____   7. First, we dug for worms and (look) for insects.

_____   8. Then we baited the hook and (sit) down.

_____   9. It (be) so boring, I thought I would fall asleep.

_____   10. Even though the fish (taste) good, I will never go fishing again.

_____   11. Now, it (be) time to visit my Grandpa.

_____   12. He (make) honey.

_____   13. Actually, the bees (produce) the honey.

_____   14. Grandpa regularly (collect) the honey from the bee hives.

_____   15. Tomorrow, I (write) my cousin to tell her to take up beekeeping instead of fishing!

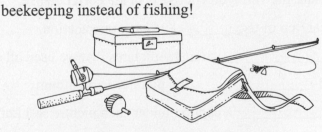

Write a Description

What hobby do you enjoy? On a separate sheet of paper, describe your hobby. (If you don't have a hobby yet, use your imagination and write as if you do have one.) Tell how you got started with that hobby and explain why it is fun. Be sure to use the correct tenses for your verbs.

Notes for Home: Your child used verb tenses (present, past, and future) to complete sentences. **Home Activity:** Invite your child to write an advertisement for his or her hobby. Encourage your child to make sure each verb uses the correct tense.

Grammar: Using Correct Verb Tenses

> Read each sentence. Underline the verb.
>
> **Present Tense:** Levi studies a book about Roman ruins.
>
> **Past Tense:** I finally completed the difficult assignment.
>
> **Future Tense:** They will grow vegetables in the summer.

> Verbs in the **present tense** tell about action that is happening now. Verbs in the **past tense** tell about action that already happened. Verbs in the **future tense** tell about action that will happen.

Directions: Read each sentence. Underline the verb. Write **present, past,** or **future** on the line to identify the tense of the verb.

_____ **1.** The clerk stayed busy all that time.

_____ **2.** Mr. Corm finally stopped here Tuesday.

_____ **3.** Two rivers flood their banks

_____ **4.** Deep puddles are everywhere.

_____ **5.** Schools and businesses closed.

_____ **6.** They will open again in a few days.

_____ **7.** Mrs. Allen will begin a new class in the fall.

Directions: Choose a verb that makes sense in each sentence and write it on the line. Make sure the verb you choose is in the correct tense.

8. Last year, ten of us _____ on vacation.

9. We _____ so many pictures that we used all our film.

10. Today I _____ the pictures in an album.

11. I _____ a caption under each picture so I know who and what is in each one.

12. Later I _____ the album to my family and friends.

13. I hope they _____ the pictures!

14. At the very least, the pictures _____ them of the fun time we had.

Notes for Home: Your child labeled verb tenses and wrote verbs in the present, past, and future tenses in sentences. *Home Activity:* Ask your child to describe to you one of his or her favorite experiences from school this year. Remind your child to use verbs in the correct tenses.

Name _____

Grammar: Using Correct Verb Tenses

Directions: Read all the sentences. Then use the correct form of the verb in ( )
to complete each sentence. Write the verb on the line.

_____   1. My family (have) a Saturday morning tradition.

_____   2. I (tell) you about why we have the tradition and when it
started.

_____   3. It all (begin) two years ago when we lived in another city.

_____   4. My brother (sneak) into the kitchen and (select) the
ingredients.

_____   5. Then my father (join) him while my mother and I slept.

_____   6. The two of them (make) blueberry waffles with whipped
cream.

_____   7. The delicious smell of the waffles (drift) down the hallway to
my bedroom.

_____   8. My mother (smell) it too.

_____   9. We went into the kitchen and (find) breakfast was ready!

_____ 10. Now my father and brother (prepare) breakfast every
Saturday morning.

_____ 11. We (talk) about the tradition as if we have been doing it
forever.

_____ 12. Soon our tradition (change).

_____ 13. My brother (have) marching band practice on Saturday
mornings.

_____ 14. He (leave) very early in the morning to get there on time.

_____ 15. When that happens, I (begin) to help my father prepare
Saturday breakfast.

_____ 16. Then my family (have) a new tradition!

Write a Family Story

Think about a funny or exciting experience you had with your family. What happened? Does
your family still talk about it? On a separate sheet of paper, write a family story to tell about your
experience. Remember to use verbs in the correct tenses.

Notes for Home: Your child wrote verbs in the correct tenses in sentences. *Home Activity:*
Provide your child with three verbs, such as *to jump, to laugh,* and *to write,* and have him or
her correctly use each verb in the present, past, and future tenses in sentences.

© Scott Foresman 5

Name _____

Word Study: Possessives

Directions: Read the sentences below. Rewrite each underlined phrase using an
apostrophe (') and **s** to show possession. For example, **the ball of the boy** can
be written as **the boy's ball.** Write the new phrase on the line.

_____   **1.** It is <u>the job of the worker bee</u> to look for flower nectar.

_____   **2.** They visited <u>the hive that belongs to the beekeeper</u>.

_____   **3.** <u>The wife of the beekeeper</u> shows visitors the honey house.

_____   **4.** <u>The combs of the hive</u> were filled with honey.

_____   **5.** Everyone enjoys <u>the flavor of honey</u>.

Directions: Read the phrases below. Rewrite each phrase using the possessive
form. Write the new phrase on the line. Remember, for plural nouns that end in
-s, add only an apostrophe, as in **the sisters' bikes.**

_____   **6.** the job of bees

_____   **7.** the honey of beekeepers

_____   **8.** the market of farmers

_____   **9.** the enjoyment of the families

_____   **10.** the bees of a hive

_____   **11.** the nectar of a flower

_____   **12.** the responsibility of a farmer

_____   **13.** the harvests of many seasons

_____   **14.** the crops from many farms

_____   **15.** the eggs of the queen bee

 Notes for Home: Your child formed singular and plural possessives, such as *the boy's ball*
and *the sisters' bikes.* **Home Activity:** Point out objects that belong to one person or more. Ask
your child to use possessives to tell who owns them.

Name _____

Spelling: Capitalization

Pretest Directions: Fold back the page along the dotted line. On the blanks, write the spelling words as they are dictated. When you have finished the test, unfold the page and check your words.

1. _____

2. _____

3. _____

4. _____

5. _____

6. _____

7. _____

8. _____

9. _____

10. _____

11. _____

12. _____

13. _____

14. _____

15. _____

16. _____

17. _____

18. _____

19. _____

20. _____

1. Her sister went to **Houston**.

2. It gets very cold in **Alaska**.

3. I have never been to **Kentucky**.

4. We are going to **Little Rock**.

5. Where is **Duluth** on the map?

6. Much of **Arizona** is desert.

7. **Miami** is in Florida.

8. Hoosiers are from **Indiana**.

9. **Alabama** is in the south.

10. I live in **South Carolina**.

11. Have you been to **Baltimore**?

12. Cars are made in **Detroit**.

13. **Los Angeles** is near the ocean.

14. **Hawaii** is made up of islands.

15. I want to go back to **Memphis**.

16. Jefferson lived in **Virginia**.

17. Eugene is a city in **Oregon**.

18. **Pittsburgh** is my hometown.

19. **Texas** is a large state.

20. It is warm in **Florida**.

Notes for Home: Your child took a pretest on capitalized words. *Home Activity:* Help your child learn misspelled words before the final test. Have your child divide misspelled words into parts (such as syllables) and concentrate on each part.

Think and Practice

Spelling: Capitalization

Word List				
Houston	Duluth	Alabama	Los Angeles	Oregon
Alaska	Arizona	South Carolina	Hawaii	Pittsburgh
Kentucky	Miami	Baltimore	Memphis	Texas
Little Rock	Indiana	Detroit	Virginia	Florida

Directions: Choose the words from the box that name U.S. states. Write the words in alphabetical order.

1. _____   7. _____

2. _____   8. _____

3. _____   9. _____

4. _____   10. _____

5. _____   11. _____

6. _____

Directions: Choose the word from the box that answers each question. Write the word on the line.

_____ **12.** Which city has the word *angel* in it?

_____ **13.** Which city has the word *his* in it?

_____ **14.** Which city has the word *pit* in it?

_____ **15.** Which city rhymes with *truth?*

_____ **16.** Which city has *us* in the middle?

_____ **17.** Which city means the same as *pebble?*

_____ **18.** Which city rhymes with *exploit?*

_____ **19.** Which city has the word *more* in it?

_____ **20.** Which city has the word *am* in the middle?

Notes for Home: Your child spelled names of cities and states. *Home Activity:* Look at a map of the United States with your child. Together, try to find all the states and cities that are spelling words. Have your child identify the capital letter or letters in each name.

Spelling: Capitalization

Directions: Proofread this article. Find five spelling mistakes. Use the proofreading marks to correct each mistake.

≡	Make a capital.
/	Make a small letter.
∧	Add something.
ꝰ	Take out something.
⊙	Add a period.
¶	Begin a new paragraph.

Many cities and states are famous for their products. In detriot, many people make cars. In Florida, thousands work on citrus farms. Lots of farmers have cotton fields in Alabama and South carolina, while others have tobacco fields in virgina. Oregon has lumberjacks, huseton has oil workers, and pitsburgh has many steel workers.

Spelling Tip

Hawaii

The end of the word **Hawaii** can be tricky to spell. Remember this hint: See **Hawaii** with your two eyes **(ii).**

Word List

Houston	Duluth	Alabama	Los Angeles	Oregon
Alaska	Arizona	South Carolina	Hawaii	Pittsburgh
Kentucky	Miami	Baltimore	Memphis	Texas
Little Rock	Indiana	Detroit	Virginia	Florida

Write a Report

Find out more about the different states and cities listed in the box. On a separate sheet of paper, write a report with your information. Try to use at least five cities or states.

Notes for Home: Your child spelled names of cities and states. *Home Activity:* Begin to spell each spelling word slowly, one letter at a time. When your child recognizes the word, have him or her complete its spelling.

Spelling: Capitalization

Word List				
Houston	Duluth	Alabama	Los Angeles	Oregon
Alaska	Arizona	South Carolina	Hawaii	Pittsburgh
Kentucky	Miami	Baltimore	Memphis	Texas
Little Rock	Indiana	Detroit	Virginia	Florida

Directions: Choose the word from the box that best matches each clue. Use a map of the United States to help you. Write the word on the line.

_____ **1.** This state is between Canada and Russia.

_____ **2.** This state is south of Oklahoma.

_____ **3.** This state is south of Utah.

_____ **4.** This state is between Ohio and Illinois.

_____ **5.** This state is east of West Virginia.

_____ **6.** This state is just north of Tennessee.

_____ **7.** This state is between Mississippi and Georgia.

_____ **8.** This state is just south of North Carolina.

_____ **9.** This state is actually a group of islands.

_____ **10.** This state is south of Washington state.

_____ **11.** This state is south of Georgia.

Directions: Choose the word from the box that names a city located in each state below. Use a map of the United States to help you. Write the word on the line.

_____ **12.** Tennessee

_____ **13.** Arkansas

_____ **14.** Pennsylvania

_____ **15.** Texas

_____ **16.** Michigan

_____ **17.** Florida

_____ **18.** California

_____ **19.** Minnesota

_____ **20.** Maryland

Notes for Home: Your child spelled names of cities and states. *Home Activity:* Say each spelling word aloud. See if your child can locate the state or city on a map of the United States. Then have your child close his or her eyes and spell the word.

Outlining

An **outline** is a plan that shows how a story, article, report, or other text is organized. You can use an outline to better understand how a text is organized or as a way to organize your own thoughts before you write something of your own.

Directions: Read the following outline. Then answer the questions.

Occupations

I. Outdoor jobs

    A. Forest ranger

        1. Cut down dead trees

        2. Watch for forest fires

        3. Plant new trees

    B. Landscaper

        1. Plant gardens

        2. Mow lawns

II. Indoor jobs

    A. Lab technician

        1. Conduct experiments

        2. Analyze results

    B. School teacher

        1. Instruct students

        2. Evaluate students

1. What other main topic is shown in the outline besides outdoor jobs? _____

2. What two subtopics are listed under the first main topic? _____

_____

3. What subtopics are listed under the second main topic? _____

_____

4. What details are listed under the subtopic "Lab technician"? _____

_____

5. Which subtopic has the most details? _____

Directions: Read the following article. Then complete the outline below.

Where Would You Like to Work?

There are two main kinds of jobs you can have—outdoor jobs and indoor jobs. Working outdoors offers many benefits. For example, you get to enjoy fresh air. You also see pretty landscapes. In addition, you get to be more active. On the other hand, outdoor work can present disadvantages too. Sometimes you may have to work in the rain. Some days may be unbearably cold or hot.

Working indoors has its benefits. For example, you may be in a climate-controlled environment, so you don't get too hot or too cold. Also, it is usually easy to get from place to place, without any rough roads or hills to climb. On the other hand, indoor work also has disadvantages. You may start to feel "cooped up" on long days. You may have to work in a room with poor air circulation.

Occupations

I. _____

   A. Benefits

      1. Enjoy fresh air

      2. _____

      3. _____

   B. _____

      1. Work in rain

      2. _____

II. Indoor jobs

   A. _____

      1. _____

      2. _____

   B. Disadvantages

      1. _____

      2. _____

 Notes for Home: Your child practiced organizing information in an outline. *Home Activity:* Talk with your child about the different jobs that people in your family have. Then invite your child to create an outline that organizes the information you discussed together.

Family Times

Name_____

Summary

Pig Thinks He's a Sheepdog!

Babe wants to herd sheep, just like his foster mom, Fly, an old sheepdog. The only problem is that Babe is a pig, the first ever on Farmer Hogget's farm. Babe makes friends with a sheep named Ma, but the closest he ever comes to herding anything is when he practices on the ducks in the barnyard. When sheep rustlers try to steal the sheep, however, Babe proves his worth as a sheep-pig.

Reading Skills

Summarizing

Summarizing means telling in a few sentences the main ideas of an article or the important events in a story. A good summary is brief and does not include unnecessary details, repeated words, or unimportant ideas.

For example, the summary of "Babe to the Rescue" in the left column mentions Babe's desire to herd sheep, his foster mother Fly, his friendship with Ma, and the sheep rustlers.

The summary does not give details about sheepherding, describe what Babe looks like, or quote dialogue from the story.

Activity

Finish the Story. Have your child tell you the rest of "Babe to the Rescue," including how Babe saved the sheep and what Mrs. Hogget did about it. Together, draw pictures of several important scenes from the story. Have your child write a caption for each one. Encourage your child to use the pictures to retell the story to a family member or friend.

Activity

Summarize a Tale. Think of a favorite fairy tale or folk tale with talking animals as characters. Summarize the tale aloud, describing only the most important events.

Family Times

Tested Vocabulary

Words to Know

Knowing the meanings of these words is important to reading "Babe to the Rescue." Practice using these words to learn their meanings.

chaos great confusion

civil polite

confusion state of disorder or being mixed-up

instinct a way of acting that is born in an animal

raid sudden attack

sensible having good judgment

unexpected happening without warning

Grammar

Contractions

A **contraction** is a shortened form of two words. An **apostrophe (')** shows where one or more letters have been left out.

Pair of Words	Contraction
does not	doesn't
should have	should've
I am	
_____	they're
had not	_____
will not	_____
she is	_____
_____	we've

Activity
Describe a Pet. Complete the table above. Then use contractions from the table to tell about a family pet or favorite animal. For example, **My cat Fluffy <u>doesn't</u> catch mice. <u>She's</u> afraid of them!**

Tested Spelling Words

© Scott Foresman 5

Summarizing

- **Summarizing** means telling just the main ideas of an article or the plot of a story.

- A good summary is brief. It does not include unnecessary details, repeated words or thoughts, or unimportant ideas.

Directions: Reread "What Do Animals Say?" Then complete the table. Write one sentence to summarize each portion of the article indicated. Then write a summary of the entire article.

Portion of Article	Summary
Paragraph 1	1.
Paragraphs 2–4	2.
Paragraph 5	3.
Paragraph 6	4.
Paragraph 7	5.

Notes for Home: Your child read an article and summarized each part of it. *Home Activity:* Read a story with your child. Stop at various points during the story and have your child summarize what happened in only a few sentences.

Vocabulary

Directions: Match each word on the left with its definition on the right.
Write the letter of the definition next to the word.

_____ **1.** civil

_____ **2.** instinct

_____ **3.** raid

_____ **4.** unexpected

_____ **5.** sensible

a. without warning

b. having good judgment

c. inborn way of acting

d. polite

e. sudden attack

Check the Words You Know

__ chaos
__ civil
__ confusion
__ instinct
__ raid
__ sensible
__ unexpected

Directions: Read the news report. Choose the word from
the box that best completes each sentence. Write the word
on the matching numbered line below.

BIG STORM HITS PRAIRIE TOWN

The storm was entirely **6.** _____. At first, there
was great **7.** _____. Everyone ran to a huge tree
on the prairie for shelter. Then a **8.** _____ young
girl said, "That's not safe. Lightning could strike
you!" Her **9.** _____ was right. In spite of the
10. _____, she led the people to safe shelter in
a nearby barn.

6. _____

7. _____

8. _____

9. _____

10. _____

Write a Story

On a separate sheet of paper, write a story that tells about a war
or battle that took place. Use as many vocabulary words as you can.

Notes for Home: Your child identified and used vocabulary words from "Babe to the
Rescue." *Home Activity:* Think of a word. Say a word to your child that means the opposite.
See if your child can guess your word. For example, the opposite of *foolish* is *sensible*.

© Scott Foresman 5

Summarizing

- **Summarizing** means telling just the main ideas of an article or the plot of a story. A good summary is brief. It does not include unnecessary details, repeated words or thoughts, or unimportant ideas.

Directions: Read the following four summaries of the opening of "Babe to the Rescue." Then answer the questions below.

A. Fly and Babe went to the pond where the ducks swam. After the ducks came out of the water, Babe tried to round them up and bring them to Fly. His efforts failed.

B. Fly and Babe went to the pond where the ducks swam. The pond was soupy green. Babe tried to round up the ducks after they came out of the water. His efforts failed.

C. Fly and Babe went to the pond where the ducks swam. Fly was a sheepdog. She was also a collie. Babe tried to round up the ducks when they came out of the water.

D. Fly and Babe went to the pond where the ducks swam. After the ducks came out of the water, Babe tried to round them up. When Babe spoke with Fly, he said, "Yes, Mum."

1. Which of the four summaries is best? Explain why.

_____

_____

2. What unnecessary detail is given in Summary B?

_____

_____

3. What unnecessary detail is given in Summary C?

_____

_____

4. What unnecessary detail is given in Summary D?

_____

_____

5. Summarize in a few sentences the part of the story about the sheep rustlers. Write your summary on a separate sheet of paper.

Notes for Home: Your child identified characteristics that make a good summary. ***Home Activity:*** Watch a TV show or movie with your child. Then ask your child to summarize the story. Discuss whether the summary included the most important parts of the story.

Selection Test

Directions: Choose the best answer to each item. Mark the letter for the answer you have chosen.

Part 1: Vocabulary

Find the answer choice that means about the same as the underlined word in each sentence.

1. Your telephone call was <u>unexpected</u>.
    A.   too long
    B.   made incorrectly
    C.   not planned for
    D.   not wanted

2. The cat followed its <u>instinct</u>.
    F.   markings
    G.   inborn way of acting
    H.   owner
    J.   sense of smell

3. The speaker stopped in <u>confusion</u>.
    A.   state of being embarrassed
    B.   state of feeling ill
    C.   state of being frightened
    D.   state of not knowing what to do

4. The salesperson was very <u>civil</u>.
    F.   polite
    G.   friendly
    H.   eager
    J.   cold

5. There was <u>chaos</u> on the field.
    A.   joy
    B.   lack of order
    C.   sorrow
    D.   movement

6. The <u>raid</u> was planned for Thursday.
    F.   surprise party
    G.   instructional gathering
    H.   sudden attack
    J.   formal test

7. Please try to be <u>sensible</u>.
    A.   having good judgment
    B.   being brave
    C.   being generous
    D.   having good taste

Part 2: Comprehension

Use what you know about the story to answer each item.

8. What does Babe first try to herd?
    F.   puppies
    G.   piglets
    H.   ducks
    J.   lambs

9. Unlike Fly, Babe tries to herd sheep by—
    A.   shouting at them.
    B.   standing in one place.
    C.   speaking politely to them.
    D.   nipping at their heels.

10. Why is Babe's style of herding different from a normal sheepdog's?
    F.   Fly wants him to be different.
    G.   Babe was not born with a sheepdog's instincts.
    H.   Farmer Hoggett teaches Babe a new method of herding.
    J.   Pigs are not intelligent animals.

11. Ma does not like sheepdogs because they—
    A.   are rude to sheep.
    B.   talk to sheep.
    C.   try to herd sheep.
    D.   are stupid.

GO ON

12. Which is the best summary of the first half of this story?
    F. Babe makes friends with Ma, an old ewe, by telling her she doesn't look old.
    G. Babe practices his herding skills with Fly's help and makes friends with Ma.
    H. Babe herds some ducks and talks with Fly.
    J. When Babe meets Ma, she tells him that she doesn't like sheepdogs, which she calls wolves.

13. Which is the best summary of the second half of this story?
    A. When Ma rejoins the flock and Mr. Hoggett goes away, Babe tries to steal the sheep.
    B. Mrs. Hoggett decides to keep Babe because he makes so much noise.
    C. Sheep rustlers come to the Hoggetts' farm one day while Mr. Hoggett and Fly are away.
    D. Babe saves the sheep from rustlers, and Mrs. Hoggett decides to keep him.

14. Which part of this story is fantasy?
    F. sheep stealers
    G. dogs that can herd sheep
    H. talking animals
    J. dogs that obey human commands

15. Based on her decision to keep Babe, you can tell that Mrs. Hoggett highly values—
    A. loyalty.
    B. money.
    C. an easy life.
    D. being meek and quiet.

STOP

Summarizing

- **Summarizing** means telling just the main ideas of an article or the plot of a story. A good summary is brief. It does not include unnecessary details, repeated words or thoughts, or unimportant ideas.

Directions: Read the following five summaries of the same story.

A. Once on a farm, a hen, a cow, and a bee were hungry. The cow gave milk and the bee made honey. The cow was white with brown spots. The hen laid eggs. They all ate custard!

B. Once on a farm, a hen, a cow, and a bee were hungry. The cow gave milk, the bee made honey, and the hen laid eggs. They mixed the foods together and had custard to eat!

C. Once on a farm, a hen, a cow, and a bee were hungry. The farm was a year old. The cow gave milk, the bee made honey, and the hen laid eggs. They mixed the foods and had custard!

D. Once on a farm, a hen, a cow, and a bee were hungry. The cow gave milk and the hen laid eggs. They mixed the foods together and had custard!

E. Once on a farm, a hen, a cow, and a bee were hungry. The cow gave milk, the bee made honey, and the hen laid eggs. They mixed the foods together and had custard! It all happened on a farm.

Directions: Complete the table. Think about the details in each summary. Explain why each summary is or is not a good summary. Tell which summary is the best.

Summary	Good Summary?
Summary A	**1.**
Summary B	**2.**
Summary C	**3.**
Summary D	**4.**
Summary E	**5.**

Notes for Home: Your child identified characteristics of a good summary. *Home Activity:* Read a story with your child. Invite your child to summarize the most important details for you. Check that the summary contains only key story events.

Compare and Contrast

Directions: Read the passage. Then read each question about the passage. Choose the best answer to each question. Mark the letter for the answer you have chosen.

Pigs and Sheep

Both pigs and sheep are common farm animals that are raised for the products they furnish to people. These animals provide food but also other things. Most pigs and sheep are raised in order for people to be able to have products made with their skin, hair, and meat.

Although pigs and sheep are never likely to be mistaken for one another, they actually share several qualities. That is, both of these animals are used by people for some of the same products.

First, both pigs and sheep provide people with meat. Sheep yield lamb chops and mutton, while pigs give ham, sausage, bacon, and pork chops. In addition, the fat and skin of both pigs and sheep are used to produce leather, soap, glue, and fertilizer.

Of course, you are aware of using the hair of sheep. It is the wool that is a common product for weaving into heavy warm clothing. You might not as quickly think of using the hair of pigs. In fact, you might not think of pigs as having much hair. Certainly, it is not as abundant as the wool of sheep. Although pigs do not grow wool, their hair is used as bristles for brushes. Pig hair is also used as stuffing for mattresses and for baseball gloves.

1. The article explains how pigs and sheep are—
   A. alike only.
   B. different only.
   C. alike and different.
   D. like other animals.

2. Both pigs and sheep are used to produce—
   F. mutton.
   G. ham.
   H. sausage.
   J. soap.

3. One difference between pigs and sheep is that—
   A. pigs live on farms.
   B. sheep grow wool.
   C. sheep supply meat.
   D. pigs supply meat.

4. One way that pigs and sheep are alike is that both—
   F. are used for leather.
   G. look the same.
   H. yield pork chops.
   J. yield bacon.

5. Bristles for brushes are a product supplied by—
   A. sheep only.
   B. pigs only.
   C. both pigs and sheep.
   D. neither pigs nor sheep.

Notes for Home: Your child read an article and identified comparisons and contrasts that the writer made. **Home Activity:** Choose two separate items in your home. Talk with your child about ways that the two items are alike and different.

Writing Across Texts

Directions: Think about the different ways Babe in "Babe to the Rescue" and the shepherd boy in "Cry Wolf" care for sheep. Think about what the effect is. Then fill in the following chart.

	Babe	**The Shepherd Boy**
How did each character treat the sheep?	Treated them with respect	3.
How did each react to the threat of danger?	1.	4.
How did others react to the way Babe and the shepherd boy cared for the sheep?	2.	5.

Write a Letter

Imagine you are the shepherd boy in "Cry Wolf" and you want to convince the villagers to trust you again. Write a letter to them explaining why you cried wolf and how you will make it up to them.

Notes for Home: Your child compared and contrasted information from two texts. *Home Activity:* Read a story with your child about an animal character. Then discuss how the character is like or different from one of the characters in "Babe to the Rescue" or another animal story.

Grammar: Using Correct Verb Tenses

Directions: Use the correct form of the verb in ( ) to complete each sentence.
Write the verb on the line.

_____ 1. Often a farmer's day hasn't (start) until he feeds the pigs.

_____ 2. By the end of the day, the pigs have (finish) all their food.

_____ 3. That electric fence isn't (keep) other animals out.

_____ 4. The fence is (cause) the piglets to stay together.

_____ 5. The piglets always (stay) close to their mother.

Directions: Circle the correct verb form in ( ) to complete each sentence.

6. After a year, a pig has (growed/grown) to its adult size.

7. Pigs usually aren't (keeped/kept) as pets.

8. Pigs aren't (knowed/known) for their cleanliness, but they are very clean animals.

9. Farmers are always (taking/taken) fresh straw to the pigs' pen.

10. Pigs often are (lain/lying) in mud to keep cool, not because they are filthy!

Directions: Add a word or words to each verb to form a sentence. Write the
complete sentence on the line.

11. eat

_____

12. am eating

_____

13. ate

_____

14. have eaten

_____

15. will eat

_____

Notes for Home: Your child practiced using the correct tense of verbs. *Home Activity:* Have
your child read aloud a simple story book. Then have him or her identify the tenses of the verbs.

Practice

Grammar: Contractions

A **contraction** is a word made by combining two words. An **apostrophe (')**
shows where letters have been left out.

Many contractions are formed by joining a verb and **not.** An apostrophe takes
the place of **o** in **not.** There is only one contraction that includes a spelling
change: **will not** becomes **won't.**

<u>Do not</u> worry.　　She <u>will not</u> be gone long.
<u>Don't</u> worry.　　She <u>won't</u> be gone long.

Other contractions are formed by joining a pronoun and a verb.

<u>I am</u> sure that <u>you are</u> right.
<u>I'm</u> sure that <u>you're</u> right.

Directions: Draw a line to match each word pair on the left with its contraction
on the right.

1. they would	you've
2. she has	isn't
3. he is	he's
4. we have	she's
5. did not	didn't
6. I will	couldn't
7. you have	they'd
8. could not	I'll
9. it will	we've
10. is not	it'll

Directions: Write the two separate words that each underlined contraction
combines.

_____ **11.** <u>I'm</u> proud of our flock of unusual types of hens.

_____ **12.** <u>It's</u> actually a special collection of my dad's.

_____ **13.** He <u>doesn't</u> mind paying the breeders to ship them here.

_____ **14.** Once every morning, suddenly, <u>they'll</u> all fly up in the air.

_____ **15.** <u>You've</u> got to see it to believe it.

Notes for Home: Your child identified and formed contractions—short words formed by
combining two words. *Home Activity:* Invite your child to discuss whether it is a good idea
to have an unusual pet, such as an iguana or a ferret. Ask your child to use contractions.

© Scott Foresman 5

Grammar: Contractions

Directions: Write a contraction to replace the underlined words in each sentence.

_____ 1. <u>I am</u> thinking of getting a pet rabbit.

_____ 2. We <u>have not</u> ever had a family pet.

_____ 3. Rabbits make good pets because they <u>are not</u> noisy.

_____ 4. <u>It is</u> fun to hold a rabbit gently and pat its soft fur.

_____ 5. I <u>must not</u> decide on a pet until I learn more about rabbits.

_____ 6. Peacocks might be a good choice because <u>they are</u> beautiful.

_____ 7. <u>We are</u> going to visit a peacock farm.

_____ 8. It <u>is not</u> very far from my home.

_____ 9. At the farm, I learned that the female peacock <u>does not</u> have a beautiful tail.

_____ 10. <u>She is</u> not colorful like the male bird.

Directions: Choose the contraction from the box that best completes each sentence. Write each contraction on the line to the left. Remember that verbs should agree with their subject.

he'd	don't	wasn't	they'll	weren't

_____ 11. A new hired hand decided that _____ save money for the farmer.

_____ 12. "If we _____ buy food for the barn cats," he thought, "they will catch more mice!"

_____ 13. Yet after a few weeks, the mouse population _____ smaller, but larger!

_____ 14. The farmer told him why the cats _____ catching more mice.

_____ 15. "To keep their supply of food," the farmer explained, "_____ leave more mice alive."

Write a Journal Entry

If you were a bird or an animal, which one would you be? On a separate sheet of paper, write a journal entry describing your life as a pet. You might be a watchdog, a peacock, or even an owl. Describe your activities, your friends, and what you eat. Use contractions in your journal entry.

Notes for Home: Your child used apostrophes to write contractions. *Home Activity:* Play a game with contractions. Say a contraction, such as *it's,* and have your child give the two words it combines *(it is).* Switch roles after five contractions.

Grammar: Contractions

Draw a line under each contraction in the sentences below.

1. I am ready. I'm ready.

2. You are on time. You're on time.

3. They will join us later. They'll join us later.

The shorter sentences have contractions. The words **I'm, you're,** and **they'll** are contractions. These contractions were formed by combining pronouns with verbs.

I am = I'm   you are = you're   they will = they'll

A **contraction** is made by combining two words. Pronouns can be combined with verbs to form contractions. Use an apostrophe (') to show where a letter or letters have been left out.

Directions: Match the pairs of words on the left with the correct contraction on the right.

1. you would	we'll	**6.** he is	we'd
2. they have	you'd	**7.** she had	I'll
3. they are	thcy've	**8.** we would	he's
4. we will	it's	**9.** it will	she'd
5. it is	they're	**10.** I will	it'll

Directions: Complete the second sentence in each pair. Write the contraction for the underlined words in the first sentence.

11. <u>I have</u> new skates.

_____ wanted them for a long time.

12. Tomorrow <u>we are</u> going to the park.

_____ planning to skate on the pond.

13. <u>It is</u> supposed to be cold tomorrow.

_____ below freezing today.

14. <u>We will</u> meet at the park.

_____ be wearing our warmest clothing.

Notes for Home: Your child practiced identifying and using contractions. *Home Activity:* Invite your child to choose a book and read it together, looking for contractions. Then have your child use some of the contractions in sentences.

Grammar: Contractions

Directions: Combine each pronoun in the Pronoun Pool with a verb in the Verb Pool. Write twelve contractions.

Pronoun Pool

I   we

he   they

she   you

it

Verb Pool

are   had

will   is

have

am

1. _____   4. _____   7. _____   10. _____

2. _____   5. _____   8. _____   11. _____

3. _____   6. _____   9. _____   12. _____

Directions: Rewrite the paragraph using contractions to replace the underlined words.

    <u>I have</u> got several gemstones at home. <u>They are</u> pretty to look at, and <u>I would</u> like to show them to you. If I turn on a special light, <u>they will</u> glow in the dark. <u>It is</u> a spectacular sight, and <u>I am</u> sure <u>you will</u> find it interesting. Please bring your brothers because I think <u>they would</u> be fascinated. I know <u>they have</u> a collection of their own. Maybe <u>we will</u> trade some stones.

13.–19. _____

_____

_____

_____

_____

Write a Paragraph

Write a paragraph about some things you collect or would like to collect. Use contractions in some of your sentences. Write on a separate sheet of paper.

Notes for Home: Your child formed contractions and changed word pairs within a paragraph into contractions. *Home Activity:* Have your child write a list of five contractions, and then ask him or her to use them to tell a scary story.

Word Study: Unusual Possessives

Directions: Some plural nouns do not end in **-s.** To make them possessive, add an **apostrophe (')** and the letter **s.** Rewrite each phrase using the possessive form. Write the new phrase on the line.

_____ 1. the honks of the geese

_____ 2. the laughter of the children

_____ 3. the conversation of the men

_____ 4. the voices of the women

_____ 5. the squeaks of the mice

Directions: Some singular nouns end in **-s.** To make them possessive, add an **apostrophe (')** and the **s.** Rewrite each phrase using the possessive form. Write the new phrase on the line.

_____ 6. the orders of the boss

_____ 7. the desks of the class

_____ 8. the singing of the chorus

_____ 9. the color of the dress

_____ 10. the contents of the glass

Directions: Read each sentence. Circle the correct possessive form in ( ).

11. The animals heard the main (boss's/boss') words, and they started to make noise.

12. The farmer could hear the many (sheep's/sheep') cries.

13. Then he heard the (mens/men's) low voices.

14. He saw the two (thieves's/thieves') truck.

15. Quietly, he crept to the truck and let out all four of the (tires'/tire's) air.

 Notes for Home: Your child learned how to form unusual possessives, such as *sheep's.* **Home Activity:** Make a list of irregular plurals, such as *mice* and *men,* and singular nouns that end in -*s,* such as *Chris.* Have your child write sentences using the possessive form of each word.

© Scott Foresman 5

Spelling: Possessives

Pretest Directions: Fold back the page along the dotted line. On the blanks, write the spelling words as they are dictated. When you have finished the test, unfold the page and check your words.

1._____

2._____

3._____

4._____

5._____

6._____

7._____

8._____

9._____

10._____

11._____

12._____

13._____

14._____

15._____

16._____

17._____

18._____

19._____

20._____

1. These are my **friend's** toys.
2. Has **today's** mail arrived yet?
3. **Dad's** magazine came today.
4. **Mom's** books are on the shelf.
5. My little **sister's** doll was broken.
6. My **sisters'** dresses are blue.
7. That **child's** face needs washing.
8. The **children's** drawings are here.
9. Did you see that **person's** hat?
10. **People's** intentions are good.
11. My **grandmother's** cat is sick.
12. Her **grandfather's** car is outside.
13. Our **uncle's** name is Steven.
14. Their **uncles'** homes are old.
15. The **doctor's** coat is white.
16. That is the **doctors'** entrance.
17. My **cousin's** hair is red.
18. Their **cousins'** names are long.
19. That **woman's** coat is brown.
20. That store sells **women's** clothes.

© Scott Foresman 5

Notes for Home: Your child took a pretest on words that show ownership, or possessives. *Home Activity:* Help your child learn misspelled words before the final test, concentrating on whether one person or more than one person owns something.

Think and Practice

Spelling: Possessives

Word List			
friend's	sisters'	grandmother's	doctors'
today's	child's	grandfather's	cousin's
Dad's	children's	uncle's	cousins'
Mom's	person's	uncles'	woman's
sister's	people's	doctor's	women's

Directions: Choose the words from the box that name ownership by one person or thing. Write the words on the lines.

1. _____   8. _____

2. _____   9. _____

3. _____   10. _____

4. _____   11. _____

5. _____   12. _____

6. _____   13. _____

7. _____

Directions: Choose the word from the box to complete each equation, using a plural possessive noun. Write your word on the line.

_____ **14.** the pets of the children = the _____ pets

_____ **15.** the offices of the doctors = the _____ offices

_____ **16.** the jobs of the people = the _____ jobs

_____ **17.** the farm of the cousins = the _____ farm

_____ **18.** the ducks of the uncles = the _____ ducks

_____ **19.** the votes of the women = the _____ votes

_____ **20.** the hogs of the sisters = the _____ hogs

Notes for Home: Your child spelled possessive nouns—words that show ownership. *Home Activity:* Look at magazine pictures together. Invite your child to identify people and their possessions, such as *the farmer's hat,* and spell each possessive noun.

Spelling: Possessives

Directions: Proofread this diary entry. Find five spelling mistakes.
Use the proofreading marks to correct each mistake.

≡	Make a capital.
/	Make a small letter.
∧	Add something.
℘	Take out something.
⊙	Add a period.
¶	Begin a new paragraph.

Dear Diary,

   Today's trip to our uncle's farm was fun! I rode my
grandmothers horse. Later, it was my two cousin's
turns. The horse licked my one cousin's face! Later we
took a childrens' tour of the farm. I saw Moms' favorite
duck and Dad's favorite pig. My grandfather's favorite
is the old hen who lays an egg every day. I think farm
animals' lives are better than peoples' lives!

Spelling Tip
sister's   sisters'
To form possessives of singular nouns,
add an **apostrophe (')** and **s: sister's.**
For plural nouns that end in **-s,** add an
apostrophe ('): sisters'. For plural
nouns that do not end in **-s,** add
apostrophe (') and **s: children's.**

Word List

friend's	grandmother's
today's	grandfather's
Dad's	uncle's
Mom's	uncles'
sister's	doctor's
sisters'	doctors'
child's	cousin's
children's	cousins'
person's	woman's
people's	women's

Write a Diary Entry

Imagine you are a farm animal who keeps a diary. On a separate sheet of paper,
write a diary entry that describes a typical day on the farm. Try to use at least
five of your spelling words.

Notes for Home: Your child spelled possessive nouns—words that show ownership. *Home
Activity:* Have your child make a list of items or places around the house, using possessive
nouns. For example: *Mom's favorite chair* or *my twin sisters' room.*

Spelling: Possessives

Word List				
friend's	sister's	person's	uncle's	cousin's
today's	sisters'	people's	uncles'	cousins'
Dad's	child's	grandmother's	doctor's	woman's
Mom's	children's	grandfather's	doctors'	women's

Directions: Choose the word from the box that is the possessive form of the underlined word in each sentence. Write the possessive noun on the line.

_____ **1.** The vacation of the <u>children</u> was spent on a farm.

_____ **2.** They visited the farm of the <u>cousins</u> in Iowa.

_____ **3.** On the farm, the work of a <u>person</u> is important.

_____ **4.** The job of the <u>grandmother</u> is to feed the chicks.

_____ **5.** The job of the <u>uncles</u> is to milk the cows.

_____ **6.** The job of the <u>women</u> is to collect chicken eggs.

_____ **7.** The job of one <u>child</u> is to feed hay to the horses.

_____ **8.** The suggestion of <u>Mom</u> was to help out with chores.

_____ **9.** Shearing the sheep was one chore of <u>today</u>.

_____ **10.** The children assisted with the help of <u>Dad</u>.

_____ **11.** The task of the <u>sister</u> was to gather the wool.

_____ **12.** Later the animals received an exam of a <u>doctor</u>.

Directions: Choose the word from the box that is the possessive form of each word below. Write the word on the line.

13. friend _____

14. cousin _____

15. grandfather _____

16. people _____

17. sisters _____

18. doctors _____

19. uncle _____

20. woman _____

Notes for Home: Your child spelled possessive nouns—words that show ownership. **_Home Activity:_** Read a magazine article with your child. Together, identify possessive nouns that you find. Have your child tell whether each noun is singular or plural.

Magazines/Periodicals/Almanacs

Periodicals are materials published at regular time periods, such as weekly, monthly, and so on. **Magazines** are a type of periodical that contain news articles, opinion columns, advertisements, cartoons, reports, and so on. The *Readers' Guide to Periodic Literature* is a good resource for locating magazine articles about specific topics.

Directions: Suppose you found the following articles in the *Readers' Guide.* Use these sample entries to answer the questions that follow.

ANIMALS, FARM
    See also
  Farming

A horses's life: just say neigh. N. Johansen.
   Farming Mag Ap 4 '98 p 87–90
All vets are off: a shortage of animal doctors.
   L. Landon. Time Mag D 13 '98 p 45
An udder disgrace: the milk strike continues.
   J. Jackson. US News Report Ja '98 p 23–24
Chicks and ducks and geese better scurry: a
   cold winter's coming. Weather Gazette.
   N '98 p 12–13
Do pigs really eat like pigs? D. Taylor.
   Farmer's Guide F 16 '98 p 90–94
Don't be a chicken with your chickens.
   G. McMillan. Farming Mag Jl 16 '98
   p 44–45

Ducks and swans: what's the difference?
   B. Barello. Science Digest D 14 '98 p 34–35
Honk if you love geese! N. Michelson.
   Agriculture and You. My '98 p 56–58
Is any animal really as stubborn as a mule? M.
   Vicars. Science Digest F 12 '98 p 87–89
Never pull the wool over a sheep's eyes.
   T. Albright. Newsweek Mag Jl 14 '98
   p 29–32
New feed for a new age. G. O'Tooney.
   Science Digest Mr 14 '98 p 99–101
New ways to shear sheep at the baa-baa shop.
   P. Nelson. Farmer's Guide Ag '98 p 78–80
Should farmers clone sheep? J. Miller. Time
   Mag Mr 10 '98 p 55–58
Why did the chicken cross the road? and
   other farm animal jokes. F. Mock. Humor
   Mag F '98 p 17

1. In which magazine does the article "Honk If You Love Geese!" appear?

_____

2. What is the date of the *Farmer's Guide* that carries the article "Do Pigs Really Eat Like Pigs?"

_____

3. Who wrote the article "New Ways to Shear Sheep at the Baa-Baa Shop"?

_____

4. On what page or pages does the article "Never Pull the Wool Over a Sheep's Eyes" appear?

_____

5. What other listing is given by the *Readers' Guide* for more information about farm animals?

_____

An **almanac** is a book published each year that contains calendars, weather information, dates of holidays, and charts and tables of current information in many different subject areas.

Directions: Use the almanac index to answer the questions that follow.

Agriculture, U.S.
Congressional committees 159
Corn blight 428
History 54
Income 498

Animals
Endangered wildlife 330
Farm animal revenues 229
Sheep cloning 109
Use in research 24

6. For a report on farm animals, would you find more helpful information under "Agriculture, U.S." or under "Animals"?

_____

7. On what page of the almanac would you find information on farm animal revenues?

_____

8. Information about what topic appears on page 109 of the almanac? _____

_____

9. If you wanted to learn about problems farmers have had with corn crops, which page would you turn to?

_____

10. When might an almanac be a more useful resource than a book? Explain.

_____

_____

Notes for Home: Your child learned how to find information in magazines and an almanac. *Home Activity:* With your child, look through the table of contents of a magazine or almanac. Choose a specific topic, and see if your child can find it in the magazine or almanac.

Name _____

Comparison/Contrast Chart

Directions: Write the titles and main-character names from two stories, and identify the problem each character faces. Follow the directions in the first column to complete the chart.

List the story titles and characters.		
Describe each character's problem.		
List ways in which the characters' efforts to solve the problems are similar.		
List ways in which the characters' efforts to solve the problems are different.		
Tell how well you think each character solves the problem.		

Directions: Write a possible topic sentence.

_____

_____

Notes for Home: Your child used this chart to compare and contrast two story characters' efforts to solve problems. *Home Activity:* Ask your child to explain how well each character dealt with the problem he or she faced.

Elaboration
Precise and Vivid Verbs

- You can make sentences clearer by replacing unclear verbs with **precise** verbs.
- You can make sentences more interesting by replacing **dull** verbs with **vivid** verbs.

Directions: For each sentence, pick a more precise or vivid verb from the box to replace the underlined verb. Rewrite each sentence, using the new verb. Make sure you select verbs that make sense in the sentences.

Verbs			
act	earns	stay	watches
draw	prefer	talk	whispers

1. Some story characters <u>are</u> with great courage.

   _____

2. Other characters <u>are</u> in one place for a long time.

   _____

3. My friend <u>sees</u> mystery movies for every clue.

   _____

4. I <u>see</u> comedies over mysteries.

   _____

5. In some comedy stories, animals can <u>say</u>.

   _____

6. It can be hard to hear a person who <u>says</u>.

   _____

7. It's fun to see cartoonists <u>make</u> characters.

   _____

8. A successful artist <u>makes</u> a lot of money.

   _____

Notes for Home: Your child has improved sentences by choosing verbs that express ideas clearly. *Home Activity:* With your child, read a newspaper or magazine article to find verbs that vividly describe action or express ideas.

Name _____

Self-Evaluation
Comparison/Contrast Paper

Directions: Think about the final draft of your comparison/contrast paper. Then answer each question in the chart.

	Yes	No	Not sure
1. Did I include similarities between the two characters' decisions or actions?			
2. Did I explain differences between the characters' decisions or actions?			
3. Are my important ideas expressed clearly?			
4. Did I use transition words or phrases well?			
5. Did I proofread and edit carefully to correct errors?			

6. What is the best part of my comparison/contrast paper?

_____

_____

_____

7. Write one thing that you would change about this paper if you had the chance to write it again.

_____

_____

_____

_____

Notes for Home: Your child has answered questions about preparing and writing a comparison/contrast paper. *Home Activity:* Ask your child what writing strategies he or she learned that may help in the writing of future papers.

© Scott Foresman 5

Family Times

Name_____

Summary

The Yangs Celebrate Their First Thanksgiving!

The Yang family has emigrated from China to Seattle. They are invited to the Conners' home for their first Thanksgiving celebration. The cultural differences between the families cause some embarrassment, as when Mrs. Yang tries to compliment one guest by telling her that she looks fat. (In China, being fat is a sign of good fortune.) Nevertheless, the Yangs still enjoy their first taste of an American tradition.

Reading Skills

Compare and Contrast

Sometimes in a story, you can compare and contrast characters or their actions. To **compare** is to tell how two or more people or things are alike. To **contrast** is to tell how two or more people or things are different. For example: The Yangs are like the Conners because both families are musical. The Yangs are different from the Conners because the Yangs come from China.

Sometimes authors use clue words like *similar to* or *unlike* to compare and contrast. What clue words can you find in the above examples? (The clue words are *like* and *different from*.)

Activity

Talk Turkey! Have your child describe all the funny things that happen at the Conners' Thanksgiving table as a result of the cultural differences between the American and Chinese families.

Activity

Take Two and Talk. Pick out two items from your home, such as two chairs, two clocks, or two dinner plates. Talk together about the ways that the two items are alike and different.

Family Times

Tested Vocabulary

Words to Know

Knowing the meanings of these words is important to reading "The Yangs' First Thanksgiving." Practice using these words to learn their meanings.

dismayed troubled greatly

impression effect produced on a person

insult say something rude

records the known facts about a person, group, and so on

sprouts shoots of plants

winced flinched slightly

Grammar

Adjectives

An **adjective** is a word that describes a person, place, or thing. An adjective may tell what kind, how many, or which one. An adjective may come before or after the word it describes.

They served a <u>large</u> turkey. (what kind)

The turkey was <u>delicious</u>. (what kind)

I ate <u>two</u> pieces of pie. (how many)

I like <u>this</u> holiday. (which one)

Activity

Describe Your Home. Use adjectives to describe some of the people or things in your home. Make lists of the adjectives that tell what kind, how many, and which one.

Tested Spelling Words

Compare and Contrast

- To **compare** is to tell how two or more things are alike. To **contrast** is to tell how two or more things are different.

- Authors sometimes use clue words such as *similar to, like,* or *as* to compare things. They may use clue words such as *different from, but,* or *unlike* to contrast things.

Directions: Reread "A Visitor from Japan." Then complete the diagram. Write what the story says and what you already know about people and places in Japan on the left. Write about the people and places in America on the right. Write things that both countries have in common in the middle. Some ideas have been given to help you get started.

Japan **Both Countries** **America**

1. _____

_____

_____

speak Japanese

sit on straw mats

wear kimonos and clogs

2. _____

_____

_____

5. _____

_____

_____

_____

big, modern, crowded cities

eat with forks, knives, and spoons

3. _____

_____

_____

4. _____

_____

_____

Notes for Home: Your child read a story and learned how to compare and contrast. *Home Activity:* With your child, look at family photographs of two people, places, or things. Invite your child to describe how the people, places, or things in the photos are alike and different.

Vocabulary

Directions: Choose the word from the box that best matches each definition. Write the word on the line.

_____ **1.** say something rude

_____ **2.** shoots of plants

_____ **3.** drew back or flinched slightly

_____ **4.** troubled greatly

_____ **5.** department in hospital that keeps written accounts

Check the Words You Know
__ dismayed
__ impression
__ insult
__ records
__ sprouts
__ winced

Directions: Read the diary entry. Choose the word from the box that best completes each sentence. Write the word on the matching numbered line to the right.

Dear Diary,

   Boy, am I upset! I couldn't be more
6. _____. We had our class potluck supper
tonight. I'm positive Amy Jones **7.** _____ when
I brought out my casserole of eels and bean
8. _____. I never dreamed she would **9.** _____
me like that! Could I be wrong? I don't
think so. Tomorrow I'll ask Leah if she
got the same **10.** _____. More later.

6. _____
7. _____
8. _____
9. _____
10. _____

Write a Funny Story

On a separate sheet of paper, write a funny story about a holiday dinner or other important event your family celebrates. Use as many vocabulary words as you can in your story.

Notes for Home: Your child identified and used vocabulary words from "The Yangs' First Thanksgiving." *Home Activity:* Ask your child to make expressions that match the words *dismayed* and *winced.* Take turns doing the same for the other words about strong feelings.

Name _____

Compare and Contrast

- To **compare** is to tell how two or more things are alike. To **contrast** is to tell how two or more things are different.

- Authors sometimes use clue words such as *similar to, like,* or *as* to compare things. They may use clue words such as *different from, but,* or *unlike* to contrast things.

Directions: Reread what happens in "The Yangs' First Thanksgiving" after Mrs. Conner tries to get Mrs. Hanson to take a piece of pie. Then answer the questions below.

Mother was staring at Mrs. Hanson and Mrs. Conner during this exchange. We Chinese think that being fat is good. It's a sign of good fortune. Thin people are considered unfortunate and miserable.

But I knew here, being thin is supposed to be attractive. A lot of the girls in school are worried about their weight, and some of them even go on diets.

I saw Mother open her mouth. Don't say it, Mother, I wanted to shout. Don't say it!

But she did. Radiating good will, Mother said, "Why you're not skinny at all, Mrs. Hanson. You're actually quite fat!"

From YANG THE THIRD AND HER IMPOSSIBLE FAMILY by Lensey Namioka. Copyright © 1995 by Lensey Namioka (Text); Illustrations © by Kees de Kiefte. By permission of Little, Brown and Company.

1. What is the author contrasting in this scene?

_____

2. What clue word does the writer use to show contrast?

_____

3. How is Mother different from Mrs. Hanson and Mrs. Conner?

_____

_____

4. Tell why Mrs. Hanson will probably feel insulted by Mother's remark.

_____

_____

5. In what other ways are the Yangs different from the Conners and their guests? On a separate sheet of paper, describe another example of contrast from the story.

Notes for Home: Your child read a story and identified comparisons and contrasts. *Home Activity:* Work with your child to compare and contrast two people, places, or things.

Selection Test

Directions: Choose the best answer to each item. Mark the letter for the answer you have chosen.

Part 1: Vocabulary

Find the answer choice that means about the same as the underlined word in each sentence.

1. She made a good <u>impression</u>.
   A. sound
   B. effect on people
   C. statement of facts
   D. look on one's face

2. Stefanie <u>winced</u> when she heard the yell.
   F. cried out
   G. burst into laughter
   H. shrugged
   J. drew back suddenly

3. Mr. Jackson got a bag of <u>sprouts</u>.
   A. shoots of plants
   B. small twigs
   C. flower buds
   D. small bushes

4. She is in charge of the <u>records</u> department.
   F. where products are made
   G. having information about patients or workers
   H. where medicines are stored
   J. for very ill patients

5. Why are you so <u>dismayed</u>?
   A. very sneaky
   B. shy
   C. greatly troubled
   D. quiet

6. Did Mark mean to <u>insult</u> his guest?
   F. pay no attention to
   G. invite again
   H. talk louder than
   J. say something rude to

Part 2: Comprehension

Use what you know about the story to answer each item.

7. The Yang family lives in—
   A. Shanghai, China.
   B. Washington, D.C.
   C. Seattle.
   D. Hong Kong.

8. What do most of the kids at the Thanksgiving meal have in common?
   F. playing music
   G. playing baseball
   H. doing carpentry
   J. taking care of pets

9. Mrs. Yang is horrified by the idea of—
   A. cooking anything.
   B. her children making new friends.
   C. roasting a turkey.
   D. shaking hands.

10. The narrator of this story is looking forward to dinner at the Conners' because she wants to—
    F. talk with Holly Hanson.
    G. try cranberries for the first time.
    H. get to know Matthew.
    J. learn how to prepare a turkey.

GO ON

11. Why are the Yangs horrified when Mr. Conner starts to scoop stuffing out of the turkey?
   A. They do not want to eat food that has been served by a man.
   B. They do not like the taste of onions.
   C. They think the turkey has not been prepared properly.
   D. They think a lot of meat has been wasted.

12. Unlike in America, most people in China think that—
   F. young people should be served first.
   G. the hosts should serve themselves before serving others.
   H. every family should have a pet.
   J. it is an honor to be old.

13. Why does Mrs. Hanson become upset during dinner?
   A. She feels insulted by Mother.
   B. Mary spills cranberries on her dress.
   C. She does not like turkey.
   D. Mary says she plays viola better than Holly.

14. Unlike in America, people in China think that it is—
   F. very rude to discuss money.
   G. rude to ask questions about a person's family.
   H not proper for women to work outside the home.
   J. good to be fat.

15. What lesson does this story teach about meeting with people from other countries?
   A. Except for differences in language, people everywhere are the same.
   B. There may be misunderstandings between people who were raised to behave differently.
   C. It is impossible to learn what people from other countries believe.
   D. There is always one right way to behave, no matter where you were born and raised.

STOP

Compare and Contrast

- To **compare** is to tell how two or more things are alike. To **contrast** is to tell how two or more things are different.

- Authors sometimes use clue words such as *similar to, like,* or *as* to compare things. They may use clue words such as *different from, but,* or *unlike* to contrast things.

Directions: Read the story below.

I remember the first time we went to one of Vito's parties. It was unlike any party I had ever attended. First of all, it was at night. My parties were always in the afternoon. When we arrived, we saw a huge tent in the yard, covered with twinkling lights. I usually had my parties inside. The food was also a surprise. Instead of the cake and punch that I was used to, they had meatballs, spaghetti, and garlic bread. And what a crowd they had—more than 100 people! My parents never let me invite more than ten people to my parties. Boy, did we have a great time. I went home hoping to be invited to Vito's next party.

Directions: Complete the table. Give details about each party. Then write whether the author is comparing or contrasting and why.

Describe the . . .	Vito's Party	Writer's Parties
Place	tent in the backyard	inside
Time	night	1.
Food	2.	3.
Size	4.	no more than ten guests
5. Conclusion:		

Notes for Home: Your child read a story and looked for comparisons and contrasts. **Home Activity:** Work with your child to compare and contrast two parties or celebrations you have attended. Make a list that shows how the two events are alike and different.

Summarizing

Directions: Read the passage. Then read each question about the passage. Choose the best answer to each question. Mark the letter for the answer you have chosen.

America's Patriotic Holidays

Two of our nation's most important patriotic holidays are Memorial Day and Independence Day. Memorial Day is observed on the last Monday in May, regardless of the date. It honors all those who died in our nation's wars. Independence Day always falls on the fourth of July, regardless of the day of the week. It celebrates the signing of the Declaration of Independence.

Most Americans feel that Memorial Day is a serious occasion. Many towns hold parades in which war veterans march. Ceremonies are held to remember the war dead. Often an important citizen will give a speech, and a firing of guns and the playing of taps bring the ceremony to a close.

Independence Day, by contrast, is a time for celebration. Towns and families hold afternoon picnics in which there frequently are games, contests, music, and plenty of food. The high point comes at nightfall. In towns across America on Independence Day, fireworks explode in brilliant shades of red, silver, and blue.

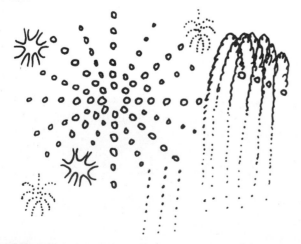

1. What is the main idea of the second paragraph?
   A. Memorial Day is a serious occasion.
   B. We should honor our war dead.
   C. Speeches should be kept short.
   D. Taps are an important custom.

2. What is the main idea of the third paragraph?
   F. Picnics are fun.
   G. Independence Day is a fun holiday.
   H. Fireworks are an important custom on Independence Day.
   J. Celebrations are an important American custom.

3. A summary of the details about Memorial Day should mention—
   A. taps.   C. ceremonies.
   B. speeches. D. gun fire.

4. What would be the *least* important detail to include in a summary about Memorial Day?
   F. Memorial Day honors the many fallen soldiers.
   G. Memorial Day is a serious holiday.
   H. An important citizen may give a speech.
   J. Memorial Day is marked by parades and ceremonies.

5. Which would be the *most* important detail to include in a summary about Independence Day?
   A. food   C. contests
   B. games   D. fireworks

Notes for Home: Your child read a nonfiction article and practiced summarizing. *Home Activity:* Read a story with your child. Then have him or her summarize it. Encourage your child to keep the summary brief and to include only the most important ideas or events.

Name _____

Writing Across Texts

Directions: "The Yangs' First Thanksgiving" and "Harvest Moon" both take place during holidays: Thanksgiving and the Harvest Moon festival. These holidays are alike in some ways, but differ in others. Read the sentences below and write each one on the chart under the name of the holiday to which it applies. If the statement applies to both holidays, write it under both.

1. This holiday takes place in the fall.

2. People usually eat turkey.

3. It is a time when families and friends get together.

4. People often eat in the afternoon, so their food can digest.

5. The mooncakes may be in the shape of the animal that represents the current Chinese year.

6. People eat harvest mooncakes

7. It is a time of giving thanks.

8. People make good luck toasts to the harvest moon.

9. It is a time of feasting.

10. Pilgrims and Native Americans celebrated at the first of these.

Thanksgiving	The Harvest Moon Festival	Both

Write a Comparison-Contrast Paragraph

Use the information in the chart above to write a paragraph comparing the two holidays of Thanksgiving and the Harvest Moon festival. Write your paragraph on a separate sheet of paper.

Notes for Home: Your child used information from two different selections to compare and contrast holidays. ***Home Activity:*** Talk with your child about special holiday traditions in your family. Compare them with traditions of people you know.

Name _____

Grammar: Complete Subjects

REVIEW

Directions: Underline the complete subject in each sentence.

1. Different people celebrate holidays in different ways.

2. My best friend walks with her family through the woods on Thanksgiving.

3. The natural beauty helps them appreciate the holiday more.

4. My favorite cousin serves Thanksgiving dinner at a shelter every year.

5. The pleasant, friendly faces make the holiday meaningful for her.

6. Several hours of hard work make her really hungry too.

7. A wonderful visit to Plymouth in Massachusetts is my family's custom.

8. The first Thanksgiving celebration took place there.

9. My home is only an hour away from that historic spot.

10. Our Thanksgiving meal is always a special event.

Directions: Add a complete subject to each predicate to create a sentence. Your subject should have at least three words. Write your sentence on the line.

11. may be different this year

_____

_____

12. will visit us at Thanksgiving

_____

_____

13. might be part of the meal

_____

_____

14. can be interesting and fun

_____

_____

15. may enjoy a traditional American holiday

_____

_____

© Scott Foresman 5

Notes for Home: Your child identified and used complete subjects in sentences. *Home Activity:* Have your child write some sentences about celebrations in your family. Then ask your child to underline the complete subject in each sentence.

Name _____

Grammar: Adjectives

An **adjective** describes the person, place, or thing that is named by a noun or identified by a pronoun. Many adjectives come before the words they describe. Adjectives can tell what kind, which one, or how many.

<u>sweet</u> relish (what kind)
<u>this</u> week (which one)
<u>four</u> hours (how many)

The words **a, an,** and **the** are called **articles.** They are used before nouns or before words that modify, or describe, nouns.

• Use **a** before singular words that begin with a consonant sound:
<u>a</u> celebration; <u>a</u> lovely dinner.

• Use **an** before singular words that begin with a vowel sound or a silent **h:** <u>an</u> announcement; <u>an</u> hour.

• Use **the** before singular or plural words beginning with any letter: <u>the</u> song; <u>the</u> efforts.

Directions: Underline every article and every adjective in each sentence.

1. The Fourth of July is a loud and lively tradition in the USA.
2. Many people celebrate with festive parties.
3. Some parks offer brilliant displays of fireworks.
4. Colorful rockets explode in the smoky sky.
5. Happy families watch the spectacular sights.
6. Concerts of patriotic music often accompany these displays.
7. In a big city, famous singers and even Miss America appear on stage.
8. A concert in Washington, D.C., Boston, or Philadelphia may be televised to the entire country.
9. The audience at an outdoor concert may wear red, white, and blue T-shirts or caps.
10. When the bandleader announces traditional songs, the enthusiastic concert goers wave small flags and sing.

Directions: Read each sentence. For each underlined word, write whether the article or adjective tells **what kind, which one,** or **how many.**

_____ 11. This holiday recalls an <u>historic</u> event.

_____ 12. The <u>thirteen</u> colonies declared independence.

_____ 13. <u>Those</u> colonies had been under England's rule.

_____ 14. <u>The</u> Declaration of Independence was signed on July 4, 1776.

_____ 15. Every year we recall these <u>brave</u> patriots.

Notes for Home: Your child identified adjectives, words that describe people, places, and things. *Home Activity:* Point out items in your home. Ask your child to describe the items by offering adjectives that tell what kind, which one, or how many.

Grammar: Adjectives

Directions: Read each sentence. Write the articles and adjectives on the line. For each article or adjective you find, write whether it tells **what kind, which one,** or **how many.**

1. Thanksgiving is an annual holiday.

   _____

2. Large families often gather on this day.

   _____

3. Some people take the time to offer sincere thanks.

   _____

4. The group may eat juicy turkey and tasty pie.

   _____

5. Americans look forward to this joyous event.

   _____

Directions: Write an adjective on the line to complete each sentence.

_____ 6. Thanksgiving is a _____ occasion.

_____ 7. _____ people express their thankfulness.

_____ 8. They find _____ ways to observe the day.

_____ 9. _____ individuals talk about the Pilgrims.

_____ 10. The Pilgrims found a _____ home here.

_____ 11. At first their lives were _____.

_____ 12. Then a _____ Native American helped them.

_____ 13. The Pilgrims and Native Americans began a _____ friendship.

_____ 14. Together they held a _____ feast.

_____ 15. This feast was the _____ Thanksgiving.

Write a Description

Invent a new holiday. On a separate sheet of paper, describe how the holiday should be celebrated. Use adjectives in your writing to make your sentences more interesting.

Notes for Home: Your child identified adjectives, words that describe people, places, and things. **Home Activity:** Read a story with your child. Have your child point out adjectives that appear in the sentences. Then ask him or her to tell what each adjective describes.

Grammar: Adjectives

Look at the sneakers on the right.
Write words that describe these sneakers.

_____

_____

Read the words you wrote that answer the question **what kind,
which one,** or **how many.** These words are called **adjectives.**

An **adjective** describes the person, place, or thing that is named by a noun or identified by
a pronoun. The words **a, an,** and **the** are called **articles.** They appear before nouns or
before adjectives that are in front of nouns.

Directions: Circle the articles in each sentence. Then underline the noun that follows each
article.

1. An elephant hid in the refrigerator.

2. We found a footprint in the pudding.

3. We saw a peanut on the shelf.

4. An embarrassed elephant fell out of the freezer.

Directions: Underline two adjectives and one article in each sentence. Then write each adjective
and article in the correct space in the chart.

5. One breakfast was the tastiest meal I ever ate.

6. Some people drink a glass of fresh juice.

7. Many children eat a bowl of cold cereal.

8. Two eggs and toast make a delicious breakfast.

	How Many?	**What Kind?**	**Article**
5.			
6.			
7.			
8.			

Notes for Home: Your child used adjectives to describe a picture and identified articles (*a,
an,* and *the*) and adjectives in sentences. *Home Activity:* Ask your child to write a list of at
least five adjectives that tell more about a picture in a magazine.

Grammar: Adjectives

Directions: Circle the adjectives that tell **What kind.** Underline the adjectives that tell **How Many.** Draw two lines under the adjectives that tell **Which one.** Put an X on the articles.

1. Many years ago there were long periods of cold temperatures in this area.

2. Large, frozen rivers covered some parts of the magnificent planet.

3. Several huge, icy sheets cut wide valleys in the mountainous areas.

4. A few glaciers dug enormous holes into that soft, brown earth.

5. Some large holes became deep lakes.

6. Many lakes were formed by those powerful glaciers.

7. One lake made by an ancient glacier is Cayuga.

Directions: Unscramble each adjective and write it on the line.

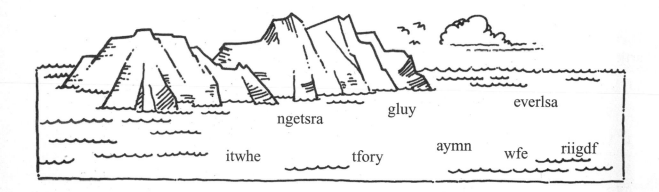

ngetsra   gluy   everlsa

itwhe   tfory   aymn   wfe   riigdf

8. _____

9. _____

10. _____

11. _____

12. _____

13. _____

14. _____

15. _____

Write a Description

Write sentences that describe what the land looks like where you live. Use at least five adjectives. Write on a separate sheet of paper.

Notes for Home: Your child identified and unscrambled adjectives and used them in a paragraph. *Home Activity:* Write a list of five adjectives that describe something in your kitchen. Write the list again, but scramble the letters. Have your child unscramble the adjectives.

Word Study: Inflected Endings -ed, -ing

Directions: Two endings that are commonly added to verbs are **-ed** and **-ing.** If the verbs end in **e,** drop the **e** before adding **-ed** or **-ing.** Read the words in the table. Find the words that dropped the **e** before adding the ending. Write the base word on the lines.

1. _____
2. _____
3. _____
4. _____
5. _____

Base Word	Add -ed	Add -ing
relieve	relieved	relieving
cook	cooked	cooking
illustrate	illustrated	illustrating
invite	invited	inviting
hope	hoped	hoping
embarrass	embarrassed	embarrassing
arrive	arrived	arriving
help	helped	helping

Directions: Add **-ed** and **-ing** to each base word. Write the new word on the line.

Base Word	Add -ed	Add -ing
excite	6. _____	16. _____
introduce	7. _____	17. _____
work	8. _____	18. _____
interest	9. _____	19. _____
slice	10. _____	20. _____
complain	11. _____	21. _____
dine	12. _____	22. _____
wince	13. _____	23. _____
start	14. _____	24. _____
boil	15. _____	25. _____

Notes for Home: Your child read and wrote words with the endings *-ed* and *-ing.* **Home Activity:** Read a magazine article with your child. List any words with *-ed* or *-ing* endings. Discuss whether the spelling of each verb was changed before *-ed* or *-ing* was added.

Spelling: Homophones

Pretest

Pretest Directions: Fold back the page along the dotted line. On the blanks, write the spelling words as they are dictated. When you have finished the test, unfold the page and check your words.

1._____	1. Please **write** to me.
2._____	2. You must do what is **right**.
3._____	3. Ted wants to **buy** a candy bar.
4._____	4. The book is **by** a famous author.
5._____	5. This letter is **to** your mother.
6._____	6. There are **too** many choices.
7._____	7. Are you **bored** by this movie?
8._____	8. I need some nails and a **board**.
9._____	9. **It's** easy to ride a bike.
10._____	10. The bird spread **its** wings.
11._____	11. Jason **threw** the baseball to me.
12._____	12. The kids ran **through** the yard.
13._____	13. You must **knead** the dough.
14._____	14. I **need** to see you tomorrow.
15._____	15. This is the library's **main** branch.
16._____	16. The lion shook his **mane**.
17._____	17. I forget things about the **past**.
18._____	18. The truck **passed** the school bus.
19._____	19. Are you **allowed** to go?
20._____	20. She was reading **aloud**.

Notes for Home: Your child took a pretest on homophones, words that sound alike but are spelled differently and have different meanings. *Home Activity:* Help your child learn to connect the spelling of the word with its meaning.

Spelling: Homophones

Word List				
write	to	it's	knead	past
right	too	its	need	passed
buy	bored	threw	main	allowed
by	board	through	mane	aloud

Directions: Read each sentence. Then match each underlined word to its definition. Write the word on the line.

He <u>threw</u> the ball <u>through</u> the window.

tossed   from end to end

You <u>need</u> to <u>knead</u> the dough to make bread.

must   press together

1. _____   2. _____   5. _____   6. _____

Are you going <u>to</u> the ball game <u>too</u>?

also   in the direction of

We <u>buy</u> our milk <u>by</u> the gallon.

in the amount of   purchase

3. _____   4. _____   7. _____   8. _____

Directions: Choose the word from the box that best completes each sentence. Write the word on the line to the left.

_____   9. Did you _____ the thank-you letter?

_____   10. Please do it _____ now.

_____   11. The lions were the _____ circus attraction,

_____   12. The biggest lion had a magnificent _____.

_____   13. The _____ meeting went on for hours.

_____   14. I was so _____ I nearly fell asleep.

_____   15. Father _____ the potatoes to me.

_____   16. We finished eating at half _____ four.

_____   17. I think _____ time for dessert.

_____   18. I gave the dog a piece of cake in _____ bowl.

_____   19. You're not _____ to talk loudly in the library.

_____   20. You also can't read _____ in the library.

Notes for Home: Your child spelled homophones—words that sound the same but have different spellings and meanings. *Home Activity:* Make up short sentences using one spelling word in each sentence. Say each sentence and have your child spell the word you used.

Proofread and Write

Spelling: Homophones

Directions: Proofread the rules for how to behave at a special dinner. Find seven spelling mistakes. Use the proofreading marks to correct each mistake.

≡	Make a capital.
/	Make a small letter.
∧	Add something.
⌧	Take out something.
⊙	Add a period.
¶	Begin a new paragraph.

Always place your napkin in your lap before eating.

Hold the fork in your left hand, and the knife in your write.

If you need to have a dish past, always ask politely.

Never sing or read allowed at the table, unless asked too do so.

Avoid yawning, even if you are bord.

When you are thru eating, wait for others to finish before

leaving the table.

Remember to thank your host buy the time you leave.

Spelling Tip

it's   its

Homophones are words that sound alike but have different spellings and meanings. Don't confuse the homophones **its** and **it's. It's** means **it is. Its** is a possessive pronoun that means **belonging to it.** Remember: **It's** easy to remember **its** spelling: **i-t.**

Write a Set of Rules

On a separate sheet of paper, write your own rules for another social situation, such as talking on the telephone or meeting new people. Try to use at least five of your spelling words.

Word List

write	threw
right	through
buy	knead
by	need
to	main
too	mane
bored	past
board	passed
it's	allowed
its	aloud

Notes for Home: Your child spelled homophones—words that sound exactly alike but have different spellings and meanings. **Home Activity:** Write each pair of homophones on index cards. Take turns choosing a card and writing a sentence that uses both words.

Spelling: Homophones

REVIEW

Word List

write	to	it's	knead	past
right	too	its	need	passed
buy	bored	threw	main	allowed
by	board	through	mane	aloud

Directions: Choose the word from the box that has the same or nearly the same meaning as each word or words below. Write the word on the line.

1. wooden plank _____

2. finished _____

3. purchase _____

4. uninterested _____

5. most important _____

6. squeeze _____

7. hair _____

8. near _____

9. require _____

10. pitched _____

Directions: Choose a pair of homophones from the box to complete each sentence. Write the words on the lines to the left.

_____ 11. It's _____ late _____ go to the parade.

_____ 12.

_____ 13. We _____ the marchers when we drove _____ the bank.

_____ 14.

_____ 15. I should _____ myself a note _____ now before I forget.

_____ 16.

_____ 17. When the cat meows, _____ time for _____ dinner.

_____ 18.

_____ 19. The teacher _____ the students to read _____ to one another.

_____ 20.

Notes for Home: Your child spelled homophones—words that sound alike but are spelled differently and have different meanings. **Home Activity:** Help your child write a short rhyming poem using several of the spelling words.

Research Process/Evaluate Reference Sources

There are many different resources you can use to find information, such as atlases, almanacs, CD-ROMs, and the Internet. When beginning a research project, follow these steps to make the best use of your time.

Research Process

1. Set a purpose.
2. Form and revise questions.
3. Evaluate and choose sources.
4. Collect, organize, and present information.

© Scott Foresman 5

Name _____

Directions: Suppose you wanted to do a research report about holidays. Think about the research process and the resources you might use. Then answer the questions below.

1. First, narrow down the topic for your report on holidays. What holiday or aspect of holidays are you most interested in? Write your topic on the line below.

_____

2. What questions about your topic do you want to answer through your research? List at least two questions.

_____

_____

_____

_____

3. List two resources you might use to begin your research into the questions above and explain why these are good resources to use. Consider whether such resources are reliable, accurate, sufficient, and up-to-date.

_____

_____

_____

_____

4. What might your finished report look and sound like? For example, could you use a diagram, a map, or a recording of a speech or music? Describe how you could organize and present your report.

_____

_____

_____

_____

5. How might the research process help you make the best use of your time? Explain.

_____

_____

_____

_____

© Scott Foresman 5

Notes for Home: Your child wrote about the steps in the research process. *Home Activity:* Watch a news report on television with your child. Talk about the research the news team probably had to do before giving the report.

Family Times

Name_____

Summary

Dusty and His Dogs Win Alaskan Sled-Dog Race!

In 1995, a 15-year-old named Dusty entered a sled race for teens held annually along Alaska's Iditarod Trail. His sled, loaded with supplies, was pulled by Huskies, a breed of dog well-suited to the cold climate. The weather was well below freezing, but Dusty and his Huskies pushed on. They encountered many obstacles along the narrow and snowy path. But by the end of the 158-mile course, Dusty was the winner. Happy trails to you, Dusty!

Reading Skills

Main Idea and Supporting Details

Main ideas are the most important ideas about the topic of a paragraph, an article, or a story. **Supporting details** tell more about a main idea. For example:

❖ This article is about Dusty competing in the Iditarod. One main idea is that Dusty faced many hardships and dangers during the race.
❖ In the article, Dusty's sled skids into a tree. Later, the dogs run into a snowmobile and get tangled in their lines. A second tangle occurs minutes later! All these details support the main idea that Dusty and his dogs faced hardships and danger.

Activity
Listen to the News. Have your child pretend to be a newscaster reporting on the Jr. Iditarod. Have him or her describe the excitement that takes place during the race.

Activity
Fill in the Blanks. Make a general statement about someone in your family. For example: **Dana is helpful.** Then have others suggest details that support your main idea.

Family Times

Tested Vocabulary

Words to Know

Knowing the meanings of these words is important to reading "The Jr. Iditarod Race." Practice using these words to learn their meanings.

announcer person who introduces programs, reads news, and so on

cargo load of goods

delays periods of time when things are put off or held up

injuries damages

obstacles things that stand in the way; hindrances

overtakes catches up and moves ahead

skids slides

wilderness region with no people living in it

Grammar

Using Adjectives to Improve Sentences

An **adjective** is a word that describes a person, place, or thing. Adjectives can make your writing more interesting and your meaning clearer. Read each pair of sentences below. Note how the use of adjectives makes the second sentence in each pair more interesting and clearer.

The Iditarod is a race.
The Iditarod is an <u>Alaskan</u> <u>dogsled</u> race.

Dogs pull a sled.
<u>Ten</u> dogs pull a <u>long</u>, <u>heavy</u> sled.

Activity
Add Adjectives. Have someone say a simple sentence, such as: **We have a car.** Then take turns adding adjectives to make the sentence clearer or more interesting.

Tested Spelling Words

Main Idea and Supporting Details

- The **main idea** is the most important idea about the topic of a paragraph, article, or story. **Supporting details** tell more about the main idea.

- When the main idea is not directly stated, you will have to decide what is most important and put it in your own words.

Directions: Reread "Saving Nome." Then complete the table. Decide on the most important idea about the topic. Then list important supporting details that tell more about that idea.

Topic The diphtheria epidemic in Nome
Main Idea 1.
Detail Nome wasn't reachable by ship in winter.
Detail 2.
Detail 3.
Detail 4.
Detail 5.

Notes for Home: Your child read a story, identified its main idea, and described important supporting details. *Home Activity:* With your child, read a small section of a simple magazine article. Ask your child to identify the main idea of the section and list some supporting details.

Vocabulary

Directions: Draw a line to connect each word on the left with its definition on the right.

1. skids   damages

2. obstacles   catches up and moves ahead

3. cargo   slides

4. injuries   things that get in the way or slow you down

5. overtakes   load of goods

Directions: Choose the word from the box that best completes each sentence. Write the word on the line to the left.

_____ 6. We awoke before dawn to load the _____ into the camper van.

_____ 7. Our plan was to drive to the mountains and spend two weeks in the _____.

_____ 8. As we drove, we listened to the radio _____ give a traffic report.

_____ 9. She said to expect long _____ on the mountain road.

_____ 10. I hope we don't face any other _____ on our vacation.

Write a Sports Announcement

Imagine you are a radio announcer covering a big sports event. How will you convey to your listeners what you see? Write your account of what happens, blow by blow. Use as many vocabulary words as you can.

Notes for Home: Your child identified and used new vocabulary words from "The Jr. Iditarod Race." *Home Activity:* With your child, write a postcard describing a real or imaginary trip to the wilderness. Encourage your child to use as many of the vocabulary words as possible.

Main Idea and Supporting Details

- The **main idea** is the most important idea about the topic of a paragraph, article, or story. When the main idea is not stated, you have to figure it out and state it in your own words.

- **Supporting details** tell more about the main idea.

Directions: Reread what happens in "The Jr. Iditarod Race" as Dusty and his team enter the woods. Then answer the questions below.

> They cross the lake safely, following the red plastic cones marking the route. But as they enter the woods, Dusty is on edge. He's never done this part of the trail, and it's crowded with obstacles. Snowmobiles roar along the same trail, and within ten miles he has to cross four roads. Sometimes the roads are so slick the dogs fall, or they get confused by the cars and spectators. Dusty knows he just needs to survive this part until he hits the main Iditarod trail.
>
> From IDITAROD DREAM. Copyright © 1996 by Ted Wood. Reprinted with permission from Walker and Company. All Rights Reserved.

1. In a few words, write the topic of this paragraph.

   _____

2. State the main idea of the paragraph in your own words.

   _____

   _____

3. List three supporting details for the main idea.

   _____

   _____

   _____

4. Is the description of the red plastic cones marking the route a supporting detail? Why or why not?

   _____

   _____

5. What are the topic and main idea of "The Jr. Iditarod Race"? On a separate sheet of paper, identify the topic, state the main idea, and list supporting details.

Notes for Home: Your child read a paragraph from a nonfiction text and identified the main idea and supporting details. **Home Activity:** With your child, read a newspaper article. Help him or her to identify its main idea and supporting details.

Selection Test

Directions: Choose the best answer to each item. Mark the letter for the answer you have chosen.

Part 1: Vocabulary

Find the answer choice that means about the same as the underlined word in each sentence.

1. There were many <u>obstacles</u> in the street.
   A. people looking at something
   B. things that stand in the way
   C. large holes that need to be filled
   D. booths where people sell things

2. Jenna hiked into the <u>wilderness</u>.
   F. wild place with no people living in it
   G. piece of land surrounded by water
   H. area full of ancient buildings
   J. border separating two countries

3. What did the <u>announcer</u> just say?
   A. someone who acts on a stage
   B. person who introduces a program or event and tells what happens
   C. someone who writes news articles
   D. person who represents the government of a foreign country

4. Workers carried the <u>cargo</u>.
   F. passengers
   G. broken machines
   H. sails on a ship
   J. load of goods

5. What should you do if your car <u>skids</u>?
   A. stops suddenly
   B. catches on fire
   C. gets a flat tire
   D. slides

6. The hiker had some <u>injuries</u>.
   F. wounds; hurt body parts
   G. hot meals
   H. successes; wins
   J. favorite sights

7. My horse <u>overtakes</u> the leader.
   A. bumps into
   B. moves ahead of
   C. loses to
   D. makes a noise at

8. There were many <u>delays</u> during the trip.
   F. surprising events
   G. pleasant meetings
   H. stops along the way
   J. dangers to avoid

Part 2: Comprehension

Use what you know about the selection to answer each item.

9. Both the Iditarod and Jr. Iditarod races are held to honor—
   A. the coming of pioneers to Alaska.
   B. the earliest Eskimo mushers.
   C. a dog team that carried medicine to Nome.
   D. Alaska's natural beauty.

GO ON

10. What is this selection mostly about?
    F.   how Dusty Whittemore and his family became involved in mushing
    G.   the fifteen young people who competed in the 1995 Jr. Iditarod
    H.   how the Jr. Iditarod is different from the adults' race
    J.   the experiences of the boy who won the 1995 Jr. Iditarod

11. Which detail supports the idea that sled dogs love to run and pull sleds?
    A.   "It's zero degrees, which is perfect for the dogs."
    B.   "Dusty has to walk each dog from the truck."
    C.   "The dogs are so excited by the other teams it takes every hand to hold them in place."
    D.   "QT and Blacky have splits in the webs between their toes."

12. What can you tell about Dusty from how he acts in the early part of the race?
    F.   He doesn't realize that mushing can be a dangerous sport.
    G.   He stays clear-headed when faced with a problem.
    H.   He panics when something unexpected occurs.
    J.   He keeps imagining victory and forgets to pay attention to what is happening.

13. You can tell from this selection that sled dogs—
    A.   are very calm and patient.
    B.   are more powerful than a moose.
    C.   need no training to mush correctly.
    D.   remember places they have been before.

14. Which sentence states an opinion?
    F.   "The handlers step away and Dusty flies from the start."
    G.   "Back on the trail, he uses his track brake to slow the dogs."
    H.   "The team is running perfectly now, strong and fast."
    J.   "It takes him five minutes to straighten them out and get under way."

15. What part of the story shows that Dusty follows the spirit of the race?
    A.   People think Dusty has mistreated his dogs.
    B.   Dusty got lost in the race the year before.
    C.   Snowmobilers almost run into Dusty's dogs.
    D.   Dusty helps the other racers build a fire.

STOP

Main Idea and Supporting Details

- The **main idea** is the most important idea about the topic of a paragraph, article, or story. When the main idea is not stated, you have to figure it out and state it in your own words.

- **Supporting details** tell more about the main idea.

Directions: Read the story below.

This year Misty entered a 100K bicycle marathon. Because it was her first marathon, Misty was nervous. On the day before the race, she studied a map of the marathon's route, mentally preparing for its challenges. She checked and doubled-checked the brakes on her bike. She also measured the air pressure in her tires and made sure her bike helmet fit correctly. Misty was careful to fill out the emergency card that all racers must carry. It had the name of a person to call in case she was sick or injured during the race. On the day of the race, Misty felt confident that she was prepared for anything.

Directions: Complete the diagram. Describe the story's main idea and give details that support the main idea.

Main Idea

1.

Supporting Details
She studied a map of the route.

2.

3.

4.

5.

Notes for Home: Your child read a nonfiction passage and identified its main idea and supporting details. *Home Activity:* With your child, read a section from a school textbook. Help him or her identify the main idea and supporting details of the section read.

© Scott Foresman 5

Generalizing

Directions: Read the passage. Then read each question about the passage. Choose the best answer to each question. Mark the letter for the answer you have chosen.

Siberian Huskies

Siberian Huskies were originally bred as sled dogs. These dogs were bred by the Chukchi people of northeastern Asia. In general, the breed's compact size, quickness, and endurance make it perfect for pulling loads over long distances.

In 1909, the first team of Siberian Huskies was brought to Alaska to compete in the All Alaska Sweepstakes Race. Soon, many Alaskan dog breeders were breeding Siberian Huskies. The dogs became popular in Alaska for racing, and they also became popular in other parts of the United States as family pets.

If you are thinking about getting a Siberian Husky for a pet, there are three important things to know about them. First, all Siberian Huskies love to run. A fenced-in yard is important so that your dog has plenty of room to run. Second, Siberian Huskies shed. If dog hair bothers you or anyone in your family, this is probably not the dog for you. Finally, Siberian Huskies are friendly and love company. If you will have to leave your dog alone for long periods of time, consider a different breed of dog.

1. What clue words in the first paragraph signal a generalization?
   A. originally
   B. in general
   C. perfect
   D. Siberian Huskies

2. Which generalization is valid based on information given in the passage?
   F. Siberian Huskies are loners.
   G. Siberian Huskies make great sled dogs.
   H. Siberian Huskies are slow, but steady runners.
   J. Siberian Huskies are easy dogs to care for.

3. Why isn't the first sentence of the second paragraph a generalization?
   A. It tells a historical fact.
   B. It doesn't give enough information about the team.
   C. It doesn't tell what most Huskies have in common.
   D. It doesn't say whether the team won the race.

4. What clue word in the third paragraph signals a generalization?
   F. all
   G. second
   H. first
   J. finally

5. Which of the following generalizations is faulty based on information given in the passage?
   A. Siberian Huskies are compact in size.
   B. Siberian Huskies love to run.
   C. Siberian Huskies originated in Siberia.
   D. Siberian Huskies are quick runners, but tire easily.

Notes for Home: Your child read an article and identified generalizations in it. *Home Activity:* Use the following clue words to take turns making generalizations with your child: *many, all, most, never, always, often.* For example: *All my children have dark hair.*

Writing Across Texts

Directions: Dusty in "The Jr. Iditarod Race" prepares himself and his dogsled team for an Alaskan tradition—the Iditarod race. Mary Yang, from "The Yangs' First Thanksgiving," may find many of these traditions unfamiliar but exciting. Some may be similar to things from her own traditions. In the table below, make a list of traditions that Dusty might explain to Mary and what Mary may think of them.

Dusty's Traditions	Mary's Reactions
Sled dogs are working dogs, not pets.	In China, dogs are not kept as pets.
1.	2.
3.	4.
5.	6.
7.	8.
9.	10.

Write a Story

Through our experiences and traditions, we learn about who we are, where we come from, and what we think is important. Think about Mary, from the story "The Yangs' First Thanksgiving." Suppose Mary's family had moved to Alaska. Write a story about Mary meeting Dusty as he prepared for the Jr. Iditarod. Think about traditions that might be new or similar to traditions from Mary's own culture. Write your story on a separate sheet of paper.

Notes for Home: Your child used information from different sources to write a story. *Home Activity:* As you read a story or article with your child, discuss how its ideas connect to other reading your child has done.

Grammar: Adjectives

REVIEW

Directions: Underline each adjective. Draw a circle around each article.

1. In February 1978, Naomi Uemura began an amazing trip.

2. Mr. Uemura, with several dogs and a sled, would try to reach the faraway North Pole.

3. It would be a long and dangerous trip.

4. Mr. Uemura would have to deal with frigid weather and many difficult conditions.

5. The strong, speedy dogs needed constant, careful care.

6. Dogs with frozen paws or empty stomachs cannot pull a heavy sled.

7. One day Mr. Uemura was attacked by an enormous angry bear.

8. The brave team traveled six hundred miles over the frozen Arctic.

9. For fifty-four difficult days, Mr. Uemura and the loyal dogs moved over the ice.

10. On April 30, 1978, Mr. Uemura became the first person to reach the North Pole alone over land.

Directions: Complete each sentence with an article or with an adjective that tells how many or how much. More than one word may work in a sentence. Choose an article or an adjective from the box that makes sense. Write your new sentences on the lines.

no   a *or* an   many   sixty   several

11. There are _____ dogsled drivers who dream of racing in the Iditarod.

_____

12. About _____ "mushers" actually do compete each year.

_____

13. Some enter the race even if they have _____ chance of winning.

_____

14. Training for the race is not _____ easy task.

_____

15. Teams must win _____ shorter races before they can run the Iditarod.

_____

Notes for Home: Your child identified and used adjectives as well as the articles *a, an,* and *the* in sentences. **Home Activity:** Ask your child questions about persons, places, and things at school. Have your child write sentences, using adjectives and articles.

Grammar: Using Adjectives to Improve Sentences

Adjectives describe persons, places, or things that nouns or pronouns identify. Adjectives tell what kind, which one, or how many. You can improve your sentences by using adjectives. They add vivid and precise details so that readers can picture what you are writing about.

Without Adjectives: Dogs run in yards.
With Adjectives Added: <u>Five</u> <u>large</u> dogs run in <u>grassy</u> yards.

Be careful not to use more adjectives than you need: <u>Two</u> <u>large</u>, <u>long</u>, <u>tall</u>, <u>alert</u> Dobermans sat in the kennel's waiting room.

Directions: Underline each adjective. Circle the noun or pronoun it modifies.

1. Dogs come in a wide variety of interesting breeds.

2. Friendly dogs make wonderful companions.

3. Intelligent dogs can perform amazing tasks.

4. Expert trainers teach them important skills.

5. Some fierce dogs guard homes and businesses.

6. Other dogs guide blind people on busy sidewalks.

7. Special dogs herd stray sheep on big farms.

8. Some large dogs rescue injured climbers.

9. Dogs have a long tradition of good deeds.

Directions: Add an adjective to make each sentence more vivid or more precise. Write the adjective on the line to the left.

_____ 10. Police rely on _____ dogs in their work.

_____ 11. These dogs receive _____ training.

_____ 12. Some dogs search for _____ criminals.

_____ 13. Other dogs can accurately sniff out _____ clues.

_____ 14. Rescue dogs search for _____ persons.

_____ 15. Dogs and police do _____ work together.

Notes for Home: Your child identified and used adjectives in sentences. Adjectives describe people, places, and things. *Home Activity:* Look at pictures in a magazine together. Invite your child to name adjectives that describe the people, places, or things in each picture.

Grammar: Using Adjectives to Improve Sentences

Directions: Think of a different adjective to replace the one that is underlined.
Write each new adjective on the line.

_____ **1.** Football is a <u>nice</u> American tradition.

_____ **2.** Many <u>good</u> teams play on New Year's Day.

_____ **3.** <u>Big</u> crowds fill stadiums around the country.

_____ **4.** The Rose Bowl is a <u>fine</u> football contest.

_____ **5.** Before the game a <u>pretty</u> parade is held.

Directions: Choose at least two adjectives to improve each sentence.
Write each new sentence on the line.

6. A band marches in the parade.

_____

_____

7. Floats of flowers travel on streets.

_____

_____

8. Spectators cheer with voices.

_____

_____

9. Music and laughter are heard.

_____

_____

10. People in costumes take part in the celebration.

_____

_____

Write a Description

Imagine you are at a football game or parade on New Year's Day. On a separate
sheet of paper, describe the people, places, and things that you see. Use precise
and vivid adjectives in your sentences.

Notes for Home: Your child used adjectives—words that describe people, places, and
things—to improve sentences. **Home Activity:** Have your child think of an object and offer
adjectives to describe it *(cold, white, big)*. See if you can guess the object *(refrigerator)*.

Grammar: Using Adjectives to Improve Sentences

RETEACHING

Read the sentence. Write an adjective on each line in the second sentence to make the sentence more vivid.

Children play games on the playground.

_____ children play _____ games on the _____ playground.

Adjectives describe persons, places, or things that nouns or pronouns identify. They can tell **what kind, which one,** or **how many.** Adjectives add details to sentences to help readers understand more clearly what the writing is about. Make sure you do not use too many adjectives in your writing.

Directions: Underline each adjective. Circle the noun or pronoun it modifies.

1. You must focus the new camera before you take a picture.

2. I'm sorry my little brother was rude.

3. After receiving her difficult orders, the proud soldier left.

4. Ginny was nasty in her refusal to attend the party.

5. Don't let Luke fool you; he has a soft heart.

6. Linda is gloomy when it rains.

7. "A good morning to you," Miss Sprolls called in a bright tone.

8. Here comes another cheerful person.

9. Holly was thoughtful, and her long silence worried her mother.

10. The bright ribbon was wrapped around the large box and tied in a bow.

Directions: Add an adjective to make each sentence more vivid or precise. Write the adjective on the line to the left.

_____ 11. My younger brother's _____ truck barreled down the street made of blocks.

_____ 12. His _____ people had to be moved out of the way to avoid it.

_____ 13. I asked my _____ brother why the truck was going so fast.

_____ 14. He said, "Watch. Do you see this _____ man running down the street?"

_____ 15. "He forgot to turn off the _____ truck when he got out!"

Notes for Home: Your child learned how to use adjectives to improve sentences. *Home Activity:* Say sentences describing your home. Have your child think of adjectives to make the sentences more vivid and interesting. Then have him or her say the sentences with adjectives.

Grammar: Using Adjectives to Improve Sentences

Directions: Think of some adjectives that could describe a favorite gift you've received, and write the name of the gift in the center circle. Then write one adjective in each oval. Picture the gift in your mind to help you think of words that tell how it looks, sounds, smells, feels, or tastes.

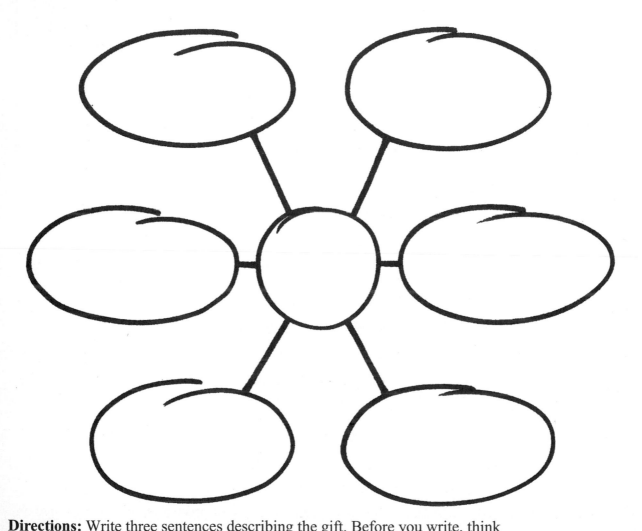

Directions: Write three sentences describing the gift. Before you write, think about what quality or characteristic of the gift you want to describe, and decide how you might use adjectives in your sentences.

_____

_____

_____

_____

Notes for Home: Your child wrote adjectives that described a favorite gift and used those adjectives in sentences. ***Home Activity:*** Together, write a list of at least eight adjectives that describe your child's favorite food.

Word Study: Inflected Endings -er, -est

Directions: The endings **-er** and **-est** are added to words to show comparisons.
Read the base words below. Add **-er** and **-est** to each word. Write the new word
on the line.

Base Word	Add -er	Add -est
warm	1. _____	2. _____
high	3. _____	4. _____
short	5. _____	6. _____
new	7. _____	8. _____

Directions: Read each sentence. Circle the word that ends with either **-er** or **-est.**
Write the base word on the line.

_____ 9. The goal of any race is to be quicker than the competition.

_____ 10. In many sports, the team with the highest score wins.

_____ 11. In dogsled racing, the person with the coolest head often wins.

_____ 12. Dogsled races only occur in the north, where the weather is colder.

_____ 13. Lower temperatures usually mean good track conditions.

_____ 14. Warmer temperatures and melting snow can slow down a team.

_____ 15. A slower pace will lose a race.

_____ 16. It is important to stay away from the softer patches of snow.

_____ 17. Some races may be harder to win than others!

_____ 18. The last night of the race often seems like the longest.

_____ 19. It's always nice to get the loudest cheer at the finish line.

_____ 20. It feels great to know you have the fastest time among all the people racing.

Notes for Home: Your child identified words with the endings *-er* and *-est*. **Home Activity:**
Make a list of words that have these endings. Have your child use them to make comparisons
about two objects (use *-er* words) and more than two objects (use *-est* words).

Spelling: Including All the Letters

Pretest Directions: Fold back the page along the dotted line. On the blanks, write the spelling words as they are dictated. When you have finished the test, unfold the page and check your words.

Pretest

1._____
2._____
3._____
4._____
5._____
6._____
7._____
8._____
9._____
10._____
11._____
12._____
13._____
14._____
15._____
16._____
17._____
18._____
19._____
20._____

1. What is the **answer**?

2. Sixty seconds make a **minute**.

3. Something **happened** today.

4. Let's go to the **library**.

5. The store **opened** last week.

6. What is the **length** of the track?

7. I am **getting** a dog.

8. We leave **when** the bell rings.

9. I have **finished** my work.

10. **Maybe** they will come tomorrow.

11. His mom likes **mystery** novels.

12. It is time to go to the **dentist**.

13. I am not **actually** afraid.

14. The car is five feet in **width**.

15. My sundae has **caramel** topping.

16. Please pass the **pumpkin** pie.

17. I found a **quarter** on the stairs.

18. I ate a roast beef **sandwich**.

19. The monkey **grabbed** the banana.

20. Thunder can be **frightening**.

© Scott Foresman 5

Notes for Home: Your child took a pretest on words that have difficult letter combinations. *Home Activity:* Help your child learn misspelled words before the final test. Your child can underline the word parts that caused the problems and concentrate on those parts.

Spelling: Including All the Letters

Word List

answer	opened	finished	actually	quarter
minute	length	maybe	width	sandwich
happened	getting	mystery	caramel	grabbed
library	when	dentist	pumpkin	frightening

Directions: Choose the word from the box that is formed by adding an ending to each base word. Write the word on the line.

1. open _____

2. actual _____

3. happen _____

4. frighten _____

5. get _____

6. grab _____

7. finish _____

Directions: Choose the word from the box that best matches each definition. Write the word on thc linc.

_____ **8.** It's a fall vegetable.

_____ **9.** It's a home for books.

_____ **10.** It's a popular luncheon food made with bread.

_____ **11.** It means the same as "perhaps."

_____ **12.** It's the same as sixty seconds.

_____ **13.** It's a sticky candy you put on apples.

_____ **14.** It's the distance you measure from end to end.

_____ **15.** It's a reply.

_____ **16.** It's the distance across.

_____ **17.** It's a tooth doctor.

_____ **18.** It's something that is hard to figure out, like a puzzle.

_____ **19.** It's a word you use to ask about the time something begins.

_____ **20.** It's the same as one-fourth.

Notes for Home: Your child spelled words that have more letters than one might expect.
Home Activity: Have a spelling bee with your child, taking turns spelling the words from the box. If one of you spells a word incorrectly, the other must try to spell it correctly.

Proofread and Write

Spelling: Including All the Letters

Directions: Proofread the letter. Find five spelling mistakes. Use the proofreading marks to correct each mistake.

≡	Make a capital.
/	Make a small letter.
∧	Add something.
℘	Take out something.
⊙	Add a period.
¶	Begin a new paragraph.

Dear Paul,

When I opend your letter, I had just finushed feeding our new husky puppy. Then I saw the picture of your new puppy! Isn't it cool? We both have huskies! I got some books out of the libary about dogsled racing. It acually sounds like a really fun sport. Maybe some day we'll compete in the Iditarod. Write back and tell me how your dog is geting along.

Love,

Keiko

Spelling Tip

Some words have more letters than you might think. When spelling these words, pronounce each syllable carefully. You'll be less likely to leave out letters.

Word List

answer
minute
happened
library
opened
length
getting
when
finished
maybe
mystery
dentist
actually
width
caramel
pumpkin
quarter
sandwich
grabbed
frightening

Write a Letter

On a separate sheet of paper, write a letter that Paul might send back to Keiko. Try to use at least five of your spelling words.

Notes for Home: Your child spelled words that have more letters than one might expect. *Home Activity:* On a piece of paper, write the spelling words with the letters scrambled. Invite your child to unscramble the letters to spell each word.

Spelling: Including All the Letters

Word List

answer	opened	finished	actually	quarter
minute	length	maybe	width	sandwich
happened	getting	mystery	caramel	grabbed
library	when	dentist	pumpkin	frightening

Directions: Write the word from the box that belongs in each group of words.

1. distance, long measure, _____

2. squash, gourd, _____

3. second, hour, _____

4. doctor, veterinarian, _____

5. soup, salad, _____

6. gym, cafeteria, _____

7. nickel, dime, _____

8. folk tale, science fiction, _____

9. fudge, butterscotch, _____

10. wideness, measure side to side, _____

Directions: Choose the word from the box that best completes each sentence in the paragraph. Write the word on the matching numbered lines to the right.

My Most Embarrassing Moment

It was my first dogsled race and I was **11.** _____ quite nervous. Then, **12.** _____ the race began, I **13.** _____ the reins and told my dogs to "Mush!" The dogs' **14.** _____ was to bark and take off. Then it **15.** _____. A bag of supplies somehow **16.** _____ and everything spilled out. I pulled hard on the reins, **17.** _____ a bit too hard. It was **18.** _____ how fast the sled flipped over. As I was **19.** _____ up, I saw four other sleds pass us. I knew then I'd be lucky if I **20.** _____ the race at all!

11. _____

12. _____

13. _____

14. _____

15. _____

16. _____

17. _____

18. _____

19. _____

20. _____

Notes for Home: Your child spelled words that have more letters than might be expected. *Home Activity:* Challenge your child to pronounce each spelling word carefully and then spell it. Talk about how sounding out each syllable makes it easier to spell these words.

Graphs

Graphs present information visually. **Circle graphs** have a pie shape and show the division of something into parts or percentages. **Bar graphs** use vertical or horizontal bars to show amounts that you can compare easily. **Line graphs** use lines to represent information that shows how something changes over a period of time.

Directions: Use the three graphs to answer the questions on the next page.

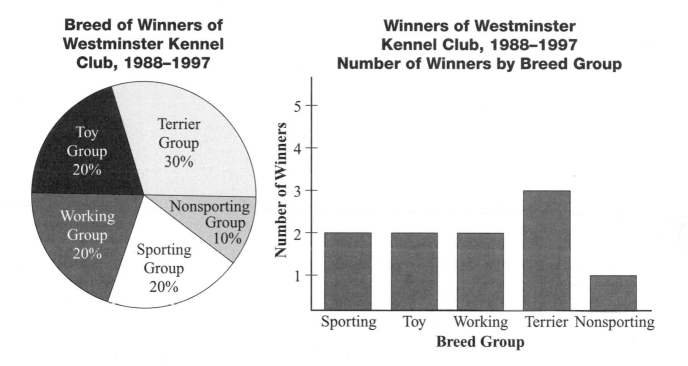

Breed of Winners of Westminster Kennel Club, 1988–1997

Terrier Group 30%
Toy Group 20%
Nonsporting Group 10%
Working Group 20%
Sporting Group 20%

Winners of Westminster Kennel Club, 1988–1997 Number of Winners by Breed Group

Number of Winners
Breed Group
Sporting Toy Working Terrier Nonsporting

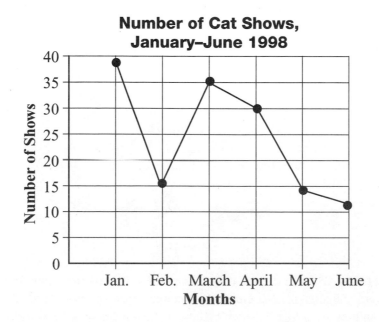

Number of Cat Shows, January–June 1998

Number of Shows
Jan. Feb. March April May June
Months

1. From 1988 to 1997, what percentage of Westminster Kennel Club winners were dogs in the Terrier Group?

_____

2. From 1988 to 1997, how many Westminster Kennel Club winners were from the Nonsporting Group?

_____

3. Which dog breed groups had the same percentage of wins during the 10-year period? How do you know?

_____

_____

4. Between which two months was there the greatest change in the number of cat shows? Between which two months was there the smallest change in the number of cat shows?

_____

5. How many more cat shows were held in March 1998 than in February 1998? _____

6. Does the bar graph tell you which breed won in 1997? Explain. _____

_____

7. Does the line graph tell you where the cat shows were held? Explain. _____

_____

8. If the percentages were not shown on the circle graph, could you still tell which dog breed had the greatest percentage of wins? Explain.

_____

_____

9. Suppose you had kept track of how much your dog weighed each month from birth until now. Which type of graph would best show how much your dog had grown? Explain.

_____

_____

10. Do you find one type of graph easier to read and understand than another? Explain.

_____

_____

Notes for Home: Your child analyzed three types of graphs. *Home Activity:* Help your child keep a weather record for one week. Then work together to make a line graph showing high and low temperatures or a bar or circle graph showing the number of cloudy or sunny days.

Family Times

Name_____

Summary

Ohkwa'ri Survives His First Overnight . . . Alone

Ohkwa'ri is an 11-year-old boy who lives with fifty other Mohawk Indian families in a big longhouse. Ohkwa'ri is given permission to stay in his own small, private lodge. During his first night alone, he is awakened by the sounds of raccoons, owls, and wolves. He is scared, but copes by thinking about his family and favorite stories. It's a night to remember!

Reading Skills

Predicting

To **predict** is to state what you think might happen next in a story. For example, while reading "The Night Alone," you might predict that Ohkwa'ri will leave his lodge during the night and return to the longhouse.

Base your predictions on what has already happened in the story and what you know about the characters so far. You might make the prediction above because many noises have frightened Ohkwa'ri during the night. As you continue reading, you can check to see if your predictions are accurate.

Activity
Listen to the Night. Darken your room and shut out all noise, if possible. Then have your child retell the story of Ohkwa'ri in detail. At various points, be silent and listen. What sounds do you hear?

Activity
Picture and Predict. Look at pictures in a magazine. For each picture, make a prediction about what may happen next. Point out the photo details that cause you to make the prediction. For example, in the picture above, you might predict that a book may fall off the shelf because it's too close to the edge.

Family Times

Tested Vocabulary

Words to Know

Knowing the meanings of these words is important to reading "The Night Alone." Practice using these words to learn their meanings.

bruised injured under the skin

lodge dwelling; house

possession thing owned

pouch bag or sack

reckless careless

Grammar

Comparative and Superlative Adjectives

An **adjective** is a word that describes a noun (a person, place, or thing). To compare two nouns, add *-er* to the adjective or use the word *more* before it. To compare three or more nouns, add *-est* or use the word *most* before it.

Adjective	Comparative	Superlative
sharp	sharper	sharpest
nice	nicer	nicest
interesting	more interesting	most interesting

Activity

Compare Rooms. Use adjectives to compare different rooms in your home. For example: **My bedroom is <u>smaller</u> than yours.** Add your adjectives to the correct column in the chart shown above.

Tested Spelling Words

Predicting

- To **predict** is to give a statement about what you think might happen next in a story or come next in an article. The statement you give is a **prediction.**

- You make predictions based on what you already know and what has already happened in the story or article.

- After you predict something, continue reading to check your prediction. As you learn new information, you might need to change your prediction.

Directions: Follow the directions for making predictions as you reread "Why Bears Have Short Tails." As you read each section of the story, tell what logical prediction can be made based on what you have read up to that point in the story. Give a reason for each prediction you make. One prediction has been done for you.

Paragraphs 1–5: Predict what will happen after Fox tells Bear how he caught the fish.

Prediction:

Bear will try what Fox told him.

  1. Reason:

_____

Paragraphs 6–9: Predict what will happen after Bear's tail freezes off.

  2. Prediction:

_____

  3. Reason:

_____

Paragraphs 10–13: Predict what will happen to Fox.

  4. Prediction:

_____

  5. Reason:

_____

Notes for Home: Your child read a legend and made predictions about what would happen next. *Home Activity:* Have your child read the first chapter of a book and predict what will happen next. Encourage your child to read the next chapter to see if his or her prediction was accurate.

Name _____

Vocabulary

Directions: Write the word from the box that belongs in each group.

1. careless, thoughtless, _____

2. bag, purse, _____

3. cabin, resort, _____

4. injured, damaged, _____

5. property, object owned, _____

<table>
<tr><td>**Check the Words You Know**</td></tr>
<tr><td>__ bruised</td></tr>
<tr><td>__ lodge</td></tr>
<tr><td>__ possession</td></tr>
<tr><td>__ pouch</td></tr>
<tr><td>__ reckless</td></tr>
</table>

Directions: Choose the word from the box that best matches each clue. Write the letters of the word on the blanks. The boxed letters spell something that you might wear or carry.

6. thing owned

7. dwelling

8. hurt

9. careless

10. bag or sack

6. □ ___ ___ ___ ___ ___

7. ___ □ ___ ___ ___

8. ___ ___ □ ___ ___ ___

9. ___ ___ ___ □ ___ ___

10. ___ ___ ___ □ ___

Something you might wear or carry: ___ ___ ___ ___ ___

Directions: Choose a word from the box that best completes each sentence. Write the word on the line to the left.

_____ 11. When we visited the Rocky Mountains we stayed in a _____.

_____ 12. Hanging from the wall was a leather _____.

_____ 13. My _____ little brother threw it across the room.

_____ 14. It hit me hard and _____ my arm.

_____ 15. I told him it hurt and that he shouldn't just grab someone else's _____.

Write a Diary Entry

Imagine that you are spending the night alone in the woods. On a separate sheet of paper, write a diary entry that describes your adventure. Tell what you see and hear and how you feel. Use as many vocabulary words as you can.

Notes for Home: Your child identified and used new vocabulary words from "The Night Alone." **Home Activity:** Help your child write a description of what it would be like to live in the woods. Encourage your child to use as many vocabulary words as possible.

Predicting

- To **predict** is to give a statement about what you think might happen next in a story or article, based on what has already happened and what you know.

- The statement you give is a **prediction.**

Directions: Reread what happens in "The Night Alone" when Ohkwa'ri returns from his first night alone in his own lodge. Then answer the questions below.

> As he walked down the rocky trail toward his canoe, which he had drawn up into the alders at the edge of the river, he wondered what food might be ready so early in the morning. His thoughts were divided between his hunger and his memory of Grabber's story. He began to walk faster as he thought of food. He no longer considered the possibility of danger. By the time Ohkwa'ri reached the place where the trail curved around a great stone to cross a rocky ledge, he was no longer watching where he put his feet.
>
> From CHILDREN OF THE LONGHOUSE by Joseph Bruchac. Copyright © 1996 by Joseph Bruchac. Used by permission of Dial Books for Young Readers, a division of Penguin Putnam Inc.

1. What clues help you predict what will happen next?

_____

_____

2. What prediction would you make after reading this paragraph?

_____

_____

3. How can you check your prediction?

_____

4. In the next paragraph, Ohkwa'ri almost steps on a rattlesnake. How does this event compare to your prediction? Explain.

_____

_____

5. On a separate sheet of paper, describe some of the predictions you made while reading "The Night Alone." Were there any events that surprised you? Did you have to change any of your predictions?

© Scott Foresman 5

Notes for Home: Your child read a paragraph and predicted what would happen next. *Home Activity:* Watch a television show with your child. As you watch, take turns making predictions about what will happen next.

Selection Test

Directions: Choose the best answer to each item. Mark the space for the answer you have chosen.

Part 1: Vocabulary

Find the answer choice that means about the same as the underlined word in the sentence.

1. Nick's arms were <u>bruised</u>.
   - A. dirty
   - B. hurt
   - C. strong
   - D. tired

2. You shouldn't be <u>reckless</u>.
   - F. filled with fear
   - G. selfish
   - H. careless; ignoring danger
   - J. lazy

3. The mover picked up each <u>possession</u> and placed it in a box.
   - A. something owned by someone
   - B. chair
   - C. something that has been damaged
   - D. book

4. That is a model of an Indian <u>lodge</u>.
   - F. home
   - G. weapon
   - H. farming tool
   - J. toy

5. Put the coins in that <u>pouch</u>.
   - A. box
   - B. bag
   - C. drawer
   - D. hole

Part 2: Comprehension

Use what you know about the story to answer each question.

6. What does Ohkwa'ri reach for twice during the night?
   - F. a snack
   - G. his mother's hand
   - H. a special stone
   - J. a deerskin robe

7. Ohkwa'ri wakes up many times during the night because—
   - A. he is cold.
   - B. he is hungry.
   - C. bears are near his lodge.
   - D. his lodge is too quiet.

8. Ohkwa'ri seems to feel that the moon and the sun are like—
   - F. members of his family that keep him company.
   - G. giant stars that care nothing for him.
   - H. animals about to attack him.
   - J. mighty gods who will protect him.

9. During his first night and morning alone, Ohkwa'ri thinks mostly about—
   - A. the dangers he faces.
   - B. the future.
   - C. his family.
   - D. his own achievements.

GO ON

10. According to this selection, the people of Ohkwa'ri's tribe used which of the following to teach lessons to young people?
  - F.   hunting maps
  - G.   diagrams
  - H.   scientific experiments
  - J.   spoken stories

11. The author most likely included the story of "Grabber" to—
  - A.   make the reader laugh.
  - B.   scare the reader.
  - C.   make the reader sad.
  - D.   teach the reader about bears.

12. When the story says that Ohkwa'ri was "no longer watching where he put his feet," a reader is most likely to predict that he will—
  - F.   die in the wilderness.
  - G.   kill a bear for food.
  - H.   soon run into danger.
  - J.   return to his little lodge instead of to his family.

13. The stories of Grabber and the two young men of the Turtle Clan suggest that—
  - A.   most young men in Ohkwa'ri's tribe are as wise as adults.
  - B.   wild animals are not very intelligent.
  - C.   it is the men, not the women, who rule Ohkwa'ri's tribe.
  - D.   young men sometimes do foolish things.

14. How does Ohkwa'ri's experience with the rattlesnake show that he is gaining in good judgment?
  - F.   He jumps when he hears the snake rattle.
  - G.   He decides to be more careful in the future.
  - H.   He realizes that he has bruised his shoulder.
  - J.   He realizes that he has missed breakfast back at the lodge.

15. You can tell from this story that the "Little People" probably are—
  - A.   Ohkwa'ri's brothers and sisters.
  - B.   spirits of the forest.
  - C.   members of the Turtle Clan.
  - D.   wild birds and animals.

STOP

© Scott Foresman 5

Predicting

- To **predict** is to give a statement about what you think might happen next in a story or article, based on what has already happened and what you know.

- The statement you give is a **prediction.**

Directions: Read the story.

The girl stood wrapped in a blanket. She fed the fire with buffalo chips. A scruffy dog came to her. A pile of fresh buffalo meat sat waiting to be made into stew. The dog whined softly, and she threw it a scrap. "Now go," she said, and the dog backed away.

An angry wail of a crying baby erupted from the wigwam. The girl went inside to check on the baby. The wailing got quieter, but the flap of the wigwam remained closed. Immediately the dog came back. It crept cautiously through the dirt, its bright eyes fixed on the pile of meat.

Directions: Complete the diagram by listing details from the story and what you know that help you make a prediction about what will happen next.

Story Details	What I Know
The dog is hungry.	A hungry dog may steal food.
1.	3.
2.	4.

5. I predict that:

Notes for Home: Your child read a story and made a prediction. *Home Activity:* Watch a movie with your child. Together, make and verify predictions about what will happen next in the movie. Change your predictions as you continue watching.

Setting/Compare and Contrast

REVIEW

Directions: Read the story. Then read each question about the story. Choose the best answer to each question. Mark the letter for the answer you have chosen.

A Taste of Independence

"Mom, can we go shopping?" Becky asked. She and her twin sister, Angela, were vacationing with their parents. At 12 years old, they had never gone shopping alone. Becky and Angela thought vacation time was a good time to start.

"All right," their mother said, "but be back for dinner." She was a little uncertain about letting the girls go by themselves, but she knew they were careful.

Three hours later, the girls hadn't returned. Dinner was long past. Becky and Angela's mother began to worry that she had made a mistake. She got in the car to look for them. Their father walked to the boardwalk on foot. He searched every video arcade, T-shirt shop, and ice cream parlor. Neon signs danced before his eyes. The din of voices and video games filled his head. He grew very worried. Where were his daughters?

Then he spotted the girls, far out on the sand. He breathed a sigh of relief. He walked out to them. There, unlike on the boardwalk, it was peaceful. The beach was deserted. Only the pounding surf and screaming gulls could be heard.

The girls waved to their dad and then ran up to him. They were surprised that he had come looking for them.

"We're sorry, Dad," Angela explained. "We had no idea it was so late. We finished shopping and came to the beach."

"After this we'll have to have more specific rules for going out alone," their father replied.

1. This story is set in a—
   A. mountain village.
   B. seaside town.
   C. big city.
   D. suburban mall.

2. This story takes place—
   F. in the present day.
   G. in the 1930s.
   H. a century ago.
   J. in the distant past.

3. What clue word signals a contrast in the fourth paragraph?
   A. then
   B. only
   C. there
   D. unlike

4. What is the writer contrasting in the fourth paragraph?
   F. Angela and Becky
   G. the boardwalk and the beach
   H. the mother and father
   J. the afternoon and the evening

5. As the setting changes from the boardwalk to the beach, the father's mood changes from—
   A. worried to angry.
   B. happy to sad.
   C. worried to relieved.
   D. angry to calm.

Notes for Home: Your child read a story and analyzed its setting and looked for comparisons and contrasts. *Home Activity:* Invite your child to compare and contrast two rooms in your home. Ask him or her to tell how these settings are alike and different.

Writing Across Texts

Directions: The story and illustrations in "The Night Alone" give details about many traditions of the Mohawk Indians. The selection "How the Sun Came" is a mythical explanation about how other traditions began. Complete the table by listing some of the traditions you read about.

Mohawk Indian Traditions
Mohawk Indians respect all things in nature, such as the moon.
1.
2.
3.
4.
5.
6.
7.
8.
9.
10.

Write a Caption

Look back at "The Night Alone" and "How the Sun Came." Think about the ways in which these stories connect to the theme "Traditions." Brainstorm a list of traditions that you read about in these stories. Then choose one tradition, illustrate it, and write a caption to go with it. Draw your illustration and write your caption on a separate sheet of paper.

© Scott Foresman 5

Notes for Home: Your child listed traditions based on a fiction story and a myth, illustrated a tradition, and wrote a caption to explain it. *Home Activity:* Talk with your child about traditions that are part of your culture. If you can, tell your child how each tradition began.

Grammar: Using Adjectives to Improve Sentences

Directions: Add one or more adjectives to improve each sentence. Write your new sentence on the line.

1. Leroy is standing in a line with skiers.

_____

2. He takes the ski lift to the top of a trail.

_____

3. At the top, the skier looks at the view.

_____

4. He loves to see the snow on the mountains.

_____

5. He takes a breath of air.

_____

Directions: Take out any unneeded adjectives in each sentence below. Write your new sentence on the line.

6. The high, steep slope is covered with fast, whooshing, graceful skiers.

_____

7. This is the first and only time Leroy has stood at this scary and challenging spot alone.

_____

8. His father, a good, experienced, and careful skier, has always been with him before.

_____

9. Leroy has worked for this big, special moment, but he feels scared, nervous, and shaky.

_____

10. Is he ready and able to ski down this steep, windy, difficult trail by himself?

_____

Notes for Home: Your child rewrote sentences, adding and taking away adjectives to make the sentences clearer. *Home Activity:* Ask your child to write a short description of a place he or she likes. Then help your child to add, take away, or change some of the adjectives.

Grammar: Comparative and Superlative Adjectives

Adjectives change form when they are used to make comparisons. Add the ending **-er** to the adjective when you are comparing two items. Add the ending **-est** to the adjective when you are comparing more than two items.

Joe is <u>tall</u>. Ed is <u>taller</u> than Joe. Al is <u>tallest</u> of all.

Sometimes you need to make spelling changes before adding **-er** or **-est.**

Dad felt <u>hungry</u>. Jay felt <u>hungrier</u>. I felt the <u>hungriest</u> of all.
Mia looks <u>slim</u>. Carol looks <u>slimmer</u>. Della looks the <u>slimmest</u> of all.

Longer adjectives use the words **more** or **most** to make comparisons. **More** is used to compare two things. **Most** is used to compare more than two. Do not use **more** or **most** with **-er** or **-est** endings.

Sue is <u>more</u> concerned than Bob. Kay is <u>most</u> concerned of all.

The adjectives **good** and **bad** have special comparative (two) and superlative (more than two) forms.

Walking is <u>good</u>. Skating is <u>better</u>. Swimming is <u>best</u> of all.
A cold is <u>bad</u>. The flu is <u>worse</u>. Pneumonia is <u>worst</u> of all.

Directions: Circle the correct adjective in ( ) to complete each sentence.

1. A cabin is (smaller/smallest) than a house.

2. A palace is the (larger/largest) home I have seen.

3. Many hotels are (bigger/biggest) than motels.

4. A tent is (better/best) than the cold, hard ground.

5. The purple and green house is the (worse/worst) looking house on the block.

Directions: Choose the correct form of the adjective in ( ) to complete each sentence. Write the adjective on the line.

_____ 6. A tepee is one of the (old) kinds of homes.

_____ 7. A cave may be (old) than a tepee.

_____ 8. Which is the (good) home of all?

_____ 9. Nothing is (good) than a snug log cabin!

_____ 10. Is a leaky tent (bad) than no tent at all?

Notes for Home: Your child used comparative and superlative adjectives to compare people and things. *Home Activity:* Ask your child to describe people, places, or things in your neighborhood, using adjectives that compare.

© Scott Foresman 5

Extra Practice

Grammar: Comparative and Superlative Adjectives

Directions: Circle the correct adjective in ( ) to complete each sentence.

1. Kim has the (most interesting/more interesting) type of home I have ever visited.

2. Her houseboat is much (neater/neatest) than any house on land.

3. Her view is the (more beautiful/most beautiful) I've ever seen.

4. A ride on a houseboat is not the (worse/worst) way to spend an afternoon.

5. In fact, it's the (nicer/nicest) ride I can imagine!

Directions: Use the correct form of the adjective in ( ) to complete each sentence. Write the adjective on the line.

_____ 6. What is the (good) home of all?

_____ 7. Is a cute little cottage by the sea the (pleasant)?

_____ 8. A cottage is (large) than a boat.

_____ 9. Some people feel that a boat is still (good) than a house ashore.

_____ 10. Kim's room is (dark) than mine.

_____ 11. My room is much (warm) than hers.

_____ 12. When it rains, my room stays (dry) than hers.

_____ 13. Kim thinks water is (nice) to live on than land!

_____ 14. She says sea air is the (fresh) you will find.

_____ 15. We both agree that her houseboat is the (cool) place we know!

Write a Description

Imagine that you could design your own "dream house." On a separate sheet of paper, describe what your home would look like. Use adjectives that compare.

Notes for Home: Your child used special forms of adjectives to compare people and things. *Home Activity:* Choose two members of your family. Ask your child to talk about how the two people are different from each other. Have your child use adjectives that compare.

Name _____

Grammar: Comparative and Superlative Adjectives

Victor   Mickey   Lou

Underline the adjective in each sentence.

1. Mickey is small.

2. Lou is smaller than Mickey.

3. Smallest of all is Victor.

Did you notice that the adjective **smaller** compared two things? Did you notice that the adjective **smallest** compared three things?

Use the **-er** form of an adjective to compare two persons, places, or things. Use the **-est** form of an adjective to compare three or more persons, places, or things. The spelling of some adjectives changes before **-er** or **-est** is added.

Directions: Complete each sentence by writing the correct form of the adjective in ( ).

1. My dog is _____ than your dog. (friendlier/friendliest)

2. That is the _____ joke in the world. (funnier/funniest)

3. Kansas is _____ than Arizona. (flatter/flattest)

4. Jetliners are _____ than helicopters. (bigger/biggest)

5. Whales are the _____ animals on earth. (heavier/heaviest)

6. Mercury is the _____ planet. (hotter/hottest)

Directions: Write the correct form of the adjective in ( ).

7. Truth is sometimes _____ than fiction. (strange)   _____

8. A hurricane is _____ than a blizzard. (rare)   _____

9. June was the _____ month of the year. (hot)   _____

10. Mount Everest is the _____ mountain in the world. (tall)   _____

11. China is a _____ country than India. (large)   _____

12. Mars is the _____ of all the other planets. (near)   _____

Notes for Home: Your child used adjectives that compare, such as *bigger* and *tallest*. **Home Activity:** Have your child compare fifth grade to first grade by writing sentences, using adjectives that compare.

Grammar: Comparative and Superlative Adjectives

Directions: Write the missing forms for each adjective below.

Adjective	Comparing Two	Comparing Three or More
1. fresh		
2.	drier	
3. wonderful		
4.		fattest
5. terrible		
6.	slimmer	
7.		nicest
8. bold		
9.		most intelligent
10.	lower	
11. trustworthy		
12.		most careful

Directions: Use the word in ( ) to write an adjective with **-er** or **-est** that completes each comparison.

13. In many places our air is _____ today than it was in the 1950s. (clean)

14. Is air _____ in cities than it is on farms? (warm)

15. Power plants use the _____ air filters of all. (large)

16. The monorail is a _____ form of transportation than the train. (new)

17. Are today's laws to control air pollution the _____ laws of all? (strict)

18. Which country produces the _____ level of air pollution? (high)

Write a Speech

On a separate sheet of paper, write a short speech about why it is important to keep our air and water clean. Use the **-er** and **-est** forms of adjectives in your sentences.

Notes for Home: Your child used the -er and -est forms of adjectives. *Home Activity:* With your child, take turns saying sentences with the -er and -est forms of adjectives. (For example: *A car is faster than a bicycle. An airplane is the fastest.*)

Word Study: Inflected Endings

When adding **-ed, -er,** or **-est** to words that end in a **consonant** and **y,** change the **y** to **i,** and then add **-ed.** For example, **fry** becomes **fried.**

When adding **-ed, -ing, -er,** or **-est** to words that end in a single consonant preceded by a single vowel, double the consonant and add the ending. For example, **hop** becomes **hopping. Thin** becomes **thinner.**

Directions: Add an ending to each word below. Write the new word on the line.

1. drop   +   -ing   =   _____

2. grab   +   -ing   =   _____

3. flat   +   -er   =   _____

4. big   +   -est   =   _____

5. cry   +   -ed   =   _____

6. pat   +   -ed   =   _____

Directions: Read the journal entry. Circle each word that ends in **-ed, -ing, -er,** or **-est.** Then write the base word for each circled word on the line.

Day 1

It is my first night alone in the woods. I'm worried. I tried to sleep, but I heard the strangest noises. I zipped and snapped all the tent flaps shut and buried my head in my pillow. But I'm still awake. I couldn't imagine a scarier place! I ran through the woods most of the day, only stopping twice to take a drink from my canteen. I'll be much happier when daylight comes.

7. _____

8. _____

9. _____

10. _____

11. _____

12. _____

13. _____

14. _____

15. _____

Notes for Home: Your child practiced changing *y* to *i* and doubling the final consonant when adding *-ed* and *-ing.* ***Home Activity:*** Read a short story with your child and find words with these endings. He or she can write the words with and without the endings.

Spelling: Adding -ed and -ing, -er and -est

Pretest Directions: Fold back the page along the dotted line. On the blanks, write the spelling words as they are dictated. When you have finished the test, unfold the page and check your words.

1._____
2._____
3._____
4._____
5._____
6._____
7._____
8._____
9._____
10._____
11._____
12._____
13._____
14._____
15._____
16._____
17._____
18._____
19._____
20._____

1. We **followed** the rules.

2. The chicks are **following** the hen.

3. This bag is **lighter** than the other.

4. You can carry the **lightest** box.

5. He **tried** to remain quiet.

6. I am **trying** to remember her.

7. Which of the two cats is **cuter**?

8. My neighbor had the **cutest** baby.

9. The children were very **excited**.

10. Fireworks can be **exciting**.

11. The teacher was **amused**.

12. The joke was very **amusing**.

13. Melons are **bigger** than oranges.

14. Sequoias are the **biggest** trees.

15. Are the presents all **wrapped**?

16. We need more **wrapping** paper.

17. We should have left **earlier**.

18. I need to catch the **earliest** flight.

19. Is math **easier** than science?

20. Do not give me the **easiest** job.

© Scott Foresman 5

Notes for Home: Your child took a pretest on adding *-ed, -ing, -er,* and *-est* to words. **Home Activity:** Help your child learn misspelled words before the final test. Dictate the word and have your child spell the word aloud for you or write it on paper.

Spelling: Adding -ed and -ing, -er and -est

Word List				
followed	tried	excited	bigger	earlier
following	trying	exciting	biggest	earliest
lighter	cuter	amused	wrapped	easier
lightest	cutest	amusing	wrapping	easiest

Directions: Choose the word from the box that is formed by adding **-er** or **-est** to each base word. Write the word on the correct line.

Base Word	Add -er	Add -est
big	1. _____	2. _____
cute	3. _____	4. _____
early	5. _____	6. _____
light	7. _____	8. _____
easy	9. _____	10. _____

Directions: Add **-ed** or **-ing** to the word in ( ) to form a word from the box and to complete each sentence. Write the word on the line.

_____ 11. Sarah is not very (excite) about tonight's sleepover.

_____ 12. She (try) spending the night at a friend's once before.

_____ 13. She started out thinking it was (excite) to be there.

_____ 14. An hour after the lights went out, Sarah was still (try) to sleep.

_____ 15. She (amuse) herself by counting the teddy bears on the wallpaper.

_____ 16. She started (follow) the teddy bears in her imagination.

_____ 17. She (wrap) herself tightly in her sleeping bag.

_____ 18. She (follow) her mother's advice to think sleepy thoughts.

_____ 19. Then she found herself (wrap) her arms around a big teddy bear.

_____ 20. Suddenly she woke up and knew she'd have an (amuse) story to tell about not sleeping!

Notes for Home: Your child spelled words that have *-ed, -ing, -er,* or *-est* endings. **Home Activity:** Think of base words that are regular verbs *(jump, play)* or adjectives *(soft, tall).* Have your child add *-ed* or *-ing* to the verbs and *-er* or *-est* to the adjectives to spell new words.

Spelling: Adding -ed and -ing, -er and -est

Directions: Proofread the letter. Find seven spelling mistakes.
Use the proofreading marks to correct each mistake.

≡	Make a capital.
/	Make a small letter.
∧	Add something.
ℐ	Take out something.
⊙	Add a period.
¶	Begin a new paragraph.

Dear Lucy,

    Yesterday I took my first airplane ride by myself. It was really exiting. I tryed to act very grown-up. Next to me was a lady with the cutest baby boy. The baby was all wraped up. I got to hold him. He felt lightter than a feather! Then he threw up on me. I pretended to be amuzed, but really it was gross. Folowing dinner was a movie. We arrived in Chicago half an hour earlier than expected. Flying is easer than I thought!

                    Your friend,

                    Karen

Spelling Tip

Words that end in -y

If a base word ends in a **consonant** and **y**, change the **y** to **i** before adding **-ed, -er,** or **-est.** Keep the **y** when adding **-ing.** For example: **try, tried, trying.**

Write a Letter

On a separate sheet of paper, write a letter Lucy might write back to Karen telling how she achieved something all by herself. Try to use at least six of your spelling words.

Word List

followed	amused
following	amusing
lighter	bigger
lightest	biggest
tried	wrapped
trying	wrapping
cuter	earlier
cutest	earliest
excited	easier
exciting	easiest

Notes for Home: Your child spelled words that end in *-ed, -ing, -er,* or *-est.* **Home Activity:** Look at video boxes, mail, or magazines to find words with these endings. Help figure out whether the spelling of the base word was changed before the ending was added.

Spelling: Adding -ed and -ing, -er and -est

REVIEW

Word List				
followed	tried	excited	bigger	earlier
following	trying	exciting	biggest	earliest
lighter	cuter	amused	wrapped	easier
lightest	cutest	amusing	wrapping	easiest

Directions: Choose the word from the box that is most opposite in meaning for each word below. Write the word on the line.

1. uglier _____
2. later _____
3. smaller _____
4. heavier _____
5. smallest _____

6. bored _____
7. led _____
8. harder _____
9. leading _____
10. hardest _____

Directions: Choose the word from the box that best completes each person's statement. Write the word on the line to the left.

_____ 11. Fast Food Worker: "Our food comes hot, _____ in foil, and ready to go."

_____ 12. Comedian: "Most people find me _____."

_____ 13. Child Actor: "Everyone says I have the _____ baby face."

_____ 14. News Photographer: "My work often takes me to _____ places."

_____ 15. Athlete: "I keep _____ to break records in my sport."

_____ 16. Store Clerk: "I'm always _____ presents for people."

_____ 17. School Bus Driver: "I have to be the _____ person awake at my house."

_____ 18. Jockey: "The _____ jockey on the fastest horse usually wins the race."

_____ 19. Politician: "I _____ my best to get elected."

_____ 20. Clown: "Are you _____ by my funny costume?"

Notes for Home: Your child spelled words that end in *-ed, -ing, -er,* or *-est.* **Home Activity:** Ask your child to explain why the base words of some spelling words were changed before an ending was added, such as *cute/cutest, big/bigger,* and *try/tried.*

Technology: Encyclopedia

Encyclopedias can be purchased on CD-ROMs or found on the Internet. The computer lets you search the entire encyclopedia for your topic using letters or a few key words. The welcome screen for an online encyclopedia might look like this:

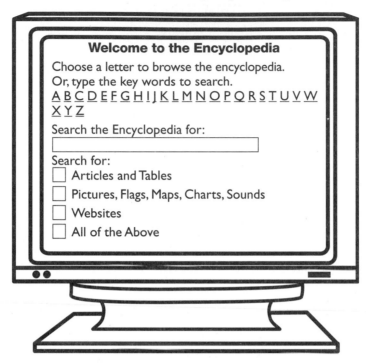

If you wanted an article about Native Americans, you could either type key words: Native AND Americans, or you could click on the letter *N*. Clicking on a letter will give you a list of articles about topics that begin with that letter.

© Scott Foresman 5

When you find an article about your topic, it will probably have links to other articles. The links will most likely be set in capital letters and underlined. Clicking on an underlined phrase will show you the other related articles.

Native American Art

The traditional arts of the indigenous native peoples of North America (see <u>NORTH AMERICA, INDIGENOUS PEOPLES OF</u>) were an important part of the everyday lives of Native Americans. Different arts were practiced in different regions. The cultures of the Eastern woodlands (see <u>IROQUOIS</u>) made pottery, baskets, beadwork, and <u>MASKS</u>. The Plains tribes (see <u>SIOUX</u>) used beads and quills to decorate hides. On the Northwest coast, native peoples used wood carving to make houses, large <u>CANOES</u>, and <u>TOTEM</u> poles. The <u>NAVAHO</u> of the Southwest had sophisticated techniques for making silver jewelry.

Directions: Use the sample computer screens to answer these questions.

1. What are two different ways to find an article about Native Americans using an online encyclopedia?

_____

2. In the second computer screen, what will you get if you click on *Nebraska?*

_____

3. In the first and second computer screens, what will you get if you click on the letter *B?*

_____

4. In the third computer screen, which link would you choose to see a related article about Native Americans who lived in the Eastern woodlands?

_____

5. Which links would you choose to find articles about the arts and crafts of the Northwest coast peoples?

_____

Notes for Home: Your child learned how to use an online encyclopedia. *Home Activity:* Ask your child to list possible key words to use to search for articles about native peoples in Alaska.

Family Times

Name_____

Summary

Ebonee Rose Leads Relay Team to Victory

Ebonee Rose, age 11, has been training with her team, the Gazelles, for the upcoming All-City Track Meet. In her diary, she records her activities, thoughts, and feelings leading up to the big race. In addition to daily workouts, Ebonee has to cope with a swollen ankle just eleven days before the race. Despite this obstacle, Ebonee manages to come through with her teammates to capture the winners' trophy.

Activity

Diaries Talk. Have your child describe Ebonee's diary entries. Then pretend you were a talking diary. What would you say to Ebonee about her thoughts and feelings?

Reading Skills

Context Clues

Context clues are words that help explain an unfamiliar word. For example, if you read "the smiling winner felt elated," you could figure out that *elated* means "very happy" from the context clues *smiling* and *winner*.

Context clues can come just before or after an unfamiliar word, or elsewhere in the story. Sometimes a context clue gives a word's meaning directly. In the sentence, "the team depended on its anchor, or final and fastest runner," the definition of *anchor* is given.

Activity

Visualize the Word. Pick out words from the vocabulary list on the next page. Perform pantomimes as visual context clues for each word. See if the other person can guess the word and give its meaning.

Family Times

Tested Vocabulary

Words to Know

Knowing the meanings of these words is important to reading "The Heart of a Runner." Practice using these words to learn their meanings.

ankle joint that connects a foot with a leg

athlete person skilled in sports or games requiring physical strength or agility

confident assured of oneself

overcame conquered an obstacle

relay race in which each member completes a part

responsible having the obligation to care for someone or something

sprint run at top speed for a short distance

Grammar

Adverbs

An **adverb** tells when, where, or how an action happens. To compare two actions, add -er to the adverb or use the word *more* before it. To compare three or more actions, add -est to the adverb or use the word *most* before it.

Ebonee ran <u>faster</u> than Marti.
Queenie ran <u>fastest</u> of all.

Ebonee went <u>more quickly</u> than Marti.
Queenie went <u>most quickly</u> of all.

Activity
Describe Actions. Have two or three people pantomime a similar action. Have other people watching describe the actions using adverbs. For example: **Dad turns <u>fast</u>, but Mom turns <u>faster</u> than Dad.**

Tested Spelling Words

Context Clues

- **Context clues** are words that can help you figure out a word that is unfamiliar to you.

- Look for specific clues by asking yourself questions like: "Does the sentence give a definition of the word or explain anything about it?"

Directions: Reread "Physical Fitness." Then complete the table. Use context clues to figure out the meaning of each word or phrase in the table.

Word or Phrase	Meaning
skills fitness	1.
agility	2.
balance	3.
coordination	4.
reaction time	5.

Notes for Home: Your child read an article and used context clues to figure out the meanings of unfamiliar words. **Home Activity:** Read a newspaper article with your child. Help your child use context clues to figure out the meanings of any unfamiliar words.

Vocabulary

Directions: Choose the word from the box that best matches each definition.
Write the word on the line.

_____ 1. joint that connects foot with leg

_____ 2. self-assured

_____ 3. conquered an obstacle

_____ 4. having the duty to take care of
someone or something

_____ 5. run a short way at top speed

Directions: Choose the word from the box that best matches each clue.
Write the word on the line.

_____ 6. It's a compound word and you'll feel good if you've done it.

_____ 7. It's what you call a person who is good at sports.

_____ 8. It's the kind of person you would want to have baby-sit your
little brother.

_____ 9. It's how you feel when you know you can do something well.

_____ 10. It's something you can do for a short while, but not for too
long.

Directions: Read the news story. Choose the word from the box that best
completes each sentence. Write the word on the matching numbered line
to the right.

┌──┐
│ **RUNNER SWEEPS STATE MEET**
│   The city has never seen an **11.** _____ like Aysha
│ Morgan. At Thursday's track competition, this young
│ unknown rose to stardom. Despite a sore **12.** _____, she
│ was able to **13.** _____ the 100-meter event in record time.
│ She also **14.** _____ an early setback to win the quarter
│ mile. Later, she led her team to victory by running the
│ fastest leg in the 400-meter **15.** _____. Sports fans, this is
│ a young woman to watch. Congratulations, Aysha!
└──┘

11. _____

12. _____

13. _____

14. _____

15. _____

Write a Description

Whom do you respect? On a separate sheet of paper, describe a person whom
you respect and tell why you respect him or her. Use as many vocabulary words
as you can in your description.

Notes for Home: Your child identified and used vocabulary words from "The Heart of a
Runner." ***Home Activity:*** With your child, write a story about an athlete your child admires.
Encourage your child to use as many of the vocabulary words as possible.

Context Clues

- **Context clues** are words that can help you figure out a word that is unfamiliar to you.

- Look for specific types of clues as you read. Context clues include synonyms, antonyms, definitions and explanations, examples, and descriptions.

Directions: Reread what happens in "The Heart of a Runner" when E.R. writes about the relay race. Then answer the questions below.

I have to tell you what an anchor is. An anchor is the final leg of a relay, the fastest runner. The anchor has to overcome any slowness of the other three runners and power on to the end. The lead runner, or lead-off, is the first leg of a relay team. That runner has to be superfast, and confident, too.

The runners in a relay depend on one another to be fast and not make mistakes. Like dropping one of the batons. I'm not mentioning any names, but you know who I mean!

Excerpt from RUNNING GIRL: THE DIARY OF EBONEE ROSE, copyright © 1997 by Sharon Bell Mathis, reprinted by permission of Harcourt Brace & Company.

1. What is an *anchor?*

_____

2. What kind of context clue helped you define *anchor?*

_____

3. Give the meaning of *leg* in the first paragraph and tell what clues you used to figure it out.

_____

_____

4. Define *lead-off* and tell what type of context clue you used to define it.

_____

_____

5. Go back to the story and find the terms *baton-passing* and *field event.* Use context clues to figure out their meanings. On a separate sheet of paper, write the meanings and tell what clues you used. Then use a dictionary to see if your definitions were correct.

© Scott Foresman 5

Notes for Home: Your child read a story and used context clues to define unfamiliar words. *Home Activity:* Read a challenging book with your child. Work together to use context clues to define words that are unfamiliar to your child.

Selection Test

Directions: Choose the best answer to each item. Mark the letter for the answer you have chosen.

Part 1: Vocabulary

Find the answer choice that means about the same as the underlined word in each sentence.

1. I hurt my <u>ankle</u>.
    A.   bone in the knee
    B.   part of the leg between the knee and hip
    C.   bottom of the foot
    D.   joint that connects the foot and leg

2. The other team looked <u>confident</u>.
    F.   unfriendly
    G.   full of energy
    H.   large
    J.   sure of themselves

3. Meghan is <u>responsible</u> for the picnic.
    A.   signed up to attend
    B.   having the duty to do something
    C.   trying to stop
    D.   curious about the reason for something

4. We watched Jeremy <u>sprint</u> down the sidewalk.
    F.   ride
    G.   walk slowly
    H.   run at top speed
    J.   hop

5. Alisha <u>overcame</u> her fears.
    A.   talked about for a long time
    B.   asked help for
    C.   got the better of; defeated
    D.   was ashamed of

6. The first event in the meet is a <u>relay</u>.
    F.   long jump
    G.   race in which each member of a team runs or swims for one part
    H.   race in which a runner must leap over a series of gates
    J.   event that involves throwing an object

7. My sister is a fine <u>athlete</u>.
    A.   person who is skilled in physical games
    B.   person who attends school
    C.   person who makes crafts
    D.   person who organizes others to get things done

Part 2: Comprehension

Use what you know about the story to answer each item.

8. Ebonee Rose was upset when she twisted her ankle because she—
    F.   knew her mother would be angry.
    G.   would be kicked off the team for the year.
    H.   did not want to miss the All-City meet.
    J.   was afraid to go to the hospital.

9. Which track star raced jackrabbits in the Mojave Desert as a child and won four medals in the 1988 Olympics?
    A.   Evelyn Ashford
    B.   Robin Campbell
    C.   Florence Griffith Joyner
    D.   Wyomia Tyus

GO ON

10. The story says, "Our fans in the <u>bleachers</u> are going crazy." <u>Bleachers</u> are—
    F.   long race tracks.
    G.   benches for people to sit on.
    H.   school buses.
    J.   large crowds of people.

11. In this story, Ebonee Rose seems to think of "Dee" as—
    A.   an opponent.
    B.   a pacer.
    C.   her mother.
    D.   a friend.

12. The story says, "The name MAIN TRACK CLUB will be <u>inscribed</u> on the brass plate beneath the golden track shoe." <u>Inscribed</u> means—
    F.   remembered.
    G.   written on stone or metal.
    H.   borrowed.
    J.   carried by the winners.

13. How do E.R.'s parents feel before the All-City Meet?
    A.   nervous but proud
    B.   worried but calm
    C.   bored and impatient
    D.   happy and relaxed

14. The author most likely included information about African American track stars in this story to—
    F.   show how heroes and heroines inspire young people.
    G.   make readers think that Ebonee Rose is a real person.
    H.   prove that Ebonee Rose is the greatest runner ever.
    J.   show that good athletes can also be good writers.

15. The author probably focuses more on E.R.'s experience in the relay instead of the long jump to show the importance of—
    A.   kindness.
    B.   teamwork.
    C.   independence.
    D.   trying new sports.

STOP

Context Clues

- **Context clues** are words that can help you figure out a word that is unfamiliar to you.

- Look for specific types of clues as you read. Context clues include synonyms, antonyms, definitions and explanations, examples, and descriptions.

Directions: Read the story below.

Dear Diary,

Today's the big day! My whole stomach feels like it's filled with butterflies! My coach says not to be <u>apprehensive</u>, but I can't help it. We're swimming against some really tough <u>opponents</u>. I hope the water isn't <u>frigid</u> the way it was last time. I don't swim as well in really cold water. We always get together before a meet, so we're going to <u>assemble</u> today at noon to go over strategy. If I <u>prevail</u> in my event, I'll go on to the finals. If I don't, I'll practice harder and try again next year. I hope I win!

Directions: Complete the table. Write a definition for each underlined word. Show how you arrived at the definition by filling in context clues from the story.

Unfamiliar Word	Definition	Context Clue
apprehensive	1.	2.
opponents	3.	4.
frigid	5.	6.
assemble	7.	8.
prevail	9.	10.

Notes for Home: Your child read a story and used context clues to define unfamiliar words. *Home Activity:* Read a newspaper article with your child and work together to use context clues to define new words. Check your definitions in a dictionary.

Name _____

Author's Viewpoint

REVIEW

Directions: Read the passage. Then read each question about the passage. Choose the best answer to each question. Mark the letter for the answer you have chosen.

Run for Your Life

Couch potatoes of the world, listen carefully. There's a very good chance that you are ruining your health sitting right there on the couch. Throw down those television remote controls and lace up your sneakers! It's time to get moving!

As a whole, American children and young people are not getting nearly enough exercise. For American adults, the situation is even worse. Many Americans do not exercise on a regular basis. (Getting up to go to the refrigerator for a soda doesn't count!)

An inactive lifestyle is dangerous at any age. It puts a person at higher risk for serious health problems. Heart disease, diabetes, and other serious diseases become more likely for people who are not active.

How can you get on the road to good health? Start by getting some regular exercise. You might choose running, jogging, walking, bicycling, gardening, or aerobics. They are all good ways to get "heart smart"! You might actually find out that you enjoy getting healthier by exercising.

1. The first paragraph suggests the author will try to—
   A. describe.
   B. explain.
   C. tell a story.
   D. persuade.

2. Which of the following words reveals how the author feels about the subject of this article?
   F. couch potatoes
   G. remote controls
   H. children
   J. young people

3. The author's opening implies that—
   A. people should never watch television.
   B. people who watch television are more relaxed.
   C. people who watch too much television don't exercise enough.
   D. couch potatoes have diabetes.

4. In this article the author—
   F. criticizes all Americans.
   G. links exercise and health.
   H. describes aerobic exercises that are dangerous.
   J. recommends consulting a doctor as soon as possible.

5. The author is strongly—
   A. in favor of regular exercise.
   B. in favor of lace-up sneakers.
   C. in favor of an inactive lifestyle.
   D. against exercise.

© Scott Foresman 5

Notes for Home: Your child read a passage and identified the author's viewpoint. *Home Activity:* Read an editorial or a letter to the editor with your child. Together, identify the author's viewpoint and look at how well the author's opinions are supported.

Writing Across Texts

Directions: Think about Ebonee Rose from "The Heart of a Runner" and Carlie Huberman from "Finding a Way to Win." Both girls compete in sports they love. How do their sports compare? Fill in the chart below to compare and contrast the two sports.

	Track and Field	**Orienteering**
Skills Needed	1.	2.
Tools Used	3.	4.
Steps Involved in a Race	5.	6.
Possible Obstacles to Overcome	7.	8.
The Goal	9.	10.

Write a Compare and Contrast Paragraph

Use the information in the chart above to write a paragraph comparing and contrasting the sports of track and field and orienteering. Tell the one in which you would rather participate. Write your paragraph on a separate sheet of paper.

Notes for Home: Your child compared and contrasted the information from two selections. *Home Activity:* As you read stories or articles with your child, discuss how the ideas are presented and how they compare with information obtained from other sources.

Grammar: Comparative and Superlative Adjectives

Directions: Complete the table below, using **-er**, **-est**, **more**, or **most**.

Adjective	Comparative Adjectives	Superlative Adjectives
friendly	1.	2.
safe	3.	4.
difficult	5.	6.
thin	7.	8.
fresh	9.	10.

Directions: Use the correct form of the adjective in ( ) to complete each sentence. Write the comparative or superlative adjective on the line.

_____ 11. In 1960, Wilma Rudolph became the (fast) woman in the world.

_____ 12. No athlete in the 1960 Olympics was (popular) than this young runner.

_____ 13. Track, or foot racing, is the (old) Olympic sport.

_____ 14. Most people have had (easy) lives than Wilma Rudolph.

_____ 15. She was a sickly and poor child, perhaps the (skinny) child in Clarksville, Tennessee.

_____ 16. However, as she grew (big), she showed a great talent for running.

_____ 17. At 16, she competed in the 1956 Olympics against (experienced) runners.

_____ 18. In a (late) Olympic competition, in 1960, she became a gold-medal champion.

_____ 19. After winning three gold medals, she was the (famous) Olympic star in the world.

_____ 20. One of her (thrilling) rewards was being invited to the White House to meet President John F. Kennedy.

Notes for Home: Your child used special forms of adjectives to compare two or more people, places, and things. *Home Activity:* Challenge your child to find comparative and superlative adjectives in a book or magazine and explain why each form is used.

Grammar: Adverbs

Adverbs tell more about verbs. An adverb tells when, where, or how an action happens. Many adverbs that tell how end in **-ly.**

The runners ran <u>quickly</u>. (how)
The time <u>soon</u> passed. (when)
The race ended <u>there</u>. (where)

Like adjectives, adverbs change form when they are used to make comparisons.

Add **-er** to an adverb when the actions of two people are being compared. This is called the **comparative form** of the adverb.

Comparative: I found a good viewing spot <u>sooner</u> than one of my cousins did.

Add **-est** when the actions of three or more people are being compared. This is called the **superlative form** of the adverb.

Superlative: Which group in that crowd had waited there <u>longest</u>?

Use **more** or **most,** instead of **-er** or **-est,** with most adverbs that end in **-ly.** Don't use **more** or **most** with **-er** and **-est** endings.

Comparative: Tyrone ran more wearily than Reggie.

Superlative: Roger ran the most wearily as the four men crossed the finish line.

Directions: Underline the adverb or adverbs in each sentence.

1. Dave runs in the New York City Marathon yearly.
2. Runners wait anxiously on the Verrazano Narrows Bridge.
3. A starter's gun loudly sounds at the start of the race.
4. Runners move hard and fast along the road.
5. They race steadily for 26.2 miles.

Directions: Choose the correct form of the adverb in ( ) to complete each sentence. Write the adverb on the line.

_____ 6. Runners' relatives cheer (more excitedly/most excitedly) of all the onlookers.

_____ 7. At the start, the inexperienced runners sometimes go (faster/fastest) than the experienced ones do.

_____ 8. Some runners wave (more cheerfully/most cheerfully) than others to spectators along the way.

_____ 9. Of all Dave's family members, his little niece took photos of the race (more successfully/most successfully).

_____ 10. At the finish line, no runner grins (more triumphantly/most triumphantly) than Dave.

Notes for Home: Your child identified adverbs—words that tell when, where, or how an action happens. ***Home Activity:*** Watch a show on television together. Ask your child to use adverbs to describe the action that he or she sees.

Grammar: Adverbs

Directions: Underline the adverb in each sentence. Write whether it tells **how, when,** or **where** on the line.

_____ **1.** Many people jog daily.

_____ **2.** They move slowly along a path.

_____ **3.** They hardly notice the passing time.

_____ **4.** Look at the joggers there.

_____ **5.** They started jogging early this morning.

Directions: Write an adverb on the line to the left to complete each sentence.

_____ **6.** Joggers run _____ on the track.

_____ **7.** Their feet _____ hit the dirt.

_____ **8.** Some joggers _____ wear headsets.

_____ **9.** Music plays _____ in their ears.

_____ **10.** The time passes _____ on the track.

Directions: Add **-er, -est, more,** or **most** to the adverb in ( ) to complete each sentence. Write the comparative or superlative form of the adverb on the line to the left.

_____ **11.** Certain older joggers exercise _____ than younger ones do. (long)

_____ **12.** Young joggers with high energy levels may run _____ than other joggers. (quickly)

_____ **13.** College students with eight o'clock classes hurry away _____ of all. (fast)

_____ **14.** Now that I'm learning to run, I watch all these joggers _____ than ever before. (closely)

_____ **15.** Someday I hope to run _____ than I do now. (smoothly)

Write Instructions

Imagine that you are a gym teacher giving instructions on how to exercise. On a separate sheet of paper, write the instructions. Use at least four adverbs in your instructions.

Notes for Home: Your child identified adverbs, words that describe verbs. *Home Activity:* Look at sentences in a book or newspaper with your child. Ask him or her to point out the adverbs. Discuss whether an adverb tells how, when, or where an action happens.

Grammar: Adverbs

> Read each pair of sentences. Circle the adverb that was added to the second sentence in each pair.
>
> 1. The reporter told us about a circus.
>
>   The reporter excitedly told us about a circus.
>
> 2. The children waited.
>
>   The children waited more patiently than their parents.

> A word that tells more about a verb is an **adverb.** Each adverb modifies a verb by telling **how, when,** or **where.** Many adverbs end in **-ly.** Adverbs have forms that are used to compare actions. Use the **-er** and **-est** forms, or **more** and **most,** to compare actions. The adverbs **well** and **badly** have special forms that show comparison.

Directions: Each verb is underlined. Write the adverb that tells about the verb.

1. The lion <u>roared</u> fiercely. _____

2. The circus vans <u>arrived</u> yesterday. _____

3. The first jumper <u>leaped</u> higher than that one. _____

4. The activity <u>stopped</u> suddenly. _____

5. Maria <u>started</u> more quickly than Harry. _____

6. Kim <u>runs</u> more gracefully than Kelly. _____

7. Workers <u>ran</u> rapidly toward the tent. _____

Directions: Write an adverb from the box to complete each sentence. The word in ( ) is a clue to the adverb.

often	carefully	most vigorously	more slowly	inside

8. Jim exercises the _____ of all my friends. (How?)

9. Violet runs _____ than Jim. (How?)

10. The lions snarled, growled, and roared _____. (When?)

11. The lion tamer _____ moved among the six lions. (How?)

 Notes for Home: Your child identified and wrote adverbs in sentences. *Home Activity:* Talk with your child about a book he or she is reading. Discuss characters' choices and behaviors. Challenge your child to describe characters' actions in detail, using adverbs.

Grammar: Adverbs

Directions: Circle the adverb that tells more about the underlined verb.

1. The large white and orange kite <u>flew</u> gracefully.

2. The wind <u>blew</u> harder than yesterday.

3. The family members carefully <u>constructed</u> the kite.

4. Kite builders often <u>enter</u> various contests.

5. Many curious and enthusiastic spectators <u>come</u> here.

6. Children <u>watched</u> the kites most excitedly of all.

7. The strong wind soon <u>became</u> a gentle breeze.

Directions: Rewrite each sentence below. Use the correct form of the word in ( ) to complete each sentence.

8. Most flowers grow (well) of all in full sun.

_____

9. Our new kite with the long tail flew (beautiful) through the sky.

_____

_____

10. Two large kites crashed (wild) in this pond.

_____

11. The wind damaged my flowers (bad) than the rain did.

_____

_____

Write Song Lyrics

Think about what it might feel like to be a kite flying through the air on a warm, breezy day. Write song lyrics from the point of view of a kite. Include at least four adverbs in your lyrics.

Notes for Home: Your child identified and wrote adverbs in sentences. *Home Activity:* Have your child create a comic strip to illustrate something he or she has seen or done today. Challenge him or her to use adverbs in captions in the comic strip.

Phonics: Schwa Sound (Within Word)

Directions: The **schwa sound** is an indistinct vowel sound heard in unstressed syllables. For example, the **a** in **ago,** the **o** in **complete,** and the **e** in **agent** are all schwa sounds. Read each sentence. Say each underlined word aloud. Write each underlined word on the line and circle the syllable that has the **schwa sound.**

_____ 1. In most cultures, people <u>compete</u> in races.

_____ 2. For <u>today's</u> race, there are more runners than usual.

_____ 3. Before the race, runners stretch and <u>exercise</u> their legs.

_____ 4. They know that it isn't wise to run on a full <u>stomach</u>.

_____ 5. Many runners feel <u>nervous</u> before a big race.

_____ 6. One athlete wiped her face with her lucky <u>handkerchief</u>.

_____ 7. She was hoping for a big <u>victory</u>.

_____ 8. However, in order to win, she must <u>overcome</u> her fears.

_____ 9. She knows she has a <u>difficult</u> race ahead of her.

_____ 10. Many people <u>identify</u> with the runner's fears.

Directions: Each word below has two **schwa sounds.** Circle the **schwa sounds** in each word.

11. different	16. emigrant	21. orchestra
12. tolerance	17. gelatin	22. passable
13. confident	18. imitation	23. president
14. together	19. literally	24. consider
15. responsibility	20. nitrogen	25. singular

Notes for Home: Your child identified the schwa sound. *Home Activity:* Read an article with your child. Ask your child to write down words that might have the schwa sound. Check the words in a dictionary. The symbol for the schwa sound looks like an upside down *e*.

Spelling: Vowels with No Sound Clues

Pretest

Pretest Directions: Fold back the page along the dotted line. On the blanks, write the spelling words as they are dictated. When you have finished the test, unfold the page and check your words.

1._____
2._____
3._____
4._____
5._____
6._____
7._____
8._____
9._____
10._____
11._____
12._____
13._____
14._____
15._____
16._____
17._____
18._____
19._____
20._____

1. The store's **manager** helped us.
2. We will elect a class **president**.
3. There is a **different** way.
4. What a **terrible** storm!
5. I **finally** finished the book.
6. This is **really** the place.
7. Are you **supposed** to do that?
8. There will **probably** be more.
9. **California** is a populous state.
10. She **especially** likes pears.
11. Don't lose your **balance**.
12. There was a **constant** noise.
13. She proved herself **innocent**.
14. I did not **realize** it was so far.
15. This is a wonderful **opportunity**.
16. Cars **pollute** the air.
17. The **prisoner** was in jail.
18. We will **celebrate** your birthday.
19. We buy milk at the **grocery** store.
20. The **elevator** does not work.

© Scott Foresman 5

Notes for Home: Your child took a pretest on words whose vowel sounds have no sound clues. *Home Activity:* Help your child learn misspelled words before the final test. Have your child divide misspelled words into parts (such as syllables) and concentrate on each part.

Spelling: Vowels with No Sound Clues

Word List				
manager	finally	California	innocent	prisoner
president	really	especially	realize	celebrate
different	supposed	balance	opportunity	grocery
terrible	probably	constant	pollute	elevator

Directions: Choose the three-syllable words from the box. Write the words in in alphabetical order. Draw lines between syllables.

1. _____   7. _____

2. _____   8. _____

3. _____   9. _____

4. _____   10. _____

5. _____   11. _____

6. _____   12. _____

Directions: Choose the word from the box that best matches each clue. Write the word on the line.

_____ **13.** You ride one of these to get to the top of a building.

_____ **14.** You do this if you throw a piece of trash in the river.

_____ **15.** This means almost the same as "chance."

_____ **16.** This is something that stays the same without changing.

_____ **17.** A gymnast needs to have this if she doesn't want to fall.

_____ **18.** This is a large state along the western coast of the United States.

_____ **19.** This means almost the same as "expected" or "required."

_____ **20.** You might use this word instead of *very* to show that something is special.

Notes for Home: Your child spelled words with unstressed vowel sounds that give no clue to their spelling, such as *grocery*. **Home Activity:** On a sheet of paper, write the consonants of each spelling word and leave blanks for the vowels. Challenge your child to fill in the vowels.

Proofread and Write

Spelling: Vowels with No Sound Clues

Directions: Proofread the student announcement. Find six misspelled words.
Use the proofreading marks to correct each mistake.

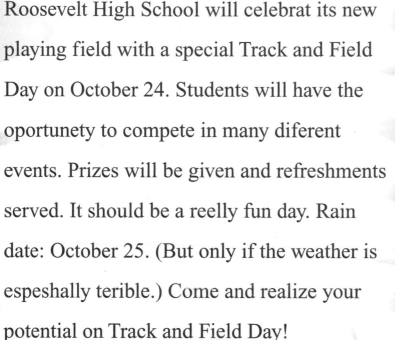

Roosevelt High School will celebrat its new
playing field with a special Track and Field
Day on October 24. Students will have the
oportunety to compete in many diferent
events. Prizes will be given and refreshments
served. It should be a reelly fun day. Rain
date: October 25. (But only if the weather is
espeshally terible.) Come and realize your
potential on Track and Field Day!

≡	Make a capital.
/	Make a small letter.
∧	Add something.
꒕	Take out something.
⊙	Add a period.
¶	Begin a new paragraph.

Spelling Tip

Spelling schwa
Sometimes knowing a
base word can help you
remember how to spell
the schwa sound, the
unstressed vowel sound
that gives no clue to its
spelling. Example:
Something that **diff*e*rs**
is **diff*e*rent.**

Word List

manager	really	balance	pollute
president	supposed	constant	prisoner
different	probably	innocent	celebrate
terrible	California	realize	grocery
finally	especially	opportunity	elevator

Write an Announcement

On a separate sheet of paper, write an announcement for
a real or imaginary event. Try to use at least five of your
spelling words.

Notes for Home: Your child spelled words with unstressed vowel sounds that give no clue to
their spelling, such as *grocery*. **Home Activity:** Write each spelling word in a list, misspelling
several words. Have your child check and correct the list.

© Scott Foresman 5

Name _____

Spelling: Vowels with No Sound Clues

Word List				
manager	finally	California	innocent	prisoner
president	really	especially	realize	celebrate
different	supposed	balance	opportunity	grocery
terrible	probably	constant	pollute	elevator

Directions: Choose the word from the box that best completes each statement. Write the word on the line to the left.

_____ 1. *City* is to *Los Angeles* as *state* is to _____.

_____ 2. *Hot* is to *cold* as *guilty* is to _____.

_____ 3. *Castle* is to *king* as *White House* is to _____.

_____ 4. *Automobile* is to *car* as *market* is to _____.

_____ 5. *Big* is to *little* as *same* is to _____.

_____ 6. *Cage* is to *bird* as *jail* is to _____.

_____ 7. *Child* is to *parent* as *worker* is to _____.

_____ 8. *Sad* is to *mourn* as *happy* is to _____.

_____ 9. *Build* is to *destroy* as *clean* is to _____.

_____ 10. *Sure* is to *certain* as *awful* is to _____.

_____ 11. *Unequal* is to *equal* as *imbalance* is to _____.

_____ 12. *Usual* is to *usually* as *final* is to _____.

Directions: Choose the word from the box that best replaces the underlined word or words. Write the word on the line.

_____ 13. You are <u>required</u> to run every day when in training.

_____ 14. If the weather is <u>always the same</u>, you can run outdoors daily.

_____ 15. Dedicated runners take every <u>good chance</u> to run.

_____ 16. Skip riding the <u>mechanical car that lifts</u> and take the stairs.

_____ 17. People don't <u>understand</u> how important proper nutrition is.

_____ 18. Eating right is <u>actually</u> just as important as working out.

_____ 19. It is <u>particularly</u> important to avoid foods that are high in fat.

_____ 20. If you eat right and train hard, you will <u>most likely</u> succeed.

Notes for Home: Your child spelled words with unstressed vowel sounds that give no clue to their spelling, such as *grocery*. **Home Activity:** Write each word on an index card. Draw a card, read it aloud, and have your child spell it. Switch roles and repeat.

Organize and Present Information/Draw Conclusions

As you read, take notes about important information. You can use your notes to help you **organize information** for a report and to help you **present information** to others. You can also use your notes to help you **draw conclusions** about the information by telling what it means.

Directions: Suppose you were planning a research report. Use the notes shown to answer the questions on the next page.

Track and field events involve running, walking, jumping, and throwing.

Some athletes are good at other events but not at the track and field events. Other athletes excel in track and field as well as other sports.

Older outdoor tracks are dirt or cinders. Newer ones use a waterproof synthetic surface. Indoor tracks are a wooden or synthetic surface with banked turns.

Track and field events of the summer Olympic Games include: Men's—runs of 100, 200, 400, 800, 1500, 5000, and 10,000 meters; hurdles of 100 and 400 meters; relays of 400 and 1600 meters; 3000-meter steeplechase; walks of 20 and 50 meters; marathon; high, long, and triple jump; discus, hammer, and javelin throw; pole vault; 16-pound shot put; and decathlon. Women's—runs of 100, 200, 400, 800, 1500, 3000, 5000, and 10,000 meters; hurdles of 100 and 400 meters; relays of 400 and 1600 meters; 10-kilometer walk; marathon; high, long, and triple jump; discus and javelin throw; 8-pound, 13-ounce shot put; and heptathlon.

The first Olympic games in Greece took place in 776 B.C. The only event was a foot race—the first competitive track and field event.

The Olympic records for men's track and field go back to 1896. The women's records are from 1928.

© Scott Foresman 5

The first U.S. woman to win an Olympic track and field event was Elizabeth Robinson in 1928 (the first year of the records). In 1896, the first year of the men's records, there were six Olympic winners in track and field from the United States—Thomas Burke, Thomas Curtis, Ellery Clark, James Connolly, Robert Garrett, and William Hoyt.

In the decathlon, heptathlon, and pentathlon, the athletes compete in several different events over a period of time.

Jackie Joyner-Kersee holds the heptathlon record with 7,215 points, set in 1988.

1. The title of your report will give the main idea. What title will you give your report?

_____

2. The information in the notes came from several different sources, but the notetaker made the mistake of not listing the sources. What reference sources could you use to verify the information in the notes and add to it?

_____

_____

3. If you wanted to present the information about the different Olympic track and field events for men and women, how might you organize this information so it is easier for readers to understand and compare?

_____

_____

_____

4. Think of things that might make your report interesting to hear and see, such as videotapes, audiotapes, graphic organizers, drawings, or posters. What might you use in your report?

_____

_____

5. Why will taking good notes as you read help you organize and present information and then draw conclusions about it? Will you use every note you wrote in your report? Explain.

_____

_____

_____

Notes for Home: Your child described how information might be organized and presented for a report. *Home Activity:* Together with your child, make a poster using information from the notes shown.

Research and Study Skills: Organize and Present Information/Draw Conclusions **427**

Family Times

Name_____

Summary

Zach and Grandfather Create a Memory Box

When Zach visits his grandparents for three weeks in the summer, he learns the sad news that Gramps is in the first stages of Alzheimer's Disease. Gramps suggests that he and Zach create a Memory Box. The two fill it with photos and other items that will always remind Zach of their good times together. Now prepared for future changes in his grandfather, Zach cherishes his Memory Box dearly.

Reading Skills

Author's Purpose

The **author's purpose** is the reason or reasons an author has for writing. Four common purposes are to entertain, to inform, to persuade, and to express. The writer of *The Memory Box* wrote to express strong feelings about a family relationship. She also wrote to inform readers about Alzheimer's Disease.

Authors usually don't state their purpose for writing. However, you can figure it out by paying close attention to the details being presented. Knowing an author's purpose can help you decide how to approach a story or article you intend to read.

Activity
Make a Memory Box. Have your child describe the items that Zach and Gramps put in the box. Then create a Memory Box that includes similar types of items.

Activity
Create a Newspaper. Imagine you were publishing your own newspaper. Talk about the sections you would include, and identify the purpose of each. Then make a Table of Contents for your newspaper.

Family Times

Tested Vocabulary

Words to Know

Knowing the meanings of these words is important to reading *The Memory Box*. Practice using these words to learn their meanings.

recall remember

reel draw in by winding

sheath case or covering for a knife

souvenirs keepsakes; items that serve as a reminder

squished pressed out something soft and wet

traditions customs that are handed down from one generation to another, such as from parents to children

Grammar

Using Adverbs to Improve Sentences

An **adverb** is a word that describes an action. By adding adverbs to sentences, you can make writing more interesting and its meaning clearer. Notice how adverbs improve these sentences:

Gramps walked through the woods.
Gramps walked absent-mindedly through the woods.

Gramps and Zach talked.
Gramps and Zach talked softly.

Activity

Add an Adverb. Have someone say a simple sentence, such as: **I read.** Then take turns adding adverbs to make the sentence clearer or more interesting, such as: **I read carefully.**

Tested Spelling Words

_____ _____ _____ _____

_____ _____ _____ _____

_____ _____ _____ _____

_____ _____ _____ _____

© Scott Foresman 5

Author's Purpose

- An **author's purpose** is the reason or reasons an author has for writing.
- Authors don't usually state a purpose so it helps to remember that the four common purposes for writing are to persuade, inform, entertain, and express.

Directions: Reread "Your Life Remembered." Then complete the web. Write the author's purpose or purposes in the middle. In the outer ovals, write words or phrases from the article that helped you identify the purpose or purposes.

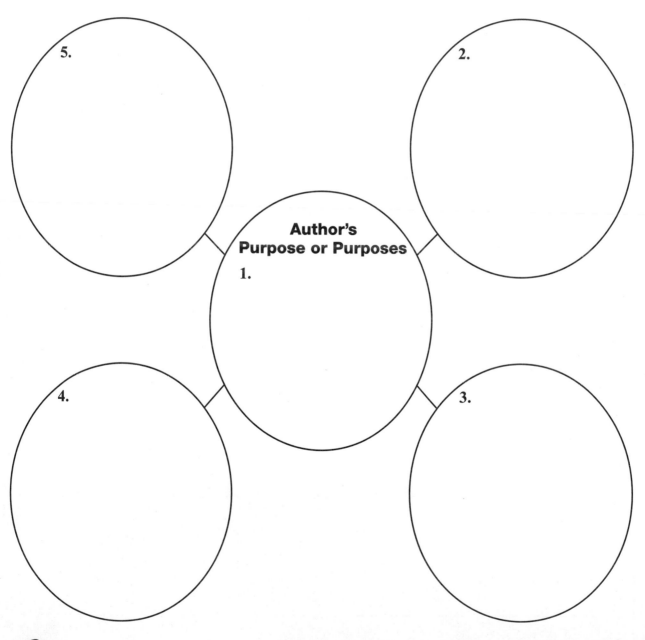

5.

2.

Author's Purpose or Purposes

1.

4.

3.

Notes for Home: Your child read an article and identified the author's purpose. *Home Activity:* Look through a magazine with your child. Invite your child to identify the author's purpose for various kinds of writing, such as editorials, poems, profiles, how-to articles, ads, or cartoons.

Vocabulary

Directions: Choose the word from the box that best completes each statement.
Write the word on the line to the left.

_____ 1. *Inflated* is to *blew up* as *flattened* is to
_____.

_____ 2. *Journals* are to *diaries* as *keepsakes* are to
_____.

_____ 3. *Think* is to *act* as *forget* is to _____.

_____ 4. *Hand* is to *glove* as *knife* is to _____.

_____ 5. *Throw* is to *catch* as *cast* is to _____.

```
+------------------------+
|        Check           |
|      the Words         |
|      You Know          |
|                        |
|  __ recall             |
|  __ reel               |
|  __ sheath             |
|  __ souvenirs          |
|  __ squished           |
|  __ traditions         |
+------------------------+
```

Directions: Choose the word from the box that best matches each clue.
Write the word in the puzzle.

Down

6. to draw in by winding
7. keepsakes
8. case or covering for a
   knife

Across

9. remember
10. beliefs and customs
    handed down from
    parents to children

Write a Letter

On a separate sheet of paper, write a thank-you
letter to a family member for all the things he or she
has done for you. Describe your good memories.
Use as many vocabulary words as you can in your letter.

 Notes for Home: Your child identified and used vocabulary words in *The Memory Box*. **Home
Activity:** Invite your child to draw a picture for at least three vocabulary words. Work together
to write sentences under the pictures that use the vocabulary words.

© Scott Foresman 5

Author's Purpose

- An **author's purpose** is the reason or reasons an author has for writing. Sometimes an author has more than one reason for writing.

- Four common purposes for writing are to persuade (convince), to inform (explain something), to entertain (amuse), or to express (describe something to help you see or feel a scene).

Directions: Reread what happens in *The Memory Box* after Zach's first dinner with Gramps and Gram. Then answer the questions below.

After dinner, we dragged our fish-full bellies to the porch to watch the sun slip into the lake. Crickets fiddled and owls hoo-ooted, but the rest of the world was quiet. All except Gram and Gramps and me in our rickety rockers on the wooden porch.

"Hmm-mmmm-m." Gramps was settling in, getting ready for another true tale. He's a great storyteller. Gram thinks so, I know, because she always puts down her cross-stitch when he begins.

THE MEMORY BOX by Mary Bahr. Text copyright © 1992 by Mary Bahr.
Excerpt reprinted by permission of Albert Whitman & Company.

1. What is happening in this scene?

_____

_____

2. How do you think Zach feels when he and Gram and Gramps are on the porch?

_____

3. What are some of the unusual words and phrases the author uses in writing this part of the story?

_____

4. What do you think is the author's purpose for writing this scene? Explain what makes you think so.

_____

_____

5. On a separate sheet of paper, tell what you think is the author's reason (or reasons) for writing *The Memory Box*. Support your answer with examples from the story.

Notes for Home: Your child read a story and identified the author's purpose for writing. ***Home Activity:*** Discuss each of the four common purposes for writing described above. Name a favorite book, story, or article that is an example of each purpose.

Selection Test

Directions: Choose the best answer to each item. Mark the letter for the answer you have chosen.

Part 1: Vocabulary

Find the answer choice that means about the same as the underlined word in each sentence.

1. Mariah put her <u>souvenirs</u> in a box.
   A. rings meant to be worn
   B. food for a light meal
   C. things that bring back memories
   D. important papers

2. I <u>recall</u> a trip to Niagara Falls.
   F. remember
   G. plan
   H. photograph
   J. describe

3. What <u>traditions</u> does your family have?
   A. pets
   B. silly names
   C. valuable objects kept for a long time
   D. beliefs and customs handed down through time

4. The baby happily <u>squished</u> the chocolate pudding.
   F. pressed something soft and wet
   G. licked something cold
   H. pointed at something far away
   J. grabbed something hard

5. It was difficult to <u>reel</u> in the kite.
   A. draw in by winding
   B. pack up
   C. sew together
   D. put in a certain order

6. Put it in the <u>sheath</u>.
   F. drawer
   G. case or covering
   H. envelope
   J. trash bag or can

Part 2: Comprehension

Use what you know about the story to answer each item.

7. What do Zach and Gramps do the first day of Zach's visit?
   A. take a hike
   B. go fishing
   C. build a box
   D. cook a meal together

8. From whose point of view is this story told?
   F. Zach's
   G. Gramps's
   H. Gram's
   J. Francie's

9. How does Zach react when Gramps says, "No matter what happens to the old person, the memories are saved forever"?
   A. He is happy to know he will always have memories of Gramps.
   B. He is bored that he will have to listen to more old stories.
   C. He realizes that Gramps has Alzheimer's.
   D. He is confused and worried that something is wrong.

GO ON

10. Which of these events happens first?
    F. Gramps gets lost.
    G. Zach sees Gramps talking to someone who is not there.
    H. Zach wonders why Gramps has not shaved.
    J. Gramps gives Zach the special knife.

11. Why does Gramps think that Zach's mom is "going to hurt"?
    A. Zach will not spend any more summers with Gram and Gramps.
    B. She will not like how Zach has changed.
    C. Zach has decided to live with Gram and Gramps instead of with his mom.
    D. She will feel sad to see Gramps when his memory is gone.

12. The author's main purpose in this story is to—
    F. entertain the reader with funny tales about a forgetful man.
    G. persuade kids to spend summers with their grandparents.
    H. express what it feels like for a family to deal with Alzheimer's.
    J. inform people about the causes of memory loss.

13. When Zach finally gets the knife he wanted, he realizes that—
    A. other things are more important than having a knife.
    B. he would rather have a newer and more valuable knife.
    C. he will have to return the knife to Gram.
    D. he will never go fishing again.

14. A "memory-box day" is best described as something that—
    F. happens when a person is alone.
    G. two people want to remember sharing with each other.
    H. happens when a man or woman gets very old.
    J. causes worry for everyone in a family.

15. What does the ending of this story suggest about Zach's view of life?
    A. He accepts things as they are.
    B. He does not take responsibility for himself.
    C. He always sees the worst in everything.
    D. He is too hopeful most of the time.

STOP

Author's Purpose

- An **author's purpose** is the reason or reasons an author has for writing. Sometimes an author has more than one reason for writing.

- Four common purposes for writing are to persuade (convince), to inform (explain something), to entertain (amuse), or to express (describe something to help you see or feel a scene.)

Directions: Read each passage below.

1. I remember staying in the water until my teeth chattered. Then my aunt would wrap me in a sun-warmed towel and give me an ice pop. I loved its cold, sweet taste on my tongue.

2. Finding a cure for Alzheimer's disease is the most important task facing modern medicine. The Alzheimer's Research Fund supports this great work. We need your generous contribution.

3. Memory is the storing of learned information and the ability to recall that which has been stored information. There are two kinds of memory: short-term memory and long-term memory.

4. I remember everything that's ever happened to me, every single thing. Did I ever tell you about the time I, uh... I, uh... uh ... Wait a minute. Hold on. It'll come to me.

5. The word *memoir* is French for "memory." In literature, a memoir may take many forms. It can be a biography, an autobiography, or an account of important events.

Directions: Complete each box. Write whether the purpose of each passage is to persuade, inform, entertain, or express. Give an explanation for each answer.

Passage 1
Author's Purpose:
Explanation:

Passage 2
Author's Purpose:
Explanation:

Passage 3
Author's Purpose:
Explanation:

Passage 4
Author's Purpose:
Explanation:

Passage 5
Author's Purpose:
Explanation:

Notes for Home: Your child read several passages and identified the author's purpose for writing each one. *Home Activity:* With your child, skim newspaper articles, editorials, and comics and identify the author's purpose or purposes for writing each one.

Plot and Theme

Directions: Read the story. Then read each question about the story. Choose the best answer to each question. Mark the letter for the answer you have chosen.

The Scrapbook

When Aunt Rose got sick and went to the hospital, Misha and his little sister Emily were both very upset. She was their favorite aunt. She often brought them books and entertained them with stories about when she was young.

Misha decided to make a scrapbook for Aunt Rose. Emily felt jealous of his idea. It seemed to her that Misha always thought of everything first and could do it better. She wanted to do something too, but her ideas didn't seem as interesting as Misha's. Misha offered to let her help, but she refused.

For the next few days, Misha worked on Aunt Rose's scrapbook. He wrote a poem, and he drew pictures. He chose favorite family snapshots. He put everything into the scrapbook. He decorated the pages with some of his favorite stickers.

Emily, meanwhile, spent a lot of time sulking. Whenever Misha tried to talk to her, she turned on her heel and walked away.

On the day they had planned to visit Aunt Rose, Misha stormed into the kitchen.

"Where's my scrapbook?" he said accusingly to Emily. She burst into tears.

"I took it," she sobbed. "I want it to be from me too."

Misha put his arm around Emily and hugged her. Emily said she was sorry. Misha told Emily to hurry and get ready to go so they could give Aunt Rose their scrapbook together.

1. What is the conflict, or problem, in this story?
   A. Aunt Rose is in the hospital.
   B. Misha and Emily are upset.
   C. Emily is jealous of Misha.
   D. Misha has to make a scrapbook.

2. The rising action of the story, where the action builds, is in—
   F. the first two paragraphs.
   G. the third and fourth paragraphs.
   H. the fifth and sixth paragraphs.
   J. the seventh and eighth paragraphs.

3. The climax, or the high point, of the story comes when—
   A. Misha confronts Emily and she cries.
   B. Emily turns on her heel and walks away.
   C. Misha finishes the scrapbook.
   D. Misha hugs Emily.

4. How is the conflict, or problem, resolved?
   F. Emily has a good cry.
   G. Misha finishes the scrapbook.
   H. Misha apologizes to Emily.
   J. Emily apologizes to Misha, who agrees to share the scrapbook.

5. Which of following best states a theme for this story?
   A. Jealous feelings should always be kept hidden.
   B. Jealousy is harmful.
   C. Jealousy is not harmful if it's kept hidden.
   D. Jealousy should be ignored.

Notes for Home: Your child read a story and identified elements of the plot and the theme. *Home Activity:* Watch a movie with your child. Then work with him or her to write a movie review, outlining the plot and identifying the theme.

Writing Across Texts

Directions: Think about how Gramps in *The Memory Box* and Ebonee Rose in "The Heart of a Runner" prepared for big events in their lives. Add examples to the Venn diagram below to show how their preparations were the same and different.

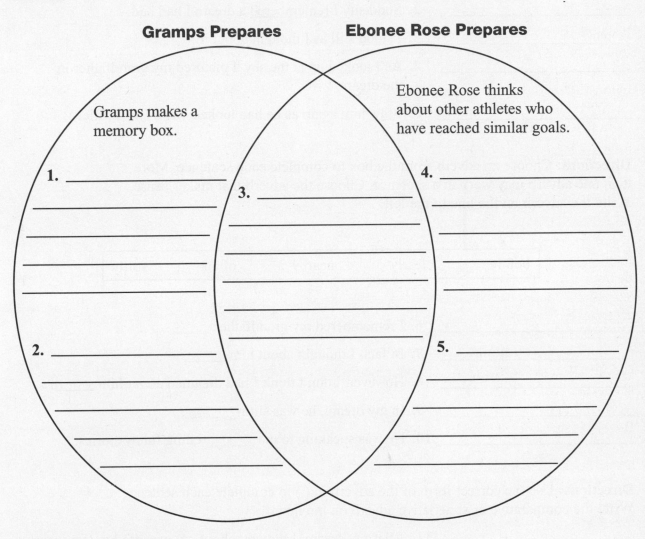

Gramps Prepares

Ebonee Rose Prepares

Gramps makes a memory box.

Ebonee Rose thinks about other athletes who have reached similar goals.

1. _____

3. _____

4. _____

2. _____

5. _____

Write Two Paragraphs

Recall the preparations for the race Ebonee Rose makes in "The Heart of a Runner" and the preparations for his loss of memory that Gramps makes in *The Memory Box*. Although the preparations were made for different reasons, they were equally meaningful to the characters. On a separate sheet of paper, write two paragraphs that compare and contrast the ways these two characters prepared for what would happen in their lives.

Notes for Home: Your child wrote two paragraphs comparing and contrasting characters from different stories. *Home Activity:* As you read stories or articles, discuss with your child how the ideas or characters are alike or different.

Grammar: Adverbs

Directions: Find the adverb in each sentence that tells about the underlined verb. Write the adverb on the line.

_____ 1. Yesterday morning I <u>walked</u> to school sleepily.

_____ 2. Suddenly I <u>remembered</u> a dream I had had.

_____ 3. I <u>stood</u> still as I thought about it.

_____ 4. As I <u>looked</u> up at the sky, I pictured my grandfather in the dream.

_____ 5. I <u>saw</u> him again as he had looked when I was little.

Directions: Choose an adverb from the box to complete each sentence. More than one adverb may work in a sentence. Choose the adverb that makes sense. Write the adverb on the line to the left.

before	clearly	nearby	often	softly

_____ 6. I remembered my grandfather _____.

_____ 7. In fact, I thought about him _____.

_____ 8. However, I don't think I had dreamed about him _____.

_____ 9. In my dream, he was sitting _____.

_____ 10. He was speaking to me _____, telling funny stories.

Directions: Use the correct form of the adverb in ( ) to complete each sentence. Write the comparative or superlative adverb on the line.

_____ 11. After my dream, I thought about my grandfather (frequently) than before.

_____ 12. When relatives visited, he always arrived (early) of all.

_____ 13. He told jokes (often) than anyone else in my family.

_____ 14. In the playground, he would swing me (high) of all.

_____ 15. There is no one I remember (lovingly) than my grandfather.

Notes for Home: Your child used adverbs—words that tell about the action of a verb—including adverbs that compare two or more actions. **Home Activity:** Take a walk with your child or look out the window. Use verbs and adverbs to talk about the actions you see.

Grammar: Using Adverbs to Improve Sentences

Adverbs tell more about verbs. They tell how, when, or where actions happen. You can improve your sentence by using adverbs. They add vivid details so that readers can picture the action in their minds.

Without Adverbs: Grandfather walked.
With Adverbs: Grandfather walked <u>slowly</u> and <u>carefully</u>.

Be careful not to use more adverbs than the sentence needs.

Grandfather walked <u>quietly</u>, <u>slowly</u>, <u>steadily</u>, and <u>carefully</u>.

Directions: Underline the adverb in each sentence. Circle the word it modifies.

1. The man talked happily about his childhood.

2. He clearly recalled many exciting moments.

3. The children listened closely to his stories.

4. Grandfather often smiled as he spoke.

5. The children stayed late at his house.

Directions: Add an adverb to make each sentence more vivid or precise. Write the adverb on the line to the left.

_____ **6.** Grandma spoke _____ about her childhood.

_____ **7.** She walked _____ to her country school.

_____ **8.** She visited _____ with her neighbors.

_____ **9.** In the summer she played _____ in the yard.

_____ **10.** Her playmates _____ joined her.

_____ **11.** They _____ thought of games to play.

_____ **12.** The summer days passed _____.

_____ **13.** In the evenings, she sat _____ on the porch.

_____ **14.** She waved _____ to all her friends.

_____ **15.** Grandma _____ wrote notes to people every week.

Notes for Home: Your child identified and wrote adverbs in sentences. An adverb can add details about actions. *Home Activity:* Watch a television show or movie together. Invite your child to name adverbs that describe the actions you see.

Grammar: Using Adverbs to Improve Sentences

Directions: Think of a different adverb to replace the one that is underlined. Write your new adverb on the line.

_____ 1. We <u>occasionally</u> hold family reunions.

_____ 2. Family members <u>often</u> meet at our home.

_____ 3. Mom <u>always</u> serves a large meal to everyone.

_____ 4. <u>Later</u>, relatives take turns telling stories.

_____ 5. Relatives <u>fully</u> enjoy this festive occasion.

Directions: Add one or two adverbs to improve each sentence. Write the new sentence on the line.

6. Uncle Joe tells jokes at each reunion.

_____

7. Aunt Mary shares pictures.

_____

8. My cousins play in the backyard.

_____

9. We all enjoy ourselves at our reunions.

_____

10. I will tell you about it.

_____

Write a Description

Think about things your family likes to do. On a separate sheet of paper, describe your family's activities. Use precise and vivid adverbs in your sentences.

© Scott Foresman 5

Notes for Home: Your child wrote sentences with adverbs. Adverbs can add details about actions. *Home Activity:* Read a short story with your child. Have him or her point out adverbs in the sentences.

Grammar: Using Adverbs to Improve Sentences

RETEACHING

Write the underlined words.

1. Puppies are <u>wonderfully</u> cute.   _____

2. Certain dogs lcarn <u>well</u>.   _____

3. Others behave <u>badly</u>.   _____

Use **adverbs** to tell more about how, when, or where actions happen. The words **well** and **badly** often are used as adverbs.

Directions: Choose the word in ( ) that correctly completes each sentence. Write it on the line.

1. My dog eats _____. (quick/quickly)

2. Sometimes she barks _____. (noisy/noisily)

3. Her voice is very _____ heard. (easy/easily)

4. That dog is _____ funny. (extremc/cxtrcmcly)

5. The animals in the show performed _____. (happy/happily)

Directions: Choose an adverb to complete each sentence. Write it on the line to the right.

6. The trainer practices with his dogs _____.   _____

7. Sometimes a dog performs _____.   _____

8. That small poodle walks _____ around the ring.   _____

9. Most show dogs behave well _____.   _____

10. The golden retriever wagged her tail _____ for the judges.   _____

11. My collie scored _____ at today's show.   _____

Notes for Home: Your child added adverbs to sentences to make them more clear and interesting. **Home Activity:** Together, take a walk or look out the window. Have your child describe what he or she sees, using adverbs to present details morc vividly.

Grammar: Using Adverbs to Improve Sentences

Directions: Choose an adverb to complete each sentence. Write it on the line.

1. The first swimmer _____ warms up in the pool.

2. We watch him _____.

3. Another swimmer joins him _____.

4. The girl in the red suit dives _____.

5. She swims _____ fast.

6. Her arms and legs move _____.

7. She must have practiced _____.

8. That last dive was _____ done.

9. Once she swam _____.

10. Now she performs _____.

11. She trains very _____.

12. She always breathes _____ in the water.

13. I swim _____.

14. My school swim team has a whole group of _____ talented swimmers.

15. Our coach tells us _____ that he is proud of us.

16. Not one of us swims _____.

17. Once we met _____ at the community pool.

18. It was so nice, we said we would rather practice _____ than anywhere else.

Write a Paragraph

On a separate sheet of paper, write a paragraph about what you like to do at a pool or a beach. Use adverbs in your sentences.

Notes for Home: Your child chose adverbs to correctly complete sentences. **Home Activity:** Make a list of adverbs, such as *carefully, slowly,* and *confidently.* Have your child choose an adverb and make up a sentence, using that adverb.

Phonics: Schwa Sound (Final Syllable)

Directions: The **schwa sound** is often found in a final, unstressed syllable. For example, the final syllables of **table, summer,** and **natural** have the schwa sound. Read the words in the box. Say each word to yourself. Sort the words by their final **schwa sounds.** Write each word in the correct column.

freckle	soccer	tackle
professional	festival	flower
water	normal	circle

Sounds like *table* | **Sounds like *summer*** | **Sounds like *natural***

1. _____ 4. _____ 7. _____

2. _____ 5. _____ 8. _____

3. _____ 6. _____ 9. _____

Directions: Read each sentence. Listen for the word that has the **schwa sound** in the final syllable. Circle the word and write it on the line.

_____ 10. I remember taking trips to go fishing.

_____ 11. Uncle Ted always caught the biggest fish.

_____ 12. We would take a photo of it for the photo album.

_____ 13. Then the fresh fish was cooked for dinner.

_____ 14. We ate, and then we would sit on the porch and whistle songs.

_____ 15. I could not think of anything I liked better.

Notes for Home: Your child identified the schwa sound heard at the end of words, such as *table, summer,* and *natural.* **Home Activity:** In the car, read signs and billboards with your child. Take note of words with the schwa sound in the final syllables.

Spelling: Vowels in Final Syllables

Pretest Directions: Fold back the page along the dotted line. On the blanks, write the spelling words as they are dictated. When you have finished the test, unfold the page and check your words.

1._____

2._____

3._____

4._____

5._____

6._____

7._____

8._____

9._____

10._____

11._____

12._____

13._____

14._____

15._____

16._____

17._____

18._____

19._____

20._____

1. I do not want **either** one.

2. Read me **another** story.

3. Th school has a new **computer**.

4. Hang the **calendar** on the wall.

5. I drew a map of the **solar** system.

6. Which place in **particular** is it?

7. Good is the opposite of **evil**.

8. We found a **fossil** of a fern.

9. To be polite is to be **civil**.

10. Please **cancel** my subscription.

11. The **label** on the bottle is red.

12. May I change the **channel**?

13. The twins had a bad **quarrel**.

14. Have you **eaten** yet?

15. I do not like **frozen** vegetables.

16. The fire engine has a loud **siren**.

17. She opened the **curtain**.

18. Who is the ship's **captain**?

19. I threw coins in the **fountain**.

20. His father always gets a **bargain**.

© Scott Foresman 5

Notes for Home: Your child took a pretest on how to spell the vowel sound in final syllables. *Home Activity:* Help your child learn misspelled words before the final test. See if there are any similar errors and discuss a memory trick that could help.

Spelling: Vowels in Final Syllables

Word List

either	particular	label	siren
another	evil	channel	curtain
computer	fossil	quarrel	captain
calendar	civil	eaten	fountain
solar	cancel	frozen	bargain

Directions: Choose the words from the box that have a final syllable that sounds like the final syllable in **open.** Write each word in the correct column.

Final syllable spelled -ain

1. _____

2. _____

3. _____

4. _____

Final syllable spelled -en

5. _____

6. _____

7. _____

Directions: Each word below has a letter missing. Decide which vowel—**e, i,** or **a**—to add to each word to form a word from the box. Write the word on the line.

8. lab_l _____

9. anoth_r _____

10. sol_r _____

11. civ_l _____

12. quarr_l _____

13. particul_r _____

14. eith_r _____

15. ev_l _____

16. comput_r _____

17. chann_l _____

18. foss_l _____

19. calend_r _____

20. canc_l _____

Notes for Home: Your child spelled words with indistinct vowel sounds in their final syllables that sound alike but are spelled differently, such as *solar* and *either. Home Activity:* Give your child clues about each spelling word. Have him or her guess and spell the word.

Proofread and Write

Spelling: Vowels in Final Syllables

Directions: Proofread the book review. Find seven spelling mistakes. Use the proofreading marks to correct each mistake.

≡	Make a capital.
/	Make a small letter.
∧	Add something.
⍺	Take out something.
⊙	Add a period.
⁋	Begin a new paragraph.

BETWEEN A BOOK'S COVERS

Memories of My Travels, by Captain Ronald Tweet, is filled with tales of the famous explorer's adventures. In one chapter, he tells of his search for the fossel of a forgotten dinosaur. In another, he describes his quest for the fountin of youth in India, where he had a close call with death after he had eaten a two-month old sandwich! On an expedition to the frozin lands of the North Pole, Sir Ronald's ship almost sinks in a dangerous chanel. My particuler favorite is his foolish quarrell with a huge anaconda in the Amazon. If you like excitement, you'll love this book. It's a bargen at $11.95!

Spelling Tip

another

If you have trouble spelling **another,** remember that it's made up of three words: **a not her.**

Word List

either
another
computer
calendar
solar
particular
evil
fossil
civil
cancel
label
channel
quarrel
eaten
frozen
siren
curtain
captain
fountain
bargain

Write a Review

On a separate sheet of paper, write a review of a book, movie, or television program you have recently read or watched. Try to use at least six of your spelling words.

Notes for Home: Your child spelled words with indistinct vowel sounds in their final syllables that sound alike but are spelled differently. *Home Activity:* With your child, sort the spelling words into separate lists according to how their final syllables are spelled.

Spelling: Vowels in Final Syllables
REVIEW

Word List

either	solar	civil	quarrel	curtain
another	particular	cancel	eaten	captain
computer	evil	label	frozen	fountain
calendar	fossil	channel	siren	bargain

Directions: Choose the word from the box that best matches each clue.
Write the word on the line.

_____ 1. This refers to rights of citizens, such as the right to vote.

_____ 2. It tells the date.

_____ 3. It's the opposite of *good*.

_____ 4. You do this when you can't meet someone as planned.

_____ 5. It can be one or the other.

_____ 6. You might dig for one.

_____ 7. You might find it at a yard sale.

_____ 8. It has a keyboard and a monitor attached to it.

_____ 9. This kind of power comes from the sun.

_____ 10. It's something you change on the television set.

_____ 11. It appears on packaged foods.

Directions: Choose the word from the box that best completes each sentence.
Write the word on the line to the left.

_____ 12. There was one day in _____ that I'll never forget.

_____ 13. We had just _____ lunch.

_____ 14. We ate _____ fish sticks that we had thawed and baked.

_____ 15. Suddenly we heard a loud police _____.

_____ 16. We all ran to the window and pulled back the _____.

_____ 17. The police were hauling a soaking wet man out of the _____.

_____ 18. _____ man had pushed him in the town's fountain.

_____ 19. They had apparently had a _____.

_____ 20. A police _____ took both men down to the station.

Notes for Home: Your child spelled words with indistinct vowel sounds in their final syllables that sound alike but are spelled differently, such as *solar* and *either*. **Home Activity:** Give your child clues to a spelling word. Have him or her guess the word and spell it.

Alphabetical Order

Resources such as encyclopedias, dictionaries, glossaries, indexes, and telephone directories list information in **alphabetical order** to make it easier for readers to find information quickly. Remember to use the first letter of the first word in each entry when you order alphabetically. If the first letters are the same, use the second letters. If the second letters are the same, use the third letters, and so on.

Directions: Suppose you wanted to find a particular photograph among the boxes of photographs below. The boxes are labeled, but they are not in any order. Someone has started to put them in alphabetical order on a shelf. On the next page, answer the questions about organizing the rest of the boxes in alphabetical order.

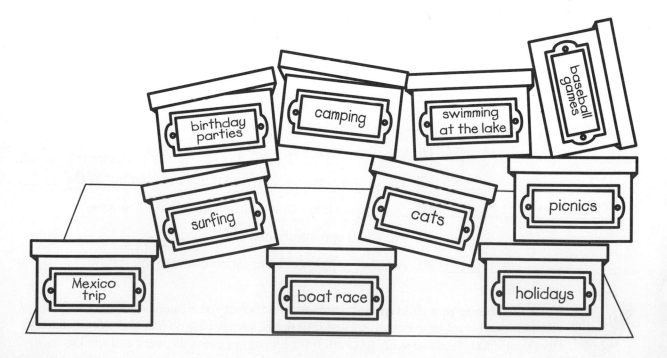

© Scott Foresman 5

Directions: Write the names of the photo boxes not on the shelf in alphabetical order.

1. _____
2. _____
3. _____
4. _____
5. _____
6. _____
7. _____
8. _____
9. _____
10. _____

11. For which boxes did you have to use the second letter of the words on the labels to alphabetize the boxes?

_____

_____

12. For which boxes did you have to use the third letter of the words on the labels to alphabetize the boxes?

_____

13. Between which two boxes would you put a photo box labeled *school trips?*

_____

14. Between which two boxes would you put a box labeled *canoeing?* _____

_____

15. Why might it be useful to sort and organize materials at school or at home by alphabetical order? Give an example of something in your class or at home that it would be helpful to organize by alphabetical order.

_____

_____

_____

_____

_____

 Notes for Home: Your child used alphabetical order to organize information. *Home Activity:* With your child, arrange the titles of some books in alphabetical order. Ignore the articles *a, the,* and *an* when alphabetizing book titles.

Name _____

How-To Chart

Directions: Fill in the how-to chart with information about your project.

Explain task _____

_____

Materials _____

_____

_____

Introduction _____

_____

Steps _____

_____

_____

_____

_____

_____

Conclusion _____

_____

_____

_____

_____

_____

© Scott Foresman 5

Notes for Home: Your child has been preparing to write a how-to report. ***Home Activity:*** Think of everyday chores such as brushing teeth, making a bed, or cleaning a room. Ask your child to outline the steps in the process. Try it out. Are there any steps missing?

Name _____

Elaboration
Add Details

> • When you write, you can elaborate by **adding interesting and specific details** that help readers easily understand your directions.
>
> • You can provide interesting and specific details by telling how things look, sound, feel, taste, and smell.

Directions: Read each sentence below. Pick a few words from the box to tell more about the process. Write your new sentence using the details.

carefully	light	creative
sturdy	unique	thick
shallow	interesting	thin
fun	completely	unusual
arrange	colorful	special
great	scrap	bright

1. You need to find a box.

_____

2. Some paint would add a nice touch.

_____

3. You can cover your box with paper.

_____

4. Poster board makes shelves.

_____

5. Put the shelves in the box.

_____

6. Add your things to the box.

_____

7. Is your box a work of art?

_____

8. Your Memory Box is a masterpiece!

_____

Notes for Home: Your child recently expanded sentences by adding interesting and specific details. *Home Activity:* Ask your child to explain three steps in a how-to process. Take turns elaborating on these steps to make them as clear as possible. Encourage your child to be specific.

© Scott Foresman 5

Name _____

Self-Evaluation Guide
How-To Report

Directions: Think about the final draft of your how-to report. Then answer each question below.

	Yes	No	Not sure
1. Are there any steps missing?			
2. Are all the steps in the right order?			
3. Are the steps clearly written and easy to follow?			
4. Did I provide all of the necessary information?			
5. Did I use words such as *first* to indicate order?			
6. Did I proofread carefully for spelling, capitalization, and punctuation?			
7. Did I accomplish what I set out to accomplish?			

8. Did I learn anything new from this report?

_____

_____

_____

9. In what way would you improve your report if you rewrote it?

_____

_____

_____

_____

© Scott Foresman 5

Notes for Home: Your child completed a self-evaluation of a writing assignment. ***Home Activity:*** Discuss the form with your child. Ask: *What did you learn from the exercise? What would you do differently next time? Are there other areas where this experience is applicable?*

Family Times

Name_____

Summary

Girls and Women March to Gain the Vote

Lila has discovered that there are unwritten rules and formal laws that prevent women and girls from having fair and equal treatment. After reading about the suffragists' struggles, Lila decides she wants to join her Grandmama in a march up Fifth Avenue to call for women's right to vote. Her impassioned speech to her papa persuades him that Lila should be allowed to march.

Reading Skills

Setting

The **setting** is the time and place in which a story takes place. "I Want to Vote!" for example, takes place in New York City in 1917.

Sometimes the time and place of a story are not stated directly. In that case, use story details to figure out what the setting is. In "I Want to Vote!" the exact place of the story isn't stated. However, the mention of a fire in Brooklyn and a march up Fifth Avenue tell you that the story takes place in New York City.

Activity
Act It Out. Have your child recount Lila's speech. Then imagine you are a guest speaker at the march for women's right to vote. Work together to write a speech that you could give.

Activity
Make a Collage. Cut out magazine and newspaper pictures of different settings. Use them to make a collage. Then talk about the details in each picture that help you identify its time and place.

I Want to Vote! 453

Family Times

Tested Vocabulary

Words to Know

Knowing the meanings of these words is important to reading "I Want to Vote!" Practice using these words to learn their meanings.

banners cloth with some designs or words on it

headlines words printed in heavy type at the top of a newspaper article

parlor living room

pavement sidewalk

splattered splashed on

stockings hosiery; long socks

trolley streetcar

Grammar

Pronouns

A **pronoun** is a word that takes the place of a noun or noun phrase. Pronouns include: *I, me, you, he, him, she, her, it, we, us, they,* and *them.* Notice how pronouns replace nouns in these sentences:

Lila helped Mike sell papers. <u>She</u> sold <u>them</u> more quickly than <u>he</u> did.

The women and girls marched. <u>They</u> were proud to march for the right to vote.

Activity
Answer with Pronouns. Take turns saying a sentence that uses at least one noun **(Mom makes great pie.)** and having the other person say an answering sentence that replaces one of those nouns with a pronoun. **(<u>It</u> is my favorite dessert.)**

Tested Spelling Words

Setting

- The **setting** is the time and place in which a story happens.

- In some stories, the author tells you exactly when and where the story takes place. In other stories, the author tells about the setting through details and you have to figure out the time and place.

Directions: Reread "The Year of Mother Jones." Then complete the table.
Provide details from the story to support each statement about the setting.

Setting	How I Know (Supporting Details from the Story)
The story takes place in Philadelphia.	1.
The story begins in November, 1903.	2.
The children work in a mill.	3.
The mill is dirty and dangerous.	4.
The strike takes place in the summer of 1903.	5.

Notes for Home: Your child read a story and identified details about its setting. ***Home Activity:*** Read a story with your child. Have him or her point out details that help identify when and where the story takes place. Talk about how important the setting is to the story.

© Scott Foresman 5

Vocabulary

Directions: Choose the word from the box that best completes each sentence. Write the word on the line.

Check the Words You Know	

Check the Words You Know

___ banners
___ headlines
___ parlor
___ pavement
___ splattered
___ stockings
___ trolley

_____ 1. Kate stared at the _____ on the newspapers: FAIR WAGES NOW!

_____ 2. Kate rode the _____ through town to the factory.

_____ 3. She saw striking workers marching along, carrying _____ and signs.

_____ 4. Even when they began to be _____ by rain, they didn't quit.

_____ 5. So much rain had fallen that the _____ was covered with deep puddles.

_____ 6. A few striking workers complained that the rainwater had soaked their shoes and _____.

Directions: Choose the word from the box that best matches each clue. Write the word on the line.

_____ 7. I am something you can ride in to travel throughout the city.

_____ 8. I am a sitting room in which you entertain guests.

_____ 9. I am a road or sidewalk covered with a hard surface.

_____ 10. I am worn over your feet and under your shoes.

Write a Song

On a separate sheet of paper, write a political song that suffragists might sing at marches, parades, or demonstrations. Use as many vocabulary words as you can.

Notes for Home: Your child identified and used vocabulary words from the story "I Want to Vote!" *Home Activity:* If possible, show your child pictures of suffragists from the 1910s and 1920s. Invite your child to make up his or her own story about the fight for the right to vote.

Name _____

Setting

- The **setting** is the time and place in which a story happens. It may be directly identified or only described through details.

- In some stories, the setting is very important. It affects what happens and why it happens.

Directions: Reread the section of "I Want to Vote!" in which the parade begins. Then answer the questions below. Think about where and when the story takes place.

> All at once, all the bands were playing and the columns of women began to move. Left, left. Lila was marching. Above her, the yellow banners streamed.
>
> Out of Washington Square they marched and onto Fifth Avenue. Before and behind came the sound of the drums, and the flags snapped in the breeze. Left, left. On they went up the street, marching in time to the music.
>
> From the curbs came the sound of whistles and cheers. Yellow streamers flew from the shop doors. White-gloved policemen held back the crowds as the bands and the marchers passed.
>
> From A LONG WAY TO GO by Zibby Oneal. Copyright © 1990 by Zibby Oneal. Used by permission of Viking Penguin, a division of Penguin Putnam Inc.

1. Where is the parade taking place?

_____

_____

2. Is the setting directly identified or implied through details? Explain.

_____

_____

3. Which details make the setting come alive for the reader?

_____

_____

4. How does the setting affect the marchers?

_____

5. How important is the time period in which the story is set? Explain your answer on a separate sheet of paper.

Notes for Home: Your child read a story and analyzed how the time and place affected the characters and events. *Home Activity:* Read a story with your child. Then talk about the way the setting (time and place) affects the characters and events.

Selection Test

Directions: Choose the best answer to each item. Mark the letter for the answer you have chosen.

Part 1: Vocabulary

Find the answer choice that means about the same as the underlined word in each sentence.

1. Lou rode the <u>trolley</u>.
    A. station wagon
    B. bicycle
    C. horse-drawn carriage
    D. streetcar

2. The milk <u>splattered</u> everywhere.
    F. splashed
    G. grew wildly
    H. smelled
    J. froze

3. The marchers carried <u>banners</u>.
    A. protective coverings
    B. signs made of cloth
    C. musical instruments
    D. small children

4. Her <u>stockings</u> were dirty.
    F. coverings for the hand
    G. drawers in a cabinet
    H. glasses used to improve eyesight
    J. coverings for the foot or leg

5. George is in the <u>parlor</u>.
    A. park
    B. garage
    C. living room
    D. basement

6. We stood on the <u>pavement</u>.
    F. street or sidewalk
    G. upper floor of a theater
    H. long, wooden porch
    J. flat stretch of sand by the sea

7. These <u>headlines</u> are not very exciting.
    A. small wrinkles on a person's face
    B. coverings or decorations for the head
    C. long lines at the store
    D. lines printed at the top of newspaper articles

Part 2: Comprehension

Use what you know about the story to answer each item.

8. At the beginning of the story, Lila and Mike were—
    F. marching in a parade.
    G. selling newspapers.
    H. fighting a fire.
    J. printing newspapers.

9. Lila read about women in Washington who refused to eat because they—
    A. were angry at the cook.
    B. did not like the food they got in jail.
    C. could not afford to buy food.
    D. would rather starve than not have the right to vote.

10. How did things change for the women in the story because there was a war on?
    F. They were allowed to vote.
    G. They had the same rights as men.
    H. They were working in offices and factories.
    J. They were not allowed to make speeches.

GO ON

11. Where does this story take place?
    A. New York
    B. Washington, D.C.
    C. Georgia
    D. California

12. When does this story take place?
    F. at the time of the Civil War
    G. in the early 1900s
    H. after World War II
    J. in the 1960s

13. How did Lila's father react to her speech?
    A. He became angry.
    B. He pretended to be bored.
    C. He was annoyed.
    D. He was impressed.

14. This story supports the idea that—
    F. women deserve the same rights as men.
    G. boys are smarter than girls.
    H. women should not be allowed to vote.
    J. women don't need to know how to drive.

15. Lila's father was wrong in thinking that she—
    A. was not as smart as George.
    B. would grow into a beautiful lady.
    C. would prefer dances and parties to learning to drive.
    D. would make speeches when she was older.

STOP

Setting

- The **setting** is the time and place in which a story happens. It may be directly identified or only described through details.

- In some stories, the setting is very important. It affects what happens and why it happens.

Directions: Read the story below.

"Penny for a shine! Penny for a shine!" Mike glanced down at his kit; polish, brushes, and soft flannel rags. He exchanged grins with Pat, who was selling newspapers across the gate.

Sunlight streamed in through the huge skylight in the roof of Pennsylvania Station. Many businessmen in dark hats, scarves, and heavy overcoats passed him, all on their way to their offices. Several of them stopped to buy papers, dropping their nickels in the box at Pat's feet.

The station was so huge it never seemed crowded or noisy, even on a busy morning. Mike wondered for a moment whether Grand Central Station was as large. Then his thoughts were interrupted as a man called to him for a shine. Time to stop daydreaming and earn his breakfast!

Directions: Complete the table. Think about details of time and place.

Setting	How Do You Know?
Time of Year/Season	1.
Time of Day	2.
Long Ago or Modern Time?	3.
Location	4.
Settings Effect on Character	Pat is happy because a busy station means many customers to buy his newspapers. 5. Mike

Notes for Home: Your child read a story and identified the setting (time and place) and its effect on the characters and events. **Home Activity:** Watch a movie or TV show with your child. Then talk about ways in which the setting was important to the story.

Making Judgments

Directions: Read the story. Then read each question about the story. Choose the best answer to each question. Mark the letter for the answer you have chosen.

Forward March!

Jack and Paul were going all the way to Washington to march in the parade with their friends Sally and Roberto. They woud travel down by train the day before. Jack had been thinking about it all week. He and Paul were good friends, and they would have a great time at the parade.

The night before, Jack and Paul got together to pack their bags. Paul noticed that Jack didn't pack an umbrella.

"Aren't you taking your umbrella, Jack? I read that it may rain tomorrow."

"I can't be bothered with an umbrella," objected Jack. "My pack is heavy enough already. Besides, why would it rain? The weather has been great all week."

Paul said nothing. He went back to his packing.

Jack watched as Paul stuffed a sweater into his pack. "Why are you taking that? Your pack will be so heavy you won't want to go anywhere! Besides, it's warm out."

"Sally travels on those trains all the time, and she says they're always cold," Paul explained. "They always have the air conditioning on full blast."

"Oh, what does she know?" scoffed Jack. "Sally always thinks it's cold. Bring that sweater if you want to, but I'm not taking one."

Paul grinned at his friend and zipped his full pack. "All set?" he asked. "We should get some sleep if we want to be awake in time for our train tomorrow!"

1. Jack thinks he won't need an umbrella because—
   A. it's too big to fit into his backpack.
   B. he has no room for it.
   C. he doesn't believe it will rain.
   D. Paul has an umbrella.

2. Jack should take an umbrella because—
   F. Paul tells him to.
   G. Paul read a forecast that predicted rain.
   H. they can sell it later.
   J. it will balance the weight of his pack.

3. Paul takes a sweater because—
   A. Sally told him it would snow.
   B. he likes to wear sweaters.
   C. he thinks it will amuse Jack.
   D. Sally told him the train would be cold.

4. Which character do you think is best prepared for whatever may happen?
   F. Jack
   G. Paul
   H. Sally
   J. Roberto

5. Which character do you think is least prepared for whatever may happen?
   A. Jack
   B. Paul
   C. Sally
   D. Roberto

Notes for Home: Your child read a story and made judgments about the characters and their actions. *Home Activity:* Talk with your child about some of the decisions he or she made recently. Together, discuss your opinion of each decision.

© Scott Foresman 5

Writing Across Texts

Directions: Think about the character Lila and children's lives as described in "I Want to Vote!" and the article "Kids Voting USA." How is being a child today different from the way it was in 1917? How has the attitude toward voting changed? Fill in the following table to record some of the differences.

Changing Times	
Today	**In the Early 1900s**
Children are encouraged to learn about voting.	Lila was discouraged from attending a suffragist parade
1.	2.
3.	4.
5.	6.
7.	8.
9.	10.

Write a Paragraph

Compare what you learned about children's lives from "I Want to Vote!" to ideas in "Kids Voting USA." On a separate sheet of paper, write a paragraph that describes some of the differences in most children's lives today compared with the lives of children in the early 1900s.

Notes for Home: Your child wrote about how times have changed since the early 1900s. *Home Activity:* Show your child an old family photograph or some other photograph of another era. Together, discuss things in the photograph that show things that were different then.

Grammar: Contractions

REVIEW

Directions: Rewrite each contraction as two separate words.

1. he'll _____
2. don't _____
3. it's _____
4. I'm _____
5. you're _____
6. didn't _____
7. they're _____
8. I've _____
9. she's _____
10. there's _____

11. won't _____
12. haven't _____
13. let's _____
14. that's _____
15. they've _____
16. she'll _____
17. we've _____
18. you've _____
19. they'll _____
20. wouldn't _____

Directions: Change the underlined words into a contraction. Then rewrite each sentence.

21. "<u>I am</u> going to the polls now!" declares my sister Lin.

_____

_____

22. "<u>They are</u> closing soon, so <u>you had</u> better hurry," says Mom.

_____

_____

23. Lin <u>does not</u> say much, but <u>she is</u> proud to be voting.

_____

_____

24. She just turned eighteen, so <u>it is</u> her first time to vote.

_____

_____

25. Lin knows that before 1920 women <u>could not</u> vote at all.

_____

_____

Notes for Home: Your child wrote contractions—word combinations such as *don't, we'll, you're*. **Home Activity:** Take a walk with your child, and try to spot contractions on neighborhood signs and posters. Name the words each contraction represents.

Practice

Grammar: Pronouns

Pronouns are words that take the place of nouns or noun phrases. Like nouns, pronouns have singular and plural forms. A singular pronoun replaces a singular noun. A plural pronoun replaces a plural noun.

<u>Lucy Stone</u> was an early suffragist. <u>She</u> argued for women's right to vote.

<u>Elizabeth Cady Stanton</u> and <u>Susan B. Anthony</u> were early suffragists too.

<u>They</u> wanted new laws about women's rights.

Pronouns
   Singular: I, me, you, she, her, he, him, it   **Plural:** we, us, you, they, them

Possessive pronouns are pronouns that show ownership. One form of possessive pronouns is used before nouns. The other form stands alone without a noun following it.

<u>Their</u> struggle for justice is part of history. Honor and respect are now <u>theirs</u>.

Possessive Pronouns
         Before a Noun: my, your, her, his, its, our, their
         By Itself: mine, yours, hers, his, ours, theirs

Directions: Underline the pronoun or pronouns in each sentence. Be sure to underline possessive pronouns too.

1. We talked about our favorite candidates.

2. Carmen and I listened to their speeches.

3. She waved at her relatives outside the polling place.

4. They smiled at us and held up signs.

5. Any right means responsibilities, so we are learning about ours.

Directions: Choose a pronoun or possessive pronoun in ( ) to replace the underlined words. Write the pronoun or possessive pronoun on the line.

_____ 6. Carmen's mom did campaign work and liked <u>campaign work</u>. (it/she)

_____ 7. Her dad made a speech in <u>her dad's</u> strong, deep voice. (his/their)

_____ 8. The candidate offered him <u>the candidate's</u> thanks afterward. (her/our)

_____ 9. Carmen and I met her, and she shook <u>Carmen's and my</u> hands. (her/our)

_____ 10. When Carmen and I are old enough, <u>Carmen and I</u> will vote in every election! (they/we)

Notes for Home: Your child identified and wrote pronouns (words that take the place of nouns). *Home Activity:* Read a short magazine or newspaper article together. Invite your child to identify all the pronouns he or she recognizes.

Grammar: Pronouns

Directions: Underline the pronoun or pronouns in each sentence. Underline the possessive pronouns too.

1. Herman said he had a question for our teacher.

2. Would she give us her permission to have a student government?

3. It would give us practice in voting and in citizenship.

4. With our classmates, we would elect a student governor.

5. Then we could decide what his or her duties would be.

6. Our classmates listened, and Herman explained his idea to them.

7. He asked Amelia, "Did your last school have a student government?"

8. "Yes," she told him. "Each grade had its own representatives."

9. Next, two of my classmates nominated me for governor.

10. Other students named their choices for student governor.

Directions: Choose a pronoun or possessive pronoun to replace the underlined word or words. Write the pronoun or possessive pronoun on the line.

_____ 11. Layla said that <u>Layla</u> had been a class treasurer the year before. (it/she)

_____ 12. Dan decided to give Layla <u>Dan's</u> vote for treasurer. (their/his)

_____ 13. Herman thanked the teacher for <u>the teacher's</u> interest and help. (her/their)

_____ 14. Our teacher praised the students for the <u>students'</u> interest in government. (its/their)

_____ 15. She added, "We will have the election next week, and I hope students will support <u>the election</u> by voting." (it/us)

Write a Letter

Think about a class project or activity you enjoyed with your classmates. On a separate sheet of paper, write a letter that describes that project or activity. Tell what different people did. Use pronouns and possessive pronouns in your letter.

Notes for Home: Your child identified and wrote pronouns in sentences. Pronouns are words that take the place of nouns. *Home Activity:* Write the pronouns *I, you, he, she, it, we,* and *they* on slips of paper. Take turns drawing a slip and using the pronoun in a sentence.

Grammar: Pronouns

Read each pair of sentences. Write the pronoun that replaces the circled word.

1. a. (Sam) has a pet snail.

   b. He has a pet snail. _____

2. a. Sam gave the snail to (Sandra.)

   b. Sam gave the snail to her. _____

Pronouns take the place of nouns or noun phrases. A pronoun can be singular or plural.

Directions: Circle the pronoun in each sentence. Write it on the line.

1. My team had never won a championship. _____

2. I was the last batter up. _____

3. My friends cheered loudly from the sidelines. _____

4. Would the winning run be mine? _____

5. Cheering teammates surrounded me at home base. _____

6. Victory was ours. _____

7. The coach congratulated us. _____

8. We shook hands with the other team. _____

9. The players were good sports about their loss. _____

Directions: Write a pronoun for the underlined word or words.

10. <u>Rosa</u> won the Most Valuable Player award. _____

11. The trophies in the bookcase are <u>Rosa's</u>. _____

12. Not all of <u>the trophies</u> are for sports. _____

13. Music interests <u>Rosa</u> too. _____

14. <u>Rosa</u> plays the violin in the school orchestra. _____

15. Rosa's favorite trophy has a violin on <u>the trophy</u>. _____

Notes for Home: Your child identified pronouns in sentences and replaced proper nouns with pronouns. *Home Activity:* Have your child write sentences about people he or she knows, replacing proper nouns with pronouns.

Grammar: Pronouns

Directions: Circle the pronoun in each sentence.

1. I like the beach.

2. Usually my friend Janice brings along a radio.

3. Sometimes Janice brings her umbrella for some shade.

4. Not even an umbrella gives complete protection from the sun and its rays.

5. We use sunscreen for added protection.

6. Sometimes the sand sticks to our skin.

7. It gets on towels and clothes.

8. Their towels feel gritty.

9. The sand does not bother us too much.

10. The ocean waves splash on his towel.

Directions: Replace the underlined word or words in each sentence with a pronoun. Then rewrite the sentence.

11. <u>Janice</u> dropped a piece of bread on the sand.

_____

12. <u>The bread</u> attracted nearby gulls.

_____

13. <u>The gulls</u> swooped down toward the food.

_____

14. The small piece of bread was not enough for all of <u>the birds</u>.

_____

Write Sentences

Write sentences that tell how you keep cool on hot days. Use pronouns in your sentences. Write on a separate sheet of paper.

Notes for Home: Your child identified pronouns in sentences and wrote new sentences with pronouns. *Home Activity:* Together, make a list of pronouns your child knows. Then make a list of proper nouns and have your child identify which pronouns match them.

Phonics: Complex Spelling Patterns

Directions: In some words, the sound **/sh/** is spelled **ci, sci,** or **ti.** Read the list of words. Say each word to yourself. Underline the letters that represent the sound **/sh/.**

1. official
2. special
3. commotion
4. spacious
5. occupation

6. imagination
7. dictionary
8. conscious
9. delicious
10. caution

11. conscience
12. luscious
13. socially
14. artificial
15. motion

Directions: Read the diary entry. Circle the words with the sound /sh/. Write the words on the lines.

May 29

Dear Diary,

  Today was a special day for our family. It was election day, and Mom just got elected to the city council! We worked very hard on her campaign. We passed out flyers and asked people to sign petitions saying they would vote for Mom. We ran commercials on the local radio and television stations. We reminded everyone we talked to that it was their constitutional right to vote. Mom told me that not so long ago women did not have the right to vote. Can you imagine that such a large percent of our population had no say in how the nation was run? It made me realize how precious our rights are, especially the right to vote. Now I can't wait till I turn 18 and can cast my own vote!

16. _____
17. _____
18. _____
19. _____
20. _____
21. _____
22. _____
23. _____
24. _____
25. _____

Notes for Home: Your child identified words with the sound /sh/ spelled *ci, sci,* and *ti.* **Home Activity:** Make a list of words with your child that end in *-tion* and have the sound /sh/. Make up rhymes with these words.

Spelling: Words with *ng, nk, th*

Pretest Directions: Fold back the page along the dotted line. On the blanks, write the spelling words as they are dictated. When you have finished the test, unfold the page and check your words.

1._____
2._____
3._____
4._____
5._____
6._____
7._____
8._____
9._____
10._____
11._____
12._____
13._____
14._____
15._____
16._____
17._____
18._____
19._____
20._____

1. The weightlifter is **strong**.
2. I brought **nothing** to the party.
3. **Everything** happened at once.
4. This **clothing** is expensive.
5. You are **among** friends.
6. Wasps might **sting** a dog.
7. Put your coat on a **hanger**.
8. The **lightning** was very bright.
9. Fill in the **blank**.
10. Open the **trunk** of the car.
11. We ate a lot on **Thanksgiving**.
12. The **chipmunk** buries a nut.
13. The sweater will **shrink**.
14. **They** talked for a long time.
15. There were no cars **then**.
16. We drove **north**.
17. I lost my watch **there**.
18. Do not come **without** her.
19. I walked **though** I was tired.
20. She **thought** it was hers.

Notes for Home: Your child took a pretest on words that include *ng, nk,* or *th*. **Home Activity:** Help your child learn misspelled words before the final test. Your child should look at the word, say it, spell it aloud, and then spell it with eyes shut.

© Scott Foresman 5

Think and Practice

Spelling: Words with *ng, nk, th*

Word List				
strong	among	blank	shrink	there
nothing	sting	trunk	they	without
everything	hanger	Thanksgiving	then	though
clothing	lightning	chipmunk	north	thought

Directions: Choose the one-syllable words from the box. Write each word in the correct column.

Contains ng

1. _____

2. _____

Contains nk

3. _____

4. _____

5. _____

Contains th

6. _____

7. _____

8. _____

9. _____

10. _____

11. _____

Directions: Write the word from the box that is associated with each word or words.

12. thunder _____

13. squirrel _____

14. zero _____

15. fashion _____

16. hook _____

17. lacking _____

18. one of _____

19. turkey _____

20. all _____

Notes for Home: Your child spelled words that have *ng, nk,* or *th*. **Home Activity:** Challenge your child to identify the four spelling words that are compound words and use each in a sentence.

Spelling: Words with *ng, nk, th*

Directions: Proofread this description. Find six spelling mistakes. Use the proofreading marks to correct each mistake.

≡	Make a capital.
/	Make a small letter.
∧	Add something.
℘	Take out something.
⊙	Add a period.
¶	Begin a new paragraph.

Next week my Grandmother is taking me to the city to see a parade celebrating Independence Day. Nothin is better than visiting the big city. Evrything their is so exciting and fast paced. I tought that I should wear red, white, and blue for the parade. In an old trunck in the attic of my house, I found the perfect costume. Finally the big day arrived. As the parade began, a bolt of lighting lit up the sky. I was worried that the parade might be canceled, but the storm passed and the parade continued. I truly enjoyed my day in the city.

Word List

strong	among	blank	shrink	there
nothing	sting	trunk	they	without
everything	hanger	Thanksgiving	then	though
clothing	lightning	chipmunk	north	thought

Write a Description

On a separate sheet of paper, write a description of something mysterious or strange. It might be a tree, a house, or an animal. You can write from experience or use your imagination. Try to use at least five of your spelling words.

Spelling Tip

there

People often mix up **there** and **their.** Remember the **here** in **there.** Both **here** and **there** refer to **where.**

Notes for Home: Your child practiced writing spelling words that contain the consonants *ng, nk,* or *th.* **Home Activity:** Help your child think of additional words that begin or end with the letters *th.* Make a list of these words.

Spelling: Words with *ng*, *nk*, *th*

REVIEW

Word List				
strong	among	blank	shrink	there
nothing	sting	trunk	they	without
everything	hanger	Thanksgiving	then	though
clothing	lightning	chipmunk	north	thought

Directions: Choose the word from the box that begins and ends with the same letter as each word below. Write the word on the line.

1. entering _____

2. workout _____

3. listening _____

4. napping _____

5. today _____

6. thorough _____

7. aging _____

8. tease _____

Directions: Choose the word from the box that best completes each person's statement. Write the word on the line.

_____ 9. Mother: "Put your coat on this _____."

_____ 10. Department Store Clerk: "Take a look at our new line of _____."

_____ 11. Beekeeper: "Sometimes I'm not careful and I get a bee _____."

_____ 12. Forest Ranger: "I have a pet _____ that I feed daily."

_____ 13. Wrestler: "You have to be _____ in my line of work."

_____ 14. Elephant: "I feed myself with my _____."

_____ 15. Trail Guide: "I don't need a compass to find _____."

_____ 16. Writer: "I just _____ of a great idea for my next book."

_____ 17. Artist: "I love filling up a _____ canvas."

_____ 18. Dry Cleaner: "I have to be careful not to _____ my customers' clothes."

_____ 19. Storyteller: "And _____ they lived happily ever after."

_____ 20. Turkey Farmer: "My favorite holiday is _____."

Notes for Home: Your child spelled words with *ng*, *nk*, and *th*. **Home Activity:** With your child, take turns making up tongue twisters using words that contain *th*. (Example: *Theo threw the third throw through the window.*)

Technology: Electronic Media

Electronic media includes audiotapes, videotapes, films, and computers. You can use computers to locate information on CD-ROMs and to search the Internet. To find a topic on the Internet, use a search engine and type in your key words.

Directions: Suppose you type "voting AND registration" in a search engine. You might get the following list that links you to related web pages. Use the list to answer the questions on the next page.

You Searched For:

| voting AND registration | **Top 6 of 3789 matches.** |

CENSUS - Voting and Registration Data Information about who votes and is registered to vote according to characteristics such as age, gender, race, amount of money earned, and so on.

Programs — Voting Rights Voting for Everyone is a group that works to eliminate any discriminatory obstacles that might prevent Asian Pacific Americans from participating in the voting process. This includes working to enforce the protections of the Voting Rights Act, encouraging voter registration through enforcement of the National Voter Registration Act, and providing data about Asian Pacific American participation.

Voting Information for Minnesota To vote, you must be: A U.S. citizen, at least 18 years old, a Minnesota resident for at least 20 days on election day, and properly registered. Election Dates and Absentee Ballot Application provided here.

Voting in Oregon Casting a ballot is as easy as mailing a letter in Oregon. Vote by mail started in 1981 when the Legislature authorized it for special district elections. Since then, it has become extremely popular and common for many elections.

League of Women Voters: Austin, Texas Qualifications for Voting: You must be a citizen of the United States. You must be at least 18 years old on the day of the election. You must be registered to vote. You may register to vote at any time.

Voting Information in Delaware, Maryland Voting Information: To be eligible to vote, one must be eighteen (18) years of age by the day after the election.

1. Which web page has information about eliminating discrimination?

_____

2. How long must you live in Minnesota to be able to vote in that state?

_____

3. In which state listed can you vote by mail? _____

4. Which web page would you go to for data about how different groups of people voted in past elections?

_____

5. What is the difference between the voting age requirement in Texas and the voting age requirement in Maryland?

_____

_____

6. What key words could you use to find out about voting in Ohio on the Internet?

_____

7. What key words could you use to find out about the history of voting rights for women?

_____

8. Suppose your library has an audiotape of interviews of older women describing their struggles to win the right to vote. How might you use a resource like this in a report on the history of women's voting rights?

_____

_____

_____

9. Suppose your library had a videotape that showed how to use a voting booth. For what kind of report might this resource be useful?

_____

_____

10. What are the advantages to searching the Internet for information? _____

_____

_____

_____

Notes for Home: Your child analyzed the results of a web page search on the Internet. *Home Activity:* Work with your child to find the requirements for voting in your area. Help your child use a telephone directory or online resources to find the voting requirements.

Name_____

Summary

Harriet Tubman Rides "Railroad" to Freedom

Harriet Tubman was a slave on a Maryland plantation. Determined to gain her freedom, she planned an escape with her brothers. When the brothers backed out, Harriet made her escape alone. She was aided by the Underground Railroad, a secret network of Quakers and other people who housed and fed slaves as the slaves made the journey to states where slavery was illegal. Once Harriet was free, she pledged to lead others to freedom.

Activity

Talk About a Hero. Have your child describe the dangers that Harriet Tubman faced during her journey. Talk about the things you admire most about her.

Reading Skills

Paraphrasing

Paraphrasing is restating something in your own words. For example, suppose you read this sentence: **Harriet escaped from the plantation.** You might paraphrase it like this: **Harriet ran away from the large farm.**

When you paraphrase, be careful not to change the original meaning or add your own opinion. The following sentence is not an accurate paraphrase, since it adds a personal opinion: **Harriet wisely ran away from the large farm.**

A stitch in time saves nine.

Activity

Rephrase That! Choose a text that everyone knows, such as a nursery rhyme or a popular saying. Have fun rephrasing the selection in your own words.

Family Times

Tested Vocabulary

Words to Know

Knowing the meanings of these words is important to reading "The Long Path to Freedom." Practice using these words to learn their meanings.

liberty freedom

plantation large farm or estate

quickened moved more quickly

runaway fugitive; slave who has escaped

slavery practice of holding people against their will

unconscious not able to think or feel

vow a solemn promise

Grammar

Subject and Object Pronouns

Pronouns are words that take the place of nouns. Pronouns used in the subject of a sentence are **subject pronouns**. For example: <u>They</u> helped Harriet.

Object pronouns tell who or what receives the action of a verb. For example: **The Quakers helped <u>her</u>.**

Subject Pronouns	Object Pronouns
I, you, he, she, it, we, they	me, you, him, her, it, us, them

Activity
Talk About Your Family. Describe a happy memory of an event that includes members of your family. Use subject and object pronouns from the table above.

Tested Spelling Words

© Scott Foresman 5

Paraphrasing

- **Paraphrasing** is explaining something in your own words.
- After you read a sentence or paragraph, think about what the author is trying to say. Then put the sentence or paragraph into your own words without changing the meaning or adding your own opinion.

Directions: Reread "A Dream of Equal Rights." Then complete the table. Paraphrase each original statement in your own words. (The beginning words of each sentence will help you find the sentence to paraphrase.)

Original Statement	My Paraphrase
Paragraph 1, Sentence 1 "Movements are born. . . ."	1.
Paragraph 1, Sentence 3 "Often, it takes. . . ."	2.
Paragraph 2, Sentence 2 "People around the nation. . . ."	3.
Paragraph 3, Sentence 3 "Many people had. . . ."	4.
Paragraph 3, Sentence 6 "His dream was. . . ."	5.

Notes for Home: Your child read an article and restated its ideas in his or her own words.
Home Activity: Read a newspaper article with your child. Have your child restate sentences or paragraphs in his or her own words.

Vocabulary

Directions: Draw a line to connect each word on the left with its definition on the right.

1. liberty	a solemn promise
2. slavery	a large farm or estate
3. vow	freedom
4. plantation	fugitive
5. runaway	holding people against their will

Check the Words You Know
___ liberty
___ plantation
___ quickened
___ runaway
___ slavery
___ unconscious
___ vow

Directions: Choose a word from the box that is the most opposite in meaning for each word or words below. Write the word on the line.

_____ **6.** captivity

_____ **7.** broken promise

_____ **8.** slowed

_____ **9.** conscious

_____ **10.** freedom

Directions: Choose the word from the box that best completes each sentence. Write the word on the line on the left.

_____ **11.** _____ was a way of life for Annie and her family for as long as Annie could remember.

_____ **12.** The master's _____ had more than fifty slaves working in the fields and the house.

_____ **13.** Annie made a _____ to herself that she would not die a slave.

_____ **14.** The punishment for a _____ slave who was caught was severe.

_____ **15.** However, for Annie, the chance for true _____ was worth any risk.

Write a Speech

On a separate sheet of paper, write a speech that a person in the 1850s might have delivered in the fight against slavery. Use as many vocabulary words as you can.

Notes for Home: Your child identified and used vocabulary words from "The Long Path to Freedom." *Home Activity:* Talk with your child about what kind of life a slave had. Use the vocabulary words in the conversation.

Paraphrasing

- **Paraphrasing** is explaining something in your own words.

- A paraphrase should include only the author's ideas and opinions. When paraphrasing, don't change the meaning or add your own opinions.

Directions: Reread what happened in "The Long Path to Freedom" when Harriet ran away with her brothers. Then answer the questions below.

> That night Harriet waited until her husband, John, fell asleep. Then she slid silently out of their cabin. She met her brothers, and they started off through the woods. Harriet took the lead. She knew the woods. They did not. Every owl that hooted, every frog that croaked startled them. They did not move very fast. And to Harriet they seemed to stomp and crash like a herd of cattle.
>
> Harriet kept encouraging them on. But at last her brothers stopped. They were frightened. They were going back.
>
> Harriet began to protest. They must go on!
>
> From THE STORY OF HARRIET TUBMAN by Kate McMullan. Copyright © 1991 by Parachute Press, Inc. Used by permission of Dell Books, a division of Bantam Doubleday Dell Publishing Group, Inc.

1. How might you paraphrase the first two sentences as a single sentence?

_____

_____

2. How might you paraphrase the last sentence in the first paragraph?

_____

_____

3. How might you paraphrase the second paragraph as a single sentence?

_____

_____

4. How might you paraphrase the final two sentences as a single sentence?

_____

_____

5. When you paraphrase, why is it important to use your own words and not the author's exact words? Explain your thinking on a separate sheet of paper.

© Scott Foresman 5

Notes for Home: Your child read a story and then retold parts of it in his or her own words. *Home Activity:* Read a newspaper article with your child. Challenge your child to restate individual sentences in his or her own words.

Selection Test

Directions: Choose the best answer to each item. Mark the letter for the answer you have chosen.

Part 1: Vocabulary

Find the answer choice that means about the same as the underlined word in each sentence.

1. Patrick fights for <u>liberty</u>.
   A. freedom
   B. life
   C. food
   D. shelter

2. Mercy lived on a <u>plantation</u>.
   F. boat
   G. large farm
   H. busy road
   J. government-owned housing

3. Ben told us about his <u>vow</u>.
   A. experience
   B. promise
   C. secret
   D. project

4. When we found the child, he was <u>unconscious</u>.
   F. chilled
   G. very hungry
   H. happy
   J. not able to think or feel

5. <u>Slavery</u> existed in ancient Greece.
   A. a system in which one person can own another
   B. type of building with columns
   C. the study of the universe
   D. a system of measurement

6. The hikers <u>quickened</u> the pace.
   F. took a rest
   G. felt better
   H. cleaned up
   J. speeded up

7. The <u>runaway</u> asked for help.
   A. person with no money
   B. person who is sick
   C. person who is from another country
   D. person who has left somewhere secretly

Part 2: Comprehension

Use what you know about the selection to answer each item.

8. According to this selection, Harriet's master was—
   F. Dr. Thompson.
   G. John Tubman.
   H. Mr. Trent.
   J. Ezekiel Hunn.

9. When Harriet Tubman realized that her mother had been tricked into remaining a slave, she knew that she—
   A. had to hire a lawyer to become free herself.
   B. would never be free.
   C. would have to go outside the legal system to become free.
   D. had to go to a judge to free her mother.

10. Harriet trusted the Quaker woman who approached her one morning because—
    F. the stranger was a female.
    G. Quakers did not believe in slavery.
    H. the woman asked Harriet's name
    J. the woman lived near Dr. Thompson's plantation.

© Scott Foresman 5

GO ON ➤

11. How were Harriet's brothers different from her?
    - A. They did not mind being slaves.
    - B. They wanted to be sold South.
    - C. They were not as brave as she was.
    - D. They were not as physically strong as she was.

12. Just before Harriet reached the Hunns' house, she—
    - F. got a pair of new shoes from Thomas Garrett.
    - G. heard slave hunters talking about a runaway girl.
    - H. sold her quilt.
    - J. put on elegant clothes to wear to the Pennsylvania border.

13. "She wanted to repay her kindness. She had no money, but she had one thing she valued." Which is the best paraphrase of these sentences?
    - A. She wanted to show she was thankful. Although she had no money, she did own one valuable item.
    - B. She wanted to get something back for being so kind. She didn't care about money, but she loved nice things.
    - C. She decided that the only way to repay the woman was with kindness, since she had no money.
    - D. She didn't want to have to pay the woman, since she had no money and only one valuable possession.

14. Harriet knows that she has found the right man in the cemetery when he—
    - F. tips his hat toward her.
    - G. says he has a ticket for the railroad.
    - H. gives her a pair of shoes.
    - J. tells her that he is a Quaker.

15. Ezekiel Hunn and Thomas Garrett would likely agree that—
    - A. slaves are property and should be returned to their owners.
    - B. a runaway slave is worth about the same as a bale of cotton.
    - C. Harriet Tubman did a foolish thing when she tried to escape.
    - D. no one has the right to own another human being.

STOP

Paraphrasing

- **Paraphrasing** is explaining something in your own words.

- A paraphrase should include only the author's ideas and opinions. When paraphrasing, don't change the meaning or add your own opinions.

Directions: Read the passage below. Each sentence is numbered.

(1) In the 1600s, slavery spread quickly in the South, where laborers toiled on large plantations that grew cotton, tobacco, and other crops. (2) But in the North, where small farms and businesses existed, there were fewer slaves. (3) During the 1700s, many American leaders began to speak out against slavery, which nonetheless continued to grow. (4) By 1860, the Southern states had about four million slaves. (5) In fact, slaves made up almost a third of the population in the region at that time.

Directions: Complete the table. Rewrite the numbered sentences in your own words.

Sentences	Paraphrases
1	**1.**
2	**2.**
3	**3.**
4	**4.**
5	**5.**

Notes for Home: Your child read a passage and then retold parts of it in his or her own words. ***Home Activity:*** Read a magazine article together with your child. Let your child restate individual sentences in his or her own words.

Main Idea and Supporting Details/Summarizing

Directions: Read the passage. Then read each question about the passage. Choose the best answer to each question. Mark the letter for the answer you have chosen.

Slavery

The practice of human slavery is something we would like to think had a short history that has long since ceased to be. It is hard to imagine how any group of people could think they could own another group of people.

It is a sad truth, however, that slavery has a long history. There is evidence that slavery was first practiced in prehistoric times. It became widespread in Greece and in the Roman Empire. During the 1500s and 1600s, slavery was established in the New World as Europeans established colonies in the Americas. They brought slaves from Africa to work on sugar plantations in the West Indies and South America. Later, slavery spread to North America.

Eventually, changing attitudes about human rights brought an end to slavery in most parts of the world. But slavery is still practiced today in parts of Africa, Asia, and South America. While the number of people living in slavery is unknown, most slaves are believed to be captives of war or persons sold into slavery to pay debts.

People who are enslaved are almost always restricted in many ways. Often they cannot legally marry or have a family. They cannot testify in court, vote, or own property. They are forced to work hard for little or no pay.

1. The main idea in the second paragraph is that—
   A. Greece had slaves.
   B. Slavery ended in places.
   C. Asia still has slavery.
   D. The practice of slavery is very old.

2. A detail that supports the main idea of the second paragraph is that—
   F. slaves are restricted.
   G. there was slavery in prehistoric times.
   H. slavery is very old.
   J. slaves can't vote.

3. The main idea in the fourth paragraph is that—
   A. slaves are restricted.
   B. slaves can't testify in court.
   C. Africa has slavery.
   D. attitudes have changed.

4. A detail that supports the main idea of the fourth paragraph is that—
   F. the New World had slavery.
   G. slavery is historic.
   H. attitudes have changed.
   J. slaves can't testify in court.

5. Which statement best summarizes the article?
   A. Slavery is everywhere.
   B. Slavery is an old and inhumane practice.
   C. Slavery has now ended.
   D. Slavery means hard work.

Notes for Home: Your child identified the main ideas and supporting details of an article and summarized it. *Home Activity:* Read a newspaper article with your child. Together, identify its main ideas and supporting details. Then have your child summarize the article.

Writing Across Texts

Directions: Think about how "The Long Path to Freedom" and "How the Underground Railroad Got Its Name" help describe the escape system for slaves known as the Underground Railroad. What might slaves have wanted to know about the Underground Railroad before they risked their lives and made the trip? Complete the following table by listing questions slaves may have had.

Questions About the Underground Railroad
What are the risks?
1.
2.
3.
4.
5.

Write a Brochure

Use questions from your table, details from both selections, and information from any other sources to write and illustrate a secret brochure designed for Underground Railroad conductors to help them help slaves understand and prepare for their journeys to freedom.

Notes for Home: Your child designed a brochure about the Underground Railroad. *Home Activity:* Help your child write a poem about what it might have been like to be hiding, or hiding someone, on the Underground Railroad.

Grammar: Pronouns

Directions: Replace each phrase with a pronoun. Write the letter of the pronoun of the line.

_____ 1. Harriet Tubman   **a.** he

_____ 2. my friend and I   **b.** she

_____ 3. the runaway slaves   **c.** we

_____ 4. the Underground Railroad **d.** it

_____ 5. Abraham Lincoln   **e.** they

Directions: Choose the correct pronoun in ( ) to complete the sentence. Write the pronoun on the line.

_____ 6. (We/Us) were walking near the State House in Boston.

_____ 7. (I/Me) was the one who noticed the statue.

_____ 8. What I learned about the statue impressed (I/me).

_____ 9. The name Colonel Robert Gould Shaw puzzled (we/us).

_____ 10. Then (we/us) read that Colonel Shaw had led a regiment of African American soldiers in the Civil War.

_____ 11. As (we/us) discovered, this Massachusetts regiment had fought bravely.

_____ 12. It saddened (I/me), though, that almost half of the regiment had been killed in a single battle.

_____ 13. A passerby told (we/us) that one soldier had been given the Medal of Honor.

_____ 14. That really impressed (I/me).

_____ 15. Would (we/us) learn other interesting facts on our trip to Boston?

Directions: Replace the underlined pronoun and verb with a contraction. Write the contraction on the line.

_____ 16. <u>I will</u> tell you about one man's remarkable rise from slavery.

_____ 17. <u>You have</u> heard of Frederick Douglass, haven't you?

_____ 18. Although <u>he had</u> been a slave, he learned to read and write.

_____ 19. <u>It is</u> amazing that, a few years after escaping, he wrote a book.

_____ 20. Today <u>he is</u> still a much-quoted historical figure.

Notes for Home: Your child identified pronouns, used *I, me, we,* and *us* in sentences, and wrote contractions. *Home Activity:* Read sentences aloud, leaving out the pronoun. Ask your child which pronoun makes sense in each sentence.

Grammar: Subject and Object Pronouns

Pronouns used as the subjects of sentences are called **subject pronouns.**

<u>He</u> traveled with friends.

<u>They</u> cared about his safety.

Singular Subject Pronouns: I, you, he, she, it

Plural Subject Pronouns: we, you, they

When you use a person's name and a pronoun in a compound subject, be sure to use a subject pronoun. When *I* is used with another noun, *I* comes last.

Aunt Kate and <u>I</u> went on the journey too.

<u>She</u> and <u>I</u> had wanted to join the group.

Pronouns that follow action verbs are called **object pronouns.**

We joined <u>him</u> near the train station.

Singular Object Pronouns: me, you, him, her, it

Plural Object Pronouns: us, you, them

Directions: Underline each subject pronoun once. Underline each object pronoun twice.

1. We accompanied them on the road.

2. He and they helped us along the way.

3. Later we met two more friends and asked them for help.

4. They led us to a restaurant owner.

5. He and the cook gave us a meal inside.

Directions: Circle the correct pronoun in ( ) to complete each sentence.

6. The two men offered (wc/us) plenty of food.

7. (They/them) asked about our trip on the road.

8. They gave Aunt Kate and (I/me) travel directions.

9. Soon (she/her) said it was time to go.

10. We had extra rolls, so we took (they/them) in a paper bag.

Notes for Home: Your child identified subject and object pronouns. *Home Activity:* Look at magazine pictures or photographs together. Ask your child to use subject pronouns and object pronouns to describe the people and actions in each picture.

Grammar: Subject and Object Pronouns

Directions: Underline the pronoun in each sentence. Write **S** on the line if the pronoun is a subject pronoun. Write **O** if it is an object pronoun.

_____ 1. We read about a slave named Kunta Kinte.

_____ 2. He traveled from Africa to America by ship, long ago.

_____ 3. The voyage was a terrible ordeal, yet Kinte survived it.

_____ 4. Traders in slavery had captured him in Africa.

_____ 5. The slave trade made them wealthy at the cost of human rights and human lives.

_____ 6. Alex Haley gave us Kinte's true story in a book called *Roots*.

_____ 7. He had heard about the young African boy from older members of the Haley family.

_____ 8. The capture of Kunta Kinte moved him greatly.

_____ 9. I thought the story was fascinating.

_____ 10. My grandparents bought me the TV film version of *Roots*.

Directions: Circle the correct pronoun in ( ) to complete each sentence.

11. (Us/We) wanted information about the TV film.

12. We admired Kunta Kinte and wondered who had played (him/he).

13. A classmate and (me/I) tried several searches on the computer catalog.

14. A librarian supplied (we/us) with printouts of reviews.

15. Your library can help (you/it) learn more about Alex Haley, Kunta Kinte, *Roots*, and slavery.

Write a Journal

Think of a person from the past that you learned about from your family or from a book or TV show. Imagine you are that person. What is your life like? What difficulties have you had to face? On a separate sheet of paper, write several entries for a journal. Tell what things you might see or have experienced. Use subject and object pronouns.

Notes for Home: Your child identified and used subject pronouns and object pronouns in sentences. *Home Activity:* Read a newspaper or magazine article together. Ask your child to identify all the subject or object pronouns he or she sees.

Grammar: Subject and Object Pronouns

> The action verb in each sentence below is underlined. Circle the pronoun or pronouns in each sentence.
>
> **1.** I <u>bought</u> a parakeet from a friend last week.
>
> **2.** Dad <u>thanked</u> her.
>
> **3.** He and I <u>left</u> with the new bird.
>
> Notice that in sentences 1 and 3, the pronouns are the subjects of the sentences. These are **subject pronouns.** In sentence 2, the pronoun comes after the action verb. It is an **object pronoun.**

> Use a **subject pronoun** as the subject of a sentence. Use an **object pronoun** after an action verb. When you use *I* or *me* and another pronoun or someone else's name, use *I* or *me* last.

Directions: Write each sentence with the correct word or words in ( ).

1. Judy and (I/me) read books about birds.

_____

2. Mom and Dad gave (me and Judy/Judy and me) some information.

_____

3. Dad and (I/me) taught the bird how to talk.

_____

Directions: Write each sentence with the correct pronoun in ( ). Circle **subject** if the pronoun is in the subject. Circle **object** if the pronoun is in the predicate.

4. Hilda and (her/she) own a parrot.

_____   subject   object

5. Fernando and (I/me) are raising pigeons.

_____   subject   object

6. Our parents help Fernando and (I/me).

_____ _____   subject   object

Notes for Home: Your child chose subject and object pronouns to complete sentences. *Home Activity:* Talk about what your family has been doing recently. Have your child write sentences about family activities, using subject and object pronouns. *(he, she, they; him, her, them)*

© Scott Foresman 5

Grammar: Subject and Object Pronouns

Directions: Circle the pronouns in each sentence below. Write each pronoun under the correct heading on the chart.

1. Tena and I made that clay sculpture of a cat.

2. It and the other sculptures are on the table.

3. The art instructors helped her and me.

4. A famous artist once spoke to us.

5. She and they worked with the students.

6. We and the other students learned a great deal.

7. You and he should visit the art class sometime.

8. Tena will show you two and him what to do.

Subject Pronouns	Object Pronouns

Directions: Complete each sentence by writing a name from the name box and the correct pronoun from the pronoun box.

Bill Emilio Kim Lucy	I me

9. _____ and _____ bought a book.

10. The store owner led _____ and _____ to it.

11. My father drove _____ and _____ to the store.

Write a Paragraph

On a separate sheet of paper, write a paragraph about a project you might do. Tell how you and a friend would work together to complete the project. Use subject and object pronouns.

Notes for Home: Your child identified subject and object pronouns in sentences. *Home Activity:* Sit around a table with a group. Play a passing game. Pass objects as fast as possible, saying a sentence with two pronouns, such as, "I pass this _____ to him" as you pass the object.

Word Study: Suffixes

Directions: Letters added to the ends of words are called **suffixes.** Suffixes can change the meaning of the base word. Add a suffix to each word below to make a new word. Write each new word on the line.

	Base Word		Suffix		New Word
1.	free	+	-dom	=	_____
2.	legal	+	-ly	=	_____
3.	own	+	-er	=	_____
4.	grate	+	-ful	=	_____
5.	joy	+	-ous	=	_____
6.	risk	+	-y	=	_____

Directions: Read the diary entry below. Find nine words that have the suffix **-ly, -er, -ful, -ous,** or **-y.** Circle the words. Then write the base word and the suffix on the line connected by a + sign. For example, for **slowly,** you would write **slow + ly.**

June 9, 1863

On a dark and rainy night, I packed my things into a bundle. Silently, I slipped from the cabin and quickly disappeared into the woods. The journey was dangerous and lonely. Each day I feared that a slave tracker was following me. But when I crossed the state line, my heart set up a thunderous beat. A joyful feeling came over me. I was on my own! I was free! And it felt wonderful!

7. _____

8. _____

9. _____

10. _____

11. _____

12. _____

13. _____

14. _____

15. _____

Notes for Home: Your child added suffixes to base words to make new words, such as *slow + ly = slowly.* **Home Activity:** Read an advertisement with your child. Help your child notice words with suffixes. Ask your child to write down the words and circle the suffixes.

Spelling: Suffixes -able, -ible, -ant, -ent

Pretest Directions: Fold back the page along the dotted line. On the blanks, write the spelling words as they are dictated. When you have finished the test, unfold the page and check your words.

1._____

2._____

3._____

4._____

5._____

6._____

7._____

8._____

9._____

10._____

11._____

12._____

13._____

14._____

15._____

16._____

17._____

18._____

19._____

20._____

1. This is a **comfortable** chair.

2. That is a **reasonable** question.

3. His shirt is hand **washable**.

4. Are you **agreeable** to the plan?

5. She owns a **valuable** painting.

6. Who is **responsible** for you?

7. I saw a **convertible** car go by.

8. The hose is **flexible**.

9. Jane is a very **sensible** person.

10. He bought a **reversible** jacket.

11. That **contestant** won the game.

12. Are you **defiant** of my orders?

13. A detective must be **observant**.

14. Their **servant** has her own car.

15. The house has a new **occupant**.

16. The **student** won an award.

17. I received an **urgent** letter.

18. We are **confident** we will win.

19. He is a **resident** of San Antonio.

20. My **opponent** played well.

Notes for Home: Your child took a pretest on words that have the suffixes *-able*, *-ible*, *-ant*, and *-ent*. **Home Activity:** Help your child learn misspelled words before the final test. Your child can underline the word parts that caused the problems and concentrate on those parts.

Think and Practice

Spelling: Suffixes -able, -ible, -ant, -ent

Word List				
comfortable	valuable	sensible	observant	urgent
reasonable	responsible	reversible	servant	confident
washable	convertible	contestant	occupant	resident
agreeable	flexible	defiant	student	opponent

Directions: Choose the words from the box that have the suffixes **-able** and **-ible.** Write each word in the correct column.

Words with -able

1. _____

2. _____

3. _____

4. _____

5. _____

Words with -ible

6. _____

7. _____

8. _____

9. _____

10. _____

Directions: Choose the word from the box that best matches each clue. Write the word on the line.

_____ 11. someone who enters a contest

_____ 12. a person who occupies a place

_____ 13. someone who serves

_____ 14. a person who studies

_____ 15. watchful, quick to notice

_____ 16. the person who resides in a place

_____ 17. something that needs immediate attention

_____ 18. disobedient

_____ 19. a person or group on the opposite side in a game or debate

_____ 20. very sure of yourself

Notes for Home: Your child spelled words that end with *-able, -ible, -ant,* and *-ent.* **Home Activity:** Start to spell each word slowly, one letter at a time. When your child recognizes the word, have him or her say the whole word and then spell it.

Spelling: Suffixes -able, -ible, -ant, -ent

Directions: Proofread this speech. Find five spelling mistakes.
Use the proofreading marks to correct each mistake.

≡	Make a capital.
/	Make a small letter.
∧	Add something.
✍	Take out something.
⊙	Add a period.
¶	Begin a new paragraph.

Ladies and gentlemen, I am an opponant of slavery who brings you an urgent message today. No servcnt can be comfortable as a forced resident or occupcnt in a home that is not agreeable. As responscble and sensible people, we must admit that slavery is not reasonible nor humane. Free all slaves, because freedom is valuable to all people!

Spelling Tip

For base words that end in
e, drop the **e** before adding
the suffixes **-able, -ible,
-ant,** and **-ent.** For most
words that end in **y,** change
the **y** to an **i** and then add
the suffix.

Word List

comfortable	responsible	contestant	student
reasonable	convertible	defiant	urgent
washable	flexible	observant	confident
agreeable	sensible	servant	resident
valuable	reversible	occupant	opponent

Write a Speech

Imagine you were asked to give a speech about a
subject you feel strongly about. On a separate sheet of
paper, write the speech you would deliver. Try to use
at least five of your spelling words.

© Scott Foresman 5

Notes for Home: Your child spelled words that end with *-able, -ible, -ant,* and *-ent.* **Home**
Activity: Spell each spelling word for your child, but purposely make one or more letters
wrong. See if your child can recognize each error and spell the word correctly.

Spelling: Suffixes -able, -ible, -ant, -ent

REVIEW

Word List				
comfortable	valuable	sensible	observant	urgent
reasonable	responsible	reversible	servant	confident
washable	convertible	contestant	occupant	resident
agreeable	flexible	defiant	student	opponent

Directions: Complete each equation to spell a word from the box. Write each word on the line.

1. serve – e + ant = _____

2. observe – e + ant = _____

3. urge – e + ent = _____

4. study – y + ent = _____

5. defy – y + i + ant = _____

6. confide – e + ent = _____

7. occupy – y + ant = _____

8. reside – e + ent = _____

9. contest + ant = _____

10. flex + ible = _____

Directions: Choose the word from the box that best completes each sentence. Write the word on the line to the left.

_____ 11. Car Salesperson: You can buy this car at a very _____ price.

_____ 12. Home Owner: I'll find out who's _____ for this broken window!

_____ 13. Clothing Store Clerk: You'll love this _____ jacket. It's green on one side and purple on the other.

_____ 14. Grandmother: Do you need another blanket, dear, or are you _____ now?

_____ 15. Team Captain: If it's _____ to everyone, we'll meet for practice at 10:00 A.M.

_____ 16. Detective: Someone has stolen a very _____ diamond necklace!

_____ 17. Scout Leader: If you get lost, the _____ thing to do is to follow the creek.

_____ 18. Baby Sitter: Oh, no! I thought the walls were all _____.

_____ 19. Driver: Let's put down the top on the _____ and drive it.

_____ 20. Chess player: My _____ must make the next move.

Notes for Home: Your child spelled words that end with *-able, -ible, -ant,* and *-ent*. **Home Activity:** Read a newspaper article with your child. Together, see how many words you can find that have the ending *-able, -ible, -ant,* or *-ent*.

Time Line

A **time line** is a line divided into years or other periods of time. The line is labeled
with events that show when events happened or will happen in time order.

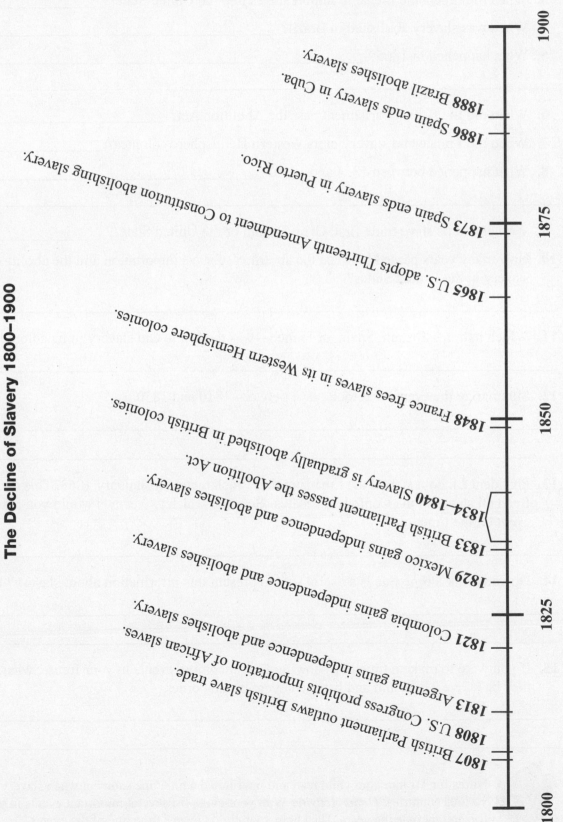

Directions: The time line below shows when slavery was abolished, or outlawed,
in various parts of the world. Use it to answer the questions on the next page.

The Decline of Slavery 1800–1900

1900

1888 Brazil abolishes slavery.

1886 Spain ends slavery in Cuba.

1875

1873 Spain ends slavery in Puerto Rico.

1865 U.S. adopts Thirteenth Amendment to Constitution abolishing slavery.

1850

1848 France frees slaves in its Western Hemisphere colonies.

1834–1840 Slavery is gradually abolished in British colonies.

1833 British Parliament passes the Abolition Act.

1829 Mexico gains independence and abolishes slavery.

1825

1821 Colombia gains independence and abolishes slavery.

1813 Argentina gains independence and abolishes slavery.

1808 U.S. Congress prohibits importation of African slaves.

1807 British Parliament outlaws British slave trade.

1800

Name _____

1. How many years does the time line show? _____

2. How many years does each of the four sections of the time line represent? _____

3. When did it become illegal to import slaves into the United States? _____

4. When was slavery abolished in Brazil? _____

5. What happened in 1865? _____

_____

6. When did the British Parliament pass the Abolition Act? _____

7. When did France end slavery in its Western Hemisphere colonies? _____

8. What happened between 1834 and 1840? _____

_____

9. Who ended its slave trade first, Great Britain or the United States? _____

10. How many years passed between the abolition of slave importation and the abolition of slavery in the United States?

_____

11. Which nation—Britain, Spain, or France—was the last to end slavery in its colonies?

_____

12. Summarize the events that took place between 1810 and 1830.

_____

_____

13. President Lincoln signed the Emancipation Proclamation in January 1863. This document freed all slaves in the Confederate states. Between which two events would you place this event on the time line?

_____

14. Do you think a time line is a useful way to present this information about slavery? Explain.

_____

_____

15. If you were to make a time line showing five upcoming events in your future, what would they be? Give a date and and list each event in time order.

_____

_____

Notes for Home: Your child read and interpreted a time line showing when slavery ended in various countries. *Home Activity:* With your child, list several important events in your child's life and include the years. Then help your child create a time line of the events.

Family Times

Name_____

Summary

<u>~</u>

Connecticut Cricket Sees New York City

Chester Cricket and Lulu Pigeon have told each other their life stories when Lulu finds out that Chester does not know much about New York City. She persuades Chester to cling to her claw while she takes him on a thrilling flight to Central Park, to the top of the Empire State Building, and to the Statue of Liberty. The thrill is almost too much when Chester falls from the Empire State Building. Lulu, however, is quick to the rescue so that the two may continue their adventure.

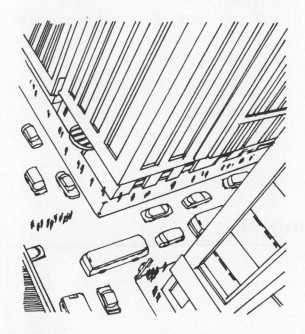

Activity
Draw a Picture. Use crayons, markers, paints, or another medium to illustrate one of Chester's adventures with Lulu. Choose a scene that is not illustrated in the selection.

Reading Skills

<u>~</u>

Visualizing

Visualizing is creating a picture in your mind as you read. An author may help you visualize by using:

❖ **imagery,** or words that create a strong picture. For example, in the story Chester sees "the jiggling reflection of the moon in the lake at Central Park." This striking image helps create a picture in the reader's mind.

❖ **sensory details,** or words that tell how something looks, sounds, smells, tastes, or feels. For example, Chester notices "the shooshing of leaves, the nighttime countryside whispering of insects and little animals" in Central Park. These details appeal strongly to the sense of hearing.

Activity
What Is It? With your eyes closed, have someone hand you a piece of food or some other object. Describe it using details of touch, smell, taste, or hearing. Try to identify the object. Then open your eyes to see whether you guessed correctly.

Family Times

© Scott Foresman 5

Tested Vocabulary

Words to Know

Knowing the meanings of these words is important to reading *Chester Cricket's Pigeon Ride.* Practice using these words to learn their meanings.

clinging hanging on to something

excursions short trips

feelers parts of an insect that are used as sensors

gale very strong wind

thrill exciting feeling

Grammar

Pronouns and Referents

A **pronoun** is a word that takes the place of a noun or noun phrase. The **referent** is the noun or noun phrase to which the pronoun refers. Pronouns and their referents may or may not be found in the same sentence. In the following sentences, the pronouns are underlined once, and then referents are underlined twice.

<u>Chester</u> thought <u>he</u> would never stop falling.

<u>Lulu</u> flew under Chester. <u>She</u> caught Chester in her claws.

Activity
Appreciate Pronouns. See if you can describe something unusual that happened to you today without using any pronouns. (This is harder than it sounds!)

Tested Spelling Words

_____   _____   _____   _____

_____   _____   _____   _____

_____   _____   _____   _____

_____   _____   _____   _____

Visualizing

- **Visualizing** is creating a picture in your mind as you read.

- An author may help you visualize by using imagery. This happens when an author uses words that give you a strong mental picture or image. *Enormous billowing clouds* is an example of imagery.

- Another way an author may help you become part of what you are reading is through sensory details. Authors use words that describe how something looks, sounds, smells, tastes, or feels to do this.

Directions: Reread "Little Billy's Swan Rides." Then complete the table. List examples of words and phrases from the story that appeal to one of the five senses.

Example	Sense
house was quiet	hearing
curtains were drawn back	1.
2.	3.
4.	5.
6.	7.
8.	9.
10.	11.
12.	13.
14.	15.

Notes for Home: Your child read a story and identified words and phrases that helped create a mental picture of story events. ***Home Activity:*** Choose a familiar place. Give clues about how this place looks, smells, and sounds. Have your child guess the place.

Name _____

Vocabulary

Directions: Read the following paragraph. Choose the word from the box that best completes each sentence. Write the word on the matching numbered line to the right.

Tom Cat's whiskers acted as **1.** _____ to help him find his way in the dark. Suddenly, a shadow came swooping down and swept him up in the air! As Tom Cat rose into the air, the very strong winds felt like a **2.** _____ against his face. **3.** _____ to whatever had snatched him, Tom yelled for help. Then he heard a deep chuckle and tilted his head back to see Harry Hawk! "Doesn't it give you a **4.** _____ to fly on exciting **5.** _____ such as these?" asked Harry innocently.

1. _____

2. _____

3. _____

4. _____

5. _____

Check the Words You Know
__ clinging
__ excursions
__ feelers
__ gale
__ thrill

Directions: Choose the word from the box that has the same or nearly the same meaning as each word or phrase below. Write the word on the line.

6. clutching _____

7. high wind _____

8. trips _____

9. excitement _____

10. an animal's sensors _____

Write a Travel Log

Where do your journeys take you? On a separate sheet of paper, write an entry in a travel log describing a real or imaginary journey. Describe the people you meet, the animals you see, and the adventures you have. Use as many vocabulary words as you can in your travel log.

Notes for Home: Your child identified and used vocabulary words from *Chester Cricket's Pigeon Ride.* **Home Activity:** Invite your child to draw a cartoon describing an adventure on a first flight. Help him or her use as many vocabulary words as possible in the speech balloons.

Visualizing

- **Visualizing** is creating a picture in your mind as you read.

- Authors may help you visualize by using imagery. These are words that give you a strong mental picture, or image.

- Another way an author may help you visualize is through sensory details. These are words that describe how something looks, sounds, smells, tastes, or feels.

Directions: Reread what happens in *Chester Cricket's Pigeon Ride* when Lulu takes Chester to Central Park. Then answer the questions below. Think about how the author uses imagery and sensory details to help you visualize.

"Here's Central Park," Lulu screeched against the wind.

And now Chester had another thrill. For there weren't only sycamore trees in the park. The cricket could smell birches, beeches, and maples—elms, oaks—almost as many kinds of trees as Connecticut itself had to offer. And there was the moon!—the crescent moon—reflected in a little lake. Sounds, too, rose up to him: the shooshing of leaves, the nighttime countryside whispering of insects and little animals, and—best of all—a brook that was arguing with itself, as it splashed over rocks. The miracle of Central Park, a sheltered wilderness in the midst of the city, pierced Chester's heart with joy.

From CHESTER CRICKET'S PIGEON RIDE by George Selden pictures by Garth Williams. Text copyright © 1981 by George Selden Thompson. Illustrations copyright © 1981 by Garth Williams. Reprinted by permission of Farrar, Straus, & Giroux, Inc.

1. Which details in the passage help you visualize what the park smells like?

_____

2. Which details in the passage help you visualize what the park sounds like?

_____

3. Which details help you visualize what the park looks like?

_____

4. What sound reminds Chester of an argument?

_____

5. How does the author help you visualize the view from the top of the Empire State Building? On a separate sheet of paper, list the sensory details and imagery he uses.

© Scott Foresman 5

Notes for Home: Your child read a story and pictured the scene in his or her mind. *Home Activity:* Have your child listen as you describe how an object looks, sounds, smells, feels, or tastes. See if your child can guess what it is. Then switch roles and repeat.

Selection Test

Directions: Choose the best answer to each item. Mark the letter for the answer you have chosen.

Part 1: Vocabulary

Find the answer choice that means about the same as the underlined word in each sentence.

1. This is such a thrill!
   - A. scary movie
   - B. exciting feeling
   - C. grand performance
   - D. sudden storm

2. He was clinging to his mother.
   - F. speaking in a soft voice
   - G. singing words over and over again
   - H. sitting next to
   - J. holding on tightly

3. They flew into the gale.
   - A. side of a mountain
   - B. tall building in a city
   - C. very strong wind
   - D. large storm cloud

4. Margo has taken many excursions.
   - F. photographs
   - G. tests
   - H. helpings
   - J. trips

5. A cricket has several feelers.
   - A. close friends
   - B. parts of an insect's body used for sensing
   - C. family members
   - D. strong emotions

Part 2: Comprehension

Use what you know about the story to answer each item.

6. Chester's friend Lulu is a—
   - F. pigeon.
   - G. cricket.
   - H. mouse.
   - J. cat.

7. How did Chester get from Connecticut to the city?
   - A. He crossed the Atlantic on a sailing vessel.
   - B. He was carried there inside a picnic basket.
   - C. He took an airplane ride.
   - D. He flew there on a pigeon's back.

8. Lulu gives Chester a—
   - F. ride on the subway.
   - G. free trip to Connecticut.
   - H. place to stay in Bryant Park.
   - J. tour of New York.

9. Which phrase best helps you see in your mind what Central Park looks like?
   - A. "Big beautiful Central Park!"
   - B. "coasted down through the air"
   - C. "a sheltered wilderness in the midst of the city"
   - D. "the best place in the city"

10. How does Chester feel about flying?
    - F. completely terrified
    - G. extremely bored
    - H. a little afraid, but excited
    - J. somewhat embarrassed

11. While flying down into Central Park, Lulu probably looks most like a—
    - A. paper airplane.
    - B. hunting bird.
    - C. hot-air balloon.
    - D. speeding bullet.

GO ON ➡

12. How can you tell that Chester is very happy in Central Park?

F. He jumps up and down.

G. He dances around with Lulu.

H. He holds on to Lulu's claw.

J. He chirps to his heart's content.

13. Which sentence from the story gives an opinion?

A. "Lulu gripped the pinnacle of the TV antenna with both her claws."

B. "They reached the Battery, . . . part of lower New York."

C. "The finest shops in all the world are on Fifth Avenue."

D. "Her right hand was holding something up."

14. After being blown off the Empire State Building, Chester most likely wants to return to the drainpipe because he—

F. is angry at Lulu for putting his life in danger.

G. needs to feel safe again.

H. wants to tell everyone about his adventure.

J. wants to pack up and leave New York.

15. Which part of this story is fantasy?

A. A cricket talks to a pigeon.

B. A pigeon flies over New York.

C. A cricket chirps in Central Park.

D. A pigeon looks at the Statue of Liberty.

STOP

Visualizing

- **Visualizing** is creating a picture in your mind as you read.

- Authors may help you visualize by using imagery. These are words that give you a strong mental picture.

- Another way an author may help you visualize is through sensory details. These are words that describe how something looks, sounds, smells, tastes, or feels.

Directions: Read the story below.

Their first trip to Yankee Stadium! Josh and Tom were excited. The view from their seats, high up in the stadium, was marvelous.

The huge field was brilliantly green. The Yankees' white uniforms gleamed in the sunshine. The sound of the stadium organ mingled with the vendors' cries of "Ice cream!" "Popcorn!" and "Hot dogs!" The smells of the hot food made Tom's mouth

water. He bought a steaming hot dog. Josh thirstily gulped a tart lemonade.

Then the voice of the announcer boomed, "Good afternoon, ladies and gentlemen. Welcome to Yankee Stadium." Josh and Tom exchanged wide grins as they settled back to enjoy the game. The seats were a bit hard, and there wasn't much room to stretch their legs, but who cared? Today was a dream come true!

Directions: Complete the web. Visualize the story details in your mind. What do you see? hear? feel? taste? smell?

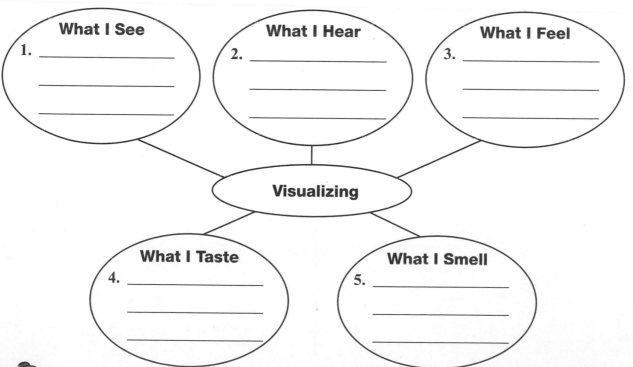

What I See
1. _____
_____
_____

What I Hear
2. _____
_____
_____

What I Feel
3. _____
_____
_____

Visualizing

What I Taste
4. _____
_____
_____

What I Smell
5. _____
_____
_____

Notes for Home: Your child read a story and visualized, or pictured, the story details in his or her mind. ***Home Activity:*** Ask your child to describe his or her favorite place. Encourage your child to describe what can be seen, heard, smelled, felt, and tasted in that place.

Paraphrasing

Directions: Read the story. Then read each question about the story. Choose the best answer to each question. Mark the letter for the answer you have chosen.

Strange Planet

Maria, the nation's newest astronaut, journeyed to the planet Backwards. No one had ever explored the territory before. Maria was overwhelmed by what she found there.

On this planet, everything appeared upside down and backwards from the way it appeared on Earth. The planet had a ground of clouds and a sky of grass. The trees grew with their leaves down and their roots up. When it rained, the rain actually traveled upward.

The people of Backwards had their faces on the backs of their heads. They greeted Maria with a "good-bye." And when they were ready to leave, they said "hello."

"This planet certainly deserves its name," Maria said to herself. She couldn't wait to get back to Earth, where everything and everyone was right side up and forward!

1. Which of the following best paraphrases the first two sentences in the first paragraph?
   A. Astronaut Maria wasn't sure she wanted to go to Backwards.
   B. Astronaut Maria was sent to the planet Backwards.
   C. Astronaut Maria was the first to explore the planet Backwards.
   D. Maria, the nation's newest astronaut, journeyed to the planet Backwards.

2. Which of the following best paraphrases the second and third sentences in the second paragraph?
   F. Clouds and grass were reversed, and trees grew upside down.
   G. The sky was grass, and the ground was clouds.

H. Leaves grew down, and roots grew up on trees.
J. The trees had no roots, and the leaves grew underground.

3. Which of the following best paraphrases the third paragraph?
   A. People had backward heads, feet, and arms.
   B. People had backward heads and said "good-bye" first and "hello" last.
   C. The people of Backwards had their faces on the backs of their heads.
   D. People had backward heads and said "hello" last.

4. Which of the following best paraphrases the last paragraph?
   F. Maria was frightened by the planet Backwards.
   G. Maria couldn't wait to get back to Earth and return to a normal life.
   H. Maria was ready to leave Backwards and return to Earth.
   J. Maria found Backwards deserving of its name and was eager to return to a right side up and forward Earth.

5. Which of the following best paraphrases the whole story?
   A. Maria traveled to Backwards and never returned to Earth.
   B. Maria loved being an astronaut.
   C. The people of Backwards do everything in reverse.
   D. Astronaut Maria explored Backwards, a planet where everything is backwards or upside down.

Notes for Home: Your child identified statements that best paraphrase a story. *Home Activity:* Say a pair of sentences to your child, such as *It would be fun to take a vacation. We could go camping.* Challenge your child to restate the same idea in a single sentence.

Name _____

Writing Across Texts

Directions: Think about how Chester the cricket traveled in the excerpt from *Chester Cricket's Pigeon Ride*. The animals in "Easy Riders" also ride on other animals. Complete the web with reasons explaining why these animals travel that way.

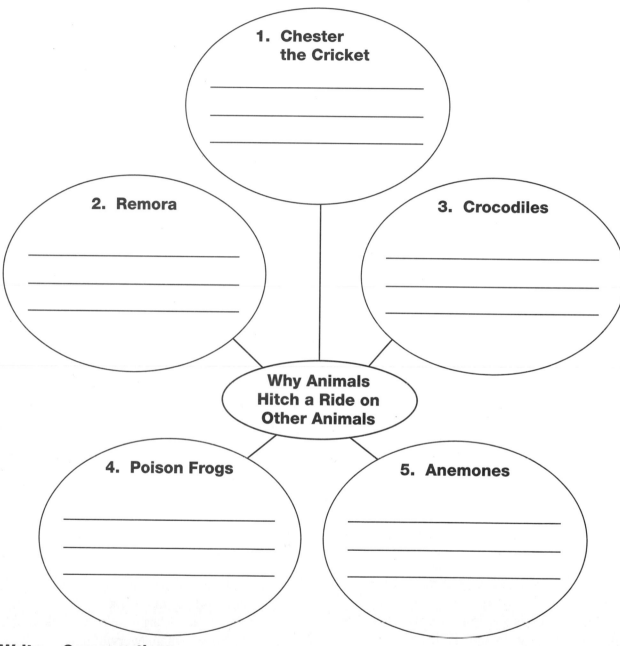

1. **Chester the Cricket**

2. **Remora**

3. **Crocodiles**

Why Animals Hitch a Ride on Other Animals

4. **Poison Frogs**

5. **Anemones**

Write a Conversation

Use the ideas from your web to write a conversation between the animals on the web above. Write on a separate sheet of paper.

Notes for Home: Your child wrote a conversation between animals who are in selections they read. *Home Activity:* With your child, read a story about an animal who depends on others. Ask your child how the animal in the story is like a person.

© Scott Foresman 5

Name _____

Grammar: Subject and Object Pronouns

REVIEW

Directions: Circle the correct pronoun in ( ) to complete each sentence. Then write **S** or **O** on the line to tell whether it is a subject pronoun or an object pronoun.

_____ 1. Gloria just read *Around the World in Eighty Days,* and (she/her) cannot stop talking about the book.

_____ 2. (It/him) was written by Jules Verne in 1873.

_____ 3. Phileas Fogg and his servant do not look for adventure, but adventure finds (they/them).

_____ 4. To win a wager, (they/them) take a journey around the world.

_____ 5. A detective mistakes Phileas Fogg for a bank robber and follows (he/him).

_____ 6. Since there are no airplanes yet, (they/them) travel by train, ship, elephant, and sailboat.

_____ 7. On Phileas Fogg's incredible journey, (he/him) collects other companions.

_____ 8. The lovely Madame Aouda, for example, is a recent widow when Mr. Fogg meets (she/her).

_____ 9. Amazingly, Mr. Fogg and his group return to London on time, where friends welcome (they/them) home.

_____ 10. Gloria loved the book, and she is recommending (he/it) to everyone.

Directions: Circle the words in ( ) that complete each sentence.

11. (Gloria and I/Gloria and me) both loved Jules Verne's book *Around the World in Eighty Days*.

12. Yesterday (Anthony and I/Anthony and me) decided to go to the library.

13. Gloria met (Anthony and I/Anthony and me) there.

14. Anthony saw a friend, but (Gloria and I/Gloria and me) went right to the computers.

15. Gloria knew what books would please (Anthony and I/Anthony and me).

16. (Gloria, Anthony, and I/Gloria, Anthony, and me) were looking for other books by Jules Verne.

17. (Gloria and I/Gloria and me) found the listings on the computer at the library.

18. *Journey to the Center of the Earth* tempted (Anthony and I/Anthony and me).

19. The title *20,000 Leagues Under the Sea* attracted (Gloria and I/Gloria and me).

20. Jules Verne would soon be taking (my friends and I/my friends and me) on some exciting journeys.

Notes for Home: Your child used the subject pronouns *I, we, you, he, she, it, they* and the object pronouns *me, us, you, him, her, it, them.* **Home Activity:** Write subject and object pronouns on cards. Then take turns choosing a card and using the pronoun in a sentence.

Grammar: Subject and Object Pronouns **507**

Practice

Grammar: Pronouns and Their Referents

Pronouns get most of their meaning from the nouns they replace. The noun or noun phrase that a pronoun replaces is called its **referent.** A referent names the person, place, or thing to which the pronoun refers. In the following sentences, the referents are underlined once, and the pronouns are underlined twice.

<u>Lisa</u> boarded the boat. Then <u>she</u> handed in her ticket.

<u>Dwayne</u> loves <u>airplanes</u>, so <u>he</u> flies in <u>them</u> often.

Pronouns and their referents must agree. In the example sentences above, the singular subject pronoun *she* agrees with its referent, *Lisa.* The plural object pronoun *them* agrees with its referent, *airplanes.*

Directions: Underline the referent or referents once and the pronoun twice in the sentences. Hint: Some pronouns are possessive pronouns

1. Tom and Keisha had no money for a vacation. They planned a fantasy trip instead.

2. Keisha wrote three travel brochures, and Tom read them.

3. Tom praised the ideas in the brochures, and Keisha smiled at him.

4. Tom chose the "Antarctica by Air" trip. He would see dark blue seas, gleaming icebergs, ice streams, and glaciers.

5. Keisha felt pleased. Then she proposed a route to Antarctica.

6. On their imaginary trip, the brother and sister traveled by ship to the tip of South America.

7. There, Tom and Keisha hired a private plane, and it flew over the ocean to the continent of Antarctica.

8. From the aircraft, Tom took the best photos of his life.

9. A helicopter pilot said he would show Tom and Keisha some wildlife.

10. The best part of her journey, Keisha said, was the sight of penguins in a natural habitat.

Notes for Home: Your child identified pronouns and referents. *Home Activity:* Invite your child to write a postcard describing an imaginary journey the family might have taken. Ask your child to use pronouns in the postcard. Then ask him or her to identify the referents.

Grammar: Pronouns and Their Referents

Directions: Use the correct pronoun to complete each sentence. Write the pronoun on the line below. Then, beside the pronoun, write its referent.

1. Sarah liked her host family members in Mexico because _____ were kind.

_____

2. Sarah's parents let _____ live with her Mexican hosts for a month.

_____

3. She had been studying Spanish at her American school and was good at _____.

_____

4. The Mexican hosts told Sarah they would speak only Spanish to _____.

_____

5. Whenever she made a mistake, they carefully explained why _____ was an error.

_____

6. She soon felt at home in Mexico, and when _____ grows up, Sarah wants to live there!

_____

7. When two Mexican children come to live with her family next summer, Sarah will help _____ feel at home.

_____

8. If they don't understand an American word, she will explain _____ to them.

_____

9. When American words have Spanish roots, the Mexican children will learn _____ quickly.

_____

10. Sarah says _____ hopes to practice her Spanish with these Mexican guests.

_____

Write a Get-Help Letter

Imagine that you have voyaged to a strange new world, but now you need to escape from it! On a separate sheet of paper, write a letter you could send in a bottle to get help. Describe your trip, and tell why you are unable to leave. Don't forget to give your location! Use pronouns and referents in your letter.

Notes for Home: Your child wrote pronouns and their referents (the nouns to which pronouns refer). *Home Activity:* Make up sentence pairs that use a noun in the first sentence and a pronoun in the second. Ask your child to identify the referent.

Grammar: Pronouns and Their Referents

In each sentence or pair of sentences, the pronoun is underlined. Circle the referent to which it refers.

1. Mrs. Grady agreed to walk our dog. <u>She</u> was going to do it for a week.

2. Dan and Mack were delighted because Mr. Lawrence chose <u>them</u> to speak first.

Pronouns get most of their meaning from the nouns they replace. The noun or noun phrase that a pronoun replaces is called its **referent.** Pronouns and their referents must agree. In the example sentences above, the singular subject pronoun *she* agrees with its referent, *Mrs. Grady*. The plural object pronoun *them* agrees with its referent *Dan and Mack*.

Directions: Underline each pronoun, and circle each referent in the sentences.

1. Mr. Thomas's students visited a radio station last month. They met the manager in her office.

2. Then the manager gave the class a tour of the building. She was very helpful.

3. Next the class went to see the studio's collection of CDs. It was huge!

4. The next person Mr. Thomas's class met was June Moon, a producer. She gave a short talk about what she did every day.

5. Later a program manager came to speak to the group. He talked about different programs the radio show put on the air.

6. The information the students learned was very valuable to them.

7. Finally, the class reached the studio of the great Deejay Spin. He gave out autographs.

8. Mr. Thomas said he was Deejay Spin's biggest fan!

9. Deejay Spin was glad to talk with the students because they were so excited to learn about what types of things deejays do.

10. After the field trip, the students organized their own radio station!

11. The class did lots of work, but it was worth the time and effort.

12. The first broadcast of the new radio station was yesterday. It was a huge success!

Notes for Home: Your child identified pronouns and their referents—nouns or noun phrases that pronouns replace. ***Home Activity:*** Listen to a radio program. Have your child write some dialogue from the program. Then have your child identify pronouns and referents in what he or she wrote.

Name _____

Grammar: Pronouns and Their Referents

Directions: Use the correct pronoun to complete each sentence. Write the pronoun on the line below. Then beside each pronoun, write its referent.

1. Maggie played a guitar in a recital last weekend. _____ was very nervous.

_____

2. Other guitar students had practiced for many hours, and _____ performed well.

_____

3. Maggie was concerned that her guitar was not in tune. _____ sounded strange when she was warming up.

_____

4. Maggie asked Luke if _____ would tune the guitar.

_____

5. Luke said to Maggie that the guitar sounded fine to _____. _____ told _____ not to be nervous.

_____

6. When it was Maggie's turn to perform, _____ felt ready.

_____

7. Maggie's parents were very proud of the performance. _____ thought _____ played beautifully.

_____

Directions: Use the referents provided to write sentences with pronouns. Make sure the pronouns and their referents agree.

8. the whole team

_____

9. one player

_____

10. the coaches

_____

11. Sheri

_____

Notes for Home: Your child identified and wrote pronouns and referents. ***Home Activity:*** Look at newspaper articles with your child. Have him or her circle pronouns and referents in six sentences. Then have him or her use two of the pronouns and their referents in new sentences.

Word Study: Suffixes

Directions: Sometimes the spelling of a base word changes when a suffix is added. In most words, when the base word ends in **-e,** drop the **-e** and add the suffix. In most words, when the base word ends in **-y,** change the **-y** to **-i** and add the suffix. Read each sentence. Combine the base word and suffix in ( ) to make one word. Write the new word on the line.

_____ 1. Traveling with my cousin is always a (please + ure).

_____ 2. Something fantastic (usual + ly) happens on our trips.

_____ 3. Our adventures make for a very interesting (converse + ation).

_____ 4. (Fortunate + ly), we have plenty of time for traveling.

_____ 5. On our last trip, we saw some (remark + able) ruins in the jungle.

_____ 6. A hidden (pass + age) led us to an amazing treasure room.

_____ 7. We were thrilled to find the (plenty + ful) riches.

_____ 8. Finding treasure is a (respect + able) way to get rich!

_____ 9. For us, the (excite + ment) of traveling never wears off.

Directions: Read the words below. Write each base word and the suffix in the correct column.

	Base word		**Suffix**
10. lazily	_____	+	_____
11. direction	_____	+	_____
12. sorrowful	_____	+	_____
13. sleepy	_____	+	_____
14. possibly	_____	+	_____
15. disappointment	_____	+	_____
16. dizziness	_____	+	_____
17. beautiful	_____	+	_____
18. imaginable	_____	+	_____
19. famous	_____	+	_____
20. musician	_____	+	_____

© Scott Foresman 5

Notes for Home: Your child made new words by adding suffixes to base words, such as *please + ure = pleasure.* **Home Activity:** Read a newspaper article with your child. Ask your child to find words with suffixes. Have your child break each word into the base word and suffix.

from **Chester Cricket's
Pigeon Ride**

Spelling: Suffixes *-ous, -ion, -ation*

Pretest Directions: Fold back the page along the dotted line. On the blanks, write the spelling words as they are dictated. When you have finished the test, unfold the page and check your words.

1._____
2._____
3._____
4._____
5._____
6._____
7._____
8._____
9._____
10._____
11._____
12._____
13._____
14._____
15._____
16._____
17._____
18._____
19._____
20._____

1. He is a **famous** writer.
2. Barking dogs make him **nervous**.
3. They sang a **joyous** song.
4. What a **marvelous** idea!
5. That was a **humorous** joke.
6. A **mysterious** man entered.
7. The boat is not **dangerous**.
8. There is a **selection** of pens.
9. She is taking speech **instruction**.
10. He has an **attraction** to parks.
11. Everyone hates **rejection**.
12. A good **education** is valuable.
13. It costs more due to **inflation**.
14. I made a **decoration**.
15. The police took our **information**.
16. This project needs **organization**.
17. They had a nice **conversation**.
18. You have a vivid **imagination**.
19. He has our **admiration**.
20. The plan takes **preparation**.

Pretest

© Scott Foresman 5

Notes for Home: Your child took a pretest on words that have the suffixes *-ous*, *-ion*, and *-ation*. **Home Activity:** Help your child learn misspelled words before the final test. Have your child divide misspelled words into parts (such as syllables) and concentrate on each part.

Think and Practice

Spelling: Suffixes -ous, -ion, -ation

Word List				
famous	humorous	instruction	inflation	conversation
nervous	mysterious	attraction	decoration	imagination
joyous	dangerous	rejection	information	admiration
marvelous	selection	education	organization	preparation

Directions: Add the suffix **-ion** or **-ation** to form a word from the box. Write the word on the line. Remember to drop the silent **e** when necessary.

Add -ion

1. instruct _____
2. select _____
3. reject _____
4. attract _____
5. decorate _____
6. educate _____
7. inflate _____

Add -ation

8. inform _____
9. converse _____
10. imagine _____
11. admire _____
12. prepare _____
13. organize _____

Directions: Add the suffix **-ous** to each base word to form a word from the box. Write the letters of each word in the blanks. The boxed letters spell one of the words you wrote, a word that tells how you might feel if you were flying for the first time. Hint: Three words will change spelling before adding **-ous.**

14. danger   14. ___ ___ [ ] ___ ___ ___ ___ ___

15. mystery   15. ___ ___ ___ [ ] ___ ___ ___ ___

16. marvel   16. ___ ___ [ ] ___ ___ ___ ___

17. nerve   17. ___ ___ ___ [ ] ___ ___

18. fame   18. ___ ___ ___ [ ] ___ ___

19. humor   19. ___ ___ ___ [ ] ___ ___ ___

20. joy   20. ___ ___ ___ ___ [ ] ___

How might you feel on your first flight?

___ ___ ___ ___ ___ ___ ___ ___

Notes for Home: Your child spelled words that end in *-ous, -ion,* and *-ation.* **Home Activity:** Read a newspaper article with your child. See how many words he or she can recognize that end in *-ous, -ion,* or *-ation.*

Name _____

Spelling: Suffixes -ous, -ion, -ation

Directions: Proofread this story. Find five spelling mistakes. Use the proofreading marks to correct each mistake.

≡	Make a capital.
/	Make a small letter.
∧	Add something.
✐	Take out something.
⊙	Add a period.
¶	Begin a new paragraph.

Joey's first trip to the marvelous city of Chicago was a joyus day. He saw famous skyscrapers like the Sears Tower and the Hancock Tower. Joey felt a great admiration for the architect of Chicago's beautiful Union Station. It seemed mystereous to him that any place could be so big.

While they were in the Art Institute, Joey's mother struck up a conversatioun with one of the guards. He shared some helpful informacion about which elevator would take them to the special exhibit. The paintings there gave Joey more educcation than he ever got in a classroom!

Word List

famous	humorous	instruction	inflation	conversation
nervous	mysterious	attraction	decoration	imagination
joyous	dangerous	rejection	information	admiration
marvelous	selection	education	organization	preparation

Write a Story

On a separate sheet of paper, write a paragraph describing things you saw on a trip to the city. Try to use at least five of your spelling words.

Spelling Tip

marvelous

How can you remember that **marvelous** has an **o** before the **u?** Think of this hint: Oh, **you (o-u)** look **marvel<u>ous</u>!**

Notes for Home: Your child spelled words that end in *-ous, -ion,* and *-ation.* **Home Activity:** Say each spelling word to your child. Have him or her identify whether it ends in *-ous, -ion,* or *-ation.* Then have your child spell the word.

© Scott Foresman 5

Proofread and Write

Name _____

Spelling: Suffixes -ous, -ion, -ation   REVIEW

Word List				
famous	humorous	instruction	inflation	conversation
nervous	mysterious	attraction	decoration	imagination
joyous	dangerous	rejection	information	admiration
marvelous	selection	education	organization	preparation

Directions: Choose the word from the box that best matches each clue.
Write the word on the line.

_____ 1. It's a talk between two or more people.

_____ 2. It's a group of people who work together.

_____ 3. It's what you use to create interesting make-believe stories.

_____ 4. It's what you do to get ready.

_____ 5. It's being turned down or turned away.

_____ 6. It's what happens when a magnet is near metal.

_____ 7. It's often seen on top of a cake.

_____ 8. It's what happens to a balloon that's blown up.

_____ 9. It's a choice that you make.

_____ 10. It's what a person feels for a hero or idol.

_____ 11. It's what you find in any encyclopedia article.

_____ 12. It's what you get from going to school.

Directions: Choose the word from the box that has the same or nearly the same
meaning as each word below. Write the word on the line.

13. directions _____   17. well-known _____

14. strange _____   18. happy _____

15. funny _____   19. worried _____

16. unsafe _____   20. wonderful _____

Notes for Home: Your child spelled words that end in *-ous, -ion,* and *-ation.* **Home Activity:**
Say each spelling word without the suffix. Have your child add the proper suffix and spell the
word.

© Scott Foresman 5

Following Directions

Following directions involves reading or listening and then doing or making something.

Directions: Follow these directions to complete the Unusual Journey puzzle. Read all the directions before you begin. Follow each step closely. Some letters have been filled in for you.

1. What is the name for a book of maps? Write the word in both columns marked **1**. (The first letter in each column is written in for you.)

2. What is the name of a book of facts that is published each year? Write the word in both columns marked **2**.

3. What is the name of a book you use to learn about a subject in school? Write the word in both columns marked **3**.

4. What is the name of a book that has words and their definitions? Write the word in both columns marked **4**.

5. What is the name for a set of books that has information about many different subjects? Write the word in both columns marked **5**.

6. Use a colored pencil or crayon to shade the space marked **6**.

7. Use different colored pencils or crayons to shade the spaces marked **7a** and **7b**.

8. Write your name in the box marked **8**.

9. Find all the letters that are set inside a diamond. Write the word the letters make after **Hot** in the box marked **9**.

10. Find all the letters that are circled. Write the word the letters make in the box marked **10**.

11. Use a pencil or crayon to color in all the empty boxes.

Directions: Use the completed puzzle to answer the questions below.

12. What type of unusual flying machine does the complete puzzle show?

_____

13. Where would you travel to have an unusual journey?

_____

14. Why is it important to read all the directions before you begin?

_____

_____

15. Why is it important to follow directions in the order they are given?

_____

_____

Name _____

from **Chester Cricket's Pigeon Ride**

Unusual Journey

The puzzle grid contains:
- Row 1: labels 5 (e), 6, 5
- Row 2: 4 (d), 4
- Row 3: 3 (t), 3
- Row 4: 2 (a), 2
- Row 5: 1 (a), 1 (a)
- Marks: b, 7a, 7b, 8, 9 Hot, 10, 's

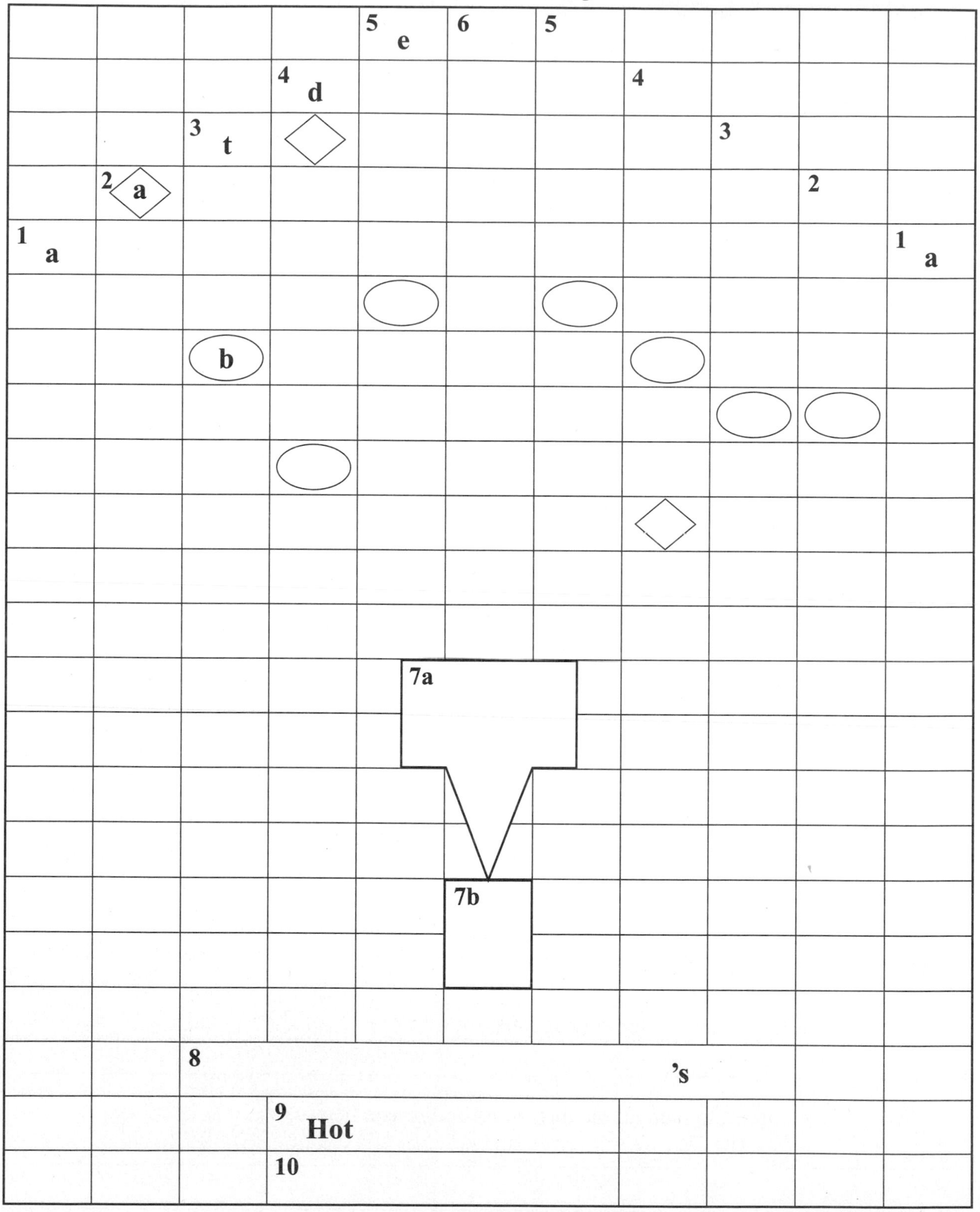

Notes for Home: Your child followed detailed directions to fill in a puzzle. ***Home Activity:*** With your child, make several lists of numbered directions to follow for writing words on a page. For example: *1. Write your name. 2. Cross out every other letter. 3. Write the letters that are left.*

518 **Research and Study Skills: Following Directions**

© Scott Foresman 5

Family Times

Name

Name_____

Summary

Japanese Diplomat Saves Jewish Refugees

Hiroki Sugihara is proud of his father. During World War II, his father was a Japanese diplomat in Lithuania. Jewish refugees fleeing the Nazis came to him pleading for visas that would permit them to leave the country. Mr. Sugihara's government ordered him not to issue the visas, but he did anyway. Before he was recalled from his post, he saved thousands of lives. Those refugees who survived the war never forgot what this brave man had done for them.

Reading Skills

Context Clues

Context clues are words that help explain the meaning of an unfamiliar word. For example, in the sentence, "My father was a diplomat, representing the country of Japan." you can infer that *diplomat* means "someone who represents a foreign country."

Sometimes a context clue directly defines or explains a word: "The five men heard that my father could give them visas—official written permission to travel through another country." You know the meaning of *visa* because its definition is stated in the sentence.

Activity

Act Out Dialogue. Imagine you are in the meeting between Mr. Sugihara and the refugees. What do you think they might have said to each other? Create dialogue for that scene. Then act it out with another person.

Activity

Define New Words. Read a short newspaper article. Circle any unfamiliar words. Try to determine what they mean from context clues. Then check the meanings in a dictionary.

© Scott Foresman 5

Family Times

Tested Vocabulary

Words to Know

Knowing the meanings of these words is important to reading *Passage to Freedom: The Sugihara Story.* Practice using these words to learn their meanings.

agreement a mutual understanding

cable insulated bundle of wires for carrying electric current

disobey refuse to do what is ordered

issue to send out

permission consent

representatives people appointed or elected to act or speak for others

superiors people who are higher in rank

translated changed from one language into another

Grammar

Prepositions and Prepositional Phrases

A **preposition** begins a group of words called a **prepositional phrase.** The phrase ends with a noun or pronoun called the **object of the preposition.** The preposition shows how the object of the preposition is related to other words in the sentence. Note how the prepositional phrases in the following sentences tell more about the other words in the sentences.

The refugees stood <u>outside the gate</u>.
Hiroki watched <u>from the window</u>.
Mr. Sugihara met <u>with five men</u>.
He gave a visa <u>to each person</u>.

Activity

Practice Prepositions. Identify the preposition and the object of the preposition in each underlined phrase above. Talk about how each preposition relates its object to other words in the sentence. Then use each preposition in another sentence.

Tested Spelling Words

520 **Passage to Freedom: The Sugihara Story**

Context Clues

- **Context clues** are words that help explain an unfamiliar word.

- Context clues can appear just before or after an unfamiliar word. But sometimes they are in a different part of the story or article, far from the unfamiliar word.

- Look for specific context clues such as definitions, explanations, examples, and descriptions.

Directions: Reread "Butterfly Memorial." Then complete the table. Write the meaning of each word in the table. Tell what context clue helped you figure out the meaning and where you found it.

Word	Meaning	Context Clues
ghetto	**1.**	The definition appears just before the word in the first paragraph.
Holocaust	**2.**	**3.**
remembrance	**4.**	**5.**

Notes for Home: Your child read an article and figured out the meanings of unfamiliar words by using context clues. *Home Activity:* Read a magazine article with your child. When you come to a word your child doesn't know, use context clues to figure out its meaning.

Vocabulary

Directions: Choose a word from the box that best completes each
sentence. Write the word on the line to the left.

_____ 1. We elected _____ to speak for the rest
of us.

_____ 2. They approached an official who had
the power to _____ passports to our
group.

_____ 3. We needed this official's _____ to
leave the island.

_____ 4. He was worried we might _____ his
orders.

_____ 5. After much discussion, we finally reached an _____.

Check the Words You Know
__ agreement
__ cable
__ disobey
__ issue
__ permission
__ representatives
__ superiors
__ translated

Directions: Choose the word from the box that best matches each clue. Write
the letters of the word on the blanks. The boxed letters spell something that a
happy child does.

6. consent

6. ☐ __ __ __ __ __ __ __

7. insulated bundle of wires
for carrying electric current

7. __ __ __ ☐ __

8. changed from one
language to another

8. __ __ ☐ __ __ __ __ __ __

9. refuse to obey

9. __ __ __ __ __ __ ☐

10. people who are higher in rank

10. ☐ __ __ __ __ __ __ __ __

Something a happy child does: __ __ __ __ __

Write an Award Citation

Imagine that one of your classmates has won an award for helping others. On a
separate sheet of paper, write a paragraph to go with the award. Describe what
the person did and the result of his or her actions. Try to use as many vocabulary
words as you can.

Notes for Home: Your child identified and used vocabulary words from *Passage to Freedom:
The Sugihara Story.* **Home Activity:** With your child, take turns telling a story using the
vocabulary words. At each turn, the teller may choose any unused word.

© Scott Foresman 5

Context Clues

- **Context clues** are words that help explain an unfamiliar word. Context clues can appear just before or after an unfamiliar word. Sometimes, they are in a different part of the story or article.

- Context clues include synonyms, antonyms, definitions and explanations, examples, and descriptions.

Directions: Reread what happened in *Passage to Freedom: The Sugihara Story* when a crowd gathered outside the Sugiharas' home. Then answer the questions below.

I couldn't help but stare out the window and watch the crowd, while downstairs, for two hours, my father listened to frightening stories. These people were refugees—people who ran away from their homes because, if they stayed, they would be killed. They were Jews from Poland, escaping from the Nazi soldiers who had taken over their country.

The five men had heard my father could give them visas—official written permission to travel through another country. The hundreds of Jewish refugees outside hoped to travel east through the Soviet Union and end up in Japan. Once in Japan, they could go to another country. Was it true? the men asked. Could my father issue these visas?

Text copyright © 1997 Ken Mochizuki. Excerpt from PASSAGE TO FREEDOM: THE SUGIHARA STORY.
Reprinted by arrangement with Lee & Low Books, Inc.

1. What does the word *refugees* mean?

_____

_____

2. What type of context clue did you use to determine the meaning of *refugees?*

_____

3. What does the word *visas* mean?

_____

_____

4. What type of context clue did you use to determine the meaning of *visas?*

_____

5. How can you be sure if you have determined the correct meaning of a word after using context clues?

© Scott Foresman 5

Notes for Home: Your child used clues within a story to figure out the meanings of unfamiliar words. **Home Activity:** Read a story with your child. Help your child try to figure out the meaning of an unfamiliar word by looking at words surrounding it.

Selection Test

Directions: Choose the best answer to each item. Mark the letter for the answer you have chosen.

Part 1: Vocabulary

Find the answer choice that means about the same as the underlined word in each sentence.

1. Mr. Park <u>translated</u> for me.
   A.   wrote out by hand
   B.   read carefully
   C.   changed into a different language
   D.   learned by heart

2. The leaders were in <u>agreement</u>.
   F.   official stopping of work by a group of employees
   G.   loud protest
   H.   sudden rise in banking costs
   J.   understanding between two or more parties

3. Did the government <u>issue</u> those uniforms?
   A.   take back
   B.   design
   C.   forbid
   D.   give out

4. Captain Jones reported to his <u>superiors</u>.
   F.   bosses
   G.   people who buy goods
   H.   friends
   J.   people who are related

5. The <u>cable</u> was damaged in the storm.
   A.   tall tower
   B.   wooden structure in a body of water
   C.   bundle of wires for sending messages electronically
   D.   power station

6. Did you <u>disobey</u> the orders?
   F.   refuse to go along with
   G.   hear
   H.   misunderstand
   J.   give

7. Several <u>representatives</u> of the company spoke at the meeting.
   A.   people who dislike something
   B.   people appointed or elected to speak or act for others
   C.   people who refuse to take charge
   D.   people who have just paid money

8. Dad gave his <u>permission</u>.
   F.   money
   G.   help
   H.   decision to allow something
   J.   words of advice

Part 2: Comprehension

Use what you know about the selection to answer each item.

9. The major events in this story take place in—
   A.   Israel.
   B.   Germany.
   C.   Poland.
   D.   Lithuania.

10. This story is told from the point of view of—
    F.   a Japanese diplomat.
    G.   a Jewish refugee.
    H.   the diplomat's son.
    J.   the diplomat's wife.

11. Why do all the refugees come to talk to the diplomat?
    A.   They want visas so they can leave the country.
    B.   They want someone to speak out against the Germans.
    C.   They want his help in returning to the homes they have left.
    D.   They want him to hide them from the German army.

GO ON

12. The selection says, "Grown-ups <u>embraced</u> each other, and some reached to the sky."
<u>Embraced</u> means—
F.   hugged.
G.   yelled at.
H.   struck.
J.   cheered for.

13. The selection says, ". . . and when we finally returned to Japan, my father was asked to <u>resign</u> from diplomatic service."
<u>Resign</u> means—
A.   join.
B.   return.
C.   quit.
D   change.

14. The most important thing to Mr. Sugihara was to—
F.   protect his family.
G.   obey his government.
H.   save people's lives.
J.   make money.

15. The author's main purpose in this selection is to—
A.   honor a brave act.
B.   explain the causes of the war.
C.   describe what it was like to be a refugee.
D.   entertain readers.

STOP

Context Clues

- **Context clues** are words that help explain an unfamiliar word. Context clues can appear just before or after an unfamiliar word. Sometimes, they are in a different part of the story or article.

- Context clues include synonyms, antonyms, definitions and explanations, examples, and descriptions.

Directions: Read the passage below.

World War II was the most catastrophic war ever, taking more lives and destroying more property than any other war. It is nearly impossible to calculate the number of people killed, wounded, and missing during the war's six years, although history experts guess that it totals about 16 million.

The war began when Germany attacked Poland on September 1, 1939. The successful test of its blitzkrieg, or lightning war, methods led Germany to take control of six more countries—Denmark, Norway, Belgium, Luxembourg, The Netherlands, and France—in only three months in 1940.

Directions: Complete the table. Tell the meaning of each word in the table and explain what context clues you used to figure out the meaning.

Word	Word's Meaning	Context Clues
catastrophic	1.	2.
calculate	3.	4.
blitzkrieg	5.	Meaning is given after the word.

Notes for Home: Your child read a story and used context clues within the story to figure out the meanings of unfamiliar words. *Home Activity:* Use a challenging word in a sentence. Have your child use context clues to explain its meaning.

Name _____

Main Idea and Supporting Details/Generalizing

REVIEW

Directions: Read the passage. Then read each question about the passage. Choose the best answer to each question. Mark the letter for the answer you have chosen.

D-Day

The D-Day invasion was an important event during World War II that made a big difference in the outcome of the war. That event occurred on June 6, 1944. On that day the Allied forces crossed the English Channel and attacked the German forces on the northern coast of France. The forces made this surprise landing on open beaches in the French region of Normandy.

The D-Day invasion required great planning. England, Canada, and the United States brought together some 3 million soldiers and 16 million tons of supplies in Great Britain. The Allies had 5,000 large ships, 4,000 small craft, and over 11,000 airplanes.

Months before the D-Day invasion, Allied planes bombed the Normandy coast to prevent Germans from taking over in the area. Allied soldiers cut rail lines, blew up bridges, and took control of landing strips to prepare for the invasion.

During the night of June 5, troops, jeeps, and even small tanks were brought in on gliders and warships. Beginning at 6:30 A.M. on June 6, German groups of soldiers on the coast were attacked by shells from Allied warships. All was ready for the largest land invasion in recent history—D-Day.

1. The main idea of the article is that—
   A. 3 million men fought.
   B. the D-Day invasion took planning.
   C. bridges were blown up.
   D. the D-Day invasion was June 6, 1944.

2. A detail that supports the main idea is that—
   F. 11,000 planes were used.
   G. Germans built up their forces.
   H. Britain was attacked.
   J. it happened in Normandy.

3. A detail that does **not** support the main idea is that—
   A. rail lines were cut.
   B. 5,000 ships were used.
   C. bridges were blown up.
   D. Normandy is in France.

4. A valid generalization you could make about the last paragraph is that—
   F. few warships were needed.
   G. all the troops, jeeps, and tanks were loaded on the morning of June 6.
   H. gliders and warships were important to the D-Day invasion.
   J. the D-Day invasion occurred on June 6, 1944.

5. A generalization you could make about the D-Day invasion is that—
   A. Germany was the enemy.
   B. Canada was in the war.
   C. many people took part in the invasion.
   D. the invasion was in June.

© Scott Foresman 5

Notes for Home: Your child identified a main idea, supporting details, and general statements about an article. *Home Activity:* Read an article with your child. Invite him or her to tell you the main idea and supporting details. Look for generalizations.

Writing Across Texts

Directions: Think about the Jewish refugees described in *Passage to Freedom: The Sugihara Story* and other events in Europe near that time. Compare that to what was happening in the United States then. Use information from "1939" to compare events in the two areas of the world.

The United States in 1939–40	Europe in 1939–40
The movie *Gone With the Wind* was released.	Jewish refugees were trying to get away from the Nazis.
1.	6.
2.	7.
3.	8.
4.	9.
5.	10.

Write a Letter

Imagine you are a Jewish refugee child described in the story. On a separate sheet of paper, write a letter to an American friend explaining what you learned and how you changed throughout this ordeal. Then write a reply from the American friend who is becoming aware of what is happening in Europe.

Notes for Home: Your child wrote two letters from other people's points of view. *Home Activity:* Together, write a letter to a special family member or friend. Encourage your child to include a description of something he or she has learned and how this has changed him or her.

Grammar: Pronouns and Referents REVIEW

Directions: Underline the pronoun in each sentence or pair of sentences. Draw a circle around its referent.

1. Leo, what do you know about D-Day?

2. On June 6, 1944, Allied troops landed in France. They began the invasion of northern Europe in World War II.

3. General Eisenhower commanded the troops. Later the American people elected him president.

4. Doreen knows an interesting story about the invasion. Is she here?

5. Doreen isn't here, but John can tell the story instead of her.

6. A Nazi spy stole the plans for the invasion, and he gave the information to the German generals.

7. The generals who saw the plans, however, didn't think much of them.

8. These leaders believed the real invasion would be elsewhere. The German army began to prepare for it.

9. Of course, the German generals were wrong, and because of them, the D-Day invasion was a success.

10. That's interesting, John. You told the story well.

Directions: Cross out the incorrect pronoun in each sentence. Then rewrite the sentence, using the correct pronoun.

11. Did you give the book about World War II to she?

_____

12. The librarian will reserve the book for we.

_____

13. I want to know more about General Patton, and the book tells about he.

_____

_____

14. Can you tell I anything about General Patton?

_____

15. Him was a very skilled general in World War II.

_____

Notes for Home: Your child identified pronouns and their referents—the nouns that they replace. *Home Activity:* Have your child write a paragraph about something that happened at school, and identify the referent of each pronoun that she or he uses.

Grammar: Prepositions and Prepositional Phrases

A **preposition** begins a group of words called a **prepositional phrase.** The
noun or pronoun that follows the preposition is the **object of the preposition.**
Prepositional phrases can be used to tell more about the words they accompany.

> The runaway horse galloped <u>toward a red house</u>.
> The runaway horse galloped <u>around a red house</u>.
> The runaway horse galloped <u>behind a red house</u>.

Notice how the prepositional phrases in the sentences above give a more vivid
and clear picture about the runaway horse.

Common Prepositions

above, across, after, around, at, before, behind, by, down,
for, from, in, into, near, of, on, to, toward, under, with

Directions: Underline the prepositional phrase in each sentence once. Draw a
second line under the preposition.

1. The ship moved with the tide.

2. The immigrants were standing by the rail.

3. Among the passengers was my father.

4. He stood between my two grandparents.

5. He watched the ship sail into the harbor.

6. It docked beside a small ferryboat.

7. The immigrants clustered around the railing.

8. Then they walked down the gangplank.

9. There was a bus on the dock.

10. It would take them to a federal building.

11. The dock felt wonderfully steady under their feet.

12. On the ship, they had felt seasick sometimes.

13. Salty ocean breezes blew around them.

14. My father gazed at the American trucks nearby.

15. His father held him by the hand, and the family boarded the bus.

Notes for Home: Your child identified prepositions such as *into* and *under* and prepositional
phrases such as *by the rail* and *around then*. **Home Activity:** Make up a two-word sentence.
Have your child add a prepositional phrase, (for example: *I ran. I ran to the milk truck.*)

Grammar: Prepositions and Prepositional Phrases

Directions: Add a prepositional phrase to each sentence using the preposition
in ( ). Write the new sentence on the line.

1. The immigrants saw the Statue of Liberty. (through)

_____

2. People cheered. (on)

_____

3. The immigrants had planned the voyage. (for)

_____

4. Anya finally smiled. (with)

_____

5. She felt welcome. (in)

_____

Directions: Add a prepositional phrase to each sentence to make it more
vivid and clear. Write the new sentence on the line.

6. Anya walked.

_____

7. She found a library.

_____

8. She sat.

_____

9. The silence was soothing.

_____

10. She fell asleep.

_____

Write a Biographical Sketch

On a separate sheet of paper, write a biographical sketch of someone who
immigrated to America. Describe why the person came to America, the journey,
and the person's new life here. Use prepositional phrases to write vivid and clear
sentences.

Notes for Home: Your child used prepositional phrases, such as *on a street.* **Home Activity:**
Say a preposition, such as *under, around, to,* or *on.* Have your child use it first in a
prepositional phrase and then in a sentence. Switch roles and repeat.

Grammar: Prepositions and Prepositional Phrases **531**

Grammar: Prepositions and Prepositional Phrases

Prepositional Phrases

Preposition	Words Between	Object
by	the	hill
beside	an old	oak
down	a winding	lane

Complete each sentence. Write words from each column.

1. The ball bounced_____.

2. The child rode a bicycle _____.

A **prepositional phrase** includes the preposition, the object of the preposition, and all the words that come between them. Every prepositional phrase starts with a preposition and ends with its object.

Directions: Write a prepositional phrase from the box below to complete each sentence.

with her fingertips	from its fur	behind a box of books
beside her pillow	in the closet	

1. Jenny found her old teddy bear _____.

2. It was lying _____.

3. She could reach it _____.

4. She brushed the dust _____.

5. She put it gently _____.

Directions: Underline the prepositional phrase. Then write **1** above the preposition and **2** above its object.

6. Chin caught a fish in the lake.

7. Marcie rowed the boat to the shore.

8. Raoul waited on the dock.

9. The three friends went inside the cabin.

10. They talked happily beside the fireplace.

Notes for Home: Your child wrote prepositional phrases and identified parts of prepositional phrases in sentences. *Home Activity:* Make a list of prepositions your child knows, and have him or her use five of them in phrases in sentences about animals.

Grammar: Prepositions and Prepositional Phrases

Directions: Read the paragraph. Underline the seven prepositional phrases and write them below.

    The skeleton contains the bones of the body. Soft material is inside the bones. Red blood cells are made in the bones. The bones of children under the age of one year are soft. Bones are held together by strong bands. Calcium helps keep the cells of the bones strong. Your bones should last a lifetime.

1. _____   5. _____

2. _____   6. _____

3. _____   7. _____

4. _____

Directions: Choose a word from each box to use in a prepositional phrase. Write each phrase. Below the phrase, write a sentence with the phrase in it.

Prepositions in under between of	Words Between the a your	Objects bones skeleton skull body

8. _____

    _____

9. _____

    _____

10. _____

    _____

Write Sentences

On a separate sheet of paper, write sentences about insects that you have seen. Use prepositional phrases in each sentence.

Notes for Home: Your child identified and wrote prepositional phrases. **Home Activity:** Have your child write directions to school, using prepositional phrases. (*First walk over the bridge. Next go down the hill.*)

Word Study: Syllabication, Common Syllable Patterns

Directions: A **syllable** is an individual part of a word that you say or hear. When a word is a compound word, it is usually divided between the two words that make up the compound word: **base • ball.** When two consonants come between two vowels (VCCV), the word is divided between the two consonants **(num • ber).** Separate each word into its syllables, using a dot **(base • ball).**

1. office _____

2. poster _____

3. downstairs _____

4. issue _____

5. outside _____

6. written _____

7. cannot _____

8. window _____

Directions: Read the words in the box. Separate each word into its syllables, using a dot **(base • ball).** Write each divided word in the correct column.

something	winter	curtains	suitcase	almost	tractor
indoors	danger	basket	flashbulb	daylight	nowhere
doctor	mittens	uptown	common	popcorn	

Compound Words

9. _____

10. _____

11. _____

12. _____

13. _____

14. _____

15. _____

16. _____

VCCV

17. _____

18. _____

19. _____

20. _____

21. _____

22. _____

23. _____

24. _____

25. _____

Notes for Home: Your child separated words into their syllable parts, such as *baseball* *(base • ball). Home Activity:* Read recipes, food packages, and game notes. Look for two-syllable words. Say each word aloud and clap to show its syllables.

Spelling: Compound Words 2

Pretest Directions: Fold back the page along the dotted line. On the blanks, write the spelling words as they are dictated. When you have finished the test, unfold the page and check your words.

Pretest

1._____

2._____

3._____

4._____

5._____

6._____

7._____

8._____

9._____

10._____

11._____

12._____

13._____

14._____

15._____

16._____

17._____

18._____

19._____

20._____

1. My **bookshelf** is full.

2. **Someone** ate the apples.

3. **Everybody** came to the party.

4. She is **nowhere** to be found.

5. She wants a chocolate **cupcake**.

6. Eleanor has a new **wristwatch**.

7. **Everyone** is here.

8. We **blindfold** the player.

9. My dad found a **typewriter**.

10. She is my only **grandparent**.

11. The girl hit a **home run**.

12. We are talking to **each other**.

13. I want ketchup on my **hot dog**.

14. Is a window seat **all right**?

15. My sister goes to **high school**.

16. Her **pen pal** lives in Tobago.

17. The stereo is in the **living room**.

18. **Peanut butter** is sticky.

19. **No one** was home when I called.

20. I got **first aid** for my injury.

Notes for Home: Your child took a pretest on compound words. *Home Activity:* Help your child learn misspelled words before the final test. Dictate the word and have your child spell the word aloud for you or write it on paper.

© Scott Foresman 5

Spelling: Compound Words 2

Word List				
bookshelf	cupcake	typewriter	hot dog	living room
someone	wristwatch	grandparent	all right	peanut butter
everybody	everyone	home run	high school	no one
nowhere	blindfold	each other	pen pal	first aid

Directions: Choose the compound words from the box that are written as one word. Write the words in alphabetical order on the lines.

1. _____

2. _____

3. _____

4. _____

5. _____

6. _____

7. _____

8. _____

9. _____

10. _____

Directions: Choose the compound word from the box that best completes each sentence. Write the word on the line to the left. Hint: Each compound word is spelled as two words, and one word of the compound word is the same as the underlined word in the sentence.

_____ **11.** The <u>school</u> that I will attend next is _____.

_____ **12.** It is too <u>hot</u> to eat a _____.

_____ **13.** <u>Run</u> around all the bases after hitting a _____.

_____ **14.** I bought a new <u>pen</u> to write to my _____.

_____ **15.** Let's <u>first</u> pack a _____ kit for the camping trip.

_____ **16.** <u>Each</u> day we find ways to help _____.

_____ **17.** I need <u>one</u> helper, but _____ is here right now.

_____ **18.** One food made from the <u>peanut</u> is _____.

_____ **19.** The <u>room</u> where we watch television is the _____.

_____ **20.** I have confidence that <u>all</u> of us will be _____.

Notes for Home: Your child spelled compound words. *Home Activity:* Say one of the words in each compound: for example, say *type* for *typewriter*. Have your child tell you the entire word and spell it.

Name _____

Spelling: Compound Words 2

Directions: Proofread this paragraph. Find five spelling mistakes.
Use the proofreading marks to correct each mistake.

Every grand parent of mine helped out in
World War II in some way. Grandpa Joe was
a doctor who gave first aid to every body in
the hospital. Grandpa Gus was a soldier that
noone could beat! Grandma Jane worked in
a war office with her new typewriter.
Grandma Gail became a nurse right after
high-school and made sure wounded
soldiers were allright.

≡	Make a capital.
/	Make a small letter.
∧	Add something.
✄	Take out something.
⊙	Add a period.
¶	Begin a new paragraph.

Spelling Tip

How can you
remember that **all
right** is not spelled
allright? Remember:
There is a space to the
right of **all** in **all
right.**

Word List

bookshelf	cupcake	typewriter	hot dog	living room
someone	wristwatch	grandparent	all right	peanut butter
everybody	everyone	home run	high school	no one
nowhere	blindfold	each other	pen pal	first aid

Write a Paragraph

Imagine that you or someone you know served in World War II. On a separate
sheet of paper, write a paragraph describing what you or the other person did in
the war. Try to use at least five of your spelling words.

Notes for Home: Your child spelled compound words. *Home Activity:* Write each spelling
word with the letters scrambled. See if your child can unscramble each word and spell it
correctly.

Spelling: Compound Words 2

Word List

bookshelf	cupcake	typewriter	hot dog	living room
someone	wristwatch	grandparent	all right	peanut butter
everybody	everyone	home run	high school	no one
nowhere	blindfold	each other	pen pal	first aid

Directions: Choose the word from the box that best completes each statement. Write the word on the line to the left.

_____ 1. *Football* is to *touchdown* as *baseball* is to _____.

_____ 2. *Ears* are to *earplugs* as *eyes* are to _____.

_____ 3. *School* is to *gymnasium* as *house* is to _____.

_____ 4. *Temperature* is to *thermometer* as *time* is to _____.

_____ 5. *Picnic* is to *sandwich* as *ballgame* is to _____.

_____ 6. *Artist* is to *paintbrush* as *author* is to _____.

_____ 7. *Food* is to *cupboard* as *book* is to _____.

_____ 8. *Salt* is to *pepper* as *jelly* is to _____.

_____ 9. *Mother* is to *parent* as *grandmother* is to _____.

_____ 10. *Doctor* is to *hospital* as *teacher* is to _____.

_____ 11. *Play* is to *teammate* as *write* is to _____.

_____ 12. *Main course* is to *stew* as *dessert* is to _____.

Directions: Unscramble the letters to find a word from the box. Write the word on the line. (Be careful with compounds that are written as two words.)

13. on neo _____

14. bevedyory _____

15. nevereoy _____

16. stirf dai _____

17. ache herot _____

18. lal thrig _____

19. emoneos _____

20. onhewer _____

Notes for Home: Your child spelled compound words. ***Home Activity:*** See how many more compound words your child can list that contain words found in each spelling word. For example, from *bookshelf* you could get *bookstore, bookmark, bookbag.*

Schedule

A **schedule** is a special chart that lists events and tells when they take place, such as the arrival and departure times of planes, trains, and buses.

Directions: The schedules below show airline flights and times between Boston, Massachusetts, and St. Louis, Missouri. Use these schedules to answer the questions on the next page.

To St. Louis, Missouri			
Flight Number	**Leave Boston**	**Arrive St. Louis**	**Frequency**
123	5:50 A.M.	8:06 A.M.	Daily
321	8:15 A.M.	10:21 A.M.	Daily
557	11:20 A.M.	1:24 P.M.	Daily
55	2:00 P.M.	4:10 P.M.	Daily
287	5:20 P.M.	7:40 P.M.	Daily
727	7:35 P.M.	9:46 P.M.	Daily Ex. Sat.

To Boston, Massachusetts			
Flight Number	**Leave St. Louis**	**Arrive Boston**	**Frequency**
222	7:54 A.M.	11:35 A.M.	Daily
354	10:23 A.M.	2:04 P.M.	Daily
408	12:50 P.M.	4:26 P.M.	Daily
292	4:20 P.M.	7:45 P.M.	Daily
156	6:55 P.M.	10:40 P.M.	Daily
166	9:30 P.M.	1:04 A.M.	Daily Ex. Sat.

1. Sara has been visiting her brother in St. Louis for the weekend. She needs to be back in Boston by noon on Monday. What is the latest flight she can take on Monday morning? What time will she arrive in Boston?

_____

_____

_____

2. Gary is attending a meeting in Boston. His meeting ends at 5:00 P.M. on Friday. It takes one hour to get to the airport. Will he be able to get home to St. Louis on Friday night, or will he have to wait until Saturday? Explain.

_____

_____

_____

3. Flights that arrive at their destinations between midnight and 5:00 A.M. are less expensive than other flights. What flight would qualify for the less expensive rate? Explain.

_____

_____

_____

4. Gayle likes to travel between 10:00 A.M. and 4:30 P.M. She wants to fly from St. Louis to Boston on Monday. She wants to return to St. Louis on Saturday. What flights could she take to make this trip during the hours she prefers?

_____

_____

_____

5. Henry lives and works in St. Louis. On Wednesday at 10:00 A.M., Henry received a call at work from a family member in Boston. He has to fly to Boston as soon as possible. It will take him an hour and a half to go home, pack, and get to the airport. What is the earliest he can arrive in Boston? Explain how you figured out the answer.

_____

_____

_____

_____

Notes for Home: Your child has read and interpreted an airline schedule. *Home Activity:* Find a schedule of television programs. Read the schedule with your child. Take turns saying what each line means. For example: The news is on today at 5:00 P.M. and at 10:00 P.M.

Family Times

Name_____

Summary

"The British Are Coming!" Warns Rider Paul Revere

In Henry Longfellow's famous poem, patriot Paul Revere receives word that British troops in Boston are on the move and are headed for the nearby town of Concord. He spreads the alarm from town to town, riding his horse through the night. Thanks to Paul Revere, the American patriots are prepared to fight the British in the first battles of the Revolutionary War.

Activity

Interview Paul Revere. With another person, conduct a mock TV news interview with Paul Revere after his famous ride. Have one person play Paul Revere, while the other plays the role of the reporter.

Reading Skills

Paraphrasing

Paraphrasing is restating something in your own words. When you paraphrase, be sure to:

- ❖ use your own words;
- ❖ keep the author's meaning;
- ❖ include only the author's ideas and opinions, not yours.

For example, suppose you read this sentence: **Paul Revere warned his countrymen that the British were coming.** You might paraphrase it this way: **Paul Revere alerted the colonists that the British were approaching.** The following paraphrase would not be accurate because it includes your opinion: **Paul Revere bravely alerted the colonists that the British were approaching.**

Activity

Practice Paraphrasing. Pose a question, such as: **What is the worst (or best) thing that happened to you today.** After each person answers, restate the answer in your own words. Have listeners judge whether your paraphrase was accurate.

Family Times

Tested Vocabulary

Words to Know

Knowing the meanings of these words is important to reading *Paul Revere's Ride*. Practice using these words to learn their meanings.

fate destiny

fearless unafraid

glimmer faint, unsteady light

lingers to stay on

magnified caused to look larger

somber gloomy

steed horse

tread walk

Grammar

Conjunctions

A **conjunction** is a word that joins words, phrases, or entire sentences. The most common conjunctions are *and, but,* and *or.*

❖ Use *and* to add information or join related ideas.
   The colonists fired once <u>and</u> then fled.
❖ Use *but* to show contrast or join different ideas.
   The colonists had great courage <u>but</u> little fighting experience.
❖ Use *or* to show a choice.
   Will the British come by land <u>or</u> by sea?

Activity
Make Idea Chains. One person says a sentence, such as: **Let's watch TV.** The next person repeats the sentence and uses a conjunction to add to it: **Let's watch TV and eat popcorn.** Keep going and see how many ideas you can combine using conjunctions: **Let's watch TV and eat popcorn, or go for a walk.** When the sentence gets too long, start over.

Tested Spelling Words

Paraphrasing

- **Paraphrasing** is explaining something in your own words.
- When you paraphrase, you restate ideas without changing their original meaning or adding your own opinion.

Directions: Reread "Samuel Adams." Then complete the table. Paraphrase each original statement in your own words. (The beginning words of each sentence will help you find the sentence to paraphrase.)

Original Statement	My Paraphrase
Introduction, Paragraph 1, Sentence 1 "Samuel Adams didn't want. . . ."	1.
Paragraph 3, Sentence 1 "On April 18 the redcoats. . . ."	2.
Paragraph 3, Sentence 3 "The more trouble there was. . . ."	3.
Paragraph 6, Sentence 1 "Samuel jumped out. . . ."	4.
Paragraph 6, Sentence 3 "John also jumped out. . . ."	5.

Notes for Home: Your child read an article and restated its ideas in his or her own words. *Home Activity:* Challenge your child to listen to part of a family conversation and then paraphrase what each speaker said.

Vocabulary

Directions: Match each word on the left with its definition on the right.
Write the letter of the definition next to the word.

_____ **1.** lingers   **a.** destiny

_____ **2.** magnified   **b.** delays in starting

_____ **3.** tread   **c.** faint, unsteady light

_____ **4.** fate   **d.** walk

_____ **5.** somber   **e.** caused to look larger

_____ **6.** glimmer   **f.** gloomy

<table>
<tr><td colspan="1">Check the Words You Know</td></tr>
<tr><td>__ fate</td></tr>
<tr><td>__ fearless</td></tr>
<tr><td>__ glimmer</td></tr>
<tr><td>__ lingers</td></tr>
<tr><td>__ magnified</td></tr>
<tr><td>__ somber</td></tr>
<tr><td>__ steed</td></tr>
<tr><td>__ tread</td></tr>
</table>

Directions: Read the help-wanted advertisement. Choose the word from
the box that best completes each sentence. Write the word on the matching
numbered line to the right.

HERO WANTED

Bold, **7.** _____ hero needed to help
American colonists fight for
freedom. The cause is serious and
the situation is **8.** _____. Must be
steady and willing to work hard.
Fast horseback riding required, so
must provide own **9.** _____. The
10. _____ of the nation may be in
your hands.

7. _____

8. _____

9. _____

10. _____

Write a Poem

On a separate sheet of paper, write a poem that alerts people to an important
problem, such as the destruction of the rain forests. Describe the problem and
some possible solutions. Use as many vocabulary words as you can.

Notes for Home: Your child identified and used vocabulary words from *Paul Revere's Ride*.
Home Activity: Have your child write a telegram announcing a heroic act by a friend, family
member, or public figure.

© Scott Foresman 5

Paraphrasing

> - **Paraphrasing** is explaining something in your own words.
>
> - When you paraphrase, include only the author's ideas and opinions and do not change the author's meaning.

Directions: Reread what happened in *Paul Revere's Ride* when Paul watched for the tower signal. Then answer the questions below.

But mostly he watched with eager search
The belfry tower of the Old North Church,
As it rose above the graves on the hill,
Lonely and spectral and somber and still.
And lo! as he looks, on the belfry's height
A glimmer, and then a gleam of light!
He springs to the saddle, the bridle he turns,
But lingers and gazes, till full on his sight
A second lamp in the belfry burns!

From "Paul Revere's Ride" from TALES OF THE WAYSIDE INN by Henry Wadsworth Longfellow, 1863.

1. How might you paraphrase lines 1 and 2 as a single sentence?

_____

_____

2. How might you paraphrase lines 5 and 6 as a single sentence?

_____

_____

3. How might you paraphrase line 7 as a single sentence?

_____

_____

4. How might you paraphrase lines 8 and 9 as a single sentence?

_____

_____

5. When you paraphrase, why is it important not to change the author's ideas and opinions?

Notes for Home: Your child read a poem and then retold parts of it in his or her own words. *Home Activity:* Read a story with your child. Have him pick out sentences and restate the same ideas in his or her own words.

Selection Test

Directions: Choose the best answer to each item. Mark the letter for the answer you have chosen.

Part 1: Vocabulary

Find the answer choice that means about the same as the underlined word in each sentence.

1. Sarah is completely <u>fearless</u>.
   A. making others afraid
   B. without fear
   C. very clever
   D. acting in a frightened way

2. The window <u>magnified</u> the tree outside.
   F. caused to look darker
   G. hid
   H. showed
   J. caused to look larger

3. Philip saw a <u>glimmer</u> in the woods.
   A. faint light
   B. dark shape
   C. tall tree
   D. red bird

4. The building looked very <u>somber</u>.
   F. wealthy
   G. elegant
   H. proper
   J. gloomy

5. The soldier wondered what his <u>fate</u> would be.
   A. position in the army
   B. what happens in the future
   C. meal
   D. punishment

6. The last guest <u>lingers</u>.
   F. delays in starting
   G. leaves
   H. travels
   J. is repaired

7. I heard the man's <u>tread</u> on the stairs.
   A. footstep
   B. loud crash
   C. squeaking noise
   D. ringing bell

8. The prince called for his <u>steed</u>.
   F. protective clothing for battle
   G. helper
   H. old-fashioned weapon
   J. horse

Part 2: Comprehension

Use what you know about the poem to answer each item.

9. Where did Paul Revere wait for the signal?
   A. in the belfry of the North Church
   B. on a farm in Lexington
   C. on the bridge in Concord
   D. across the water from the North Church

10. Revere's friend in the North Church belfry noticed that the British were—
    F. marching toward Connecticut.
    G. returning quietly to their camps.
    H. heading to Concord by boat.
    J. heading toward Paul Revere's hiding place.

GO ON →

11. "He heard the bleating of the flock, / And the twitter of birds among the trees." Which is the best paraphrase of these lines?
   - A. He scared the flock of sheep as he rode by.
   - B. The bleating of sheep made him keep riding.
   - C. He heard the sounds made by sheep and birds.
   - D. Birds and a flock of sheep waved to him.

12. "And one was safe and asleep in his bed / Who at the bridge would be first to fall." Which is the best paraphrase of these lines?
   - F. The man who would die first that day was still sleeping.
   - G. The bridge was still safe, but it fell that day.
   - H. While everyone else was sleeping, a man fell off the bridge.
   - J. A man dreamed that he would be the first to die.

13. What can you conclude from the information in this poem?
   - A. The British wanted the patriots to know they were coming.
   - B. Paul Revere's friend discovered the British troops by accident.
   - C. The patriots in Concord and Lexington were waiting for the British.
   - D. Paul Revere was secretly working for the British.

14. The speaker in this poem often mentions shadows, silence, and graveyards to—
   - F. show that Revere was a gloomy fellow.
   - G. remind the reader that war and death were coming soon.
   - H. suggest that Paul Revere's ride was all a bad dream.
   - J. give the poem a peaceful, happy mood.

15. The end of this poem suggests that Paul Revere's ride stands for—
   - A. the horror of war.
   - B. cleverness and secrecy.
   - C. fear and alarm.
   - D. the struggle for freedom.

STOP

Paraphrasing

- **Paraphrasing** is explaining something in your own words.

- When you paraphrase, include only the author's ideas and opinions and do not change the author's meaning.

Directions: Read the passage below. Each sentence is numbered.

(1) The Revolutionary War led the way for the 13 British colonies in America to win their independence and become the United States of America. (2) On April 19, 1775, the war began when American colonists battled British soldiers at Lexington, Massachusetts. (3) The war ended in 1783, eight years later.

(4) Not all Americans had been in favor of challenging the British, whom they saw as more powerful than themselves. (5) Some colonists believed that to fight against England was an act of disloyalty, even though they admitted that life in the colonies was less than perfect at the time.

Directions: Complete the diagram. Rewrite the numbered sentences in your own words.

Sentence 1:

Sentence 2:

Sentence 3:

Sentence 4:

Sentence 5:

Notes for Home: Your child read an article and then retold each sentence in his or her own words. *Home Activity:* Read a newspaper article with your child. Have him pick out sentences and restate the same ideas in his or her own words.

Visualizing

Directions: Read the story. Then read each question about the story. Choose the best answer to each question. Mark the letter for the answer you have chosen.

The Battle of Bunker Hill

Johnny was only eighteen years old, yet he was doing a man's job. He stood on Breed's Hill, next to Bunker Hill, overlooking the city of Boston. Other armed patriots stood all around him. They watched silently as the British prepared to attack.

Time stood still as Johnny waited with the others. Finally a long line of redcoats began marching up the steep hill. To Johnny, the long line of enemy soldiers looked like one huge, red monster. A drummer beat a steady rhythm as the British troops came toward him.

As the soldiers drew near, Johnny took aim with his rough, heavy rifle. It felt uncomfortable in his hands. On the captain's order, a tremendous blast of gunfire erupted. It sounded like an explosion.

Smoke from the muskets filled the air and Johnny's lungs. His mouth went dry suddenly, as if he had been chewing on cotton. Johnny reloaded his musket and prepared to fire again.

Twice, the British charged up the hill and both times the patriots drove them back. At the third charge, Johnny found he was out of gunpowder. He left the battle field, along with most of the other Americans. It didn't matter. They had won what would come to be called the Battle of Bunker Hill.

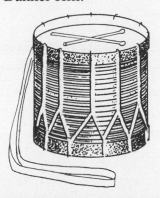

1. The image "a long line of enemy began marching" appeals to the sense of—
   A. hearing
   B. sight
   C. touch
   D. taste

2. The image "a drummer beat a steady rhythm" appeals to the sense of—
   F. hearing
   G. sight
   H. touch
   J. smell

3. The image "rough, heavy rifle" appeals to the sense of —
   A. hearing
   B. sight
   C. touch
   D. taste

4. The image "smoke from the muskets filled the air and Johnny's lungs" appeals to the sense of—
   F. hearing
   G. sight
   H. touch
   J. smell

5. The image "chewing on cotton" appeals to the sense of—
   A. hearing
   B. sight
   C. touch
   D. taste

Notes for Home: Your child read a story and used its sensory details to picture the story in his or her mind. **Home Activity:** Read a poem with descriptive details. Have your child describe what he or she sees, hears, tastes, feels, or smells, based on the details.

Writing Across Texts

Directions: How was the heroism displayed by Paul Revere in *Paul Revere's Ride* similar to Mr. Sugihara's heroism in *Passage to Freedom: The Sugihara Story?* How were these experiences alike? Complete the following table to organize your ideas.

How the Experiences of Paul Revere and Chiune Sugihara Were Alike
Both Paul Revere and Mr. Sugihara saved lives through their efforts.
1.
2.
3.
4.
5.

Write a Conversation Starter and Follow-Up Questions

Imagine meeting Paul Revere or Chiune Sugihara. What question could you ask that would be an appropriate conversation starter? What questions would help you learn about their heroism and the obstacles they faced?

Notes for Home: Your child compared characters from two different selections. **Home Activity:** Read aloud to your child two true stories about heroes. Help your child list the similarities between the heroes in both stories.

© Scott Foresman 5

Grammar: Compound and Complex Sentences

Directions: Write **compound** or **complex** to tell what kind of sentence each of the following sentences is.

_____ 1. The U. S. flag is called the Stars and Stripes, but it is also known as Old Glory.

_____ 2. Did Betsy Ross sew the first American flag, or is that just a legend?

_____ 3. Although it has never been proved, Betsy Ross's grandson told the following story.

_____ 4. It is said that George Washington visited her in 1776, and he asked her to make a flag for the new nation.

_____ 5. He gave her a rough sketch, and she added ideas of her own.

_____ 6. When the design was settled, she made the flag in her home.

_____ 7. The story is a popular one, but no one can prove it.

Directions: Combine each pair of sentences. Add a connecting word to make the kind of sentence shown in ( ). Write your new sentences on the lines.

8. The Revolutionary War began. An American flag was raised near Boston. (complex)

_____

_____

9. It had red and white stripes. It had a British symbol in the corner instead of stars. (compound)

_____

_____

10. The Continental Congress met in 1777. It approved a flag with stars and stripes. (complex)

_____

_____

 Notes for Home: Your child identified and wrote compound and complex sentences. **Home Activity:** With your child, make a list of simple sentences on a specific topic. Then add words to make each sentence first a compound and then a complex sentence.

Grammar: Conjunctions

Conjunctions such as *and, but,* and *or* can connect individual words, groups of words, or entire sentences. Conjunctions are used to make compound subjects, compound predicates, and compound sentences.

For compound sentences, you usually add a comma before the conjunction. The conjunction you use depends on your purpose.

Conjunction	Purpose
and	joins related ideas
but	joins different ideas
or	suggests a choice between ideas

Compound Subject: British troops <u>and</u> American minutemen confronted each other in many battles.

Compound Predicate: They exchanged shots on Lexington Green <u>and</u> fought again at Concord Bridge.

Compound Sentence: British troops and American minutemen exchanged shots on Lexington Green, <u>and</u> they fought again at Concord Bridge.

Directions: Underline the conjunction in each sentence.

1. American patriots fought the British and won independencc.

2. The colonists objected to unfair laws and rebelled at paying taxes to the Crown.

3. They were angry, but thcy were determined to resist.

4. Either the king or the colonists would have to give in.

5. The British marched into Lexington and ordered the rebels to go home.

Directions: Choose a conjunction in ( ) to complete each sentence. Be sure to choose the conjunction that makes the most sense. Write the conjunction on the line.

_____ 6. Some Americans were killed, (but/or) others kept fighting.

_____ 7. The British soldiers turned (and/but) fled.

_____ 8. They retreated (and/or) hoped to escape death.

_____ 9. Soldiers (and/but) officers waited anxiously for help to arrive.

_____ 10. Either General Washington (or/but) General Ward would lead the army.

Notes for Home: Your child used the conjunctions *and, but,* and *or* to connect ideas. ***Home Activity:*** Have your child use *and, but,* and *or* in sentences that describe the day's events. For example: *We played soccer, but the team didn't win.*

Grammar: Conjunctions

Directions: Circle the conjunction in each sentence.

1. George Washington organized and trained an army.

2. His troops were willing but poorly trained.

3. General Washington and his men lacked the enemy's resources.

4. His officers wanted to attack, but he decided to hold off.

5. Then the British attacked, and General Washington's troops were beaten back.

Directions: Choose a conjunction in ( ) to combine each pair of sentences.
Write the new sentence on the line.

6. The Americans retreated. The British troops followed. (and/or)

_____

_____

7. The British thought they had won. They were wrong. (or/but)

_____

_____

8. General Washington led a surprise attack on the British. It was successful. (but/and)

_____

_____

9. The Americans were happy. They were starving. (or/but)

_____

_____

10. The colonists needed to get fresh supplies of food. They would starve. (and/or)

_____

_____

Write a Description

On a separate sheet of paper, write a description of what your life might be like
if the British had won the Revolutionary War. Describe the language, food, and
customs. Use conjunctions to connect ideas.

Notes for Home: Your child used conjunctions to connect ideas. *Home Activity:* Invite your
child to make sentences using the conjunctions *and, but,* and *or.* Challenge your child to make
the sentences tell a story about the Revolutionary War.

Grammar: Conjunctions

The conjunction *and* joins related ideas in a sentence. Underline the conjunction in the sentence.

1. Reggie washed the dishes, and Dave dried them.

The conjunction *but* joins contrasting ideas in a sentence. Underline the conjunction in the sentence.

2. The boys were finished with the dishes, but they hadn't cleaned their bedroom.

The conjunction *or* suggests a choice between ideas. Underline the conjunction in the sentence.

3. Their mother wanted them to make their beds or do their laundry first.

Conjunctions such as *and*, *but*, and *or* can connect individual words, groups of words, or entire sentences. They are used to make compound subjects, compound predicates, and compound sentences.

Directions: Read each sentence. Write a conjunction—*and*, *but*, or *or*—that makes sense in the sentence.

1. Friendships are difficult, _____ they are worth it.

2. Deanna _____ I have been best friends since first grade.

3. We like to do many of the same things, such as swimming _____ singing.

4. On the weekends, we usually go to a movie _____ we rent one.

5. Our favorite thing to do is bake chocolate chip cookies _____ eat them.

6. We argue sometimes, _____ we always manage to settle our differences.

7. I listen to her side, _____ she listens to mine.

8. Then we talk about our thoughts _____ feelings.

9. Sometimes an adult _____ my older sister helps us.

10. Most of the time she _____ I get along.

11. This afternoon we are going to have lunch _____ go to the park!

Notes for Home: Your child wrote conjunctions—connecting words, such as *and*, *but*, and *or*—in sentences. **Home Activity:** Talk about what each of you did today. Encourage your child to use conjunctions correctly.

Grammar: Conjunctions

Directions: Circle the conjunction in ( ) that best fits each sentence.

1. When my family (but/and) I went camping last summer, I had a wonderful time.

2. At first I didn't want to go, (or/but) eventually I changed my mind.

3. We packed the car with food, gear, (or/and) clothes.

4. My dad made us choose between bringing a raft (but/or) inner tubes.

5. We brought the raft, (or/but) my sister was not happy about it.

6. She wanted to bring the raft (and/but) the inner tubes.

7. My mom said that if we brought both, my sister (but/or) I would have to stay home.

8. There would be no room in the car for both water toys (but/and) both of us!

9. My sister laughed (but/and) said, "I don't want to stay home!"

10. When we got to the camp site, we saw beautiful trees (and/but) flowers.

11. There were also paths through the woods (and/but) to a lake.

12. My sister and I couldn't decide if we would either hike in the woods (and/or) go swimming.

13. My mother said we could go exploring, (but/or) she didn't want to yet.

14. We went hiking, (or/but) later we went swimming.

15. When we got back, we had to wash lots of laundry (and/but) scrub our camp dishes.

Directions: Read each group of words. Add more information and the conjunction in ( ) to create a complete sentence. Write it on the line.

16. go camping again next summer (but)

_____

17. My sister and I will make lots of plans (and)

_____

18. go to a new place (or)

_____

19. take many photos (and)

_____

Notes for Home: Your child used conjunctions correctly in sentences. ***Home Activity:*** Ask your child to talk about what he or she can do now that wasn't possible at a younger age. Help your child recognize conjunctions in his or her sentences.

Word Study: Word Building

Directions: Say each pair of related words to yourself. Listen for the syllable that is stressed in each word. Write **same** if the same word part is stressed in each pair. Write **different** if different word parts are stressed in each pair.

_____ **1.** real   reality

_____ **2.** oppose   opposite

_____ **3.** sorrow   sorrowful

_____ **4.** history   historical

_____ **5.** office   officer

Directions: When you add a suffix to a word, you have built a new word. Most of the time, the base word still sounds the same. But sometimes when you add a suffix, you change the way the base word sounds. Read the paragraph below. Say each underlined word to yourself. Write each word in the correct column.

The patriot's <u>curiosity</u> was aroused by a strange ship moored on the <u>opposite</u> shore. He sent a <u>respectful</u> <u>inquiry</u> to the ship's captain to ask its purpose. No one responded. <u>Plainly</u>, he thought, the newcomers are up to no good. He feared that they were <u>dangerous</u>. He leaped onto his horse. This journey would not be a <u>pleasure</u>. By riding hard under the cover of <u>darkness</u>, he could get a <u>signal</u> to his compatriots. The <u>sooner</u> they learned the news, the better.

Base Word Sound Unchanged

6. _____

7. _____

8. _____

9. _____

10. _____

Base Word Sound Changed

11. _____

12. _____

13. _____

14. _____

15. _____

Notes for Home: Your child recognized sound changes when building new words by adding suffixes to base words. ***Home Activity:*** Read a magazine article with your child. Look for words with suffixes, and ask your child to identify which base words sound different with the suffix added.

Spelling: Related Words

Pretest Directions: Fold back the page along the dotted line. On the blanks, write the spelling words as they are dictated. When you have finished the test, unfold the page and check your words.

1._____	1. **Please** pass the stuffing.
2._____	2. We had a very **pleasant** day.
3._____	3. My scarf is made of soft **cloth**.
4._____	4. Dirty **clothes** go in the hamper.
5._____	5. The **sign** pointed north.
6._____	6. She has a lovely **signature**.
7._____	7. I had a strange **dream** last night.
8._____	8. She **dreamt** she was dancing.
9._____	9. My bicycle needs a new **part**.
10._____	10. This is only a **partial** list.
11._____	11. The cake was rich and **moist**.
12._____	12. We **moisten** the stamps.
13._____	13. Smoke makes it hard to **breathe**.
14._____	14. Take a deep **breath**.
15._____	15. His stories **create** new worlds.
16._____	16. A toad is an odd **creature**.
17._____	17. We will **elect** a new governor.
18._____	18. The **election** is tomorrow.
19._____	19. You must **practice** every day.
20._____	20. Paper shoes are not **practical**.

Notes for Home: Your child took a pretest on pairs of words that have parts spelled the same but pronounced differently. *Home Activity:* Help your child learn misspelled words before the final test by underlining the parts that are different in each pair and concentrating on those.

Spelling: Related Words

Word List

please	sign	part	breathe	elect
pleasant	signature	partial	breath	election
cloth	dream	moist	create	practice
clothes	dreamt	moisten	creature	practical

Directions: Choose the words from the box that have one syllable. Write each word on a line.

1. _____   6. _____

2. _____   7. _____

3. _____   8. _____

4. _____   9. _____

5. _____   10. _____

Directions: Complete each equation to form a word from the box. Write the word on the line.

11. practice – e + al = _____

12. assign – as + ature = _____

13. moisture – ure + en = _____

14. depart – de + ial = _____

15. please – e + ant = _____

16. select – s + ion = _____

17. create – e + ure = _____

18. practical – al + e = _____

19. creation – ion + e = _____

20. election – ion = _____

Notes for Home: Your child spelled pairs of words that have parts that are spelled the same but pronounced differently. *Home Activity:* Say a spelling word aloud. Have your child say the related word and spell it for you. Repeat for other pairs of related words.

Think and Practice

Spelling: Related Words

Directions: Proofread this diary entry. Find five spelling mistakes. Use the proofreading marks to correct each mistake.

≡	Make a capital.
/	Make a small letter.
∧	Add something.
✄	Take out something.
⊙	Add a period.
¶	Begin a new paragraph.

July 4, 1776.

Dear Diary: Today every leader in Congress will put his sigature on a document that will create a new nation—the United States! I used to think independence was only a dream, but now it's practicle and real! Now we can elect our own leaders, which will pleaze all Americans. It's like a breathe of fresh air! Today I'll wear my best cloths!

Spelling Tip

breath   **breathe**

How can you remember the difference between **breath** and **breathe?** Think of this hint: You **breathe the** air.

Word List

please	moist
pleasant	moisten
cloth	breathe
clothes	breath
sign	create
signature	creature
dream	elect
dreamt	election
part	practice
partial	practical

Write a Diary Entry

Imagine you were an American colonist at the time of the Revolutionary War. Write a diary entry that describes your experiences or your feelings about the war. Try to use at least five of your spelling words.

© Scott Foresman 5

Notes for Home: Your child spelled pairs of words that have parts that are spelled the same but pronounced differently. *Home Activity:* Write one word for each pair of related spelling words. Have your child show how the word can be changed to spell a related word.

Spelling: Related Words

Word List

please	sign	part	breathe	elect
pleasant	signature	partial	breath	election
cloth	dream	moist	create	practice
clothes	dreamt	moisten	creature	practical

Directions: Choose the word from the box that best completes each sentence.
Write the word on the line to the right.

In 1775, American colonists felt that life under English rule was harsh, not **1.** _____. Colonists could not **2.** _____ their own leaders. War seemed to be the only **3.** _____ way to win their freedom. But with untrained soldiers, victory seemed like a distant **4.** _____. After some **5.** _____, however, the soldiers got better. Soon the colonists were able to **6.** _____ a sigh of relief. In 1776, American leaders agreed to **7.** _____ a Declaration of Independence. They would **8.** _____ a new nation—the United States of America. Later, they held an **9.** _____ and George Washington became president in 1789.

1. _____

2. _____

3. _____

4. _____

5. _____

6. _____

7. _____

8. _____

9. _____

Directions: Choose the word from the box that belongs in each group of words.
Write the word on the line.

10. gasp, sigh, _____

11. fantasized, imagined, _____

12. piece, portion, _____

13. thank you, excuse me, _____

14. animal, beast, _____

15. dampen, rinse, _____

16. autograph, written name, _____

17. humid, damp, _____

18. incomplete, unfinished, _____

19. shoes, hats, _____

20. leather, plastic, _____

Notes for Home: Your child spelled pairs of words that have parts that are spelled the same but pronounced differently. *Home Activity:* Together, see if you and your child can name more words that are related to each pair. For example, *create* and *creature* are also related to *creation*.

Study Strategies

Learning and using different **study strategies** can help you better understand
what you read and help you focus on the most important information.

Directions: Three different study strategies are described on the index cards
below. Each one is a little different. Read about them and then answer the
questions that follow.

Skim and Scan

When you skim, you glance through a piece
of writing quickly to get a general idea of
what it is about. When you scan, you read
quickly to locate specific information, key
words or ideas, or to answer a specific
question.

SQ2R

SQ2R stands for Survey, Question, Read, and
Recite. First you survey a new work by
looking at its title, author, chapter titles,
headings, picture captions, and so on. Then
think of questions you want to find out
about that you think might be answered in
the reading. Then, as you read, look for
answers to the questions. Finally, recite by
telling what you learned.

K-W-L

"K-W-L" stands for "What I Know," "What I
Want to Know," and "What I Learned." The
letters go at the top of a chart. Before
reading, list what you already know in the K
column. Write questions you still have in the W
column. As you read, write answers to your
questions in the L column. Also write in the L
column additional interesting information you
discovered.

K What I Know	W What I Want to Know	L What I Learned

1. Which strategy would you use if you wanted to find major battles with their dates in an
   encyclopedia article about the Revolution? Explain.

   _____

   _____

2. Which strategy would you use for reading an article from *American History Magazine* about
   the winter of 1777 at Valley Forge? Explain.

   _____

3. Which strategy would you use for reading a new biography of Paul Revere? Explain.

_____

_____

4. Which strategy would you use to review a chapter of your textbook for a test on the American Revolution? Explain.

_____

_____

5. Which strategy would you use to decide whether to read a historical novel about Abigail Adams? Explain.

_____

_____

6. Which strategy would you use for reading a nonfiction book about the role Native Americans played in the American Revolution? Explain.

_____

_____

7. Which strategy would you use to decide whether a historical atlas would be a useful resource for your Revolutionary War research? Explain.

_____

_____

8. Which strategy would you use for reading an illustrated history of the American Revolution? Explain.

_____

_____

9. Which strategy would you use for reading a collection of letters and diaries by American colonists during the Revolution? Explain.

_____

_____

10. Suppose you were reading a nonfiction text about Paul Revere's ride. What are some questions you might ask yourself that you could then use with one of the study strategies to help you find the answers?

_____

_____

Notes for Home: Your child made decisions about which of three study strategies works best with different kinds of texts. **Home Activity:** Discuss with your child a subject you would like to know more about. Make and complete a K-W-L chart like the one shown.

Time Line

Directions: Write your topic. Between the slanted lines, write notes about the person. Below the bold line, write the dates. Identify your information sources.

Topic: _____

Information Sources: _____

Date or time: _____

Notes for Home: Your child made a time line to organize information for a research report. *Home Activity:* Think of a person of the past who did something brave or admirable. Tell your child about this person's deed and ask how the facts could be organized on a time line.

Name _____

Elaboration
Prepositional Phrases

- You can add information to sentences or make sentences clearer by using **prepositional phrases.**

- Prepositional phrases begin with **prepositions**—words such as *across, at, for, in, of, on, until,* and *with.*

Directions: Complete each sentence by picking a prepositional phrase from the box that tells more about the topic. Rewrite the sentence with the prepositional phrase in place of the blank. More than one phrase may fit a sentence. Choose one that makes sense.

Prepositional Phrases	
about new taxes	of England
across the ocean	to the presidency
by General Washington	until 1776
for many years	with battles

1. The first thirteen United States were ruled by England _____.

_____

2. King George _____ never visited those American colonies.

_____

3. Americans felt that a government _____ was too far away.

_____

4. Many people in the colonies became upset _____.

_____

5. In the Revolutionary War, the army was led _____.

_____

6. War lasted _____ before the United States became free.

_____

7. Soldiers on both sides were happy to be finished _____.

_____

8. Finally George Washington was elected _____.

_____

Notes for Home: Your child added information to sentences by using prepositional phrases, such as *across the ocean.* **Home Activity:** Ask your child to make up three sentences telling about an event in history. Have your child identify any prepositional phrases in the sentences.

Name _____

Self-Evaluation
Research Report

Directions: Think about the final draft of your research report. Then answer each question in the chart.

	Yes	No	Not sure
1. Did I find interesting information about a person and event?			
2. Did I present the information from my research clearly?			
3. Did I keep my purpose and audience in mind?			
4. Did I identify sources of special information?			
5. Did I proofread and edit carefully to correct errors?			

6. What is the best part of my research report?

_____

_____

_____

7. Write one thing that you would change about this research report if you had the chance to research or write it again.

_____

_____

_____

Notes for Home: Your child has answered questions about writing a research report. *Home Activity:* Ask your child what sources provided useful information. Ask your child whether it was difficult to find information about the person and event he or she chose to research.

Family Times

Summary

Baker Puts Neighbor on Trial

One of Pablo Perez's greatest pleasures is smelling the freshly baked breads and pastries at the shop of Manuel Gonzales. Manuel, however, resents Pablo. He thinks Pablo should pay him for all that smelling. He gets a judge to listen to his case against his neighbor. After hearing the case, the Judge asks Pablo to bring his life's savings to the court. It looks as though Manuel is about to get his money, but the Judge's final decision is a surprise—and a lesson—to everyone.

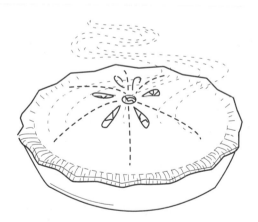

Reading Skills

Theme

Theme is an underlying meaning or message of a story. Themes can be statements, lessons, or generalizations that stand on their own.

❖ Sometimes the theme of a story or play is stated directly in the words of the author or a character. In "The Baker's Neighbor," the Judge states the theme when he says, "Good friends and neighbors are better than gold."

❖ More often, the theme is expressed indirectly. You can figure it out by asking yourself, "What does the author want me to learn or understand from reading this story?" Look for evidence in the story to support the theme.

Activity

Stage a Reading. If possible, stage a reading of "The Baker's Neighbor" with family members. Have each person take a part and read the play aloud. Follow the stage directions to make the reading as expressive as possible. Another option is to have your child summarize the story and direct people to act out different scenes using their own words.

Activity

Find the Theme. Think of a familiar fairy tale, folk tale, or fable. Retell it to your child or have your child retell it. Then talk about the story's message or meaning. Ask your child to say what he or she thinks the theme of the story is.

Family Times

Words to Know

Knowing the meaning of these words is important to reading "The Baker's Neighbor." Practice using these words to learn their meanings.

fragrance aroma

inspects examines

pastries bakery goods

pleasures things that please

privilege special favor or right

scowling looking angry or gloomy

trial deciding of a case in a court of law

Grammar

Sentences and Sentence Punctuation

A **sentence** is a group of words that makes a statement, a question, a command or a request, or an exclamation. It begins with a capital letter and ends with a special end mark.

- ❖ A **declarative** sentence makes a statement.
  Pablo is smelling the pie.
- ❖ An **interrogative** sentence asks a question.
  Why is Pablo smelling the pie?
- ❖ An **imperative** sentence gives a command or makes a request.
  Please stop it, Pablo.
- ❖ An **exclamatory** sentence shows strong feeling.
  I don't like it when you do that!

Activity
Make Sense of Sentences. Take turns saying sentences and having the other person identify the type of sentence and tell which end mark it uses.

Tested Spelling Words

Theme

- **Theme** is an underlying meaning or message of a story. Themes can be statements, lessons, or generalizations that stand on their own, such as: *Life is what you make of it.*

- Sometimes the author states the theme directly. Sometimes readers have to figure out a theme on their own by asking, "What did I learn from reading this story?"

Directions: Reread "King Midas." Then complete the table. Answer the questions in order to determine the story's theme.

Questions	Answers
What did King Midas wish for?	1.
Why did King Midas make the wish that he did?	2.
Why was Bacchus disappointed by King Midas' wish?	3.
What ultimately happened to King Midas?	4.
What lesson does this story teach you?	5.

Notes for Home: Your child read a story and identified its theme, or message. *Home Activity:* Read a story with your child. Later, talk about the lesson that it teaches. Discuss what the main characters learn from their experiences in the story.

Vocabulary

Directions: Choose the word from the box that best matches each clue. Write the word on the line.

_____ **1.** A grumpy person is always doing it.

_____ **2.** This decides if a person is guilty or not guilty.

_____ **3.** Don't eat too many of these sweet treats.

_____ **4.** It's what an inspector does.

_____ **5.** It appeals to the sense of smell.

Directions: Choose the word from the box that best completes each sentence. Write the word on the line to the left.

_____ **6.** A good baker _____ his ingredients before he starts to bake.

_____ **7.** He uses only the finest flour, sugar, and butter to make _____.

_____ **8.** A delicious _____ wafts from the bakery.

_____ **9.** His neighbors feel it is a _____ to live next door.

_____ **10.** There are so many _____ to being a baker's good friend!

Write a Recipe

What is your favorite dish? On a separate sheet of paper, write a recipe for it. List the ingredients and steps in the preparation. Don't forget to tell how good the food tastes and smells! Use as many vocabulary words as you can in your recipe.

Notes for Home: Your child identified and used vocabulary words from "The Baker's Neighbor." **Home Activity:** Act out with your child a conversation between a baker and a customer. Use as many listed vocabulary words as you can.

Theme

- **Theme** is an underlying meaning or message of a story. Themes can be statements, lessons, or generalizations that stand on their own, such as: *Life is what you make of it.*

- Sometimes the author states the theme directly. Sometimes readers have to figure out a theme on their own by asking, "What did I learn from reading this story?"

Directions: Reread what happens in "The Baker's Neighbor" when the judge makes his ruling. Then answer the questions below.

JUDGE: No, I did not tell him to pay it to you. I told him to put it on this table. Then I instructed you to count the money, which you did. In doing so, you enjoyed Pablo's money the way he enjoyed your cakes and pies. In other words, he has smelled your pastry and you have touched his gold. Therefore, I hereby declare that the case is now settled. *(He raps twice with his gavel.*

MANUEL *shamefacedly shoves purse across table to* PABLO *and turns to leave.* JUDGE *stops him.)* Just a moment, Manuel! I hope this has been a lesson to you. In the future, think less about making money and more about making friends. Good friends and neighbors are better than gold. And now, if you please—my fee!

Reprinted by permission. From PLAYS FROM FAVORITE FOLKTALES, edited by Sylvia E. Kamerman. Copyright © 1987 by Sylvia K. Burack.

1. Why does the judge tell Manuel to count Pablo's money?

_____

_____

2. What is the final judgment in the case?

_____

_____

3. What lesson does the Judge want Manuel to learn?

_____

_____

4. Which sentence might be a statement of the play's theme?

_____

_____

5. Read "The Baker's Neighbor" again. On a separate sheet of paper, restate the theme in your own words.

Notes for Home: Your child read a play and identified its theme. *Home Activity:* With your child, read a fable or folk tale and identify its theme, or big idea. Discuss what lessons the story might be trying to teach its readers.

Selection Test

Directions: Choose the best answer to each item. Mark the letter for the answer you have chosen.

Part 1: Vocabulary

Find the answer choice that means about the same as the underlined word in each sentence.

1. The traveler inspects the hotel.
   - A. enters
   - B. describes in words
   - C. visits again
   - D. looks at closely

2. Aunt Melanie brought pastries to the party.
   - F. gifts
   - G. bakery goods
   - H. things for decorating
   - J. guests

3. What is that wonderful fragrance?
   - A. smell
   - B. music
   - C. color
   - D. flavor

4. Jasper was scowling throughout the game.
   - F. clapping loudly
   - G. yelling
   - H. looking angry
   - J. whispering

5. Niki acts as if she has some special privilege.
   - A. gift
   - B. information
   - C. right
   - D. skill

6. The trial was covered in the newspaper.
   - F. big party
   - G. recount of votes in an election
   - H. championship game
   - J. deciding of a case of law

7. Mom wrote us a letter describing the pleasures of her trip.
   - A. problems
   - B. things that are enjoyed
   - C. places where one stops
   - D. reasons for doing something

Part 2: Comprehension

Use what you know about the play to answer each item.

8. After Manuel sets his pies out in the morning, he—
   - F. lies down to rest.
   - G. travels from door to door selling his pies.
   - H. invites the neighborhood children to sample his pies.
   - J. counts his money.

9. At the beginning of the play, why is Manuel angry with Pablo?
   - A. Pablo does not think Manuel's pies are very good.
   - B. Pablo makes more money than Manuel.
   - C. Pablo enjoys Manuel's pies without paying for them.
   - D. Pablo sends children to Manuel's to beg for free pies.

10. What is Pablo's attitude about work?
    - F. He works when he has to.
    - G. He thinks work is the most important thing in life.
    - H. A man should have his children support him.
    - J. He would like to work part time for Manuel.

GO ON

11. When the children ask what sound Pablo would like to be, he says that —
  A. he would like to be a song.
  B. he would like to be gold coins jingling.
  C. the question is a foolish waste of time.
  D. only children could think up such a question.

12. Which best states a theme of this play?
  F. People need to work hard to get ahead in life.
  G. When people grow up, they should stop acting like children.
  H. Some of life's simple pleasures don't have a price.
  J. It is just as bad to be greedy for food as to be greedy for money.

13. Which sentences from the story best help support the theme?
  A. "It has not yet been proved that Pablo is a thief. First he must have a fair trial."
  B. "Every night I mix the flour and knead the dough and slave over a hot oven while that shiftless, good-for-nothing Pablo sleeps."
  C. "I am a man of simple pleasures. Just the smell of a bakery makes me happy!"
  D. "I must make sure I haven't been cheated. How kind of you to remind me!"

14. The Judge decided the case the way he did because he wanted to—
  F. show everyone that stealing is punished severely.
  G. have people make fun of Manuel.
  H. scare Pablo so that he would stop smelling the pies.
  J. make Manuel truly understand why Pablo was innocent.

15. The writer probably ends the play with the Judge and Pablo eating the same pie in order to—
  A. have it end in a funny way.
  B. show that the Judge is just as greedy as Manuel.
  C. add an air of excitement.
  D. prove that the pies really taste good.

STOP

Theme

- **Theme** is an underlying meaning or message of a story. Themes can be statements, lessons, or generalizations that stand on their own, such as: *Life is what you make of it.*

Directions: Read the play below.

> **CHARACTERS: HENRY** and **LEWIS**, neighbors; **MARTHA**, Henry's wife.
> **HENRY** *(mowing his lawn and muttering):* I've had it with these rotten apples from Lewis's tree. *(shouts)* Hey, Lewis! I'm going to have that tree cut down. I don't care if we've been friends for years. I don't care if my daughter is engaged to marry your son.
> **LEWIS:** You can't have my tree cut down, you obnoxious loud-mouth! If you—
> **MARTHA** *(runs out of the house in a panic):* Henry! Lewis! Listen—Pete and Susie have been in a car accident! They are both at the hospital.
> **LEWIS and HENRY** *(talking at once):* What fools we are to fight about apples. Our children might have been killed! Come on, friend. Let's go to our children.

Directions: Complete the table. Use the questions to help you think about the story's big idea. Answer each question and then write the story's theme.

Ask Yourself . . .	Answer
What comes between Henry and Lewis's friendship?	1.
What other bond do the two friends share?	2.
What happens to make them forget their fighting?	3.
What effect does this event have on them?	4.
5. Theme:	

 Notes for Home: Your child read a passage from a play and identified its theme, or big idea. *Home Activity:* Read a story with your child. Together, identify the theme by talking about the characters and what happens to them. Think about what lessons were learned from the story.

Compare and Contrast

Directions: Read the story. Then read each question about the story. Choose the best answer to each question. Mark the letter for the answer you have chosen.

Resolving Conflict

Maggie and Beth both tend to have many conflicts with their friends. They handle these conflicts differently, however. Maggie tries to resolve problems by sitting down and talking with her friends. Beth, on the other hand, tends to dwell on the misunderstandings.

When Maggie has a disagreement with her friends, she listens to them and they listen to her. They come to understand each other's point of view and work out a resolution to their problem. Maggie's friendships don't seem to suffer from the fact that there are conflicts.

Beth refuses to sit down and talk out the differences honestly with the person with whom she disagrees. As a result, the conflicts between Beth and her friends never get resolved. The fights go on and on.

When the girls have conflicts with their parents, they use the same approaches as they do with their friends. Last week, for instance, both girls had trouble with their parents over their math grades.

Maggie agreed to sit down with her parents and talk about her math grade. She explained that she just didn't understand the new material and was too embarrassed to ask her teacher for extra help. Then she let her parents talk.

Beth, however, simply got angry when her parents brought up the subject of her math grade. She threw her math book on the floor, stormed out of the kitchen, slammed the door of her room, and sulked.

1. From the first paragraph, we learn that Maggie and Beth both—
   A. settle conflicts by talking.
   B. dwell on conflicts.
   C. tend to argue with friends.
   D. have a lot of friends.

2. In the first paragraph, the author shows contrast with the clue words—
   F. however, on the other hand.
   G. both, conflicts.
   H. resolve, dwell.
   J. sitting down, talking.

3. In the fourth paragraph, the author shows comparison with the clue word—
   A. for instance.
   B. both.
   C. when.
   D. conflicts.

4. In the fourth and fifth paragraphs, the author contrasts—
   F. the girls' grades in math.
   G. how the girls deal with their parents.
   H. the reactions of the girls' parents.
   J. the difficulty of growing up.

5. Overall, the girls are—
   A. exactly alike.
   B. completely different.
   C. alike in the way they handle conflicts.
   D. different in the way they handle conflicts.

Notes for Home: Your child read a story and identified comparisons and contrasts in the text. *Home Activity:* Have your child compare and contrast the ways that different family members or friends settle conflicts.

Writing Across Texts

Directions: Think about items and services that have been used for money or barter as shown in "All Kinds of Money." What might the characters in "The Baker's Neighbor" use for barter? Consider what special skills each has and fill in the table below with your ideas.

Character	Skill to Be Used as Barter
Pablo	1.
Manuel	2.
Carlos	3.
The Three Women	4.
The Judge	5.

Write a Paragraph

Write a paragraph about a time you or someone you know has bartered with someone else. You may have done a chore for a trip to a favorite restaurant or traded one toy for another. Use a separate sheet of paper for your paragraph.

Notes for Home: Your child applied information from a selection to his or her own life. *Home Activity:* As you read stories and articles with your child, talk about how the ideas in this reading material connect to his or her own experiences.

Grammar: Conjunctions

REVIEW

Directions: Choose the conjunction *and, but,* or *or* to complete each sentence. Write the complete sentence on the line.

1. Brittany _____ Rose went to the bakery together.

_____

2. I did not go, _____ Dan went with them.

_____

3. Will you call me _____ stop by my house later?

_____

4. I have some questions about tomorrow's test, _____ we should talk about our group project.

_____

_____

5. We have to decide whether Brittany _____ Rose will be the presenter.

_____

_____

Directions: Choose the conjunction *and, but,* or *or* to combine each pair of sentences. Write your new sentence on the line.

6. Brittany agreed to come to my house. Rose couldn't make it.

_____

7. Dan, Brittany, and I met. Dan took notes for Rose.

_____

8. We know we need to work hard. We will not get a good grade.

_____

9. I think we should use drawings. Dan thinks a videotape would be more interesting.

_____

_____

10. We want to show how bread is made at a bakery. We want to show how bread is sold.

_____

_____

Notes for Home: Your child used the conjunctions *and, but,* or *or* to complete sentences and to join two simple sentences. *Home Activity:* Look in a book or magazine for sentences with *and, but,* or *or.* Decide what sentence parts or simple sentences these conjunctions join.

© Scott Foresman 5

Grammar: Review of Sentences

A **sentence** is a group of words that makes a statement, a question, a command, a request, or an exclamation. It begins with a capital letter and ends with a punctuation mark. You can tell whether a group of words is a sentence by checking to see whether it makes a complete statement.

A **declarative sentence** makes a statement. It ends with a period.
> The two neighbors got into an argument about how to make apple pie.

An **interrogative sentence** asks a question. It ends with a question mark.
> Which one puts cinnamon into her pies?

An **imperative sentence** gives a command or makes a request. It ends with a period.
> Please, teach me how to make apple pie.

An **exclamatory sentence** shows strong feeling. It ends with an exclamation mark.
> I just love a good homemade pie!

Directions: Read each sentence. Determine whether the sentence is declarative, interrogative, imperative, or exclamatory. Write your answer on the line.

_____ 1. The peach pies are cooling in the oven.

_____ 2. Take them out after you've finished cleaning the counter.

_____ 3. Do you think any of the pies are ready yet?

_____ 4. Sometimes the pies have to cook for a little longer than you think.

_____ 5. What a great smell those pies have!

Directions: Add the correct end punctuation to complete each sentence.

6. Oh no, the apple pies are burning _____

7. Are they ruined _____

8. Get more apples from the farmers' market _____

9. Do we have enough money to buy some more apples _____

10. We need at least twenty pies for the bakery _____

11. Do you know what time the bakery opens _____

12. Please, be there at 7 A.M. _____

13. People count on our bakery opening on time _____

14. What great customers we have _____

15. It's important that we keep them happy _____

Notes for Home: Your child wrote sentences that make statements, questions, commands or requests, and exclamations. *Home Activity:* Have your child create examples of all four types of sentences by writing greeting cards to friends and family.

Grammar: Review of Sentences

Directions: Add the correct end punctuation to complete each sentence.

1. Don't you think that my bread is the best in town _____

2. No, I think mine is better _____

3. Try my cinnamon raisin bread _____

4. Why should I when I have my own _____

5. I'm just trying to be helpful _____

6. What a good friend you are _____

7. Do you like to eat bread when it's toasted _____

8. I prefer my bread freshly baked _____

9. Please, help me prepare my new recipe _____

10. What a great idea that is _____

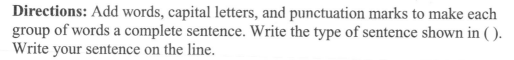

Directions: Add words, capital letters, and punctuation marks to make each group of words a complete sentence. Write the type of sentence shown in ( ). Write your sentence on the line.

11. makes bread at the bakery (declarative)

_____

12. delicious pies (exclamatory)

_____

13. when will the pies (interrogative)

_____

14. the bakery in my neighborhood (declarative)

_____

15. some bread for me (imperative)

_____

Write a Recipe

What foods do you like best? On a separate sheet of paper, write a recipe for your favorite food. Give clear steps in the directions. Use different types of sentences. List the different types of sentences you used.

Notes for Home: Your child wrote sentences that make statements, questions, commands, and exclamations. *Home Activity:* Together, write sentences on index cards but leave off the end punctuation. Take turns identifying the type of sentence and adding correct punctuation marks.

Grammar: Review of Sentences

RETEACHING

Underline the declarative sentence. Circle the interrogative sentence. Put a check mark by the imperative sentence. Circle the punctuation mark at the end of the exclamatory sentence.

1. How often do you go to the movies?

2. I go to the movies at least once a month.

3. There sure are a lot to choose from!

4. Please bring me the newspaper.

A **sentence** is a group of words that makes a statement, a question, a command or a request, or an exclamation. It begins with a capital letter and ends with a punctuation mark.

Directions: Read each sentence. Write *declarative, interrogative, imperative,* or *exclamatory* on the line to the left.

_____ 1. Listen to the wind blowing through the orchard.

_____ 2. Can you hear the soft sound?

_____ 3. I think it sounds like someone is whistling.

_____ 4. How beautiful it is!

Directions: Think about an exciting adventure you have had, or an event you have attended. Write a declarative sentence, an interrogative sentence, an imperative sentence, and an exclamatory sentence about your experience. Then label each one *declarative, interrogative, imperative,* or *exclamatory.*

5. _____

_____

6. _____

_____

7. _____

_____

8. _____

_____

Notes for Home: Your child identified and wrote four kinds of sentences. *Home Activity:* Have your child find examples of declarative, interrogative, imperative, and exclamatory sentences in books. Then have him or her explain the differences between sentence types.

Grammar: Review of Sentences

Directions: Add the correct punctuation to complete each sentence.

1. Many interesting things happen in the sky at night _____

2. Please look up there _____

3. Did you see that _____

4. It was a shooting star _____

5. How bright it was _____

6. What is a shooting star _____

7. It is a burning meteor traveling through the air _____

8. It leaves a glowing trail behind it _____

9. Here, look through my telescope _____

10. It certainly is exciting to watch the sky _____

Directions: Add words, capital letters, and punctuation marks to make each group of words a complete sentence. Write the type of sentence shown in ( ). Write your sentence on the line.

11. at my poor angelfish (imperative)

_____

12. is hiding under a piece of seaweed (declarative)

_____

13. scared it is (exclamatory)

_____

14. bought it yesterday (declarative)

_____

15. nice of him (interrogative)

_____

16. give it a little food (your choice)

_____

Notes for Home: Your child punctuated and wrote four types of sentences. *Home Activity:* Have your child write a short scene for a play. Encourage him or her to include declarative, interrogative, imperative, and exclamatory sentences as lines for the characters in the scene.

© Scott Foresman 5

Phonics: Vowel Digraphs

Directions: Read the words in the box. Each word contains the vowel combination **ea,** but the words have different vowel sounds. Write each word in the correct column.

steal	please	pleasure
tread	treat	break
great	steak	instead

Long e Sound

1. _____

2. _____

3. _____

Short e Sound

4. _____

5. _____

6. _____

Long a Sound

7. _____

8. _____

9. _____

Directions: Read the words in the box. Even though some words have the same vowel combination, the vowels have different vowel sounds. Write each word in the correct column.

pies	tough	belief	dough	tries
enough	pieces	ties	though	thief

Long o Sound

10. _____

11. _____

Short u Sound

15. _____

16. _____

Long e Sound

12. _____

13. _____

14. _____

Long i Sound

17. _____

18. _____

19. _____

Directions: Write six words that have the **long a** sound spelled **ay** as in **way** on the lines below.

20. _____

21. _____

22. _____

23. _____

24. _____

25. _____

Notes for Home: Your child distinguished between different vowel sounds for words with *ea, ou, ie,* and *ay.* **Home Activity:** With your child, write words with these vowel combinations on slips of paper. Say each word aloud and group the words that have the same vowel sounds and spellings.

Spelling: Easily Confused Words

Pretest Directions: Fold back the page along the dotted line. On the blanks, write the spelling words as they are dictated. When you have finished the test, unfold the page and check your words.

1._____

2._____

3._____

4._____

5._____

6._____

7._____

8._____

9._____

10._____

11._____

12._____

13._____

14._____

15._____

16._____

17._____

18._____

19._____

20._____

1. This is the last **of** the oranges.

2. Please turn **off** the lamp.

3. I like all fruit **except** bananas.

4. I didn't **accept** the invitation.

5. **Which** is the way to town?

6. She was a **witch** for Halloween.

7. **Where** is the grocery store?

8. We **were** lost in the hills.

9. The **weather** was stormy.

10. Tell me **whether** you will come.

11. He has a **plant** with red flowers.

12. They saw a new **planet**.

13. The ball went out of **bounds**.

14. The girls **bounce** the ball.

15. Camels live in the **desert**.

16. We will have cake for **dessert**.

17. The sun will **rise** soon.

18. They **raise** the flags up high.

19. What is for **dinner**?

20. This **diner** serves malts.

Notes for Home: Your child took a pretest on words easily confused with another word. *Home Activity:* Help your child learn misspelled words. Your child should look at the word in its sentence, think about its meaning, spell it aloud, and then spell it with eyes shut.

Spelling: Easily Confused Words

Word List				
of	which	weather	bounds	rise
off	witch	whether	bounce	raise
except	where	plant	desert	dinner
accept	were	planet	dessert	diner

Directions: Choose the word from the box that is easily confused with the word given. Write the word on the line.

1. off _____

2. except _____

3. which _____

4. where _____

5. weather _____

6. plant _____

7. bounds_____

8. dessert _____

9. rise _____

10. dinner _____

Directions: Write the word from the box that belongs in each group of words.

11. leaps, jumps, _____

12. flower, bush, _____

13. under, over, on, _____

14. breakfast, lunch, _____

15. here, there, _____

16. what, who, _____

17. swell, lift, _____

18. exclude, omit, _____

19. snow, rain, _____

20. pie, cake, _____

Notes for Home: Your child spelled words that are easily confused, such as *off* and *of*. **Home Activity**: Help your child think of other pairs of easily confused words, such as *conscience/conscious*, *adapt/adopt*, and *wreck/wreak*. Invite him or her to spell both words.

Spelling: Easily Confused Words

Proofread and Write

Directions: Proofread this letter of apology. Find five spelling mistakes. Use the proofreading marks to correct each mistake.

≡	Make a capital.
/	Make a small letter.
∧	Add something.
ꟿ	Take out something.
⊙	Add a period.
¶	Begin a new paragraph.

Dear Rita,

   I'm sorry that I yelled at you yesterday. You were right, and I was out of bounds. Please ecept my apology, which is sincere. We could plant some flowers if the whether is nice or go out to diner. I will buy you a nice desert, anything acept strawberry shortcake because I know you don't like it.

Your friend,

Carlos

Spelling Tip

Remember the number of **s**'s in **dessert** and **desert** this way: **Desserts** are **so sweet**, but a **desert** is only **sandy.**

Write a Letter

On a separate sheet of paper, write a note to a friend in which you settle a conflict or other problem between you. Try to use at least five of your spelling words.

Word List

of	plant
off	planet
except	bounds
accept	bounce
which	desert
witch	dessert
where	rise
were	raise
weather	dinner
whether	diner

© Scott Foresman 5

Notes for Home: Your child spelled words that are easily confused, such as *off* and *of*. **Home Activity:** Spell each word aloud, pausing between each letter. As soon as your child recognizes the word, have him or her say the word and tell its meaning.

Spelling: Easily Confused Words

REVIEW

		Word List		
of	which	weather	bounds	rise
off	witch	whether	bounce	raise
except	where	plant	desert	dinner
accept	were	planet	dessert	diner

Directions: Choose the word from the box that best matches each clue. Write the letters of the word on the blanks. The boxed letters answer the riddle: What do you do to place *it* and *run* in alphabetical order?

1. a very dry place

2. a foul ball is out of

3. rubber balls do this

4. atmospheric conditions

5. pledge _____ allegiance

6. Mars, for example

7. sweet item served at the end of a meal

8. a place to eat

9. an important meal

10. an ivy, for example

1. __ __ __ __ □ __ __ __

2. __ __ __ □ __ __ __ __

3. __ __ __ □ __ __ __

4. __ __ __ □ __ __ __

5. __ □ __ __

6. __ __ __ □ __ __

7. __ __ __ □ __ __ __ __ __

8. __ __ __ □ __

9. __ □ __ __ __ __

10. __ __ __ □

What would you do to place *it* and *run* in alphabetical order?

__ __ __ __ __ __ __ __ __

Directions: Unscramble the letters to find a word from the box. Write the word on the line.

11. fof _____

12. rheew _____

13. rewe _____

14. itwch _____

15. xetecp _____

16. seira _____

17. wreheth _____

18. pctace _____

19. chiwh _____

20. ires _____

Notes for Home: Your child spelled words that are easily confused, such as *off* and *of*. **Home Activity:** Challenge your child to write a sentence that uses each pair of words together in a single sentence.

Advertisement/Order Form

An **advertisement** is an announcement that tries to persuade readers, viewers, or listeners to do something, buy something, or feel a particular way about something. An **order form** is a chart that allows a person to respond to an advertisement or catalog.

Directions: Read the advertisement and order form below. Then answer the questions on the next page.

Momma's Marvelous Muffins Can't seem to wake up? One taste of Momma's Marvelous Muffins will wake you up and make you smile!

Just ask the basketball star, Harriet Hoopster. She eats Momma's Muffins every single morning, and her team has not lost a game all year.

Momma's Marvelous Muffins come in six delicious flavors: outrageous orange, raisin razzmatazz, strawberry surprise, peanut butter perfection, lemon zip, and blueberry bonanza.

Every bite is loaded with great flavor.

Order your muffins by phone, fax, mail, or in person.

Call 1-888-555-2020 today, or use the handy order form below.

Visit our web site at www.marvmuffins.com. for more information.

1. Ship to:

Name _____

Address _____

_____

Phone Number _____

2. Method of payment

____ check

____ credit card

Card number: _____

3. Muffins ordered (order in boxes of six each)

ITEM	Quantity	Price per box	Cost
Outrageous Orange		$12.00	
Raisin Razzmatazz		$12.00	
Strawberry Surprise		$12.00	
Peanut Butter Perfection		$10.00	
Lemon Zip		$10.00	
Blueberry Bonanza		$14.00	

Mail to *Momma's Marvelous Muffins,* 15390 Delicious Drive, Bakerville. MD 20888.

Or fax your completed order form to 1-888-555-2025.

Subtotal		
Add shipping and handling.		
$10–$24	$1.50	
$25–$49	$2.50	
over $50	$3.50	
Subtotal, shipping and handling		
TOTAL		

© Scott Foresman 5

Name _____

1. What information in this advertisement consists of statements of fact? _____

_____

_____

_____

2. What information in this advertisement consists of statements of opinion? _____

_____

_____

3. What exaggerated claim does this advertisement make? _____

_____

_____

4. What conclusion does the advertiser want you to draw about Harriet Hoopster's team's winning record?

_____

_____

5. If you order muffins by mail, how can you pay for them? _____

_____

6. How many muffins come in a box? _____

7. What is the price of a box of Lemon Zip muffins? _____

8. What would the shipping and handling costs be on an order worth $34.00? How do you know?

_____

_____

9. How can you send the order form to the company? _____

_____

10. Suppose your class decided to order two boxes of Outrageous Orange, one box of Strawberry Surprise, and three boxes of Blueberry Bonanza muffins. Fill out the order form. Then write the total amount you must pay on the line below.

_____

_____

Notes for Home: Your child read and interpreted an advertisement and filled out an order form. *Home Activity:* Look through magazines with your child. Talk about the ways the advertisers try to sell their merchandise. Then study an order form together and help your child fill it out.

Name_____

Summary

Boy Bakes (Gulp) Beetle Brownies

Andy is determined to win the fifth grade essay contest. He decides to write about something really interesting—edible insects. Without telling anyone, he sends away for information about edible insects and how to prepare them for eating. After he receives it, he catches some beetles and follows the directions carefully. Then he cooks the beetles in a batch of brownies. The final test comes when his unsuspecting brother Wendell tries one. Wendell's verdict? They're good!

Reading Skills

Steps in a Process

Steps in a process are the actions you take to reach a goal or make something.

❖ Sometimes steps in a process are shown by numbers or clue words. For example, the letter Andy got says, "you might put them in a covered box in the freezer first, then cook them later." The clue words here are *first, then,* and *later.*

❖ If there are no clue words, use common sense to picture the steps. Imagine the end result of the process and how each step fits in. Identifying stcps in a process will help you do experiments, solve problems, and follow directions (just like Andy).

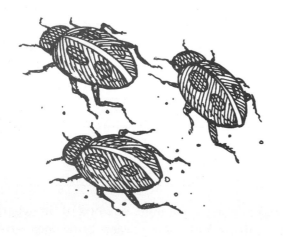

Activity
Then What Happened? Continue the story by telling how Andy's family learns the secret ingredient of his brownies, and what happens when they do.

Activity
Follow a Recipe. Cook something, such as brownies, cookies, pancakes, or muffins, using a cookbook recipe or a mix. First read through the steps and make sure you understand them. Then follow them carefully.

Family Times

Tested Vocabulary

Words to Know

Knowing the meanings of these words is important to reading "Andy's Secret Ingredient." Practice using these words to learn their meanings.

clenched gripped tightly

comparing seeing similarities and differences

cornmeal coarsely ground dried corn

essay written composition

flyer brochure

grease oil or fat for cooking

primitive of early times

Grammar

Capitalization

Use the following rules to capitalize words correctly.

- Capitalize the first word of a sentence.
  <u>W</u>ould you like to eat a beetle?
- Capitalize the first and every important word of a proper noun. Proper nouns name particular persons, places, or things.
  <u>A</u>ndy <u>M</u>oller
  <u>I</u>owa <u>S</u>tate <u>U</u>niversity
  <u>A</u>pril <u>F</u>ool's <u>D</u>ay
  <u>F</u>riday, <u>A</u>pril 1
- Capitalize parts of addresses.
  1900 <u>E</u>ast <u>L</u>ake <u>A</u>ve.
  <u>G</u>lenview, <u>IL</u> 60025
- Capitalize titles before people's names.
  <u>M</u>r. Sudermann
  <u>D</u>r. Angela Scarlotti
  <u>C</u>aptain A.J. Walker

Activity

Make a Guest List. Imagine you were having a huge party, and you could invite anyone you wanted, real or make-believe. Make up a guest list with names and addresses of people you would invite. Be sure to capitalize words correctly.

Tested Spelling Words

© Scott Foresman 5

Steps in a Process

- **Steps in a process** are the actions you take to reach a goal or to make something.
- Sometimes steps in a process are shown by numbers or clue words *(first, next, then,* and *last)*. If there are no clues, use common sense to picture the steps.

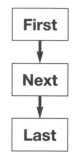

First

↓

Next

↓

Last

Directions: Reread "Beetle Research." Then write the following steps in the order that they should be performed. The first step is done for you.

Steps

Compare beetles caught at different times of the day.
Cover the cup with the stones and the wood.
Gather a jar or plastic cup, four stones, and a small piece of wood.
Remove the trap when you have finished.
Bury the cup level with the surface.
Put food in the cup to see what attracts certain species.

Making a Pitfall Trap

Gather a jar or plastic cup, four stones, and a small piece of wood.

↓

1.

↓

2.

↓

3.

↓

4.

↓

5.

Notes for Home: Your child read about a process and then identified its steps in order. *Home Activity:* Choose a job that your child performs, such as doing the laundry or setting the dinner table. Work together to list all the steps of the process in order.

© Scott Foresman 5

Vocabulary

Directions: Draw a line to connect each word on the left with its definition on the right.

1. essay   of early times

2. flyer   seeing similarities and differences

3. primitive   written composition

4. comparing   coarsely ground dried corn

5. cornmeal   brochure

Directions: Read the recipe. Choose the word from the box that best completes each sentence. Write the word on the matching numbered line to the right.

Fried Worms

This old family recipe dates all the way back to **6.** _____ times. I **7.** _____ my teeth when I first tried them, but I love them now. **8.** _____ the taste to chicken, I'd say worms are sweeter and less chewy.

Step 1: Dip one dozen fat, juicy earthworms in a beaten egg.

Step 2: Roll the worms in 1 cup of **9.** _____ or flour.

Step 3: Melt 2 tablespoons butter or **10.** _____ in a skillet.

Step 4: Fry the worms in the hot fat for 2–3 minutes, or until brown and crispy. Drain on a paper towel. Enjoy!

6. _____

7. _____

8. _____

9. _____

10. _____

Write Contest Rules

Imagine you are in charge of a creative cooking contest. On a separate sheet of paper, write the contest rules. Explain the type of contest, who can enter, and the prizes. Use as many vocabulary words as you can.

Notes for Home: Your child identified and used vocabulary words from "Andy's Secret Ingredient." *Home Activity:* Have your child write a story about the strangest food he or she has ever tasted. Guide your child to use as many vocabulary words as possible.

Steps in a Process

> - **Steps in a process** are the actions you take to reach a goal or to make something.
>
> - Sometimes steps in a process are shown by numbers or clue words *(first, next, then*, and *last)*. If there are no clues, use common sense to picture the steps.

Directions: Reread what happens in "Andy's Secret Ingredient" when Andy makes his special brownies. Then answer the questions below.

The batter was dark and moist. When the flour and eggs and sugar had been mixed, Andy put in a quarter of a cup of chopped walnuts and then, his teeth clenched, a quarter of a cup of chopped beetle.

All the time the brownies were baking, Andy wondered if he could smell the beetles.

When the brownies were done, he took them out, cooled them for twenty minutes, then cut them into squares and piled them onto a platter. He was just washing out the bowl and spoon in the sink when Wendell came into the kitchen, a screwdriver hanging out of one pocket.

Reprinted with the permission of Atheneum Books for Young Readers, an imprint of Simon & Schuster Children's Publishing Division from BEETLES, LIGHTLY TOASTED by Phyllis Reynolds Naylor. Copyright © 1987 by Phyllis Reynolds Naylor.

1. What is the first step in the process described here?

_____

_____

2. What are the second and third steps in the process?

_____

_____

3. What steps does Andy take when the brownies are done?

_____

_____

4. What is the last thing Andy does?

_____

_____

5. On a separate sheet of paper, tell how Andy prepares the beetles he has found for baking. List the steps in order.

Notes for Home: Your child read a story and identified the order of steps in a process. *Home Activity:* Using a simple recipe, bake cookies or brownies with your child. Check to make sure he or she follows the recipe steps in the correct order.

Selection Test

Directions: Choose the best answer to each item. Mark the letter for the answer you have chosen.

Part 1: Vocabulary

Find the answer choice that means about the same as the underlined word in each sentence.

1. Marisol <u>clenched</u> her fists.
   A. cleaned
   B. looked at carefully
   C. closed tightly
   D. raised

2. Jan studies how <u>primitive</u> people lived.
   F. simple, as in early times
   G. from a different country
   H. very smart
   J. of the forest

3. Grandma bought some <u>cornmeal</u>.
   A. corn kernels
   B. pancakes made from corn
   C. coarsely ground dried corn
   D. corn syrup

4. She placed the fish in the hot <u>grease</u>.
   F. oil
   G. salt
   H. spice
   J. oven

5. Our teacher was <u>comparing</u> two countries.
   A. traveling to
   B. seeing how things are alike in
   C. discussing the history of
   D. listing all the things wrong with

6. A woman handed me a <u>flyer</u>.
   F. free sample of food
   G. young turkey
   H. ticket for an airplane flight
   J. paper handed out for advertising

7. Kala finished her <u>essay</u>.
   A. daily chore
   B. speech read aloud
   C. physical exercise
   D. written composition

Part 2: Comprehension

Use what you know about the story to answer each item.

8. In what kind of project is Andy involved?
   F. an essay contest
   G. a cooking contest
   H. an animal-raising project
   J. a project to raise money

9. What is Andy's attitude toward his cousin Jack?
   A. Andy feels sorry for Jack and wants to help him.
   B. Andy feels that he and Jack make a great team.
   C. Andy feels that he and Jack are always in a competition.
   D. Andy doesn't want to do anything that Jack does.

10. Andy begins planning for his essay by—
    F. running away from the turkey.
    G. writing a letter to the university.
    H. deciding that he does not like catfish.
    J. letting Wendell eat a brownie.

11. What is the first step Andy takes in preparing the beetles?
    A. He puts them in the freezer.
    B. He washes them.
    C. He puts them in a cookie tin with a tight lid.
    D. He feeds them cornmeal.

12. Just before Andy chops the beetles into pieces, he—
    F. rolls them in cornmeal.
    G. freezes them.
    H. peels off the wings and legs.
    J. toasts them.

GO ON

13. Through his experiment with the beetles, Andy wants to show that—
   A.   beetles can live in a freezer.
   B.   people don't care what is in their food as long as it tastes good.
   C.   he can bake as well as his mother can.
   D.   people can eat bugs.

14. What will Andy probably do when he takes his brownies to school?
   F.   decide that he cannot continue with his experiment
   G.   let his classmates eat the brownies before he tells them about the beetles
   H.   write an essay about eating soul food
   J.   make a flyer to help sell his beetle brownies

15. Andy's approach to writing his essay is a good example of how to—
   A.   get along better with people.
   B.   solve problems in creative ways.
   C.   impress a girl who is a good cook.
   D.   get by without much money.

STOP

Steps in a Process

- **Steps in a process** are the actions you take to reach a goal or to make something.

- Sometimes steps in a process are shown by numbers or clue words (*first, next, then,* and *last*). If there are no clues, use common sense to picture the steps.

Directions: Read the story.

"I wonder how I would look if I put on some makeup just like Mommy wears," four-year-old Jillian said to herself as she woke up early from her nap. "I think I'll try it while Mommy is downstairs."

First Jillian scrubbed her face. Then she applied a thick layer of powder all over her face. Next she colored her eyelids blue, green, and gold. She drew over her eyebrows with eyebrow pencil. After that she smeared her lips with bright pink lipstick. She studied her face in the mirror. "I think I need some red stuff on my cheeks too," she said. So she dusted on a thick coat of blush. "Won't Mommy be surprised," Jillian thought as she made her way downstairs.

Directions: Complete the flowchart. Fill in the steps that Jillian took to make up her face.

Jillian scrubbed her face.

↓

1.

↓

2.

↓

3.

↓

4.

↓

5.

 Notes for Home: Your child read a story and identified the order of steps in a process. ***Home Activity:*** Work with your child to create a flowchart showing the order of steps in an activity you both enjoy.

Fact and Opinion/ Author's Viewpoint

REVIEW

Directions: Read the passage. Then read each question about the passage. Choose the best answer to each question. Mark the letter for the answer you have chosen.

Insects as Food

You probably think that you would never eat an insect, even if you were starving. Insects are ugly and disgusting, right?

But chances are you do eat them, or at least you use products that come from insects. Beeswax, for example, is used in lip balms. Honeycomb is sold in most American supermarkets.

Around the world, insects have long been an important food source. Insects were once a major food for Australian aborigines. In some countries, grasshoppers and large palm weevil grubs are still eaten. In South Africa, some people snack on roasted termites as if they were popcorn. In the Sinai Desert, some people eat the dry, scaly parts of certain bugs. In Mexico, a popular cake is made with the eggs of a water insect. In the United States, chocolate-covered ants are a delicacy sold in many food stores.

As someone who has eaten dishes made from insects, let me tell you that they are delicious. They are very nutritious, too, because insects are an excellent source of protein. It is simply prejudice that keeps most people from enjoying these delicacies. As with any new food, you have to give it a chance. You might be surprised at just how tasty insects can be!

1. In the first paragraph, the author assumes that most people—
   A. like insects.
   B. hate insects.
   C. have eaten insects.
   D. think insects are useful.

2. In the second and third paragraphs, the author supports his or her viewpoint by—
   F. quoting an expert.
   G. providing a variety of opinions.
   H. repeating the main idea.
   J. giving facts.

3. Which of the following is a statement of opinion?
   A. Insects have long been an important food source.
   B. Australian aborigines ate bugs.
   C. Insects are delicious.
   D. Beeswax is used in lip balms.

4. Which statement best sums up the author's viewpoint?
   F. Insects are unfairly rejected as a food source.
   G. Insects are better than most foods.
   H. Insects have no place in a modern diet.
   J. Insects are the food of the future.

5. This article is best described as—
   A. balanced.
   B. unbalanced.
   C. emotional.
   D. inaccurate.

Notes for Home: Your child read an article and identified statements of fact and opinion, as well as the author's viewpoint. ***Home Activity:*** Read a newspaper editorial with your child. Have him or her identify the facts, opinions, and author's viewpoint.

Writing Across Texts

Directions: Consider what you learned about eating bugs in "Andy's Secret Ingredient" and "Bug-a-licious!" Complete the table to answer the Central Issue question. Include both pro and con ideas and your conclusion.

Central Issue:

Would I try a dish that has insects as one of the ingredients?

Pros:

Many people around the world eat bugs safely.

1.

2.

Cons:

Some bugs are poisonous.

3.

4.

Conclusion:

5.

Write an Essay

Both "Andy's Secret Ingredient" and "Bug-a-licious!" present surprising information about bugs you can eat. Each story contains additional facts or ideas not found in the other. After reading these stories, would you try a dish that has bugs as one of the ingredients? On a separate sheet of paper, write an essay in which you explain the pros and cons of eating insects and then give your own opinion.

Notes for Home: Your child used information from different sources to write an essay. *Home Activity:* As you read stories and articles with your child, discuss ways the characters in the stories, as well as people in your own lives, solve problems creatively.

Grammar: Proper Nouns and Proper Adjectives

REVIEW

Directions: Rewrite each sentence correctly. Capitalize each proper noun.

1. My friend edward rabitoy lives on middle street.

_____

2. He goes to diamond middle school instead of to king middle school.

_____

3. His science teacher, ms. garza, has assigned edward an interesting experiment.

_____

4. I am meeting edward and his friend jonah in washington park.

_____

5. Then we will all go to the herman museum of science.

_____

Directions: Rewrite each sentence correctly. Capitalize each proper adjective and proper noun.

6. The museum on third avenue was named after a german scientist.

_____

7. He left germany to study at yale university and became an american citizen.

_____

_____

8. At the herman museum, we learned about the swiss scientist, daniel bernoulli.

_____

_____

9. He discovered the bernoulli principle, which states that the faster air or liquid moves, the less pressure it has.

_____

_____

10. edward, who is french, was testing the bernoulli principle in his science experiment.

_____

_____

Notes for Home: Your child capitalized proper nouns and proper adjectives. *Home Activity:* Ask your child to write some sentences about what he or she learned in school this week. Encourage your child to use proper nouns and proper adjectives in the sentences.

© Scott Foresman 5

Grammar: Capitalization

Capitalize the first word of a sentence.

A telescope was necessary for her space experiment, but she didn't have one.

Capitalize the first and every important word of a proper noun. Proper nouns name particular persons, places, or things.

Annie Johnson	Wednesday, December 21
Johnson Space Center	Independence Day
250 Park Place	*Journey to the Stars*

Capitalize the first letter of an abbreviation for parts of addresses. An abbreviation is a shortened form of a word. It usually ends with a period. When abbreviating state names in addresses, use two capital letters and no periods.

1558 Brummel St.
Evanston, IL 60202

Capitalize titles before people's names. Some titles may also be abbreviations.

Dr. Jacob Abboud was an expert on stars.

He liked to visit the home of Major Roger Nelson.

With the help of Ms. Rita Miller, they would spend hours observing the stars.

Directions: Rewrite the sentences using proper capitalization.

1. president matthew turner wanted an experiment to test the new telescope.

_____

_____

2. he asked his team of scientists to start working on friday, august 25.

_____

_____

3. the experiment would have to be finished by new year's day.

_____

_____

4. the leader of the team was capt. julie mora, who was an experienced astronomer.

_____

_____

5. capt. mora had taught astronomy at the university of texas in austin.

_____

_____

Notes for Home: Your child capitalized words in sentences, proper nouns, addresses, and titles. *Home Activity:* Have your child make a list of his or her five favorite holidays, five favorite books, and five favorite friends, capitalizing all proper nouns.

Extra Practice

Grammar: Capitalization

Directions: Write **C** on the line if words are correctly capitalized in the sentences. Write **NC** on the line if words are not correctly capitalized. Circle each word that should be capitalized but isn't.

_____ 1. Ms. Julia Rose came to visit her friend Rico.

_____ 2. rico was in the middle of an experiment.

_____ 3. He was doing the experiment at 16 Phillips rd.

_____ 4. Rico lived with his parents, dr. Troy Rose and major Phyllis Rose.

_____ 5. They had just moved to Nashua, New Hampshire, from Salt Lake City, Utah.

_____ 6. Julia had an idea for an experiment that her teacher, mr. mills, had told her.

_____ 7. Rico had a different idea that he'd learned from a friend in newark, new jersey.

_____ 8. Julia and Rico combined their ideas to create an experiment of their own.

_____ 9. One experiment was called *Freezing Water* and the other was called *look at the stars*.

_____ 10. They called their new experiment *Freezing the Stars*.

Directions: Add a proper noun to complete each sentence. Use the kind of proper noun in ( ). Write the proper noun on the line. Remember to capitalize proper nouns.

_____ 11. Mia liked to conduct experiments with her friend _____. (person's name)

_____ 12. They worked in the lab at _____. (name of school)

_____ 13. The school's address is _____. (street address)

_____ 14. Tomorrow school would be closed for _____. (holiday)

_____ 15. Mia and her friend will read their book of science experiments called _____. (book title)

Write a List

On a separate sheet of paper, write your "Top Ten" list of books, movies, TV shows, and magazines. Be sure to capitalize each title correctly. Then write a review of your #1 favorite, using complete sentences and proper nouns.

Notes for Home: Your child capitalized words in sentences, proper nouns, addresses, and titles. *Home Activity:* Write a postcard to a family member or friend. Have your child address the postcard and write the sentences you create together, using proper capitalization.

Grammar: Capitalization

Circle mistakes in capitalization.

1. my dog, rex, is a saint bernard.   **2.** My address is 1222 Rosamond st.

Capitalize the first word of a sentence, the first and every important word of a proper noun, the first letter of an abbreviation for parts of addresses, and titles before people's names.

Directions: Read each sentence. Rewrite the sentences, adding capital letters where they belong.

1. my friend goes to franklin school.

_____

2. Her class took a trip on friday.

_____

3. they walked down morgan avenue and turned onto eagle drive.

_____

4. The students visited the sears tower.

_____

5. amy, paul, and susie went into the gift shop.

_____

6. We could see lake michigan from the top floor of the building!

_____

7. Then I went back home to 1534 durand st.

_____

8. I told my aunt donna about my trip.

_____

9. she was very excited about it.

_____

10. She told me she walked past the building on her way to see dr. Philips, the dentist.

_____

Notes for Home: Your child used capital letters correctly in sentences. *Home Activity:* Write a letter to your child, leaving out capital letters. Have him or her circle the words that need capital letters.

Grammar: Capitalization

Directions: Write each sentence below with the correct capitalization.

1. i wonder what Roaches and Grasshoppers would taste like.

_____

2. do You think they would know at Iowa state university?

_____

3. i wonder if aunt Wanda would make a big Bug stew.

_____

4. andy was afraid of the moller's big tom turkey.

_____

5. aunt bernie always compared andy to jack.

_____

6. andy wrote a letter asking about how to prepare bugs, and he addressed it to the department of bugs.

_____

_____

7. john burrows, entomologist, wrote a letter to andy.

_____

8. andy received the letter on may 1.

_____

Directions: For each sentence, underline the word or words that need a capital letter. Then write the word or words correctly on the line.

9. Uncle Delmar took care of his car on saturday. _____

10. The soul food kitchen and carry-out was in a small building.

_____

11. The restaurant was on North street. _____

12. we really enjoyed our meal. _____

13. Now I'm going to write a letter to uncle delmar at his brother's house at 1345 martin st.

_____   _____

Notes for Home: Your child capitalized words in sentences correctly. **Home Activity:** Have your child write a letter to a character in *Andy's Secret Ingredient*. Help him or her use capital letters correctly.

Name _____

Phonics: Diphthongs and Vowel Digraphs

Directions: Read the words in the box. Each word has the letters **ow,** but the letters stand for different vowel sounds. Say each word to yourself. Listen for the words with the same vowel sound as **cow** and those with the same vowel sound as **low.** Write each word in the correct column.

| brownies |
| bowl |
| swallow |
| down |
| showing |
| however |

Vowel sound in *cow*

1. _____

2. _____

3. _____

Vowel sound in *low*

4. _____

5. _____

6. _____

Directions: Read each sentence below. One word in each sentence has a word with the vowel sound heard at the beginning of **author.** Write the word on the line. Circle the letters that stand for that vowel sound.

_____ 7. August is a good time to catch beetles.

_____ 8. The cook needed beetles because he is making a special dessert.

_____ 9. He placed the beetles on a saucer, then stored them in the freezer.

_____ 10. He rinsed them under the faucet in the sink.

Directions: Read the announcement below. Listen for words that have a vowel sound like **boy** or **oil.** Circle the words and write them on the lines.

| Everyone! Join in! |
| Make your choice! |
| Sign up for the school |
| science fair! |
| Don't boycott it this year! |
| You're sure to enjoy it! |
| You won't be disappointed! |
| See Mr. Keller for more details. |

11. _____

12. _____

13. _____

14. _____

15. _____

Notes for Home: Your child worked with the vowel sounds represented by *oi* as in *join, oy* as in *boy, ow* as in *brownies* or *low,* and *au* as in *author.* **Home Activity:** As you read with your child, look and listen for these spellings and vowel sounds.

Spelling: Using Just Enough Letters

Pretest

Pretest Directions: Fold back the page along the dotted line. On the blanks, write the spelling words as they are dictated. When you have finished the test, unfold the page and check your words.

1._____

2._____

3._____

4._____

5._____

6._____

7._____

8._____

9._____

10._____

11._____

12._____

13._____

14._____

15._____

16._____

17._____

18._____

19._____

20._____

1. Wait **until** tomorrow.

2. We **went** to the skating rink.

3. Is that **enough** food for you?

4. Do you watch too much **TV**?

5. I have **one** quarter left.

6. The cat **didn't** like water.

7. That is **a lot** of ice cream.

8. The boys **want** to play ball.

9. The librarian **doesn't** like noise.

10. The sun **always** sets at night.

11. Her **necklace** has a diamond.

12. What is the **exact** time?

13. The **burglar** wore a mask.

14. We need the right **equipment**.

15. The **chimney** is very dirty.

16. I thought it did not **exist**.

17. There was a **rumbling** below us.

18. I painted a cat **upon** the canvas.

19. She is a great **athlete**.

20. The doctor will **examine** your cut.

Notes for Home: Your child took a pretest on words that have difficult letter combinations. *Home Activity:* Help your child learn misspelled words before the final test. Your child can underline the word parts that caused the problems and concentrate on those parts.

Spelling: Using Just Enough Letters

Word List				
until	one	doesn't	burglar	rumbling
went	didn't	always	equipment	upon
enough	a lot	necklace	chimney	athlete
TV	want	exact	exist	examine

Directions: Choose the words from the box that begin with a vowel. Sort them according to which vowel they start with. Write the words in the correct column.

Begins with a

1. _____

2. _____

3. _____

Begins with u

4. _____

5. _____

Begins with e

6. _____

7. _____

8. _____

9. _____

10. _____

Begins with o

11. _____

Directions: Choose the word from the box that best replaces the underlined word or words. Write the word on the line.

_____ 12. Lauren <u>did not</u> have anything to do.

_____ 13. She decided to watch a science show on <u>television</u>.

_____ 14. When the show was over, Lauren <u>left</u> from the room.

_____ 15. "I <u>would like</u> to try an experiment!" she said.

_____ 16. "It <u>does not</u> look hard," she thought.

_____ 17. Lauren put chemicals on an old <u>piece of jewelry worn around the neck</u>.

_____ 18. Smoke from the chemicals drifted up the <u>smokestack over the fireplace</u>.

_____ 19. The experiment started <u>making a deep, rolling sound</u> like thunder.

_____ 20. "Well, I guess a <u>robber</u> won't steal *this* experiment!" she laughed.

Notes for Home: Your child spelled words using just enough letters to spell them correctly. *Home Activity*: With your child, practice spelling the words by first pronouncing each word carefully and correctly, syllable by syllable.

Spelling: Using Just Enough Letters

Directions: Proofread this recipe. Find six spelling mistakes. Use the proofreading marks to correct each mistake.

≡	Make a capital.
/	Make a small letter.
∧	Add something.
⌻	Take out something.
⊙	Add a period.
¶	Begin a new paragraph.

Salad Surprise

Eqipment: Cutting board, sharp knife, salad bowl

Ingredients: Enuff fresh lettuce to fill bowl; at least three "surprise" ingredients such as mini-crackers, raisins, nuts, or marshmallows; one-half cup bottled dressing.

- Always wash lettuce thoroughly. Examne it closely for bugs.

- Rip lettuce into alot of small pieces. Place in bowl.

- Add other ingredients, on at a time.

- Add dressing and toss untill salad is evenly coated.

Spelling Tip

When you shorten **did not** and **does not** to **didn't** and **doesn't,** you must use apostrophes.

Write a Recipe

On a separate sheet of paper, write a recipe for a dish you have created—or one that you have always dreamed of making! Give it a surprise ingredient or two. Try to use at least five of your spelling words.

Word List

until	necklace
went	exact
enough	burglar
TV	equipment
one	chimney
didn't	exist
a lot	rumbling
want	upon
docsn't	athlete
always	examine

Notes for Home: Your child spelled words using just enough letters to spell them correctly. *Home Activity:* Spell each word for your child, but misspell several words. See if he or she can catch each mistake and spell the word correctly.

Spelling: Using Just Enough Letters REVIEW

Word List

until	one	doesn't	burglar	rumbling
went	didn't	always	equipment	upon
enough	a lot	necklace	chimney	athlete
TV	want	exact	exist	examine

Directions: Choose the word from the box that best completes each statement.
Write the word on the line to the left.

_____ 1. *Knight* is to *armor* as *scuba diver* is to *diving _____*.

_____ 2. *Few* is to *many* as *a little* is to _____.

_____ 3. *Inspector* is to *inspect* as *examiner* is to _____.

_____ 4. *Satisfactory* is to *acceptable* as *sufficient* is to _____.

_____ 5. *Vague* is to *precise* as *inexact* is to _____.

_____ 6. *Knowing* is to *know* as *wanting* is to _____.

_____ 7. *No* is to *yes* as *never* is to _____.

_____ 8. *Is not* is to *isn't* as *does not* is to _____.

_____ 9. *Below* is to *under* as *on* is to _____.

_____ 10. *Wrist* is to *bracelet* as *neck* is to _____.

Directions: Write the word from the box that belongs in each group.

11. sportscaster, coach, _____

12. roaring, crackling, _____

13. radio, video, _____

14. be, live, _____

15. wouldn't, hadn't, _____

16. three, two, _____

17. now, after, _____

18. thief, robber, _____

19. came, saw, _____

20. door, roof, _____

Notes for Home: Your child spelled words using just enough letters to spell them correctly.
Home Activity: Write each word on a card and show it to your child briefly. Encourage her or
him to say each word clearly and picture how the word looks before spelling the word aloud.

Recipe

A **recipe** is a set of directions for preparing something to eat.

Directions: Use the recipe below to answer the questions on the next page.

Sharon's Spicy Scrambled Eggs

3 eggs | dash of pepper | $\frac{1}{4}$ cup minced onion

1 tablespoon milk | dash of hot pepper sauce | 1 tablespoon butter or margarine

dash of salt | $\frac{1}{4}$ cup grated cheddar cheese

Break an egg into a cup. Pick out any shell. Then pour the egg into a bowl.

Repeat for the other two eggs.

Add milk, salt, pepper, and hot sauce to eggs.

Beat eggs gently.

Melt butter or margarine in skillet over medium heat.

Add onion to the melted butter and cook for 2–3 minutes until you can see through the onion pieces. Be careful not to burn the butter or margarine.

Add egg mixture and cheese.

Stir occasionally with spatula until eggs are firm.

Sharon's suggestions for experimenting:

Use cottage cheese instead of cheddar cheese.

Separate 2 eggs into yolks and egg whites, and substitute the 2 egg whites for 2 whole eggs.

Add diced cooked potatoes.

Add chopped green chilies.

Add crumbled bacon or a nonmeat bacon substitute.

Put in more hot sauce!

Name _____

1. What is the first step in preparing this recipe? _____

_____

2. Why does the recipe say to break each egg into a cup before pouring it into a bowl?

_____

_____

3. Which ingredients do you add before beating the eggs? _____

_____

4. What do you do after beating the eggs gently? _____

_____

5. What does the second illustration show? _____

_____

6. What "experimental" ingredients do you think you would like in this recipe? Explain why.

_____

_____

7. Write your own suggestion for experimenting with this recipe. _____

_____

_____

8. What are the advantages to watching a cooking show on television? What are the disadvantages?

_____

_____

_____

_____

9. Why is it important to follow a recipe's directions in the order that they are given?

_____

_____

10. Are illustrations or photographs helpful in a recipe? Explain. _____

_____

_____

Notes for Home: Your child read and answered questions about a recipe and an illustration. *Home Activity:* Find a simple recipe for something your child likes. Read the recipe together and talk about the steps involved in following the recipe. Then make the dish together.

© Scott Foresman 5

Family Times

Summary

Elderly Woman Outsmarts Thieves

Two travelers spend the night at the home of an old woman. When they see the prize ham she keeps in a closet, they decide to steal it. But the old woman is smart and spies them putting the ham in their bag in the middle of the night. While they sleep, she replaces the ham in their bag with an adobe brick. The next morning, the two men tease the old woman with their dreams of food, but it is she who has the last laugh.

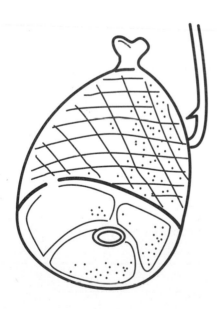

Activity
Be a Storyteller. Have your child be a storyteller and retell this folk tale in his or her own words for an audience of family members. Encourage your child to be expressive in the retelling.

Reading Skills

Plot

A **plot** includes the important events that happen in a story. A plot usually has:

❖ **conflict:** In this story, the conflict is between the travelers, who want to steal the ham, and the old woman, who is determined to keep it.
❖ **rising action:** In the story, the men steal the ham; the old woman takes it back; they tease her with dreams; she teases them back. Each event builds suspense.
❖ **climax:** The high point comes when the men open the bag to find that the old woman has outsmarted them.
❖ **outcome or resolution:** The two travelers learn a lesson and don't try any more tricks on people.

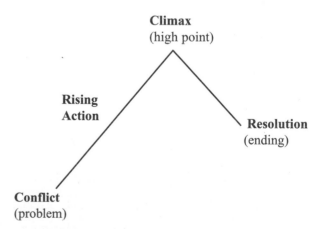

Climax
(high point)

Rising
Action

Resolution
(ending)

Conflict
(problem)

Activity
Tell a Story. With your family, make up an original plot for a story. In a round robin, have each family member contribute an element or event. As each part of the plot is created, write it down in a story map like the one shown.

Family Times

Tested Vocabulary

Words to Know

Knowing the meanings of these words is important to reading "In the Days of King Adobe." Practice using these words to learn their meanings.

fascinated highly interested

foolishness behavior that shows a lack of sense or judgment

generous large; plentiful

rascals mischievous or dishonest persons

seldom not often

Grammar

Commas in Series and in Direct Address

Commas tell you when to pause when reading. They help make the meaning of a sentence clear. Use commas to separate items in a series or names of people directly addressed.

In a Series:
The old woman ate <u>beans</u>, <u>tortillas</u>, and <u>cornmeal mush</u>.

In Direct Address:
Listen, <u>children</u>, and I'll tell you a story. We're ready, <u>Grandma</u>.

Activity

Address Your Family. Think of something you'd like to say to each member of your family. Then write your thoughts in a sentence or two addressed to each person. Use commas to separate the names of people directly addressed.

Tested Spelling Words

_____	_____	_____	_____
_____	_____	_____	_____
_____	_____	_____	_____
_____	_____	_____	_____
_____	_____	_____	_____

Plot

- A **plot** includes the important events that happen in a story.
- A plot usually has a conflict or problem, rising action, a climax, and the resolution, or outcome.

Directions: Reread "The Brahman and the Banker." Then identify each important part of the plot in the story map.

Climax: When is the Brahman's problem solved?

4. _____

_____

_____

_____

Rising Action: What actions does the Brahman do to try to solve his problem?

3. _____

_____

_____

_____

Resolution: What is explained at the end of the story?

5. _____

2. _____

_____

_____

_____

_____

_____

_____

_____

_____

_____

Conflict: What problem does the Brahman have with the banker?

1. _____

_____

_____

_____

Notes for Home: Your child identified the important events in a story. **Home Activity:** Read a story to your child, or watch one together on TV. Have your child outline the plot by identifying a character's conflict or problem, the story's rising action, the climax, and the resolution.

Vocabulary

Directions: Choose the word from the box that has the same or nearly the same meaning as each word or words below. Write the word on the line.

_____ 1. scoundrels

_____ 2. rarely

_____ 3. plentiful

_____ 4. enchanted

_____ 5. silliness

Directions: Choose the word from the box that best matches each clue. Write the word in the puzzle.

Down

6. mischievous persons
7. large; plentiful

Across

8. highly interested
9. not often
10. behavior that shows lack of judgment

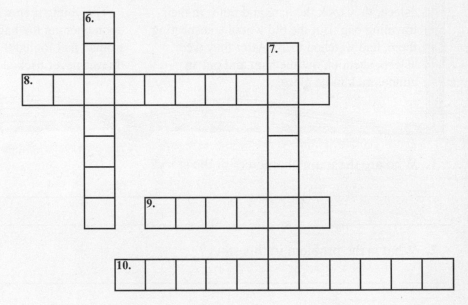

Write an Epilogue

Ever wonder what happens to the characters *after* a story ends? Pick a story you like very much. On a separate sheet of paper, tell what happens after the end of the story. You may set your epilogue weeks, months, or years in the future! Use as many vocabulary words as you can.

 Notes for Home: Your child identified and used vocabulary words from "In the Days of King Adobe." *Home Activity:* Work with your child to make a puzzle that uses all these vocabulary words. The puzzle can be a word search or crossword, for example.

Plot

- A story's **plot** is the important events that happen in a story. These parts include the conflict or problem, the rising action, the climax, and the resolution, or outcome.

Directions: Read the plot summary of "In the Days of King Adobe." Then answer the questions below.

There once was a poor but thrifty old woman who had a fine ham. One evening two young men on a journey came to her door. She gave them lodging and ham for dinner. When they saw the ham, they decided to steal it.

That night, thinking the old woman was asleep, they took the ham and put it in their traveling bag. But the old woman, suspecting them, had watched them. After they were asleep, she took out the ham and put an adobe brick in its place.

The next day at breakfast the two young rascals told her a made-up dream about Hambone the First, king of a land called Travelibag. She responded with her own dream, in which King Hambone was usurped by Adobe the Great.

The young men went on their way. Later, upon opening the bag, they saw that the old woman had fooled them. The two hungry thieves never tricked another old woman.

1. Who are the main characters in the story?

_____

_____

2. What is the problem in this story?

_____

_____

3. Describe the rising action of the story where the problem leads to other events.

_____

_____

4. What is the climax, or high point, of the story?

_____

_____

5. What is the resolution, or outcome, of the story? Write your answer on a separate piece of paper.

Notes for Home: Your child read a story summary and identified different elements of the story's plot. *Home Activity:* Watch a television show or movie with your child. Discuss the important parts of the story, the main problem characters face, and how it is resolved.

Selection Test

Directions: Choose the best answer to each item. Mark the letter for the answer you have chosen.

Part 1: Vocabulary

Find the answer choice that means about the same as the underlined word in each sentence.

1. Kayla seldom asks questions in class.
   - A. every day
   - B. often
   - C. never
   - D. not often

2. Those boys are rascals.
   - F. people who are related to each other
   - G. persons who cause mischief
   - H. people who work together
   - J. hard-working persons

3. Throughout the play, Jonas looked fascinated.
   - A. very interested
   - B. upset
   - C. very sleepy
   - D. proud

4. Everyone commented on the foolishness of the plan.
   - F. danger
   - G. lack of sense
   - H. success
   - J. difficulty

5. My grandmother served a generous bowl of soup.
   - A. steaming hot
   - B. tasty
   - C. large
   - D. leftover

Part 2: Comprehension

Use what you know about the story to answer each item.

6. At the beginning of this story, we know only that the old woman was—
   - F. very poor.
   - G. living with her family.
   - H. very rich.
   - J. going on a journey.

7. Where does the old woman live?
   - A. in the marketplace of a town
   - B. in a hotel where she works as a servant
   - C. in the middle of a wilderness
   - D. at the edge of a village

8. The old woman gets the ham by—
   - F. saving a penny a day.
   - G. stealing it.
   - H. selling bricks.
   - J. tricking the young men.

9. What can you conclude about the old woman based on the way she acts when the young men first come to her house?
   - A. She is lonely.
   - B. She is very suspicious.
   - C. She is lazy.
   - D. She dislikes young people.

GO ON

10. The main problem in this story is between the—
    F. woman's wish to eat the ham and her wish to share it.
    G. men wanting to steal the ham and their wish to respect the woman.
    H. men's wish to travel and their wish to stay with the woman.
    J. men wanting to steal the ham and the woman's wish to keep it.

11. Which of these events is part of the rising action in this story?
    A. The old woman sells most of her vegetables in the market.
    B. The young men decide not to trick the next person they stay with.
    C. The old woman buys the ham.
    D. The young man tells about his dream of King Hambone the First.

12. The old woman shows that she has a sense of humor when she—
    F. describes her dream of King Adobe.
    G. takes the ham from the traveling bag.
    H. notices the rascally look in the men's eyes.
    J. prepares the ham for supper.

13. The climax of this story occurs when the—
    A. young men steal the ham.
    B. men open the bag and find the brick.
    C. woman puts the brick in place of the ham.
    D. woman asks the men about their dreams.

14. Which fact makes it hardest to forgive the young men's behavior to the old woman?
    F. She was very generous to them.
    G. They were very hungry.
    H. She tricked them too.
    J. They had a long way to travel.

15. The author's main purpose in this story is to—
    A. explain how to cook a ham.
    B. describe the travels of two young men.
    C. teach a lesson.
    D. convince readers to help travelers in need.

STOP

Name _____

Plot

- A story's **plot** is the important events that happen in a story. These parts include the conflict or problem, the rising action, the climax, and the resolution, or outcome.

Directions: Read the folk tale.

> There was once a young woman who was rich and beautiful, but she was never satisfied.
>
> One day she took a walk on the beach. She sighed sadly and said, "I wish I were more beautiful." A fish leaped out of the surf and said, "I will grant your wish." The woman became the most beautiful woman in the world. Still she was unhappy.
>
> A week later she went to the water's edge. "Fish," she cried, "I wish I had more money."
>
> The fish said, "I will grant your wish." All the gold in the world became hers. Still she was not happy.
>
> A week later, she went to the ocean. "Fish," she cried, "I need more beauty and riches." The fish said, "There is no pleasing you." With that, the woman became plain and poor. She married a fisherman and learned to live happily ever after.

Directions: Complete the plot map by describing the different parts of the plot. Describe two events for the rising action.

Climax

4. _____

_____

_____

Rising Action

3. _____

_____

_____

Resolution or Outcome

5. _____

_____

_____

_____

2. _____

_____

_____

Conflict or Problem

1. _____

_____

_____

Notes for Home: Your child read a story and identified its important story events. *Home Activity:* Read a folk tale, fable, or myth with your child. Work together to identify the different parts of the plot. Ask yourselves what problem the characters face and how they solve it.

Context Clues

Directions: Read the story. Then read each question about the story. Choose the best answer to each question. Mark the letter for the answer you have chosen.

Now You See It, Now You Don't

Rudy is a master of <u>legerdemain</u>. He can make scarves fly from his ears and mouth. He can make birds vanish and pull rabbits out of hats. He can make nickels and dimes appear out of his assistant's nose and ears. Children gasp to see these acts. Adults shake their heads in wonder.

Rudy's hands are so <u>nimble</u> that no matter how carefully you watch, you cannot tell how he does it. He rarely rests, either—his act continues for hours without a <u>hiatus</u>. The only time he pauses in his act is when the audience applauds. Rudy is so good that the audience always applauds long and enthusiastically as Rudy bows and smiles.

There is another way in which Rudy is amazing. He is a <u>stellar</u> student, ranking first in his class despite the fact that he needs so much time to prepare for his tricks. How he finds the time to study and practice his magic is a mystery to everyone. It seems to be just one more way in which Rudy can seem to perform magic.

Today, Rudy wants to work out a new trick for the upcoming school talent show. He's starting with some <u>ersatz</u> gold—it looks real, but it isn't. Then he adds a pile of feathers and sets to work. It's the most difficult trick Rudy has attempted. He's having a hard time making it work the way he wants. You can bet that Rudy will be practicing his new trick long into the night. This, of course, will be after he has finished his school work.

1. In this story, the word <u>legerdemain</u> means—
   - **A.** sewing.
   - **B.** thievery.
   - **C.** magic tricks.
   - **D.** silliness.

2. In this story, the word <u>nimble</u> means—
   - **F.** invisible.
   - **G.** quick.
   - **H.** strong.
   - **J.** dirty.

3. In this story, the word <u>hiatus</u> means—
   - **A.** break.
   - **B.** mistake.
   - **C.** blunder.
   - **D.** accident.

4. In this story, the word <u>stellar</u> means—
   - **F.** pointed.
   - **G.** good.
   - **H.** dull.
   - **J.** outstanding.

5. The best synonym for <u>ersatz</u> is—
   - **A.** artificial.
   - **B.** real.
   - **C.** expensive.
   - **D.** fancy.

Notes for Home: Your child used context clues to figure out the meaning of unfamiliar words. *Home Activity:* Encourage your child to make a list of unfamiliar words he or she finds while reading. Discuss how context clues can be used to figure out a word's meaning.

Writing Across Texts

Directions: Complete the tables with important events from "In the Days of King Adobe" and another folk tale you have read, such as "The Baker's Neighbor." Write *humor, trickery,* or *repetition* to show which literary element, or elements the event demonstrates.

In the Days of King Adobe	
Event/Literary Element	**Event/Literary Element**
Two rascals steal a ham from a woman who has fed them and put the ham in their bag. (trickery)	6.
1.	7.
2.	8.
3.	9.
4.	10.
5.	

Write Two Paragraphs

Folk tales commonly rely on humor, trickery, or repetition of actions or events. On a separate sheet of paper, write two paragraphs that compare and contrast one or more of these elements in "In the Days of King Adobe" with another folk tale you have read, such as "The Baker's Neighbor." Use the information in the table you completed above.

Notes for Home: Your child wrote two paragraphs comparing and contrasting information from different folk tales. *Home Activity:* As you read stories and articles with your child, discuss ways the ideas, events, or characters connect to other literature your child has read.

Grammar: Compound Subjects and Objects

Directions: Combine each set of sentences by using a compound subject. Write your new sentences on the lines. (Remember to make each verb agree with its subject.)

1. Stories about tricksters are found in many cultures. Myths about tricksters are also found.

_____

_____

2. The fox appears as the trickster in various stories. The coyote and the raven also appear as the trickster in various stories.

_____

_____

3. An animal may be the victim of the wily trickster. A human might be the victim also. Even an insect can be the trickster's victim.

_____

_____

Directions: Combine each set of sentences by using a compound object. Write your new sentences on the lines.

4. Some societies have used real-life jesters for entertainment. Sometimes they have also used musicians.

_____

_____

5. Jesters entertained Egyptian pharaohs. Similar figures entertained the Aztecs of Mexico. Jesters kept the nobles of Europe entertained too.

_____

_____

_____

Notes for Home: Your child used compound subjects and compound objects to combine sentences. ***Home Activity:*** Look through a book, a magazine, or a newspaper with your child. List all the sentences with compound subjects and objects that you find.

Grammar: Commas

A **series** is a list of three or more items. Items may be words (such as nouns, adjectives, or verbs) or phrases (such as prepositional phrases). Use commas to separate the items in a sentence. A comma is used after each item in the series except the last.

> We ate beans, tortillas, and tacos.
> All the food was spicy, delicious, and plentiful.
> After dinner we cleaned up, talked for a while, and then walked home.
> We walked through the tunnel, across the road, and over the bridge.

A comma is also used to set off the names of people who are **directly addressed.** Use two commas if the name comes in the middle of a sentence.

> Maria, is dinner ready?
> Do you know, Hal, what time it is?
> You should go home now, Ali.

Directions: Write **C** on the line if commas are used correctly in each sentence. Write **NC** if they are not used correctly.

_____ 1. Nick and Sam, welcome to our new restaurant.

_____ 2. Tonight we will celebrate with food, music, and dancing.

_____ 3. Would you like to help us prepare the chicken salad pasta and watermelon?

_____ 4. We'll move the hot plates from the oven, to the waiter's trays, and then onto the tables in the dining room.

_____ 5. I'm really glad you could come celebrate with us Nick and Sam.

Directions: Rewrite each sentence, adding commas to set off items in a series and names directly addressed.

6. Nick thanks for helping out.

_____

7. It's a fun worthwhile and helpful thing to do.

_____

8. I think Sam that you should clear the table now.

_____

9. Then you can serve dessert thank the customers and eat the leftovers.

_____

10. It's been great working with you two as volunteers Nick and Sam.

_____

Notes for Home: Your child used commas in a series and in direct address. *Home Activity:* Have your child create lists of favorite things in groups of three or more. Together, write a sentence about each group, using commas to separate the list of items as shown above.

Grammar: Commas

Directions: Add commas to punctuate each sentence correctly. Rewrite each
sentence on the line.

1. Harold what do you know about your heritage?

_____

2. We can learn about a culture from its folk tales Nicole.

_____

3. The Middle East has folk tales that are scary funny or sad.

_____

4. Greg do you know any Chinese folk tales about the Monkey King?

_____

5. Many cultures have trickster tales with coyotes rabbits and spiders.

_____

6. Anansi the Spider is a character from African trickster tales Ashley.

_____

7. Tricksters often hide behind rocks beneath bushes and in the branches of trees.

_____

_____

8. The Native Americans George have trickster tales of their own.

_____

9. We tell trickster tales at home in school and around a campfire at summer camp.

_____

10. I especially like the coyote stories Leah!

_____

Write a Story

On a separate piece of paper, write a story describing how a trickster played a
trick on someone else. Use commas to set off items in a series or the name of
anyone directly addressed.

Notes for Home: Your child used commas to separate items in a series and to set off the
names of people directly addressed. **Home Activity:** With your child, list names on slips of
paper. Take turns using each name as a form of direct address in a sentence.

Grammar: Commas

Add commas where they belong.

1. Lilly please hand me that glass.

2. Do you really think George that that is a good idea?

3. I have to do my homework shop for books and go to hockey practice.

4. Please pick up eggs milk butter and cereal on your way home.

Use **commas** to separate items in a series. Each item may be one or more words. Also use a comma to set off the name of a person who is directly addressed. Use two commas if the name comes in the middle of the sentence.

Directions: Add commas where they belong. Rewrite the sentence correctly.

1. Lions elephants and tigers live in the game reserve.

_____

2. The jungle was dark damp hot and mysterious.

_____

3. John did you see how that road ran up the hill?

_____

4. The mosquitoes were huge noisy and annoying.

_____

5. The guide carried a map Sonja and led us in the right direction.

_____

6. Our vehicle was fast Dave.

_____

7. The boat went across the lake up the river and into the harbor.

_____

8. The lake looked cool refreshing and inviting.

_____

9. Marta you should have seen those hippopotamuses!

_____

Notes for Home: Your child added commas in sentences. *Home Activity:* Have your child write a letter to a younger person, telling that child what he or she needs to know about fifth grade. Help your child to use commas correctly in series and in direct address.

Grammar: Commas

Directions: Write **C** on the line if commas are used correctly in each sentence.
Write **NC** if they are not used correctly.

_____ **1.** The plain was dry dusty and treeless.

_____ **2.** A buffalo and a mustang ran across the field Sheila.

_____ **3.** Over the hill, around the lake, and into the forest ran the doe.

_____ **4.** The guide raced down the hill, over the ditch, and into the heavy underbrush.

_____ **5.** The guide was experienced Terry.

Directions: Rewrite each sentence, adding commas to set off items in a series
and names directly addressed.

6. I like ships trains and planes.

_____

7. Travel is fun Elizabeth if you know where to go.

_____

8. Europe Asia and Africa are my favorite continents.

_____

9. Australia is a large distant and beautiful land.

_____

10. Anne would you like to go there one day?

_____

11. Kangaroos bandicoots dingos and wombats are some unusual Australian animals.

_____

12. I would like to see what a bandicoot looks like Tina.

_____

13. Australians live in large cities in small towns and on vast ranches.

_____

Write a Travel Journal

Imagine you have just gotten back home from an amazing journey to an exotic place. Write about
your adventures. Include details about the people, places, animals, sights, sounds, and smells.
Use a separate sheet of paper.

Notes for Home: Your child identified and rewrote sentences with correct placement of
commas. *Home Activity:* Talk with your child about what your family will do this weekend or
on a vacation. Have your child write sentences listing items to remember.

© Scott Foresman 5

Phonics: *r*-Controlled Vowels

Directions: Read the words in the box. Listen for the vowel sounds heard in **star, for, deer,** and **dirt.** Sort the words according to their vowel sounds. Write each word in the correct column.

beard	cornmeal	guitar	peer	serious	worked
burn	farthest	large	purple	steer	world
circle	fear	morning	series	tortilla	worthy

Sounds like *star*

1. _____
2. _____
3. _____

Sounds like *deer*

4. _____
5. _____
6. _____
7. _____
8. _____
9. _____

Sounds like *for*

10. _____
11. _____
12. _____

Sounds like *dirt*

13. _____
14. _____
15. _____
16. _____
17. _____
18. _____

Directions: Read each sentence below. Listen for words that have the vowel sound in **dirt.** The sound may be spelled **or, ir,** or **ur.** Write each word on the line.

_____ 19. The large dinner left them bursting at the seams.

_____ 20. Their bellies were so full that their shirt buttons nearly popped!

_____ 21. It was the first good meal they had had in days.

_____ 22. To thank their hostess, they promised to do work in payment for the meal.

_____ 23. They felt a little labor was worth the good meal.

_____ 24. It also wouldn't hurt them to do some physical activity.

_____ 25. But the hostess assured them that there was no reason for them to leave their chairs.

Notes for Home: Your child identified words with vowels combined with the letter *r,* such as *star, for, deer,* and *dirt.* **Home Activity:** Read a story with your child. Help your child listen and look for words with these sounds. Say the words together to hear the sounds.

Spelling: More Vowels with *r*

Pretest Directions: Fold back the page along the dotted line. On the blanks, write the spelling words as they are dictated. When you have finished the test, unfold the page and check your words.

1._____

2._____

3._____

4._____

5._____

6._____

7._____

8._____

9._____

10._____

11._____

12._____

13._____

14._____

15._____

16._____

17._____

18._____

19._____

20._____

1. They became **aware** of a sound.

2. We have to **prepare** for our trip.

3. It is nice of you to **share**.

4. **Declare** your allegiance!

5. The **spare** tire is flat.

6. **Beware** of the dog.

7. Cheese is a **dairy** food.

8. The **stairway** was dimly lit.

9. Many bison lived on the **prairie**.

10. The mechanics **repair** the car.

11. This book is very **dear** to me.

12. Their father grew a **beard**.

13. Lights **appear** in the distance.

14. The workers were **weary**.

15. I **smear** the paint on the paper.

16. The **volunteer** firefighters came.

17. To be a doctor is a good **career**.

18. The room looked **cheery**.

19. He was a true **pioneer**.

20. **Reindeer** live in Scandinavia.

Notes for Home: Your child took a pretest on words that have vowel sounds with the letter *r*. *Home Activity:* Help your child learn misspelled words before the final test. Dictate the word and have your child spell the word aloud for you or write it on paper.

Spelling: More Vowels with *r*

Word List				
aware	spare	prairie	appear	career
prepare	beware	repair	weary	cheery
share	dairy	dear	smear	pioneer
declare	stairway	beard	volunteer	reindeer

Directions: Choose the words from the box that have the vowel sound with **r** that you hear in **steer**. Sort them according to how the vowel sound is spelled. Write each word in the correct column.

Vowel-r spelled ear

1. _____
2. _____
3. _____
4. _____
5. _____

Vowel-r spelled eer

6. _____
7. _____
8. _____
9. _____
10. _____

Directions: Choose the word from the box that best matches each clue. Write the word on the line.

_____ **11.** When you get ready, you do this.

_____ **12.** When you fix something, you do this.

_____ **13.** A person who knows something is this.

_____ **14.** This is a type of farm that produces milk and cheese.

_____ **15.** When you give someone part of what you have, you do this.

_____ **16.** It's what you call the steps to go upstairs and downstairs.

_____ **17.** When you're sure of yourself, you say things this way.

_____ **18.** This word signals a warning.

_____ **19.** It's something extra, such as a tire in a car.

_____ **20.** It's the place where the land is flat.

Notes for Home: Your child spelled words where the letter *r* changes a word's vowel sound, as in *aware* and *cheery*. **Home Activity:** As you read with your child, look for words that have the vowel sound with *r* you hear in *spare* and *dear*.

Spelling: More Vowels with *r*

Directions: Proofread this radio announcement. Find seven spelling mistakes. Use the proofreading marks to correct each mistake.

≡	Make a capital.
/	Make a small letter.
∧	Add something.
℘	Take out something.
⊙	Add a period.
¶	Begin a new paragraph.

Beware! A man with a beerd is playing tricks on people. He can appear anywhere. His usual approach is to offer to repare something, such as a broken starway or window. Then he will smeer paint on it and disappear. He makes a carere out of destructive practical jokes, so stay awear. He is friendly and cheary, but don't be fooled!

Spelling Tip

Watch out for words that have the same vowel sound but different spellings, such as **aware** and **repair**, or **smear** and **career**.

Write Interview Questions

Imagine you are a reporter. On a separate sheet of paper, write some questions you could ask the man who plays tricks on people. Try to use at least five of your spelling words.

Word List

aware	dear
prepare	beard
share	appear
declare	weary
spare	smear
beware	volunteer
dairy	career
stairway	cheery
prairie	pioneer
repair	reindeer

Notes for Home: Your child spelled words where the letter *r* changes a word's vowel sound, as in *aware* and *cheery*. **Home Activity:** Write the spelling words, but leave blanks for the vowel-*r* combinations *(are, air, ear, eer)*. Invite your child to fill in the blanks.

Spelling: More Vowels with *r*

Word List

aware	spare	prairie	appear	career
prepare	beware	repair	weary	cheery
share	dairy	dear	smear	pioneer
declare	stairway	beard	volunteer	reindeer

Directions: Choose the word from the box that best replaces the underlined word.
Write the word on the line.

_____ 1. My grandmother was an early <u>settler</u> in this region.

_____ 2. Her journey across the <u>plains</u> was long and difficult.

_____ 3. At the end of each day's travel she was <u>tired</u>.

_____ 4. She never did <u>seem</u> to be discouraged, however.

_____ 5. She was always <u>happy</u> and ready to push on.

_____ 6. Once a wheel broke and she was unable to <u>fix</u> it.

_____ 7. Luckily another family had an <u>extra</u> to give her.

_____ 8. In those times, families would always <u>give</u> whatever they had.

_____ 9. They were <u>conscious</u> of the dangers of their journey.

_____ 10. They tried to <u>be ready</u> themselves for anything.

Directions: Choose the word from the box that best matches each clue.
Write the word on the line.

_____ 11. These animals pull a holiday sled.

_____ 12. These food products include milk and cheese.

_____ 13. It's what grows on a man's face.

_____ 14. It's what a person does for a living.

_____ 15. It's what you do when you offer your time and help.

_____ 16. It's what a warning sign may say.

_____ 17. It's what babies often do with their food.

_____ 18. It's how you start a friendly letter.

_____ 19. It's what you climb to get to a second floor.

_____ 20. It means almost the same as *say*.

Notes for Home: Your child spelled words where the letter *r* changes a word's vowel sound, as in *aware* and *cheery*. **Home Activity:** Together, write short rhymes using the spelling words. Include other words with the same vowel sounds and spellings.

Questions for Inquiry

A good way to begin a research project is by **asking yourself questions** about your topic. These questions will help guide you as you research information to find answers for your questions. As you research and read, revise your questions as needed.

Directions: Suppose you are doing research on tricksters. Many cultures have folk tales about tricksters—characters who use tricks to show a special trait. Some are animals and some are people. Sometimes the tricks are to teach a hard lesson, and sometimes they are just pranks. Choose one of the tricksters described below as a topic for a research report. Then answer the questions on the next page.

Coyote is a clever and sometimes naughty character in Native American folk tales. He sometimes doesn't play fair, but there is always a point to his antics.

Reynard the Fox is sly. He knows the weaknesses of those he plays tricks on. Often his tricks let people know that they need to think more of others than of themselves.

Till Eulenspiegel is a German character. He uses his abilities as a trickster to help the townsfolk and sometimes the whole country.

Anansi is a spider in African and Caribbean folk tales. He often shows his cleverness by getting the better of the larger animals and teaching them that size isn't everything.

© Scott Foresman 5

1. Which trickster will your report be about? _____

2. What would you like to know about your topic? Think of at least three questions that you could use to guide you as you start your research.

_____

_____

_____

Directions: Which of the following resources do you think might be helpful in finding answers to your questions? Explain why.

3. *The Times of London World Atlas* _____

_____

4. *Famous Folk Tales from Around the World* _____

_____

5. *Encyclopedia of Myth and Folklore* _____

_____

6. *A Celebration of African Folk Tales* _____

_____

7. "Why Germans Love Till Eulenspiegel" (article) _____

_____

8. *The Illustrated Guide to Native American Mythology* _____

_____

9. "Fox Meets Coyote: A Comparison of Two Popular Folk Tale Characters" (article)

_____

10. Why might you revise your questions during the research process? _____

_____

_____

_____

_____

Notes for Home: Your child formed questions for research and considered how to find the answers. ***Home Activity:*** Together with your child, write two or three questions about a topic you would like to know more about. Discuss how to find the answers.

Family Times

Summary

Family Critic Gets Constructive

Felicia is a natural-born critic. She criticizes everything from the color of her sister's nail polish to the contents of the family refrigerator. One day Felicia confides to her mother that her friends are mad at her and she doesn't know why. Her mother explains that negative criticism hurts people's feelings. She encourages Felicia to be constructive in her criticism. Felicia takes her mother's words to heart and turns over a new leaf. Her first project is fixing up the messy family broom closet. What will Felicia do next?

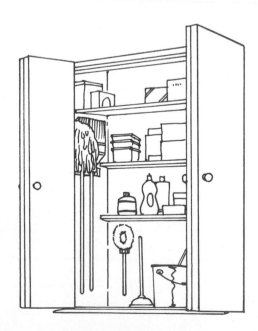

Activity

Be a Critic. Have your child be a critic and review the story for you, telling you what he or she liked and didn't like about it.

Reading Skills

Making Judgments

Making judgments means forming opinions about someone or something.

❖ **Characters** make judgments about situations and other characters. In "Just Telling the Truth," Felicia judges other people harshly until her mother gives her a new idea. How do you think other characters judge Felicia?

❖ **Readers** make judgments about a story's characters, authors, and ideas. For example, you probably formed an opinion about Felicia. Is your opinion supported by evidence from the story?

❖ **Authors** make judgments on the subject of their writing. You can evaluate their judgments by looking for supporting evidence in the story or article.

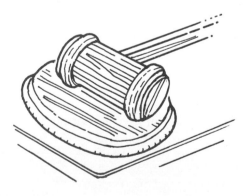

Activity

You Be the Judge. Read an editorial or a letter to the editor in a newspaper or magazine. First decide what judgments the writer is making and look for evidence supporting these judgements. Then make your own judgment of the writer's ideas. Can you support your opinion?

Family Times

Tested Vocabulary

Words to Know

Knowing the meanings of these words is important to reading "Just Telling the Truth." Practice using these words to learn their meanings.

career occupation or profession

critical inclined to find fault or disapprove

efficient workable and effective

maneuvered moved skillfully

opinion what one thinks or believes

resolved decided

shattered broken

survey examine

Grammar

Quotations and Quotation Marks

A person's exact words are a **direct quotation.** To show that you are giving someone else's words and not your own, enclose the quotation in **quotation marks.**

- ❖ Begin a direct quotation with a capital letter and end with proper punctuation.
- ❖ Use a comma to separate who is speaking from what is said.

Felicia said, "I hate that color."
"Who cares?" Marilyn replied.
"We'd better clean this mess up," Mother said, "or someone could slip and fall."

Activity
Conduct a Poll. Ask family members their opinion about a household topic, such as where to go on a family trip or what food makes the best dessert. Write up your poll results in the form of direct quotations.

Tested Spelling Words

_____   _____   _____   _____

_____   _____   _____   _____

_____   _____   _____   _____

_____   _____   _____   _____

Making Judgments

- **Making judgments** means forming opinions about someone or something.
- Characters make judgments about situations and other characters. Authors make judgments on the subject of their writing. Readers make judgments about characters, authors, and ideas. A reader's judgment should be supported by evidence in the story or article.

Directions: Reread "Can You Change Your School Lunch?" Then complete the table. Give supporting evidence for each judgment. Then make your own judgment about the author's ideas.

Judgments (Opinions)	Supporting Evidence
Justin's opinion: The school lunches needed to be improved.	1.
Justin's opinion: The school lunches did improve.	2.
Author's opinion: You can change your own school's lunches.	3.
Your opinion of the author's ideas: 4.	5.

Notes for Home: Your child identified supporting evidence for opinions in the article and made judgments about the author's ideas. *Home Activity:* Help your child write a letter about something he or she thinks should be changed.

© Scott Foresman 5

Vocabulary

Directions: Choose the word from the box that best completes each sentence. Write the word on the matching numbered line to the right.

★★★★★★★★★★★★★★★★★★★★

A SURE FIRE HIT

"My New **1.** _____" is a moving story about a fearless young woman's job search. Jean is a warm-hearted but extremely **2.** _____ person. She gets her dream job because she is an **3.** _____ worker, but then she gets fired for arguing with her boss. The conflict is **4.** _____ when Jean learns to accept people. People then learn to accept her. In my **5.** _____, this film has "Oscar" written all over it.

1. _____
2. _____
3. _____
4. _____
5. _____

Directions: Choose the word from the box that best matches each clue. Write the word on the line.

_____ **6.** It's what the chess champion did.

_____ **7.** A college degree will help you start this.

_____ **8.** It's what surveyors do.

_____ **9.** You have a right to yours.

_____ **10.** It's what the china plate did after falling.

Write a List

What *really* bothers you—barking dogs, smelly feet, annoying siblings? On a separate sheet of paper, list ten things that bother you a lot. Next to each entry, explain why it annoys you. Use as many vocabulary words as you can in your list.

Notes for Home: Your child identified and used vocabulary words from "Just Telling the Truth." *Home Activity:* With your child, write a review of a book, television show, or movie like the one shown above. Guide your child to use as many vocabulary words as possible.

Making Judgments

- **Making judgments** means forming opinions about someone or something. Characters, authors, and readers all make judgments.

Directions: Reread what happens in "Just Telling the Truth" when Felicia tells her mother she doesn't know why her friends were mad at her. Then answer the questions below.

Her mother looked at her for a long time. "Are you sure," she said finally, "you don't know why? You haven't even got an idea?"

"Well," Felicia hesitated, "I told the truth. Maybe they didn't like that."

"Felicia," her mother said gently, "there's a difference between truth and opinion. The truth is facts. Opinion is what you think. You told them what you thought."

"And they didn't like that. Shouldn't I say what I think?"

Her mother frowned. "Look, if you have a great idea for something and someone comes along and says, 'Boy, what a dumb idea, this is wrong and this is wrong,' wouldn't you feel bad?"

Copyright © 1973 by Ellen Conford. From FELICIA THE CRITIC published by Little, Brown and Company. Reprinted by permission of McIntosh and Otis, Inc.

1. Do you agree that "the truth is facts"? Why or why not?

_____

_____

2. How would you answer Felicia when she says, "Shouldn't I say what I think?"

_____

_____

3. What point is Felicia's mother trying to make?

_____

_____

4. What is your opinion of Felicia's mother? Explain.

_____

_____

5. What lesson does Felicia learn in "Just Telling the Truth"? On a separate sheet of paper, tell what Felicia learned and whether you think it was a worthwhile lesson for people to learn.

Notes for Home: Your child read a story and made judgments about its characters and ideas. *Home Activity:* Read a newspaper editorial with your child. Ask him or her to make judgments about the ideas expressed.

Selection Test

Directions: Choose the best answer to each item. Mark the letter for the answer you have chosen.

Part 1: Vocabulary

Find the answer choice that means about the same as the underlined word in each sentence.

1. Aunt Jessie told us about her new <u>career</u>.
    A. job or occupation
    B. apartment
    C. hobby or activity
    D. goal

2. Mr. Marlow <u>maneuvered</u> the car.
    F. bought
    G. fixed quickly
    H. started
    J. moved skillfully

3. My brother explained his <u>opinion</u>.
    A. dream
    B. what one believes
    C. experience
    D. what one plans

4. Why is Laura so <u>critical</u>?
    F. forgetful
    G. often sad
    H. tending to be shy
    J. quick to find fault

5. The vase was <u>shattered</u>.
    A. painted
    B. washed
    C. broken
    D. put away

6. Try to develop more <u>efficient</u> habits.
    F. thoughtful of others
    G. working in an effective way
    H. tending to save money
    J. careful

7. Nell told us what she had <u>resolved</u>.
    A. completed
    B. ruined
    C. heard
    D. decided

8. Mom came in to <u>survey</u> the damage.
    F. look at
    G. repair
    H. blame someone for
    J. clean up

Part 2: Comprehension

Use what you know about the story to answer each item.

9. Felicia's friends don't like her attitude about—
    A. what a club should be.
    B. walking to school alone.
    C. Cheryl's mother.
    D. her sister Marilyn.

10. When Felicia first comes home from school, she—
    F. paints her nails.
    G. makes a snack.
    H. cleans the floor.
    J. starts a building project.

11. Marilyn is partly responsible for the broken jar because she—
    A. was the first to use the peanut butter.
    B. left it on the table.
    C. startled Felicia, causing Felicia's arm to hit it.
    D. screamed when Felicia was picking up the jar.

12. You can tell from Felicia's problems at school that she—
    F. tries to be cruel to others.
    G. does not have any friends.
    H. doesn't care what other people think.
    J. doesn't understand the effect she has on others.

13. Felicia decides to change the broom closet because she wants to—
  A. keep her mother from becoming angry about the broken jar.
  B. get more attention from Marilyn.
  C. practice being constructive.
  D. put off doing her homework.

14. Telling Felicia to become a constructive critic is good advice because it—
  F. fools Felicia into thinking everyone likes her.
  G. gives Felicia a way to go out and get a job right away.
  H. makes Felicia see that there's nothing wrong with how she acts.
  J. gives Felicia a way to get along with others while still being herself.

15. How does Felicia show that she has understood her mother's advice about becoming a constructive critic?
  A. She interrupts her mother when her mother is trying to cook.
  B. She doesn't understand why her mother won't return the roast.
  C. She asks her mother if she would mind hearing suggestions about the broom closet.
  D. She yells at Marilyn to come look at what she has done with the closet.

STOP

Name _____

Making Judgments

- **Making judgments** means forming opinions about someone or something. Characters, authors, and readers all make judgments.

Directions: Read the story below.

Richard walked into the cafeteria wearing his new athletic shoes.

"Wow! Look at those awesome shoes!" cried Mark.

"Awesomely expensive, I bet," said Paul. "How much did you pay for them, Richard?"

"Only $95," said Richard proudly. "They were on sale."

"I've got to get a pair of those myself," said Mark. "Then I'll be one cool dude!"

"You're crazy," replied Paul. "You can get a pair just as good for half that money without the fancy designer label."

"You have to have the label," replied Richard. "They're the best. Just like the basketball player on the commercial says."

"You believe everything you hear on TV?" asked Paul.

Before Richard could reply, Paul had left the table with his empty tray.

"What's the matter with him?" asked Mark.

"Oh, he's just jealous, that's all," said Richard.

Directions: Complete the table. Make a judgment about the characters' actions and ideas.

What do you think of . . .	Judgments
1. Mark's response to Richard's shoes?	1.
2. Paul's response?	2.
3. Paul's judgment of Richard's shoes?	3.
4. Richard's judgment of Paul?	4.
5. Do you agree with Paul's judgment of the shoes? Explain your thinking.	

© Scott Foresman 5

Notes for Home: Your child read a story and made judgments about the actions and ideas of its characters. *Home Activity:* Discuss with your child some favorite fictional characters from books or movies. Ask your child to make a judgment about the characters' actions and ideas.

Character

Directions: Read the story. Then read each question about the story. Choose the best answer to each question. Mark the letter for the answer you have chosen.

The Lonely Critic

Anne and Teresa smiled and laughed as they left the movie theater. Joe walked close behind them. He had a serious expression as he rushed to keep up with Anne, Teresa, and their other friends.

"I really liked it," said Anne to the others as they walked outside.

"So did I," added Teresa. "It was so funny and entertaining."

"Didn't you love it when the dog got into the driver's seat?" commented another friend. One or two others in the group nodded their heads in agreement.

"Well," Joe said loudly, "I can't believe any of you liked it. The script was an absolute embarrassment. The acting was awful. The camera work was terrible, and the director doesn't know the first thing about filmmaking."

The others looked at each other and rolled their eyes.

"Joe thinks he knows everything," Anne whispered to Teresa.

"I'll say," Teresa whispered back.

"Who wants to grab some pizza and talk about the movie?" Joe asked. "There are a lot more things I could tell you about filmmaking."

"No thanks, we've got to get home," said Anne and Teresa at the same time. "It's getting late." One by one the others said they had to be up early in the morning.

Joe shrugged. "Suit yourselves," he said.

1. From what he says, Joe seems to—
   A. value his own opinion highly.
   B. value his friends' opinions.
   C. want to learn about movies.
   D. want to talk about himself.

2. You can tell from what Anne and Teresa say about Joe that he is—
   F. well liked.
   G. a film expert.
   H. good company.
   J. a know-it-all.

3. Which is **not** a clue to Joe's character?
   A. His friends roll their eyes.
   B. His friends turn down his invitation.
   C. His friends liked the movie.
   D. His friends whisper about him.

4. Joe might best be described as—
   F. good-natured.
   G. critical.
   H. emotional.
   J. kind.

5. What is missing from the story that would help you know more about Joe?
   A. his actions.
   B. his friends' actions.
   C. his thoughts.
   D. his words.

Notes for Home: Your child read a story and drew conclusions about the characters. *Home Activity:* Take turns describing people you know by what they say and do, as well as by what others say about them. Then, take turns trying to guess who is being described.

© Scott Foresman 5

Writing Across Texts

Directions: Consider the problems facing Andy and Felicia in the stories "Andy's Secret Ingredient" and "Just Telling the Truth." For each problem they encountered, they found a solution. Use information from the stories to complete the problem and solution diagrams below.

Andy's Problems   **Andy's Solutions**

Andy needed to find out what bugs could be eaten safely.	→	1.

2.	→	3.

4.	→	5.

Felicia's Problems   **Felicia's Solutions**

At lunch, Phyllis scowled at Felicia and said, "Eat your corn chips, Felicia."	→	6.

7.	→	8.

9.	→	10.

Write a Comparison/Contrast Paragraph

Both Andy, from "Andy's Secret Ingredient," and Felicia, from "Just Telling the Truth," creatively solved their problems. Use information from the stories to write a paragraph in which you compare and contrast the creative ways Andy and Felicia solved their problems. Write your paragraph on a separate sheet of paper.

Notes for Home: Your child combined and used information from two stories to write a comparison/contrast paragraph. ***Home Activity:*** As you read other stories and articles together, encourage your child to compare and contrast them.

Grammar: Sentence Capitals and End Punctuation

Directions: Rewrite each sentence correctly. Add the correct capitalization and end punctuation.

1. do you always read the reviews before you see a movie.

_____

2. What a ridiculous question that is?

_____

3. make up your own mind about the movies you see?

_____

4. I Do think it's nice to have some guidance, don't you!

_____

5. good reviewers know how to criticize without being unkind?

_____

Directions: Write a sentence in response to each sentence given. Include at least one declarative, interrogative, imperative, and exclamatory sentence.

6. Give your opinion of the last movie you saw.

_____

7. Write a question you might ask a movie critic.

_____

8. Write a sentence you might use in a movie review.

_____

9. Write a piece of advice you might give to a movie goer.

_____

10. Write a question or comment about movie reviews.

_____

© Scott Foresman 5

Notes for Home: Your child wrote sentences that began with a capital letter and ended with a period, a question mark, or an exclamation mark. ***Home Activity:*** Have your child write a note to a friend. Include examples of declarative, interrogative, imperative, and exclamatory sentences.

Grammar: Quotations and Quotation Marks

A person's exact words are a **direct quotation.** Direct quotations begin with capital letters and end with proper punctuation marks. To show you are using someone else's words and not your own, enclose a quotation in **quotation marks.**

"Critics review books and movies," my mother said.

My father added, "You can find reviews in the newspaper."

Use a comma to separate a quotation from the words that tell who is speaking. Put commas and end marks inside the last quotation mark. Sometimes words that tell who is speaking may interrupt a direct quotation. Then two sets of quotation marks are used. The words that tell who is talking may be followed by a comma or end punctuation. Use a comma if the second part of the quotation does not begin a new sentence. Use end punctuation and a capital letter if it does.

"Have you read the review?" she asked.

"I haven't," I said, "but I want to."

"The critic liked the book," Ann said. "He thought it was fascinating."

Directions: Write **C** if quotation marks are used correctly in each sentence. Write **NC** if the quotation marks are not used correctly.

_____ 1. "Let's see a movie, Tim said."

_____ 2. "Which one"? I asked.

_____ 3. "Well," he hesitated, "I really don't know."

_____ 4. I said, "Let's see what the critics thought."

_____ 5. "Do we have a newspaper?" he asked.

_____ 6. "I think so I answered.

Directions: Add quotation marks and other punctuation marks to complete each sentence.

7. Here's the newspaper Mom said.

8. Do you know I asked where the movie reviews are?

9. Tim answered They're on this page.

10. Give me a minute to read these said Tim.

11. Then he said The critics liked this movie.

12. I want to see it I said. What time is it playing?

13. What is the rating my mother asked.

14. It's rated G Tim said.

15. I stood up and said Let's get going!

Notes for Home: Your child used quotation marks to show a speaker's exact words. ***Home Activity:*** Say aloud a brief series of sentences and have your child write them down, using quotation marks to show your exact words and words to tell who is talking.

Grammar: Quotations and Quotation Marks

Directions: Add quotation marks, commas, end marks, and capital letters to complete each sentence. Write the new sentence on the line.

1. do you want to see a movie Amy asked

_____

2. I don't think so I answered movies aren't fun

_____

3. how about playing a game she asked

_____

4. I doubt it I said games are boring

_____

5. let's go skating Amy urged

_____

6. skating is really boring I complained

_____

7. then she asked do you want to visit David

_____

8. why would I want to do that I shrieked he lives so far away

_____

9. it's not his fault Amy shouted

_____

10. you're right I answered let's go visit him

_____

Write a Conversation

Think of a movie, book, or TV show you have recently discussed with friends or family. Write what different people said about it. Use quotation marks to show the speaker's exact words. Be sure to tell who each speaker is.

Notes for Home: Your child practiced punctuating quotations, a speaker's exact words. *Home Activity:* With your child, read some stories. Have your child point out the dialogue and explain the use of the quotation marks.

© Scott Foresman 5

Grammar: Quotations and Quotation Marks

Quotation marks help identify and set off the exact words of a speaker.
Circle the speaker's exact words in each sentence below.

1. Wai remarked, "This is an interesting book."

2. "Can you find one like it for me?" asked Lin.

3. "Yes," said the librarian, "I think I can."

4. "Wow!" cried Lin. "Thank you very much."

Use quotation marks to show the exact words of a speaker. Don't overuse the word **said.**
Vary the verbs that tell who spoke.

Directions: Write each sentence correctly. Add the necessary punctuation. Use
capital letters where needed.

1. Mr. Part said "the new computers have arrived

_____

2. can we begin using them today asked Lee

_____

3. Mr. Part replied "first we must connect them and test them

_____

4. maybe" he said "some of you can help me"

_____

5. "I will open the boxes" Josie said "I am good at that"

_____

6. be sure that you do not drop anything warned Mr. Part

_____

7. Lee asked should I read the instruction booklet

_____

8. "I think" replied Mr. Part "that is an excellent idea"

_____

Notes for Home: Your child capitalized and punctuated quotations correctly. *Home Activity:*
Have your child eavesdrop on a conversation between you and another family member. Have
him or her write some of the dialogue, punctuating sentences correctly.

Grammar: Quotations and Quotation Marks

Directions: Write each sentence. Add the necessary punctuation.

1. Did you bring your new camera? asked Judy.

_____

2. I brought the camera, Olga replied, and two rolls of film.

_____

3. They also sell film at the museum store, commented Judy.

_____

4. We can put the pictures on the bulletin board, suggested Ramon.

_____

5. That is an excellent idea for a project, Olga remarked.

_____

Directions: Unscramble each set of words to write a sentence with quotations. Add punctuation marks and capital letters where needed.

6. asked class a our going is Raphael on trip

_____

7. will Ms. Smith yes be replied the museum going to we

_____

8. many the see Jane there at interesting museum things commented to are

_____

9. cried boy great sounds this a like trip Raphael

_____

10. Amy wish could I we now right leave said

_____

© Scott Foresman 5

Notes for Home: Your child wrote quotations with correct capitalization and punctuation. *Home Activity:* Watch a TV program with your child. Have him or her write part of the dialogue between two TV show characters, punctuating sentences correctly.

Phonics: Complex Spelling Patterns

Directions: Looking at spelling patterns can help you figure out how to pronounce a word. Some words have simple spelling patterns such as **cat** or **lake.** These spelling patterns can be written as **CVC (consonant-vowel-consonant)** or **CVCe (consonant-vowel-consonant-*e*).** But many words have more complex spelling patterns. Carefully read each word in the box. Sort the words according to their spelling patterns by following the instructions below.

accident	curiously	gorgeous
actually	definite	grumbling
appreciated	disinterest	hesitated
constructive	dubiously	maneuvered
criticism	efficient	uncertainly

Write the words that have three vowels in a row—**VVV.**

1. _____ 2. _____ 3. _____

Write the words that have three consonants in a row—**CCC.**

4. _____ 5. _____

Write the word that has four consonants in a row—**CCCC.**

6. _____

Write the words that start with the pattern **VCCV.**

7. _____ 8. _____ 9. _____

Write the words that alternate consonants and vowels.

10. _____ 11. _____

Write the words that don't seem to follow a pattern.

12. _____ 14. _____

13. _____ 15. _____

Notes for Home: Your child recognized words with complex spelling patterns, such as *efficient* and *gorgeous.* **Home Activity:** Read a newspaper article with your child. Have your child look for consonant and vowel patterns in longer words.

Spelling: Getting Letters in Correct Order

Pretest Directions: Fold back the page along the dotted line. On the blanks, write the spelling words as they are dictated. When you have finished the test, unfold the page and check your words.

1._____

2._____

3._____

4._____

5._____

6._____

7._____

8._____

9._____

10._____

11._____

12._____

13._____

14._____

15._____

16._____

17._____

18._____

19._____

20._____

1. He is **lonely** without his friends.

2. She owns one **hundred** books.

3. He is my best **friend**.

4. The settlers **built** a cabin.

5. This is a **beautiful** vase.

6. Have you **heard** the news?

7. I heard the news on the **radio**.

8. **Their** feet were getting cold.

9. Who **caught** the most fish?

10. I am **bored** with this program.

11. The **guard** fell asleep.

12. Many people **pierce** their ears.

13. Someone **shrieked** outside.

14. Who will **receive** first prize?

15. What a **horrible** noise!

16. They make **jewelry** for a living.

17. Rocks **tumble** down the hill.

18. We walked to the **northern** cliff.

19. The field is only half an **acre**.

20. The **museum** is open late.

Notes for Home: Your child took a pretest on words with difficult letter combinations. *Home Activity:* Help your child learn misspelled words before the final test. Have your child underline the word parts that caused the problem and concentrate on those parts.

© Scott Foresman 5

Spelling: Getting Letters in Correct Order

Word List				
lonely	beautiful	caught	shrieked	tumble
hundred	heard	bored	receive	northern
friend	radio	guard	horrible	acre
built	their	pierce	jewelry	museum

Directions: Choose the words from the box that contain two or more vowels in a row. Sort them according to their vowel pattern. Write each word in the correct column.

Spelled ea or eau

1. _____

2. _____

Spelled ua

3. _____

Spelled io

4. _____

Spelled ei

5. _____

6. _____

Spelled eu

7. _____

Spelled au

8. _____

Spelled ui

9. _____

Spelled ie

10. _____

11. _____

12. _____

Directions: Choose the word from the box that best completes each sentence. Write the word on the line to the left.

_____ 13. My aunt lives on an _____ of land in Maine.

_____ 14. In that _____ state, the winters are long and cold.

_____ 15. My aunt makes beautiful _____ out of sea glass and sells it to tourists in the summer.

_____ 16. She picks which pieces to use by letting the glass gently _____ out of her basket.

_____ 17. She charges as much as one _____ dollars for some pieces.

_____ 18. Some people think that because my aunt works by herself she might be _____.

_____ 19. She loves her work, though, and never gets _____ even when she does the same thing over and over.

_____ 20. Personally, I think it would be _____ to be so isolated, but she likes it.

Notes for Home: Your child spelled words with letter combinations that are often mixed up. *Home Activity:* Write down the spelling words with the letters scrambled. Challenge your child to unscramble the letters to spell each word correctly.

Spelling: Getting Letters in Correct Order

Directions: Read this e-mail message. Find six spelling mistakes. Use the proofreading marks to correct each mistake.

≡	Make a capital.
/	Make a small letter.
∧	Add something.
✍	Take out something.
⊙	Add a period.
¶	Begin a new paragraph.

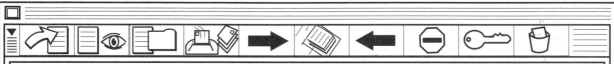

To All Museum Staff:

It has come to my attention that some of you are listening to the radio during work hours. The gaurd cuaght two people when thier radio made a horibel squawking noise. We have one hundred people working here. They all herd the music peirce the quiet. From now on, please be considerate and do not play the radio during work hours.

The Management

Spelling Tip

jewelry

Many people misspell **jewelry** by mixing up its letters. Remember: there is a **jewel** in **jewel**ry.

Word List

lonely	guard
hundred	pierce
friend	shrieked
built	receive
beautiful	horrible
heard	jewelry
radio	tumble
their	northern
caught	acre
bored	museum

Write an E-Mail Message

On a separate sheet of paper, write an e-mail message in which you criticize someone's bad behavior and suggest an alternative. Be constructive, not insulting. Try to use at least four spelling words.

Notes for Home: Your child spelled words with letter combinations that are often mixed up. *Home Activity:* Have a spelling bee with your child. Take turns saying words from the list for the other person to spell and use in a sentence.

Spelling: Getting Letters in Correct Order

REVIEW

Word List				
lonely	beautiful	caught	shrieked	tumble
hundred	heard	bored	receive	northern
friend	radio	guard	horrible	acre
built	their	pierce	jewelry	museum

Directions: Choose the word from the box that best completes each tongue twister. Write the word on the line to the left. Hint: The answer will start with the same letter as the first word in each sentence.

_____ 1. Rita would rather _____ a rose from Ralph than Ronald.

_____ 2. Patty plans to _____ the paper with a pointed pen.

_____ 3. Fred, a family _____, fried fish for folks at the fair.

_____ 4. Greg greeted the gabby _____ at the gate.

_____ 5. Theda and Thelma took _____ three tan tank tops to Tahiti.

_____ 6. Marcia and Mark managed a _____ of miniature models.

_____ 7. An _____ offers a lot after all.

_____ 8. Return the _____ to Rachel for repair.

_____ 9. Happy Hal has half a _____ hobbies.

_____ 10. Ten tip-top clowns _____ to tunes together.

Directions: Choose the word from the box that is associated with each word below. Write the word on the line.

11. shriek _____

12. beauty _____

13. bore _____

14. catch _____

15. hear _____

16. horror _____

17. build _____

18. north _____

19. jewel _____

20. lone _____

Notes for Home: Your child spelled words with letter combinations that are often mixed up. *Home Activity:* Help your child create a set of flash cards with these words. Use the cards to help your child practice spelling the words.

Textbook/Trade Book

A **textbook** is a book you use in school to learn about a subject. You can use the chapters, headings, subheadings, captions, and index to locate information in a textbook. A **trade book** is any book that is not a textbook, a periodical, or a reference book.

Directions: Use the sample pages from a textbook and a trade book below to answer the questions on the next page.

Chapter 4: American Artists of 19th and 20th Centuries

Artists in the United States used many painting styles. In this chapter you will read about women and men who created their own styles as well as adapted the styles of other painters.

Lesson 1

Mary Cassatt (1844–1926)

Mary Cassatt was born in the United States but lived and painted in France for much of her life.

Many of her best known oil paintings are of mothers and children. She became **associated** with the art school known as **Impressionism.**

Check Your Understanding

1. With what style of art did Mary Cassatt become linked?
2. Where did Mary Cassatt live most of her life?

associated connected (with)
Impressionism (See glossary and Chapter 2.)

Mary Cassatt, a Woman for Her Time and Ours

This American artist, associated with the French Impressionist movement, was born in Pittsburgh, Pennsylvania, in 1844. We often think of her paintings as sincere renderings of the power of the bond between mothers and children.

In 1866, after completing her study at the Pennsylvania Academy of Fine Arts with Thomas Eakins, Mary Cassatt moved to France. She spent the rest of her life in France, where she died in 1926.

In France, Mary Cassatt had the good fortune to become a close friend of Edgar Degas and other Impressionist painters of the time. Her style adds a welcome sensitivity, which many other of her contemporaries did not attain.

Mary Cassatt, a Woman for Her Time and Ours

1. What chapter is shown in the textbook? What is the title of the chapter? _____

_____

2. For what kind of class might you use this textbook? Explain. _____

_____

3. What is the title of the trade book? What do you think this book would be about?

_____

_____

4. Why might someone want to read this trade book? _____

_____

5. How are the textbook and trade book sample pages alike? How are they different?

_____

_____

_____

_____

6. Which book would contain detailed information about the artist's childhood? Explain.

_____

_____

7. Why are the words *associated* and *Impressionism* boldfaced in the textbook?

_____

8. Why do you think the textbook includes questions? _____

_____

_____

9. What subjects do you think Mary Cassatt painted most often? Explain.

_____

_____

10. Explain how you could use both a textbook and trade books for a research report.

_____

_____

Notes for Home: Your child compared a sample textbook and trade book. *Home Activity:* Ask your child to show you a textbook from school and explain to you how it is organized and what kind of information it has. Then do the same with a trade book from home or the library.

Family Times

Summary

Artists Trick the Eye with Trompe L'Oeil

Trompe l'oeil is French for "to trick the eye," and that's exactly what artists do when they work in this style. A trompe l'oeil door, for example, should make you think, at least for a moment, that it <u>is</u> a door, not a painting of a door. This article tells about the tradition of trompe l'oeil art, including the work of modern painters and sculptors, and describes favorite trompe l'oeil subjects, such as landscapes, doors, and even people. As the article makes clear, fooling the eye can be fun for both artists and viewers.

Reading Skills

Visualizing

Visualizing is creating a picture in your mind as you read. Authors help you visualize by using:

- ❖ **imagery:** In "Is It Real?" the description of "worn out work boots . . . scuffed, scratched, and battered" is a striking image that makes it easy to visualize the boots.
- ❖ **sensory details:** Most of the details in "Is It Real?" appeal to the sense of sight, but some, such as "cracked leather," also appeal to the sense of touch.

Activity

Interview an Expert. Ask your child questions about trompe l'oeil art. Have your child be the "expert" who answers your questions. If unanswered questions remain, help your child use home or library resources to learn more about this art style.

Activity

Practice Visualizing. Describe in detail a photograph, poster, sculpture, or artistic object in your home. Have another family member visualize and identify it based on your description. Switch roles and play again.

Family Times

Words to Know

Knowing the meanings of these words is important to reading "Is It Real?" Practice using these words to learn their meanings.

artistic of art or artists

deceive fool

realistic like the real thing

represent show in a picture or statue

sculpture work produced by carving or modeling figures from marble, stone, wood, or other substances

style manner, method, or way

viewer one who looks at something

Compound and Complex Sentences

Use compound and complex sentences to combine ideas and improve your writing.

❖ A **compound sentence** contains two simple sentences joined by a conjunction, such as *and, but,* or *or.*
Sentences:
That painting is strange. I like that painting.
Compound Sentence:
That painting is strange, but I like it.
❖ A **complex sentence** is made up of a simple sentence and a sentence part that cannot stand alone. In the following sentence, *When I look at it* cannot stand on its own.
Complex Sentence:
When I look at it, I think of a bright summer day.

Activity
Describe a Trip. Talk about a visit you made to a museum, show, or sports event. At first use only simple sentences. Then allow yourself to use compound and complex sentences as well. Which was harder to do?

Tested Spelling Words

_____ _____ _____ _____

_____ _____ _____ _____

_____ _____ _____ _____

© Scott Foresman 5

Visualizing

- **Visualizing** is creating a picture in your mind as you read.

- Pay attention to description, imagery, and sensory words that help you imagine what you are reading. Also think about what you already know about the places, people, and things being described.

Directions: Reread "Mrs. Middlesome-Merry's Art Studio." Then complete the table. Tell what story details you used to help you visualize different parts of the story.

I Visualized	Using These Story Details
Mrs. Middlesome-Merry	1.
Mrs. Middlesome-Merry's apron	2.
Mrs. Middlesome-Merry's apron pocket	3.
Mrs. Middlesome-Merry's stairs	4.
Mrs. Middlesome-Merry's studio	5.

Notes for Home: Your child read a story and identified vivid images that helped him or her visualize the details. *Home Activity:* Describe a place, such as your kitchen. Give clues about things a person might see, hear, feel, taste, or smell there. Have your child guess the place.

Vocabulary

Directions: Choose the word from the box that best completes each statement. Write the word on the line to the left.

_____

_____

_____

_____

_____

1. *Literature* is to *literary* as *art* is to _____.

2. *Depend* is to *trust* as *mislead* is to _____.

3. *Paint* is to *painting* as *stone* is to _____.

4. *False* is to *real* as *fake* is to _____.

5. *Food* is to *taster* as *picture* is to _____.

Directions: Choose the word from the box that best completes each sentence. Write the word on the line to the left.

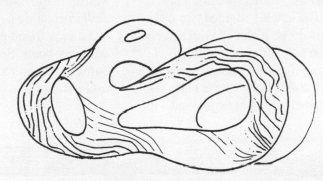

_____

_____

_____

_____

_____

6. The paintings we saw at the museum were as _____ as photographs.

7. We also visited the _____ exhibit and saw many different statues carved out of marble.

8. The statues _____ the artists' ideas.

9. Some were done in a very modern _____.

10. One _____ sat for a long time just staring at an especially interesting piece.

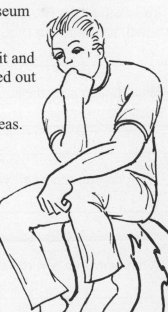

Check the Words You Know
__ artistic
__ deceive
__ realistic
__ represent
__ sculpture
__ style
__ viewer

Write an Essay

On a separate sheet of paper, write an essay about an art style or art work you especially like. Look at the paintings and sculpture in an art book for ideas. Use as many vocabulary words as you can in your essay.

Notes for Home: Your child identified and used vocabulary words from "Is It Real?" *Home Activity:* Have your child make an art project and then describe the process on an index card. Encourage your child to use as many vocabulary words as possible in the description.

Visualizing

- **Visualizing** is creating a picture in your mind as you read.

- Authors may help you visualize by using imagery. These are words that give you a strong mental picture, or image.

- Another way an author may help you visualize is through sensory details. These are words that describe how something looks, sounds, smells, tastes, or feels.

Directions: Reread the passage below from "Is It Real?" about the time when Marilyn Levine had difficulty finishing her sculpture on time. Then answer the questions below.

Worried that the teacher would think she was too slow, she quickly molded two disks like the rubber tips on a pair of crutches. She placed these on both sides of her single ceramic shoe, so it looked like someone with an injured foot had hobbled to the party on crutches. The teacher was as impressed with Marilyn's quick-thinking as he was by her skill in creating a realistic shoe.

Later, a friend gave Levine a pair of worn-out work boots. Scuffed, scratched, and battered, the boots had a strange appeal. They told a story.

From ARTISTIC TRICKERY: THE TRADITION OF TROMPE L'OEIL by Michael Capek.
Copyright © 1995 Lerner Publications. Reprinted by permission.

1. To which of the five senses does the phrase "molded two disks" appeal: touch, taste, sight, smell, hearing?

_____

2. What image does the author use to help you visualize the sculpture?

_____

_____

3. What do you see when you visualize Marilyn's finished sculpture?

_____

_____

4. What words help you visualize the work boots in the second paragraph?

_____

_____

5. Close your eyes and visualize Marilyn Levine's *Black Gloves*. Then, on a separate sheet of paper, describe what you see in your own words.

Notes for Home: Your child read an article and visualized images from it. *Home Activity:* Close your eyes while your child describes an object or a room in your home. Guess what is being described by the details your child uses.

© Scott Foresman 5

Selection Test

Directions: Choose the best answer to each item. Mark the letter for the answer you have chosen.

Part 1: Vocabulary

Find the answer choice that means about the same as the underlined word in each sentence.

1. Max likes to <u>deceive</u> people.
   A. ignore
   B. refuse to help
   C. fool
   D. steal from

2. He has an interesting <u>style</u> of painting.
   F. place to work
   G. manner
   H. name
   J. amount of work

3. The <u>viewer</u> enjoyed the movie.
   A. actor
   B. someone who looks at something
   C. owner
   D. someone who makes something

4. What was she trying to <u>represent</u> in her picture?
   F. show
   G. explain
   H. buy
   J. fix

5. That painting is so <u>realistic</u>.
   A. like the actual thing
   B. expensive
   C. dark and ugly
   D. looking as if done by a child

6. We bought a <u>sculpture</u> for the garden.
   F. fountain
   G. art object that is usually carved or molded
   H. small bush
   J. tall wooden frame for vines to grow on

7. She has so many <u>artistic</u> interests.
   A. painted
   B. of money
   C. different
   D. related to art

Part 2: Comprehension

Use what you know about the story to answer each item.

8. In "trompe l'oeil," the artist tries mainly to—
   F. fool the eye.
   G. ask a riddle.
   H. show life as it should be.
   J. make people laugh.

9. Trompe l'oeil is an art form that—
   A. was recently invented.
   B. involves only one or two artistic techniques.
   C. is very hard to produce successfully.
   D. has been around for centuries.

10. Marilyn Levine's *Black Gloves* shows—
    F. a painting of the gloves.
    G. a life-size figure of a man wearing the gloves.
    H. leather gloves that look like ceramic.
    J. ceramic gloves that look like leather.

11. Which of these stories from the selection best proves how trompe l'oeil can fool people?
    A. Duane Hanson's *Traveler* portrays a person who looks tired.
    B. Some artists make floors look as if they are covered with litter.
    C. People said they smelled peanuts while looking at *Fresh Roasted*.
    D. The Greeks appreciated trompe l'oeil before the Romans did.

GO ON

12. Which would be another good title for this selection?

    F.   "Why Audrey Flack Painted *Strawberry Tart Supreme*"

    G.   "When *Fresh Roasted* Was Painted"

    H.   "How Artists Trick the Viewer"

    J.   "Where to See Trompe l'oeil"

13. Which sentence best helps the reader visualize what is being discussed?

    A.   ". . . looking like they were sliced just minutes ago, the apples and oranges seem to spill right out of the picture."

    B.   "And the more familiar you become with the game, the more fun it is."

    C.   "Throughout history, dozens of artistic movements and fads have come and gone."

    D.   "Many different artistic styles and techniques have been used to create trompe l'oeil."

14. Which would be the best evidence that trompe l'oeil can fool people?

    F.   A woman admires a mural on a bathroom wall.

    G.   A child laughs at a painting of a clown.

    H.   A man tries to open the door on a mural of a house.

    J.   A teacher studies a painting of a pair of shoes.

15. Which of these best fits the definition of trompe l'oeil art?

    A.   a ceramic frog made to look like a real frog that sits in a real pond

    B.   a drawing of a historical figure wearing the clothes of that time

    C.   a painting of flowers in which each blossom is a blot of color

    D.   a life-size photograph of a real person

Visualizing

- **Visualizing** is creating a picture in your mind as you read.
- Authors may help you visualize by using imagery. These are words that give you a strong mental picture, or image.
- Another way an author may help you visualize is through sensory details. These are words that describe how something looks, sounds, smells, tastes, or feels.

Directions: Read the passage.

Optical illusions fascinate people. Flat images on paper take on new life when you look at them carefully. There's even a kind of modern art that uses optical illusions to trick the eye. It's called "Op Art" for *optical art*. Some Op Artists use colors and patterns to create the illusion of movement. For example, a painter might swirl a pattern of wavy stripes on a large canvas. By using hues of vivid purple and yellow, the stripes might appear to be vibrating.

Op Art paintings also create the illusion of three dimensions. If you run your hand over these paintings, you'll feel a flat, smooth surface. To the eye, however, they appear to have bumps and holes. It's almost impossible to see them as they really are. If you haven't seen any Op Art before, it is definitely worth a look, or two, or three . . .

Directions: Complete each box. Tell what details in the passage appeal to the senses of sight and touch that help you visualize the descriptions of different types of Op Art paintings.

Sight	Touch 
1.	4.
2.	
3.	5.

 Notes for Home: Your child read a passage and visualized what it describes. *Home Activity:* Read a short poem or descriptive paragraph with your child. Share the mental pictures formed while you each read.

Fact and Opinion

Directions: Read the passage. Then read each question about the passage. Choose the best answer to each question. Mark the letter for the answer you have chosen.

The Eyes Have It

The use of optical illusions in art has a long history. The ancient Greeks used trompe l'oeil techniques thousands of years ago. The painter Zeuxis, for example, reportedly painted such realistic grapes that the birds tried to eat them! Much later, the Italian painter Caravaggio painted insects in his pictures of fruit bowls to make them look more real.

I like optical illusion in art. It's fun to feel that your eyes are telling you one thing while your brain tells you something else.

In real life, however, it is always unpleasant when our eyes get fooled. On a hot summer's day, you might think you see water on a hot highway—but it's an optical illusion. Mirages in the desert are another type of optical illusion. They can be even more upsetting, especially if you're thirsty.

Why are some optical illusions upsetting? It's a matter of survival. To function each day, we need our eyes and brains to work together. We're uncomfortable when they don't. In art, optical illusions are a kind of game. But life is never a game. Life is serious business.

1. Which of the following is **not** a statement of fact?
   A. The use of optical illusions in art has a long history.
   B. The ancient Greeks used trompe l'oeil techniques thousands of years ago.
   C. Later, the Italian painter Caravaggio painted insects in his pictures of fruit bowls to make them look more real.
   D. I like optical illusions in art.

2. "In real life, however, it is always unpleasant when our eyes get fooled" is—
   F. a statement of fact.
   G. a statement of opinion.
   H. a combination of fact and opinion.
   J. a question.

3. "Mirages in the desert are another type of optical illusion" is—
   A. a statement of fact.
   B. a statement of opinion.
   C. both a statement of fact and opinion.
   D. a question.

4. Which of the following is a statement of fact?
   F. To function each day, we need our eyes and brains to work together.
   G. We're always uncomfortable when they don't.
   H. But life is never a game.
   J. Life is serious business.

5. This passage contains—
   A. only facts.
   B. only opinions.
   C. a mixture of facts and opinions.
   D. only one opinion.

Notes for Home: Your child read a passage and identified statements of fact and opinion.
Home Activity: Work with your child to list statements of fact and opinion about a favorite food, such as *Oranges contain Vitamin C. I think they taste great!*

Writing Across Texts

Directions: Consider what you learned about the eye and its functions in the feature "See the Picture!" Complete the table by listing the names and functions of important parts of the eye used for sight. Then list the jobs your eyes do.

Parts of the Eye and Their Functions	Jobs the Eyes Do
cornea: bends light rays as they near the eye	7.
1.	8.
2.	9.
3.	10.
4.	
5.	
6.	

Write an Explanation

Use the information in "Is It Real?" and "See the Picture!" to explain how your eyes help you see and understand a work of art such as a trompe l'oeil painting or sculpture. Include information from the table above in your writing. Write your explanation on a separate sheet of paper.

Notes for Home: Your child used information from different sources to write an explanation. *Home Activity:* As you read stories and articles with your child, talk about how the ideas in this reading material connect to other reading he or she has done.

© Scott Foresman 5

Grammar: Correcting Sentence Fragments and Run-Ons

Directions: Read each item. On the line at the left, write **S** if it is a sentence or pair of sentences. Write **F** if it contains a fragment. Write **R** if it is a run-on. Then, correct each fragment or run-on. Write the corrected sentence or sentences on the lines.

_____ 1. When a picture plays a trick on your eyes, it is called an optical illusion.

_____

_____ 2. Not only humans are tricked by optical illusions. Birds and fish too.

_____

_____ 3. Look down a long, straight road it seems to grow narrower.

_____

_____ 4. Trees along the road seem to get smaller. As they get farther away.

_____

_____ 5. The road and trees stay the same size, of course. The change is an optical illusion.

_____

_____ 6. Compare a white house with a dark house. Of the same size.

_____

_____ 7. Although they are the same size. The white house will look larger.

_____

_____ 8. These are real examples, optical illusions can also be created.

_____

_____ 9. Draw a faraway object the same size as a nearer one, and the faraway object will look bigger.

_____

_____ 10. Sometimes an illusion fools the eye, other times it fools the brain.

_____

Notes for Home: Your child corrected sentence fragments and run-on sentences. **Home Activity:** Together with your child, write a paragraph or two about a family incident. Correct any fragments or run-ons.

Grammar: Review of Compound and Complex Sentences

You can make your writing more interesting by varying your sentences. A **simple sentence** contains one complete subject and one complete predicate. A **compound sentence** is like two simple sentences with related ideas joined with a comma and a conjunction such as *and, but,* or *or*.

Simple Sentences: The artist is a genius. The mural is beautiful!

Compound Sentence: The artist is a genius, and the mural is beautiful!

A **complex sentence** is a simple sentence combined with a sentence part that cannot stand on its own. The sentence part has a subject and predicate. It is joined to the sentence with a word such as *if, because,* or *when*.

Complex Sentence: When the blue paint is gone, I'll paint the sky pink.

                         sentence part   **simple sentence**

Directions: Write whether each sentence is **compound** or **complex**.

_____ 1. Water colors are nice, but they can fade.

_____ 2. Some artists paint, and others sculpt.

_____ 3. If materials are not available, an artist can't work.

_____ 4. Sculptors carve rock, or they mold clay.

_____ 5. Because they are artists, painters are creative.

_____ 6. They work hard, and they like to be praised.

Directions: Write a compound sentence by joining the two simple sentences with *and, but,* or *or* and a comma. Write the compound sentence on the line.

7. Tricia took an art class. She liked it a lot.

_____

8. She learned how to paint. She enjoyed working with clay.

_____

9. Tricia could paint a watercolor. She could sculpt a figure from clay.

_____

_____

10. Tricia usually paints every day. She took last Sunday off.

_____

Notes for Home: Your child identified compound and complex sentences and then combined simple sentences to form compound sentences. *Home Activity:* Invite your child to read a comic strip and combine the simple sentences to create compound sentences.

Grammar: Review of Compound and Complex Sentences   **665**

Extra Practice

Grammar: Review of Compound and Complex Sentences

Directions: Write a compound sentence by joining the two simple sentences with a conjunction in ( ) and a comma. Write the compound sentence on the line.

1. We went to an art museum. It was closed. (or/but)

_____

2. Sally went home. I took a walk. (but/or)

_____

3. I arrived at the park. I saw some artists at work. (and/but)

_____

4. They seemed young. Their work was great. (but/or)

_____

5. I watched them paint. Then I went home. (or/and)

_____

Directions: Make a complex sentence by adding a simple sentence to the end of each sentence part.

6. Because he loved painting optical illusions, _____

_____

7. When he ran out of paint, _____

_____

8. If the store didn't have any more paint, _____

_____

9. When he had finished painting the optical illusion, _____

_____

10. If the painting confused people, _____

_____

Write a Description

On a separate sheet of paper, write a description of your favorite art work. It can be a famous work of art, a not-so-famous work of art, or even art you created yourself. Use compound and complex sentences in your descriptions.

Notes for Home: Your child wrote compound and complex sentences. *Home Activity:* With your child, take turns saying two simple sentences and having the other person combine them with *or, and,* or *but.*

© Scott Foresman 5

Grammar: Review of Compound and Complex Sentences

RETEACHING

Circle the simple sentences in the compound sentence.

1. My brother likes spaghetti, and I like lasagna.

Circle the simple sentence and underline the other sentence part in the complex sentence.

2. We were unable to go to the party because the weather was nasty.

A **simple sentence** contains one complete subject and one complete predicate. A **compound sentence** is like two simple sentences with related ideas joined with a comma and a conjunction such as *and, but,* or *or.* A **complex sentence** is a simple sentence combined with another part that cannot stand on its own as a separate sentence.

Directions: Write a compound sentence by joining the two simple sentences with a comma and a conjunction. Write the compound sentence on the line.

1. Ballet looks easy. The dancers must work hard.

_____

2. They go to classes regularly. They never stop practicing.

_____

3. Dancers learn movements. They practice them over and over.

_____

Directions: Write a complex sentence by combining the simple sentence with a word such as *when, because, although,* or *if* and the other sentence part. Add capital letters and punctuation where needed. Write each new sentence on the line.

4. professional dancers are very good at what they do   they have practiced for a long time

_____

_____

5. young girls are good enough and have practiced   they can learn to dance with toe shoes.

_____

_____

Notes for Home: Your child wrote compound and complex sentences. *Home Activity:* Talk with your child about how compound and complex sentences are formed. Have him or her show you examples on this page.

Grammar: Review of Compound and Complex Sentences

Directions: Make a complex sentence by adding a simple sentence to the end of each sentence part.

1. When we got home from school, _____

_____

2. Since it was so late, _____

_____

3. If I hadn't packed extra T-shirts, _____

_____

4. When Martin talked to Brian, _____

_____

5. Although he never told anyone, _____

_____

Directions: Read each sentence. Write *compound* or *complex* on the line.

_____ 6. When I saw the frightening dog, I crossed the street.

_____ 7. The dog was big, and it had a long tail.

_____ 8. I stayed away from it because I was scared.

_____ 9. When I heard it yelp, I had to laugh.

_____ 10. Its bark was high and quiet, and it wagged its tail happily.

Write an Animal Adventure Story

Think about an adventure an animal might have. What would the animal see? Where would it go? How would it react to different situations? On a separate sheet of paper, write an animal adventure story, using compound and complex sentences.

Notes for Home: Your child identified and wrote compound and complex sentences. *Home Activity:* Have your child find compound and complex sentences in a book or newspaper. Then have him or her point out the two separate parts of five of the sentences.

Phonics: Word Building

Directions: Sometimes when you add a prefix or a suffix to a word, the sound of the base word doesn't change. For example, when **-ness** is added to **dark,** the result is **darkness.** The sound of **dark** does not change. Other times, when you add a prefix or a suffix to a word, the sound of the base word changes. Add a suffix to each base word to make a new word. Write the new word on the line. Then tell whether the sound of the base word changes.

Base Word		Suffix		New Word	Change or No Change?
1. art	+	-ist	=	_____	_____
2. remark	+	-able	=	_____	_____
3. locate	+	-ion	=	_____	_____
4. assign	+	-ment	=	_____	_____
5. sign	+	-al	=	_____	_____

Directions: Sometimes when you add a prefix or suffix, the stressed syllable changes. Read the word pairs below. Underline the stressed syllable in each word, for example: <u>im</u>itate and imi<u>ta</u>tion.

6. artist	artistic	11. normal	normality
7. reality	realism	12. economy	economical
8. prefer	preference	13. history	historical
9. exhibit	exhibition	14. process	procession
10. represent	representation	15. edit	edition

Directions: Read the paragraph below. Five words with suffixes are underlined. Write the base word for each underlined word on the line.

The art <u>exhibition</u> was not a huge success. It had a strong <u>representation</u> of the modern art world, and the <u>artistic</u> level of the paintings was high. However, most images were too abstract. Viewers expressed a <u>preference</u> for <u>realism</u>, for pictures of the familiar, everyday world.

16. _____

17. _____

18. _____

19. _____

20. _____

Notes for Home: Your child examined how the sounds of words change when a suffix is added, such as *artist* and *artistic.* **Home Activity:** Point out words in a story that have suffixes. Have your child compare each word to its base word to see if the sounds change.

Spelling: Related Words

Pretest Directions: Fold back the page along the dotted line. On the blanks, write the spelling words as they are dictated. When you have finished the test, unfold the page and check your words.

1. _____
2. _____
3. _____
4. _____
5. _____
6. _____
7. _____
8. _____
9. _____
10. _____
11. _____
12. _____
13. _____
14. _____
15. _____
16. _____
17. _____
18. _____
19. _____
20. _____

1. He writes a newspaper **column**.
2. My brother is a **columnist**.
3. My **face** is sunburned.
4. Watch her **facial** expressions.
5. My sister has a beautiful **voice**.
6. Her **vocal** cords are sore.
7. The tree **limb** fell in the storm.
8. Athletes keep themselves **limber**.
9. He walks too **fast**.
10. Please **fasten** your seat belt.
11. Grandmother is very **wise**.
12. **Wisdom** comes with experience.
13. The machine finished its **cycle**.
14. My **bicycle** needs a new pedal.
15. We are all **human** beings.
16. Your behavior is quite **humane**.
17. The bridge is not **stable**.
18. **Stability** is difficult to achieve.
19. This is your **final** warning.
20. She spoke with great **finality**.

Notes for Home: Your child took a pretest on pairs of words that are related to one another. *Home Activity:* Help your child learn misspelled words before the final test. Your child can underline the parts that are different in each pair and concentrate on those parts.

Spelling: Related Words

Word List				
column	voice	fast	cycle	stable
columnist	vocal	fasten	bicycle	stability
face	limb	wise	human	final
facial	limber	wisdom	humane	finality

Directions: Choose the word pairs from the box in which **all** of the letters of one word are contained in the longer related word. Write each word in the correct column.

Shorter Word

1. _____

3. _____

5. _____

7. _____

9. _____

11. _____

Longer Related Word

2. _____

4. _____

6. _____

8. _____

10. _____

12. _____

Directions: Choose a pair of words from the box to complete each sentence. Write the words on the lines to the left.

_____ 13. The skin on my _____ felt better after the _____ treatment.

_____ 14.

_____ 15. A structure won't be very _____ if its foundation lacks _____.

_____ 16.

_____ 17. Before I sing, I do _____ exercises to warm up my _____.

_____ 18.

_____ 19. It's not _____ to question the _____ of your elders.

_____ 20.

Notes for Home: Your child spelled pairs of words that have parts that are spelled the same but pronounced differently. *Home Activity:* Say one word from the list and have your child say the related word. Then ask him or her to spell both words.

Proofread and Write

Spelling: Related Words

Directions: Proofread this flyer. Find six spelling mistakes. Use the proofreading marks to correct each mistake.

☰	Make a capital.
/	Make a small letter.
∧	Add something.
⌒	Take out something.
⊙	Add a period.
¶	Begin a new paragraph.

Mandrake the Magician

—All New Illusions!

Come one, come all! He's fast, wize, and limber! In his finil show in the area, Mandrake will perform illusions with his face, hands, and vioce. He'll have you spinning, so fastn your seatbelts. Show includes the famous "Human Bicicle" trick and the "Tower of Wisedom" illusion. You won't believe your eyes!

Spelling Tip

bicycle
Many people have trouble spelling **bicycle.** Remember this tip: <u>I</u> know <u>why</u> it's spelled B-<u>I</u>-C-<u>Y</u>-C-L-E.

Word List

column	wise
columnist	wisdom
face	cycle
facial	bicycle
voice	human
vocal	humane
limb	stable
limber	stability
fast	final
fasten	finality

Write a Poster

Imagine that you are a master of optical illusions. On a separate sheet of paper, create a poster advertising your latest show. Try to use at least five of your spelling words.

Notes for Home: Your child spelled pairs of words that have parts that are spelled the same but pronounced differently. *Home Activity:* Write each word on a slip of paper. Take turns picking a word and writing a sentence for each word.

Name _____

Spelling: Related Words

REVIEW

Word List				
column	voice	fast	cycle	stable
columnist	vocal	fasten	bicycle	stability
face	limb	wise	human	final
facial	limber	wisdom	humane	finality

Directions: Choose the word from the box that best matches each clue. Then write the word from the box that is related to it.

Clue	Matching Word	Related Word
coming at the end	1. _____	2. _____
scholarly	3. _____	4. _____
arm or leg	5. _____	6. _____
solid as a rock	7. _____	8. _____
the front of the head	9. _____	10. _____

Directions: Choose the word from the box that best completes each statement. Write the word on the line to the left.

_____ 11. *Late* is to *early* as *slow* is to _____.

_____ 12. *Seasonal* is to *season* as *cyclical* is to _____.

_____ 13. *Mean* is to *cruel* as *kind* is to _____.

_____ 14. *Author* is to *book* as *columnist* is to _____.

_____ 15. *Locate* is to *local* as *voice* is to _____.

_____ 16. *Three* is to *tricycle* as *two* is to _____.

_____ 17. *Shoe* is to *tie* as *seatbelt* is to _____.

_____ 18. *Monkey* is to *animal* as *person* is to _____.

_____ 19. *Book* is to *author* as *column* is to _____.

_____ 20. *Seeing* is to *eyes* as *singing* is to _____.

Notes for Home: Your child spelled pairs of words that have parts that are spelled the same but pronounced differently. *Home Activity:* Work with your child to think of other pairs of related words, such as *oppose* and *opposite* or *history* and *historical*.

Spelling: Related Words 673

Technology: Pictures and Captions

Most CD-ROM encyclopedias include **pictures with captions.** If you use an
online encyclopedia, it may provide a special search function just for pictures.
The welcome screen for an online encyclopedia might look like this:

Welcome to the Encyclopedia

Choose a letter to browse the encyclopedia.
Or, type the key words to search. Use AND between key words.
A B C D E F G H I J K L M N O P Q R S T U V W X Y Z

Search the Encyclopedia for:

Search for:

☐ Articles

☐ Pictures, Flags, Maps, Charts, Sounds

☐ Web Sites

☐ All of the Above

If you need help, click here.

If you want both articles and pictures, then check the first two boxes. If you just want
pictures, check only the second box.

Directions: Use the computer screen above to answer these questions.

1. Explain how to get just pictures of optical illusions. _____

_____

_____

_____

_____

2. Explain how to find both articles and pictures about American oil painters.

_____

_____

_____

_____

_____

Name _____

Online reference sources and web pages often include pictures with captions. You can usually click on either the picture or the caption to get more information. For example, a page about optical illusions might look like the one below. To get more information, you can click on any of the three pictures, any of the three underlined captions, or any of the four underlined links at the bottom of the page.

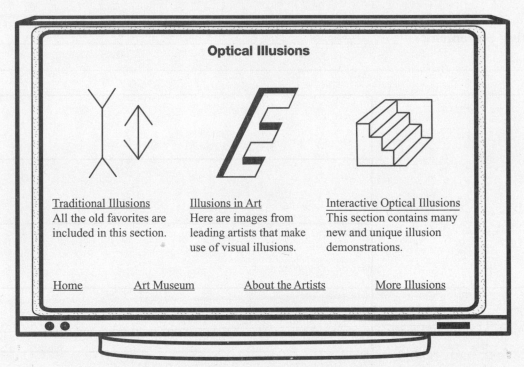

Optical Illusions

Traditional Illusions
All the old favorites are included in this section.

Illusions in Art
Here are images from leading artists that make use of visual illusions.

Interactive Optical Illusions
This section contains many new and unique illusion demonstrations.

Home   Art Museum   About the Artists   More Illusions

Directions: Use the web page above to answer these questions.

3. Where could you click to find a demonstration of an interactive optical illusion?

_____

_____

4. Where could you click to find a biography of the artist Scott Kim? _____

_____

_____

5. How are captions in an online encyclopedia similar to captions in a print encyclopedia? How are they different?

_____

_____

_____

_____

© Scott Foresman 5

Notes for Home: Your child learned how to access and interpret pictures and captions that might be found on a CD-ROM or web page. *Home Activity:* Use a book, magazine, or newspaper to discuss with your child the information shown in a picture and its caption.

Research and Study Skills: Technology: Pictures and Captions 675

Persuasive Argument Organizer

Directions: Complete the entire organizer. In each box, write a reason that supports the arguing statement. Next to each box, write three sentences that explain the reason.

Title: _____

Arguing Statement: _____

_____

<table>
<tr><td rowspan="3"></td><td></td></tr>
<tr><td></td></tr>
<tr><td></td></tr>
<tr><td rowspan="3"></td><td></td></tr>
<tr><td></td></tr>
<tr><td></td></tr>
<tr><td rowspan="3"></td><td></td></tr>
<tr><td></td></tr>
<tr><td></td></tr>
</table>

Concluding Statement: _____

Notes for Home: Your child recently completed a persuasive argument organizer. *Home Activity:* Ask your child how he or she chose the topic for the persuasive argument. Have your child give you convincing reasons why he or she chose the topic.

© Scott Foresman 5

Name _____

Elaboration
Adding Persuasive Words

- When you write a persuasive argument, remember to elaborate by **adding persuasive words,** in order to sound more convincing.

Directions: Elaborate each sentence by adding persuasive words. Use the words in parentheses to help you. Here is an example.

Do your homework so you will learn more. (it's important)

It's important to do your homework so you will learn more.

1. Do not eat too many sweets. (it's much healthier)

_____

2. Bring a raincoat on your camping trip. (you'll be so glad)

_____

_____

3. Keep your room neat and clean. (you'll feel better)

_____

_____

4. Save some of your allowance. (you'll be much better off)

_____

_____

5. Be a good sport. (your friends will respect you more)

_____

6. Get your chores done first. (you'll worry less)

_____

7. Kids need time to relax. (of course)

_____

8. Fifth graders shouldn't be treated like babies. (it's obvious)

_____

_____

Notes for Home: Your child elaborated sentences by adding persuasive phrases. *Home Activity:* Ask your child to listen for persuasive phrases in commercials, the next time he or she watches television or listens to the radio.

Name _____

Self-Evaluation Guide
Persuasive Argument

Directions: Think about the final draft of your persuasive argument. Then answer each question below.

	Yes	No	Not sure
1. Did I use the correct form for a five-paragraph essay?			
2. Did I use good reasons that will persuade my reader?			
3. Are my reasons organized in order of importance?			
4. Did I use persuasive words in my argument?			
5. Did I proofread and edit carefully to avoid errors?			

6. What is the best reason you used in your persuasive argument?

_____

_____

_____

_____

7. How would you change this argument if your audience were your classmates? Explain.

_____

_____

_____

_____

Notes for Home: Your child wrote and evaluated a five-paragraph persuasive argument .
Home Activity: Ask your child to explain one new writing skill that he or she learned during this project.

Directions: Use the tables below to find the percentage score for the total number correct out of the total number of items. The last entry in each table shows the total number of items.

Number Correct	1	2	3	4	5
Percentage Score	20%	40%	60%	80%	100%

Number Correct	1	2	3	4	5	6	7	8	9	10
Percentage Score	10%	20%	30%	40%	50%	60%	70%	80%	90%	100%

Number Correct	1	2	3	4	5	6	7	8	9	10	11	12	13	14	15
Percentage Score	7%	13%	20%	27%	33%	40%	47%	53%	60%	67%	73%	80%	87%	93%	100%

Number Correct	1	2	3	4	5	6	7	8	9	10
Percentage Score	5%	10%	15%	20%	25%	30%	35%	40%	45%	50%
Number Correct	11	12	13	14	15	16	17	18	19	20
Percentage Score	55%	60%	65%	70%	75%	80%	85%	90%	95%	100%

Number Correct	1	2	3	4	5	6	7	8	9	10	11	12	13
Percentage Score	4%	8%	12%	16%	20%	24%	28%	32%	36%	40%	44%	48%	52%
Number Correct	14	15	16	17	18	19	20	21	22	23	24	25	
Percentage Score	56%	60%	64%	68%	72%	76%	80%	84%	88%	92%	96%	100%	

Number Correct	1	2	3	4	5	6	7	8	9	10	11	12	13	14	15
Percentage Score	3%	7%	10%	13%	17%	20%	23%	27%	30%	33%	37%	40%	43%	47%	50%
Number Correct	16	17	18	19	20	21	22	23	24	25	26	27	28	29	30
Percentage Score	53%	57%	60%	63%	67%	70%	73%	77%	80%	83%	87%	90%	93%	97%	100%

1.	Ⓐ	Ⓑ	Ⓒ	Ⓓ
2.	Ⓕ	Ⓖ	Ⓗ	Ⓙ
3.	Ⓐ	Ⓑ	Ⓒ	Ⓓ
4.	Ⓕ	Ⓖ	Ⓗ	Ⓙ
5.	Ⓐ	Ⓑ	Ⓒ	Ⓓ
6.	Ⓕ	Ⓖ	Ⓗ	Ⓙ
7.	Ⓐ	Ⓑ	Ⓒ	Ⓓ
8.	Ⓕ	Ⓖ	Ⓗ	Ⓙ
9.	Ⓐ	Ⓑ	Ⓒ	Ⓓ
10.	Ⓕ	Ⓖ	Ⓗ	Ⓙ
11.	Ⓐ	Ⓑ	Ⓒ	Ⓓ
12.	Ⓕ	Ⓖ	Ⓗ	Ⓙ
13.	Ⓐ	Ⓑ	Ⓒ	Ⓓ
14.	Ⓕ	Ⓖ	Ⓗ	Ⓙ
15.	Ⓐ	Ⓑ	Ⓒ	Ⓓ

Sequence

- **Sequence** is the order in which things happen. Keeping track of the sequence of events will help you better understand what you read.
- Words such as *then* and *after* are often clues to a sequence. Words such as *meanwhile* and *during* show that several events can happen at once.
- By arranging events in sequence, you can see how one thing leads to another.

Directions: Reread the excerpt from *Homer Price*. On the lines below, write the steps from the box in the order that Mr. Murphy follows them to build a musical mousetrap.

Steps
Make a bargain with the town mayor.
Finally, let the mice go.
Drive up and down the streets.
First, build an organ out of reeds.
Fasten the mousetrap to the car.
Then, compose a tune the mice like.
Let the mice run into the trap.
Next, drive the car to a town.
Then, start the musical mousetrap.
Drive the mice to the city limits.

How to Remove Mice with a Musical Mousetrap

1. **First, build an organ out of reeds.**
2. **Then, compose a tune the mice like.**
3. **Fasten the mousetrap to the car.**
4. **Next, drive the car to a town.**
5. **Make a bargain with the town mayor.**
6. **Then, start the musical mousetrap.**
7. **Drive up and down the streets.**
8. **Let the mice run into the trap.**
9. **Drive the mice to the city limits.**
10. **Finally, let the mice go.**

Notes for Home: Your child read a story and identified the order in which events occurred. *Home Activity:* Choose a task that your child performs, such as making the bed, and work together to create a list of steps that are required to complete the task.

Sequence   3

Vocabulary

Directions: Choose the word from the box that best matches each clue. Write the word on the line.

Check the Words You Know
__ cafeteria
__ demonstration
__ diary
__ racket
__ switch
__ triggered

__racket__ 1. This might keep you from sleeping.

__cafeteria__ 2. You might go here if you're hungry.

__diary__ 3. You may not want anyone to read this.

__switch__ 4. You flip this to turn on a light.

__demonstration__ 5. You might do this at a science fair.

Directions: Write the word from the box that belongs in each group.

6. sparked, began, __triggered__

7. restaurant, diner, __cafeteria__

8. explosion, noise, __racket__

9. journal, log, __diary__

10. show, display, __demonstration__

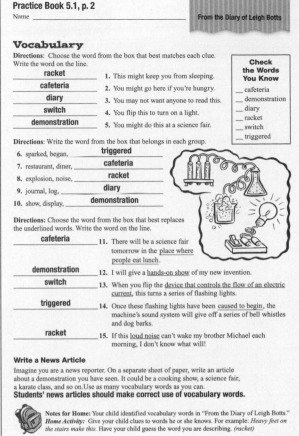

Directions: Choose the word from the box that best replaces the underlined words. Write the word on the line.

__cafeteria__ 11. There will be a science fair tomorrow in the place where people eat lunch.

__demonstration__ 12. I will give a hands-on show of my new invention.

__switch__ 13. When you flip the device that controls the flow of an electric current, this turns a series of flashing lights.

__triggered__ 14. Once these flashing lights have been caused to begin, the machine's sound system will give off a series of bell whistles and dog barks.

__racket__ 15. If this loud noise can't wake my brother Michael each morning, I don't know what will!

Write a News Article

Imagine you are a news reporter. On a separate sheet of paper, write an article about a demonstration you have seen. It could be a cooking show, a science fair, a karate class, and so on. Use as many vocabulary words as you can. **Students' news articles should make correct use of vocabulary words.**

Notes for Home: Your child identified vocabulary words in "From the Diary of Leigh Botts." *Home Activity:* Give your child clues to words he or she knows. For example: *Heavy feet on the stairs make this.* Have your child guess the word you are describing. *(racket)*

4   Vocabulary

Sequence

- **Sequence** is the order in which things happen.
- Words such as *then* and *after* are often clues to a sequence. Words such as *meanwhile* and *during* show that two or more things happen at the same time.

Directions: Reread what happens in "From the Diary of Leigh Botts" when Leigh builds a burglar alarm for his lunchbox. Then answer the questions below. Think about the sequence in which things happen in the story.

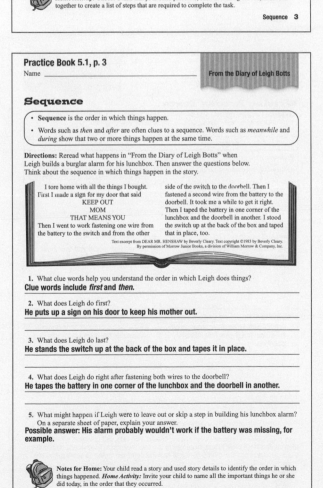

> I tore home with all the things I bought. First I made a sign for my door that said
> **KEEP OUT**
> **MOM**
> **THAT MEANS YOU**
> Then I went to work fastening one wire from the battery to the switch and from the other side of the switch to the doorbell. Then I fastened a second wire from the battery to the doorbell. It took me a while to get it right. Then I taped the battery in one corner of the lunchbox and the doorbell in another. I stood the switch up at the back of the box and taped that in place, too.
>
> Text excerpt from DEAR MR. HENSHAW by Beverly Cleary. Text copyright ©1983 by Beverly Cleary. By permission of Morrow Junior Books, a division of William Morrow & Company, Inc.

1. What clue words help you understand the order in which Leigh does things?
Clue words include *first* and *then*.

2. What does Leigh do first?
He puts up a sign on his door to keep his mother out.

3. What does Leigh do last?
He stands the switch up at the back of the box and tapes it in place.

4. What does Leigh do right after fastening both wires to the doorbell?
He tapes the battery in one corner of the lunchbox and the doorbell in another.

5. What might happen if Leigh were to leave out or skip a step in building his lunchbox alarm?
On a separate sheet of paper, explain your answer.
Possible answer: His alarm probably wouldn't work if the battery was missing, for example.

Notes for Home: Your child read a story and used story details to identify the order in which things happened. *Home Activity:* Invite your child to name all the important things he or she did today, in the order that they occurred.

Sequence   5

Selection Test

Directions: Choose the best answer to each item. Mark the letter for the answer you have chosen.

Part 1: Vocabulary

Find the answer choice that means about the same as the underlined word in each sentence.

1. We met in the cafeteria.
   - (A) place to buy and eat meals
   - B. storage area
   - C. small theater or stage area
   - D. entrance hall

2. The demonstration was very helpful.
   - F. act of criticizing or judging something
   - G. act of repairing something
   - (H) act of showing or explaining something
   - J. act of designing something

3. For her invention, she needed a switch.
   - A. the engine that makes a machine go
   - B. a source of power
   - C. a thin, metal wire
   - (D) a device to turn power on and off

4. Someone triggered the alarm.
   - F. stopped
   - G. repaired
   - (H) set off
   - J. disabled

5. He opened the diary.
   - A. a book of poetry or verse
   - (B) a book for writing down each day's thoughts or happenings
   - C. a book of instructions for using something
   - D. a book in which pictures or clippings are pasted

6. They were making a racket.
   - (F) loud noise
   - G. strange sight
   - H. terrible mess
   - J. cage or trap

Part 2: Comprehension

Use what you know about the story to answer each item.

7. What had happened to Leigh at school before this story begins?
   - A. Kids made fun of his lunchbox.
   - B. Someone took his notebook.
   - C. He got into trouble with the teacher.
   - (D) Someone took his lunch.

8. Leigh went to the hardware store to buy the things he needed to make a—
   - F. new lunchbox.
   - (G) burglar alarm.
   - H. doorbell.
   - J. flashlight.

9. To make his invention, what did Leigh do first?
   - A. He bought wire and a bell.
   - B. He made a cardboard shelf inside his lunchbox.
   - (C) He went to the library for books about batteries.
   - D. He connected a battery to a switch.

10. Leigh was smiling when he got to school on Monday because he—
    - F. always smiled at school.
    - G. was eager to show Mr. Fridley his invention.
    - H. had a new lunchbox.
    - (J) was thinking about catching the lunch thief.

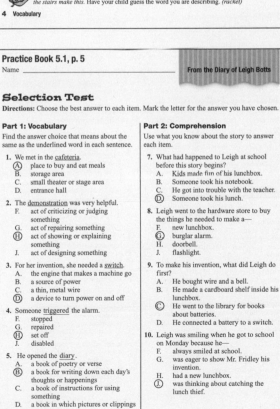

GO ON ▶

6   Selection Test

11. Why was Leigh expecting to hear his alarm go off during class on Monday morning?
- (A) Someone usually stole his food before lunchtime.
- B. He had set the alarm to go off before lunch.
- C. He had agreed to show his teacher how the alarm worked.
- D. His mom had packed his lunch carefully.

12. Which of these statements from the story is a generalization?
- F. "The kids were surprised, but nobody made fun of me."
- G. "My little slices of salami rolled around cream cheese were gone, but I expected that."
- (H) "Boys my age always get watched when they go into stores."
- J. "I tore home with all the things I bought."

13. At lunchtime, Leigh began to realize he had a problem just after he—
- (A) set his lunchbox on the table.
- B. showed his invention to the principal.
- C. set off the alarm.
- D. opened the lunchbox lid.

14. What was the most important result of Leigh's invention?
- F. No one stole his lunch.
- (G) Leigh felt like some sort of hero.
- H. It made a lot of noise.
- J. Mr. Fridley was grinning.

15. The author of this selection probably wanted to—
- A. give information about electrical circuits.
- B. teach a lesson about being a thief.
- C. explain how to make a lunchbox alarm.
- (D) tell a story about a boy and how he solves his problem.

STOP

Sequence

- **Sequence** is the order in which things happen.
- Words such as *then* and *after* are often clues to a sequence. Words such as *meanwhile* and *during* show that two or more things happen at the same time.

Directions: Read the following story.

Dear Diary,
I had a great time today washing cars! It was to raise money for my class. First I put on some old clothes that Mom said I could get wet and dirty. Then I reported to the parking lot where the car wash was being held. I filled my buckets with soap and warm water. As each car drove up, I washed it with soapy water and a large sponge. Next I hosed off the soapy water. Then I applied a wax with a soft towel. Afterward I shined the car with another towel. Pretty soon, it looked like new! It was really fun! At the end of the day, I gave Ms. Miller all the money I collected.

Directions: Read the steps in the box below. Write them in the chart in the order that they occurred in the story.

> He shined the car with a towel.
> He handed over all the money he collected.
> He put on old clothes.
> He applied wax with a soft towel.
> He washed the car with soapy water.

1. **He put on old clothes.**
2. **He washed the car with soapy water.**
3. **He applied wax with a soft towel.**
4. **He shined the car with a towel.**
5. **He handed over all the money he collected.**

Making Judgments

REVIEW

Directions: Read the story. Then read each question about the story. Choose the best answer to each question. Mark the letter for the answer you have chosen.

Wanted: More Vacation

So much work and too little play is not good for anybody, especially school students. That's what we have—too much work and too little play. Getting more vacation is a way to correct that problem.

I think that we students should be given much more vacation time than we get right now. Currently in our school, we're off only one week in winter, one week in spring, two months in summer, and all national holidays. It's not enough. We work hard in school, and we need time to relax. We need more time than we get now. Actually, we need a lot more time.

Students should get more vacation time because I feel we go to school too much during the year. I've only checked with my best friend Matt, but I think the whole school would agree with me on this. They all understand the importance of time away from books and homework. They would agree that more time for ballgames and television would be a good idea.

Adults who work in business get vacation, so why shouldn't kids? Yes, school is important, but so is vacation. It's something that all kids deserve. Now is the time to see that we get what we deserve.

1. The writer's opinion is that students should—
- A. vacation all year.
- B. keep the same vacation days.
- C. get more school time.
- (D) have more vacation time.

2. In the third paragraph, the arguments—
- F. are wrong because the facts are wrong.
- (G) contain no supporting facts.
- H. will convince everyone who reads it.
- J. are supported clearly with facts.

3. What does the author use to support his argument in the third paragraph?
- A. many details
- B. statistics
- (C) his and one other person's opinion
- D. true stories

4. In the fourth paragraph, the writer gives the impression that—
- (F) students have no vacation.
- G. adults never work.
- H. vacations are costly.
- J. students don't want vacations.

5. In general, the writer supports his opinion—
- A. very well.
- (B) poorly.
- C. convincingly.
- D. fairly.

Writing Across Texts

Directions: Complete the table with information from the selections "From the Diary of Leigh Botts" and "The Rampanion." **Possible answers given.**

Leigh	Alison
Problem:	**Problem:**
Someone has been stealing Leigh's lunch.	3. **Alison needs to roll her wheelchair over curbs that lack a ramp; she had to make an invention for school.**
How Leigh tries to solve it:	**How Alison tries to solve it:**
1. **He makes an alarm that would sound when someone opened his lunch box.**	4. **She made a model and then built an aluminum ramp with sides and a sticky bottom.**
Degree of success:	**Degree of success:**
2. **Leigh needs to do more work on his invention, but it gets him lots of attention.**	5. **Alison won a prize at an inventor's showcase; the prize was a trip to Florida.**

Write an Essay

What problems do Leigh Botts and Alison DeSmyter try to solve in these selections? Do they succeed? What do you think they learn in the process? Write a brief essay in which you compare and contrast Alison's and Leigh's approaches to problem-solving. Use the information from the table above and write your essay on a separate sheet of paper. **Essays will vary, but students should use information from their tables to compare the two inventors. They might notice, for example, that both discover a sense of satisfaction from trying to solve problems.**

Grammar Practice Book 5.1, p. 1

Name _____

Grammar: Sentences

REVIEW

Directions: Read each group of words. Write S if it is a sentence. Write NS if it is not a sentence.

_____ S _____ 1. Anthony has had his dog, Buddy, for six years.
_____ NS _____ 2. Came home from school one day.
_____ S _____ 3. The dog was gone.
_____ NS _____ 4. His treasured friend and playmate.
_____ S _____ 5. He looked for his dog immediately.
_____ S _____ 6. First he checked all of Buddy's favorite places.
_____ NS _____ 7. Every yard and hiding place in the neighborhood.
_____ NS _____ 8. Called his friends and asked for their help.
_____ S _____ 9. Someone came to the door.
_____ S _____ 10. A neighbor had found Buddy.

Directions: Add a word or group of words to complete each sentence. Write the complete sentence on the line. Remember to start each sentence with a capital letter. **Possible answers given.**

11. Eva's pet parrot, Scratch, _____.
Eva's pet parrot, Scratch, flew up into a tall tree.

12. _____ was very excited and upset.
Eva was very excited and upset.

13. The bird _____.
The bird could have flown further away.

14. The neighbors _____.
The neighbors came out to see what had happened.

15. _____ flew down to sit on Eva's shoulder.
Then Scratch flew down to sit on Eva's shoulder.

Notes for Home: Your child identified and wrote complete sentences. *Home Activity:* Look at a favorite magazine. Together read the titles of some articles and the captions under the pictures. Have your child identify which groups of words are sentences and which are not.

Grammar: Sentences **11**

Grammar Practice Book 5.1, p. 2

Name _____

Grammar: Sentences

A **sentence** is a group of words that makes a statement, a question, a command, a request, or an exclamation. You can tell if a group of words is a sentence by checking whether it expresses a complete thought. Each sentence begins with a capital letter and ends with a punctuation mark.

Sentence: The computer has many uses.
Not a sentence: Has many uses.

Directions: Read each group of words. Write S if it is a sentence. Write NS if it is not a sentence.

_____ S _____ 1. The computer is a remarkable invention.
_____ NS _____ 2. The first computer.
_____ S _____ 3. Do you have a computer?
_____ S _____ 4. Some computers are very expensive.
_____ NS _____ 5. A computer in my house.

Directions: Choose the group of words in ( ) that will complete each sentence. Write the complete sentence on the line.

6. _____ was also an important invention.(The electric light/Provided light for the house)
The electric light was also an important invention.

7. The lightbulb _____. (helped people in many ways/a bright light)
The lightbulb helped people in many ways.

8. Electric light _____. (in the house/helped people work at night)
Electric light helped people work at night.

9. _____ replaced candles. (To light the house/The lightbulb)
The lightbulb replaced candles.

10. Mr. Edison _____. (was a great inventor/the inventor)
Mr. Edison was a great inventor.

Notes for Home: Your child identified groups of words that make a sentence. *Home Activity:* Ask your child to talk about inventions that save time or have made life easier. Encourage your child to use complete sentences to tell about the invention.

12 Grammar: Sentences

Grammar Practice Book 5.1, p. 3

Name _____

Grammar: Sentences

Directions: Match each word group on the left with a word group on the right to make a sentence that makes the most sense. Draw a line between the word groups that go together.

1. A good invention begins — provides power for a flashlight.
2. Many inventions — can help you see at night.
3. A computer — often sells her inventions.
4. A lamp — are helpful to people.
5. A battery — with a good idea.
6. The inventor — can help you search the Internet.

Directions: Add a word or group of words to complete each sentence. Write the complete sentence on the line. **Possible answers given.**

7. The first computers **were too large to carry**.
8. A computer **can help in many ways**.
9. **I like to** send e-mail messages.
10. **The keyboard** contains keys used for typing.
11. Most computers need **electricity to operate**.
12. **My best friend and I** play video games.
13. While I was playing a video game **my computer shut down**.
14. **I'm glad** that we have computers at school.
15. If computers had not been invented, **our lives might be very different**.

Write a Description

Think about the different inventions you use every day. Choose one invention that you feel is especially important. On a separate sheet of paper, describe the invention and tell why it is important. Use complete sentences in your writing. **Students might describe a range of inventions including home computers, telephones, cars, TV, etc. Check to see that students use complete sentences.**

Notes for Home: Your child formed sentences by matching groups of words and by supplying missing words. *Home Activity:* Open a book. Read aloud only part of a sentence. See if your child can make a complete sentence that includes the words you read.

Grammar: Sentences **13**

Grammar Practice Book 5.1, p. 4

Name _____

Grammar: Sentences

RETEACHING

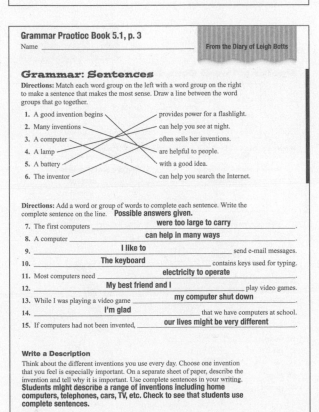

Mark the word group that best describes the picture. The best description tells a complete thought. It is a complete sentence.

1. The children _____
2. Are planting a tree. _____
3. The children are planting a tree. ✓

A **sentence** is a group of words that makes a statement, a question, a command, a request, or an exclamation.

Directions: Write **sentence** after each complete sentence. If the word group is not a sentence, write **not a sentence.**

1. Some trees produce fruit. **sentence**
2. Apples and pears. **not a sentence**
3. Very beautiful to see. **not a sentence**
4. The fruit gets ripe on the tree. **sentence**
5. Fruit growers protect the trees. **sentence**
6. Plenty of sun and water. **not a sentence**
7. We pick apples every fall. **sentence**

Directions: Circle each word group that is a sentence. Draw a line through each word group that is not a sentence.

8. (Trees do not eat food.)
9. ~~Food from water, air, and light.~~
10. (Roots get food from the ground.)
11. ~~Carries the food all the way to the trunk.~~
12. ~~Deep below the surface of the ground.~~
13. (Water travels up the trunk to the branches.)
14. ~~The green leaves.~~
15. (Some leaves stay green all year.)

Notes for Home: Your child identified groups of words that make sentences. *Home Activity:* Talk with your child about plants in your home or outside. Encourage your child to use complete sentences in your conversation.

14 Grammar: Sentences

Name _____

Grammar: Sentences

Directions: Draw a line through each word group that is not a sentence. On the lines, write the word groups that are sentences.

1.–9. Fish are found in fresh water and salt water. ~~All over the world.~~ ~~Many different shapes, sizes, and colors.~~ Most fish are covered with scales. These flat, bony structures protect the body of the fish. ~~Also have fins.~~ Fins are on the body of the fish. ~~Move through the water.~~ All fish can breathe under water.

Fish are found in fresh water and salt water. Most fish are covered

with scales. These flat, bony structures protect the body of the fish.

Fins are on the body of the fish. All fish can breathe under water.

_____

_____

_____

Directions: Write complete sentences. Add words to each group below.

Possible answers given.

10. A major source of food.
Fish are a major source of food.

11. With hooks, lines, and poles.
People can catch them with hooks, lines, and poles.

12. Large nets.
They can also use large nets.

13. Caught in the nets.
Fish get caught in the nets.

14. Schools of fish.
Schools of fish swim by.

Write an Underwater Adventure Journal Entry
On a separate sheet of paper, write a journal entry about an underwater adventure. Be sure each sentence is complete.
Check that students have used complete sentences.

 Notes for Home: Your child identified and wrote complete sentences. **Home Activity:** Write a list of words or phrases that relate to marine life. Let your child say complete sentences that each word suggests to him or her.

Grammar: Sentences **15**

Name _____

Phonics: r-Controlled Vowels

Directions: Read the words in the box. Say the words to yourself. Listen for the vowel sounds that the letters **ar, er, or,** and **ir** represent. Some sound like **her.** Some sound like **car.** Some sound like **for.** Sort the words by sound. Write each word in the correct column. **Order may vary.**

garbage	morning	worry
portable	story	parked
first	surf	alarm

her
1. first
2. surf
3. worry

car
4. garbage
5. parked
6. alarm

for
7. portable
8. morning
9. story

Directions: Read the following "to-do" list. Each item has a word with a missing letter. Write the word on the line with the correct letter filled in.

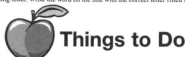
Things to Do

hardware
10. Go to the h_rdware store.

burglar
11. Buy stuff for my b_rglar alarm.

work
12. W_rk on my new invention.

short
13. Take a sh_rt nap.

dirt
14. Clean any d_rt from my invention.

turn
15. T_rn it on and test it.

 Notes for Home: Your child sorted and wrote words with r-controlled vowels, like *first, car,* and *short.* **Home Activity:** Read some ads in newspapers and magazines to help your child recognize other words with these vowel sounds and spellings.

16 Phonics: r-Controlled Vowels

Name _____

Spelling: Vowel Sounds with r

Pretest Directions: Fold back the page along the dotted line. On the blanks, write the spelling words as they are dictated. When you have finished the test, unfold the page and check your words.

1. army
2. starve
3. scar
4. garbage
5. argue
6. apartment
7. guitar
8. Arkansas
9. hamburger
10. return
11. purpose
12. surface
13. curl
14. purse
15. furniture
16. courage
17. journal
18. courtesy
19. nourish
20. journey

1. His brother joined the **army.**
2. We must eat or **starve.**
3. The cut left a small **scar.**
4. The **garbage** can is full.
5. I do not want to **argue.**
6. Their **apartment** was large.
7. Jess plays songs on her **guitar.**
8. King River is in **Arkansas.**
9. Thea eats well-done **hamburger.**
10. **Return** your library books.
11. He did it on **purpose.**
12. The **surface** of the water is clear.
13. A cat will **curl** up to sleep.
14. What is in the woman's **purse**?
15. The **furniture** was very old.
16. A lion tamer has **courage.**
17. I write in my **journal** every day.
18. Show **courtesy** toward others.
19. I **nourish** myself with good food.
20. Lylia is going on a long **journey.**

Notes for Home: Your child took a pretest on words that have vowel sounds with the letter *r.* **Home Activity:** Help your child learn misspelled words before the final test. Your child should look at the word, say it, spell it aloud, and then spell it with eyes shut.

Spelling: Vowel Sounds with *r* **17**

Name _____

Spelling: Vowel Sounds with r

Word List			
army	apartment	purpose	courage
starve	guitar	surface	journal
scar	Arkansas	curl	courtesy
garbage	hamburger	purse	nourish
argue	return	furniture	journey

Directions: Choose the words from the box that have the vowel sound with **r** that you hear in **hurt.** Write each word in the correct column. **Order may vary.**

Vowel-r sound spelled ur
1. hamburger
2. return
3. purpose
4. surface
5. curl
6. purse
7. furniture

Vowel-r sound spelled our
8. courage
9. journal
10. courtesy
11. nourish
12. journey

Directions: Decide where to add the letters **ar** in each letter group to spell a word from the box. Write the word on the line.

13. guit — guitar
14. sc — scar
15. my — army
16. kansas — Arkansas
17. stve — starve
18. gue — argue
19. gbage — garbage
20. aptment — apartment

 Notes for Home: Your child spelled words where the letter *r* changes the vowel sound. **Home Activity:** Read a magazine article with your child. Together, see how many words you can find that have the same vowel sounds and spellings as *scar, curl,* and *journal.*

18 Spelling: Vowel Sounds with *r*

Spelling Workbook 5.1, p. 3

Name _____

Spelling: Vowel Sounds with *r*

Directions: Proofread this journal entry. Find five spelling mistakes. Use the proofreading marks to correct each mistake.

> June 13—I have been writing in my
> Jurnal since March. Since then I
> have been working on our apartment.
> First, I rearranged the furniture.
> Then I painted. I had to aregue with
> Dad about painting the serface of
> the kitchen counter. It took courage
> to paint it purple! Now, though, I've
> decided to retern to the original
> color, and both Dad and I are happy.
> Maybe I'll even put the furniture back.

Proofreading Marks
- ≡ Make a capital.
- / Make a small letter.
- ∧ Add something.
- ⌿ Take out something.
- ⊙ Add a period.
- ⁋ Begin a new paragraph.

Spelling Tip
return
How can you remember that **return** has a **u** in the middle? Think of this hint: Make a "U" turn to **return**. Check the journal entry to see if this word is spelled correctly.

Write a Journal Entry
Imagine you have a problem you need to solve. On a separate sheet of paper, write a journal entry that describes your problem plus an idea for solving it. Try to use at least five of your spelling words.
Answers will vary, but each journal entry should include at least five spelling words.

Word List
army
starve
scar
garbage
argue
apartment
guitar
Arkansas
hamburger
return
purpose
surface
curl
purse
furniture
courage
journal
courtesy
nourish
journey

Notes for Home: Your child spelled words where the letter *r* changes the vowel sound, such as in *scar, curl,* and *journal*. **Home Activity:** Write each spelling word with the letters scrambled. See if your child can unscramble each word and spell it correctly.

Spelling: Vowel Sounds with *r* **19**

Spelling Workbook 5.1, p. 4

Name _____

Spelling: Vowel Sounds with *r*

REVIEW

Word List

army	argue	hamburger	curl	journal
starve	apartment	return	purse	courtesy
scar	guitar	purpose	furniture	nourish
garbage	Arkansas	surface	courage	journey

Directions: Choose the word from the box that best completes each statement. Write the word on the line to the left. Look at the pairs of words that are being compared. See the example below.

Crawl is to *baby* as *walk* is to *adult.*

Arkansas	1. *City* is to *Little Rock* as *state* is to _____.
guitar	2. *Blow* is to *horn* as *strum* is to _____.
army	3. *Sailors* are to *navy* as *soldiers* are to _____.
garbage	4. *Groceries* are to *food* as *trash* is to _____.
apartment	5. *Car* is to *bicycle* as *palace* is to _____.
argue	6. *Friends* are to *agree* as *enemies* are to _____.
scar	7. *Metal* is to *scratch* as *skin* is to _____.
starve	8. *Air* is to *suffocate* as *food* is to _____.
hamburger	9. *Pig* is to *sausage* as *cow* is to _____.
purse	10. *Laundry* is to *basket* as *money* is to _____.
furniture	11. *Coat* is to *clothing* as *table* is to _____.
courage	12. *Coward* is to *fear* as *hero* is to _____.
return	13. *Begin* is to *finish* as *leave* is to _____.
purpose	14. *Intentionally* is to *intention* as *purposely* is to _____.

Directions: Choose the word from the box that has the same or nearly the same meaning as the word or words below. Write the word on the line.

15. politeness **courtesy**
16. feed **nourish**
17. trip **journey**
18. daily record **journal**
19. roll up **curl**
20. face or side **surface**

Notes for Home: Your child spelled words in which the letter *r* changes the vowel sound. **Home Activity:** Look around the room with your child. Together, see how many items you can find whose names have the same vowel sounds and spellings as in *scar, curl,* and *journal*.

20 Spelling: Vowel Sounds with *r*

Practice Book 5.1, p. 9

Name _____

Locate/Collect Information

You can **locate and collect information** from many different sources, such as books, magazines, newspapers, audiotapes, videotapes, CD-ROMs, and web sites on the Internet. You can also talk to people who are experts on the subject you are researching. When doing research, you need to pick the reference source that best suits the purposes of your project.

Directions: Use the following resource list from a library media center to answer the questions on the next page.

Library Media Center: Inventors/Inventions

Audiotapes
- *The Genius of Thomas Edison,* narrated by Maria Walsh. Recorded Sound Productions, 1997. (30 min.)
- *Great Inventions of the Nineteenth Century,* narrated by Joseph Smith. Educational Tapes, Inc., 1993. (30 min.)
- *Meet the Inventors: Interviews with 26 Real Kid Inventors,* narrated by Charles Osborne. Facts on Tape, 1998. (45 min.)

Videotapes
- *The Art and Science of Computers.* Documentary. Edu-films, Inc., 1994. (45 min.)
- *Computers, Computers, Computers!* Documentary. Millennium Technology Films, 1998. (60 min.)
- *The Life and Times of Thomas Alva Edison.* Documentary. Insight Productions, 1994. (58 min.)

Pictures and Print
- Smithson, Stephen. *Picture This: A Photo Collection of Great Inventions.* Chicago: AllStar Books, 1992.
- See librarian at desk for access to our photo archives of local inventors and inventions.

Internet Web Sites
- information on Alexander Graham Bell
  http://www.agbell.com/Inventions.html
- information on child inventors (under 18 years old)
  http://www.KidsInvent.org

Resource People: Inventors
- Becker, Cassandra. 43 Maple Drive, Hollistown. 555-5487.
- Danbury, Robert. 2356 Norfolk Street, Oakdale. 555-6110.
- Foxworthy, Nancy. 99200 Central Avenue, Hollistown. 555-0002.

Resource People: Experts on Specific Topics
- Lederer, David. 9 Kenosha Drive, Oakdale. 555-7360. Expert on Alexander Graham Bell.
- Prager, Benjamin, Ph.D. 1334 Rainbow Hill, Hollistown. 555-0741. Expert on Thomas Edison (published author).

Research and Study Skills: Locate/Collect Information **21**

Practice Book 5.1, p. 10

Name _____

1. If you were doing a report on Thomas Edison, which audiotape and videotape resources would be best to use?
audiotape: *The Genius of Thomas Edison;* **videotape:** *The Life and Times of Thomas Alva Edison.*

2. What would be the best web site to use to find out about Alexander Graham Bell?
http://www.agbell.com/Inventions.html

3. Why are photographs useful for researching inventions? **Possible answer: Photographs would show you what the inventions look like.**

4. Name an inventor you could interview. **Possible answer: Cassandra Becker, Robert Danbury, Nancy Foxworthy**

5. Which resource person would be the best source for information about Thomas Edison?
Benjamin Prager

6. If you were doing a report on inventions made by children, which two resources would be best to use?
audiotape: *Meet the Inventors: Interviews with 26 Real Kid Inventors;* **Internet web site: http://www.KidsInvent.org.**

7. For a report on computers, which two resources would be best to use? **videotapes:** *The Art and Science of Computers* and *Computers, Computers, Computers!*

8. For information about a recent invention, why might it be more useful to interview a person familiar with the invention than to use only books?
Possible answer: You may get more recent information from a person familiar with the invention. A book might not mention the invention if the book is not very recent.

9. How are the two groups of resource people different from each other?
Possible answer: One group is inventors, while the other group is experts on specific topics.

10. Why might you want to use different sources when researching?
Possible answer: Different sources will give you different kinds of information that you might need.

Notes for Home: Your child chose resources to fit specific research purposes. **Home Activity:** With your child, list the resources he or she might use to do a report on the history of your family.

22 Research and Study Skills: Locate/Collect Information

Character

- **Characters** are the people or animals in a story.
- You can learn about characters from the things they think, say, and do.
- You can also learn about characters from the way that other characters in the story treat them and what they say about them.

Directions: Reread "No Friends." Then complete the table. Use the examples of things that characters do and say to tell what it shows about Lucy.
Possible answers given.

	Example	What It Shows About Lucy
What Lucy Does	She leans on the window and blinks back tears.	1. **She is very sad.**
	She makes a face when asked to go to the store.	2. **She is angry and annoyed.**
What Lucy Says	"I wish we still lived in Guelph."	3. **She is homesick.**
	"There's nothing to do here."	4. **She is bored and lonely.**
What Mrs. Bell Says	"We only got here yesterday."	5. **She is impatient.**

 Notes for Home: Your child analyzed characters—the people or animals in a story. *Home Activity:* Play "Guess Who?" Think of someone you both know. Describe the way that person acts and talks, and challenge your child to guess who it is. Switch roles and play again.

Character **25**

Vocabulary

Directions: Choose the word from the box that best replaces the underlined word or words. Write the word on the line.

faith _____ 1. Billy and Carla had <u>belief without proof</u> that they would find the golden key and win the game.

retraced _____ 2. They <u>went back over</u> their steps to make sure they had followed all the clues.

cemetery _____ 3. The last clue took them to a large stone statue in a <u>graveyard</u>.

withdrew _____ 4. Carla reached up to the statue's hand and <u>took out</u> the golden key.

darted _____ 5. Then Carla and Billy <u>moved quickly</u> to home base to claim their prize!

> **Check the Words You Know**
> __ alternating
> __ anticipation
> __ cemetery
> __ darted
> __ faith
> __ retraced
> __ scent
> __ withdrew

Directions: Choose the word from the box that best matches each clue. Write the letters of the word on the blanks. The boxed letters spell something that you should have in yourself.

6. belief without proof

7. happening by turns

8. state of looking forward to something

9. a smell or odor

10. took out

6. f a i t h

7. a l t e r n a t i n g

8. a n t i c i p a t i n g

9. s c e n t

10. w i t h d r e w

What you should have in yourself: f a i t h

Write a Report
Imagine you are a dog trainer. On a separate sheet of paper, write a report about a dog that you have been training. What methods do you use to get the dog to behave? How does the dog respond to your directions? Use as many vocabulary words as you can.
Students' reports should make correct use of vocabulary words.

 Notes for Home: Your child identified and used vocabulary words from "Faith and Eddie." *Home Activity:* Using a dictionary, find simple definitions for a variety of words and read them aloud to your child. See if your child can guess each word. Keep a list of "Words I Know."

26 Vocabulary

Character

- **Characters** are the people or animals in a story.
- You can learn about characters from what they think, say, and do.
- You can also learn about characters from the way other characters in the story treat them or talk about them.

Directions: Reread what happens in "Faith and Eddie" when Faith comes home from school one day. Then answer the questions below. Think about what you learn about the characters of Faith and Eddie.

> That afternoon, Faith rushed through the door, her eyes all red and swollen. She sank to her knees and hugged me and sobbed.
> "Oh, Eddie," she said. "I hate it. I just hate it."
> I pressed my muzzle up into her face and licked her cheek. It tasted salty.
>
> "The kids at school hate me," she said. "The teacher hates me. I can't understand a thing anyone says and they can't understand me, either." She sniffled. "Diego keeps making fishy faces at me."
> At that she buried her face into my neck and cried.
>
> From FAITH AND THE ELECTRIC DOGS by Patrick Jennings. Copyright © 1996 by Patrick Jennings. Reprinted by permission of Scholastic Inc.

1. What does Faith do when she gets home?
She cries about school as she hugs Eddie.

2. Why does Faith think her teacher and classmates hate her?
She thinks they don't like her because she can't communicate well with them and because one student makes faces at her.

3. How does Eddie react to Faith's behavior?
He is very loving, showing affection by licking her cheek.

4. What does Faith's behavior tell you about the type of person she is?
Possible answers: She is a sensitive and emotional person. She wants very much to get along with others.

5. What do you learn about Eddie's character from the rest of the story? On a separate sheet of paper, write your answer and give examples to support it.
Possible answers: He is loyal and caring as he tracks down Faith when she runs away. He is intelligent and clever when he plays fetch with Faith. He has a sense of humor when he talks to the reader and makes funny comments.

 Notes for Home: Your child read a story and used story details to analyze its characters. *Home Activity:* Name a family member or friend. Talk with your child about the type of person that individual is, based on the way he or she thinks, talks, and behaves.

Character **27**

Selection Test

Directions: Choose the best answer to each item. Mark the letter for the answer you have chosen.

Part 1: Vocabulary
Find the answer choice that means about the same as the underlined word in each sentence.

1. She had <u>faith</u> in the plan.
   A. a position of leadership
   B. lack of confidence
   C. belief without proof
   D. strong interest

2. We <u>retraced</u> the journey.
   F. plotted on a map or chart
   G. went back over
   H. took a new route
   J. told about again

3. They walked through a <u>cemetery</u>.
   A. graveyard
   B. meadow
   C. narrow street
   D. city square

4. A mouse <u>darted</u> under the leaves.
   F. made tunnels
   G. sat silently without stirring
   H. crept quietly
   J. moved suddenly and quickly

5. His shirt had <u>alternating</u> stripes.
   A. forming a smooth wavy pattern
   B. arranged in an unexpected or disorganized manner
   C. blending together to create a single color
   D. first one and then the other, by turns

6. The children looked up in <u>anticipation</u>.
   F. state of being amazed
   G. state of looking forward to something
   H. state of being disappointed
   J. state of avoiding something

7. This plant is known for its <u>scent</u>.
   A. color
   B. size
   C. smell
   D. shape

8. She opened the drawer and <u>withdrew</u> a small package.
   F. took out
   G. discovered
   H. hid
   J. returned

Part 2: Comprehension
Use what you know about the story to answer each item.

9. Which character is the narrator of the story?
   A. Faith
   B. Hector
   C. Bernice
   D. Eddie

10. Who is Coco?
    F. a household servant
    G. Faith's tutor
    H. a family friend
    J. Faith's mother

11. In what way is Eddie an unusual dog?
    A. He comforts Faith when she is sad.
    B. He plays Fetch and Tug-of-war.
    C. He understands everything people say.
    D. He talks to Faith just as a person would.

12. From the story you can tell that Faith—
    F. loves to go on adventures.
    G. is very unhappy about living in Mexico.
    H. is trying hard to succeed in school.
    J. makes friends with almost everyone she meets.

GO ON ➡

28 Selection Test

© Scott Foresman 5

---

686 Answers

13. Why does Eddie rush through the city without paying much attention to his old street-dog chums?
 Ⓐ He is worried about Faith.
 B. He no longer needs dog friends now that he has a home.
 C. He does not like other dogs.
 D. He no longer recognizes the dogs he once knew.

14. Which detail tells you what time of year the story takes place?
 F. Eddie learned to play Fetch.
 G. Faith and Eddie went outside after dinner.
 Ⓗ Graves were still decorated from the Days of the Dead.
 J. A crescent moon glimmered behind the wispy fog.

15. Eddie wants to help Faith. Which of his actions has an effect that is different from what he intended?
 A. howling by the front gate until Milagros opens it
 B. hurrying to the school and looking through the window
 C. following his nose across a stream and a pasture
 Ⓓ howling in the graveyard so that Faith will hear him

STOP

Character

- **Characters** are the people or animals in a story.
- You can learn about characters from the things they think, say, and do.
- You can also learn about characters from the way other characters in the story treat them or talk about them.

Directions: Read the story below.

Tory wasn't very happy when her brother Joey received a new puppy. She thought it was a nicer gift than any their parents had ever given her.

"How come he gets a great pet and I don't?" Tory whined.

That night, Tory took the dog's bone and hid it. The next morning, Mother asked, "Tory? Have you seen the puppy's bone?"

Tory just shook her head and walked away.

That afternoon, Father said, "Tory, we know you're a loving girl. And here's a present just for you." He handed her a new pet gerbil in a cage.

"Thanks!" Tory cried. Later she brought back the dog's bone, apologized to her family, and happily played with her gerbil until bedtime.

Directions: Complete the table. Think about what you learned about Tory's character from the things she thinks, says, and does, and from what others say about her.

Tory's Character	Examples
Tory is jealous.	1. What Tory thinks: **She thinks her parents have given Joey a nicer gift than she ever got.**
	2. What Tory says: **"How come he gets a great pet and I don't?"**
	3. What Tory does: **She hides the dog's bone.**
Tory is loving.	4. What Father says: **"Tory, we know you're a loving girl."**
	5. What Tory does: **She returns the bone, apologizes to her family, and plays with her pet gerbil.**

 Notes for Home: Your child read a story and used story details to analyze a character. **Home Activity:** Invite your child to describe his or her own personality, based on things he or she often does, says, or thinks. Then describe your own personality to your child.

Setting

REVIEW

Directions: Read the story. Then read each question about the story. Choose the best answer to each question. Mark the letter for the answer you have chosen.

A Sore Vacation

Alex looked around at the neat, clean room. He sat carefully on the edge of the chair. He was careful not to let his back touch anything. This was a nice chair. He would like to settle back into it. If he just felt better, he would like this chair. On the other hand, if he felt better, he wouldn't be here.

Everything about the room would be comfortable if only he felt better. He looked up as the doctor came into the room.

"Take off your shirt and sit down," ordered the doctor.

Alex could barely sit. His whole body was sore from the sunburn. He was glad to have his shirt off, although it hurt getting it off. He was sure the room got brighter in the glow of his red skin.

Alex tried to relax as the doctor applied lotion to his body. He jerked every time he felt the doctor's fingers. At the same time, he was glad to feel the cool, soft lotion. He wished he could just get into a bathtub full of it.

This vacation had seemed like such a good idea. The travel poster showed clear water and beautiful sand. That was just what Alex wanted.

As soon as he arrived, he was out on the beach in front of the hotel. After a long plane ride, he had been glad to relax in the sun.

"Nobody told me Mexico could be this hot," Alex said. "I should have come here for winter vacation instead of in July."

"Take my advice. Next time, try not to fall asleep in the sun," the doctor said.

1. The setting of the story is—
 A. Alex's hotel lobby.
 B. beside a pool.
 Ⓒ a doctor's office.
 D. at the beach.

2. A clue to the setting is—
 F. the hot sun.
 G. Alex's vacation.
 Ⓗ the neat, clean room.
 J. the travel poster.

3. The time of year is—
 Ⓐ summer.
 B. autumn.
 C. winter.
 D. spring.

4. The best word to describe Mexico in July is—
 F. cool.
 G. warm.
 H. chilly.
 Ⓙ hot.

5. Alex wouldn't have burned if he had—
 A. gone to the beach.
 Ⓑ sat in the shade.
 C. gone out at noontime.
 D. worn sunglasses.

 Notes for Home: Your child read a story and used details to answer questions about the setting. **Home Activity:** Have your child look around the room and describe the setting in detail.

Writing Across Texts

Directions: The left column shows a list of difficult times that Faith experiences in the story "Faith and Eddie." On the right side, write how Eddie seems to make things better in these difficult situations. **Possible answers given.**

What Faith Does	How Eddie Makes It Better
Faith moves to a new country where she does not speak the language.	She gets a new dog.
Faith has a bad day in school.	1. **She hugs Eddie to feel better.**
Faith draws her family tree during her Spanish lesson.	2. **She shows Eddie as part of the family.**
Faith leaves school by herself and gets lost.	3. **Eddie tracks Faith around town until he finds her.**
Faith thinks Eddie is a strange dog and runs away from him.	4. **Eddie outruns Faith and makes her stop running.**
Faith realizes the dog is Eddie.	5. **He licks her face and makes her laugh.**

Write a Paragraph

The stories you read in this unit are linked by a common theme: how relating to others teaches us about the important things in life. On a separate sheet of paper, write a paragraph explaining why having a good friend like Eddie is important. How would Faith's life be different if she hadn't had a friend like Eddie? Compare Faith's situation to Leigh Botts's. How might Leigh Botts's situation have been different if he had a friend to confide in? **Paragraphs will vary, but should reflect an understanding of the unit theme.**

 Notes for Home: Your child used information from a reading selection to write about how a friend makes a girl's life better. **Home Activity:** Discuss with your child any stories you both know that reflect this unit's theme.

Grammar: Sentences and End Punctuation

Directions: Add the correct end mark to each sentence.

1. Making new friends can be hard __.__
2. Sometimes friends will disagree with one another __.__
3. Have you ever disagreed with a friend __?__
4. You should talk about your feelings with a good friend __.__
5. Sandra is my best friend __. or !__
6. A good friend respects your decisions __.__
7. Even best friends can have different feelings and values __.__
8. Each person is, after all, different __.__
9. Don't you agree __?__
10. Of course, you must be a good friend too __. or !__

Directions: Use the end mark in ( ) to write five sentences about friendship. Remember to begin each sentence with a capital letter. **Possible answers given.**

11. (period)
A real friend is understanding.

12. (period)
That person is a friend in good times and bad times.

13. (exclamation point)
I have the best friend in the world!

14. (period)
We have been friends since second grade.

15. (question mark)
Do you have a good friend?

 Notes for Home: Your child identified the correct end mark for sentences and wrote complete sentences. *Home Activity:* With your child, look through a paragraph in one of his or her favorite books. Ask your child to explain why the particular end mark is used.

Grammar: Subjects and Predicates

A **sentence** must have both a **subject** and a **predicate**.

The **complete subject** is made up of all the words that tell whom or what the sentence is about. A complete subject may have several words or only one word.

The **complete predicate** is made up of all the words in the predicate. The complete predicate tells what the subject is or does. It may have several words or only one word.

<u>Mexico</u> is south of the U.S. border.
<u>Nearly all Mexicans</u> speak Spanish.
complete subject   complete predicate

The most important word in the complete subject is called the **simple subject.** It usually is a noun or a pronoun. Some simple subjects, such as *Mexico City*, have more than one word.

The most important word in the complete predicate is the verb. It is called the **simple predicate.** Some simple predicates can have more than one word, such as *have attracted.*

The beautiful sights of <u>Mexico City</u> <u>have attracted</u> many tourists.

Directions: For each sentence, underline the complete subject once. Underline the complete predicate twice.

1. <u>Many English words</u> <u>come from Spanish.</u>
2. <u>These words</u> <u>include</u> *canyon, patio,* and *rodeo.*
3. <u>Many Americans and Canadians</u> <u>use these words often.</u>
4. <u>Most native people in Mexico</u> <u>speak two languages.</u>
5. <u>They</u> <u>know Spanish and their native language.</u>

Directions: For each sentence, underline the simple subject once and the simple predicate twice.

6. The official <u>language</u> of Mexico <u>is</u> Spanish.
7. <u>People</u> <u>speak</u> Spanish all over Latin America.
8. Many <u>Americans</u> <u>use</u> Spanish too.
9. Some American <u>states</u> <u>have</u> Spanish names.
10. Such <u>places</u> <u>include</u> California and Florida.

 Notes for Home: Your child identified subjects and predicates in sentences. *Home Activity:* Have your child write sentences that tell what happened in school this week. Ask him or her to identify the complete and simple subjects and predicates in each sentence.

Grammar: Subjects and Predicates

Directions: Tell what is underlined in each sentence. Write **S** for subject or **P** for predicate.

S 1. Most people in Mexico <u>live in cities and towns.</u>
P 2. The largest Mexican city <u>is Mexico City.</u>
P 3. Many Mexican towns <u>are hundreds of years old.</u>
S 4. <u>A typical town or village</u> includes a plaza.
S 5. <u>The older buildings</u> are made of stone or adobe.

Directions: Use the nouns and verbs shown below to write complete sentences. Then, underline the complete subject of each sentence once and the complete predicate twice. Finally, circle the simple subject and the simple predicate in each sentence. **Possible answers given.**

6. farmers   live
Many (farmers) (live) in small villages.

7. roads   curve
The narrow (roads) (curve) through the country.

8. rain   falls
A light (rain) (falls) on the crops.

9. people   wear
The (people) (wear) light clothing in hot weather.

10. merchants   sell
Food (merchants) (sell) fruits and vegetables.

Write a Description

Think of a place you would like to visit. On a separate sheet of paper, write a description of the place. Tell what things you see and what people do there. In each sentence, underline the complete subject once and the complete predicate twice.
Check that students have identified the complete subjects and predicates.

 Notes for Home: Your child identified and wrote subjects and predicates in sentences. *Home Activity:* Pick out easy sentences from a newspaper. Ask your child to identify the subject and predicate in each one.

Grammar: Subjects and Predicates

Imagine that you are a detective. Read the sentence to find out who did what.

The young boy walked quietly into the room.

Who walked quietly into the room? Write all the words in the subject of the sentence.
The young boy

What did the young boy do? Write all the words in the predicate of the sentence.
walked quietly into the room.

The **complete subject** is made up of all the words that tell whom or what the sentence is about. The subject names someone or something. It may have one word or many words. The **complete predicate** is made up of all the words in the predicate of a sentence. The predicate tells what the subject is or does. It may have one word or many words.

Directions: Circle the complete subject in each sentence. Write each complete subject under the heading **Who Did It?**

	Who Did It?
1. (Sherlock Holmes) solved many mysteries.	**Sherlock Holmes**
2. (People) asked him to solve many mysteries.	**People**
3. (The police) came to him for help.	**The police**
4. (Doctor Watson) helped Holmes with his work.	**Doctor Watson**
5. (Holmes) had many adventures.	**Holmes**

Directions: Circle the complete predicate in each sentence. Write each complete predicate under the heading **What Did They Do?**

	What Did They Do?
6. The crime victims (counted on Holmes)	**counted on Holmes**
7. Two men (looked for clues)	**looked for clues**
8. The criminals (hid from Holmes)	**hid from Holmes**
9. Criminals (could not trick him)	**could not trick him**

Notes for Home: Your child identified and wrote subjects and predicates of sentences. *Home Activity:* Look at a magazine or newspaper article with your child. Have him or her underline the subjects and circle the predicates of five sentences.

Grammar: Subjects and Predicates

Directions: Decide if the underlined part is the complete subject or the complete predicate. Circle the correct answer.

1. <u>Pearl oysters</u> are different from clams.   (subject)   predicate
2. People <u>may find a small pearl in an ordinary oyster.</u>   subject   (predicate)
3. <u>These pearls</u> are not worth very much.   (subject)   predicate
4. <u>Pearl oysters</u> grow in warm southern seas.   subject   (predicate)
5. <u>Pearl divers</u> look for pearls under water.   subject   (predicate)
6. <u>People all over the world</u> prize pearls.   (subject)   predicate

Directions: Underline the complete subject and circle the complete predicate.

7. <u>Oysters</u> (are useful creatures.)
8. <u>Fishermen</u> (grow oysters as a sea crop.)
9. <u>Most oysters</u> (live in the quiet, shallow waters of bays.)
10. <u>Hole boring snails</u> (are enemies of oysters.)
11. <u>Oysters</u> (live in many parts of the world.)
12. <u>Many oysters</u> (make pearls.)
13. <u>The shells</u> (are very beautiful.)
14. <u>Some people</u> (eat raw oysters.)
15. <u>Oysters</u> (breathe with gills.)
16. <u>Some oysters</u> (live more than twenty years.)

Write a Newscast

On a separate sheet of paper, write a newscast about the things that live in the sea. Be sure to use a complete subject and complete predicate in each sentence.

Check that students have used complete subjects and complete predicates.

 Notes for Home: Your child identified complete subjects and predicates of sentences. *Home Activity:* Write two subjects. (For example: *Black pearls* and *Oyster shells*) Have your child make up predicates to go with the subjects and write the complete sentences.

Grammar: Subjects and Predicates   **37**

Phonics: Vowel Digraphs

Directions: Read each sentence. Say the underlined word to yourself. Listen for the vowel sounds that the letters **ee**, **ai**, and **oa** represent. Circle the word in ( ) that has the same **vowel sound** as the underlined word.

1. My dog howled, then sat to <u>wait</u> for me.   (fate)/fat
2. I rubbed my <u>cheek</u> against his warm fur.   (weak)/wreck
3. I took him for a quick walk in the wet <u>rain</u>.   (plane)/plan
4. We walked along the sand near the <u>coast</u>.   (most)/moss
5. We watched the fishing <u>boats</u> come in.   (robe)/rob

Directions: Read the postcard below. Say the underlined words to yourself. Match each underlined word with a word below that rhymes. Write the word on the correct line.

> Dear Mom,
>
> Camp is great! Guess what? My friend, Liza, has a seeing eye dog named Kip. Kip is very calm. He never jumps on my <u>knees</u>. He is patient while Liza <u>feeds</u> him. It's <u>plain</u> that he loves her. He goes <u>straight</u> to her when she calls. They swim together each day. When he shakes himself off, we all get <u>soaked</u>! I wish I had a dog like Kip.
>
> Love,
> Terri

6. ate   **straight**   9. joked   **soaked**
7. cane   **plain**   10. reads   **feeds**
8. ease   **knees**

 Notes for Home: Your child practiced working with words with these long vowel sounds: *long e* (*see*), *long a* (*rain*) and *long o* (*coast*). **Home Activity:** Write *see*, *rain*, and *coast* on separate sheets of paper. Take turns listing words that have the same vowel sounds and spellings.

38   Phonics: Vowel Digraphs

Spelling: Short e and Long e

Pretest Directions: Fold back the page along the dotted line. On the blanks, write the spelling words as they are dictated. When you have finished the test, unfold the page and check your words.

1. heavy
2. ahead
3. measure
4. already
5. jealous
6. meadow
7. weapon
8. said
9. again
10. against
11. degree
12. cheese
13. succeed
14. speech
15. breeze
16. goalie
17. piece
18. believe
19. thief
20. chief

1. The weight is **heavy**.
2. Let's plan **ahead**.
3. **Measure** the triangle.
4. The bus **already** came.
5. She is not **jealous** of others.
6. Flowers grow in the **meadow**.
7. The soldier held his **weapon**.
8. Did you hear what I **said**?
9. Let's play **again**.
10. Lean **against** the wall.
11. Juan earned a college **degree**.
12. Say **cheese** for the camera!
13. Sara is determined to **succeed**.
14. The principal gave a **speech**.
15. The **breeze** cooled us off.
16. Our **goalie** blocked the point.
17. Please, cut a **piece** of pizza.
18. I **believe** it is true.
19. The **thief** took it.
20. Hail to the **chief**.

 Notes for Home: Your child took a pretest on words that have the short *e* and long *e* sounds. *Home Activity:* Help your child learn misspelled words before the final test. Your child can underline the word parts that caused the problems and concentrate on those parts.

Spelling: Short *e* and Long *e*   **39**

Spelling: Short e and Long e

Word List			
heavy	meadow	degree	goalie
ahead	weapon	cheese	piece
measure	said	succeed	believe
already	again	speech	thief
jealous	against	breeze	chief

Directions: Choose the words from the box that have the **long e** sound. Write each word in the correct column. **Order may vary.**

Long e spelled ee
1. degree
2. cheese
3. succeed
4. speech
5. breeze

Long e spelled ie
6. goalie
7. piece
8. believe
9. thief
10. chief

Directions: Write the **short e** word from the box that begins and ends with the same letters as each word below.

11. mellow   **meadow**   16. jobs   **jealous**
12. accident   **against**   17. accepted   **ahead**
13. hay   **heavy**   18. anybody   **already**
14. action   **again**   19. woman   **weapon**
15. spend   **said**   20. mile   **measure**

HEAVY CHEESE

 **Notes for Home:** Your child spelled words with the short *e* sound spelled *ea* and *ai* (*ahead*, *said*) and the long *e* sound spelled *ee* and *ie* (*cheese, piece*). **Home Activity:** Read a brief newspaper article with your child. Together, find all the short *e* and long *e* words you can.

40   Spelling: Short *e* and Long *e*

© Scott Foresman 5

Name _____

Faith and Eddie

Spelling: Short *e* and Long *e*

Directions: Proofread this description. Find five spelling mistakes.
Use the proofreading marks to correct each mistake.

What are my best friends like? For one
thing, they are never jelous of me. They
like to see me succeed and to get
ahead. My best friends would never turn
against me. Also, they trust me and
always beleeve what I have said to
them. They don't mind if I give them a
peace of advice. If you have friends like
that, you are already a very lucky
person indeed!

Proofreading Marks	
≡	Make a capital.
/	Make a small letter.
∧	Add something.
ℒ	Take out something.
⊙	Add a period.
¶	Begin a new paragraph.

Spelling Tip
piece
Don't confuse the word
piece with **peace**.
Remember this hint: I
want a **piece** of **pie**.

Word List
heavy
ahead
measure
already
jealous
meadow
weapon
said
again
against
degree
cheese
succeed
speech
breeze
goalie
piece
believe
thief
chief

Write a Description
Think about a good friend. How does your friend act?
What does your friend look like? What sorts of
activities do you both enjoy? What makes this person
a good friend? On a separate sheet of paper, write a
description of your friend. Try to use at least five of
your spelling words.
**Answers will vary, but each description should
include at least five spelling words.**

Notes for Home: Your child spelled words with the short *e* sound spelled *ea* and *ai* (*ahead,
said*) and the long *e* sound spelled *ee* and *ie* (*cheese, piece*). **Home Activity:** Together, look at
pictures in a magazine to find items whose names have the short *e* and long *e* sounds.

Spelling: Short *e* and Long *e* 41

Name _____

Faith and Eddie

Spelling: Short *e* and Long *e*

REVIEW

Word List			
heavy	meadow	degree	goalie
ahead	weapon	cheese	piece
measure	said	succeed	believe
already	again	speech	thief
jealous	against	breeze	chief

Directions: Choose the word from the box that best matches each clue. Write the
letters of the word on the blanks. The boxed letters tell what you'll find in each
word.

1. think to be true — 1. b e **l** i e v e
2. a position on the soccer team — 2. **g** o a l i e
3. one more time — 3. a g a i **n**
4. a college title — 4. **d** e g r e e
5. a gun, for example — 5. w e a p o **n**
6. a cool wind — 6. **b** r e e z e
7. spoke — 7. **s** a i d
8. a formal talk — 8. s p e e c **h**
9. a grassy field — 9. m e a d o **w**
10. use a ruler — 10. m e a s u r **e**
11. opposed to — 11. a g a i n s **t**
12. a dairy product — 12. **c** h e e s e

What you'll find in each word: **long or short *e***

Directions: Choose the word from the box that is most opposite in meaning
for each word or words below. Write the word on the line.

13. light **heavy**
14. fail **succeed**
15. whole **piece**
16. behind **ahead**
17. not yet **already**
18. donor **thief**
19. follower **chief**
20. content **jealous**

Notes for Home: Your child spelled words with the short *e* sound spelled *ea* and *ai* (*ahead,
said*) and the long *e* sound spelled *ee* and *ie* (*cheese, piece*). **Home Activity:** Have your child
spell each spelling word and tell whether it has a short *e* or long *e* sound.

42 Spelling: Short *e* and Long *e*

Name _____

Faith and Eddie

Dictionary/Glossary

A **dictionary** is a book of words and their meanings. A **glossary** is a short
dictionary in the back of some books. It includes definitions of words used in
the book. Words are listed in alphabetical order. **Guide words** appear at the top
of each page and show the first and last entry word for that page.

Directions: Use this section of a dictionary page to answer the questions that follow.

245 fretful/frogman

fret•ful (fret′fəl), cross, discontented, or worried; ready
to fret: *My baby brother is fretful because his ear hurts.*
adjective.
fric•tion (frik′shən), 1 a rubbing of one thing against
another, such as skates on ice, hand against hand, or a
brush on shoes: *Matches are lighted by friction.* 2 the
resistance to motion of surfaces that touch: *Oil reduces
friction.* 3 a conflict of differing ideas and opinions;
disagreement; clash: *Constant friction between the two
nations brought them dangerously close to war. noun.*
Fri•day (frī′dā), the sixth day of the week; the day after
Thursday. *noun.*

a hat	i it	oi oil	ch child
ā age	ī ice	ou out	ng long
ä far	o hot	u cup	sh she
e let	ō open	ú put	th thin
ē equal	ò order	ü rule	ᵀᴴ then
ér term	ô author		zh measure

a in *about*
e in *taken*
i in *pencil*
o in *lemon*
u in *circus*

fried (frīd), 1 cooked in hot fat: *fried eggs.* 2 See **fry.**
I fried the ham. The potatoes had been fried. 1 *adjective,*
2 *verb.*
friend (frend), 1 a person who knows and likes another.
2 a person who favors and supports: *He was a generous
friend of the art museum.* 3 a person who belongs to the
same side or group: *Are you a friend or an enemy? noun.*

From SCOTT FORESMAN BEGINNING DICTIONARY by E.L. Thorndike and Clarence L. Barnhart. Copyright © 1997 by Scott Foresman and Company.

1. Using the guide words, list two other words that might appear on this page.
Possible answers: friendly, fright

2. According to the pronunciation key at the top right side of the page, the vowel sound in *fried*
sounds like the long *i* sound in what other word?
ice

3. Which definition of *friend* is used in the following sentence?
Tyrell has been my best friend for years.
The first meaning is used: a person who knows and likes another.

4. How many syllables do the words *Friday* and *friend* each have? **Friday has two
syllables. *Friend* has one syllable.**

5. Write a sentence using the third meaning of *friction*. **Possible answer: There was
friction between the two unhappy neighbors.**

6. Which word on the dictionary page can be used as a verb? **fried**

Research and Study Skills: Dictionary/Glossary 43

Name _____

Faith and Eddie

Directions: Use this section of a glossary from a textbook to answer the
questions that follow.

eyelid/glutton

eye•lid (ī′lid), the movable cover of skin, upper or
lower, by means of which we can shut and open our
eyes. *noun.*
fam•i•ly (fam′əlē), 1 a father, mother, and their
children: *A new family moved to our block.* 2 all of a
person's relatives: *a family reunion. noun,* plural
fam•i•lies.
fife (fīf), a small, shrill musical instrument like a
flute, played by blowing. Fifes are used with drums
to make music for marching. *noun.* [*Fife* comes
from German *Pfeife,* meaning "pipe."]
gar•lic (gär′lik), the bulb of a plant related to the
onion, used in cooking. Its flavor is stronger than
that of an onion. *noun.*

ges•ture (jes′chər), 1 a movement of the hands, arms,
or any part of the body, used instead of words or
with words to help express an idea or feeling:
*Speakers often make gestures with their hands to
stress something they are saying.* 2 to make
gestures; use gestures. 1 *noun,* 2 *verb.* **ges•tures,
ges•tured, ges•tur•ing.**
gla•cier (glā′shər), a large mass of ice formed from
the snow on high ground and moving very slowly
down a mountain or along a valley. *noun.* [*Glacier*
comes from the French *glace,* which comes from the
Latin *glacies,* meaning "ice."]

7. Which definition of *gesture* is used in the following sentence? How can you tell?
The coach gestured secretly to the player.
The second meaning is used. Possible answer: The word is used as a verb.

8. Which entry word on the glossary page has the most syllables? How many syllables does the
word have?
The word *family* has three syllables.

9. Which word comes from a German word? What does the German word mean?
The word *fife* comes from the German word *Pfeife,* meaning "pipe."

10. In what ways is a glossary similar to a dictionary? How is a glossary different from a
dictionary?
**Possible answer: Both present words in alphabetical order, give their spellings,
number of syllables, pronunciations, meanings, and parts of speech. A glossary
shows only words used in the book in which it appears. A dictionary includes many
more words than a glossary.**

Notes for Home: Your child used a dictionary and a glossary to find information about
words. *Home Activity:* With your child, select various words from a dictionary or glossary.
Discuss all the information you find about that word.

44 Research and Study Skills: Dictionary/Glossary

© Scott Foresman 5

Name _____

Looking for a Home

Generalizing

- **Generalizing** is making a statement that tells what several people or things have in common.
- Sometimes a clue word such as *most, all, sometimes, always,* or *never* signals that a generalization is being made.
- A valid generalization is supported by facts and logic. A faulty generalization is not.

Directions: Reread "A Special Family." Then complete the table. Tell whether each statement is a generalization. Explain your reasons for all answers.

Possible reasons given.

Statement	Generalization (Yes or No?)	Reason
Joshua has a few memories of his Korean foster family.	1. No	2. It doesn't say what people have in common.
Most Asians in the Levins' school have Asian parents.	3. Yes	4. It says what several people have in common.
Eric Levin is an adopted child.	5. No	6. It doesn't say what people have in common.

Directions: Complete the table. Tell whether each generalization is **valid** or **faulty.** Explain your reasons for all answers.

Statement	Generalization (Valid or Faulty?)	Reason
All the Levin children have musical talent.	7. Faulty	8. It is not supported by facts. Only Eric's musical talent is mentioned
The Levins do many things together as a family.	9. Valid	10. It is supported by facts. They eat, shop, work, and play together.

Notes for Home: Your child identified generalizations. *Home Activity:* Ask your child to look around a room in your home and make a generalization about it, such as *All the walls are painted white.* Then talk about whether you agree with the generalization.

Generalizing **47**

Name _____

Looking for a Home

Vocabulary

Directions: Choose a word from the box that best matches each definition. Write the word on the line.

Check the Words You Know
__ awe
__ bitter
__ determined
__ horrified
__ panicked
__ select
__ suspicious

_____ horrified _____   1. shocked; terrified

_____ panicked _____   2. acted as if there was an emergency without having real cause

_____ bitter _____   3. miserable; angry

_____ awe _____   4. a feeling of wonder

_____ suspicious _____   5. doubtful

Directions: Choose the word from the box that best completes each statement. Write the word on the line to the left.

_____ awe _____   6. The boys looked in _____ at the huge train.

_____ select _____   7. They began to _____ their seats.

_____ determined _____   8. Each boy was _____ to find a good seat.

_____ panicked _____   9. However, no one _____ in the rush to sit down.

_____ bitter _____   10. None felt angry or _____ about the seats they found.

Directions: Choose the word from the box that best completes each statement. Write the word on the line to the left.

_____ suspicious _____   11. *Respect* is to *respectful* as *suspicion* is to _____.

_____ horrified _____   12. *Terrify* is to *terrified* as *horrify* is to _____.

_____ bitter _____   13. *Sleepy* is to *alert* as *happy* is to _____.

_____ select _____   14. *Toss* is to *throw* as *choose* is to _____.

_____ awe _____   15. *Hopeful* is to *hope* as *awesome* is to _____.

Write a Description
On a separate sheet of paper, describe a real or imaginary trip by train, boat, or airplane. Include vivid sensory details to tell what you see, hear, smell, touch, or taste. Use as many vocabulary words as you can.
Students' descriptions should make correct use of vocabulary words.

Notes for Home: Your child identified and used vocabulary words from "Looking for a Home." *Home Activity:* Ask your child to describe events that would cause a person to feel *awe, bitter, determined, horrified, panicked,* and *suspicious.*

48 Vocabulary

Name _____

Looking for a Home

Generalizing

- **Generalizing** is making a statement that tells what several people or things have in common.
- Sometimes a clue word such as *most, always,* or *never* signals that a generalization is being made.
- A valid generalization is supported by facts and logic. A faulty generalization is not.

Directions: Read this passage from "Looking for a Home" that tells about the placement of orphan train riders. Then answer the questions below. Think about ways that the author makes generalizations in her writing.

Most placements were successful, and the program grew. During the first 20 years an average of 3,000 children rode the orphan trains each year. Brace continued to raise the needed money through his speeches and his writing. Railroads gave discount fares to the children, and wealthy people sometimes paid for whole trainloads of children.

Unfortunately, many children who needed homes were not allowed to go on the trains. It was always difficult to find homes for older children, and while some teenagers as old as 17 were successfully placed, 14 was usually the oldest a rider could be. It was always easiest to find homes for babies.

From ORPHAN TRAIN RIDER: ONE BOY'S TRUE STORY by Andrea Warren. Copyright ©1996 by Andrea Warren. Reprinted by permission of Houghton Mifflin Company. All rights reserved.

1. What clue words can you find in the passage that signal a generalization?
Clue words include *most, sometimes, many, always, some,* and *usually.*

2. What facts does the author offer to support her generalizations?
She cites the average number of children who rode the trains annually. She names those who raised and donated money.

3. Explain why the sentence about Charles Loring Brace is or is not a generalization.
It is not a generalization since it doesn't tell what several people or things have in common.

4. Explain why this generalization is valid or faulty: *Most orphans as old as 17 were easily placed*
It is faulty since the passage indicates that the opposite is true.

5. What generalizations can you make about Lee and his two brothers from "Looking for Home"? Explain your thinking on a separate sheet of paper. **Possible answers: All three brothers had only one another to rely on. They all were afraid of being separated. They all were healthy.**

Notes for Home: Your child read a nonfiction article and identified generalizations that the author made. *Home Activity:* Talk with your child about members in your family. Encourage him or her to make general statements about ways that some of the members are alike.

Generalizing **49**

Name _____

Looking for a Home

Selection Test

Directions: Choose the best answer to each item. Mark the letter for the answer you have chosen.

Part 1: Vocabulary
Find the answer choice that means about the same as the underlined word in each sentence.

1. Eduardo panicked when he saw the house.
   - Ⓐ felt a great and sudden fear
   - B. felt a loss of confidence
   - C. felt a sense of relief
   - D. felt wild and silly

2. Anna wanted to select one.
   - F. send
   - G. complete
   - Ⓗ choose
   - J. try

3. Gillian was determined.
   - A. sent for punishment
   - Ⓑ firm; with her mind made up
   - C. making the best of it
   - D. very respectful

4. The sight horrified us.
   - F. amused
   - G. filled with anger
   - H. made sad
   - Ⓙ shocked very much

5. The stars filled him with awe.
   - A. shame
   - B. anger
   - Ⓒ wonder
   - D. joy

6. It was a bitter experience.
   - Ⓕ causing pain or grief
   - G. exhausting
   - H. causing delight or joy
   - J. surprising

7. The girl's actions made him suspicious.
   - A. unsafe
   - B. embarrassed or shy
   - C. curious
   - Ⓓ unwilling to trust

Part 2: Comprehension
Use what you know about the selection to answer each item.

8. Where did Lee and his brothers come from?
   - F. Texas
   - G. New Jersey
   - H. Iowa
   - Ⓙ New York

9. Children on the orphan trains were taken to other parts of the country to—
   - A. make money.
   - Ⓑ find new homes.
   - C. go to school.
   - D. make new friends.

10. Why did Lee feel a sense of dread when he got back on the train after the first children were chosen?
    - F. He was afraid no one would ever choose him.
    - G. He was tired of the train food.
    - Ⓗ He felt sure he would be separated from his brothers.
    - J. He wanted to stay in that town.

11. What happened to Lee at the Rodgerses' house?
    - A. He got a haircut.
    - Ⓑ He got separated from Leo.
    - C. He got his own bedroom.
    - D. He felt welcome in his new home.

12. Which of these events happened last?
    - Ⓕ Lee spoke rudely to Ben Nailling.
    - G. The Rodgerses decided to keep only Leo.
    - H. A man and woman took Gerald.
    - J. Lee accidentally killed some chicks.

GO ON

50 Selection Test

Answers 691

13. What was the most important difference between Lee's experience at the Naillings' and his other experiences?
   A. The bedroom was sunny.
   B. He was firmly disciplined.
   C. He felt wanted.
   D. There was lots of food.

14. Which statement is a valid generalization based on the facts in this selection?
   F. Children on the orphan trains often fought with each other.
   G. The oldest orphan train riders were always chosen first.
   H. The matrons on the orphan trains treated the children kindly.
   J. Most brothers and sisters traveling together ended up in different homes.

15. The author of this selection most likely thinks that—
   A. orphans enjoy long train rides.
   B. every child needs love and a good home.
   C. the orphan trains were a useful experience for the children.
   D. Lee Nailling was not a nice boy.

STOP

Generalizing

- **Generalizing** is making a statement that tells what several people or things have in common.
- Sometimes a clue word such as *most, always,* or *never* signals that a generalization is being made.
- A valid generalization is supported by facts and logic. A faulty generalization is not.

Directions: Read the following passage.

Railroad trains are an important means of transportation. Every day, thousands of passenger trains carry people to work, home, and other places. Other trains carry products such as coal, grain, and lumber. Trains are the fastest means of transportation except for airplanes. Some passenger trains travel over 200 miles an hour. Trains can also carry heavier loads than any other means of transport except ships. A freight train can haul thousands of tons across a country. Nearly every country has at least one railroad line running through it.

Directions: Complete the table. Tell if the first three statements are generalizations or not. Tell if the last two statements are valid or faulty generalizations. Give reasons for your answers.

Statement	Generalization	Valid or Faulty?	Reason
Railroad trains are an important means of transportation.	1. Yes		2. It states what trains have in common.
One freight train carried grain to Iowa last week.	3. No		4. It doesn't tell what several things have in common.
Some passenger trains travel over 200 miles per hour.	5. Yes		6. It tells what some trains have in common.
Most freight trains cannot carry more than 1,000 pounds.	Yes	7. Faulty	8. A freight train can carry thousands of tons.
Nearly every country has at least one railroad line.	Yes	9. Valid	10. A logical statement as trains are important for transportation.

Notes for Home: Your child identified generalizations in a nonfiction article. **Home Activity:** Choose a category of food, such as fruits, vegetables, or meats. Encourage your child to make general statements about ways that foods in that category are alike.

Sequence

REVIEW

Directions: Read the passage. Then read each question about the passage. Choose the best answer to each question. Mark the letter for the answer you have chosen.

How to Adopt

Deciding to adopt a child is a big decision for any couple. It is also a big decision for those who are currently caring for the child. There are many parts involved in giving a child a happy home.

The couple wishing to adopt a child first must apply to an adoption agency. The adoption agency will take steps to find out whether it is a good idea for this couple to adopt a child.

After the couple applies, the adoption agency assigns a caseworker to investigate. The caseworker needs to know the couple's background. The caseworker also checks the couple's health and their finances.

If the agency feels that the couple will be good parents and the child will be safe and happy with them, the agency has the child live in the couple's home for 6 to 12 months. This is an important time for deciding whether or not the adoption can become legal.

If the child and the couple still want the adoption, a lawyer then prepares an adoption request. The request is given to a court. If the court approves, the adoption becomes legal and the child and parents become a family.

1. The first step in the process to adopt a child is—
   A. telling the child.
   B. finding a lawyer.
   C. applying to an agency.
   D. writing to the judge.

2. The first thing that an adoption agency does is—
   F. contact the judge.
   G. find the child.
   H. contact a lawyer.
   J. investigate the people who want to adopt a child.

3. Before a child can be adopted, he or she must—
   A. apply to the judge.
   B. get lawyer approval.
   C. live with the people who want to adopt him or her.
   D. investigate the people who want to adopt him or her.

4. After a lawyer prepares an adoption request, it is given to the—
   F. parents.
   G. court.
   H. child.
   J. adoption agency.

5. The final step in making an adoption legal is—
   A. the court's approval.
   B. the child's approval.
   C. the parents' approval.
   D. the lawyer's approval.

Notes for Home: Your child read a nonfiction article and then identified the order in which steps were presented. **Home Activity:** Review with your child the important things that have happened in his or her life so far. Have your child name the events in the order that they occurred.

Writing Across Texts

Directions: Review "Looking for a Home" and "What Were Orphan Trains?" Trace the experiences Lee Nailling and Claretta Carman Miller had from leaving their families to coming to live with the families who would eventually adopt them. Add a brief description of each experience to the table below. **Possible answers given.**

	Lee	Claretta
Birth Families:	Father sent him to an orphanage after his mother died. Lee was often punished and didn't have enough to eat.	3. Her parents neglected her and she was taken away from them.
First families they went to from orphan train:	1. A family agreed to take both Leo and Lee, but then decided they could only keep Leo; the brothers didn't get to say good-bye.	4. A large family adopted Claretta so they would have a servant.
Families who finally adopted them:	2. Lee was reluctant at first to stay with the Naillings, but he soon found the Nailling family to be loving and caring.	5. Mrs. Carman nursed Claretta back to health and provided a loving home.

Write a Compare/Contrast Paragraph

Before finding successful placements with new families, many orphans on the trains had unpleasant experiences. Trace the experiences of Lee Nailling and Claretta Carman Miller. What did they probably learn about people when they met the families who finally adopted them? Use the information from the table above to write a paragraph comparing and contrasting the children's experiences. Write your paragraph on a separate sheet of paper. **Paragraphs will vary. Check that students indicate that both Lee and Claretta had numerous negative experiences, but they finally were fortunate to find loving families to raise them.**

Notes for Home: Your child used information from different texts to write a compare/contrast paragraph. **Home Activity:** As you read stories and articles with your child, talk about how the ideas or experiences described connect to other reading they have done.

© Scott Foresman 5

Grammar: Subjects and Predicates — REVIEW

Directions: For each sentence, underline the complete subject once and the complete predicate twice.

1. Families have changed in unexpected ways!
2. Many different groups make a family today.
3. Often, one adult in the family has to work outside of the home.
4. Many mothers are working today.
5. Very young children sometimes go to day care centers.
6. Sometimes an older relative will help care for younger children.
7. Some families have only one parent in the house.
8. Some children live with one parent and one step-parent.
9. Grandparents are the only adults at home in other families.
10. Some young people live with foster parents.

Directions: Write sentences that include the following simple subjects and predicates. Remember to begin each sentence with a capital letter and end each one with the correct punctuation mark. **Possible answers given.**

11. brothers and sisters   make
Brothers and sisters make a family fun.

12. grandparents   tell
Do your grandparents tell you about family history?

13. Mom   works
Mom works three days a week.

14. parents   spend
My parents spend time with me each day.

15. family   is
My family is the best in the world!

Notes for Home: Your child identified complete and simple subjects and predicates and wrote sentences with subjects and predicates. *Home Activity:* Give your child several different words. Ask him or her to use each of those words as the simple subject in a sentence.

Grammar: Four Kinds of Sentences

There are four kinds of sentences. Each begins with a capital letter and has a special end mark.

A **declarative sentence** makes a statement. It ends with a period.

Many children live with foster parents.

An **interrogative sentence** asks a question. It ends with a question mark.

What are foster parents?

An **imperative sentence** gives a command or makes a request. It ends with a period. The subject *(you)* is not shown, but it is understood.

Please tell me what foster parents do.

An **exclamatory sentence** shows strong feeling. It ends with an exclamation mark.

How interesting that is!

Directions: Write whether each sentence is **declarative**, **interrogative**, **imperative**, or **exclamatory**.

interrogative	1. What jobs does a foster parent do?
declarative	2. Many foster parents open their homes to children.
interrogative	3. Can anyone become a foster parent?
imperative	4. Call a state agency for more information.
exclamatory	5. What a helpful suggestion you made!
declarative	6. I'm glad I could help.

Directions: Read each sentence. Rewrite and correct each incorrect sentence.

7. foster parents are licensed by the state.
Foster parents are licensed by the state.

8. I have heard that some foster children stay until they are adults?
I have heard that some foster children stay until they are adults.

9. What happens after that!
What happens after that?

10. What a good question that is!
correct

Notes for Home: Your child identified sentences that make a statement, ask a question, give a command or make a request, or show strong feeling. *Home Activity:* Ask your child to write sentences about a topic and to identify each type of sentence.

Grammar: Four Kinds of Sentences

Directions: Write whether each sentence is **declarative**, **interrogative**, **imperative**, or **exclamatory**.

interrogative	1. Can foster parents adopt a foster child?
declarative	2. Many foster parents do adopt their foster children.
declarative	3. Fostering and adopting both mean taking care of children.
imperative	4. Tell me more about it later.
declarative	5. I like taking care of babies.
exclamatory	6. How I would love to bring up a family!

Directions: Rewrite each sentence. Add the correct capitalization and end punctuation.

7. what must a family do to adopt a child
What must a family do to adopt a child?

8. read this book about adoption
Read this book about adoption.

9. what a huge number of laws there are
What a huge number of laws there are!

10. approval for adoption may take a year or more
Approval for adoption may take a year or more.

Write a Conversation

On a separate sheet of paper, write several sentences that you might hear spoken between two relatives—a brother and sister, a mother and child, or an aunt and uncle. Supply one example of each type of sentence: declarative, interrogative, exclamatory, and imperative.
Students should start each sentence with a capital letter and finish with the correct end punctuation.

Notes for Home: Your child identified sentences that make a statement, ask a question, give a command or make a request, or show strong feeling. *Home Activity:* Take turns creating different kinds of sentences.

Grammar: Four Kinds of Sentences — RETEACHING

Read the sentences below. Circle the end punctuation in each one.

1. There are two lions in the cage.
2. Do only lions and horses have manes?
3. How fierce that lion looks!
4. Stay back from the wall.

A **declarative sentence** makes a statement. It ends with a period. An **interrogative sentence** asks a question. It ends with a question mark. An **imperative sentence** gives a command or makes a request. It ends with a period. An **exclamatory sentence** expresses strong feeling. It ends with an exclamation mark. All sentences begin with a capital letter.

Directions: Circle the end punctuation in each sentence. Then write **declarative**, **interrogative**, **imperative**, or **exclamatory**.

1. Zoos are fun places to visit.	declarative
2. I have a wonderful idea.	declarative
3. Meet me at the bus stop.	imperative
4. Isn't this a perfect day for a trip?	interrogative
5. How smart you are to bring a camera!	exclamatory

Directions: Write the correct punctuation mark at the end of each sentence. Circle any letter that should be capitalized. Then write each sentence correctly.

6. please hand me the camera ___.
Please hand me the camera.

7. how exciting it is to see a baby panda ___!
How exciting it is to see a baby panda!

8. in which countries are pandas found ___?
In which countries are pandas found?

9. the pandas are eating bamboo stalks ___.
The pandas are eating bamboo stalks.

10. please take some pictures of the pandas ___.
Please take some pictures of the pandas.

Notes for Home: Your child identified and wrote four kinds of sentences. *Home Activity:* Point to sentences in a magazine or newspaper and have your child identify whether they are declarative, interrogative, imperative, or exclamatory.

Name _____

Looking for a Home

Grammar: Four Kinds of Sentences

Directions: Write the correct punctuation mark at the end of each sentence. Then identify each sentence as **declarative, interrogative, imperative,** or **exclamatory.**

1. How many different kinds of birds are there __?__   interrogative
2. Find out if all birds can fly __.__   imperative
3. Flying birds have light bodies and strong wings __.__   declarative
4. Is an ostrich light enough to fly __?__   interrogative
5. Look at this picture of an ostrich __.__   imperative
6. What a funny-looking bird it is __!__   exclamatory
7. An ostrich is often heavier than an adult human __.__   declarative

Directions: Write each sentence. Use capital letters and end punctuation correctly.

8. a bird's wing feathers are used for flying
A bird's wing feathers are used for flying.

9. are birds' tail feathers important for flying
Are birds' tail feathers important for flying?

10. read this article for more information about birds
Read this article for more information about birds.

11. how important those tail feathers are for steering and balance
How important those tail feathers are for steering and balance!

12. feathers also keep birds warm
Feathers also keep birds warm.

13. i enjoy collecting feathers that have fallen on the ground
I enjoy collecting feathers that have fallen on the ground.

14. how many feathers have you collected
How many feathers have you collected?

 Notes for Home: Your child identified and wrote the correct punctuation for four kinds of sentences. **Home Activity:** Write declarative, interrogative, imperative, and exclamatory sentences and have your child add the correct punctuation at the end.

Grammar: Four Kinds of Sentences   **59**

Name _____

Looking for a Home

Phonics: Diphthongs

Directions: Read each sentence. Look at the words in ( ). Both words make sense, but only one word has a vowel sound like **cow.** Circle the correct word.

1. The (crew/**crowd**) was waiting for the train.
2. Someone (**shouted**/shushed) his name.
3. The steam drifted (**about**/above) him.
4. In the distance, he saw a (horse/**house**).
5. When he arrived, the boy (**found**/thought) he liked his new home.

Directions: Read the clue in ( ). Choose the letters **ou** or **ow** to complete each word. It's tricky! These letters stand for the same sound. Write the correct letters on the blanks.

6. ar __o__ __u__ nd   (in a circle)
7. br __o__ __w__ n   (the color of toast)
8. all __o__ __w__ ed   (let someone do something)
9. gr __o__ __u__ nd   (the land under our feet)
10. m __o__ __u__ th   (the place on a face to eat and speak)
11. fr __o__ __w__ n   (look unhappy)

Directions: Complete each sentence with a word that has the same vowel sound as **crowd** and **mouth.** Write the word on the line to the left.

_____south_____   12. The train traveled _____, not north.

_____out_____   13. It took the children _____ of the city and into the country.

_____town_____   14. After a long journey, the train stopped in a small _____, very different from the big city.

_____down_____   15. The conductor helped the children _____ the steps and onto the platform.

 Notes for Home: Your child practiced reading and writing words with letters **ou** and **ow** that represent the same vowel sound, such as *mouth* and *crowd.* **Home Activity:** Together, make a list of words with these spellings and this vowel sound. Make up rhymes that use pairs of these words.

60   Phonics: Diphthongs

Name _____

Looking for a Home

Spelling: Vowel Sounds in *boy* and *out*

Pretest Directions: Fold back the page along the dotted line. On the blanks, write the spelling words as they are dictated. When you have finished the test, unfold the page and check your words.

1. choice
2. noisy
3. spoil
4. poison
5. Illinois
6. loyal
7. destroy
8. annoy
9. oyster
10. voyage
11. powder
12. towel
13. downtown
14. drown
15. growl
16. amount
17. our
18. outside
19. couch
20. surround

1. You have to make a **choice.**
2. Drums can be very **noisy.**
3. Old fruit will **spoil.**
4. On the bottle it said **poison.**
5. Chicago is a big city in **Illinois.**
6. Good friends are always **loyal.**
7. Rain will **destroy** the drawing.
8. Wasps **annoy** me.
9. The **oyster** made a pearl.
10. He went on a long **voyage.**
11. The recipe needs baking **powder.**
12. Bring your **towel** to the pool.
13. I like to shop **downtown.**
14. You must swim or **drown.**
15. The dog will **growl.**
16. They paid the wrong **amount.**
17. This is **our** house.
18. Let's play **outside.**
19. Please sit on the **couch.**
20. Ants **surround** the ice cream.

 Notes for Home: Your child took a pretest on words that have the vowel sounds heard in *boy* and *out.* **Home Activity:** Help your child learn misspelled words before the final test. Dictate the word and have your child spell the word aloud for you or write it on paper.

Spelling: Vowel Sounds in *boy* and *out*   **61**

Name _____

Looking for a Home

Spelling: Vowel Sounds in *boy* and *out*

Word List			
choice	loyal	powder	amount
noisy	destroy	towel	our
spoil	annoy	downtown	outside
poison	oyster	drown	couch
Illinois	voyage	growl	surround

Directions: Choose the words from the box that have the vowel sound in **boy.** Write each word in the correct column. **Order may vary.**

Vowel sound spelled oy
1. loyal
2. destroy
3. annoy
4. oyster
5. voyage

Vowel sound spelled oi
6. choice
7. noisy
8. spoil
9. poison
10. Illinois

Directions: Write the word from the box that belongs in each group of words. Hint: The word will have the vowel sound in **out.**

11. inside, between, __outside__
12. oink, moo, __growl__
13. chair, table, __couch__
14. uptown, midtown, __downtown__
15. napkin, cloth, __towel__
16. circle, enclose, __surround__
17. liquid, paste, __powder__
18. swim, sink, __drown__
19. your, their, __our__
20. cost, price, __amount__

 Notes for Home: Your child spelled words that have the vowel sounds heard in *boy* spelled *oi* and *oy* and *out* spelled *ow* and *ou.* **Home Activity:** Together, write the spelling words on slips of paper. Take turns choosing words and saying them aloud for the other person to spell.

62   Spelling: Vowel Sounds in *boy* and *out*

© Scott Foresman 5

Spelling: Vowel Sounds in *boy* and *out*

Directions: Proofread this letter. Find five spelling mistakes. Use the proofreading marks to correct each mistake.

☰	Make a capital.
╱	Make a small letter.
∧	Add something.
⤴	Take out something.
⊙	Add a period.
¶	Begin a new paragraph.

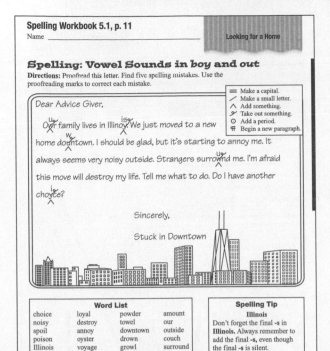

Dear Advice Giver,

    Our family lives in Illinoy. We just moved to a new home downtown. I should be glad, but it's starting to annoy me. It always seems very noisy outside. Strangers surrownd me. I'm afraid this move will destroy my life. Tell me what to do. Do I have another choyce?

                                    Sincerely,

                                    Stuck in Downtown

Word List

choice	loyal	powder	amount
noisy	destroy	towel	our
spoil	annoy	downtown	outside
poison	oyster	drown	couch
Illinois	voyage	growl	surround

Spelling Tip

Illinois
Don't forget the final **-s** in **Illinois**. Always remember to add the final **-s**, even though the final **-s** is silent.

Write a Reply

Imagine you are the "Advice Giver" who received the letter above. On a separate sheet of paper, write a reply that tells "Stuck in Downtown" what to do. Try to use at least five of your spelling words.
Answers will vary, but each reply should include at least five spelling words.

Notes for Home: Your child spelled words with the vowel sounds heard in *boy* spelled *oi* and *oy* and *out* spelled *ow* and *ou*. **Home Activity:** Spell each spelling word slowly, one letter at a time. When your child knows the word, have him or her complete its spelling.

Spelling: Vowel Sounds in *boy* and *out*

REVIEW

Word List

choice	loyal	powder	amount
noisy	destroy	towel	our
spoil	annoy	downtown	outside
poison	oyster	drown	couch
Illinois	voyage	growl	surround

Directions: Choose the word from the box that best answers each question. Write the word on the line.

Illinois	1.	What state is west of Indiana?
voyage	2.	What do you call a trip across the ocean?
couch	3.	What piece of furniture can you relax on?
poison	4.	What is very dangerous if swallowed?
towel	5.	What do you use to dry off after a shower?
downtown	6.	What place is the opposite of *uptown*?
oyster	7.	What sea creature has a pearl in its shell?
outside	8.	What is the opposite of *inside*?
powder	9.	What is soft, dry, and dusty?
growl	10.	What sound does a hungry stomach make?

Directions: Choose the word from the box that has the same or nearly the same meaning as each word or words below. Write the word on the line.

11. loud	**noisy**		16. owned together	**our**
12. enclose	**surround**		17. ruin	**destroy**
13. selection	**choice**		18. decay	**spoil**
14. sink	**drown**		19. sum	**amount**
15. bother	**annoy**		20. faithful	**loyal**

Notes for Home: Your child spelled words that have the vowel sounds heard in *boy* spelled *oi* and *oy* (*choice*, *loyal*) and *out* spelled *ow* and *ou* (*towel*, *couch*). **Home Activity:** Read a short story with your child. Look for words that have the vowel sounds heard in *boy* and *out*.

Poster/Announcement

An **announcement** gives specific facts about an event. Like a news article, an announcement should answer the questions: *who?*, *what?*, *when?*, *where?*, and *why?* A **poster** is a type of announcement printed on a large sheet of paper and posted for the public to view.

Directions: Use the information on the poster to answer the questions on the next page.

Public Notice

Centerville Foster Care Agency
1592 Boulevard West, Room 507
Centerville, NY 10129

Anyone wishing to foster or adopt a child or children should schedule an appointment with the Centerville Foster Care Agency for an interview between the hours of 9:30 A.M. and 4:45 P.M. on Friday, October 15.

- Please bring documents showing who you are, where you live, and what kind of work you do.
- You will also need to bring a completed foster application or adoption application form. Forms are available from Centerville Foster Care Agency at the address above, Monday through Friday, 8:30 A.M.–5:00 P.M. You can also call our offices, and an application will be mailed to your home.
- This first interview will take approximately 45 minutes. Follow-up interviews will be scheduled as needed.
- Anyone unable to interview on the date and time assigned above may call our offices to schedule an interview at 555-1214, Monday through Friday, 8:30 A.M.–5:00 P.M.

We look forward to meeting you!

---

1. What event does this poster announce? **It announces the fact that the agency is holding interviews for anyone interested in fostering or adopting a child.**

2. Where should people go if they want an interview with the Centerville Foster Care Agency?
1592 Boulevard West, Room 507, Centerville, NY 10129

3. On what day and at what time will the interviews be held? **Friday, October 15, between 9:30 A.M. and 4:45 P.M.**

4. What should people bring with them to the interview?
People should bring documents showing who they are, where they live, and what kind of work they do. They also need a completed application form.

5. During what times may people call for an application to be mailed to them?
Monday through Friday, 8:30 A.M. to 5:00 P.M.

6. What should applicants do if they cannot be at the agency for an interview during the time specified in the poster?
They should call the office to schedule an interview.

7. If an applicant arrives at 10:30 A.M. for an interview, about what time can he or she expect the interview be done?
about 11:15 A.M.

8. Would a person have to have more than one interview before he or she could foster or adopt a child? Explain.
Yes, the poster mentions follow-up interviews so it's likely that more than one interview is needed.

9. What are two ways a person can get an application form? **A person can get an application form by going to the agency or by calling to have one mailed to him or her.**

10. What 5 "W" questions should an announcement answer?
who?, what?, when?, where?, and why?

Notes for Home: Your child answered questions about information on a poster. **Home Activity:** Find an announcement in the newspaper, such as a wedding announcement. With your child, discuss all the information the announcement provides.

Cause and Effect

- A **cause** is why something happens. An **effect** is what happens.
- A cause may have more than one effect. An effect may have more than one cause.
- Sometimes a clue word such as *because* or *since* signals a cause-effect relationship. Sometimes there is no clue word, and you need to think about why something happened.

Cause → Effect

Directions: Reread "Baseball and Brothers." Then complete the table. Provide each missing cause or effect.

Cause (Why did it happen?)	Effect (What happened?)
1. Girls can't play major-league baseball.	Meg says she hates baseball and thinks about giving it up.
2. Mrs. O'Malley loves the game, and she's the best player in her league.	Mrs. O'Malley still plays baseball.
Mrs. O'Malley wants Meg to stop thinking about her problems, and she wants Charles to eat more peas.	3. Mrs. O'Malley asks Meg to sing "Yankee Doodle" to Charles.
4. Meg has sung the song many times before.	Singing "Yankee Doodle" is very easy for Meg.
5. Meg loves baseball, even if there are no women in the professional leagues.	Meg finds it difficult to walk away from baseball.

 Notes for Home: Your child read a story and identified causes and effects. *Home Activity:* Help your child relate causes and effects by starting a sentence, such as *You eat breakfast because _____.* Ask your child to complete the sentence by giving a cause, or reason.

Cause and Effect **69**

Vocabulary

Directions: Read the want ad. Choose the word from the box that best completes each sentence. Write the word on the matching numbered line to the right.

JOB AVAILABLE

We have a position open for a school 1. _____.
Job involves keeping classrooms and 2. _____
clean. Not easy work! The principal will be
3. _____ you regularly to prove your worth.
Do a good job and be a 4. _____ part of our
team. Do a poor job and get 5. _____
immediately. Call 555-1234.

1. custodian
2. corridors
3. challenging
4. valuable
5. cut

Check the Words You Know
__ challenging
__ corridors
__ custodian
__ cut
__ valuable

Directions: Choose the word from the box that best matches each clue. Write the word in the puzzle.

Down
6. calling in question
7. long hallways
8. worth something
9. dismissed; let go

Across
10. a janitor

Write a Diary Entry
Imagine you are a school janitor. On a separate sheet of paper, write a diary entry that tells about your day. Use as many vocabulary words as you can. **Students' diary entries should make correct use of vocabulary words.**

 Notes for Home: Your child identified and used vocabulary words from "Meeting Mr. Henry." *Home Activity:* Take turns using each vocabulary word in a sentence.

70 Vocabulary

Cause and Effect

- A **cause** is why something happens. An **effect** is what happens.
- A cause may have more than one effect. An effect may have more than one cause.
- Sometimes a clue word such as *because* or *since* signals a cause-effect relationship. Sometimes there is no clue word and you need to think about why something happens.

Directions: Reread what happens in "Meeting Mr. Henry" when Jason plays imaginary baseball with Mr. Henry. Then answer the questions below. Think about each thing that happens and why it happens.

And then right there in the middle of Eberwoods School, old, gray-haired Mr. Henry, the school custodian, went into a full windup.

And as he did, something strange happened. He didn't look so old. He looked tall and young and powerful as he kicked high and came down over his head with a smooth motion and fired the imaginary ball. I swung. "Run!" he yelled.

I ran. I didn't look down the other corridor where the imaginary ball went. I lifted my feet and ran hard and hit first base with my left shoe. The base slid far down the smooth, waxed floor.

Mr. Henry laughed and slapped me on the back. "Now, if you'd moved like that when you hit that ground ball, you'd still be on your team. You run like that and you'll be getting your share of hits and then some."

From FINDING BUCK MC HENRY by Alfred Slote. Copyright © 1991 by Alfred Slote. Used by permission of HarperCollins Publishers.

1. What causes Mr. Henry to seem younger to Jason?
Mr. Henry kicks high, motions smoothly, and throws hard when he pitches. These activities make him seem younger.

2. Why is Jason able to run faster now than he did in the game?
He doesn't look to see where the ball goes before starting to run.

3. According to Mr. Henry, what is the reason Jason was cut from the team?
Jason hadn't run quickly enough after hitting the ball.

4. What effect does Mr. Henry's practice session have on Jason?
Jason begins to run more quickly.

5. How does Jason change by the end of the story? What causes that change? On a separate sheet of paper, explain your answer.
Possible answer: He has become more self-confident and eager to play baseball again. The causes are Mr. Henry's advice and practice session.

 Notes for Home: Your child used details from a story to identify causes and effects. *Home Activity:* Talk with your child about things that have happened to him or her or to you recently. Invite your child to explain what caused each thing to happen.

Cause and Effect **71**

Selection Test

Directions: Choose the best answer to each item. Mark the letter for the answer you have chosen.

Part 1: Vocabulary
Find the answer choice that means about the same as the underlined word in each sentence.

1. My parents were challenging my answer.
   A. finding difficult to understand
   B. adding details to
   C. demanding proof of
   D. restating in different words

2. We walked quickly down the corridors.
   F. long hallways
   G. flights of stairs
   H. long ramps
   J. narrow streets

3. Joe's father is a custodian.
   A. guard
   B. coach
   C. driver
   D. janitor

4. Of the six players, only Allie was cut from the team.
   F. hurt
   G. dismissed
   H. named
   J. chosen

5. He knew the old book was valuable.
   A. popular
   B. falling apart
   C. stolen
   D. worth money

Part 2: Comprehension
Use what you know about the story to answer each item.

6. Where was Jason's team playing ball?
   F. Eberwoods School
   G. Tiger Stadium
   H. The Grandstand
   J. Sampson Park School

7. Jason offered to carry the bases into the gym because he
   A. wanted to help Mr. Henry.
   B. enjoyed talking with Mr. Henry.
   C. wanted to avoid talking with his teammates.
   D. hoped to get some batting tips.

8. Which sentence best describes Mr. Henry?
   F. He's always joking and fooling around.
   G. He doesn't like his job much.
   H. He observes people carefully.
   J. He loves baseball cards.

9. In what way were Josh Gibson, Satchel Paige, and Cool Papa Bell alike?
   A. They were all great pitchers.
   B. They all played for the Pittsburgh Crawfords.
   C. They were all known for their speed.
   D. They all played center field.

10. Jason knows about famous baseball players from the past because he—
    F. collects baseball cards.
    G. has seen them play.
    H. plays baseball.
    J. has read books about them.

GO ON →

72 Selection Test

© Scott Foresman 5

11. What was Jason's problem as a baseball player, according to Mr. Henry?
   A. He took his eye off the ball.
   B. He didn't wait for a good pitch.
   C. He stood watching the ball after he hit it.
   D. He was too chubby to run fast.

12. What will Jason do when he gets to The Grandstand?
   F. sign up for a new team
   G. look for information about the players Mr. Henry knew
   H. sell some of his baseball cards
   J. find out about the newest baseball cards

13. Mr. Henry probably compares Jason with Willie Mays and Roy Campanella to—
   A. help him gain confidence in himself.
   B. convince him that he is bound for the major leagues.
   C. help him understand his mistakes.
   D. make him feel embarrassed.

14. What does Mr. Henry think about Jason?
   F. He could be a famous player some day.
   G. He is foolish to be so interested in baseball.
   H. He should play a position other than catcher.
   J. He will get to play on a team if he gets more hits.

15. What did Mr. Henry prove to Jason?
   A. Baseball is easy to play.
   B. He could see without looking.
   C. Willie Mays was born to play baseball.
   D. Keeping the school clean is more important than baseball.

STOP

Cause and Effect

- A **cause** is why something happens. An **effect** is what happens.
- A cause may have more than one effect. An effect may have more than one cause.
- Sometimes a clue word such as *because* or *since* signals a cause-effect relationship. Sometimes there is no clue word, and you need to think about why something happens.

Directions: Read the following story.

Jessie was very excited when he awoke that morning. He had hardly been able to sleep all night. Today was a special day because Grandpa had tickets to take him to a baseball game that night.

Around five o'clock, Grandpa and Jessie drove to the ball park. The game was sold out, so finding a parking spot was hard. Their seats were high in the bleachers, and Jessie could hardly see what was happening on the field. But that didn't stop him from eating four hot dogs during the game.

Who won the game? Jessie doesn't remember because he fell asleep by the sixth inning. But he *does* remember the stomachache he had the next day!

Directions: Complete the table. Think about each thing that happened and why it happened. Fill in each missing cause or effect.

Cause (Why It Happens)	Effect (What Happens)
Because Jessie is so excited,	he is hardly able to sleep.
1. **Because Grandpa is taking Jessie to a baseball game,**	today is a special day for Jessie.
Because the game is sold out,	2. **it is hard to find a parking space.**
Because the seats are far back,	3. **Jessie can hardly see what is happening on the field.**
4. **Because Jessie eats so many hot dogs,**	he gets a stomachache.
5. **Because Jessie fell asleep by the sixth inning,**	he doesn't know who won the game.

 Notes for Home: Your child read a story and used story details to identify causes and effects. **Home Activity:** Read a brief newspaper or magazine article with your child. Ask your child to identify events that are described in the article and tell the reason why each event happened.

Drawing Conclusions

REVIEW

Directions: Read the story. Then read each question about the story. Choose the best answer to each question. Mark the letter for the answer you have chosen.

The First Game

Today would be Amy's first game in the Little League. She had been awake since before the sun came up. She had dressed before breakfast. She wondered if her uniform still fit right. She brushed her teeth three times. She walked Champ twice.

At last, it was time to go to the ballpark. Amy was quiet in the car. She didn't even notice her favorite songs on the radio. She bit her nails as her mother drove her to the ballpark.

"Stop that," Mother said. "You're going to be just fine." Amy wanted to believe that. Mother was usually right. She tried to think of other things as she bent her glove back and forth.

At the park, Amy joined her teammates on their side of the field. They got together and started their team cheer. They started practicing swinging the bats. They practiced throwing the ball. They listened to their coach remind them of their plans for winning the game.

From the stands she could hear cries of, "Go, Amy! Go, Fireball!" Fireball was a nickname her cousins had given her when she was little. She liked the nickname and was glad her team and the fans used it.

During the game, Amy didn't have time to worry. She struck out twelve batters. She got a single at her first turn at bat. Then she got a double in her next turn. By the end of the game, Amy wore a smile that no one could remove.

1. Before the beginning of the game, Amy feels—
   A. hungry.
   B. tired.
   C. nervous.
   D. confused.

2. Amy tries to think of other things because she—
   F. is bored in the car.
   G. wants to relax.
   H. doesn't like baseball.
   J. doesn't like her glove.

3. Amy's position on the team is—
   A. catcher.
   B. outfield.
   C. first base.
   D. pitcher.

4. Amy's playing is—
   F. poor.
   G. average.
   H. good.
   J. uneven.

5. After the game, Amy feels—
   A. embarrassed.
   B. happy.
   C. nervous.
   D. angry.

 **Notes for Home:** Your child read a story and drew conclusions based on its details. **Home Activity:** Read a story together with your child. Afterward, invite your child to tell you what conclusions he or she can draw about how a character feels or why an event happened.

Writing Across Texts

Directions: Review "From the Diary of Leigh Botts" and "Meeting Mr. Henry." In the table below, make notes about what happens at the beginning, middle, and end of both stories. Think about what the boys learn from their experiences. Do they solve their problems? How do they feel? **Possible answers given.**

Leigh	Jason
Beginning	
He feels sorry for himself since someone has been stealing his lunch.	1. **He feels bad because he has just been dropped from the team.**
Middle	
2. **He decides to make an alarm and concentrates on his invention until he makes something that works.**	3. **He discovers that not everyone who is good gets recognition, and that he's better than he thought.**
End	
4. **He doesn't solve the problem, but gets attention and feels better for doing something productive.**	5. **He decides to learn about these ball players and is determined to work harder at his game.**

Write a Compare/Contrast Paragraph

Like Leigh Botts, Jason finds himself with a problem. Trace what happens in the beginning, middle, and end of both stories. Compare how the boys face their problems and explain what both boys learn from their experiences. Use the information in the table above to compare the two boys. Write your paragraph on a separate sheet of paper. **Possible answer might include: Leigh works on a lunch box alarm that brings him attention; Jason decides to pay attention and play harder. Both learn that working to solve a problem is better than just feeling sorry for themselves.**

 Notes for Home: Your child used information from stories to compare and contrast characters and show what the characters learned. **Home Activity:** As you read stories with your child, compare and contrast characters from different stories.

© Scott Foresman 5

Name _____

Meeting Mr. Henry

Grammar: Declarative and Interrogative Sentences

REVIEW

Directions: Write the correct end mark at the end of each sentence. Then, write **D** on the line to the left if the sentence is declarative. Write **I** if it is an interrogative sentence.

I	1. Did you know that the first World Series game was played in 1903 **?**
D	2. The Pittsburgh Pirates played the Boston Red Sox **.**
I	3. Would 100,000 fans be a big crowd today **?**
D	4. Pittsburgh won 5 to 3 **.**
I	5. What very famous person was on the Boston team **?**
D	6. His name was Cy Young **.**
D	7. Winners of the first World Series were each paid $1,182 **.**
D	8. Now a Cy Young Award is presented every year **.**
I	9. Who do you think receives the award **?**
D	10. It goes to the best pitcher in the American League and the National League **.**

Directions: Rewrite each of these declarative sentences as interrogative sentences. Be sure to use the correct end punctuation. **Possible answers given.**

11. The World Series games are the best games.
Are the World Series games the best games?

12. I try to watch every minute of every single game.
Do you try to watch every minute of every single game?

13. Tickets for the World Series games are hard to get.
Are tickets for the World Series games hard to get?

14. All the games are shown live on television.
Are all the games shown live on television?

15. I think baseball players deserve the fame they get.
Do you think baseball players deserve the fame they get?

Notes for Home: Your child punctuated and wrote declarative sentences (statements) and interrogative sentences (questions). *Home Activity:* Ask your child several questions. Have your child change each question into a statement.

Grammar: Declarative and Interrogative Sentences **77**

Name _____

Meeting Mr. Henry

Grammar: Compound and Complex Sentences

A **simple sentence** expresses one complete thought. A **compound sentence** contains two simple sentences joined by a comma and a word such as *and, but,* and *or.*

Simple sentences: Baseball players run bases. Custodians sweep floors.
Compound sentence: Baseball players run bases, and custodians sweep floors.

A **complex sentence** is made up of a simple sentence and another part. In a complex sentence, the other part cannot stand alone as a simple sentence. The other part is joined to the sentence with a word such as *if, because,* or *when.*

Complex sentence: When a home run is hit, the crowd cheers.
not a sentence   simple sentence

Directions: Write whether each sentence is **compound** or **complex.**

compound	1. Babe Ruth hit many home runs, but it took much effort.
complex	2. If he struck out, he tried even harder the next time.
compound	3. He had many hits, but not all of them were home runs.
complex	4. When he became too old to play, he retired.
complex	5. Because of his talent, Babe Ruth became very famous.
compound	6. Fans loved to see home runs, and they loved the great hitter.

Directions: Choose the group of words that will complete each sentence and makes sense. Write the complete sentence on the line. Add a comma, if necessary.

7. You can hit the ball over the fence _____.
(because you need to practice first/but you need to practice first)
You can hit the ball over the fence, but you need to practice first.

8. The ball was pitched _____.
(after the game was over/and the batter struck out)
The ball was pitched, and the batter struck out.

9. Although many players hit the ball hard, _____.
(but they sometimes hit home runs/only a few can hit home runs)
Although many players hit the ball hard, only a few can hit home runs.

10. Many people play baseball _____.
(if the player is good/but only a few play professionally)
Many people play baseball, but only a few play professionally.

Notes for Home: Your child identified compound and complex sentences. *Home Activity:* Say a simple sentence, such as *I went to work today.* Challenge your child to expand it by changing it into either a complex or a compound sentence.

78 Grammar: Compound and Complex Sentences

Name _____

Meeting Mr. Henry

Grammar: Compound and Complex Sentences

Directions: Make a compound sentence by joining the simple sentences, using a comma and one of these words: *and, but,* or *or.*

1. It was early in the season. We were playing our first game.
It was early in the season, and we were playing our first game.

2. Our best player strolled to the plate. She hit a home run.
Our best player strolled to the plate, and she hit a home run.

3. The fans rose to their feet. The ball went over the fence.
The fans rose to their feet, and the ball went over the fence.

4. Both teams played their best. Only one team can win the game.
Both teams played their best, but only one team can win the game.

5. Our team practiced every day. We still lost the game.
Our team practiced every day, but we still lost the game.

Directions: For each complex sentence, tell whether the underlined part of the sentence could stand on its own as a simple sentence. Write **S** if it is a sentence. Write **NS** if it is not a sentence.

S	6. If baseball had not been invented, <u>our lives would be very different</u>.
NS	7. <u>Because the runner was fast</u>, she made it to first base.
NS	8. Few people are great players <u>when they first play the game</u>.
S	9. After practicing for many years, <u>he became a good player</u>.
NS	10. <u>When fans cheer</u>, the players feel appreciated.

Write a Paragraph

Think of a baseball game or other sporting event that you have watched. On a separate sheet of paper, describe the game. Include compound and complex sentences in your description.
Check that students have correctly formed compound and complex sentences.

Notes for Home: Your child formed compound sentences and identified parts of a complex sentence. *Home Activity:* Look for examples of compound and complex sentences in a newspaper. Have your child underline the sentence parts that can stand alone as a sentence.

Grammar: Compound and Complex Sentences **79**

Name _____

Meeting Mr. Henry

Grammar: Compound and Complex Sentences

RETEACHING

Read the simple sentences. The subjects are underlined once and verbs are underlined twice.

1. <u>Ed</u> <u>collects</u> buttons.   2. <u>Jan</u> <u>saves</u> string.

Sentences 1 and 2 are joined by a comma and the conjunction *and* below. The comma and conjunction that join them in the following compound sentence are circled.

3. Ed collects buttons, and Jan saves string.

Read each group of words

4. If it rains this afternoon   5. Margo will stay at the library.

The first group of words cannot stand alone as a complete sentence. The second group of words is a simple sentence. Both groups of words make up the following **complex sentence.**

6. If it rains this afternoon, Margo will stay at the library.

A **compound sentence** contains two or more simple sentences joined by a conjunction. A compound sentence contains at least two complete subjects and two complete predicates. A **complex sentence** is made up of a simple sentence and another part. The other part is joined to the sentence with a word such as *if, because,* or *when.*

Directions: Write **compound** or **complex** for each sentence.

1. Morris opened the sardine can, and Lee toasted the bread.   compound
2. Mark sleeps late because today is Saturday.   complex
3. Victor will do his homework, or he will draw a picture.   compound
4. The light blinked quickly when she flipped the switch.   complex
5. If the weather is nice, we will continue our walk.   complex
6. Lee cooked dinner, and Linnea made dessert.   compound
7. I mopped the floor, and my sister washed the dishes.   compound
8. Maureen and Joe swept the stairs because their father asked them to do it.   complex
9. Jan will feed the dog, or her brother will do it.   compound
10. If you need help, I will walk your dog.   complex

Notes for Home: Your child distinguished between compound and complex sentences. *Home Activity:* After a discussion of the topic, have your child write an article about housework. Be sure your child uses at least two compound and two complex sentences.

80 Grammar: Compound and Complex Sentences

© Scott Foresman 5

Name _____

Meeting Mr. Henry

Grammar: Compound and Complex Sentences

Directions: Underline each compound sentence. Circle each complex sentence.

1. Canada is our northern neighbor, and Mexico is our southern neighbor.
2. Mexico has a population of over 100 million people, but Canada has fewer than 40 million.
3. (Although you may see a bullfight in Mexico, you probably wouldn't see one in Canada.)
4. The capital of Canada is Ottawa, and the capital of Mexico is Mexico City.
5. (I think both countries are fascinating because of their unique cultures.)
6. (If I ever have the chance, I will visit both countries.)

Directions: Write a compound sentence. Use the conjunction in ( ) and the two simple sentences.

7. The Aztecs ruled ancient Mexico. They built a city named Tenochtitlán. (and)
The Aztecs ruled ancient Mexico, and they built a city named Tenochtitlán.

8. Cold chocolate was the Aztecs' favorite drink. Only the wealthy could buy it. (but)
Cold chocolate was the Aztecs' favorite drink, but only the wealthy could buy it.

Directions: Combine each pair of word groups to make complex sentences. Use the word in ( ). You may need to change some capital letters to lowercase.

9. You visit Toronto, Ontario   You may take a trip to Niagara Falls. (if)
If you visit Toronto, Ontario, you may take a trip to Niagara Falls.

10. Niagara Falls may be crowded when you visit it   It is such a popular place. (because)
Niagara Falls may be crowded when you visit it because it is such a popular place.

Write a Story

On a separate sheet of paper, write a story about two cities or two countries. Use compound and complex sentences in your writing.
Check that students have used compound and complex sentences.

Notes for Home: Your child created both compound and complex sentences. **Home Activity:** Listen for examples of compound and complex sentences in radio or TV commercials. Have your child tell how he or she knows which sentence is compound and which is complex.

Grammar: Compound and Complex Sentences **81**

Name _____

Meeting Mr. Henry

Phonics: Common Word Patterns

Directions: Read each word below. Some words have the pattern **consonant-vowel-consonant-e** as in **game**, which forms a **long vowel** sound. Other words have the pattern **vowel-consonant-consonant-vowel** as in **number**, which has a **short vowel** sound for the first vowel. Sort the words according to their word patterns. Write each word in the correct column.

| base | powder | bike | elbow | five |
| center | harder | lesson | home | mule |

CVCe game

1. base
2. bike
3. home
4. five
5. mule

VCCV number

6. center
7. powder
8. harder
9. lesson
10. elbow

Directions: Circle all the words that have a pattern like **game**.

11. It was (time) for the (game) to start.
12. With a big swing, she (made) a great hit.
13. It was a (race) to first (base.)
14. She (made) it to first just in (time.)
15. I (like) to watch Lisa (make) such good plays.

Directions: Circle all the words that have a pattern like **number**.

16. One (lesson) we can learn from baseball is how to work as a team.
17. Mike puts all the bases in a big (basket.)
18. The player in (center) field hit a home run.
19. "(Batter) up!" shouted the coach.
20. There have been many great players in the (history) of baseball.

Notes for Home: Your child learned to recognize some common word patterns such as *CVCe* (home) and *VCCV* (basket). **Home Activity:** Look for these patterns and vowel sounds in a variety of print material such as signs, food packages, billboards, and store names.

82 Phonics: Common Word Patterns

Name _____

Meeting Mr. Henry

Spelling: Long Vowels a, i, o

Pretest Directions: Fold back the page along the dotted line. On the blanks, write the spelling words as they are dictated. When you have finished the test, unfold the page and check your words.

1. brain
2. plain
3. claim
4. complain
5. favorite
6. stranger
7. aliens
8. vacation
9. sidewalk
10. slide
11. survive
12. crime
13. bowling
14. owner
15. arrow
16. snowball
17. whole
18. globe
19. antelope
20. slope

1. Use your **brain** to think.
2. I draw on **plain** paper.
3. What seat did you **claim**?
4. Don't **complain**, just fix it.
5. Spring is my **favorite** season.
6. Fact can be **stranger** than fiction.
7. The **aliens** went home.
8. I want to go on a **vacation**.
9. We ran on the **sidewalk**.
10. He slid down the **slide**.
11. You need water to **survive**.
12. Stealing is a **crime**.
13. Lin is at the **bowling** alley.
14. Who is the **owner** of this dog?
15. The **arrow** points up.
16. She threw a **snowball**.
17. Lisa ate the **whole** pie.
18. Spin the **globe**.
19. The **antelope** plays on the range.
20. The **slope** is steep.

Notes for Home: Your child took a pretest on words that have the long vowels a, i, and o. **Home Activity:** Help your child learn misspelled words before the final test. Your child can underline the word parts that caused the problems and concentrate on those parts.

Spelling: Long Vowels *a, i, o* **83**

Name _____

Meeting Mr. Henry

Spelling: Long Vowels a, i, o

Word List

brain	favorite	sidewalk	bowling	whole
plain	stranger	slide	owner	globe
claim	aliens	survive	arrow	antelope
complain	vacation	crime	snowball	slope

Directions: Choose the words from the box that have the **long a** sound. Write each word in the correct column. **Order may vary.**

Long a spelled ai

1. brain
2. plain
3. claim
4. complain

Long a spelled a

5. favorite
6. stranger
7. aliens
8. vacation

Directions: Choose the word from the box that rhymes with the underlined word or words and completes the sentence. Write the word on the line to the left.

slope	9. I certainly <u>hope</u> you don't fall down a _____.
sidewalk	10. If I were you, <u>I'd walk</u> on the _____.
owner	11. A gift's <u>donor</u> is usually its _____.
bowling	12. You do some <u>strolling</u> in a game of _____.
snowball	13. There is <u>no ball</u> that stings like a _____.
whole	14. Will you eat a <u>roll</u>, either half or _____?
slide	15. It's fun to <u>ride</u> on a slippery _____.
arrow	16. If it's sharp and <u>narrow</u>, it might be an _____.
antelope	17. "Sorry, you <u>can't elope</u>," said the papa _____.
crime	18. It's never a good <u>time</u> to commit a _____.
globe	19. I bought a long <u>robe</u> and a brand-new _____.
survive	20. If you're still <u>alive</u>, you've managed to _____.

Notes for Home: Your child spelled words that have the long a, i, or o sound (*brain, stranger, slide, arrow, slope*). **Home Activity:** Together with your child, name other words that have the long a, i, or o sound. See how many of these words your child can spell correctly.

84 Spelling: Long Vowels *a, i, o*

© Scott Foresman 5

Name _____

Meeting Mr. Henry

Spelling: Long Vowels *a, i, o*

Directions: Proofread this letter. Find five spelling mistakes. Use the proofreading marks to correct each mistake.

Dear Aunt Esther,

On vacation, Dad took our whoal family to our first baseball game. Now it's my favorite sport—even more than boling! It's so cool how players slide! After the game, we met the team oner and some players on the sidewalk. I can't complain about having this much fun!

Love,

Dave

≡	Make a capital.
/	Make a small letter.
∧	Add something.
◞	Take out something.
⊙	Add a period.
¶	Begin a new paragraph.

Spelling Tip

whole   owner
Remember that **long o** can be spelled with **consonant-vowel-consonant-e**, as in **whole**, but it can also be spelled with **ow**, as in **owner**. Remember which spelling to use.

Word List

brain	survive
plain	crime
claim	bowling
complain	owner
favorite	arrow
stranger	snowball
aliens	whole
vacation	globe
sidewalk	antelope
slide	slope

Write a Letter

Imagine you are Dave's Aunt Esther. On a separate sheet of paper, write a friendly letter back to Dave. Try to use at least five of your spelling words. **Answers will vary, but each letter should include at least five spelling words.**

Notes for Home: Your child spelled words that have the long *a, i,* or *o* sounds (*brain, stranger, slide, arrow, slope*). **Home Activity:** Say each spelling word aloud. Have your child tell whether the word has a long *a, i,* or *o* sound. Then have your child spell the word.

Spelling: Long Vowels *a, i, o*   85

Name _____

Meeting Mr. Henry

Spelling: Long Vowels *a, i, o*

REVIEW

Word List

brain	favorite	sidewalk	bowling	whole
plain	stranger	slide	owner	globe
claim	aliens	survive	arrow	antelope
complain	vacation	crime	snowball	slope

Directions: Choose the word from the box that best completes each sentence. Write the word on the line to the left.

___globe___ 1. Baseball is a popular game all over the _____.

___favorite___ 2. It has often been called America's _____ pastime.

___bowling___ 3. Baseball is a more popular sport than _____.

___whole___ 4. A _____ baseball game lasts nine innings.

___slope___ 5. The pitcher stands on a small _____ called a mound.

___survive___ 6. A good baseball pitcher can _____ an entire game.

___crime___ 7. In baseball, it's not a _____ to steal bases.

___slide___ 8. Runners _____ into bases and kick up dirt!

___arrow___ 9. A good runner moves as swiftly as a speeding _____.

___complain___ 10. A good sport doesn't _____ if he or she loses.

Directions: Choose the word from the box that best matches each clue. Write the word on the line.

___antelope___ 11. It's a very fast animal.

___aliens___ 12. They're strangers from another planet!

___stranger___ 13. He's new in town.

___owner___ 14. She's the one who bought it.

___snowball___ 15. It's round and cold.

___brain___ 16. It lets you think.

___plain___ 17. It's not fancy.

___vacation___ 18. It's a rest from work.

___sidewalk___ 19. It's made of cement and is often found in front of houses.

___claim___ 20. It's something you make when you say, "I didn't do that."

Notes for Home: Your child spelled words that have the long *a, i,* or *o* sound (*brain, stranger, slide, arrow, slope*). **Home Activity:** Pick a spelling word. Give a hint about the word. (Example: *It's a long a word. It's in your head.*) See if your child can guess the word. (*brain*)

86   Spelling: Long Vowels *a, i, o*

Name _____

Meeting Mr. Henry

Technology: Card Catalog/Library Database

Libraries list the materials in their collections using a **card catalog** or a **computer database.** You can search for materials by author, title, or subject. Be sure to type words carefully when using a database. If you are not sure exactly what you want, you can use key words in the title, author's name, or subject to search the database. Always use the last name of an author first. Each listing will have a special **call number.** Use the call number to locate the item in the library.

Directions: Look at the starting screen for searching the library database below. Tell what number and words you should type to get information about each book or group of books.

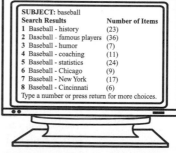

Search Our Public Library
1 Title (exact search)
2 Title (key words)
3 Author (exact name)
4 Author (key words)
5 Subject (exact search)
6 Subject (key words)
Type a number or press return for more choices.

1. books about the baseball player Babe Ruth ___5; Babe Ruth___

2. books written by the baseball player Joe DiMaggio ___3; DiMaggio, Joe___

3. books about how to coach baseball ___6; baseball AND coaching___

4. a book called *Learning How to Play Baseball* ___1; Learning How to Play Baseball___

5. a book you heard about that you remember has the word *pitching* in the title
___2; pitching___

Research and Study Skills: Technology: Card Catalog/Library Database   87

Name _____

Meeting Mr. Henry

If you search on a broad subject category, the computer may give you categories of choices. For example, the computer screen below shows that a library has 23 books or other items about the history of baseball.

Directions: Use the information on the computer screen to answer the questions that follow.

SUBJECT: baseball

Search Results	Number of Items
1 Baseball - history	(23)
2 Baseball - famous players	(36)
3 Baseball - humor	(7)
4 Baseball - coaching	(11)
5 Baseball - statistics	(24)
6 Baseball - Chicago	(9)
7 Baseball - New York	(17)
8 Baseball - Cincinnati	(6)

Type a number or press return for more choices.

6. What number should you type to find books about New York baseball teams? ___7___

7. What number should you type to find information about when baseball was invented? ___1___

8. What number should you type to find books about the baseball player Hank Aaron? ___2___

9. If you wanted to search for more books about baseball by Alfred Slote, the author of "Meeting Mr. Henry," would a subject search be the best way to search? Explain.
No, it would be better to search by the author's name than subject.

10. Do you think it is easier to use a library database or to look at cards in a card catalog? Explain.
Answers may vary. Check that students support their answers.

Notes for Home: Your child learned how to use an online card catalog at a library. **Home Activity:** Ask your child to make a list of five topics. At the library, work with your child to use the online catalog to find materials about these topics.

88   Research and Study Skills: Technology: Card Catalog/Library Database

© Scott Foresman 5

---

700   Answers

Name _____

Eloise Greenfield

Author's Purpose

- The **author's purpose** is the reason an author has for writing. The purpose is usually not stated directly in the writing. Sometimes an author has more than one purpose for writing.
- Four common purposes for writing are to persuade (convince), to inform (explain something), to entertain (amuse), or to express (describe something to help you see or feel a scene).

Directions: Reread "First Steps." Then complete the chart. For each passage given, write the author's purpose or purposes for writing. Choose from these purposes: to persuade, to inform, to express strong feeling, to entertain. You may use a purpose more than once.

Passage	Author's Purpose
I remember the very first time I walked by myself. My sister Alexis was in high school then.	1. to inform
I was kind of scared, but I wanted to do it, so I pushed up off the arms of my wheelchair.	2. to inform
I was so happy I'd made it that far. I looked up to heaven and said, "Thank you."	3. to express strong feeling
Then I had to walk just a few more steps to get to the door—and I did it!	4. to express strong feeling
She was so surprised. She burst out laughing and gave me a big hug.	5. to entertain; to express strong feeling

 Notes for Home: Your child learned about the purposes an author may have for writing. *Home Activity:* Read the TV listings with your child. Pick out various television programs and discuss the purpose of each one.

Author's Purpose **91**

Name _____

Eloise Greenfield

Vocabulary

Directions: Read the announcement. Choose the word from the box that best completes each sentence. Write the word on the matching numbered line to the right.

■PUBLIC NOTICE■

A new apartment 1. _____ is being built at 300 Main Street in our 2. _____. The town 3. _____ has ruled that any local 4. _____ may apply for an apartment there. If you are interested and have not yet 5. _____, please do so by December 31. Applications are available at City Hall.

1. project
2. community
3. council
4. resident
5. applied

Check the Words You Know
__ applied
__ community
__ council
__ in-between
__ project
__ resident

Directions: Choose the word from the box that best matches each clue. Write the letters of the word on the blanks. The boxed letters spell something that many people in apartments pay.

6. a group of apartment buildings
7. being between
8. a group of people with power to make rules
9. people living in the same area
10. a person with a permanent home

6. p r o j e c t
7. i n - b e t w e e n
8. c o u n c i l
9. c o m m u n i t y
10. r e s i d e n t

What many people in apartments pay: r e n t s

Write a Set of Rules
On a separate sheet of paper, write a set of rules you'd like to see enforced in your town. It could be rules about keeping the neighborhood clean or quiet or about keeping dogs on leashes. Use as many vocabulary words as you can. **Students' rules should make correct use of vocabulary words.**

 Notes for Home: Your child identified and used vocabulary words from "Eloise Greenfield." *Home Activity:* Read an article with your child. Encourage him or her to figure out the meanings of unfamiliar words using context clues—words surrounding the unfamiliar words.

92 Vocabulary

Name _____

Eloise Greenfield

Author's Purpose

- The **author's purpose** is the reason an author has for writing. Sometimes an author has more than one reason for writing. The author's purpose is usually not stated directly.
- Often an author's purpose is to persuade (convince), to inform (explain something), to entertain (amuse), or to express (describe something to help you see or feel a scene).

1. Reread "Eloise Greenfield." What is the author's purpose or purposes in telling the story?

Possible answer: Her purpose is to inform readers about life for African Americans in the 1920s and 1930s.

Students may choose more than one purpose. Accept answers that are reasonably supported. Possible answers given.
Directions: Read each paragraph. For each one, identify the author's purpose. Put an X on the line beside your choice or choices. Then explain your choice.

2. Everyone has the right to decent housing. Too many people in our community are living on the streets. Proposition 37 will solve this problem. It provides for low-income housing without new taxes. So vote *yes* on 37!

___ entertain   **X** persuade   ___ inform   ___ express
The author wants to persuade readers to vote yes on 37.

3. If you can't finish your ice cream, my dog will gladly do it for you. Last night he ate my sundae while my back was turned. Can't finish that cone? Give my dog a call. He's got a beeper.

X entertain   ___ persuade   ___ inform   ___ express
The author presents a silly image of his dog to entertain readers.

4. I love my neighborhood. On summer evenings, a warm glow settles over the street. The old folks sit and rock on their porches. The little kids ride bikes in the street. The moms gossip on the sidewalk. It's the homiest, friendliest place you'll ever see.

___ entertain   ___ persuade   ___ inform   **X** express
The author expresses pride in his or her neighborhood.

5. Beginning in the 1890s, many African Americans left their homes in the South and moved to northern cities. They moved to escape poverty and discrimination. Historians call this mass movement the Great Migration.

___ entertain   ___ persuade   **X** inform   ___ express
The author presents factual information to tell about the Great Migration.

 Notes for Home: Your child read a story and several paragraphs, and then determined each author's purpose for writing. *Home Activity:* Look through various parts of a magazine or newspaper with your child. Ask him or her to identify the purpose for writing each feature.

Author's Purpose **93**

Name _____

Eloise Greenfield

Selection Test

Directions: Choose the best answer to each item. Mark the letter for the answer you have chosen.

Part 1: Vocabulary
Find the answer choice that means about the same as the underlined word in each sentence.

1. She <u>applied</u> for a job.
   A. wished
   B. had the skills
   (C) made a request
   D. studied

2. He was the town's <u>resident</u> artist.
   (F) living in a place permanently
   G. highly regarded
   H. traveling from place to place
   J. living alone

3. Mae is a member of the <u>council</u>.
   A. a club for singers
   B. a group of employees
   (C) a group of people who make rules
   D. a club for checkers players

4. That summer was an <u>in-between</u> time.
   F. having a quality of sadness
   (G) being or coming in the middle
   H. not interesting; boring
   J. showing strong feeling

5. They lived in a <u>project</u>.
   A. a grid formed by several streets
   B. a place where people live outdoors
   C. an unfinished building or group of buildings
   (D) a group of apartment buildings built and run as a unit

6. He was a leader in the <u>community</u>.
   (F) a group of people living in one place
   G. a group of people with the same last name
   H. a band or company, especially a group of performers
   J. a group of persons that has the duty to make laws

Part 2: Comprehension
Use what you know about the selection to answer each item.

7. Where was Eloise Greenfield's father when she was born?
   A. at home helping out
   B. working at Mr. Slim Gordon's store
   (C) downtown playing checkers
   D. out of town

8. Langston Terrace was located in—
   F. Parmele, North Carolina.
   (G) Washington, D.C.
   H. Chicago.
   J. Atlanta.

9. From her stories about school, you can tell that Eloise was a—
   (A) quiet child.
   B. good student.
   C. popular girl.
   D. troublemaker.

10. Why did Eloise's parents want to move to Langston Terrace?
    F. They had friends in the neighborhood.
    G. It was named for a famous black congressman.
    (H) They needed more space.
    J. The houses were very beautiful.

11. How was her home at Langston Terrace different from other places Eloise had lived?
    A. It was in the city.
    B. It had only one room.
    C. Daddy's cousin Lillie was there.
    (D) Her family had a whole house to themselves.

 GO ON

94 Selection Test

© Scott Foresman 5

12. Why was it difficult for families at Langston Terrace to save enough money to buy a house?
  (F.) Whenever they earned more money, their rents increased.
  G. They had to pay fees for the many social activities.
  H. The rents there were higher than in other parts of the city.
  J. They were too busy enjoying life to think about saving money.

13. What happened after Eloise's sister Vedie was born?
  A. Eloise went to a new school.
  (B.) The family moved to a three-bedroom house.
  C. Eloise celebrated her ninth birthday.
  D. The family moved to Washington.

14. The author tells about two events from when she was in grade school. She probably chose these particular events to help the reader understand—
  F. what kind of schools she went to.
  G. why she became famous.
  (H.) what kind of child she was.
  J. what life was like in olden times.

15. In this selection, the author's main purpose is to—
  A. explain the difficulties of being poor.
  (B.) share childhood memories.
  C. give information about housing in the city.
  D. entertain the reader with humor.

Author's Purpose

- The **author's purpose** is the reason an author has for writing. Sometimes an author has more than one reason for writing. The author's purpose is usually not stated directly.

- Often an author's purpose is to persuade (convince), to inform (explain something), to entertain (amuse), or to express (describe something to help you see or feel a scene).

Directions: Read each brief passage.

1. I was in my local bakery this morning and a duck walked in. He ordered a doughnut and told the owner, "Put it on my bill."

2. Students in this school want the right to plan the cafeteria menu. After all, it's the students who have to eat the food. We know best what we like. So let us choose the foods.

3. Last night I watched a great fireworks display in the neighborhood. Dozens of rockets shot up in the sky and exploded like crazy rainbows. The steady boom-boom of firecrackers sounded like beating drums.

4. Today our town council approved money to put up a stoplight at the corner of Broad and Main Streets. The corner has been the site of several accidents in recent years.

5. I visited our town library, and I think they should definitely order new books. Most of the books they have now are at least five to ten years old. We need new books to keep up with current times around here!

Directions: Complete the diagram. Think about the author's purpose in each passage above. Write whether the purpose is to persuade, inform, entertain, or express. Explain each answer. **Possible answers given.**

Author's Purpose	Explanation
1. entertain	The author tells a funny story about a talking duck.
2. persuade	The author wants the school to let the students choose the food.
3. express	The author conveys the excitement of the fireworks.
4. inform	The author presents factual information about the funding of a stoplight.
5. persuade	The author wants to persuade the reader that the library needs new books.

Notes for Home: Your child read paragraphs and determined the author's purpose for writing. **Home Activity:** Read a short story with your child. Have your child identify the author's purpose in writing the story.

Sequence

REVIEW

Directions: Read the story. Then read each question about the story. Choose the best answer to each question. Mark the letter for the answer you have chosen.

My New Home

As I think about living in Hicksville, I vividly remember the day we moved there. I hadn't known much about the town, and I didn't know anything at all about the neighborhood. Mom seemed to know I would like it. I was both scared and excited. Would I like the house? Would I make new friends?

I could hardly wait to see my new home. As soon as we got there, I raced from my parents' car and went straight into the house. It looked so much bigger than the old apartment.

"Where's my room?" I asked. Dad pointed to the long staircase.

"At the top of the stairs and to the right," Dad said.

I found my room right away because I recognized my boxes. My clothes, my music, and all my other things were in those boxes. As I began unpacking a box of school clothes, I heard a barking noise outside. I looked through my window.

I couldn't believe it. In the next yard were two dogs. I loved dogs, although I had none of my own. I went outside and looked over the backyard fence. A boy about my own age was feeding one of the dogs. The dog glanced at me and wagged its tail but kept eating. The boy came over to the fence.

"Hi," the boy said. "You must be the new neighbor."

1. The first thing the narrator does after getting to the new house is—
  A. go to the narrator's room.
  B. look out the window.
  (C.) leave the car.
  D. hear a dog bark.

2. In the room, the narrator first—
  (F.) starts to unpack.
  G. sees the window.
  H. hears dogs barking.
  J. meets the boy next door.

3. Just before looking out the window, the narrator—
  A. goes downstairs.
  B. hears the neighbors talking.
  (C.) hears barking.
  D. carries a box.

4. The narrator goes outside and looks over the fence because he or she—
  F. wants to meet a neighbor.
  G. is bored.
  H. hears voices.
  (J.) loves dogs.

5. The last thing the narrator does in the story is—
  A. return to the car.
  (B.) meet the neighbor.
  C. meet the dogs.
  D. unpack a box.

Notes for Home: Your child read a story, and then identified the order in which events happened. **Home Activity:** With your child, read a magazine or newspaper article that tells about an event that took place. Then have your child describe the event to you, in his or her own words, in order.

Writing Across Texts

Directions: A story you read recently was called "Looking for a Home." The same title might also fit Eloise Greenfield's autobiography. Complete the table below by listing details about each selection. **Possible answers given.**

Questions	Eloise Greenfield	Looking for a Home
What is the setting for each selection?	Langston Terrace	farms in Texas
Who is the main character?	1. Eloise Greenfield	2. Lee Nailling
What genre, or type of writing, is each selection?	3. autobiography	4. biography
With whom did the main character of each selection live?	5. family, other relatives	6. chain of different families who adopted him
What was each main character looking for?	7. a comfortable home, close neighbors	8. anyone who would care for him and care about him
How did the main character feel about his or her experiences?	9. happy, secure	10. untrusting after many disappointments, but happy once he found a true home

Write a Comparison/Contrast Paragraph

Compare and contrast the experiences of the main characters of the two selections. Write your paragraph on a separate sheet of paper. **Paragraphs will vary. Check that students use the information in the table to compare and contrast the experiences of Eloise Greenfield and Lee Nailling, recognizing that their experiences were quite different, but they both found themselves in a happy home in the end.**

Notes for Home: Your child used information from different texts to compare and contrast the experiences of two people. **Home Activity:** As you read stories and articles, encourage your child to compare and contrast characters.

Eloise Greenfield

REVIEW

Grammar: Imperative and Exclamatory Sentences

Directions: Write the correct end mark at the end of each sentence. Write **I** on the line to the left if the sentence is an imperative sentence. Write **E** if it is an exclamatory sentence.

I	1. Look around your neighborhood ___ .
I	2. Take your time ___ .
E	3. What a big surprise you'll find ___ !
I	4. Stop and smell the sweet air ___ .
E	5. These flowers are beautiful ___ !
I	6. Look closely at the tall building across the street ___ .
E	7. It must have forty floors ___ !
I	8. Listen to the music coming from the band stand ___ .
E	9. Those musicians are really great ___ !
E	10. That trumpet player hits the highest notes ___ !

Directions: Write four imperative sentences that explain to someone else how to do something. Then write an exclamatory sentence. Remember to begin each sentence with a capital letter and end each one with the correct punctuation.   **Possible answers given.**

11. **Put your dog in a tub of soapy water.**

12. **Use a sponge to wash him.**

13. **Rinse him off carefully.**

14. **Dry him with several towels.**

15. **This is much harder than it sounds!**

Notes for Home: Your child identified sentences that gave commands and expressed strong feelings. *Home Activity:* Tone of voice is an important part of reading imperative and exclamatory sentences. Take turns creating and saying these types of sentences aloud.

Grammar: Imperative and Exclamatory Sentences **99**

Eloise Greenfield

Grammar: Correcting Sentence Fragments and Run-ons

A **sentence fragment** may begin with a capital letter and end with a period, but it does not express a complete thought. Some fragments can be corrected by adding words to them to make a complete sentence. Some fragments can be corrected by attaching them to a related sentence.

> **Sentence fragment:** Different kinds of neighborhoods.
> **Corrected sentence:** Children live in different kinds of neighborhoods.

> **Sentence and a fragment:** We live in the country. Where we can grow vegetables.
> **Corrected sentence:** We live in the country where we can grow vegetables.

A **run-on sentence** is two or more sentences combined with just a comma, or with no joining word or punctuation at all. Correct a run-on sentence by writing two separate sentences or by changing it to a compound sentence.

> **Run-on sentence:** Some young people live in the city others live in the country.
> **Separate sentences:** Some young people live in the city. Others live in the country.
> **Compound sentence:** Some young people live in the city, and others live in the country.

Directions: Read each group of words. Write **SF** if it is a sentence fragment. Write **S** if it is a complete sentence.

SF	1. Neighborhoods in large cities.	SF	4. The quiet country with little noise.
S	2. Tall buildings stand on each block.	S	5. Children walk along country roads.
SF	3. Noisy traffic all day long.	S	6. Country life has its charms.

Directions: Correct each run-on sentence either by writing two sentences or by writing a compound sentence.   **Possible answers given.**

7. City children visit museums they also attend plays.
City children visit museums and also attend plays.

8. City life is fast, there is much to do and see.
City life is fast. There is much to do and see.

9. The country is quiet some young people prefer that.
The country is quiet, but some young people prefer that.

10. They enjoy open fields, farm animals are near.
They enjoy open fields. Farm animals are near.

Notes for Home: Your child identified sentence fragments and corrected run-on sentences. *Home Activity:* Write examples of sentence fragments and run-on sentences like those above for your child to correct. Then discuss the way your child has corrected each sentence.

100 Grammar: Correcting Sentence Fragments and Run-ons

Eloise Greenfield

Grammar: Correcting Sentence Fragments and Run-ons

Directions: Correct each fragment. Write the corrected sentence on the line.   **Possible answers given.**

1. Attended the block party.
Most of the neighborhood attended the block party.

2. A group of happy neighbors.
A group of happy neighbors told jokes and laughed.

3. The mayor of the town.
The mayor of the town stopped by for a short visit.

4. The glee club sang. A song about our block.
The glee club sang a song about our block.

5. Volunteers cleaned up. After everyone had left.
Volunteers cleaned up after everyone had left.

Directions: Read each item. Write **S** if it is a correct sentence. Write **RS** if it is a run-on sentence, and rewrite the sentence correctly.   **Possible answers given.**

6. The neighborhood held a block party it was fun.
RS; The neighborhood held a block party. It was fun.

7. People brought food, a band played all day.
RS; People brought food, and a band played all day.

8. Neighbors chatted, and some people sang.
S

9. Children played in the street no cars were allowed.
RS; Children played in the street, and no cars were allowed.

10. We had a great time it didn't end until dark.
RS; We had a great time. It didn't end until dark.

Write About Your Neighborhood

On a separate sheet of paper, describe your neighborhood. Check and correct any fragments or run-ons.   **Check that each sentence is complete.**

Notes for Home: Your child corrected run-on sentences and sentence fragments. *Home Activity:* Have your child explain what run-on sentences and sentence fragments are and how to correct them.

Grammar: Correcting Sentence Fragments and Run-ons **101**

Eloise Greenfield

RETEACHING

Grammar: Correcting Sentence Fragments and Run-ons

Read the run-on sentence. Then read the corrections of the run-on sentence.

Run-on Sentence	Corrected Sentences
Our team won the race we were happy.	1. Our team won the race. We were happy. 2. Our team won the race, and we were happy.

Read the sentence fragment. Then read the correction of the sentence fragment.

Sentence Fragment	Corrected Sentence
All of the leaves and the flower petals.	All of the leaves and the flower petals were brightly colored.

A **run-on sentence** is two or more sentences combined with just a comma or with no joining word or punctuation. A **sentence fragment** may begin with a capital letter and end with a period, but it does not express a complete thought.

Directions: Correct each run-on sentence. Write a compound sentence by adding a comma and the conjunction *and*, *but* or *or*.

1. Craig ran his first race last week Jay ran a race soon after.
Craig ran his first race last week, and Jay ran a race soon after.

2. Lee's running shoes are badly worn mine are new.
Lee's running shoes are badly worn, but mine are new.

Directions: Add words to each sentence fragment and write each new sentence.   **Possible answers given.**

3. Marcella, Sophie, and Caroline in the park.
We saw Marcella, Sophie, and Caroline in the park.

4. Through the field and toward the pond.
They were walking through the field and toward the pond.

Notes for Home: Your child corrected sentence fragments and run-on sentences. *Home Activity:* Have your child write a list of rules for recognizing sentence fragments and run-ons. Then have him or her use the list to teach other family members.

102 Grammar: Correcting Sentence Fragments and Run-ons

Grammar Practice Book 5.1, p. 25

Name _____

Eloise Greenfield

Grammar: Correcting Sentence Fragments and Run-ons

Directions: Underline each sentence fragment. Make each fragment a complete sentence by adding words to it or by joining the fragment to another sentence. Rewrite the paragraph.

1.–7. Jacob Riis was a photographer. And a journalist. Born in Denmark, Riis came to the United States in 1870. Started at the *New York Evening Sun* in 1890. Tried to improve housing and law enforcement. He also pushed for child-labor laws. His photographs showed that people needed better living conditions. **Possible answers given.**

Jacob Riis was a photographer and a journalist. Born in Denmark, Riis came to the United States in 1870. Riis started at the *New York Evening Sun* in 1890. He tried to improve housing and law enforcement. He also pushed for child-labor laws. His photographs showed that people needed better living conditions.

Directions: Rewrite each run-on sentence as a compound sentence. **Possible anwers given.**

8. Clouds are signs of rain fog is a low cloud.
   Clouds are signs of rain, and fog is a low cloud.

9. Some clouds are made of water drops others have ice crystals.
   Some clouds are made of water drops, and others have ice crystals.

10. A rainbow formed after the shower it disappeared quickly.
    A rainbow formed after the shower, but it disappeared quickly.

11. The pond froze the stream did not.
    The pond froze, but the stream did not.

12. The clouds blew away the sun came out.
    The clouds blew away, and the sun came out.

Write About a Day

On a separate sheet of paper, write about a day when the weather changed your plans. Check to make sure there are no sentence fragments or run-ons in your writing.

Make sure students have not written sentence fragments or run-ons.

 Notes for Home: Your child corrected run-on sentences and added words to sentence fragments to make them complete sentences. *Home Activity:* Say sentence fragments about the weather. Have your child make a sentence from each sentence fragment.

Grammar: Correcting Sentence Fragments and Run-ons **103**

Practice Book 5.1, p. 48

Name _____

Eloise Greenfield

Phonics: Complex Spelling Patterns

Directions: Words that end in *-ough* or *-ought* can be tricky. They don't all sound alike. Read the sentences. Then read the words in ( ). Circle the word that has the same vowel sound as the underlined word in the sentence.

1. They saved <u>enough</u> money to buy a house. (though (tough))
2. They <u>brought</u> their belongings with them. ((though) bough)
3. The new neighborhood was <u>rough</u>. (though (tough))
4. People sometimes <u>fought</u> on his block. ((brought) found)
5. The police <u>ought</u> to do something about it. (out (thought))
6. He never got in fights, <u>although</u> others did. (loud (dough))

Directions: Read the poster below. The phrase in ( ) is a clue to the missing word. Choose the word from the box with the same vowel sound as the word in ( ). Make sure the words make sense in the sentence. Write the word on the line.

Hey everyone! We _____ (sounds like *fought*) you could use a party!

We _____ (sounds like *fought*) lots of food at the store.

Even _____ (sounds like *dough*) you have a lot of work to do, come join us!

It's a _____ (sounds like *tough*) job, but someone has to have fun!

though	thought	rough	bought

7. ___**thought**___   9. ___**though**___

8. ___**bought**___   10. ___**rough**___

 Notes for Home: Your child matched vowel sounds for words that end in *-ough* and *-ought* such as *though* and *thought*. *Home Activity:* Make up several short sentences that include words ending in *-ough* or *-ought*. Say the sentences aloud and have your child write them.

104 Phonics: Complex Spelling Patterns

Spelling Workbook 5.1, p. 17

Name _____

Eloise Greenfield

Spelling: Vowel Sounds in *rule, use, off*

Pretest Directions: Fold back the page along the dotted line. On the blanks, write the spelling words as they are dictated. When you have finished the test, unfold the page and check your words.

1. choose
2. school
3. broom
4. scoop
5. booth
6. threw
7. crew
8. drew
9. jewel
10. future
11. music
12. usually
13. humor
14. Utah
15. taught
16. naughty
17. daughter
18. laundry
19. sausage
20. launch

1. **Choose** a shirt to wear.
2. It is time to go to **school**.
3. The **broom** is made of straw.
4. He uses a shovel to **scoop** sand.
5. There is a phone **booth** inside.
6. They **threw** away the garbage.
7. A work **crew** paved the road.
8. What a nice picture you **drew**!
9. I have found my lost **jewel**.
10. What will the **future** be like?
11. Tad likes all kinds of **music**.
12. I **usually** eat lunch outside.
13. His sense of **humor** is strange.
14. Have you ever been to **Utah**?
15. The teacher **taught** them to read.
16. It is **naughty** to be rude.
17. The couple has one **daughter**.
18. Put your **laundry** in the dryer.
19. **Sausage** is good at breakfast.
20. The ship will **launch** tomorrow.

 **Notes for Home:** Your child took a pretest on words that have vowel sounds such as those in *rule, use,* and *off*. *Home Activity:* Help your child learn misspelled words before the final test. See if there are any similar errors and discuss a memory trick that could help.

Spelling: Vowel Sounds in *rule, use, off* **105**

Spelling Workbook 5.1, p. 18

Name _____

Eloise Greenfield

Spelling: Vowel Sounds in *rule, use, off*

Word List			
choose	threw	music	naughty
school	crew	usually	daughter
broom	drew	humor	laundry
scoop	jewel	Utah	sausage
booth	future	taught	launch

Directions: Choose the words from the box that have the vowel sound you hear in *off*. Write each word in the correct column. **Order may vary.**

Vowel sound spelled *augh*

1. ___**taught**___
2. ___**naughty**___
3. ___**daughter**___

Vowel sound spelled *au*

4. ___**laundry**___
5. ___**sausage**___
6. ___**launch**___

Directions: Complete each equation to spell a word from the box. Write the word on the line.

7. useful – eful + ually = **usually**
8. creep – eep + ew = **crew**
9. change – ange + oose = **choose**
10. Utopia – opia + ah = **Utah**
11. fuel – el + ture = **future**
12. brown – wn + om = **broom**
13. jest – st + wel = **jewel**
14. scheme – eme + ool = **school**
15. museum – eum + ic = **music**
16. huge – ge + mor = **humor**
17. boat – at + oth = **booth**
18. scar – ar + oop = **scoop**
19. thread – ad + w = **threw**
20. drive – ive + ew = **drew**

 Notes for Home: Your child spelled words that have the vowel sounds heard in *rule* spelled *oo* and *ew* (*school, threw*), *use* spelled *u* (*music*), and *off* spelled *augh* and *au* (*taught, laundry*). *Home Activity:* Say each spelling word to your child. See if your child can spell it correctly.

106 Spelling: Vowel Sounds in *rule, use, off*

© Scott Foresman 5

Spelling: Vowel Sounds in *rule, use, off*

Directions: Proofread this description. Find five spelling mistakes. Use the proofreading marks to correct each mistake.

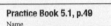

My neighborhood is usỉally very

busy. Mr. Jones is always out with

his broom in front of the lỏndry

room. A crẻẉ of workers is often

working on the school or another

building. You can hear music and

smell sởsage coming from the

local cafe. I choose to think of my

neighborhood as a jẻẉel because

I treasure it greatly.

| ≡ Make a capital. |
| / Make a small letter. |
| ∧ Add something. |
| ℐ Take out something. |
| ⊙ Add a period. |
| ¶ Begin a new paragraph. |

Spelling Tip
choose
Some people forget that **choose** has two o's, not one. Remember: When you **choose**, you often pick between **two** things.

Word List
choose
school
broom
scoop
booth
threw
crew
drew
jewel
future
music
usually
humor
Utah
taught
naughty
daughter
laundry
sausage
launch

Write a Description
On a separate sheet of paper, write a description of your neighborhood or one you would like to live in. Try to use at least five of your spelling words.
Answers will vary, but each description should include at least five spelling words.

Notes for Home: Your child spelled words that have the vowel sounds heard in *rule* spelled *oo* and *ew* (school, threw), use spelled *u* (music), and *off* spelled *augh* and *au* (taught, laundry). *Home Activity:* Scramble the letters of each spelling word and have your child unscramble the words.

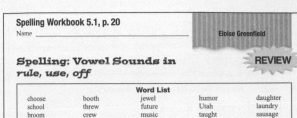

Spelling: Vowel Sounds in *rule, use, off*

REVIEW

Word List				
choose	booth	jewel	humor	daughter
school	threw	future	Utah	laundry
broom	crew	music	taught	sausage
scoop	drew	usually	naughty	launch

Directions: Choose the word from the box that best matches each clue. Write the word in the puzzle.

Down
1. send up in the air
2. female child
4. learning place
5. small stall

Across
3. kind of meat
6. bad
7. instructed
8. dirty clothes

Directions: Choose the word from the box that best matches each clue. Write the word on the line.

music 9. It's what a piano makes.
crew 10. It's a group of sailors.
broom 11. It's what you sweep with.
Utah 12. It's one of the states in the United States.
jewel 13. It's a real gem.
scoop 14. It's how you get ice cream.

drew 15. It's what the artist did.
humor 16. It's what a good joke has.
future 17. It's all ahead of you.
usually 18. It means "commonly."
choose 19. It's what you do when you vote.
threw 20. It's what the pitcher did.

Notes for Home: Your child spelled words that have the vowel sounds heard in *rule* spelled *oo* and *ew* (school, threw), use spelled *u* (music), and *off* spelled *augh* and *au* (taught, laundry). *Home Activity:* Write the spelling words without the vowels. Ask your child to correct them.

Manual

A **manual** is a written set of directions that helps readers understand or use something. It usually comes in the form of a booklet or a book.

Directions: Use the pages from a manual for a refrigerator to answer the questions that follow.

Know Your
Refrigerator

_____

Table of Contents

Appliance Registration	2
Automatic Icemaker	6
Care and Cleaning	7–10
Drawers	7
Lightbulbs	8
Icemaker	9
Shelves	10
Food Storage	5
Installation	4
Model and Serial Numbers	3
Power Switch	3
Safety Instructions	4
Temperature Controls	5

Temperature Controls
There are two types of controls for your refrigerator. The fresh food control uses numbers. The freezer control uses letters. When installing, set the fresh food control at 5 and the freezer control at C as shown in the diagrams.

The fresh food control maintains the temperatures throughout the refrigerator. Setting the control to OFF will stop the cooling in both the fresh food area and the freezer area, but this will not shut off the power to the refrigerator.

FRESH FOOD
5 INITIAL SETTING
9 COLDEST

The freezer control moves a damper that changes the amount of cold air that moves from the freezer to the fresh food compartment.

Damper
Initial Setting C
Coldest E
FREEZER

5

---

1. What is the purpose of this manual? **Possible answer: The purpose is to explain the use and care of a refrigerator.**

2. When might you use this manual? Give an example. **Possible answer: You might use this manual to install a new refrigerator or to figure out how clean it properly.**

3. The table of contents is listed in alphabetical order. Why might this be helpful?
Possible answer: If you wanted to look up something specific about the refrigerator, then you could locate the information more quickly if the table of contents is in alphabetical order.

4. On which page would you find information to clean the drawers? **page 7**

5. What kinds of information would you expect to find on page 4? **You could find information about installing the refrigerator and safety instructions for using the refrigerator.**

6. What are the two types of temperature controls? **the fresh food control and the freezer control**

7. At what settings should you put the two temperature controls when you are installing the refrigerator?
You should set the fresh food control at 5 and the freezer control at C.

8. What is the coldest setting for each temperature control? **fresh food control: 9; freezer control: E**

9. Why are diagrams like the ones shown helpful in a manual?
Possible answer: They make it easier to understand the directions for using what is shown.

10. If you were using this manual to help install a new refrigerator, why is it important to follow the directions for installation exactly as they are written?
Possible answer: If you do not follow the directions as they are written, you may install the refrigerator incorrectly.

 Notes for Home: Your child answered questions about a refrigerator manual. *Home Activity:* Together with your child, read part of a manual you have at home, such as a manual for operating your TV. Talk about the different kinds of information that the manual gives.

© Scott Foresman 5

Name _____

Time Line

Directions: Write the main events of your personal narrative in time order on the slanted lines. Identify the date or time each event happened. Add more lines if you need them. **The time line should be filled out completely.**

Date

Notes for Home: Your child used a time line to organize prewriting notes for a personal narrative. *Home Activity:* Work with your child to make a time line of important family dates.

Unit 1: Writing Process **111**

Name _____

Elaboration
Combine Sentences

- When you write, you can elaborate by **combining short, choppy sentences** into one longer, more interesting sentence.
- You can make compound sentences by joining short sentences with *and, but,* or *or.*
- You can make a complex sentence by joining short sentences with words such as *when, if,* or *because.*

Directions: Use the word in parentheses to combine the sentences. Remember to capitalize the first word of your new sentence. **Answers will vary. Possible answers given.**

1. (when) We will learn about Texas history. We will visit the Alamo.
When we visit the Alamo, we will learn about Texas history.

2. (but) Lupe is a forward on her soccer team. I am the goalie on my team.
Lupe is a forward on her soccer team, but I am the goalie on my team.

3. (and) My birthday is July 8. Lupe's birthday is July 9.
My birthday is July 8, and Lupe's birthday is July 9.

4. (or) We can drive to Dallas. We can drive to Padre Island.
We can drive to Dallas, or we can drive to Padre Island.

5. (but) Some parts of Texas are flat. Other parts are hilly.
Some parts of Texas are flat, but other parts are hilly.

6. (if) Lupe will come to visit me in Florida next summer. Her parents have to agree.
If her parents agree, Lupe will come to visit me in Florida next summer.

7. (because) Lupe and I have become good friends. We like the same things.
Lupe and I have become good friends because we like the same things.

8. (when) Our schools are getting online. Lupe and I will e-mail each other.
When our schools get online, Lupe and I will e-mail each other.

Notes for Home: Your child made compound and complex sentences by combining simple sentences. *Home Activity:* Ask your child to think of sentences beginning with the words *when, if,* and *because.*

112 Unit 1: Writing Process

Name _____

Self-Evaluation Guide
Personal Narrative Checklist

Directions: Think about the final draft of your personal narrative. Then answer each question below. **Students' responses should show that they have given thought to the personal narratives that they have written.**

	Yes	No	Not sure
1. Does my narrative flow smoothly from beginning to middle to end?			
2. Do I use enough details to let my audience know how I feel about the event?			
3. Did I keep my audience and purpose in mind?			
4. Did I use vivid words to express myself?			
5. Did I proofread and edit carefully to avoid errors?			

6. Which sentence of your personal narrative do you think is the most well-written? Explain.

_____

_____

_____

7. Was your topic a good one for a personal narrative, or should you have chosen a different topic? Explain.

_____

_____

_____

Notes for Home: Your child has just completed a self-evaluation of a personal narrative. *Home Activity:* Ask your child to tell you about the personal narrative he or she has just written.

Unit 1: Writing Process **113**

Practice Book 5.2, p. 51

Name _____

The Diver and the Dolphins

Steps in a Process

- The actions you take to make something or to reach a goal are the **steps in a process.**
- When you read, look for clues that help you follow the steps. Clues may be numbers, illustrations, or words such as *first, next, then,* and *last.*
- If there are no clues, think of what you already know about how the process might be done.

Directions: Reread "First-Aid ABCs." Then complete the flowchart by listing in order the steps you should take if you suspect that someone is choking. **Possible answers given.**

Step 1: Ask the person if he or she is choking.

↓

Step 2: Have someone dial 911 for emergency medical help.

↓

Step 3: If the person can't speak, wrap your arms around the person's waist and make a fist.

↓

Step 4: Place the thumb side of your fist on the middle of the person's abdomen and grasp your fist with your other hand.

↓

Step 5: Press your fist into the abdomen with a quick upward thrust.

↓

Step 6: Repeat until the food or object comes out of the person's mouth.

Notes for Home: Your child read an article and showed the order of the steps for the Heimlich maneuver. *Home Activity:* Have your child describe the steps of the Heimlich maneuver in order. Then take turns acting out the Heimlich maneuver, without using any thrusting force.

116 Steps in a Process

Name _____

Vocabulary

Directions: Choose the word from the box that best completes each statement. Write the word on the line to the left.

_____ **communicate**

_____ **dolphins**

_____ **cooperate**

_____ **injured**

_____ **desperate**

1. *Bus* is to *travel* as *telephone* is to _____.
2. *Desert* is to *camels* as *ocean* is to _____.
3. *Enemy* is to *argue* as *friend* is to _____.
4. *Medal* is to *honored* as *bandage* is to _____.
5. *Separation* is to *separate* as *desperation* is to _____.

Check the Words You Know
__ communicate
__ cooperate
__ desperate
__ dolphins
__ doomed
__ hovered
__ injured

Directions: Choose the word from the box that best matches each clue. Write the word in the puzzle.

Down
6. stayed near
7. sea mammals

Across
8. headed for a terrible fate
9. work together
10. hurt

Puzzle answers:
- 6 down: **h o v e r e d** (h at top)
- 7 down: **d o l p h i n s**
- 8 across: **d o o m e d**
- 9 across: **c o o p e r a t e**
- 10 across: **i n j u r e d**

Write a Persuasive Paragraph

Think of a problem that an ocean creature has, such as polluted waters, lack of food, or safe resting places. On a separate sheet of paper, write a paragraph that persuades readers to help this ocean creature. Use as many vocabulary words as you can. **Students' paragraphs should make correct use of vocabulary words.**

Notes for Home: Your child identified and used vocabulary words from "The Diver and the Dolphins." *Home Activity:* Using a dictionary, find simple definitions for words and read them aloud to your child. See if your child can guess each word.

Name _____

Steps in a Process

- The actions you take to make something or to reach a goal are the **steps in a process**.
- When you read, look for clues that help you follow the steps. Clues may be numbers, illustrations, or words such as *first, next, then,* and *last*.
- If there are no clues, think of what you already know about how the process might be done.

Directions: Reread what happens in "The Diver and the Dolphins" when Wayne frees the baby dolphin. Then answer the questions below. Think about the order of the steps.

> I gently held the baby on the sea floor, then cut the trailing fishing line free until all that was left was the part embedded under the baby's tender skin. Getting it out with as little pain for the baby as possible was going to be the hard part.
>
> Then, bit by bit, I started pulling the embedded line loose so I could cut it with my knife. As I pulled it up, more blood flowed out.
>
> I looked around for sharks, not wanting to get in the way if the parent dolphins needed to protect their baby from attack.
>
> Seeing no sharks, I gently continued to pull some line free.... Finally, all the line was cut free except for a short piece attached to the hook.

From DOLPHIN ADVENTURE by Wayne Grover. Copyright 1990 by Wayne Grover. By permission of Greenwillow Books, a division of William Morrow & Company, Inc.

1. What process is being described?
The process is cutting a fishing line free from a baby dolphin.

2. Write all the steps Wayne took to get the line free. Number the steps in correct order.
Possible answer: 1. hold the baby down; 2. cut the trailing line; 3. pull the embedded line loose; 4. check for sharks; 5. pull the rest of the line loose

3. What clue words does the writer use to indicate the order of the steps?
then, finally

4. Did Wayne work quickly or slowly? How do you know?
Wayne worked slowly, "bit by bit," so he wouldn't hurt the baby dolphin.

5. On a separate sheet of paper, write all the steps Wayne took to get the hook out of the dolphin's flesh. Number the steps in the correct order. **Possible answer: 1. calm dolphin; 2. slip the knife into the wound; 3. cut the hook free; 4. pull out the knife and the hook; 5. stop the bleeding; 6. release the dolphin**

Notes for Home: Your child read a story and described the steps in a process. *Home Activity:* Work with your child to describe the steps in a simple process, such as making a sandwich or getting ready for school.

Name _____

Selection Test

Directions: Choose the best answer to each item. Mark the letter for the answer you have chosen.

Part 1: Vocabulary

Find the answer choice that means about the same as the underlined word in each sentence.

1. He was <u>desperate</u>.
   A. ready to try anything
   B. totally out of control
   C. very sad
   D. greatly pleased

2. The dogs <u>hovered</u> as we ate.
   F. stayed in or near one place
   G. moved about in a secret way
   H. paid no attention
   J. gave long, sad cries

3. They were trying to <u>communicate</u>.
   A. blend in with others
   B. show sorrow for another's suffering
   C. help someone in need
   D. send and receive information

4. We watched the <u>dolphins</u>.
   F. kinds of seals
   G. fish that live in lakes
   H. kinds of sharks
   J. mammals that live in the sea

5. The king was <u>doomed</u>.
   A. weakened in spirit
   B. certain to have an unhappy end
   C. very excited
   D. having the most power

6. The children were learning to <u>cooperate</u>.
   F. speak clearly
   G. try hard to win
   H. work together with others
   J. find the way home

7. The horse was <u>injured</u>.
   A. hurt
   B. exhausted
   C. filled with anger
   D. tied down

Part 2: Comprehension

Use what you know about the selection to answer each item.

8. What noise were the dolphins making as they approached Wayne Grover?
   F. splashing
   G. clicking
   H. crying
   J. swishing

9. The baby dolphin's wound was caused by —
   A. a diver's knife.
   B. sharks.
   C. a fish hook.
   D. a boat.

10. What did Wayne Grover do first in the process of helping the baby dolphin?
   F. He went to the surface to breathe.
   G. He cut the fishing line.
   H. He tried to loosen the hook with his finger.
   J. He used his knife on the hook.

11. Grover stroked the baby dolphin to—
   A. find the wound.
   B. help it breathe.
   C. calm it.
   D. stop the bleeding.

Name _____

12. Why was Grover especially fearful of sharks while he worked to help the baby dolphin?
   F. Sharks are attracted to blood.
   G. Sharks often attack divers who stay in one place.
   H. Sharks often hunt for young dolphins.
   J. Sharks follow the sounds that dolphins make.

13. What was the last step Grover took before he let the baby dolphin go?
   A. He slipped the knife into the wound.
   B. He took the hook out of the muscle.
   C. He held the dolphin down with his leg.
   D. He pressed hard on the wound to stop the flow of blood.

14. You can tell from reading this selection that the author—
   F. learned how to speak with dolphins.
   G. was frightened by this experience.
   H. was very moved by this experience.
   J. gained a new respect for sharks.

15. Which action by the father dolphin best supports the idea that the dolphin parents were asking Wayne Grover to help their baby?
   A. The father shot away when Grover reached out to touch him.
   B. After bringing the baby to Grover, the father lifted Grover's arm.
   C. The father raced off to attack a large bull shark.
   D. The father returned quickly when the mother clicked.

Steps in a Process

- The actions you take to make something or to reach a goal are the **steps in a process.**
- When you read, look for clues that help you follow the steps. Clues may be numbers, illustrations, or words such as *first, next, then,* and *last.*
- If there are no clues, think of what you already know about how the process might be done.

Directions: Read the story.

The best part of Dr. Lisa Carson's day is talking to the children who visit Sea View Park. Dr. Lisa, as the kids call her, is the aquarium director.

"What is your job?" the children always ask Dr. Lisa.

"I take care of the creatures at Sea View Park," she replies. "First thing every morning, I check all the tanks. I make sure

nothing has fallen into the water. I make sure the water isn't too hot or too cold. Next, I feed all the fish, dolphins, and whales. Every creature has a different breakfast! Third, I check the fish to make sure they are healthy. I look at their scales and their eyes. I also see how well they are moving. Then, I check with the other animal workers. Finally, I make up the schedule of the day's events."

Directions: Complete the table. Think about what it says in the story to help you order the steps Dr. Lisa takes each morning. Give clue words for the steps given.

Dr. Lisa's Morning Routine	Clue Word
She checks all the tanks.	1. **first**
2. **She feeds the fish, dolphins, and whales.**	next
She checks the fish.	3. **third**
4. **She checks with the other animal workers.**	then
5. **She makes up the day's schedule.**	finally

Notes for Home: Your child read a story, identified the steps in a process, and wrote the clue words that signal the order of each step. **Home Activity:** Have your child make a numbered list showing the steps necessary to make breakfast.

Steps in a Process **121**

Cause and Effect

REVIEW

Directions: Read the story. Then read each question about the story. Choose the best answer to each question. Mark the letter for the answer you have chosen.

Fun with Fins

"Let's go scuba diving, Nick!" Luis said on the phone.

"Great idea!" I answered. "I'll check with my parents and get back to you this afternoon."

My parents knew I was a good diver, so they gave me permission right away.

I called Luis back, and we made plans to dive at Crescent Reef in a week. Crescent Reef was one of our favorite spots.

Since I had not been scuba diving in a while, I spent the week rereading my safety manual. I studied the rules carefully. I reviewed how to use the breathing equipment and how to fasten the weight belt. I read about how long it is safe to stay in the deep water. I felt a lot more confident as a result.

On the day of the dive, Luis picked me up early. I loaded my diving equipment. Then I went back for the extras. Luis laughed when he saw my pack. On the four-hour drive to get to the reef, though, he was glad I had packed food and water bottles. On the four-hour drive back, he was glad I'd brought the extra dry towels too.

Thanks to my planning, the dive was a great success. We had the best time! I can't wait to do it again.

1. Nick asked his parents if he could go scuba diving because—
   Ⓐ he needed to get their permission first.
   B. he thought it was a great idea.
   C. Luis told him to ask.
   D. diving was his favorite sport.

2. One effect of Nick's not having dived for a while was that—
   F. he asked permission first.
   G. he packed a lot of food.
   Ⓗ he reread his safety manual to review the diving rules.
   J. he felt confident.

3. Rereading his safety manual caused Nick to—
   Ⓐ feel more confident.
   B. study the rules harder.
   C. pack more food.
   D. be a better friend.

4. Why did Nick pack food, water, and extra dry towels?
   F. Luis always forgot to pack.
   Ⓖ They had to drive four hours each way.
   H. They were leaving early.
   J. His parents told him to do it.

5. Why was Nick and Luis's diving trip a great success?
   A. Luis is a good friend.
   B. The weather was good.
   Ⓒ Nick planned the trip carefully.
   D. Nick wanted to go again.

Notes for Home: Your child read a story and identified causes and effects. **Home Activity:** Invite your child to explain the causes (why something happens) and effects (what happens) of playing a sport such as baseball or soccer.

122 Cause and Effect

Writing Across Texts

Directions: Consider what you learned about dolphins in "The Diver and the Dolphins" and "Dolphin Behavior." Add five more details to each side of the table below to show that dolphins are social animals. **Possible answers given.**

The Diver and the Dolphins	Dolphin Behavior
The dolphin family circles the diver. The dolphin family makes clicking noises at the diver.	Dolphins feed, play, rest, touch, and resolve conflicts together. A baby stays close to its mother for six months.
1. **The dolphins look at the diver.**	6. **Up to age three, dolphins play in nursery groups.**
2. **Dolphins take care of their young.**	7. **Dolphins form lifelong friendships.**
3. **The parent dolphins bring the baby dolphin near the diver for help.**	8. **Dolphins rub their fins together.**
4. **The parent dolphins protect the diver and the baby dolphin from sharks.**	9. **Dolphins communicate in whistles.**
5. **The father dolphin appears to thank the diver.**	10. **Young adult dolphins baby-sit the little dolphins.**

Write Details to Support a Topic Sentence
Use supporting details from the table and the reading selections to write a paragraph that supports the following topic sentence: *Dolphins are social animals.*
Paragraphs will vary. Check that all supporting details relate to the topic sentence and are based on information found in the selections.

Notes for Home: Your child has combined and used information from more than one source. **Home Activity:** As you read a story or an article with your child, discuss the details that authors use to support their topic sentences.

Writing Across Texts **123**

Grammar: Subjects

REVIEW

Directions: Underline the complete subject in each sentence. Then circle each simple subject.

1. Most (people) find dolphins to be very appealing creatures.
2. These friendly, intelligent (mammals) have even become film and TV stars.
3. A very popular (movie) in 1963 was called *Flipper.*
4. (Flipper) is a wounded dolphin in the movie.
5. A young (boy) and his (family) nurse Flipper back to health.
6. The devoted (dolphin) returns later to save the boy from sharks.
7. Many (viewers) were charmed by the dolphin movie star.
8. The movie's (success) led to an equally popular TV series.
9. Another (film) about Flipper was made more than thirty years later, in 1996.
10. A (boy) and a (dolphin) once again develop a special relationship.

Directions: Use each group of words as a complete subject in a sentence. Write your sentence on the line. Then circle the simple subject. **Possible answers given.**

11. the intelligent dolphin
The intelligent (dolphin) is easy to train.

12. movies about animals
(Movies) about animals appeal to audiences.

13. dolphins and dogs
(Dolphins) and (dogs) are the most popular animal stars.

14. trained seals
Trained (seals) are popular also.

15. almost any animal
Almost any (animal) can be trained to appear in a movie.

Notes for Home: Your child recognized and used subjects in sentences. **Home Activity:** Read part of a story about an animal with your child. Ask your child to identify the subjects of the sentences.

124 Grammar: Subjects

© Scott Foresman 5

Grammar: Nouns

A **noun** is a word that names one or more persons, places, or things. Some nouns name things you cannot see, such as ideas or feelings.

Person: doctor   **Place:** school   **Thing:** book   **Thing (Idea):** freedom

Nouns may be found in the subject of a sentence, in the predicate, or in both the subject and the predicate.

Directions: Write whether each noun names a person, place, or thing.

1. dolphin ___thing___
2. ocean ___place___
3. protection ___thing___
4. sailor ___person___
5. vacation ___thing___

6. boat ___thing___
7. island ___place___
8. fin ___thing___
9. scientist ___person___
10. loyalty ___thing___

Directions: Underline the noun or nouns in each sentence. Write S above the noun if it is the subject. Write P if it is in the predicate.

11. <u>Scientists</u> study the <u>intelligence</u> of <u>animals</u>. (S, P, P)
12. <u>Biologists</u> carry out <u>tests</u> in <u>laboratories</u>. (S, P, P)
13. Some <u>workers</u> observe <u>dolphins</u> in the <u>sea</u>. (S, P, P)
14. Certain <u>dolphins</u> can live in fresh <u>water</u>. (S, P)
15. Actually, <u>dolphins</u> are small <u>whales</u>, and they have <u>beaks</u>. (S, P, P)
16. These <u>mammals</u> make many different special <u>sounds</u>. (S, P)
17. <u>Communication</u> goes on among these fascinating <u>creatures</u>. (S, P)
18. A young <u>calf</u>, or baby <u>dolphin</u>, will respond to a <u>whistle</u> from its <u>mother</u>. (S, S, P, P)
19. Trained <u>dolphins</u> carry <u>messages</u> between <u>people</u>. (S, P, P)
20. These remarkable <u>mammals</u> have rescued <u>people</u> in <u>danger</u> of being drowned. (S, P, P)

Notes for Home: Your child identified nouns—words that name people, places, or things. **Home Activity:** Read a newspaper article together. Ask your child to point out each noun and tell whether it names a person, a place, or a thing.

Grammar: Nouns

Directions: Underline the nouns in each sentence. Write **PER** above the noun if it names a person, **PL** if it names a place, or **T** if it names a thing. Remember, some nouns name things you cannot see, such as ideas.

1. <u>Children</u> visit the <u>exhibits</u> at the <u>aquarium</u> daily. (PER, T, PL)
2. A <u>guide</u> shares <u>facts</u> about the <u>fish</u> and other <u>creatures</u> of the <u>sea</u>. (PER, T, T, T, PL)
3. Two <u>youngsters</u> are quietly watching a <u>tuna</u> swim in the <u>tank</u>. (PER, T, T)
4. Many of the <u>children</u> in the <u>room</u> ask <u>questions</u> and talk about the <u>answers</u>. (PER, PL, T, T)
5. The <u>leader</u> gives out <u>booklets</u> with <u>information</u>. (PER, T, T)

Directions: Add a noun that makes sense to complete each sentence. Write the noun on the line to the left. **Possible answers given.**

___fish___ 6. The giant glass tank holds tropical _____.
___colors___ 7. The various fish have bright, beautiful _____.
___worker___ 8. A _____ feeds the fish at the same time each day.
___tank___ 9. A large turtle paddles steadily upward in another _____.
___glass___ 10. Children and adults are watching it closely through the _____.

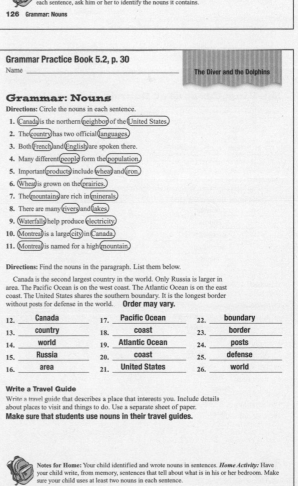

Write a Poem

On a separate sheet of paper, write a poem about an ocean creature's adventure. Include at least one noun that names a person, one that names a place, and two that each name a thing, including an idea. The poem does not have to rhyme. **Check that students have included at least one noun that names a person, one that names a place, and two that each name a thing, including an idea.**

Notes for Home: Your child identified nouns—words that name people, places, and things. **Home Activity:** Say sentences to your child that tell about your day. After your child writes each sentence, ask him or her to identify the nouns it contains.

Grammar: Nouns

RETEACHING

Complete the sentence. Write one word for each picture. **Possible answers given.**

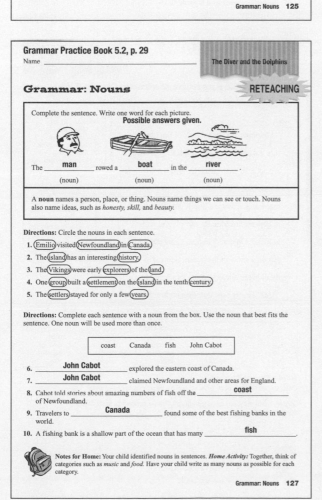

The ___man___ rowed a ___boat___ in the ___river___.
    (noun)   (noun)   (noun)

A **noun** names a person, place, or thing. Nouns name things we can see or touch. Nouns also name ideas, such as *honesty, skill,* and *beauty.*

Directions: Circle the nouns in each sentence.

1. (Emilio) visited (Newfoundland) in (Canada).
2. The (island) has an interesting (history).
3. The (Vikings) were early (explorers) of the (land).
4. One (group) built a (settlement) on the (island) in the tenth (century).
5. The (settlers) stayed for only a few (years).

Directions: Complete each sentence with a noun from the box. Use the noun that best fits the sentence. One noun will be used more than once.

| coast   Canada   fish   John Cabot |

6. ___John Cabot___ explored the eastern coast of Canada.
7. ___John Cabot___ claimed Newfoundland and other areas for England.
8. Cabot told stories about amazing numbers of fish off the ___coast___ of Newfoundland.
9. Travelers to ___Canada___ found some of the best fishing banks in the world.
10. A fishing bank is a shallow part of the ocean that has many ___fish___.

Notes for Home: Your child identified nouns in sentences. **Home Activity:** Together, think of categories such as *music* and *food.* Have your child write as many nouns as possible for each category.

Grammar: Nouns

Directions: Circle the nouns in each sentence.

1. (Canada) is the northern (neighbor) of the (United States).
2. The (country) has two official (languages).
3. Both (French) and (English) are spoken there.
4. Many different (people) form the (population).
5. Important (products) include (wheat) and (iron).
6. (Wheat) is grown on the (prairies).
7. The (mountains) are rich in (minerals).
8. There are many (rivers) and (lakes).
9. (Waterfalls) help produce (electricity).
10. (Montreal) is a large (city) in (Canada).
11. (Montreal) is named for a high (mountain).

Directions: Find the nouns in the paragraph. List them below.

Canada is the second largest country in the world. Only Russia is larger in area. The Pacific Ocean is on the west coast. The Atlantic Ocean is on the east coast. The United States shares the southern boundary. It is the longest border without posts for defense in the world. **Order may vary.**

12. ___Canada___
13. ___country___
14. ___world___
15. ___Russia___
16. ___area___
17. ___Pacific Ocean___
18. ___coast___
19. ___Atlantic Ocean___
20. ___coast___
21. ___United States___
22. ___boundary___
23. ___border___
24. ___posts___
25. ___defense___
26. ___world___

Write a Travel Guide

Write a travel guide that describes a place that interests you. Include details about places to visit and things to do. Use a separate sheet of paper. **Make sure that students use nouns in their travel guides.**

Notes for Home: Your child identified and wrote nouns in sentences. **Home Activity:** Have your child write, from memory, sentences that tell about what is in his or her bedroom. Make sure your child uses at least two nouns in each sentence.

Phonics: Consonant Sounds for *c* and *g*

Directions: Read the sentences below. Two words in each sentence have the letter **c**. One word has a **hard-c** sound as in **care**. The other word has a **soft-c** sound as in **face**. Circle the words with the **hard-c** sound. Underline the words with the **soft-c** sound.

1. I (decided) to try to (call) the dolphin.
2. My (voice) seemed to (encourage) the dolphin.
3. In (fact,) the dolphin (surfaced) immediately.
4. I (carefully) placed my hand on its skin.
5. The dolphin soon (became) peaceful.

Directions: Read the sentences below. Two words in each sentence have the letter **g**. One word has a **hard-g** sound as in **get**. The other word has the **soft-g** sound as in **giant**. Circle the word with the **hard-g**. Underline the word with the **soft-g**.

6. A large dolphin was (snagged) in the net.
7. It (began) to thrash its huge tail.
8. The situation (grew) dangerous.
9. One gentle (tug) released it.
10. I imagined the dolphin (gave) me a smile.

Directions: Find the word in each sentence that has both a **hard** and a **soft** consonant sound. Write the word on the line.

engaging	11. Dolphins can be very engaging and gentle creatures.
language	12. They speak their own language using signals.
convinced	13. I'm convinced they like me to come dive near them.
circling	14. I see them circling around me in the water.
encourage	15. I encourage their playful behavior.

 Notes for Home: Your child identified words with hard-c sounds (*care*), soft-c sounds (*face*), hard-g sounds (*get*), and soft-g sounds (*giant*). **Home Activity:** Read a book about sea animals with your child. Have your child to find and pronounce words with these letters and sounds.

Spelling: Consonant Sounds /j/ and /k/

Pretest Directions: Fold back the page along the dotted line. On the blanks, write the spelling words as they are dictated. When you have finished the test, unfold the page and check your words.

1.	major	1. Her father is an Army **major**.
2.	subject	2. Yolanda's best **subject** is math.
3.	junior	3. He is a **junior** camp counselor.
4.	judge	4. The **judge** banged her gavel.
5.	lodge	5. We stayed at a mountain **lodge**.
6.	ridge	6. The **ridge** is very high.
7.	ledge	7. The window **ledge** is icy.
8.	legend	8. The **legend** was interesting.
9.	general	9. A **general** commands troops.
10.	Georgia	10. Peaches are grown in **Georgia**.
11.	character	11. A good **character** is important.
12.	chorus	12. Rachel joined the **chorus**.
13.	orchestra	13. The **orchestra** plays today.
14.	mechanic	14. He is a good **mechanic**.
15.	chord	15. This is a hard **chord** to play.
16.	raccoon	16. A **raccoon** ate our food.
17.	occur	17. When did the accident **occur**?
18.	accurate	18. This clock is not **accurate**.
19.	occasion	19. Do you fish on **occasion**?
20.	accuse	20. Did they **accuse** him?

 Notes for Home: Your child took a pretest on words that have the consonant sounds of /j/ and /k/. **Home Activity:** Help your child learn misspelled words before the final test. Your child should look at the word, say it, spell it aloud, and then spell it with eyes shut.

Spelling: Consonant Sounds /j/ and /k/

Word List

major	ridge	character	raccoon
subject	ledge	chorus	occur
junior	legend	orchestra	accurate
judge	general	mechanic	occasion
lodge	Georgia	chord	accuse

Directions: Choose the words from the box that have the consonant sound /k/ heard at the beginning of **car**. Write each word in the correct column. **Order may vary.**

Consonant /k/ spelled ch		Consonant /k/ spelled cc	
1.	character	6.	raccoon
2.	chorus	7.	occur
3.	orchestra	8.	accurate
4.	mechanic	9.	occasion
5.	chord	10.	accuse

Directions: Write the word from the box that belongs in each group of words. Hint: Each word has the consonant sound /j/ heard at the beginning of **jail**.

11. freshman, sophomore, _junior_
12. Alabama, Mississippi, _Georgia_
13. regular, common, _general_
14. myth, story, _legend_
15. greater, important, _major_
16. hill, mountain, _ridge_
17. topic, theme, _subject_
18. inn, hotel, _lodge_
19. lawyer, jury, _judge_
20. edge, cliff, _ledge_

 Notes for Home: Your child spelled words that have the consonant sounds /j/ (*junior, ridge, general*) or /k/ (*character, occur*). **Home Activity:** Help your child think of and spell additional words with these sounds and spellings. Then check the spellings in the dictionary.

Spelling: Consonant Sounds /j/ and /k/

Directions: Proofread this report. Find four spelling mistakes. Use the proofreading marks to correct each mistake.

Dolphins are the subjeck of my report.
It is not acurate to call dolphins fish. They
are actually mammals. Dolphins are
warm-blooded and have lungs like other
mammals. They are highly intelligent and
in general are friendly and playful with
humans. On one ocassion, I saw dolphins
put on a show in the ocean. Several of
them made clicking sounds together like a
corus. This is how dolphins communicate.

Make a capital.
⁄ Make a small letter.
∧ Add something.
ℐ Take out something.
⊙ Add a period.
¶ Begin a new paragraph.

Spelling Tip

chorus   orchestra
The consonant sound /k/ can be spelled ch, c, or cc. Remember: You can **hear** the **ch**orus and or**ch**estra.

Word List

major	lodge	general	orchestra	occur
subject	ridge	Georgia	mechanic	accurate
junior	ledge	character	chord	occasion
judge	legend	chorus	raccoon	accuse

Write a Factual Paragraph

On a separate sheet of paper, write a paragraph about a sea animal or a fish. Try to use at least four of your spelling words.
Answers will vary, but each paragraph should contain at least four spelling words.

 Notes for Home: Your child spelled words that have the consonant sounds /j/ (*junior, ridge, general*) or /k/ (*character, occur*). **Home Activity:** Hold a spelling bee with your child, family, and friends using these spelling words.

Spelling: Consonant Sounds /j/ and /k/

REVIEW

Word List

major	ridge	character	raccoon
subject	ledge	chorus	occur
junior	legend	orchestra	accurate
judge	general	mechanic	occasion
lodge	Georgia	chord	accuse

Directions: Choose the word from the box that answers each question. Write the word on the line.

Georgia   1. In what state are peaches and peanuts grown?

judge   2. Who decides who wins a contest?

raccoon   3. What animal appears to wear a mask?

general   4. Which word can mean both "widespread" and "a commanding officer"?

orchestra   5. What group plays music?

junior   6. What would add to your name if you were named after your father?

chord   7. What rhymes with *lord* and refers to something musical?

lodge   8. In what kind of building might you stay on a skiing vacation?

Directions: Choose the word from the box that contains each word below. Write the word on the line. Use each word only once.

9. rid   **ridge**

10. act   **character**

11. use   **accuse**

12. rate   **accurate**

13. sub   **subject**

14. us   **chorus**

15. or   **major**

16. end   **legend**

17. me   **mechanic**

18. edge   **ledge**

19. as   **occasion**

20. cur   **occur**

Notes for Home: Your child spelled words that have the consonant sounds /j/ (*junior, ridge, general*) or /k/ (*character, occur*). **Home Activity:** Take turns picking a spelling word and giving clues about it like those above. Another person must guess the word and spell it.

Chart/Table

A **chart** organizes information in a visual way. It may include words, numbers, or both. A **table** is a type of chart that organizes information in rows and columns.

Directions: Use the table to answer the questions that follow.

Type of Whale	Scientific name	Where It Lives	Length
Dall porpoise	*Phocoenoides dalli*	Pacific Ocean	up to 6 feet (1.8 meters)
pilot whale	*Globicephala melaena*	Atlantic Ocean	up to 20 feet (6 meters)
white-sided dolphin	*Lagenorhynchus albirostris*	North Atlantic Ocean	up to 9 feet (2.7 meters)
killer whale	*Orcinus orca*	all oceans	up to 30 feet (9 meters)
bottle-nosed dolphin	*Tursiops truncatus*	all oceans	up to 9 feet (2.7 meters)
common porpoise	*Phocoena phocoena*	all oceans	up to 6 feet (1.8 meters)
common dolphin	*Delphinus delphis*	all oceans	up to 8 feet (2.4 meters)

1. What is the scientific name for the bottle-nosed dolphin? **Tursiops truncatus**

2. Where does the pilot whale live? **Atlantic Ocean**

3. How long may a killer whale be? **up to 30 feet (9 meters)**

4. What kind of dolphin has the scientific name *Phocoena phocoena*? **common porpoise**

---

5. Which type of whale may be the longest in length? **killer whale**

6. Which types of dolphins may be the shortest in length? **Dall's porpoise and common porpoise**

7. Which type of dolphin is found only in the Pacific Ocean? **Dall's porpoise**

8. Which types of dolphins may be found in all oceans? **killer whale, bottle-nosed dolphin, common porpoise, common dolphin**

9. How much longer may a common dolphin be than a common porpoise? **up to 2 feet (0.6 meters)**

10. Where can the white-sided dolphin be found? **North Atlantic Ocean**

11. Which dolphin has the scientific name *Lagenorhynchus albirostris*? **white-sided dolphin**

12. Is every pilot whale 20 feet long? Explain. **Possible answer: No, the table says a pilot whale's length is up to 20 feet meaning that they could be less than 20 feet. It's an approximate measurement, not an exact one.**

13. Which types of dolphins are found in only one ocean? **Dall's porpoise, pilot whale, white-sided whale**

14. Are most full-grown dolphins longer or shorter than most fifth graders? Explain. **Most dolphins grow to be 6 feet or longer, so they would be longer than most fifth graders.**

15. Are tables useful for comparing information? Explain. **Yes, the rows and columns of a table make it easier to compare information.**

Notes for Home: Your child analyzed information in a table. **Home Activity:** Work with your child to create a table with information about different family members. Columns on the chart might list information such as each person's name, age, color of hair, color of eyes, and height.

Graphic Sources

- A **graphic source** is something that shows information visually. Pictures, charts, graphs, and maps are graphic sources.
- Graphic sources can help you better understand what you read because they provide a lot of information that can be seen quickly.

Directions: Reread "Hurricane Seasons." Then use the bar graph and the text to answer the questions below.

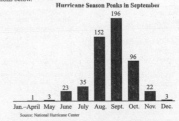

Hurricane Season Peaks in September

| Jan.–April | May | June | July | Aug. | Sept. | Oct. | Nov. | Dec. |
| 1 | 3 | 23 | 35 | 152 | 196 | 96 | 22 | 3 |

Source: National Hurricane Center

1. Read the labels on the bar graph and text. What does the bar graph show? **It shows the number of hurricanes per month (from 1886 to 1993).**

2. How do you know to which years the bar graph refers? **You know by reading the text.**

3. The text says that more than 80% of the hurricanes occur from August through October. How does the bar graph help show this information? **The bars for August through October are the three highest bars in the graph. The bars form a "peak" at September.**

4. Would you use the text or the bar graph to compare different months? **You would use the bar graph to make a comparison.**

5. Which month has the second highest number of hurricanes? **August**

Notes for Home: Your child read a short text and studied a related bar graph. **Home Activity:** Together with your child, read a weather report and study a weather map from a newspaper. Discuss what information each reveals and how the map can help you understand the text.

Practice Book 5.2, p. 62

Name _____

The Fury of a Hurricane

Vocabulary

Directions: Read the following weather bulletin. Choose the word from the box that best completes each sentence. Write the word on the matching numbered line to the right.

WEATHER BULLETIN

Our weather radar has managed to **1.** ____ a dangerous **2.** ____ that is blowing over the Atlantic Ocean. We **3.** ____ that the **4.** ____ winds will hit our area around noon tomorrow. Since they could do heavy **5.** ____, all residents are advised to board up their windows.

1. __identify__
2. __hurricane__
3. __predict__
4. __mightiest__
5. __damage__

Check the Words You Know
__ damage
__ ecology
__ hurricane
__ identify
__ mightiest
__ predict
__ pressure
__ recovered

Directions: Choose the word from the box that best matches each clue. Write the word in the puzzle.

Down

6. the force per unit of area
7. relationship between living things and the environment
8. tell before an event happens
10. harm or injury

Across

9. got back something lost

6.p	7.				8.p	
9.r	e	c	o	v	e	r	10.d
e		o			d		a
s		l			i		m
s		o			c		a
u		g			t		g
r		y					e
e							

Write a Weather Report

Imagine you witnessed a storm. On a separate sheet of paper, report what happened. Use as many vocabulary words as you can.
Students' weather reports should make correct use of vocabulary words.

 Notes for Home: Your child identified and used new vocabulary words from "The Fury of a Hurricane." *Home Activity:* Imagine you and your child are weather reporters. Use as many vocabulary words as possible to describe a terrible storm.

Vocabulary **139**

Practice Book 5.2, p. 63

Name _____

The Fury of a Hurricane

Graphic Sources

- A **graphic source** shows information, such as a picture, graph, or map, visually.
- As you read, compare the written words to the graphic sources for a better understanding of the main ideas.

Directions: Study the following maps from "The Fury of a Hurricane." Then use the maps to answer the questions below.

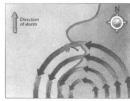 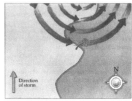

If hurricane winds first blow from the east, they will blow from the west after the eye has passed.

From HURRICANES: EARTH'S MIGHTIEST STORMS by Patricia Lauber. Copyright © 1996 by Patricia Lauber. Reprinted by permission of Scholastic Inc.

Directions: Refer to the graphics to answer the questions below.

1. According to the compass and the arrow, in which direction is the storm moving?
The storm is moving north.

2. What do the maps show?
They show a hurricane passing over land. The first map shows a point of land before the eye of the hurricane passes over; the second shows the same point of land after the eye has passed over.

3. How does the caption help you interpret the maps?
The caption summarizes what the map shows.

4. How do the maps help you understand what the text is saying about wind direction?
Possible answer: The maps help you picture the direction of the hurricane's winds.

5. Choose another graphic source from "The Fury of a Hurricane." On a separate piece of paper, tell how the graphic source helps you understand the information in the text.
Choices of graphic sources will vary. Students should note that they make it easier to form a mental picture of a hurricane and the damage it inflicts.

 Notes for Home: Your child analyzed two maps and a caption. *Home Activity:* Use newspapers to discuss with your child what is shown in a different graphic source, such as a schedule or a bar graph.

140 Graphic Sources

Practice Book 5.2, p. 65

Name _____

The Fury of a Hurricane

Selection Test

Directions: Choose the best answer to each item. Mark the letter for the answer you have chosen.

Part 1: Vocabulary

Find the answer choice that means about the same as the underlined word in each sentence.

1. These are the __mightiest__ storms.
   A. most frightening
   B. longest lasting
   C. most interesting
   Ⓓ most powerful

2. The __ecology__ of the area has changed.
   F. population growth
   G. physical features such as rocks
   H. kinds of houses
   Ⓙ relation between living things and their environment

3. They ran to take shelter from the __hurricane__.
   Ⓐ a storm with violent winds that begins over tropical waters
   B. a seasonal wind that brings rain from April to October
   C. a cloud shaped like a funnel
   D. a storm with heavy snow

4. People in the area soon __recovered__.
   F. got help or support
   G. became smaller
   Ⓗ got back to normal
   J. were hit again

5. The storm did not cause much __damage__.
   A. loss of courage
   Ⓑ harm or injury
   C. change in how people live
   D. feeling that nothing good can happen

6. Did you __predict__ that this would happen?
   Ⓕ tell ahead of time
   G. make up one's mind
   H. feel afraid
   J. take for granted

7. The weather report shows an area of low __pressure__ to the west.
   A. amount of water in the air
   B. wind speed
   Ⓒ weight of the atmosphere on the earth's surface
   D. calm area in the center of a storm

8. We wanted to __identify__ each tree.
   F. find a use for
   Ⓖ give a name to
   H. look at carefully
   J. protect the life of

Part 2: Comprehension

Use what you know about the selection to answer each item.

9. Beginning in 1979, hurricanes for the first time were named after—
   Ⓐ men.
   B. women.
   C. animals.
   D. cities.

10. As a hurricane forms, the warm air—
    F. becomes colder.
    G. sinks into the water.
    Ⓗ goes up.
    J. becomes very dry.

11. On each side of a hurricane, the—
    A. warm air sinks.
    Ⓑ winds blow in different directions.
    C. rain turns to snow.
    D. water turns different colors.

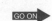

Selection Test **141**

Practice Book 5.2, p. 66

Name _____

The Fury of a Hurricane

12. During Hurricane Andrew, the greatest damage was caused by—
    F. clouds.
    G. rain.
    H. thunder.
    Ⓙ wind.

13. When Hurricane Andrew hit Florida, help was slow to arrive because—
    A. the army was not prepared.
    B. too many people were using telephones at once.
    Ⓒ people did not realize how great the damage was.
    D. members of the government refused to spend money.

14. Which conclusion does this selection best support?
    Ⓕ Hurricanes and human activities have changed Florida's environment.
    G. Areas hit by hurricanes generally recover quickly.
    H. People should be doing more to stop hurricanes.
    J. Hurricanes have ruined most of Florida.

15. The author's main purpose in writing this selection is to—
    A. entertain with an exciting story.
    B. describe the towns of Homestead and Florida City.
    C. express strong opinions about hurricanes.
    Ⓓ give information about hurricanes.

142 Selection Test

© Scott Foresman 5

Graphic Sources

- A **graphic source** shows information, such as a picture, graph, or map, visually.
- As you read, compare the written words to the graphic sources for a better understanding of the main ideas.

Directions: Read the following passage and study the table. Then answer the questions below.

Hundreds of tropical storms are born every year in the world's oceans. Many never reach land and blow themselves out over the water. Only those that reach wind speeds of at least 74 miles per hour are classified as hurricanes. There are four more classes, or categories, of hurricanes above that. Of course, even a hurricane of the lowest category can cause a lot of damage. A hurricane like Hurricane Andrew, with wind speeds of up to 195 mi/hr, is truly a destructive force.

Category	Wind Speed	Force
1	74–95 mi/hr	weak
2	96–110 mi/hr	average
3	111–130 mi/hr	strong
4	131–155 mi/hr	very strong
5	more than 155 mi/hr	terrible

1. What does the table show?
It shows how hurricanes are classified.

2. How does the table help you understand the text?
It gives more details about the subject and tells more about each category.

3. When does a tropical storm become a hurricane?
When it reaches wind speeds of 74 miles per hour.

4. Describe a hurricane of average force.
A hurricane of average force would be Category 2 with wind speeds of 96–110 miles per hour.

5. What category of hurricane was Hurricane Andrew? Explain.
Hurricane Andrew had wind speeds of 195 miles per hour which is a Category 5 in the table.

 Notes for Home: Your child read a nonfiction article and analyzed a table. *Home Activity:* Look through a newspaper and find a picture or chart. Help your child describe what this graphic source shows.

Graphic Sources **143**

Author's Purpose and Text Structure

REVIEW

Directions: Read the passage. Then read each question about the passage. Choose the best answer to each question. Mark the letter for the answer you have chosen.

Fighting the Floodwaters

The city of New Orleans has always had a problem with flooding. The city's location is part of the reason. New Orleans lies between two great bodies of water, the Mississippi River on the south and Lake Pontchartrain on the north. When the Mississippi River rises from heavy rainfall to the north, the extra water naturally tries to spread out into the city. There is danger to the city from the river during heavy rains. Hurricanes traveling along the Gulf Coast also bring a threat of flooding in the city.

Another reason New Orleans often has water problems is that the city itself is like a saucer in a way. Its edges are higher than its middle. The middle dips below sea level. When a hurricane hits or when the river floods, there is always a chance that the city will fill with water.

The Orleans Levee Board was created to address the problem of flooding. The Levee Board taxes citizens and uses the money to build high banks along the river called *levees* and floodwalls.

Over the years, millions of dollars have been spent on hurricane and flood protection. Today the city is safeguarded by a complex system of levees, floodwalls, and floodgates. The longest of the levees and floodwalls are along the Mississippi River and Lake Pontchartrain.

1. This text is—
   A. fiction.
   B. nonfiction.
   C. poetry.
   D. drama.

2. This passage—
   F. describes a terrible flood.
   G. argues that levees are useful.
   H. provides flood statistics.
   J. describes a way to solve a flooding problem.

3. The organization of this text is best described as—
   A. cause and effect.
   B. problem and solution.
   C. comparison and contrast.
   D. sequence of events.

4. This passage is—
   F. funny.
   G. emotional.
   H. informative.
   J. persuasive.

5. What do you think is the author's purpose for writing?
   A. to entertain
   B. to express
   C. to persuade
   D. to inform

 Notes for Home: Your child read a passage and identified the author's purpose and the organization of the text. *Home Activity:* Work with your child to analyze a newspaper article. Study the way the article is organized and evaluate the author's purpose.

144 Author's Purpose and Text Structure

Writing Across Texts

Directions: Consider what you learned in the selections "The Fury of a Hurricane" and "Flying into a Hurricane." Complete the web with details that show what you know about Earth's mightiest storms. **Possible answers given.**

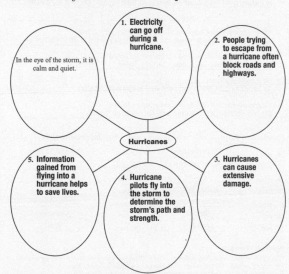

In the eye of the storm, it is calm and quiet.

1. Electricity can go off during a hurricane.

2. People trying to escape from a hurricane often block roads and highways.

Hurricanes

5. Information gained from flying into a hurricane helps to save lives.

4. Hurricane pilots fly into the storm to determine the storm's path and strength.

3. Hurricanes can cause extensive damage.

Write a Diary

Imagine you lived in South Florida when Hurricane Andrew came ashore. Use descriptive, sensory details, as well as the facts that you listed above to create a diary about your feelings and experiences during the storm. **Students' diary entries will vary. Check that students have used sensory, descriptive details, as well as facts, about hurricanes.**

Notes for Home: Your child listed details about a hurricane gathered from different sources. *Home Activity:* Read and share news information, especially information about weather, with your child. Discuss the facts and experiences included in this information.

Writing Across Texts **145**

Grammar: Nouns

REVIEW

Directions: Circle each noun in the following sentences.

1. Do you know the difference between blizzards and other storms?
2. A blizzard involves snow rather than rain.
3. Strong winds blow the snow with great force.
4. Visibility is greatly reduced for several hours.
5. People in the northern sections of the country worry about blizzards.
6. Fortunately, forecasters are often able to issue warnings about stormy conditions.
7. Men and women rush to stores to buy food, flashlights, and other supplies.
8. The threat of being snowed in for a long time is very real.
9. Drivers on snowy streets and roads may be stuck in their cars for hours.
10. Snowstorms leave behind a world of whiteness, beauty, and silence.

Directions: Use each of the following nouns in a sentence about a storm. Write the sentence on the line. Underline every noun in the sentence. **Possible answers given.**

11. clouds
Large, black clouds covered the sky.

12. wind
The noise of the strong wind frightened people.

13. highway
The highway was full of cars stuck in the snow.

14. danger
The drivers were in great danger from the cold.

15. trees
Many beautiful trees were blown over by the storm.

 Notes for Home: Your child identified and wrote sentences with nouns—words that name people, places, and things. *Home Activity:* Play a noun game. Give a prediction about the weather. Each time you use a noun, have your child raise his or her hand.

146 Grammar: Nouns

Answers 713

Grammar Practice Book 5.2, p. 32

Name _____

The Fury of a Hurricane

Grammar: Proper Nouns

A **proper noun** names a particular person, place, or thing. Begin the first word and every other important word in a proper noun with a capital letter. All other nouns are **common nouns**. Common nouns are not capitalized.

Common nouns: scientist, school, country
Proper nouns: Dr. Mark. E. Shen, Pace College, United States of America

Directions: Write whether each noun is **common** or **proper**.

1. hurricane — common
2. Hurricane Earl — proper
3. Cape Cod — proper
4. state — common
5. Mr. Taylor — proper
6. California — proper
7. peninsula — common
8. the District of Columbia — proper
9. month — common
10. September — proper

Directions: Rewrite each sentence. Capitalize proper nouns where necessary.

11. A class led by ms. miller learned about hurricanes.
A class led by Ms. Miller learned about hurricanes.

12. Many hurricanes have formed over the ocean and hit the americas.
Many hurricanes have formed over the ocean and hit the Americas.

13. Hurricane david struck the dominican republic.
Hurricane David struck the Dominican Republic.

14. Did a hurricane named diane rip through rhode island?
Did a hurricane named Diane rip through Rhode Island?

15. Hurricanes usually hit between june and october.
Hurricanes usually hit between June and October.

 Notes for Home: Your child identified proper nouns—nouns that name particular persons, places, or things. *Home Activity:* Read a story or an article together. Invite your child to identify each proper noun.

Grammar: Proper Nouns **147**

Grammar Practice Book 5.2, p. 33

Name _____

The Fury of a Hurricane

Grammar: Proper Nouns

Directions: Write **C** if the noun is common. Write **P** if the noun is proper. If it is a proper noun, write it correctly on the line.

1. rainstorm — C
2. university of texas — P; University of Texas
3. new york city — P; New York City
4. blizzard — C
5. dr. fernandez — P; Dr. Fernandez
6. weather reporter — C
7. channel 7 — P; Channel 7
8. newspaper — C
9. biologist — C
10. pacific ocean — P; Pacific Ocean

Directions: Read the following journal entry. Replace each underlined word or phrase with a proper noun. Write the proper noun on the line with the matching number. **Possible answers given.**

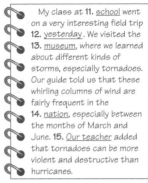

My class at 11. school went on a very interesting field trip 12. yesterday. We visited the 13. museum, where we learned about different kinds of storms, especially tornadoes. Our guide told us that these whirling columns of wind are fairly frequent in the 14. nation, especially between the months of March and June. 15. Our teacher added that tornadoes can be more violent and destructive than hurricanes.

11. Bridge School
12. Tuesday
13. Museum of Science
14. United States
15. Mr. Johnson

Write a Weather Broadcast
Imagine you are a TV meteorologist. On a separate sheet of paper, write a weather report that tells about today's weather in your area. Use several proper nouns in your report.
Proper nouns might include the names of radio stations or personnel, flooded streets, parts of the country, mountain ranges, or large bodies of water. Check for correct capitalization of proper nouns.

 Notes for Home: Your child identified and wrote proper nouns—words that name particular people, places, and things. *Home Activity:* Look at different labels on objects around your home. See how many proper nouns your child can find printed on them.

148 Grammar: Proper Nouns

Grammar Practice Book 5.2, p. 34

Name _____

The Fury of a Hurricane

Grammar: Proper Nouns

RETEACH

The proper nouns are underlined. Circle the capital letters in the proper nouns.

Last Thursday William went with Janet to the Museum of Natural History in New York City.

Use capital letters to begin the important words in proper nouns. Capitalize the names of people, pets, months, days, holidays, and particular places and things.

Directions: Circle the proper nouns in each sentence below.

1. Scientists scheduled the shuttle launch for August.
2. On Wednesday Jamie watched the shuttle launch.
3. He and his family arrived in Florida last June.
4. He attends Jefferson School near Orlando.
5. Next Friday he will show a film of the launch to Ms. Diaz.
6. The pilot could see the Atlantic Ocean below the shuttle.
7. The United States looked very small from the shuttle's window.

Directions: Write a proper noun to complete each sentence.

Answers will vary. Check that students used capital letters correctly.

8. The day of the week I like best is — Saturday
9. I live with my family in the state of — North Carolina
10. The name of the town I live in is — Charlotte
11. My best friend's name is — Andrew
12. The school I attend is called — Elm School
13. My favorite holiday is — Fourth of July
14. I like the weather during the month of — June
15. A famous place I would like to visit is — Grand Canyon
16. My teacher's name is — Mr. Ford
17. A good name for a dog is — Yipper

 Notes for Home: Your child identified proper nouns. *Home Activity:* Make a list of familiar places and people, such as *doctor, bookstore, school, aunt,* and so forth. Have your child write a proper noun for each word on the list, such as *Doctor Marine.*

Grammar: Proper Nouns **149**

Grammar Practice Book 5.2, p. 35

Name _____

The Fury of a Hurricane

Grammar: Proper Nouns

Directions: Write each sentence. Capitalize each proper noun.

1. In december of 1606, three ships set sail from london, england, for america.
In December of 1606, three ships set sail from London, England, for America.

2. The four-month voyage across the atlantic ocean ended in april, 1607.
The four-month voyage across the Atlantic Ocean ended in April, 1607.

3. The settlers named their colony for king james I of england.
The settlers named their colony for King James I of England.

4. On saturday aunt marta and I will visit Jamestown, virginia.
On Saturday Aunt Marta and I will visit Jamestown, Virginia.

5. My dog, patches, will miss me until our return on sunday.
My dog, Patches, will miss me until our return on Sunday.

Directions: Write a proper noun for each common noun. **Possible answers given.**

6. state — North Carolina
7. holiday — Memorial Day
8. month — October
9. inventor — Thomas Edison
10. school — Riverside Elementary
11. pet — Stripes
12. lake — Lake Erie
13. river — Mississippi River
14. language — Italian
15. country — United States
16. friend — Jay
17. ocean — Indian Ocean
18. day — Thursday
19. town — Vale

Write an Itinerary
Plan a trip. Write a vacation itinerary describing where you would go, what you would see, and who would go with you. Use proper nouns. Write on a separate sheet of paper.
Make sure that students have capitalized proper nouns correctly.
Students' itineraries may include plans with family members or visits to famous places.

 Notes for Home: Your child used correct capitalization to write proper nouns in sentences. *Home Activity:* Have your child fill in a calendar for the month, using capitals for proper nouns, such as *Uncle Ed's birthday* or *Memorial Day.*

150 Grammar: Proper Nouns

© Scott Foresman 5

Phonics: Silent Consonants

Directions: Silent consonants are letters you don't hear when you say a word. Read the groups of words below. Say each word to yourself. Circle the word that has the silent consonant. Underline the consonant that is silent.

1. kitten
   kite
   (knocked)
   keep

2. (wrist)
   ring
   rack
   rust

3. gate
   (ghost)
   gale
   gone

4. icing
   icicle
   igloo
   (island)

5. (wrong)
   won
   rang
   wind

6. baseball
   (bomb)
   burger
   basket

7. corridor
   careful
   charter
   (column)

8. forget
   forest
   (foreign)
   forgive

9. (knife)
   kissing
   kept
   kilometer

Directions: Read the weather report. Find six words with silent consonants. Write each word on the line.

° WEATHER BULLETIN

A large storm will hit our area sometime today. Radar signs show us that it will bring strong winds and heavy downpours. If you live near the coast, take cover. Listen for the warning whistle. We know it will be hard, but stay off the roads. Watch out for fallen tree limbs. Fasten all your shutters and doors and stay inside.

10. _____ signs
11. _____ listen
12. _____ whistle
13. _____ know
14. _____ limbs
15. _____ fasten

Notes for Home: Your child identified words with silent consonants, such as the g in *design*. *Home Activity:* Read or listen to a local weather report with your child. Ask your child to point out any words with silent consonants.

Phonics: Silent Consonants **151**

Spelling: Words with *kn, mb, gh, st*

Pretest Directions: Fold back the page along the dotted line. On the blanks, write the spelling words as they are dictated. When you have finished the test, unfold the page and check your words.

1. _____ knowledge
2. _____ know
3. _____ knew
4. _____ knuckle
5. _____ knitting
6. _____ knapsack
7. _____ numb
8. _____ bomb
9. _____ tomb
10. _____ climber
11. _____ plumbing
12. _____ ghost
13. _____ spaghetti
14. _____ aghast
15. _____ glisten
16. _____ listening
17. _____ fasten
18. _____ hustle
19. _____ mistletoe
20. _____ whistle

1. Her **knowledge** is very great.
2. I **know** many people.
3. No one **knew** how to do it.
4. He cracked his **knuckle**.
5. Grandmother is **knitting**.
6. This **knapsack** is very large.
7. My feet are cold and **numb**.
8. The team defused the **bomb**.
9. This **tomb** is ancient.
10. The **climber** scaled the cliff.
11. **Plumbing** is a hard job.
12. He thought he saw a **ghost**.
13. We ate **spaghetti** for lunch.
14. They were **aghast** at the idea.
15. The wet stones **glisten**.
16. Are you **listening** to me?
17. **Fasten** your seatbelts.
18. They **hustle** down the hall.
19. **Mistletoe** lives on trees.
20. Can you **whistle** a tune?

Notes for Home: Your child took a pretest on words that include the letters *kn, mb, gh,* and *st*. *Home Activity:* Help your child learn misspelled words before the final test. Your child can underline the word parts that caused the problems and concentrate on those parts.

152 Spelling: Words with *kn, mb, gh, st*

Spelling: Words with *kn, mb, gh, st*

Word List

knowledge	knitting	tomb	spaghetti	fasten
know	knapsack	climber	aghast	hustle
knew	numb	plumbing	glisten	mistletoe
knuckle	bomb	ghost	listening	whistle

Directions: Choose the words from the box that either begin or end with a silent consonant. Write each word in the correct column. **Order will vary.**

Begins with a Silent Consonant
1. knowledge
2. know
3. knew
4. knuckle
5. knitting
6. knapsack

Ends with a Silent Consonant
7. numb
8. bomb
9. tomb

Directions: Choose the word from the box that best completes each sentence. Write the word on the line to the left.

fasten	10. Always _____ your seat belt when riding in a car.
mistletoe	11. The _____ plant has small, waxy white berries and green leaves.
climber	12. The _____ reached the snowy mountaintop.
plumbing	13. We have leaky _____ in our house.
spaghetti	14. My favorite meal is _____ and meatballs.
ghost	15. We didn't have a _____ of a chance of winning.
hustle	16. They had to _____ to make the early train.
aghast	17. His parents were _____ at his bad grades.
listening	18. "Are you _____ to me?" asked the teacher.
glisten	19. Sweat will _____ on your skin when you exercise.
whistle	20. Does your dog come when you _____?

Notes for Home: Your child spelled words with *kn, mb, gh,* and *st* in which the two letters together stand for only one sound. *Home Activity:* Help your child think of and spell additional words that have the letters *mb* and *st* where the *b* and *t* are silent, such as *comb, limb* and *wrestle*.

Spelling: Words with *kn, mb, gh, st* **153**

Spelling: Words with *kn, mb, gh, st*

Directions: Proofread this letter. Find five spelling mistakes. Use the proofreading marks to correct each mistake.

Dear Dan,

Last night a tornado hit our area. I knew something was wrong when I heard the wind whisle loudly. My mom was lisening to the radio. She stopped her knitting and told me to fasten the door. We spent the night in the cellar. I was num with fear.

Aren't you glad you live in another state?

Your friend,

Mark

≡	Make a capital.
/	Make a small letter.
∧	Add something.
℘	Take out something.
⊙	Add a period.
¶	Begin a new paragraph.

Spelling Tip

Sometimes two consonants together stand for one sound. Remember to keep the *k* when spelling words with **kn**.

Word List

knowledge	plumbing
know	ghost
knew	spaghetti
knuckle	aghast
knitting	glisten
knapsack	listening
numb	fasten
bomb	hustle
tomb	mistletoe
climber	whistle

Write a Letter

On a separate sheet of paper, write a letter that Dan might send back to Mark. Describe a natural disaster that Dan experienced, such as a flood or blizzard. Try to use at least five of your spelling words.
Answers will vary, but each letter should include at least five spelling words.

Notes for Home: You child spelled words that have *kn, mb, gh,* or *st* in which the two letters together stand for only one sound. *Home Activity:* Say each word aloud. Have your child spell it and tell you which consonant is silent.

154 Spelling: Words with *kn, mb, gh, st*

© Scott Foresman 5

Spelling Workbook 5.2, p. 28

Name _____

The Fury of a Hurricane

Spelling: Words with *kn, mb, gh, st*   REVIEW

Word List				
knowledge	knitting	tomb	spaghetti	fasten
know	knapsack	climber	aghast	hustle
knew	numb	plumbing	glisten	mistletoe
knuckle	bomb	ghost	listening	whistle

Directions: Choose the word from the box that best matches each clue. Write the word on the line.

ghost	1. Anything that is dim, pale, or shadowy is like this.
spaghetti	2. This kind of noodle can be fun to eat.
knitting	3. If you like sewing, you might like this too.
plumbing	4. This brings water to your kitchen sink.
climber	5. This person is always going up or down.
listening	6. Some students should do less talking and more of this.
tomb	7. An Egyptian pyramid is an example of this.
knowledge	8. By studying, you get more of this every year.

Directions: Write the word from the box that belongs in each group.

9. sparkle, shine, **glisten**
10. understand, think, **know**
11. to flop, to fail, to **bomb**
12. plant, white berries, **mistletoe**
13. zip, button, **fasten**
14. backpack, bookbag, **knapsack**
15. elbow, wrist, **knuckle**
16. cold, stiff, **numb**
17. hum, sing, **whistle**
18. horrified, terrified, **aghast**
19. realized, understood, **knew**
20. hurry, rush, **hustle**

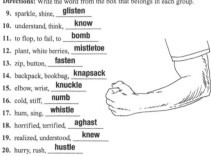

 Notes for Home: Your child spelled words that have the letters *kn, mb, gh,* and *st* in which the two letters together stand for only one sound. **Home Activity:** Make a crossword puzzle with your child using words from the box. Decide where the words will intersect. Then write clues.

Spelling: Words with *kn, mb, gh, st*   **155**

Practice Book 5.2, p. 69

Name _____

The Fury of a Hurricane

Parts of a Book

Parts of a book include its cover, title page, copyright page, table of contents, chapter titles, captions, section heads, other text features, glossary, and index.

Directions: Use the parts of a book shown below to answer the questions on the next page.

Natural Disasters Since 1900
by Ronald O'Day

Chronicle Publication Society
New York, NY

Title Page

Copyright © 1985 Ronald O'Day

All rights reserved. No part of this book may be reproduced in any form without written permission of the publisher. Permission requests should be addressed to Chronicle Publishing Society, 100 Main Street, New York, NY, 10000.

O'Day, Ronald.
Natural Disasters Since 1900/by Ronald O'Day.
Includes index.
ISBN 1-33000-219-6
1. Earthquakes, Volcanoes, Floods, Storms.

Copyright Page

Table of Contents	
Chapter 1 **What Is a Disaster?**	3
Chapter 2 **Earthquakes**	6
Why Earthquakes Occur	8
Predicting Earthquakes	15
Famous Earthquakes	18
Chapter 3 **Volcanoes**	24
How Volcanoes Form	26
Kinds of Volcanoes	29
Famous Volcanoes	35
Chapter 4 **Floods**	39
River Floods	41
Seacoast Floods	43
Famous Floods	48
Chapter 5 **Storms**	51
Hurricanes	53
Tornadoes	55
Famous Storms	59

Table of Contents

Index

Rivers, see Floods
Storms
air, 52
blizzard, 52
clouds, 52
cyclone, 53
dust storm, 61
hail, 51
hurricane, 53–54
lightning, 59
rain, 59
sandstorm, 62
sleet, 51
snow, 52
thunder, 59
tornado, 55–58
weather, 51–52
wind, 53–56
Volcanoes
active, 29
ash, 24–28
craters, 24
eruptions, 28
inactive, 29
lava, 26

Index

156 Research and Study Skills: Parts of a Book

Practice Book 5.2, p. 70

Name _____

The Fury of a Hurricane

1. What is the title of this book? **Natural Disasters Since 1900**

2. Who wrote this book? **Ronald O'Day**

3. When was the book published? **1985**

4. If you were seeking information about the Johnstown flood of 1889, would this book be helpful to you? Explain.
No, the book only discusses disasters since 1900.

5. If you were seeking information about the California earthquake of 1989, would this book be helpful? Why or why not?
No, the book was published in 1985 and would not include a disaster that occurred in 1989.

6. How many chapters are there in this book? **five**

7. What is the main topic of Chapter 3? **Volcanoes**

8. In which chapter would you learn about tornadoes? **Chapter 5**

9. In which chapter would you learn about causes of an earthquake? **Chapter 2**

10. On which page or pages are sandstorms discussed? **page 62**

11. On which page or pages are blizzards discussed? **page 52**

12. What is the meaning of the index entry "Rivers, see Floods"? **Possible answer: The entry "Rivers" cross-references another related entry, "Floods." You can look up the entry "Floods" to find information related to both rivers and floods.**

13. Which part of a book will help you decide how up-to-date its information is? Explain.
Possible answer: The copyright page will tell you when a book was published. You can use that information to help you decide how up-to-date its information is.

14. If you were seeking information on the volcanic eruption of Mt. St. Helens in Washington on May 18, 1980, would this book be helpful to you? Explain.
Yes, this eruption occurred after 1900 but before 1985, so the book might include information on this volcano.

15. Which chapter might explain what the term *disaster* means? **Chapter 1**

 Notes for Home: Your child used the parts of a book (the title page, copyright page, table of contents, and index) to find information. **Home Activity:** Choose a book. Have your child identify and talk about the different parts of the book.

Research and Study Skills: Parts of a Book   **157**

Practice Book 5.2, p. 71

Name _____

Dwaina Brooks

Fact and Opinion

- A **fact** is something that can be proved true or false. Statements of fact can be proved by checking reference books, observing, measuring, and so on.
- An **opinion** tells a person's ideas or feelings. It cannot be proved true or false, but it can be supported or explained.

Directions: Reread "A Volunteer's Help." Then complete the table. Read each statement about Ellen's flood volunteer work, and answer the questions at the top of each column. **Possible ways to check facts are given.**

Statements	Does it state a fact or an opinion?	If an opinion, are there any clue words? If a fact, how could you try to prove it?
Ellen and her friends gathered 15 cartons of food and toys.	1. **Fact**	2. **Count the cartons and check their contents.**
I felt really sad.	3. **Opinion**	4. **I felt**
I thought there should be something we could do to help.	5. **Opinion**	6. **I thought**
Lots of kids brought stuff in.	7. **Fact**	8. **Check with the teacher.**
I felt good about it.	9. **Opinion**	10. **I felt**

 Notes for Home: Your child read a story and identified statements of fact and opinion. **Home Activity:** Read a movie or TV review with your child. Together, decide which statements are statements of fact and which are statements of opinion.

160 Fact and Opinion

© Scott Foresman 5

Name _____

Dwaina Brooks

Vocabulary

Directions: Match each word on the left with its definition on the right. Write the letter of the definition next to the word.

d	1. advised	a. things sent and received	
a	2. deliveries	b. not lucky	
e	3. donate	c. arranged	
c	4. organized	d. told how to do	
b	5. unfortunate	e. give money or help	

Check the Words You Know
___ advised
___ deliveries
___ donate
___ organized
___ unfortunate

Directions: Choose the word from the box that best completes each statement. Write the word on the line to the left.

deliveries 6. *Pony* is to *ponies* as *delivery* is to _____.

unfortunate 7. *Happy* is to *sad* as *lucky* is to _____.

donate 8. *Invent* is to *create* as *give* is to _____.

advised 9. *Acted* is to *performed* as *counseled* is to _____.

organized 10. *Long* is to *short* as *jumbled* is to _____.

Directions: Choose the word from the box that best completes each sentence. Write the word on the line.

donate 11. Keitha and Matt _____ their time at the local food bank.

organized 12. Last month the food bank _____ a drive to collect canned goods from the community.

advised 13. Keitha and Matt designed flyers that _____ people on what kinds of goods were most needed and when donations could be dropped off at the food bank.

unfortunate 14. The food bank also provides meals to any _____ person who needs it.

deliveries 15. Since Matt is old enough to drive, he makes _____ of hot meals to people who can't leave their homes.

Write a News Story
On a separate sheet of paper, write a news story about someone who did a good deed. Use as many vocabulary words as you can.
Students' news stories should make correct use of vocabulary words.

Notes for Home: Your child identified and used vocabulary words from "Dwaina Brooks." *Home Activity:* Discuss with your child ways people can help out others. Use the vocabulary words, such as: *You can donate your time to visiting someone in a nursing home.*

Name _____

Dwaina Brooks

Fact and Opinion

- A **fact** is a statement that can be proved true or false. Even if it is false, it is still a statement of fact.
- An **opinion** is someone's ideas or feelings. Opinions cannot be proved true or false.

Directions: Reread this passage from "Dwaina Brooks" about Dwaina's accomplishments and goals. Then answer the questions below.

In a little more than two years, Dwaina Brooks, now in sixth grade, has organized several thousand meals for unfortunate people in the Dallas area. She and her mother and the classmates who sometimes still join in have perfected the art of helping others and having fun at the same time. They do it by doing something they already love to do: cooking and putting meals together.

Dwaina hopes to become a doctor and open her own clinic someday, but she thinks it's crazy to wait till then to start caring for others. "Kids should get going," she says. "There aren't enough jobs out there, especially for people without diplomas. Not even at McDonald's. We should try to help. If we don't act, there will be more and more homeless people. . . ."

From IT'S OUR WORLD TOO! by Phillip Hoose. Copyright ©1993 by Phillip Hoose. By permission of Little, Brown and Company.

1. Is the first sentence a statement of fact or a statement of opinion? Explain.
It is a statement of fact. It can be proved true or false.

2. List two ways you could verify the statement made in the opening sentence.
Possible answer: Ask Dwaina; check the records of homeless shelters in Dallas.

3. Reread the quote from Dwaina. Is she stating facts or is she stating her opinion when she says, "Kids should get going."
Possible answer: She is stating an opinion since this is a belief that can't be proved true or false.

4. How might you prove that there are not enough jobs for people without diplomas?
Possible answer: You could check employment statistics.

5. On a separate sheet of paper, write two statements of fact and two statements of opinion from the rest of the article. **Facts might include details about her program for feeding the homeless. Opinions might include statements about her energy, courage, or compassion.**

Notes for Home: Your child read a nonfiction article and identified statements of fact and opinion. *Home Activity:* Work with your child to recognize statements of fact and opinion in a television or movie review.

Name _____

Dwaina Brooks

Selection Test

Directions: Choose the best answer to each item. Mark the letter for the answer you have chosen.

Part 1: Vocabulary
Find the answer choice that means about the same as the underlined word in each sentence.

1. Leon agreed to <u>donate</u> his old bike.
   A. fix up
   (B) give to a cause
   C. rent out
   D. set the value of

2. Alice made <u>deliveries</u> for her uncle.
   (F) acts of carrying and giving out things
   G. requests or orders
   H. acts of collecting and organizing things
   J. reasons for doing something

3. The librarian <u>advised</u> me.
   A. refused to help
   B. gave an order to
   (C) offered suggestions to
   D. tried to prevent

4. They <u>organized</u> the clothing.
   F. used again
   G. cleaned and repaired
   H. looked at carefully
   (J) put together in order

5. He was an <u>unfortunate</u> man.
   (A) not lucky
   B. not powerful
   C. not happy
   D. not interesting

Part 2: Comprehension
Use what you know about the selection to answer each item.

6. What grade was Dwaina in when she started making meals for the homeless?
   F. third
   (G) fourth
   H. fifth
   J. sixth

7. Dwaina got the idea of making meals for the homeless when she—
   A. saw homeless people on the street.
   (B) talked to a homeless man on the telephone.
   C. visited a homeless shelter.
   D. discussed the homeless with her class at school.

8. Which of these events happened first?
   (F) A baker gave Dwaina twenty free boxes.
   G. Dwaina took 105 meals to the homeless center.
   H. Crystal and Stephanie helped make sandwiches.
   J. Two men helped carry the boxes into the homeless center.

9. Which word best describes Dwaina?
   A. nosy
   B. quiet
   C. wealthy
   (D) caring

10. Dwaina and her mother decided to buy day-old bread instead of fresh bread because it—
   (F) saved money.
   G. tasted better.
   H. lasted longer.
   J. was sold nearby.

GO ON

Name _____

Dwaina Brooks

11. Which sentence states an opinion?
   A. Dwaina gave her lunch money to a homeless shelter.
   B. They spent three days shopping and preparing.
   (C) Kids should pitch in to help the homeless.
   D. Dwaina and her classmates made more than 300 meals in one night.

12. Which statement is a valid generalization based on the facts in this selection?
   F. Most people who help the homeless were once homeless themselves.
   (G) Many homeless people once had lives that were going along okay.
   H. Most homeless people need only one good meal.
   J. Many children are looking for ways to help homeless people.

13. Which sentence states a fact?
   A. We should all take care of other people.
   B. Dwaina Brooks will be a great doctor.
   C. Dwaina Brooks is the most generous girl in her school.
   (D) There are hundreds of homeless people in Dallas.

14. What can you tell about the author of this selection?
   F. He is a lot like Dwaina.
   G. He is related to Dwaina.
   H. He has helped Dwaina.
   (J) He admires Dwaina.

15. Which title below best fits this story?
   (A) "Kids Can Make a Difference"
   B. "How to Make Hundreds of Sandwiches"
   C. "Coming Home on Fridays"
   D. "Life in a Homeless Shelter"

STOP

Answers 717

Fact and Opinion

- A **fact** is a statement that can be proved true or false. Even if it is false, it is still a statement of fact.
- An **opinion** is someone's ideas or feelings. Opinions cannot be proved true or false.

Directions: Read the passage from a news article below.

> **1.** Every morning, Bob Jackson and his mother walked past the empty lot. **2.** "What a mess!" Bob said one day. **3.** "We should do something about it." **4.** "That's a great idea," his mom replied. **5.** "The town owns this lot," she added. **6.** "You have to call them first to get permission."
>
> **7.** The next day, Bob spoke to his friends. **8.** "The empty lot is the worst problem facing our town," he started. **9.** "I spoke to the town clerk and she said we can clean it up. **10.** I think we can make this lot the most beautiful place in town."

Directions: Imagine you are a fact checker for the local newspaper. For each sentence in the passage, tell whether it is a statement of fact or opinion. For each statement of fact, tell what you could do to prove it true or false.

Possible fact-checking methods given.

Sentence	Fact or Opinion	How to Prove Facts
1.	Fact	Ask Bob or his mother.
2.	Opinion	
3.	Opinion	
4.	Opinion	
5.	Fact	Call town hall and ask.
6.	Fact	Call town hall and ask.
7.	Fact	Call Bob and his friends.
8.	Opinion	
9.	Fact	Ask the town clerk.
10.	Opinion	

 Notes for Home: Your child read a passage and distinguished between statements of fact and opinion. **Home Activity:** Read a magazine article with your child. Work together to decide which statements are facts and which are opinions.

Fact and Opinion **165**

Steps in a Process

REVIEW

Directions: Read the passage. Then read each question about the passage. Choose the best answer to each question. Mark the letter for the answer you have chosen.

Working for the Homeless

Thursdays are one day of the week when Becky and her mother work together. They work as volunteers at a local soup kitchen. They cook and serve food to anyone who comes in.

There is a regular routine Becky, her mother, and the other volunteers always follow. They feed from 50 to 125 people every week, and they need to be well organized.

The first thing Becky does when she arrives is wash her hands. Then she puts on an apron. Then she goes to work on getting things ready for the next day. Next she scrubs and chops vegetables for the next day's meal. She puts the vegetables into several large pots on the stove.

Next it's time to work on the Thursday evening meal. Every Thursday the meal is chili. Chili is very popular at the soup kitchen. As each person files by a low counter, Becky dishes up a bowl of chili. She likes seeing the smiles as the smell of hot chili fills the room.

After everyone has been served, Becky helps clean up the kitchen. She washes the table tops and then wipes the trays.

At the end of the night, Becky is tired. She and her mother talk about the experience on the way home.

"Working in the soup kitchen is not always what people would call fun," Becky says, "but I really love doing it."

1. This article describes the process of—
   A. chopping vegetables.
   Ⓑ working in a soup kitchen.
   C. fighting homelessness.
   D. dishing up chili.

2. First, Becky—
   F. scrubs vegetables.
   G. washes counters.
   H. puts on her apron.
   Ⓙ washes her hands.

3. Right before she serves dinner, Becky always—
   A. cleans the kitchen.
   Ⓑ helps prepare the next day's meal.
   C. puts on her apron.
   D. washes her hands.

4. Last, Becky—
   Ⓕ helps clean up the kitchen.
   G. dishes up bowls of chili.
   H. puts on her apron.
   J. scrubs and chops vegetables.

5. What would happen if Becky forgot to put pots on the stove?
   A. She would be punished.
   B. The food would get burned.
   Ⓒ Dinner for the next day would not get cooked.
   D. The chili might taste spicy.

 Notes for Home: Your child read a story and identified steps in a process. **Home Activity:** Invite your child to list the steps necessary to brush his or her teeth.

166 Steps in a Process

Name _____

Writing Across Texts

Directions: Dwaina Brooks and the diver in "The Diver and the Dolphins" were alike in some ways and different in other ways. In the table below, write your ideas about what made these two caring people so special. **Possible answers given.**

Dwaina	The Diver
Dwaina was a generous and caring class leader.	He respected and protected all animals.
1. When she learned about the problems of homeless people, Dwaina tried to find out what could be done to help.	He figured out the dolphins' problem.
2. She got her family and friends involved.	4. He seemed to be able to communicate with animals.
3. Her work fed thousands of homeless people.	5. He saved the life of a dolphin.

Write a Poem

Write a poem of praise about these real-life, caring people. Use these lines to help you get started:
One works alone.
One works with others.
Poems will vary. Poems can rhyme or be free verse, but should include descriptive details, as well as facts, about both people.

 Notes for Home: Your child listed ideas from two selections about real-life heroes. **Home Activity:** Talk about the environment with your child. Discuss ways you and your family can show your concern for the world around you.

Writing Across Texts **167**

Grammar: Proper Nouns

REVIEW

Directions: Beside each noun, write **C** if it is common. If it is proper, write **P**, and then write the noun correctly.

1. shelter — **C**
2. california — **P; California**
3. grant park — **P; Grant Park**
4. kindergarten — **C**
5. street — **C**
6. los angeles — **P; Los Angeles**
7. house — **C**
8. al smith — **P; Al Smith**
9. volunteer — **C**
10. church — **C**
11. saturday — **P; Saturday**
12. boston celtics — **P; Boston Celtics**
13. mario — **P; Mario**
14. gomez trucking — **P; Gomez Trucking**

Directions: Rewrite each sentence. Capitalize all proper nouns.

15. My brother mario was walking down fourth avenue one monday in june.
My brother Mario was walking down Fourth Avenue one Monday in June.

16. He noticed ms. katz, owner of hot hamburgers, throwing out boxes of food.
He noticed Ms. Katz, owner of Hot Hamburgers, throwing out boxes of food.

17. My brother volunteers at the drew shelter in amestown, and he had a thought.
My brother volunteers at the Drew Shelter in Amestown, and he had a thought.

18. By july, mario and friends were collecting leftover food from ms. katz.
By July, Mario and friends were collecting leftover food from Ms. Katz.

19. They borrowed a truck from mr. chan and drove the food to the fifth ave. food shelter.
They borrowed a truck from Mr. Chan and drove the food to the Fifth Ave. Food Shelter.

20. From there, volunteers delivered it to the glendale shelter and other homeless shelters in the area.
From there, volunteers delivered it to the Glendale Shelter and other homeless shelters in the area.

 Notes for Home: Your child distinguished common and proper nouns and spelled proper nouns with capital letters. **Home Activity:** Look through a magazine article with your child. Have your child list all the proper nouns she or he finds.

168 Grammar: Proper Nouns

© Scott Foresman 5

Grammar: Plural Nouns

Plural nouns name more than one person, place, or thing. Plural nouns are formed in different ways.

- Add **-s** to most singular nouns to form the plural.
  can/cans   bowl/bowls   house/houses   meal/meals   volunteer/volunteers
- Add **-es** to singular nouns ending in **ch, sh, x, z, s,** and **ss**.
  lunch/lunches   wish/wishes   box/boxes   gas/gases   glass/glasses
- If a noun ends in a **vowel** and **y**, add **-s**.
  donkey/donkeys   key/keys   journey/journeys
- If a noun ends in a **consonant** and **y**, change **y** to **i** and add **-es**.
  city/cities   county/counties   library/libraries   copy/copies
- Some nouns have **irregular plural** forms.
  You'll need to remember the spelling changes for nouns such as these. A dictionary can help you with irregular plurals too.
  ox/oxen   child/children   woman/women   tooth/teeth   mouse/mice
- For many nouns ending in **f** or **fe**, change **f** or **fe** to **v** and add **-es**.
  wolf/wolves   life/lives   leaf/leaves   knife/knives   shelf/shelves
- Some nouns have the same singular and plural forms.
  fish   sheep   deer   series   headquarters

Directions: Write the plural form of each singular noun. Use a dictionary if you need help.

1. watch   **watches**
2. toy   **toys**
3. foot   **feet**
4. shelter   **shelters**
5. baby   **babies**
6. fox   **foxes**
7. helper   **helpers**
8. moose   **moose**
9. dish   **dishes**
10. man   **men**
11. boss   **bosses**
12. loaf   **loaves**
13. turkey   **turkeys**
14. elk   **elk**
15. bus   **buses**
16. stripe   **stripes**
17. memory   **memories**
18. task   **tasks**
19. zebra   **zebras**
20. half   **halves**

 Notes for Home: Your child formed plural nouns. *Home Activity:* Point out different singular items in your home. Have your child write the word that names each item, such as *floor, stove,* or *puppy*. Then have your child write the plural form of each noun.

Grammar: Plural Nouns   **169**

Grammar: Plural Nouns

Directions: Write the plural form of each singular noun.

1. check   **checks**
2. woman   **women**
3. push   **pushes**
4. rose   **roses**
5. sandwich   **sandwiches**
6. dress   **dresses**
7. tooth   **teeth**
8. monkey   **monkeys**
9. tax   **taxes**
10. penny   **pennies**
11. knife   **knives**
12. deer   **deer**

Directions: Write the plural form of the noun in ( ) to complete each sentence.

adults — 13. The (adult) on our street formed a special group.
wives — 14. All the husbands and (wife) looked for ways to help others living in the neighborhood.
children — 15. The (child) contributed ideas also.
people or persons — 16. Through the years, the group has helped many (person) in need.
groceries — 17. They ask supermarkets to donate (grocery).
Volunteers — 18. (Volunteer) collect and clean used clothing.
boxes — 19. Then they deliver the food and clothing in large (box).
branches — 20. Today the group has many (branch) all over the city.

Write a Proposal
Make a plan for helping other people. On a separate sheet of paper, describe your plan. Use as many plural nouns as possible and underline them.
Check that students have made appropriate spelling changes when writing plural nouns.

 Notes for Home: Your child formed plural nouns—words that name more than one person, place, or thing. *Home Activity:* Look at magazine and newspaper advertisements together. Have your child identify several singular nouns. Then have him or her spell the plural forms.

170   Grammar: Plural Nouns

Grammar: Plural Nouns

RETEACHING

Follow the hint on each machine. Change each singular noun to a plural noun.

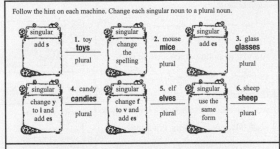

singular / add s — 1. toy / **toys** / plural
singular / change the spelling — 2. mouse / **mice** / plural
singular / add es — 3. glass / **glasses** / plural
singular / change y to i and add es — 4. candy / **candies** / plural
singular / change f to v and add es — 5. elf / **elves** / plural
singular / use the same form — 6. sheep / **sheep** / plural

A **plural noun** names more than one person, place, or thing. Most nouns add an ending in the plural form. Some nouns change their spelling in the plural form.

Directions: Write the plural form of each noun.

1. roof   **roofs**
2. thief   **thieves**
3. foot   **feet**
4. tray   **trays**
5. woman   **women**
6. bush   **bushes**
7. deer   **deer**
8. spy   **spies**
9. ax   **axes**

Directions: Rewrite each sentence. Change the underlined singular noun to a plural noun.

10. Howard spotted the wild strawberry.
   Howard spotted the wild strawberries.

11. The leaf hid some of them.
   The leaves hid some of them.

12. We quickly filled the box.
   We quickly filled the boxes.

 Notes for Home: Your child identified plural forms of nouns. *Home Activity:* Name objects in one room of your home. Have your child write the plural forms of the names of the objects.

Grammar: Plural Nouns   **171**

Grammar: Plural Nouns

Directions: Underline each plural noun.

1. A bird has feathers.
2. Wolves and foxes are mammals.
3. Alligators and crocodiles are reptiles.
4. Some animals travel in packs.
5. A monkey can hang by its tail in trees.
6. Many lizards live in the desert.
7. Ducks have webbed feet.
8. A frog lays eggs in the water.

Directions: Write the plural form of each noun.

9. lady   **ladies**
10. wolf   **wolves**
11. goose   **geese**
12. fox   **foxes**
13. hiss   **hisses**
14. birch   **birches**
15. feather   **feathers**
16. ostrich   **ostriches**
17. woman   **women**
18. puppy   **puppies**
19. boss   **bosses**
20. couch   **couches**
21. man   **men**
22. ranch   **ranches**
23. branch   **branches**
24. monkey   **monkeys**
25. foot   **feet**
26. baby   **babies**
27. salmon   **salmon**
28. canary   **canaries**
29. bush   **bushes**
30. pouch   **pouches**
31. half   **halves**
32. moose   **moose**
33. class   **classes**
34. summer   **summers**
35. guppy   **guppies**
36. boot   **boots**

Write a Funny Story
Write a funny story about animals. Include details about how they look and what they do. Use plural nouns. Write on a separate sheet of paper.
Check to make sure that students have spelled plural nouns correctly.

 Notes for Home: Your child wrote the plural forms of nouns. *Home Activity:* Read sentences with plural nouns from a magazine or newspaper. Have your child identify the plural nouns and write them in new sentences.

172   Grammar: Plural Nouns

Word Study: Compound Words

Directions: **Compound words** are words formed from two other words, such as *something* and *bookshelf*. Combine a word from the left box with a word from the right box to form a compound word that makes sense. Write both words and the resulting compound word on the lines below.

mail	pop
bread	night
fore	basket
with	up
any	out

head	ball
body	stairs
out	doors
corn	stick
gown	box

Order may vary.

	Left Box		**Right Box**		**Compound Word**
1.	mail	+	box	=	mailbox
2.	bread	+	stick	=	breadstick
3.	fore	+	head	=	forehead
4.	with	+	out	=	without
5.	any	+	body	=	anybody
6.	pop	+	corn	=	popcorn
7.	night	+	gown	=	nightgown
8.	basket	+	ball	=	basketball
9.	up	+	stairs	=	upstairs
10.	out	+	doors	=	outdoors

Directions: Read each sentence. Part of a compound word is missing. Choose the word that best completes the compound word and makes sense in the sentence. Write the whole compound word on the line to the left. **Possible answers given.**

outside	11. I was out_____ on my front porch.
summertime	12. Since it was summer_____, it was very hot.
someone	13. I heard some_____ call out my name.
somewhere	14. The sound came from _____where behind me.
baseball	15. It was my best friend Sue, who wanted me to play base_____ with her.

 Notes for Home: Your child formed compound words, such as *something*. *Home Activity:* Experiment with common words children see around the house. Have your child put two words together to try to make a compound word. Check each word in a dictionary.

Spelling: Compound Words 1

Pretest Directions: Fold back the page along the dotted line. On the blanks, write the spelling words as they are dictated. When you have finished the test, unfold the page and check your words.

1.	mailbox	1.	The **mailbox** is full.
2.	nearby	2.	There are many stores **nearby**.
3.	into	3.	We went **into** the library.
4.	sometimes	4.	**Sometimes** I forget to be polite.
5.	sunset	5.	It was a beautiful **sunset**.
6.	anything	6.	Is there **anything** I can do?
7.	daylight	7.	It was broad **daylight**.
8.	something	8.	Did you hear **something**?
9.	haircut	9.	Carl needs a **haircut**.
10.	notebook	10.	I lost my **notebook**.
11.	earthquake	11.	The **earthquake** was scary.
12.	hideout	12.	The bandits have a **hideout**.
13.	textbook	13.	Read your history **textbook**.
14.	volleyball	14.	We played **volleyball** today.
15.	horseback	15.	**Horseback** riding is fun.
16.	handwriting	16.	Renaldo has neat **handwriting**.
17.	kickstand	17.	My bike's **kickstand** broke.
18.	rattlesnake	18.	The **rattlesnake** almost bit me.
19.	fireplace	19.	This **fireplace** is made of stone.
20.	housework	20.	**Housework** can be tiring.

 Notes for Home: Your child took a pretest on compound words. *Home Activity:* Help your child learn misspelled words before the final test. Dictate the word and have your child spell the word aloud for you or write it on paper.

Spelling: Compound Words 1

		Word List		
mailbox	sunset	haircut	textbook	kickstand
nearby	anything	notebook	volleyball	rattlesnake
into	daylight	earthquake	horseback	fireplace
sometimes	something	hideout	handwriting	housework

Directions: Combine a word from each box below to form a compound word from the word list. Write the compound word on the line. **Order may vary.**

some	back
note	quake
some	out
hide	place
horse	thing
kick	stand
earth	times
rattle	book
fire	snake

1.	sometimes
2.	notebook
3.	something
4.	hideout
5.	horseback
6.	kickstand
7.	earthquake
8.	rattlesnake
9.	fireplace

Directions: Find two words in each sentence that make up a compound word from the box at the top of the page. Write the word on the line.

housework	10. Our house needs a lot of work done to it.
volleyball	11. It took just a single volley for the ball to go out.
into	12. I looked in the cupboard to see what was left.
mailbox	13. He dropped the piece of mail in the box.
anything	14. Isn't there any way I can give this thing back?
sunset	15. We watched the sun as it set in the sky.
daylight	16. During the day, the light is very bright.
nearby	17. It is near the stream that runs by our house.
textbook	18. I wrote the text for the book, but I didn't illustrate it.
handwriting	19. My hand is sore from writing.
haircut	20. My hair is long, and I need to get it cut.

 Notes for Home: Your child spelled compound words, longer words formed by joining two or more shorter words. *Home Activity:* Together, see how many items you can find in your home that have names that are compound words. List them, and check a dictionary.

Spelling: Compound Words 1

Directions: Proofread this advertisement. Find four spelling mistakes. Use the proofreading marks to correct each mistake.

Volunteers Wanted!

Are you a young person looking for somethin~g~ to do this summer? Shady Rest Home is looking for young people who live nearb~y~e to spend a few hours a week with our residents. We need volunteers to read, play vol~l~eyball and other games, or just visit and talk. Sometimes you might be needed to help in the kitchen or do some light housew~o~rk. If interested, call 555-3725 or drop a note into a mailbox today.

≡	Make a capital.
/	Make a small letter.
∧	Add something.
℘	Take out something.
⊙	Add a period.
¶	Begin a new paragraph.

Spelling Tip

Remember to keep all the letters of the shorter words when spelling compound words. For example: **hide** + **out** = **hideout**.

	Word List	
mailbox		earthquake
nearby		hideout
into		textbook
sometimes		volleyball
sunset		horseback
anything		handwriting
daylight		kickstand
something		rattlesnake
haircut		fireplace
notebook		housework

Write an Advertisement

On a separate sheet of paper, write your own advertisement offering a service or selling a product. Try to use at least four of your spelling words.
Answers will vary, but each advertisement should include at least four spelling words.

 Notes for Home: Your child spelled compound words, longer words formed by joining two or more shorter words. *Home Activity:* Look at the words in the box that your child didn't use in his or her writing exercise. Ask him or her to use several of these words in a sentence.

© Scott Foresman 5

Spelling Workbook 5.2, p. 32

Name _____ Dwaina Brooks

Spelling: Compound Words 1   REVIEW

Word List

mailbox	anything	earthquake	handwriting
nearby	daylight	hideout	kickstand
into	something	textbook	rattlesnake
sometimes	haircut	volleyball	fireplace
sunset	notebook	horseback	housework

Directions: Write the word from the box that is associated with each place.

1. stationery store **notebook**
2. barbershop **haircut**
3. post office **mailbox**
4. school **textbook**
5. stable **horseback**
6. sports shop **volleyball**
7. bicycle shop **kickstand**
8. desert **rattlesnake**

Directions: Choose the word from the box that best completes each sentence. Write the word on the line to the left.

earthquake 9. Many homes were destroyed by the _____.

fireplace 10. All that was left standing of one house was the brick _____.

something 11. Rebecca wanted to do _____ to help the victims.

handwriting 12. She filled out an application in her best _____.

daylight 13. She awoke at _____ to join the group of volunteers.

hideout 14. They scoured the disaster area looking for anyone concealed in a _____.

into 15. She shone her flashlight _____ dark spaces and holes.

anything 16. She listened carefully but didn't hear _____.

Sometimes 17. _____ she felt like giving up.

nearby 18. Then several children were located in a _____ basement.

sunset 19. By _____ Rebecca was exhausted.

housework 20. She couldn't even think of the _____ that would be needed to get these homes back in order.

Notes for Home: Your child spelled compound words, longer words formed by joining two or more shorter words, such as *housework* and *fireplace.* *Home Activity:* Challenge your child to make up a story using as many of the compound words listed above as possible.

Spelling: Compound Words 1   **177**

Practice Book 5.2, p. 79

Name _____ Dwaina Brooks

Newspaper

A **newspaper** is a daily or weekly publication containing news, advertisements, features, editorials, and other useful information, such as TV listings. You can scan headlines to help you find articles you would like to read.

Directions: Scan the headlines from different parts of a newspaper. Then answer the questions that follow.

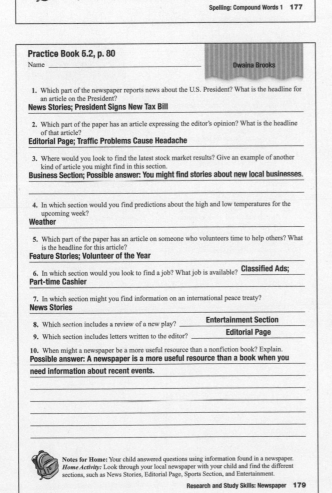

178   Research and Study Skills: Newspaper

Practice Book 5.2, p. 80

Name _____ Dwaina Brooks

1. Which part of the newspaper reports news about the U.S. President? What is the headline for an article on the President?
News Stories; President Signs New Tax Bill

2. Which part of the paper has an article expressing the editor's opinion? What is the headline of that article?
Editorial Page; Traffic Problems Cause Headache

3. Where would you look to find the latest stock market results? Give an example of another kind of article you might find in this section.
Business Section; Possible answer: You might find stories about new local businesses.

4. In which section would you find predictions about the high and low temperatures for the upcoming week?
Weather

5. Which part of the paper has an article on someone who volunteers time to help others? What is the headline for this article?
Feature Stories; Volunteer of the Year

6. In which section would you look to find a job? What job is available? **Classified Ads;**
Part-time Cashier

7. In which section might you find information on an international peace treaty?
News Stories

8. Which section includes a review of a new play? **Entertainment Section**

9. Which section includes letters written to the editor? **Editorial Page**

10. When might a newspaper be a more useful resource than a nonfiction book? Explain.
Possible answer: A newspaper is a more useful resource than a book when you need information about recent events.

Notes for Home: Your child answered questions using information found in a newspaper. *Home Activity:* Look through your local newspaper with your child and find the different sections, such as News Stories, Editorial Page, Sports Section, and Entertainment.

Research and Study Skills: Newspaper   **179**

Practice Book 5.2, p. 81

Name _____ Everglades

Author's Viewpoint

- **Author's viewpoint** is the way an author thinks about the subject of his or her writing.
- To learn an author's viewpoint, think about the author's opinion and choice of words. Sometimes you can figure out an author's viewpoint even when it is not stated directly.
- Unbalanced, or biased, writing happens when an author presents only one viewpoint. Balanced writing presents both sides of an issue equally.

Directions: Reread "Action Against Pollution." Then complete the table. Identify key words or phrases that reveal the viewpoint of the two authors. Then tell the authors' viewpoint.
Possible answers given.

Statement	What It Reveals
Young people realize that actions speak louder than words.	1. Authors are in favor of doing something rather than just talking about it.
. . . they're taking responsibility through a wide variety of actions that will help make the world a better place.	2. Authors approve of the actions the young people are taking.
When kids returned to class, they decided to do something about the problem.	3. Authors feel students knew how to develop a plan.
Thanks to their hard work and determination, it now has more than 2,500 chapters in 20 countries around the world.	4. Authors give proof that the plan worked.

Authors' Viewpoint

5. **Kids who work to help the environment are doing the right thing.**

Notes for Home: Your child read an article and identified the authors' viewpoint. *Home Activity:* Together with your child, read a column from the editorial page of a newspaper. Help your child figure out the author's viewpoint.

182   Author's Viewpoint

© Scott Foresman 5

Answers   721

Name _____

Everglades

Vocabulary

Directions: Write the word from the box that belongs in each group.

1. leaked, drained, __seeped__
2. amazing, unbelievable, __miraculous__
3. edge, border, __brim__
4. thought, considered, __pondered__
5. amounts, numbers, __quantities__

> **Check the Words You Know**
> __ brim
> __ miraculous
> __ pondered
> __ prospered
> __ quantities
> __ seeped

Directions: Choose the word from the box that best matches each clue. Write the word in the puzzle.

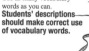

```
6.              7.          8.
p r o s p e r e d      s
        o              e
9. q u a n t i t i e s  e
        d              p
        e              e
10.   b r i m          d
        e
        d
```

Across

6. It's what the rich person did.
9. Eggs by the dozen are these.
10. A cup can be filled to here.

Down

7. It's what the careful planner did.
8. It's what the leaky bag did.

Write a Description

Imagine a beautiful lake or pond and the animals and plants that live there. On a separate sheet of paper, describe the place. Use as many vocabulary words as you can. **Students' descriptions should make correct use of vocabulary words.**

Notes for Home: Your child identified and used new vocabulary words from *Everglades*. **Home Activity:** Think of words your child knows. Give your child clues about each word. For example: *It's something that rings and is used for talking to others. (telephone)*

Name _____

Everglades

Author's Viewpoint

- An **author's viewpoint** is the way an author thinks about the subject of his or her writing. You can learn an author's viewpoint by looking at the words used and the opinions expressed.
- Balanced writing presents both sides of an issue. Unbalanced, or biased, writing presents one side more than another.

Directions: Reread what happens in *Everglades* as the storyteller completes his story. Then answer the questions below. Think about how the author reveals her viewpoint in the article.

> Another child looked around. "And where did the mammals and snails and one-celled plants and animals go?"
>
> They vanished when the engineers dug canals in the Everglades and drained the fresh water into the sea to make land. Farmers tilled the land; business people built towns and roads upon it. Pesticides and fertilizers flowed into the river waters and poisoned the one-celled animals and plants. The snails died, the fish died, the mammals and birds died.
>
> "But this is a sad story," said a fifth child.
>
> Text Copyright ©1995 by Jean Craighead George. Used by permission of HarperCollins Publishers.

Possible answers given.

1. How do you think the author feels about the destruction of the Everglades?
The author is saddened by it.

2. What words does the author use that convey this viewpoint?
She repeats "died" and calls it "a sad story."

3. Is the description of what happened to the creatures balanced or unbalanced? Explain.
Unbalanced, since it only presents the environmentalist's side of the story

4. State, in your own words, the viewpoint the author has about what happened to the creatures.
Most of the development of the Everglades has had a destructive effect on plants and animals.

5. On a separate sheet of paper, identify the author's viewpoint as expressed in the article as a whole. Support your answer with examples.
While the author is saddened by the destruction of the Everglades, she is hopeful for its future. The storyteller tells a "new story" describing the return of the animals and plants to the Everglades.

Notes for Home: Your child read a passage, described the author's viewpoint, and identified whether the writing shows a bias. **Home Activity:** Work with your child to read a letter to the editor and identify the author's viewpoint and bias.

Name _____

Everglades

Selection Test

Directions: Choose the best answer to each item. Mark the letter for the answer you have chosen.

Part 1: Vocabulary

Find the answer choice that means about the same as the underlined word in each sentence.

1. Dinah sat quietly and <u>pondered</u>.
   - (A) thought carefully
   - B. worried
   - C. stared at closely
   - D. became sad

2. It was a <u>miraculous</u> day.
   - F. long and tiring
   - (G) marvelous; wonderful
   - H. full of jokes and teasing
   - J. upsetting; disturbing

3. Water spilled over the <u>brim</u>.
   - A. a stone wall
   - B. a cover
   - C. a large pile
   - (D) an edge

4. Water <u>seeped</u> into the basement.
   - F. ran through pipes
   - G. flowed quickly
   - H. fell steadily
   - (J) leaked slowly

5. There were <u>quantities</u> of small fish.
   - A. small clusters
   - B. something hidden
   - (C) large numbers
   - D. something dark

6. The wildlife <u>prospered</u>.
   - F. became fewer in number
   - G. spread out in different directions
   - (H) grew or developed well
   - J. became too crowded

Part 2: Comprehension

Use what you know about the selection to answer each item.

7. What is the Everglades?
   - A. a round, deep lake
   - (B) a shallow, warm river
   - C. a long, thin piece of land
   - D. an ocean bay

8. Limestone is made from—
   - F. water.
   - G. tiny one-celled animals.
   - (H) seashells.
   - J. grass and trees.

9. Alligators can live in saw grass because of—
   - (A) their leathery skin.
   - B. the abundance of birds.
   - C. their sharp teeth.
   - D. the blowing winds.

10. Which of these came to the Everglades first?
   - F. Spanish conquistadors
   - (G) panthers
   - H. Calusa people
   - J. orchid hunters

11. Which sentence states an opinion?
   - A. Hunters shot tens of thousands of egrets.
   - B. *Seminole* means "runaway."
   - C. Alligators were hunted for their hides.
   - (D) This is a sad story.

GO ON

Name _____

Everglades

12. What can you tell about the author of this selection?
   - (F) She has a great love for the beauty of the natural world.
   - G. She would like to build a new home in the Everglades.
   - H. She sees no future for the creatures of the Everglades.
   - J. She thinks storytellers should tell happy stories, not sad ones.

13. Which sentence best describes this selection?
   - A. It is mostly make-believe, but some of it is based on facts.
   - (B) It is mostly based on facts, but the author's choice of words expresses her point of view.
   - C. It is mostly based on old legends.
   - D. It is mostly opinions, with some facts to support the opinions.

14. Which of these human acts does the author think was harmful to the Everglades?
   - (F) draining water from the Everglades to make land
   - G. catching fish in the Everglades
   - H. making tools out of seashells found in the Everglades
   - J. poling a dugout canoe through the Everglades

15. The author would most likely agree with which of these statements?
   - A. Some of the plants and animals of the Everglades should probably be restored, but only the ones people like.
   - B. People should continue to make money from the rich resources in the Everglades.
   - (C) The wonders of nature in the Everglades can return only if people change their ways.
   - D. The Everglades was never a good environment for fishing.

STOP

© Scott Foresman 5

Author's Viewpoint

- An **author's viewpoint** is the way an author thinks about the subject of his or her writing. You can learn an author's viewpoint by looking at the words used and the opinions expressed.

- Balanced writing presents both sides of an issue. Unbalanced, or biased, writing presents one side more than another.

Directions: Read the two passages below.

Passage 1
The timber industry employs thousands of workers. Without trees to cut, many people would be out of work. Their families would go hungry. Some misguided people complain that by cutting down the forest, we are destroying the habitat of certain animals and birds. This is unlikely. Birds can always fly to a new home and animals can survive almost anything. What's important is to keep people working and make America strong.

Passage 2
The world of many animals is very fragile. Cutting down a forest where these creatures have lived for generations is like a death sentence. They cannot adapt to the destruction of their environment and will die. These forests must be protected from greedy developers and lumber companies. They only want to get rich. New laws must be passed to end the killing of innocent creatures.

Directions: Complete the table. Think about the words used in the two passages and the opinions expressed that reveal each author's viewpoint.

Possible answers are given.

Author's Viewpoint	Words Used	Opinions Expressed
Passage 1 Forests must be cut down to keep lumber workers employed.	1. **go hungry, misguided people, unlikely**	2. **Cutting forests keeps people working and America strong. Animals and birds won't be harmed.**
Passage 2 3. **Cutting forests is wrong because it endangers wildlife.**	4. **death sentence, greedy developers, the killing of innocent creatures**	5. **Cutting forests destroys habitats and kills animals and birds. The lumber companies only care about making money.**

 Notes for Home: Your child read two passages and identified each author's viewpoint. *Home Activity:* Work with your child to read or listen to an advertisement. Talk about the words and the opinions that are used to try to convince people to buy the product.

Author's Viewpoint **187**

Cause and Effect REVIEW

Directions: Read the passage. Then read each question about the passage. Choose the best answer to each question. Mark the letter for the answer you have chosen.

Here Today—Gone Tomorrow?

Remember the dinosaurs? They are now extinct. They disappeared about 63 million years ago. Nobody knows exactly why. Remember the dodo? Remember the moa? Remember the passenger pigeon? The dodo, moa, and passenger pigeon are species of birds that are now extinct. They all disappeared within the last 200 years. Some of the mammals that have also become extinct in the last 200 years include a form of zebra called a quagga and a sea mammal called Steller's sea cow.

Over millions of years, many species have died out because natural conditions changed. However, the process of extinction may not be over. Many plants and animals *today* are in danger of becoming extinct. There are several reasons for this more recent pattern of extinction. Pollution, highway construction, overhunting, and wetland drainage all contribute to the extinction of plant and animal species. These reasons are all caused by humans.

Since the 1800s, the process of extinction has speeded up. This is a result of more people as well as more business and industry. Humans have changed the world more in the past 200 years than in all the previous centuries of human history. These changes are so rapid that many plants and animals cannot adapt. As a result of the changes, the plants and animals die out.

1. What has caused species to die out over millions of years?
   A. too much pollution
   B. too many people
   (C) changing natural conditions
   D. growth of industry

2. What is the effect stated in the second paragraph?
   (F) Many of today's plant and animal species are endangered.
   G. Wetlands are drained.
   H. Water is polluted.
   J. Highways are built.

3. The process of extinction has speeded up because of—
   (A) more people on the earth.
   B. slowed industrial growth.
   C. clean air and water.
   D. animals' ability to adapt.

4. What is the effect of environmental changes that are too rapid?
   F. People now have more time for entertainment.
   G. Plants and animals adapt easily with changes.
   (H) Plants and animals cannot adapt.
   J. Habitats stay the same.

5. What happens if plants and animals cannot adapt?
   A. They reproduce.
   (B) They die out.
   C. They thrive.
   D. They get lost.

 Notes for Home: Your child read a nonfiction article and identified causes and effects. *Home Activity:* Work with your child to identify causes and effects. Use "Because" statements such as *I hurt my arm because I tripped over the rock.*

188 Cause and Effect

Writing Across Texts

Directions: The Everglades have suffered many changes over the years—some natural and some caused by humans. In the left column, add five natural changes you read about in "The Fury of a Hurricane." In the right column, add five man-made changes you read about in *Everglades.*

Possible answers given. Note that some answers may appear in both columns.

Save Our National Park

The Fury of a Hurricane	Everglades
All the trees in Hurricane Andrew's path were felled.	Many areas of the Everglades were drained by engineers.
1. **A tangled mass of dead and dying plants lay on the ground.**	6. **Hunters killed alligators and egrets.**
2. **Foreign plants invaded the damaged areas of the park.**	7. **Most of the orchids were picked and sold.**
3. **Some animals lost their food supply when native plants were driven out.**	8. **Canals were built through the Everglades.**
4. **The mangrove trees were shredded.**	9. **Pesticides poisoned animals and plants.**
5. **The loss of mangroves affected many food chains and food webs.**	10. **Towns and roads were built in the area.**

Write an Editorial

Using facts and details from "The Fury of a Hurricane" and *Everglades,* write an editorial to express your opinion on one of the following statements.

- Natural changes, such as those caused by hurricanes, pose the most serious threat to the Everglades.

- Changes caused by humans, such as chemical pollution, pose the most serious threat to the Everglades.

Write your editorial on a separate sheet of paper.
Editorials will vary. Check that students have expressed a strong opinion about the changes in the Everglades and that they have supported their opinions with facts from the selections.

 Notes for Home: Your child read and listed details about changes in the Florida Everglades. *Home Activity:* As you read a story or article, have your child express opinions about its topic.

Writing Across Texts **189**

Grammar: Plural Nouns REVIEW

Directions: Write the plural form of each singular noun.

1. swamp	**swamps**	7. calf	**calves**
2. bench	**benches**	8. deer	**deer**
3. tooth	**teeth**	9. crocodile	**crocodiles**
4. key	**keys**	10. tree	**trees**
5. mouse	**mice**	11. knife	**knives**
6. body	**bodies**	12. ax	**axes**

Directions: Use the plural form of the noun in ( ) to complete each sentence. Write the plural noun on the line to the left.

tourists — 13. Millions of _____ visit the Everglades. (tourist)

families — 14. From all over the world, _____ come to see this tropical area. (family)

children — 15. Adults and _____ are fascinated by its scenery and wildlife. (child)

people — 16. Will these _____ join in helping to save the endangered area? (person)

sheep — 17. Crocodiles are not as soft and cuddly as _____, but they are worth saving. (sheep)

marshes — 18. Unusual plants and wildlife live in the Everglades' _____. (marsh)

Volunteers — 19. _____ who are willing to clean up the area are always needed. (Volunteer)

lives — 20. Cleanup efforts may save the _____ of many plants and animals. (life)

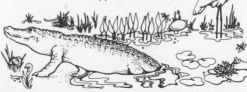

 Notes for Home: Your child wrote the plural forms of both regular and irregular nouns. *Home Activity:* Look through a magazine or catalog, and challenge your child to use singular nouns to name things in the pictures, then write the plural form of each noun.

190 Grammar: Plural Nouns

Answers 723

Grammar Practice Book 5.2, p. 42

Name _____

Everglades

Grammar: Possessive Nouns

A **singular possessive noun** shows that one person, place, or thing has or owns something.

- To make a singular noun show possession, add an **apostrophe (')** and **-s**
  the feathers of the bird   the bird's feathers

A **plural possessive noun** shows that more than one person, place or thing has or owns something.

- When a plural noun ends in **-s**, add just an **apostrophe (')** to make the noun show possession.
  the scales of the alligators   the alligators' scales

- When a plural noun does not end in **-s**, add an **apostrophe (')** and **-s** to show possession.
  the laughter of the people   the people's laughter

Directions: Circle the correct possessive noun in ( ) to complete each sentence.

1. The (library's/librarys') story hour will begin today at two o'clock.
2. The (children's/childrens') favorite storyteller will be there.
3. The (storyteller's/storytellers') name is Nina.
4. (Nina's/Ninas') voice is soft, but clear.
5. Nina tells different (culture's/cultures') stories.

Directions: Add an apostrophe to each underlined possessive noun. Rewrite the noun on the line.

Native Americans'
stories'
character's
Mother Earth's
story's

6. I love the various Native Americans stories best.
7. These stories characters can be kind, wise, or tricky.
8. One characters name was Mother Earth.
9. Mother Earths children were the human race.
10. The storys message was that we should care for Earth as we would care for our own mother.

 Notes for Home: Your child learned how to use and punctuate possessive nouns. **Home Activity:** Ask your child to list items he or she owns, describing clothing, books, and so on. Help your child use possessive nouns to show ownership (Al's skis, the twins' toys).

Grammar: Possessive Nouns   **191**

Grammar Practice Book 5.2, p. 43

Name _____

Everglades

Grammar: Possessive Nouns

Directions: Rewrite each underlined phrase to show possession. Write the new phrase on the line to the left.

alligator's name
America's alligators
China's alligators
Alligators' snouts
These creatures' eggs
Florida's crocodiles
Crocodiles' teeth
This reptile's snout
These animals' skins
crocodile's eggs

1. The name of the alligator comes from the Spanish word for lizard.
2. Alligators of America are found in the southeast.
3. Alligators of China live in the Yangtze River.
4. The snouts of alligators are broad and flat.
5. The eggs of these creatures hatch in the hot sun.
6. Crocodiles of Florida bury themselves in mud to hibernate.
7. The teeth of crocodiles can crush the bones of small animals.
8. The snout of this reptile is long and narrow.
9. The skins of these animals were used to make shoes and handbags.
10. Today, some people eat the eggs of a crocodile.

Write an Advertisement
Imagine you've been hired to help save an endangered species! On a separate sheet of paper, create an advertisement that teaches people ways to save creatures like alligators and crocodiles. You may need to do some research first to learn more about a particular species. Use singular and plural possessive nouns in your advertisement.
Check to see that students use and punctuate their possessive nouns correctly.

Notes for Home: Your child learned how to use and punctuate possessive nouns. **Home Activity:** Take a walk with your child. Ask your child to use possessive nouns to show that one person, place, or thing owns something, such as Mr. Wong's house.

192   Grammar: Possessive Nouns

Grammar Practice Book 5.2, p. 44

Name _____

Everglades

Grammar: Possessive Nouns   RETEACH

Write the words that tell who owns the bicycles.

1. One girl's bicycle was pink. _____ **girl's**
2. The twins' bicycle has two seats. _____ **twins'**
3. The men's bicycles have large frames. _____ **men's**

The words **girl's**, **twins'**, and **men's** are possessive nouns. The possessive form of a noun shows ownership.

A **possessive noun** shows ownership. Possessive nouns are formed by adding an apostrophe (') and -s or only an apostrophe.

Directions: Write the possessive noun in each sentence.

1. The dog's tail wagged. _____ **dog's**
2. My grandfather's bicycle is in good condition. **grandfather's**
3. James's bicycle needs a new set of brakes. **James's**
4. The workers' tools are at the repair shop. **workers'**
5. One man's hammer has a broken handle. **man's**
6. The owner's daughter also works at the shop. **owner's**
7. The customers' problems usually are simple. **customers'**

Directions: Write the possessive form of each noun.

8. painter   **painter's**   15. pony   **pony's**
9. uncle   **uncle's**   16. children   **children's**
10. families **families'**   17. fox   **fox's**
11. goose   **goose's**   18. deer   **deer's**
12. woman   **woman's**   19. friends   **friends'**
13. sister   **sister's**   20. father   **father's**
14. guest   **guest's**   21. ladies   **ladies'**

 Notes for Home: Your child wrote the possessive forms of nouns. **Home Activity:** Have your child list characters from a favorite book or movie. Then have him or her write the possessive form of each name followed by the name of something the character owns. (Tom's marbles)

Grammar: Possessive Nouns   **193**

Grammar Practice Book 5.2, p. 45

Name _____

Everglades

Grammar: Possessive Nouns

Directions: Circle each singular possessive noun. Underline each plural possessive noun. Then write each possessive noun.

1. The cook's knife was too dull to cut the meat. **cook's**
2. The dishwashers' gloves were made of rubber. **dishwashers'**
3. Ms. Santiago tasted the baker's cakes. **baker's**
4. Then she shook the man's hand. **man's**
5. Other workers' smiles brightened the room. **workers'**
6. The waitresses' dresses were long. **waitresses'**
7. The owner's family ate at the center table. **owner's**
8. The child's birthday cake was beautiful. **child's**
9. All of the children's eyes opened wide at the sight. **children's**
10. The family's birthday song filled the restaurant. **family's**
11. Some customers' voices added volume to the song. **customers'**

Directions: Write the possessive form of each underlined noun.

12. The ladies coats were left at the front rack. **ladies'**
13. One guest sister arrived at the party very late. **guest's**
14. The woman car was in a traffic jam. **woman's**
15. Other drivers cars had blocked the entire street. **drivers'**
16. The traffic officers cars flashed their lights. **officers'**
17. The men dogs waited in the front yard. **men's**
18. My friend birthday is tomorrow. **friend's**

Write a Family Memoir
Write a family memoir, or personal record, that tells about things your family has that were saved from past generations. Use singular and plural possessive nouns. Write on a separate sheet of paper.

Make sure students have punctuated and written possessive nouns correctly.

 Notes for Home: Your child wrote possessive forms of nouns. **Home Activity:** Have your child make a list of jobs that people have in your community. Then have your child say the possessive forms of the job titles and a tool each person might use. (The chef's spoon)

194   Grammar: Possessive Nouns

© Scott Foresman 5

Word Study: Base Words

Directions: Many words are formed by adding letters at the beginning or end of a word. The word you start with is called the **base word**. Read each sentence. Find the base word in the underlined word. Write the base word on the line.

sparkle	1. The water <u>sparkled</u> in the bright sun.
bloom	2. Flowers once <u>bloomed</u> everywhere.
spill	3. The waters were <u>spilling</u> over with fish.
grace	4. Wild birds <u>gracefully</u> flew above the marshy waters.
fill	5. The sounds of insects <u>filled</u> the air.
appear	6. Some animals have all but <u>disappeared</u>.
harm	7. Other kinds of wildlife remain <u>unharmed</u>.
do	8. Many people would like to <u>undo</u> the damage.
work	9. Some <u>workers</u> help care for injured birds.
like	10. The Everglades today are <u>unlike</u> the Everglades of long ago.

Directions: Combine each base word and ending to make a new word. You might need to add or take away letters to spell the word correctly. Write the word on the line.

11. leather	+	-y	=	leathery
12. sun	+	-y	=	sunny
13. cut	+	-ing	=	cutting
14. quick	+	-ly	=	quickly
15. glitter	+	-ed	=	glittered

Notes for Home: Your child identified base words in longer words, such as *appear* in *disappeared*, and used base words to form longer words. **Home Activity:** Read a magazine article with your child. Look for words made of base words and endings.

Word Study: Base Words **195**

Spelling: Short Vowels *a, i, o, u*

Pretest Directions: Fold back the page along the dotted line. On the blanks, write the spelling words as they are dictated. When you have finished the test, unfold the page and check your words.

1.	handle	1.	The pump **handle** is loose.
2.	perhaps	2.	**Perhaps** they will not come.
3.	anger	3.	Please control your **anger**.
4.	accident	4.	There was an auto **accident**.
5.	adventure	5.	Traveling can be an **adventure**.
6.	before	6.	We will finish **before** them.
7.	because	7.	She cried **because** she was sad.
8.	decided	8.	Have you **decided** what to do?
9.	pretend	9.	Let's **pretend** to be airplanes.
10.	belong	10.	The clothes **belong** to Sue.
11.	possible	11.	Is it really **possible**?
12.	solve	12.	Detectives might **solve** the case.
13.	problem	13.	This is a hard math **problem**.
14.	lobster	14.	Sarah likes to eat **lobster**.
15.	python	15.	The **python** is a large snake.
16.	swung	16.	The monkey **swung** in the tree.
17.	jungle	17.	The **jungle** was full of noises.
18.	shuttle	18.	The space **shuttle** took off.
19.	blood	19.	I hate the sight of **blood**.
20.	flood	20.	The **flood** caused damage.

Notes for Home: Your child took a pretest on words that have the short vowels *a, i, o,* and *u*. **Home Activity:** Help your child learn misspelled words before the final test. Have your child divide misspelled words into parts (such as syllables) and concentrate on each part.

196 Spelling: Short Vowels *a, i, o, u*

Spelling: Short Vowels *a, i, o, u*

Word List			
handle	before	possible	swung
perhaps	because	solve	jungle
anger	decided	problem	shuttle
accident	pretend	lobster	blood
adventure	belong	python	flood

Directions: Choose the words from the box that have the **short u** sound heard in **sun** or the **short i** sound heard in **begin**. Write each word in the correct column.

Short u spelled u *Order may vary.*

1. swung
2. jungle
3. shuttle

Short u spelled oo

4. blood
5. flood

Short i spelled e

6. before
7. because
8. decided
9. pretend
10. belong

Directions: Choose the word from the box that best replaces the underlined word or words. Write the word on the line.

accident	11. We took in our new dog, Flash, purely by <u>chance</u>.
adventure	12. Getting him home was an <u>exciting, dangerous experience</u>.
lobster	13. My sister pinched him so hard putting on his collar, he must have thought she was a <u>hard-shelled sea animal</u>.
handle	14. She quickly learned to <u>control</u> the dog gently.
python	15. My brother gave Flash a squeeze like a <u>big, thick snake</u>.
problem	16. Our cat, though, presents a serious <u>dilemma</u>.
anger	17. Fluff still has moments of <u>rage</u> about sharing our attention.
Perhaps	18. <u>Maybe</u> Flash and Fluff will get along well soon.
possible	19. It's <u>not impossible</u> that a cat and dog can be friends.
solve	20. With a little training and separate rooms, we will <u>figure out</u> this difficulty.

Notes for Home: Your child spelled words that have the short vowel sounds *a, i, o,* or *u* (*handle, before, possible, swung, good*). **Home Activity:** Say these words with your child and look at how the vowel sounds are spelled. Add other words that have the same vowel sounds and spellings.

Spelling: Short Vowels *a, i, o, u* **197**

Spelling: Short Vowels *a, i, o, u*

Directions: Proofread this article. Find five spelling mistakes. Use the proofreading marks to correct each mistake.

For many years the Everglades were in danger of being destroyed. Then the people of Florida desided to solve the problim before it was too late.

Water that had been dammed up was allowed to flud into the area. Underpasses were built so wild animals could travel safely under highways. Exotic plants that didn't bilong there were removed bicuz they choked out native plants.

These solutions helped save the Everglades.

Proofreading Marks	
≡	Make a capital.
/	Make a small letter.
∧	Add something.
✎	Take out something.
⊙	Add a period.
¶	Begin a new paragraph.

Spelling Tip

blood   flood
The **short u** sound can be spelled **u** or **oo**. Remember to spell **blood** and **flood** with two o's by remembering that liquids can <u>ooze</u>.

Word List	
handle	possible
perhaps	solve
anger	problem
accident	lobster
adventure	python
before	swung
because	jungle
decided	shuttle
pretend	blood
belong	flood

Write a Science Article

On a separate sheet of paper, write a short article about how people in your community or state are protecting the environment. Try to use at least five of your spelling words. **Students may need to do some research before writing their articles. Answers will vary, but each article should include at least five spelling words.**

Notes for Home: Your child spelled words that have the short vowel sounds *a, i, o,* or *u* (*handle, before, possible, swung, good*). **Home Activity:** Have your child find other verb forms of *decided, pretend,* and *swung,* such as *deciding, pretended,* and *swing.*

198 Spelling: Short Vowels *a, i, o,* and *u*

Name _____

Everglades

Spelling: Short Vowels *a, i, o, u*

REVIEW

Word List

handle	before	possible	swung
perhaps	because	solve	jungle
anger	decided	problem	shuttle
accident	pretend	lobster	blood
adventure	belong	python	flood

Directions: Choose the word from the box that is the most opposite in meaning for each word or words below. Write the word on the line.

1. impossible **possible**
2. solution **problem**
3. after **before**
4. real **pretend**

5. drought **flood**
6. undecided **decided**
7. joy **anger**
8. deliberate **accident**

Directions: Choose the word from the box that best matches each clue. Write the word on the line.

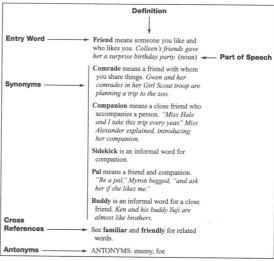

handle 9. part of a teapot
lobster 10. a tasty shellfish
blood 11. a fluid in the body
belong 12. what members do to a club
swung 13. the past tense of *swing*
python 14. a huge kind of snake
perhaps 15. the same as *maybe*
jungle 16. found in a rainforest
shuttle 17. a bus that runs back and forth
adventure 18. an exciting experience
solve 19. what detectives do to crimes
because 20. why things happen

 Notes for Home: Your children identified spelling words from opposites and clues. *Home Activity:* Challenge your child to write a paragraph using as many spelling words as possible.

Name _____

Everglades

Thesaurus

A **thesaurus** is a kind of dictionary in which synonyms (words that have the same or similar meanings), antonyms (words that have opposite meanings), and other related words are classified under headings. You can use a thesaurus to help you find new and interesting words when writing.

Directions: Use the thesaurus entry to answer the questions that follow.

Definition

Entry Word → **Friend** means someone you like and who likes you. *Colleen's friends gave her a surprise birthday party.* (noun) ← **Part of Speech**

Synonyms → **Comrade** means a friend with whom you share things. *Gwen and her comrades in her Girl Scout troop are planning a trip to the zoo.*

Companion means a close friend who accompanies a person. *"Miss Hale and I take this trip every year," Miss Alexander explained, introducing her companion.*

Sidekick is an informal word for companion.

Pal means a friend and companion. *"Be a pal," Myron begged, "and ask her if she likes me."*

Buddy is an informal word for a close friend. *Ken and his buddy Yuji are almost like brothers.*

Cross References → See **familiar** and **friendly** for related words.

Antonyms → ANTONYMS: enemy, foe

From EVERYDAY SPELLING by James Breers, Ronald L. Cramer, W. Dorsey Hammond. © 1998 Addison-Wesley Educational Publishers Inc.

Name _____

Everglades

1. What entry word is shown? **friend**

2. Name the part of speech of the entry word. **noun**

3. What synonyms are given for the entry word? **comrade, companion, sidekick, pal, and buddy**

4. Rewrite this sentence using one of the synonyms from the entry: *My friend Marta and I went on a swamp tour in New Orleans.*
Check that students replace *friend* with one of the synonyms shown.

5. Rewrite this sentence by replacing the underlined words with a word from the entry: *The alligator is no friend to the birds who live in the swamp.*
The alligator is an enemy (or "a foe") to the birds who live in the swamp.

6. Would you use *sidekick* when introducing a visiting friend to your school principal? Explain.
Possible answer: No, *sidekick* is an informal word so it is probably not the best word to use in a more formal situation.

7. What would you do if you wanted to find additional words that have meanings similar to the entry word?
Possible answer: You could look up *familiar* and *friendly*, the two related words cross-referenced in the entry.

8. How does knowing the meaning of *friend* help you understand how to use *foe* in a sentence?
Possible answer: Since *foe* is an antonym of *friend*, you know that *foe* means the opposite of *friend*.

9. If you looked up the entry word *large* in a thesaurus, what synonyms might you find? What antonyms might you find?
Possible synonyms: big, huge, gigantic; Possible antonyms: small, little, tiny

10. Why might a thesaurus be a helpful reference source when you are writing a report for class?
Possible answer: You can use a thesaurus to help you find new and more interesting or precise words to use in your writing.

 Notes for Home: Your child answered questions about a thesaurus entry. *Home Activity:* If a thesaurus is available, challenge your child to look up five words and tell what information is shown. If not available, work together to write five thesaurus entries.

Name _____

Missing Links

Drawing Conclusions

- When you form opinions based on facts and details, you are **drawing conclusions**.
- To draw a conclusion, use logic and clues from what you've read, as well as your own knowledge and experience.
- To check your conclusion, ask yourself if it makes sense. Are there other possible conclusions?

Directions: Reread "Granny's Missing Food." Then complete the table. Write a conclusion for each piece of evidence given. Write evidence that supports each conclusion drawn. **Possible answers given.**

Evidence	Conclusions
Chicken, fruit, and cookies are missing from Granny's house.	1. There may be a thief in her house.
2. **He calls her "Granny." She calls him "my grandson."**	The woman is the narrator's grandmother.
Clooz has only one business card.	3. **He isn't a very successful detective.**
4. **The dog died last spring.**	The dog did not steal Granny's food.
Clooz and the narrator trade funny looks when Granny points to the newspapers she got from the checkout line at the supermarket.	5. **Newspapers found in the supermarket check-out line don't always have true facts.**

 Notes for Home: Your child read a story and used story details, as well as logic, to draw conclusions. *Home Activity:* Offer clues about what you did today. Ask your child to draw conclusions about your activities.

© Scott Foresman 5

---

726 Answers

Vocabulary

Directions: Choose the word from the box that best matches each definition. Write the word on the line.

counter   1. a long, flat, raised surface in a store, restaurant, or a bank

sapphire   2. precious gem, brilliant blue in color

jewelry   3. ring, bracelet, necklace, or other ornament to be worn

smudge   4. smear of dirt or grease

indicates   5. points out; shows; suggests

Check the Words You Know
__ counter
__ indicates
__ jewelry
__ sapphire
__ smudge

Directions: Choose the word from the box that best completes each sentence. Write the word on the matching numbered line to the right.

I wanted to buy the perfect gift for my older sister's graduation. I went to the local **6.** _____ store to look at some necklaces. The sales clerk behind the large **7.** _____ where the jewelry was displayed was very helpful. While looking for a gift, I saw the most beautiful blue stone in a gold necklace. The sales clerk told me that the stone was a **8.** _____. The clerk told me the color and cut of the stone **9.** _____ that it is an excellent piece of jewelry. The necklace was so beautiful that I put my face close to the display case and made a big **10.** _____ on the glass. That was embarrassing! The necklace was too expensive, but I did find a very nice pair of earrings for my sister.

6. _jewelry_
7. _counter_
8. _sapphire_
9. _indicates_
10. _smudge_

Write a Story

Imagine that a robbery has taken place at a local jewelry store, and you are the detective in charge. On a separate sheet of paper, write a story about searching the crime scene for clues. What do you find? Use as many vocabulary words as you can. **Stories will vary. Check that included vocabulary words are used correctly.**

Notes for Home: Your child identified and used new words from the story "Missing Links." *Home Activity:* Act out a radio drama with your child about a jewelry robbery. Use the vocabulary words in your dialogue.

Drawing Conclusions

- When you form opinions based on facts and details, you are **drawing conclusions**.
- To draw a conclusion, use logic and clues from what you've read, as well as your own knowledge and experience. To check your conclusion, ask yourself if it makes sense. Are there other possible conclusions?

Directions: Reread what happens in "Missing Links" when Amanda and Sherlock inspect the smashed jewelry case. Then answer the questions below. Use story details to help you draw conclusions.

> The case that Amanda had been looking into just a few minutes before was now smashed and almost empty. All the cuff links, the tie pins, and the beautiful ring were gone.
> "What happened?" Amanda asked the salesman excitedly.
> "I don't know, I don't know. I must have been putting some ladies' jewelry away in the next counter . . . there was so much confusion . . . I just didn't see . . . but I haven't been near the case. I know you're not supposed to touch anything. The police will probably want to check for fingerprints."
> Sherlock, apparently, was already doing just that. He had his magnifying glass out and was peering intently into the shattered display case.
>
> From FLUTE REVENGE by Andrew Bromberg.
> Copyright © 1982 by William Morrow and Company, Inc. By permission of Greenwillow Books.

Possible answers given.

1. What has happened to the items from the jewelry case?
They have been stolen.

2. What conclusion can you draw about the salesman from the way that he speaks?
The salesman seems to be confused and uncertain about what happened.

3. Why does the salesman say you're not supposed to touch anything?
The police will want to look for fingerprints, so no one should touch anything before that happens.

4. Why does Sherlock study the case through his magnifying glass?
Sherlock wants to find any clues that the robber might have left.

5. What conclusions can you draw about Amanda and Sherlock from the whole story? On a separate sheet of paper, write your conclusions. Support them with evidence from the story.
They are intelligent, brave, curious, and like mysteries. They figure out who stole the jewelry; the panic in the store doesn't scare them; they like to see everything that's going on; and they can "never resist a good mystery."

Notes for Home: Your child used story details to draw conclusions. *Home Activity:* Work with your child to draw conclusions about a movie you've seen or a book you've read together. Talk about why something happened or how the characters might feel in a certain situation.

Selection Test

Directions: Choose the best answer to each item. Mark the letter for the answer you have chosen.

Part 1: Vocabulary

Find the answer choice that means about the same as the underlined word in each sentence.

1. Miko put the box on the <u>counter</u>.
   A. small container with a cover
   B. large, square floor
   Ⓒ display table or cabinet in a store
   D. room where things are stored

2. Someone stole her <u>jewelry</u> case.
   F. flat pouch for carrying paper money
   G. belief or plan
   Ⓗ rings, bracelets, or other ornaments to be worn
   J. collection of coins

3. The clock <u>indicates</u> that it is two o'clock.
   Ⓐ shows
   B. pretends
   C. discovers
   D. hides

4. A <u>sapphire</u> ring was missing.
   F. hard gray or pink rock
   Ⓖ clear blue precious stone
   H. gold band
   J. deep red gem

5. He had a <u>smudge</u> on his chin.
   A. short beard
   B. healed cut
   C. small dimple
   Ⓓ dirty mark

Part 2: Comprehension

Use what you know about the story to answer each item.

6. Amanda and Sherlock went to the department store to—
   F. play computer games.
   G. look at men's jewelry.
   H. solve a mystery.
   Ⓙ buy a tie for their dad.

7. What happened while Sherlock and Amanda were in the department store?
   A. A fire broke out in the store.
   Ⓑ The sprinklers went off.
   C. Amanda stole a sapphire ring.
   D. The manager announced a big sale.

8. The salespeople were racing back and forth because they were trying to—
   F. put out the fire.
   G. keep the customers happy.
   Ⓗ protect their merchandise.
   J. catch a thief.

9. The sprinklers probably stopped suddenly because—
   A. the store ran out of water.
   B. they were not working properly.
   Ⓒ someone turned them off.
   D. someone opened the emergency exit.

10. Why was Sherlock studying the salesman's tie with his magnifying glass?
   Ⓕ He was looking for clues.
   G. He forgot his glasses at home.
   H. Amanda suggested he should.
   J. The spot was impossible to see otherwise.

GO ON

---

11. Amanda and Sherlock could not stay until the police arrived because they—
   A. would be in the way.
   Ⓑ would be late getting home.
   C. might become suspects.
   D. didn't know anything about solving mysteries.

12. The stolen jewelry was most likely hidden in—
   Ⓕ a loaf of bread.
   G. the baker's hat.
   H. the sprinklers.
   J. Sherlock's eclair.

13. You can tell that the baker is not very smart because he—
   A. could not bake a loaf of bread properly.
   B. didn't charge enough for the bread.
   C. didn't try to keep his bread dry.
   Ⓓ was wearing the stolen ring.

14. Which fact best supports the idea that Sherlock might make a good detective someday?
   F. He carries a magnifying glass with him wherever he goes.
   G. He has the same first name as the famous detective, Sherlock Holmes.
   Ⓗ He notices clues that help solve the mystery.
   J. He and his sister Amanda work well together.

15. The title of this story probably refers to the missing cuff links and to—
   A. loaves of bread.
   B. Sherlock and Amanda.
   C. the thieves.
   Ⓓ the clues needed to solve the mystery.

STOP

Drawing Conclusions

- When you form opinions based on facts and details, you are **drawing conclusions**.
- To draw a conclusion, use logic and clues from what you've read, as well as your own knowledge and experience. To check your conclusion, ask yourself if it makes sense. Are there other possible conclusions?

Directions: Read the story.

"How is the case going, Mom?" Amy asked her mother at dinner one night.

"We still don't have an answer," her mother replied, "but I think we're getting close."

"Is your theory the right one?" Amy asked.

"Well, dear," said her mother, "all we really know for sure is that the will isn't in any of the obvious places. We've looked in the safe-deposit box and searched every room in the mansion. Some of the other detectives agree with me that the grandfather hid the will because of the hints in the letter he left for his granddaughter. If we could decode that letter I'm sure we could find the will."

"I know you'll figure it out," said Amy, "I'm just glad you made it home in time for dinner for once!"

Directions: Complete the table. Write a conclusion for each set of evidence given. Write evidence that supports each conclusion given. **Possible answers given.**

Conclusion	Evidence
Amy's mom is a detective.	1. **Amy's mom is working with "other detectives" to find a missing will.**
The grandfather hid the will.	2. **The will isn't in any obvious places. The grandfather left hints about the will in a letter.**
3. **The grandfather wants his grandaughter to find the will.**	The grandfather left his granddaughter a letter hinting where the will is hidden.
Detectives are like code-breakers.	4. **If they could decode the letter, it would tell them where the will was hidden.**
5. **Amy's mother works long hours.**	Amy is glad her mom is home for dinner "for once."

 Notes for Home: Your child used story details to draw conclusions. *Home Activity:* Watch a television show with your child and draw some conclusions about the characters—how they feel, what they are like, and why they act the way they do.

Drawing Conclusions **209**

Predicting

REVIEW

Directions: Read the story. Then read each question about the story. Choose the best answer to each question. Mark the letter for the answer you have chosen.

Thrills and Chills

Suddenly, the lion moved! He stretched his neck, shook himself, yawned, and jumped from his pedestal. He then looked at the two girls and took a step toward them.

"Run for it!" Jill screamed.

Instead of moving, Tracy stared. "This is a mystery," she whispered. "How did that lion move?"

"I don't know. I just want to get out of here," Jill said, trembling.

The lion looked from Jill to Tracy, then turned away. He stalked away down the avenue, head high, looking straight ahead. As they watched, fascinated, he disappeared from sight.

Tracy and Jill stared at one another, then went to look at the empty pedestal. "Look!" cried Tracy. "There's a note here." She picked it up and read it aloud.

> You have just witnessed an amazing sight.
> Tell all your friends to come to the museum for tomorrow night's grand opening of Laser Lights!

"So that's how he moved," said Tracy.

"What do you mean?" asked Jill.

"That was no lion! That was a laser show demonstration to promote a new museum exhibit."

The two girls heard a sound high above them. They turned and looked. A museum staff person was standing in a special projection booth. He waved and called out, "Hope to see you tomorrow night."

1. After reading the first paragraph, you would probably predict that—
   A. the girls are going to attack the lion.
   B. the lion is going to attack the girls.
   C. the girls will stand still.
   D. the girls will feed the lion.

2. What do you think about Tracy after she speaks for the first time?
   F. Tracy loves lions.
   G. Tracy is dreaming.
   H. Tracy is more surprised than scared.
   J. Tracy is more scared than Jill.

3. What clue word or words in the note would probably cause you to change your initial prediction?
   A. witnessed
   B. amazing
   C. laser lights
   D. friends

4. After listening to Tracy's explanation, Jill will likely feel—
   F. scared.
   G. relieved.
   H. angry.
   J. sad.

5. What do you predict Jill and Tracy will do next?
   A. They will agree never to go to the museum again.
   B. They will go searching for the lion.
   C. They will complain to museum security.
   D. They will go to the Laser Lights opening.

 Notes for Home: Your child read a story and predicted events in the story. *Home Activity:* As you watch a movie with your child, make predictions about the characters and events. Make new predictions as needed as you continue watching.

210 Predicting

Writing Across Texts

Directions: Think again about how the main characters in "Missing Links" and "Dwaina Brooks" use initiative to solve problems they see in the world around them. Fill in the rest of the problem-and-solution chart below. **Possible answers given.**

Sherlock and Amanda	Dwaina
Problem: Sherlock and Amanda want to find out who stole the jewelry.	**Problem:** Dwaina wants to figure out how to feed the homeless in Dallas.
Attempts to solve the problem:	Attempts to solve the problem:
1. Sherlock investigates the spot on the salesman's tie with his magnifying glass.	6. Dwaina convinces her mother to help prepare food for people at the shelter.
2. Sherlock and Amanda realize that the baker set off the sprinklers.	7. She uses her lunch money to buy food.
3. Sherlock and Amanda figure out that the baker is a thief.	8. She collects coupons and donations from merchants and family members.
4. Amanda figures out where the jewels are hidden.	9. She gives a persuasive speech to her classmates and teachers.
Solution:	Solution:
5. Sherlock and Amanda determine that the salesman and the baker stole the jewels together.	10. Dwaina's efforts help feed thousands of homeless people.

Write a Paragraph

On a separate sheet of paper, write one or two paragraphs to describe how Sherlock, Amanda, and Dwaina show initiative. Be sure to include specific examples from the selections. **Paragraphs will vary. Check that students have supported writing with examples from both selections.**

 Notes for Home: Your child compared fictional characters with a real-life person described in an article. *Home Activity:* As you read other stories or articles, have your child tell how characters' traits, such as initiative, bravery, intelligence, or determination, help them solve problems.

Writing Across Texts **211**

Grammar: Possessive Nouns

REVIEW

Directions: Circle the possessive noun in ( ) that correctly completes each sentence.

1. The (detective's/detectives') hat blew off as she ran for the bus.
2. She reached the corner just as the (buses/bus's) doors closed.
3. Was that the (criminal's/criminals') face smiling from the bus?
4. Detective (Moss/Moss's) face certainly did not have a smile on it.
5. Her (life's/lives') work was solving mysteries.
6. She thought she had found this (mysterys'/mystery's) solution.
7. The (suspect's/suspects') escape on the bus was a terrible setback.
8. The passing (cars'/car's) loud horns sounded to her like cruel laughter.
9. She would rest at (Janes'/Jane's) house and decide what to do next.
10. She had to find the thief who was stealing (womens'/women's) purses.

Directions: Add an apostrophe to make each underlined word or words possessive. Write the possessive noun on the line.

company's	11. The door to the <u>companys</u> safe stood wide open.
boxes'	12. Someone had smashed the cash <u>boxes</u> lids and stolen all the money.
police officers'	13. Now it was the two <u>police officers</u> job to ask questions.
secretaries'	14. Had the door to the <u>secretaries</u> offices been locked or unlocked?
workers'	15. Why was one of the <u>workers</u> keys found on the floor?
boss's	16. Had the <u>boss</u> wife really telephoned him at six o'clock?
children's	17. Whose <u>childrens</u> toys were scattered around the room?
sheep's	18. Why was a pile of <u>sheep</u> wool lying next to the safe?
witnesses'	19. The <u>witnesses</u> statements did not agree.
today's	20. The officers knew that <u>todays</u> mystery would not be easily solved.

 Notes for Home: Your child formed possessive nouns—nouns that show that a person, place, or thing owns or has something. *Home Activity:* Point to things in your home or outside your window. Ask questions such as "Whose bike is that?" Have your child write the answers.

212 Grammar: Possessive Nouns

© Scott Foresman 5

Grammar Practice Book 5.2, p. 47

Name _____

Missing Links

Grammar: Commas with Nouns in Series and in Direct Address

A list of three or more nouns forms a **series**. A **comma** is used after each word in a series except the last.

> Dinosaurs, snakes, lizards, and crocodiles were missing from the zoo.

When you speak or write to someone, you often use that person's name or title. This use of a noun is called **direct address**. One comma sets off the noun when it appears at the beginning or the end of a sentence. Two commas are used when it appears in the middle.

> Students, today we will learn about how to write a mystery.
> What do you know about mysteries, Anna?
> The mystery novel that you suggested, Josh, is excellent.

Directions: Write **C** if the sentence is punctuated correctly. Write **NC** if it is not correct. Then, write correctly any sentence marked **NC**.

1. Items such as jewelry, money, and appliances were taken from the house.
C _____

2. Chris do you know how the detective solved the mystery?
NC; Chris, do you know how the detective solved the mystery?

3. Footprints, fingerprints, and broken glass were all important clues.
C _____

4. How they know where to look for evidence is also a mystery, Leroy.
C _____

5. Detectives, Tina have found the criminal in hundreds of investigations.
NC; Detectives, Tina, have found the criminal in hundreds of investigations.

Directions: Add commas to each sentence to set off nouns used in a series or in direct address.

6. The elusive thief was spotted in Europe, the Americas, and other continents.

7. Evidence to solve the case was found in Central Asia, Mike.

8. The criminal, Sophia, was close to escaping.

9. While the thief was hiding in Florida he ate fish, shellfish, and plants.

10. Sarah, some mysteries are never solved.

 Notes for Home: Your child learned how to use commas with nouns in a series and in direct address. *Home Activity:* Ask your child to make a list of different kinds of dinosaurs. Then have your child write a sentence using commas to set off nouns in a series.

Grammar: Commas with Nouns in Series and in Direct Address **213**

Grammar Practice Book 5.2, p. 48

Name _____

Missing Links

Grammar: Commas with Nouns in Series and in Direct Address

Directions: Add commas to each sentence to set off nouns in a series or in direct address.

1. The items that the thief took from the store included rakes, seeds, and shovels.

2. Liz, the thief might have enjoyed gardening.

3. The detective searched for clues in vacant lots, gardens, and fields.

4. This is the biggest mystery of the year, Tim.

5. One of the clues, Ashley, was a freshly planted garden in the vacant lot.

Directions: Read the following paragraph. Add commas where necessary.

> Class, today we are going to read the first half of a mystery. I know that most of you enjoy solving mysteries. We will also spend time working on math, spelling, and science. Tonya, Juan, Kerry, and Simon, you will each lead a group. Remember, class, each group will try to solve the mystery after reading just half of the story.

Write a News Report

Imagine you have solved the mystery of the disappearance of a set of valuable jewels from a museum. On a separate sheet of paper, write a news report about your discovery. Tell how you solved the mystery. What clues did the thieves leave behind? Use commas to set off nouns in a series and in direct address.
Nouns in a series might include a description of the jewels. Nouns used in direct address might be included in quoted eyewitness reports.

 Notes for Home: Your child learned how to use commas. *Home Activity:* With your child, write sentences describing things you see around you, such as books, clothes, and plants. Encourage your child to explain how to use commas to punctuate nouns in a series.

214 Grammar: Commas with Nouns in Series and in Direct Address

---

Grammar Practice Book 5.2, p. 49

Name _____

Missing Links

RETEACHING

Grammar: Commas with Nouns in Series and in Direct Address

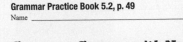

Each sentence shows one way to use a comma. Circle each comma.

1. Tanya, go home please.
2. Then, Ray, you follow her.
3. We will go right now, Juan.
4. Dora, Amy, and Tony will come.

A **comma** can tell a reader where to pause. Use a comma to separate words in a series of three or more items. Use a comma to set off the name of someone directly spoken to in **direct address**.

Directions: Add commas where they are needed.

1. I hope to become an astronaut one day, June.
2. Jenny, tell me about Sally Ride.
3. She was the first American woman in space, Maria.
4. An astronaut's life must be fascinating, exciting, and sometimes scary.
5. I would miss my family, my friends, and my cat on a space voyage.
6. You could use the communication system, Ruby, to relay messages.
7. How much food, water, and equipment can fit in a spacecraft?
8. Gina, let's go to the library.
9. Let's find out more about space travel, astronauts, and moonwalks.

Directions: Write a sentence to answer each question. **Answers will vary. Check for correct use of commas.**

10. What are the names of three of your classmates?
John, Kate, and Tina are three of my classmates.

11. What are three of your favorite sports?
I love to play soccer, baseball, and basketball.

12. Which birds live in your town or city?
There are robins, wrens, chickadees, and crows in my city.

 Notes for Home: Your child used commas in a series and in direct address. *Home Activity:* Have your child use newspapers or magazines to find and highlight examples of commas in a series and commas in direct address.

Grammar: Commas with Nouns in Series and in Direct Address **215**

Grammar Practice Book 5.2, p. 50

Name _____

Missing Links

Grammar: Commas with Nouns in Series and in Direct Address

Directions: Add commas where they are needed.

1. John Glenn did not orbit the earth before Alan Shepard's space flight, Danielle.
2. Kim, who is your favorite hero?
3. I think Thomas Edison, Martin Luther King, Jr., and Abraham Lincoln helped the most people.
4. I think, Laurie, someone like Charles Lindbergh is a true hero.
5. Pecos Bill, Paul Bunyan, and Calamity Jane are my favorite folk heroes.
6. John Henry was strong, hardworking, and brave.
7. Was he a real person, Jill?
8. I think so, Bonnie, but I don't know for sure.

Directions: Write a complete sentence for each direction. **Answers will vary. Make sure students have used commas correctly.**

9. Name three states you would like to visit.
I would like to visit Wyoming, Colorado, and Washington.

10. Name three breakfast foods.
For breakfast I eat cereal, waffles, and fruit.

11. Name the four seasons.
The four seasons are winter, spring, summer, and fall.

12. Name three of your favorite vegetables.
Three of my favorite vegetables are broccoli, green beans, and corn.

13. Name three kinds of transportation.
Trains, cars, and airplanes are three kinds of transportation.

14. Name three favorite story characters.
I like Leigh Botts, Dwaina Brooks, and Amanda.

Write a Restaurant Review

Write a restaurant review that includes descriptions of your three favorite foods in each food group. Use commas where they are needed. Write on a separate sheet of paper.
Make sure students have used commas correctly.

 Notes for Home: Your child used commas in a series and in direct address. *Home Activity:* Have your child write a description of a favorite sports team or electronic game. Encourage your child to use words in a series in the description.

216 Grammar: Commas with Nouns in Series and in Direct Address

---

© Scott Foresman 5

Answers 729

Name _____

Missing Links

Word Study: Prefixes

Directions: Letters added to the beginnings of words are called **prefixes**. Prefixes can change the meaning of the base word. Add the prefixes to each word below to make a new word. Write each new word on the line.

1.	re	+	heat	=	**reheat**
2.	pre	+	occupied	=	**preoccupied**
3.	un	+	believable	=	**unbelievable**
4.	pre	+	school	=	**preschool**
5.	re	+	turn	=	**return**
6.	un	+	changed	=	**unchanged**
7.	pre	+	paid	=	**prepaid**
8.	re	+	view	=	**review**

Directions: Read the detective's report. Circle the words that contain the prefixes *un-*, *re-*, and *pre-*. Write the prefix and the base word on the line connected by a + sign. For example, **prepaid**, you would write **pre** + **paid**.

Detective's Report: Case No. 57

Submitted by Lydia Lookout, P. I.

I was hired to investigate the disappearance of peanuts from the local grocery store. Bob, the owner of the small neighborhood store, was very (unhappy) about the missing peanuts. He had suspected one or two people as thieves but Bob felt that it would be (unfair) to (prejudge) his loyal customers. Bob was (unable) to solve the mystery, so he hired me to solve the case. I told Bob that I couldn't (replace) the missing peanuts, but I could find the thief. After two days on the case, I was still (uncertain) about the disappearing peanuts. I decided to stay overnight in the store to catch the thieves in action. Sometime after midnight, I heard a noise and turned on the lights. The store was filled with happy squirrels eating peanuts. The next day Bob called a roofer to (repair) the hole where the squirrels had entered the store.

9.	**un + happy**
10.	**un + fair**
11.	**pre + judge**
12.	**un + able**
13.	**re + place**
14.	**un + certain**
15.	**re + pair**

 Notes for Home: Your child formed new words by adding the prefixes *un-*, *re-*, and *pre-*. **Home Activity:** Read a newspaper story with your child. Help your child find words that have these prefixes. Have your child write each word and circle its prefix.

Word Study: Prefixes **217**

Name _____

Missing Links

Spelling: Prefixes *dis-*, *un-*, *mid-*, *pre-*

Pretest Directions: Fold back the page along the dotted line. On the blanks, write the spelling words as they are dictated. When you have finished the test, unfold the page and check your words.

1.	**discovered**	1.	We **discovered** it just in time.
2.	**disorder**	2.	The room was in total **disorder**.
3.	**disappoint**	3.	I am sorry to **disappoint** you.
4.	**disobey**	4.	They **disobey** orders.
5.	**disapprove**	5.	Does she **disapprove** of him?
6.	**unsure**	6.	The driver is **unsure** how to go.
7.	**unclear**	7.	The writing was too **unclear**.
8.	**unable**	8.	Are you **unable** to help today?
9.	**unbuckle**	9.	You may **unbuckle** your seatbelt.
10.	**unlimited**	10.	He has an **unlimited** supply.
11.	**midweek**	11.	The news came **midweek**.
12.	**midyear**	12.	It is time for a **midyear** review.
13.	**midway**	13.	The games are on the **midway**.
14.	**midnight**	14.	The bell tower chimed **midnight**.
15.	**midstream**	15.	The deer stood in **midstream**.
16.	**pretest**	16.	We will have a **pretest** tomorrow.
17.	**preschool**	17.	They are too old for **preschool**.
18.	**precook**	18.	The restaurants **precook** meals.
19.	**prepaid**	19.	We **prepaid** for our tickets.
20.	**prerecorded**	20.	This program was **prerecorded**.

 Notes for Home: Your child took a pretest on words that begin with *dis-*, *un-*, *mid-*, and *pre-*. **Home Activity:** Help your child learn misspelled words before the final test. See if there are any similar errors and discuss a memory trick that could help.

218 Spelling: Prefixes *dis-*, *un-*, *mid-*, *pre-*

Name _____

Missing Links

Spelling: Prefixes *dis-*, *un-*, *mid-*, *pre-*

Word List

discovered	disapprove	unbuckle	midway	preschool
disorder	unsure	unlimited	midnight	precook
disappoint	unclear	midweek	midstream	prepaid
disobey	unable	midyear	pretest	prerecorded

Directions: Add the prefix **dis-**, **un-**, **mid-**, or **pre-** to each word below to form a word from the box. Write the word on the line.

1. covered	**discovered**	6. stream	**midstream**
2. night	**midnight**	7. approve	**disapprove**
3. recorded	**prerecorded**	8. sure	**unsure**
4. year	**midyear**	9. buckle	**unbuckle**
5. obey	**disobey**	10. clear	**unclear**

Directions: Choose the word from the box that best matches each clue. Write the word in the puzzle.

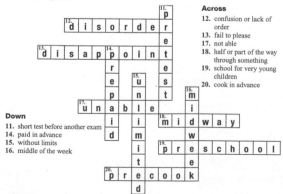

Across
12. confusion or lack of order
13. fail to please
17. not able
18. half or part of the way through something
19. school for very young children
20. cook in advance

Down
11. short test before another exam
14. paid in advance
15. without limits
16. middle of the week

 Notes for Home: Your child spelled words that begin with *dis-*, *un-*, *mid-*, and *pre-*. **Home Activity:** Read each word aloud from the box. Ask your child to identify and spell the base word. For example, *buckle* is the base word for *unbuckle*.

Spelling: Prefixes *dis-*, *un-*, *mid-*, *pre-* **219**

Name _____

Missing Links

Spelling: Prefixes *dis-*, *un-*, *mid-*, *pre-*

Directions: Proofread these rules. Find six spelling mistakes. Use the proofreading marks to correct each mistake.

☰	Make a capital.
/	Make a small letter.
∧	Add something.
⟋	Take out something.
⊙	Add a period.
¶	Begin a new paragraph.

Rules for Our Trip to the Shopping Mall

We will be in a big crowd tomorrow at the shopping mall, so everyone remember these rules!

1. Do not dissobey the instructions of the teacher or the group leader. If you do, it will cause great disordar.

2. If you have disckovered that you are unnclear about which bus you belong on, ask the teacher. Space on each bus is not unlimitied, so you must go on the bus you were assigned.

3. We will eat middway through the day. The lunch is prepaid, so you don't need to bring any money for food.

We want everyone to have fun, so please remember these rules and be on time tomorrow!

Spelling Tip
discovered

How can you remember that **discovered** begins with **disc**, not **disk**? When something is **dis**covered, you can see (**c**) it!

Write Rules

Imagine you are in charge of a group that is visiting a shopping mall. On a separate sheet of paper, make a list of rules for the group to follow. Try to use at least five of your spelling words.
Answers will vary, but each list of rules should include at least five spelling words.

Word List

discovered	midweek
disorder	midyear
disappoint	midway
disobey	midnight
disapprove	midstream
unsure	pretest
unclear	preschool
unable	precook
unbuckle	prepaid
unlimited	prerecorded

 Notes for Home: Your child spelled words that begin with *dis-*, *un-*, *mid-*, and *pre-*. **Home Activity:** Read a magazine article with your child. See how many words you can find that start with the prefixes *dis-*, *un-*, *mid-*, or *pre-*.

220 Spelling: Prefixes *dis-*, *un-*, *mid-*, *pre-*

© Scott Foresman 5

Spelling: Prefixes *dis-, un-, mid-, pre-* REVIEW

Word List

discovered	disapprove	unbuckle	midway	preschool
disorder	unsure	unlimited	midnight	precook
disappoint	unclear	midweek	midstream	prepaid
disobey	unable	midyear	pretest	prerecorded

Directions: Choose the word from the box that best completes each sentence. Write the word on the line.

__preschool__ 1. When I was in _____ I was too young to work at our family store.

__Midway__ 2. _____ through the fifth grade I began to help my parents at the store.

__discovered__ 3. I soon _____ that I enjoyed stocking the shelves.

__disorder__ 4. After school I wanted to straighten the items that were in _____.

__disobey__ 5. I would never _____ when my parents asked me to complete a task.

__unable__ 6. Mother was _____ to hide a smile at her delight in my contribution to the store.

__unclear__ 7. If I was _____ about how to do something, mother helped.

__unlimited__ 8. My love for helping at the store was endless and _____.

Directions: Choose the word from the box that has the same or nearly the same meaning as each word or phrase below. Write the word on the line.

__midnight__	9. twelve o'clock A.M.	__prepaid__	15. already paid
__midweek__	10. Wednesday	__unbuckle__	16. unfasten
__midyear__	11. June	__prerecorded__	17. taped
__disapprove__	12. frown on	__unsure__	18. doubtful
__pretest__	13. quiz	__disappoint__	19. let down
__midstream__	14. middle of the stream	__precook__	20. preheat

Notes for Home: Your child spelled words that begin with *dis-, un-, mid-,* and *pre-*. **Home Activity:** Name one of these prefixes: *dis-, un-, mid-,* or *pre-*. Have your child identify the spelling words that begin with that prefix, and have him or her write a sentence for each one.

Spelling: Prefixes *dis-, un-, mid-, pre-* **221**

Technology: Telephone Directory

A **telephone directory** is a book that lists entries that give the names, phone numbers, and addresses for individual people and businesses. The **white pages** list entries for individual people and businesses in alphabetical order. The **yellow pages** list entries and ads for businesses. Entries are grouped by category or type of business, such as *jewelry.* You can find this same information using a computer and the Internet. You can search online to find phone numbers for people and businesses in other cities, states, and even countries.

Directions: The computer screen shows you how to search a directory of online white pages. Use the computer screen to answer the questions that follow.

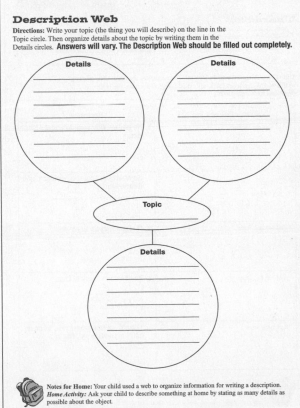

Enter the first and last name of the person and click Find! For better results, enter the city and state also.
Last Name (required) _____
First Name _____
City _____ State _____
Country _____
Find! If you need help, click here.

1. What entries will you get if you type "Gomez" in the box for Last Name, "Boston" in the box for City, and "MA" in the box for State?
You will get entries for all the people who live in Boston, Massachusetts, who have the last name of Gomez and are listed in the directory.

2. Would typing "Pamela" in the box for First Name and "USA" in the box for Country give you good search results? Explain.
Possible answer: No, there isn't enough information for a good search. A last name is required.

3. You know Nan Worth lives in Florida. Tell how to find her phone number and address.
Type "Worth" for Last Name; "Nan" for First Name; "FL" for State and click Find.

4. What should you do if you need help using this online telephone directory?
Click on the underlined words click here.

222 Research and Study Skills: Technology: Telephone Directory

---

Directions: The computer screen shows you how to search a directory of online yellow pages. Use the computer screen to answer the questions that follow.

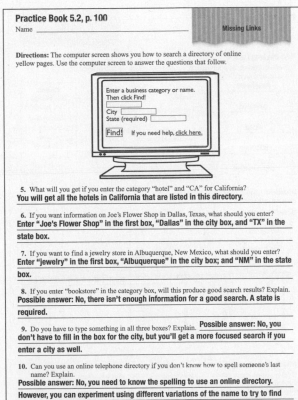

Enter a business category or name. Then click Find!
City _____
State (required) _____
Find! If you need help, click here.

5. What will you get if you enter the category "hotel" and "CA" for California?
You will get all the hotels in California that are listed in this directory.

6. If you want information on Joe's Flower Shop in Dallas, Texas, what should you enter?
Enter "Joe's Flower Shop" in the first box, "Dallas" in the city box, and "TX" in the state box.

7. If you want to find a jewelry store in Albuquerque, New Mexico, what should you enter?
Enter "jewelry" in the first box, "Albuquerque" in the city box; and "NM" in the state box.

8. If you enter "bookstore" in the category box, will this produce good search results? Explain.
Possible answer: No, there isn't enough information for a good search. A state is required.

9. Do you have to type something in all three boxes? Explain. **Possible answer: No, you don't have to fill in the box for the city, but you'll get a more focused search if you enter a city as well.**

10. Can you use an online telephone directory if you don't know how to spell someone's last name? Explain.
Possible answer: No, you need to know the spelling to use an online directory. However, you can experiment using different variations of the name to try to find the person you want.

Notes for Home: Your child answered questions about using an online telephone directory. **Home Activity:** Use your telephone books. Ask your child to find one person and a type of business to practice using both the white and yellow pages.

Research and Study Skills: Technology: Telephone Directory **223**

Name _____

Description Web

Directions: Write your topic (the thing you will describe) on the line in the Topic circle. Then organize details about the topic by writing them in the Details circles. **Answers will vary. The Description Web should be filled out completely.**

Details

Details

Topic

Details

Notes for Home: Your child used a web to organize information for writing a description. **Home Activity:** Ask your child to describe something at home by stating as many details as possible about the object.

224 Unit 2: Writing Process

Elaboration
Sense Words

- One way to elaborate is by adding **sense words** that help readers picture things clearly.
- You can provide vivid images by telling how things look, sound, feel, taste, and smell.

Directions: Substitute or add words from the box to the sentences below to make them more interesting. Write the new sentences using the words you picked.

Answers will vary. Possible answers given.

snatch	dark	deadly
bumping	crashing	unsuspecting
damp	sharp	warm
special	squeaks	silently
unusual	high-pitched	slither
strike	fierce	pounce
crawl	dangerous	suddenly

1. Animals have ways of discovering food and danger.
Animals have special ways of discovering food and danger.

2. Bats fly through caves.
Bats fly through damp, dark caves.

3. They make sounds that echo off obstacles.
They make high-pitched squeaks that echo off obstacles.

4. These sounds prevent them from going into rocks.
These sounds prevent them from crashing into sharp rocks.

5. Big-eared rabbits listen for enemies.
Big-eared rabbits listen for deadly enemies.

6. Rattlesnakes have pits that detect bodies.
Dangerous rattlesnakes have pits that detect warm bodies.

7. These snakes move toward prey.
These snakes slither toward unsuspecting prey.

8. Suddenly they move and get their dinner.
Suddenly they strike and snatch their dinner.

 Notes for Home: Your child recently expanded sentences by adding sense words. *Home Activity:* Ask your child to describe an animal using sense words. For example: *The fluffy, spotted puppy chased the noisy bike.*

Unit 2: Writing Process **225**

Self-Evaluation Guide
Descriptive Paragraph

Students' responses should show that they have given thought to the description that they have written.

Directions: Think about the final draft of your description. Then answer each question below.

	Yes	No	Not sure
1. Does my description tell about something in nature?			
2. Did I use descriptive words and images to give readers a good picture of this thing?			
3. Did I keep my audience and purpose in mind?			
4. Did I present my ideas in an organized way?			
5. Did I proofread and edit carefully to avoid errors?			

6. What part of your description do you think gives the best picture of your topic?

_____
_____
_____

7. Write one thing that you could change to make this description even better (a word, phrase, or sentence).

_____
_____
_____
_____

 Notes for Home: Your child recently wrote a description. *Home Activity:* Encourage your child to tell you one way he or she tried to make this description vivid.

226 Unit 2: Writing Process

Practice Book 5.3, p. 101

Name _____

Going with the Flow

Character

- **Characters** are the people or animals in a stories.
- You learn about characters from their words, actions, and the way other characters act toward them.

Directions: Reread "Jerome's Dream." Then complete the table. Give examples of things that characters think, say, and do to show what Jerome is like.
Possible answers given.

What the Characters Think, Do, and Say	Examples
What Jerome Thinks	1. He wishes Tilly wouldn't speak for him.
	2. He wishes school kids wouldn't help him so much.
What Jerome Says	3. "I wann tricycle to rrr-ride!"
What Jerome Does	4. He becomes angry at Liza.
What Liza Says	5. "How's Jerome gonna ride, when he can't even walk yet, Papa?"

 Notes for Home: Your child read a story and analyzed its main character. *Home Activity:* Think of a relative or neighbor. Describe things that the person frequently thinks, does, or says. Have your child guess who the person is, based on your clues. Switch roles and repeat the activity.

Character **229**

Practice Book 5.3, p. 102

Name _____

Going with the Flow

Vocabulary

Directions: Choose the word from the box that best completes each sentence. Write the word on the line to the left.

___volunteers___   1. Many _____ took part in the school games.

___gestured___   2. The principal raised her hands and _____ for the games to begin.

___skied___   3. Some students _____ down nearby mountain slopes.

___dribbling___   4. Others were good at _____ basketballs indoors.

___conversation___   5. All over school, people's _____ was about the games.

Check the Words You Know
__ conversation
__ dribbling
__ gestured
__ interpreter
__ skied
__ volunteers

Directions: Choose the word from the box that best matches each clue. Write the word in the puzzle.

Down
6. people who offer their services
7. informal talk
8. signaled by hand
9. glided on skies

Across
10. one who translates

Crossword:
6. v o l u n t e e r s (down)
7. c o n v e r s a t i o n (down)
8. g e s t u r e d (down)
9. s k i e d (down)
10. i n t e r p r e t e r (across)

Write a Broadcast
Imagine you are a sportscaster. On a separate sheet of paper, write a broadcast that describes a real or imaginary sports competition. Describe the action as if it were happening right now in front of your eyes. Use as many vocabulary words as you can. **Students' broadcasts should make correct use of vocabulary words.**

Notes for Home: Your child identified vocabulary words in *Going with the Flow*. *Home Activity:* Work with your child to write a sports article about a favorite sport or athlete, using as many vocabulary words as you can.

230 Vocabulary

© Scott Foresman 5

Character

- **Characters** are the people or animals in stories.
- You learn about them from their words, actions, and the way other characters act toward them.

Directions: Reread what happens in *Going with the Flow* when Mark attends his new class for the first time. Think about what you've read, and then answer the questions below.

> "Hi, Mark. How are you?" Mrs. LaVoie signed and mouthed the words silently to me across the room.
> The whole fifth grade was watching us.
> "This is dumb!" I signed back.
> "They've never met a deaf kid before," she replied. "They..."
>
> I didn't wait for her to finish. I had to get out of there. I raced down the center aisle, nearly tripped over the leg of some big, long-haired guy with a smirk on his face, and ran out the door.
> Mrs. LaVoie found me in the gym under one of the bleachers. She put a hand on my arm.
>
> From GOING WITH THE FLOW by Claire H. Blatchford. Copyright Text 1998 by Claire H. Blatchford, illustrations 1998 by Janice Lee Porter. Used by permission of Carolrhoda Books, Inc. All rights reserved.

Possible answers given.

1. What do the other students do when Mark signs with Mrs. LaVoie?
They watch them.

2. How does Mark feel about being in his new class? How do you know?
He doesn't like being there. He signs that it's "dumb."

3. Why does Mark leave the room?
He feels angry and embarrassed.

4. How does Mrs. LaVoie treat Mark?
She treats him with understanding. She puts a hand on his arm to comfort him.

5. How does Mark change by the end of the story? Write your answer on a separate sheet of paper. Give examples from the story to support your answers.
He feels less angry and more like a part of the group. With Keith's encouragement and support, he joins the school basketball team.

 Notes for Home: Your child read a story and used story details to analyze a character. *Home Activity:* Watch a TV show or movie with your child, and then have your child describe his or her favorite character in the story.

Character **231**

Selection Test

Directions: Choose the best answer to each item. Mark the letter for the answer you have chosen.

Part 1: Vocabulary

Find the answer choice that means about the same as the underlined word in each sentence.

1. I didn't understand that <u>conversation</u>.
   - (A) a friendly talk
   - B. a long book
   - C. a math test
   - D. a movie

2. A group of <u>volunteers</u> met at the town hall.
   - F. people who have been elected to represent others
   - G. teachers
   - (H) people who offer to work or help for free
   - J. government workers

3. Nell works as an <u>interpreter</u>.
   - A. person who helps others learn to study better
   - (B) person who translates one language into another
   - C. writer for a newspaper
   - D. coach who teaches others how to play a sport

4. Mike <u>gestured</u> excitedly.
   - F. called out in a loud voice
   - G. argued against something
   - H. jumped up and down
   - (J) made hand movements

5. The girl <u>skied</u> very well.
   - A. picked out skis
   - B. explained how to ski
   - C. waxed the skis
   - (D) glided on skis

6. All the players need to practice their <u>dribbling</u>.
   - (F) moving a ball by bouncing
   - G. communicating without words
   - H. throwing a ball into a basket
   - J. passing a ball from one player to another

Part 2: Comprehension

Use what you know about the story to answer each item.

7. Who follows Mark into his classroom on the first day at his new school?
   - A. his mother
   - B. his fifth-grade teacher
   - (C) his interpreter
   - D. the principal

8. Just after he rushes out of the classroom, Mark—
   - F. takes a bus home.
   - G. goes to eat in the cafeteria.
   - (H) hides in the gym.
   - J. calls his friend Jamie.

9. After his first day at school, Mark feels—
   - A. confident that he will succeed.
   - B. ignored by his classmates.
   - C. sure that he will make friends.
   - (D) sorry for himself.

10. Mark wants to move back to Vermont mainly because he wants to—
   - F. play basketball.
   - (G) be with other deaf people.
   - H. ski in races against Jamie.
   - J. go to a better school.

 GO ON

232 Selection Test

---

11. You can tell that his father thinks Mark should—
   - (A) give the new school a chance before he gives up.
   - B. forget the friends he had in Vermont.
   - C. pretend he is not deaf so he will be accepted by others.
   - D. move back to Vermont.

12. What is the first sign that Keith is a kind person?
   - F. He smirks at Mark on Mark's first day in class.
   - G. He laughs when Mark asks if his name is Teeth.
   - (H) He offers to take notes for Mark.
   - J. He asks Mark to play basketball.

13. Keith trips Mark during the basketball game because he—
   - A. knows that Mark is a better player than he is.
   - B. is slower than Mark and cannot get out of his way.
   - C. is trying to get Mark to give up and leave the basketball team.
   - (D) thinks Mark is playing without respect for him and the other players.

14. What makes the biggest difference in Mark's life?
   - (F) He joins the basketball team.
   - G. Some of the boys laugh at him.
   - H. Mrs. LaVoie helps him.
   - J. He gets angry while playing basketball.

15. As a result of playing basketball with Keith, Mark learns to—
   - (A) try to fit in by working with others.
   - B. look after himself first.
   - C. realize that being deaf is not a problem.
   - D. accept that he will always be left out.

 STOP

Selection Test **233**

Character

- **Characters** are the people or animals in stories.
- You learn about them from their words, actions, and the way other characters act toward them.

Directions: Read the story below.

> Sharon's knees shook as she stood at the foul line. At that moment, she wondered why she had ever decided to play basketball.
> "Don't worry, Sharon!" Coach Miller yelled. "You can make it!"
> "I hope I can," Sharon said softly. She took a deep breath and let the ball go.
>
> It hit the basket rim and fell to the side. She had missed the first shot!
> Sharon bounced the ball several times. Then she shot again. Whoosh! The ball sailed through the hoop! Sharon jumped up and down, flashing a victory sign with her fingers. Her team had won the game!

Directions: Complete the table. Think what you learn about Sharon's character from things she thinks, says, and does, and from what other characters say.

Sharon's Character	Examples
Sharon is nervous.	1. What she thinks: **She wonders why she ever decided to play basketball.**
	2. What she does: **Her knees shake. She takes a deep breath.**
	3. What she says: **"I hope I can."**
	4. What Coach Miller says: **"Don't worry, Sharon! You can make it!"**
Sharon is happy.	5. What she does: **She jumps up and down and flashes a victory sign.**

Notes for Home: Your child read a story and used story details to analyze a character. *Home Activity:* Think of someone you and your child both know. Describe what that person often says, does, or thinks. Have your child guess who the person is. Reverse roles and repeat.

234 Character

Name _____

Going with the Flow

Drawing Conclusions and Predicting

REVIEW

Directions: Read the story. Then read each question about the story. Choose the best answer to each question. Mark the letter for the answer you have chosen.

Seeing the Problem

It was Tony's first day in his new school. As the newest student, Tony was seated in the back of the classroom.

Tony's new teacher, Mr. Brown, said they would start the day with a spelling lesson. Tony knew that the spelling book was blue, and he got it out of his book bag. Mr. Brown called on Tony. He asked Tony to read the spelling words which were written on the board.

Tony looked at the board. He squinted his eyes. He leaned his head forward and stared for a minute. When he didn't say anything, one or two children giggled.

Mr. Brown asked Tony if he would like to sit in the front of the room. Tony agreed. He picked up his book bag and spelling book and moved to a new seat at the very front of the class.

Mr. Brown then asked Tony once again to read the spelling words on the board. Tony squinted again and finally said, "I'm sorry, but I can't."

After class, Mr. Brown asked Tony to stay a few minutes. Tony hoped he hadn't done anything wrong on his first day.

Mr. Brown said, "Tony, I'd like you to visit the school doctor. She can give you an eye test."

1. Tony squints because he—
   A. dislikes being in the back of the classroom.
   B. has trouble seeing.
   C. can't hear the teacher.
   D. is in pain.

2. Tony doesn't read the words because he—
   F. dislikes Mr. Brown.
   G. dislikes reading.
   H. is embarrassed.
   J. can't see them clearly.

3. Mr. Brown changes Tony's seat to the front so that—
   A. he can talk to Tony.
   B. Tony is with his friends.
   C. Tony is closer to the chalkboard.
   D. Tony won't misbehave.

4. The eye doctor will probably tell Tony that he—
   F. needs glasses.
   G. is fine.
   H. should switch classes.
   J. should sit up front.

5. You could find out if your prediction is right by—
   A. rereading the passage.
   B. asking a friend.
   C. making another prediction.
   D. reading the rest of the story.

Notes for Home: Your child drew conclusions and made predictions based on story details. *Home Activity:* As you read with your child, pause often to let your child predict what will happen next. After reading, have your child draw conclusions about the characters and events.

Drawing Conclusions and Predicting **235**

Writing Across Texts

Directions: Think about Mark from *Going with the Flow* and what happened to him when he moved to a new school. Then think back to the story "Faith and Eddie." Remember what happened when Faith started school in Mexico. How are the characters' experiences in a new school the same? How are they different? Organize your thoughts in the Venn diagram below. **Possible answers given.**

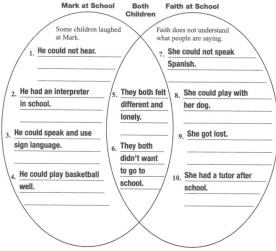

Mark at School — **Both Children** — **Faith at School**

Some children laughed at Mark.

Faith does not understand what people are saying.

1. He could not hear. _____

2. He had an interpreter in school. _____

3. He could speak and use sign language. _____

4. He could play basketball well. _____

5. They both felt different and lonely. _____

6. They both didn't want to go to school. _____

7. She could not speak Spanish. _____

8. She could play with her dog. _____

9. She got lost. _____

10. She had a tutor after school. _____

Write a Paragraph

In *Going with the Flow*, you learned about a boy who struggles to fit in at his new school. In "Faith and Eddie," you read about a girl who moves to a new country. How was Mark's situation the same or different than Faith's? On a separate sheet of paper, write a paragraph that tells which character's situation would be more difficult, and why. **Paragraphs will vary. Check that students based their opinions on information from each selection.**

Notes for Home: Your child compared and contrasted the situations of two story characters to make a judgment. *Home Activity:* Read a story to your child. Discuss how one character's life is the same or different from another character's life. Ask your child: *Who* would you rather be?

236 Writing Across Texts

Grammar: Predicates

REVIEW

Directions: Underline the complete predicate in each sentence. Then circle each simple predicate.

1. Joey's father took a new job in Tampa, Florida.
2. He told Joey about the move.
3. Joey thought about the meaning of a move to Florida.
4. He faced a new school, a new home, and new friends.
5. Tears came to his eyes.
6. Joey said good-bye to his friends one summer day.
7. Joey's room in the new house in Florida doubled the space of his old room.
8. A boy Joey's age lived right next door.
9. He took Joey to the nearby beach.
10. The nightmare of the move changed on that very first day!

Directions: Add a simple or complete predicate to each subject to form a sentence. Write the sentence on the line. **Possible answers given.**

11. My friends at school _____.
My friends at school eat together.

12. My family's house _____.
My family's house was sold yesterday.

13. New people and new places _____.
New people and new places scare me most of the time.

14. One advantage of a new school _____.
One advantage of a new school is making new and interesting friends.

15. A home in Florida _____.
A home in Florida sounds wonderful!

Notes for Home: Your child identified simple and complete predicates. *Home Activity:* Ask your child to find a paragraph he or she wrote at school. Have your child identify the complete and simple predicate in each sentence.

Grammar: Predicates **237**

Grammar: Verbs

An **action verb** tells what action the subject of a sentence does.

The players <u>shoot</u> the ball accurately. They <u>ran</u> fast down the court.

Sometimes an action verb tells about an action that you cannot see, such as an action in someone's mind.

The players <u>think</u> all the time. They <u>surprised</u> us with their skill.

A **linking verb** does not show action. Instead, it links, or joins, the subject to a word in the predicate. That word helps to tell what the subject is or is like.

The players <u>are</u> new. They <u>seem</u> talented.

The most common linking verbs are *am, is, are, was,* and *were.* Other verbs often used as linking verbs are *become, seem, feel,* and *look.*

Directions: Underline the action verb in each sentence.

1. The ancient Aztecs <u>played</u> a form of basketball.
2. They <u>threw</u> a balled-up animal skin at a wooden hoop.
3. Dr. James Naismith <u>invented</u> modern basketball in 1891.
4. He <u>nailed</u> two empty peach baskets to the wall.
5. Next, he <u>formed</u> teams of eighteen players.

Directions: Underline the linking verb in each sentence.

6. Thirteen rules <u>were</u> part of the game.
7. The first basketballs <u>looked</u> uneven!
8. They <u>felt</u> squishy too.
9. Now, the balls <u>are</u> orange cowhide and nylon.
10. Basketball <u>is</u> an international sport.

Notes for Home: Your child identified action verbs and linking verbs. *Home Activity:* Ask your child to list ways he or she could help new classmates become part of the group. Guide your child to identify action verbs and linking verbs in the list.

238 Grammar: Verbs

© Scott Foresman 5

Name _____

Going with the Flow

Grammar: Verbs

Directions: Circle the verb in each sentence. Write **A** if the verb is an action verb. Write **L** if it is a linking verb.

__A__ 1. Professional basketball (began) in 1896.

__A__ 2. A group of players (rented) a hall in New Jersey.

__L__ 3. They (were) very popular with the fans.

__A__ 4. That night, each player (earned) fifteen dollars!

__L__ 5. By the 1930s, basketball (was) a major sport.

Directions: Add a verb to complete each sentence. Try to use action verbs and linking verbs in your sentences. Write the verb on the line to the left. **Possible answers given.**

__happened__ 6. The first NBA game _____ on November 1, 1946.

__played__ 7. The Toronto Huskies _____ the New York Knicks.

__was__ 8. Admission _____ free for fans taller than 6 feet, 8 inches.

__cheered__ 9. The fans _____ loudly for their favorite players.

__is__ 10. Today, basketball _____ popular with people of all ages.

__is__ 11. The exercise _____ good for both amateur and professional players.

__stay__ 12. Good players _____ alert on the basketball court.

__helps__ 13. It also _____ if you have quick hands and feet.

__are__ 14. Now, there _____ professional women's basketball teams.

__is__ 15. Basketball _____ even an Olympic sport.

Write a Letter

How do you "go with the flow"? On a separate sheet of paper, write a letter telling a friend how you have learned to work with other people. Describe a problem you have faced and how you solved it. Use action and linking verbs. **Check that students use action and linking verbs in their letters.**

Notes for Home: Your child identified and wrote action verbs and linking verbs. *Home Activity:* Invite your child to describe how to do something, such as how to make a sandwich or throw a basketball. Encourage your child to use both action and linking verbs.

Grammar: Verbs **239**

Name _____

Going with the Flow

Grammar: Verbs

RETEACHING

Underline each simple subject once. Underline each simple predicate twice.

1. The snail crawls.   3. The snake slithers.   5. He was certain.

2. The ants march.   4. I am sure.   6. They are positive.

Notice that the simple predicates in sentences 1–3 are verbs that show action. The action verbs tell what the simple subject does. The simple predicates in sentences 4–6 are linking verbs—verbs that link subjects to words in the predicates.

An **action verb** tells the action that the subject of a sentence does. A **linking verb** helps to tell what the subject is or is like.

Directions: Underline the verb or verbs in each sentence.

1. My friend visits me on Saturdays.

2. My younger cousins are happy to watch television on the weekends.

3. They sometimes race from one room to another.

4. We laugh at their silly riddles, but we are glad to hear them.

5. I often cook lunch for them.

Directions: Write a verb to complete each sentence. Use a verb from the box below. One verb will be used more than once.

are	climb	drink	read	listen	is	chases

6. Each time the house _____ **is** _____ filled with much laughter.

7. My brother _____ **chases** _____ our cousins out of his room.

8. They _____ **drink** _____ their milk with long straws.

9. Karen and Bud never _____ **listen** _____ to the rules of our games.

10. They _____ **are** _____ a little too young.

11. I _____ **read** _____ with them until their bedtime.

12. At that time they _____ **are** _____ very quiet.

13. Then I _____ **climb** _____ into my own bed, tired from the long day.

Notes for Home: Your child identified and used verbs in sentences. *Home Activity:* Have your child listen to a favorite song and identify the verbs used in the lyrics.

240 Grammar: Verbs

Name _____

Going with the Flow

Grammar: Verbs

Directions: Circle the verb in each sentence.

1. Mary Cassatt (lived) in Pittsburgh, Pennsylvania.

2. She (traveled) to France from America in 1868.

3. Cassatt (studied) the paintings of French artists.

4. Then she (was) a painter herself.

5. She (painted) pictures of mothers with their children.

6. Her paintings (are) in many museums today.

Directions: Write the scrambled words in the correct order. Circle the verbs.

7. Mandy a visited in museum Boston
   Mandy (visited) a museum in Boston.

8. Mary Cassatt's an paintings she of exhibition saw
   She (saw) an exhibition of Mary Cassatt's paintings.

9. Mandy her camera with pictures took
   Mandy (took) pictures with her camera.

10. guide facts told artist's the about life a
    A guide (told) facts about the artist's life.

11. paintings then Cassatt's were questions about there
    Then there (were) questions about Cassatt's paintings.

12. poster a bought at gift Mandy the shop
    Mandy (bought) a poster at the gift shop.

13. were things new many to discover art about there
    There (were) many new things (to discover) about art.

Write a Description

Describe what it might be like to paint a picture. Use verbs. What might you think, feel, and do as you paint? Write on a separate sheet of paper.
Students' descriptions should include thoughts, feelings, and actions. Make sure students use verbs correctly.

Notes for Home: Your child correctly reordered words in sentences and identified each verb. *Home Activity:* Have your child use a highlighter pen to identify verbs in newspaper articles or magazines. Ask whether each verb is an action verb or a linking verb.

Grammar: Verbs **241**

Name _____

Going with the Flow

Word Study: Regular Plurals

Directions: To form the plural of most nouns, add **-s**. For nouns that end in **x, s, ss, ch,** or **sh,** add **-es.** For nouns that end in **consonant** and **y,** change the **y** to **i** and add **-es.** Write the plural form for each noun below.

1. player — **players**
2. bleacher — **bleachers**
3. basketball — **basketballs**
4. box — **boxes**
5. lunch — **lunches**
6. turkey — **turkeys**

7. enemy — **enemies**
8. glasses — **glasses**
9. teacher — **teachers**
10. photograph — **photographs**
11. signal — **signals**
12. victory — **victories**

Directions: Read the sports article. Make each word in ( ) plural. Write the plural word on the line. You might need to change the spelling of a word to make it plural.

We Are the Champions!

(Sign) for the game had been posted for (month). When the night finally arrived, you could see in the players' (eye) that something special was going to happen. (Word) can't do justice to how the team played that night. Their (hand) were everywhere, shooting, dribbling, stealing. The star made great (pass) and shot from all corners of the court. No (speech) were given that day, but the final score spoke for itself. We will all have great (memory) of this game for a long time to come.

13. **Signs**
14. **months**
15. **eyes**
16. **Words**
17. **hands**
18. **passes**
19. **speeches**
20. **memories**

Notes for Home: Your child practiced forming plural nouns, such as *steps* and *boxes.* **Home Activity:** Read the labels on game boxes and food packages with your child. Help your child notice plural words. Look to see whether *-s* or *-es* were added.

242 Word Study: Regular Plurals

© Scott Foresman 5

Spelling Workbook 5.3, p. 41

Spelling: Adding -s and -es

Pretest Directions: Fold back the page along the dotted line. On the blanks, write the spelling words as they are dictated. When you have finished the test, unfold the page and check your words.

1. months
2. friends
3. grades
4. cowboys
5. valleys
6. donkeys
7. missiles
8. costumes
9. pictures
10. mornings
11. matches
12. bushes
13. benches
14. speeches
15. passes
16. kisses
17. dresses
18. batteries
19. companies
20. centuries

1. It takes **months** to do this.
2. Wes will miss his old **friends**.
3. Study to improve your **grades**.
4. **Cowboys** ride horses.
5. The **valleys** are green and grassy.
6. **Donkeys** pulled the hay cart.
7. **Missiles** are dangerous.
8. Sew the **costumes** for the play.
9. These **pictures** are good.
10. Most **mornings**, he takes the bus.
11. Corey's tie **matches** his socks.
12. Daria hid in the **bushes**.
13. Fans watched from the **benches**.
14. Nobody listens to her **speeches**.
15. Did you check their hall **passes**?
16. His mom **kisses** him goodbye.
17. **Dresses** come in many colors.
18. My **batteries** are running low.
19. **Companies** give people jobs.
20. It's been done for **centuries**.

 Notes for Home: Your child took a pretest on adding -s and -es to nouns. **Home Activity:** Help your child learn misspelled words before the final test. Your child should look at the word, say it, spell it aloud, and then spell it with eyes shut.

Spelling: Adding -s and -es **243**

Spelling Workbook 5.3, p. 42

Spelling: Adding -s and -es

Word List

months	valleys	pictures	benches	dresses
friends	donkeys	mornings	speeches	batteries
grades	missiles	matches	passes	companies
cowboys	costumes	bushes	kisses	centuries

Directions: Write the word from the box that is formed by adding **-es** to each base word. Hint: In some cases, you need to change the **y** to **i** before adding **-es**.

1. match   matches
2. bench   benches
3. kiss   kisses
4. dress   dresses
5. speech   speeches

6. pass   passes
7. bush   bushes
8. century   centuries
9. company   companies
10. battery   batteries

Directions: Choose the word from the box that is formed by adding **-s** to each base word. Write the letters of the word on the blanks. The boxed letters spell something you do to form plurals.

11. valley
12. grade
13. donkey
14. cowboy
15. month
16. friend
17. costume
18. morning
19. picture
20. missile

11. v a l l e y s
12. g r a d e s
13. d o n k e y s
14. c o w b o y s
15. m o n t h s
16. f r i e n d s
17. c o s t u m e s
18. m o r n i n g s
19. p i c t u r e s
20. m i s s i l e s

Something you do to form plurals: a d d o n s o r e s

 Notes for Home: Your child spelled words that have -s and -es added to them to form plurals. **Home Activity:** Pick out items from the room whose names your child can spell. Then have your child spell the plural by adding -s or -es.

244 Spelling: Adding -s and -es

Spelling Workbook 5.3, p. 43

Spelling: Adding -s and -es

Directions: Proofread this letter. Find five spelling mistakes. Use the proofreading marks to correct each mistake.

≡ Make a capital.
∕ Make a small letter.
∧ Add something.
𝒫 Take out something.
⊙ Add a period.
¶ Begin a new paragraph.

Dear Jenna,

It's been two months since we moved here after Dad switched companys. I've made some new friends, and my grades are okay. I got two new dresses and hung new pictures on my wall. However, some mornings I wish I were back in my old home.

Hugs and kisses,

Tina

Word List

months	donkeys	matches	kisses
friends	missiles	bushes	dresses
grades	costumes	benches	batteries
cowboys	pictures	speeches	companies
valleys	mornings	passes	centuries

Write a Friendly Letter
Imagine you are Tina's friend Jenna. On a separate sheet of paper, write a friendly letter that tells what it is like when your best friend moves away. Try to use at least five of your spelling words.
Answers will vary, but each letter should include at least five spelling words.

Spelling Tip
Adding -es
Add **-es** to words that end in **sh, ch, s, ss,** or **x.** If the word ends in **consonant** and **y**, change **y** to **i** before adding **-es.**

 Notes for Home: Your child spelled words that have -s and -es added to them to form plurals. **Home Activity:** Say each spelling word aloud, leaving off the final sound /s/. For example, say picture, not pictures. Have your child spell the plural form of the word.

Spelling: Adding -s and -es **245**

Spelling Workbook 5.3, p. 44

Spelling: Adding -s and -es

Word List

months	valleys	pictures	benches	dresses
friends	donkeys	mornings	speeches	batteries
grades	missiles	matches	passes	companies
cowboys	costumes	bushes	kisses	centuries

Directions: Choose the word from the box that best completes each sentence. Write the word on the line to the left.

friends — 1. Our _____ next door are leaving the neighborhood.
months — 2. They've been planning to move for _____.
mornings — 3. They've been waking early in the _____ to pack.
companies — 4. One of the moving _____ sent its van over today.
bushes — 5. We stood near the rose _____ and watched the movers.
pictures — 6. They carried out _____ that once hung on the walls.
dresses — 7. They took girls' _____ that had hung in a closet.
benches — 8. They took wooden _____ from the backyard.
speeches — 9. Some neighbors praised the family in brief _____.
kisses — 10. After hugs and _____, the family drove away.

Directions: Write the word from the box that matches each clue.

missiles — 11. sky rockets
donkeys — 12. similar to mules
costumes — 13. actors' outfits
matches — 14. candle lighters
grades — 15. A and B+, for example
cowboys — 16. horse riders
centuries — 17. hundreds of years
valleys — 18. between hills
batteries — 19. used in flashlights
passes — 20. thrown in football

 Notes for Home: Your child spelled words that have -s and -es added to them to form plurals. **Home Activity:** Spell a word that names one thing, such as table or glass. See if your child can spell the plural by adding -s or -es.

246 Spelling: Adding -s and -es

© Scott Foresman 5

Evaluate Information/Draw Conclusions

Directions: Read the article below and the advertisement on the next page. Then answer the questions that follow the advertisement.

Ready? Get Set . . . Move!

Moving to a new home can be very challenging. It's not just all the packing and unpacking. If you're planning a move in the near future, here are some tips that will help you get where you're going.

Set Your Dates

It may sound obvious, but before you move, you must know exactly *when* you're moving. Whether you're leaving a house or an apartment, timing is everything. So check exactly when you're leaving your old home and arriving at your new home.

Notify All Services

Before you exit your old home, notify all important services. This includes utility companies, such as gas, electric, and telephone, and the bank. Most importantly, notify the U.S. post office of your change of address. The post office will forward your mail for up to six months. After that, letters may be returned.

Notify People

At least one month before you move, make a list of everyone you want to have your new address. This includes family, friends, neighbors, co-workers, doctors, dentists, and any other people with whom you communicate on a regular basis. The post office will supply you with cards that you can send to each person with your new address. If you already know your new telephone number, include that on the card as well.

Pack It Up

Perhaps the hardest part of any move is physically moving items from home to home. Plan ahead, and be sure to have plenty of boxes, tape, and other packing materials. Pack carefully. Mark your boxes to indicate the contents. Keep a list of what gets packed in each box and its condition. Double check to make sure you've left nothing behind.

Get Settled

Remember how you had to notify all your old services to discontinue? Well, now you've got the opposite task. Once in your new home, be sure all your new services have been activated. Is your telephone working? Do you have gas and electricity? Have you opened new bank accounts? Of course, in time you'll realize things you've forgotten. But the more that gets done immediately, the easier it will be to cope later!

Moving Day Checklist
Have I notified. . .

___ family	___ U.S. government (tax forms)	___ magazine subscriptions
___ friends	___ U.S. post office	___ newspaper subscriptions
___ neighbors	___ bank	___ clubs/organizations
___ co-workers	___ telephone company	___ others
___ doctors	___ gas/electric company	_____
___ dentists	___ landlord	_____

Research and Study Skills: Evaluate Information/Draw Conclusions **247**

MOVING? WE CAN HELP!

Whether moving across the street or across the country, you need the services of a reliable mover. **Transport Movers** are the finest professional movers in the country.

• We are trustworthy, efficient, and economical.
• Other movers often break items in transport, but we almost never do. (And if we do, we'll reimburse you the full value of the item.)
• We require no more than three days' notice to be at your doorstep on the day you move.
• To find out more about **Transport Movers**, just call this toll free number: 1-800-555-MOVE.

Transport Movers
Moving Across America

1. What is the topic of the article in the pamphlet shown on the previous page?
how to prepare for moving

2. What are the five main points in the article? **1. Set your dates for moving in and out.**
2. Notify all services and the post office. 3. Notify people. 4. Get enough packing
materials and pack everything carefully. 5. Get settled in your new home by having
services turned on.

3. How reliable do you think the information is in the article? Explain.
Possible answer: It is reliable because the pamphlet doesn't try to sell you anything.

4. What opinions are presented in the advertisement from Transport Movers?
Transport Movers are the finest professional movers in the country. They are
trustworthy, efficient, and economical.

5. Do you feel the information in the advertisement is as reliable as the information in the article? Explain.
Possible answer: The advertisement is not as reliable because it comes from a
company trying to get you to use their services. The authors of the pamphlet are not
seeking to make money by moving people.

 Notes for Home: Your child read an article and an advertisement, evaluated their information, and then drew conclusions about them. *Home Activity:* Read a newspaper or magazine article and advertisement with your child. Talk about the main ideas presented.

248 Research and Study Skills: Evaluate Information/Draw Conclusions

Graphic Sources

• A **graphic source**, such as a picture, graph, or map shows information visually.

• Before you read, look for graphic sources of information that could give you an idea of what the article or story is about.

• As you read, compare the written words to the graphic source for a better understanding of the main ideas.

Standard Time Zones in the United States

10:00 Pacific Time Zone D
11:00 Mountain Time Zone C
12:00 Central Time Zone B
1:00 Eastern Time Zone A

0   250   500 Miles
0   250   500 Kilometers

Directions: Reread "Train Time." Use the text and map to answer each question. **Possible answers given.**

1. What does the map show?
The map shows the standard time zones in the United States.

2. What information does the map give that the article does not?
The map shows exactly where the time zones divide the United States.

3. How do you know that the map shows the United States after 1883, not before?
The article explains that before 1883, there were no time zones in the United States.

4. How does the map help show the main idea in a different way than the text does?
The map clearly shows that each time zone is exactly one hour different from the preceding time zone.

5. If it were 3:00 Pacific Time, what time would it be Eastern Time? **6:00 Eastern Time.**

 Notes for Home: Your child read an article and got information from a related map. *Home Activity:* Together with your child, look at a map of your city, state, or country. Have your child describe locations of certain places, or the distances between two places on the map.

Graphic Sources **251**

Vocabulary

Directions: Choose the word from the box that best completes each sentence. Write the word on the line.

downpour _____ 1. Last night's heavy _____ caused massive mud slides in our town.

schedules _____ 2. The _____ for buses, trains, and postal service were all ruined.

rugged _____ 3. The mud slides caused local roads and trails to become even more _____ and difficult to use.

heroic _____ 4. People who came to help did a _____ job.

rescuers _____ 5. The mayor gave an award to the _____ for their brave work.

Check the Words You Know
___ dispatched
___ downpour
___ heroic
___ locomotives
___ rescuers
___ rugged
___ schedules

Directions: Choose the word from the box that best matches each clue. Write the letters of the word on the blanks. The boxed letters spell something you can take on trains.

6. train engines   6. l o c o m o [t] i v e s

7. rough and uneven   7. [r] u g g e d

8. very brave   8. h e r o [i] c

9. heavy rainfall   9. d o w n [p] o u r

10. sent off   10. d i [s] p a t c h e d

Something you take on trains: [t] [r] [i] [p] [s]

Write a Journal Entry

On a separate sheet of paper, write a journal entry about an imaginary train trip that runs into trouble. Describe the problem and how it was solved. Use as many vocabulary words as you can. **Students' journal entries should make correct use of vocabulary words.**

Notes for Home: Your child identified and used new vocabulary words from *Kate Shelley: Bound for Legend*. **Home Activity:** Make up a story with your child of a daring rescue, using the vocabulary words. When finished, share your story with others.

252 Vocabulary

Name _____

Kate Shelley: Bound for Legend

Graphic Sources

- A **graphic source**, such as a picture, graph, or map, shows information visually.
- Before you read, look for graphic sources of information that could give you an idea of what the article or story is about.

Directions: Look at the map of the vicinity of Kate Shelley's home from *Kate Shelley: Bound for Legend*. Then answer the questions below.

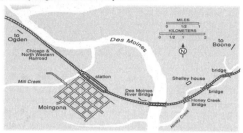

From KATE SHELLEY: BOUND FOR LEGEND by Robert D. San Souci, paintings by Max Ginsburg.
Copyright © 1995 by Max Ginsburg, paintings. Used by permission of Dial Books for Young Readers, a division of Penguin Putnam Inc.

1. In which direction does a train travel from Moingona to the Honey Creek Bridge?
The train travels east.

2. Is the Shelley house closer to the Honey Creek Bridge or to the station at Moingona?
It is closer to the bridge.

3. If you traveled by train from Ogden to Boone, what bridges and stations would you travel past along the way?
You would first travel past the Moingona station, then the Des Moines River Bridge, then the Honey Creek Bridge, and then past the two unnamed bridges.

4. Which bridge is closest to the Moingona station?
The Des Moines River Bridge is the bridge closest to the station.

5. How does the map help you better understand the story? Explain your answer on a separate sheet of paper. **Possible answer: The map helps you picture how far Kate had to travel from Honey Creek Bridge to the station and back to bring help.**

Notes for Home: Your child answered questions about a map. *Home Activity:* Look at a map with your child. Talk about the information you can find by reading the map, such as distances between two locations.

Name _____

Kate Shelley: Bound for Legend

Selection Test
Directions: Choose the best answer to each item. Mark the letter for the answer you have chosen.

Part 1: Vocabulary
Find the answer choice that means about the same as the underlined word in each sentence.

1. The newspaper included a report about the downpour.
   - Ⓐ heavy rainfall
   - B. ruined plan
   - C. huge fountain
   - D. falling prices

2. Please pick up some schedules.
   - F. books about historic events
   - G. lists of addresses and phone numbers
   - Ⓗ times of arrival and departure
   - J. guides to interesting places

3. That museum has some old locomotives.
   - A. uniforms of railroad engineers
   - Ⓑ engines used to push or pull trains
   - C. oil lanterns
   - D. letters and diaries

4. The rescuers looked into the cave.
   - F. scientists
   - Ⓖ people trying to save others
   - H. artists
   - J. people traveling to new places

5. We hiked across the rugged land.
   - A. damp and muddy
   - B. green and grassy
   - C. dry and dusty
   - Ⓓ rough and uneven

6. The mayor dispatched the rescue team.
   - F. said good things about
   - Ⓖ sent out
   - H. gave instructions to
   - J. welcomed

7. The girl told us about her heroic acts.
   - A. unusual
   - B. against the law
   - C. unknown
   - Ⓓ very brave

Part 2: Comprehension
Use what you know about the selection to answer each question.

8. How did fifteen-year-old Kate Shelley spend most of her time?
   - F. She attended school with her younger brothers and sisters.
   - G. She helped her father on the railroad.
   - H. She swam in the nearby stream and played with her friends.
   - Ⓙ She ran the family farm.

9. Which of these events happened first?
   - A. Kate heard a pusher engine fall into Honey Creek.
   - B. Kate moved the farm animals to higher ground.
   - C. Kate decided to try to stop the midnight train bound for Chicago.
   - Ⓓ Kate helped her mother bring in the laundry.

 GO ON

Name _____

Kate Shelley: Bound for Legend

10. When Kate decided that she had to go through the storm to the train station, her mother was—
    - Ⓕ worried that she would be hurt.
    - G. eager for Kate to face the danger.
    - H. furious at Kate for disobeying her.
    - J. confident that Kate would be safe.

11. According to the map in this selection, a train heading in a westerly direction as it passed the Shelley house was going toward—
    - A. Boone.
    - Ⓑ Ogden.
    - C. Chicago.
    - D. Ohio.

12. What was Kate's most terrifying moment while crossing the Des Moines River Bridge?
    - F. realizing that the ties were two feet apart
    - G. seeing the spot where her brother had died
    - H. seeing the lights of the railway station in the distance
    - Ⓙ seeing a huge tree rushing toward the bridge

13. Which sentence states an opinion?
    - A. "She turned and headed for the Des Moines River Bridge."
    - B. "As it headed for the fallen trestle, the engineer kept sounding the whistle."
    - Ⓒ "The girl is crazy."
    - D. "But the structure proved solid, and the storm was quieting at last."

14. Traveling east from Moingona, a train would first come to the—
    - Ⓕ Des Moines River Bridge.
    - G. Shelley House.
    - H. Honey Creek Bridge.
    - J. town of Boone.

15. Of all the honors Kate received, which did she think was the best?
    - A. a medal from the state of Iowa
    - B. whistles from trains that passed by
    - Ⓒ a lifetime pass on the railroad
    - D. greetings from passengers on the trains

 STOP

Name _____

Kate Shelley: Bound for Legend

Graphic Sources

- A **graphic source**, such as a picture, graph, or map, shows information visually.
- Before you read, look for graphic sources of information that could give you an idea of what the article or story is about.

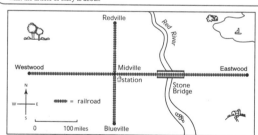

Directions: Look at the map. Use information from the map to answer the questions below.

1. About how many miles is it from Westwood to Eastwood?
It is about 500 miles. Accept reasonable estimates.

2. How could you get by train from Redville to Eastwood?
Take a train to Midville, and then switch to a train to Eastwood.

3. In which direction do you travel from Redville to Blueville?
You travel south.

4. About how many miles is it from Midville to Westwood?
It is about 200 miles. Accept reasonable estimates.

5. Why are maps like this used in stories?
Possible answer: Maps show the settings for stories and help readers picture where events occur.

Notes for Home: Your child answered questions about a map. *Home Activity:* With your child, draw a map of your neighborhood. Then talk about the information you can find by reading the map. Write a story about your neighborhood and include your map.

© Scott Foresman 5

Practice Book 5.3, p. 117

Name _____

Text Structure

REVIEW

Directions: Read each passage. Then read each question about the passages. Choose the best answer to each question. Mark the letter for the answer you have chosen.

All About Trains

1. Trains can carry heavier cargo than airplanes. One locomotive engine can pull many cars full of freight. Planes, on the other hand, can carry only one cargo load of freight at a time. Planes travel faster than trains, though, which can mean that the cargo gets to its destination faster than it would by train.

2. At one time, Americans couldn't get from coast to coast by train. The train tracks did not go all the way across the United States. Then, in the early 1860s, the railroad companies decided to begin building a transcontinental railroad.

3. Some early trains carried large sums of money. Companies would send payrolls and other kinds of payments in cash by rail. As a result, the trains were often the targets of robbery.

4. In 1804, the steam locomotive was invented. This made it possible for a locomotive to pull cars along a train track. By 1831, there was steam-powered train service in the United States.

5. There are many kinds of railroad cars, and they have different purposes. A Pullman car is one with sleeping compartments in which passengers can sleep overnight. A hopper car hauls freight. A tank car carries oil and other liquids. A stock car holds cattle.

1. The text structure of the first passage is—
   A. cause and effect.
   B. problem and solution.
   C. chronological order.
   D. compare and contrast.

2. The text structure of the second passage is—
   F. cause and effect.
   G. problem and solution.
   H. chronological order.
   J. compare and contrast.

3. The text structure of the third passage is—
   A. cause and effect.
   B. problem and solution.
   C. chronological order.
   D. compare and contrast.

4. The text structure of the fourth passage is—
   F. cause and effect.
   G. problem and solution.
   H. chronological order.
   J. compare and contrast.

5. The text structure of the fifth passage is—
   A. cause and effect.
   B. problem and solution.
   C. chronological order.
   D. compare and contrast.

Notes for Home: Your child read individual passages and identified the way the information was organized in each one. **Home Activity:** Read a magazine or newspaper article with your child. Talk together about the way that the information is organized in the article.

Text Structure 257

Name _____

Writing Across Texts

Directions: Consider what you know about frontier life and what you learned in *Kate Shelley: Bound for Legend* and "The Last Western Frontier." What do you think you would like about frontier life? What would you dislike? Add examples to each column to complete the table below. **Possible answers given.**

What I Would Like About Frontier Life	What I Would Not Like About Frontier Life
I would get to work on a farm.	I would have lots of chores.
1. There would be lots of space around me.	6. I might live in a sod house.
2. I could get free land.	7. I might have to use a wooden plow.
3. I could ride horses.	8. I would have to do hard work.
4. I could keep chickens.	9. It might be boring without TV or telephones.
5. My family would work and eat together.	10. It might be dangerous.

Write an Opinion

Imagine what it might have been like to be a pioneer in the westward expansion as described in both Kate Shelley's story and in "The Last Western Frontier." What are some reasons you would like frontier life? Why would you dislike it? Use information from each selection to write a paragraph that supports your feelings. Write your paragraph on a separate sheet of paper. **Paragraphs will vary. Check to see that students have used information from both selections to support their opinions.**

Notes for Home: Your child wrote an opinion about frontier life in the 1800s. **Home Activity:** Together with your child, discuss challenges faced by all families who move to a new place.

258 Writing Across Texts

Grammar Practice Book 5.3, p. 56

Name _____

Grammar: Verbs

REVIEW

Directions: Circle the verb in each sentence. Write **A** if the verb is an action verb. Write **L** if the verb is a linking verb. Remember, an **action verb** tells what action the subject of a sentence is performing or does. A **linking verb** links, or joins, the subject to a word in the predicate. A linking verb helps to tell what the subject is or is like.

L	1. Rescuers usually (are) people.
A	2. However, every year animals (save) the lives of many people.
L	3. For example, a cat once (was) a brave hero.
A	4. Early one morning a lady's house (filled) with smoke.
L	5. The smoke (looked) thick and dangerous.
A	6. The cat (jumped) on the lady.
L	7. The cat's warning (seemed) useless.
A	8. Again and again the cat (walked) over her body and her head.
A	9. Just in time, the lady (opened) her eyes.
A	10. She and the cat (raced) outside to safety.

Directions: Use each of the following words as verbs in a sentence. Write the sentence on the line. **Possible answers given.**

11. *looked* as an action verb
I looked through the window.

12. *looked* as a linking verb
The window looked dirty.

13. *felt* as an action verb
I felt the sandpaper.

14. *felt* as a linking verb
It felt rough.

15. *seems*
Our new neighbor seems strange!

Notes for Home: Your child identified action and linking verbs. **Home Activity:** Identify some simple verbs such as *say, run,* and *hit.* Work with your child to see how many colorful verbs you can find to substitute for these verbs. Use a thesaurus if available.

Grammar: Verbs 259

Grammar Practice Book 5.3, p. 57

Name _____

Grammar: Subject-Verb Agreement

The subject and the verb in a sentence must **agree** in number. A **singular noun subject** needs a verb whose form agrees with singular nouns. A **plural noun subject** needs a verb that agrees with plural nouns. The word **singular** refers to "one"; **plural** means "more than one." Use the following rules for verbs that tell about present time.

- If the subject is a singular noun, add **-s** or **-es** to most verbs. If a verb ends in a **consonant** and **y,** change the y to i before adding **-es.**

  Thunder <u>scares</u> the cat.
  The animal <u>scurries</u> under the bed.

- If the subject is a plural noun, do not add **-s** or **-es** to the verb.

  Cats <u>react</u> to unexpected sounds or flashes of light.

- When two subjects combine to form a compound subject, use a plural verb form.

  Thunder and lightning <u>scare</u> the cat.
  Heavy rain and hailstones <u>are</u> not favorites of hers either.

Directions: Circle the correct form of the verb in ( ) to complete each sentence.

1. Legends (tells/**tell**) about people from the past.
2. Some legends (is/**are**) based on fact.
3. Other legends (stretches/**stretch**) the truth.
4. Stories about the past (**thrill**/thrills) me sometimes.
5. Every culture (**has**/have) its own legends.
6. My grandmother (**knows**/know) a legend about Sarah Winnemucca, a member of the Paiute tribe.
7. We (listens/**listen**) to my grandmother's stories eagerly.
8. Heroes (is/**are**) often the subjects of legends.
9. Davy Crockett and Daniel Boone (has/**have**) a role in many legends about pioneers settling in the West.
10. Legends and other tales (keeps/**keep**) history alive.

Notes for Home: Your child chose forms of verbs that agree with singular subjects and plural subjects. **Home Activity:** Invite your child to write a family legend about something good a family member has done. Remind your child to check for subject-verb agreement.

260 Grammar: Subject-Verb Agreement

Answers 739

Grammar: Subject-Verb Agreement

Directions: Use the correct form of the verb in ( ) to complete each sentence. Write the verb on the line.

tells 1. My father (tell) many stories about Uncle Nick.

demonstrates 2. Uncle Nick always (demonstrate) great courage in his job as a firefighter.

respond 3. Every day, Uncle Nick and the other firefighters (respond) to fire alarms.

fight 4. Even at night, these guardians of our safety (fight) fierce blazes.

burn 5. Sometimes the fires (burn) for days.

pulls 6. Uncle Nick (pull) people out of burning buildings.

express 7. These people always (express) their gratitude to him for saving their lives.

possesses 8. Uncle Nick now (possess) several medals for bravery.

deserves 9. In my view, Uncle Nick (deserve) a hero's honors.

thinks 10. Dad (think) that Uncle Nick may even become a legend some day.

Directions: Add a verb to complete each sentence. Be sure to use the correct verb form. Write the verb on the line to the left. **Possible answers given.**

race 11. Each day, the trains _____ along the railroad tracks.

stay 12. During winter months, the passengers always _____ inside the station house.

looks 13. The conductor _____ for anything that might block the tracks.

fall 14. Sometimes, tree branches _____ on the tracks.

check 15. Workers _____ the tracks to make sure they are safe for the trains to travel.

Write a Song

What does "bravery" mean to you? On a separate sheet of paper, write a song about a brave person in the news right now. Tell how the person is brave. Set your words to a well-known tune. Be sure all the subjects and verbs in your song agree. **Check that students use the correct verb form that agrees with each subject.**

Notes for Home: Your child wrote verbs that agree with singular subjects and plural subjects. *Home Activity:* Read a news story with your child. Ask him or her to find all the subjects and verbs and to explain how they agree, or match in number.

Grammar: Subject-Verb Agreement

RETEACHING

Read each sentence. The simple subjects are underlined. Write the verbs.

1. Two boys build scenery. _____ **build** _____
2. A girl builds scenery. _____ **builds** _____

The **subject** and the **verb** in a sentence must **agree** in number.

Directions: Write the verb that correctly completes each sentence.

1. Tony and his helper _____ **paint** _____ the sets. (paint/paints)
2. Mary _____ **studies** _____ her part. (study/studies)
3. Dan and a teacher _____ **raise** _____ the rear curtains. (raise/raises)
4. The narrator _____ **appears** _____ in a costume. (appear/appears)
5. Teachers and parents _____ **help** _____ with the scenery. (help/helps)
6. Parents and guests _____ **arrive** _____ on time. (arrive/arrives)

Directions: The verb in each sentence is incorrect. Rewrite each sentence with the correct form of the underlined verb.

7. Judy and Diego moves the scenery.
Judy and Diego move the scenery.

8. Band members and the chorus joins in a song.
Band members and the chorus join in a song.

9. Classmates and visitors claps loudly.
Classmates and visitors clap loudly.

10. The stage director plan a cast party.
The stage director plans a cast party.

11. Scenery are put away.
Scenery is put away.

Notes for Home: Your child used verbs that agreed with the subjects of sentences. *Home Activity:* Write three subjects, such as *the plane, my friends,* and *the old car* and have your child write sentences using the subjects you wrote and verbs that agree.

Grammar: Subject-Verb Agreement

Directions: Edit the letter below to correct the eleven errors in subject-verb agreement. Cross out the incorrect verb form and write the correct form above it. Make sure subjects are used with the correct verb forms.

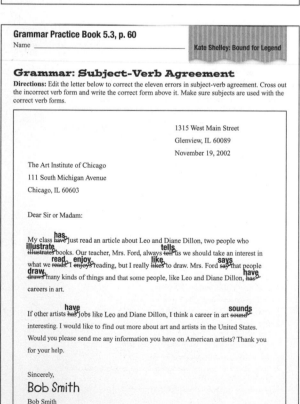

1315 West Main Street
Glenview, IL 60089
November 19, 2002

The Art Institute of Chicago
111 South Michigan Avenue
Chicago, IL 60603

Dear Sir or Madam:

My class have **has** just read an article about Leo and Diane Dillon, two people who illustrate **illustrate** books. Our teacher, Mrs. Ford, always tell **tells** us we should take an interest in what we reads **read**. I enjoys **enjoy** reading, but I really likes **like** to draw. Mrs. Ford say **says** that people draws **draw** many kinds of things and that some people, like Leo and Diane Dillon, has **have** careers in art.

If other artists has **have** jobs like Leo and Diane Dillon, I think a career in art sound **sounds** interesting. I would like to find out more about art and artists in the United States. Would you please send me any information you have on American artists? Thank you for your help.

Sincerely,

Bob Smith

Bob Smith

Notes for Home: Your child corrected a letter with errors in subject-verb agreement. *Home Activity:* Write sentences with blanks for verbs. Then have your child fill in verbs. Make sure the verbs your child writes agree with the subjects in the sentences.

Word Study: Irregular Plurals

Directions: Most plural nouns are formed by adding -s or -es. Some plural nouns do not follow a regular spelling pattern. These are called **irregular plurals**. Read the paragraph. Find each irregular plural noun and write it on the line.

The children heard the whistle as the train neared the town. Suddenly they heard a crash, and then it was quiet. They raced to the edge of town. Men and women had already begun to arrive. What a scene it was! The train had been carrying a special load. Oxen were lumbering about, and geese ran honking everywhere. The mice that had been nesting in the hay were under everyone's feet. Thankfully, no one was hurt, and the animals were all rounded up safely.

1. **children**
2. **men**
3. **women**
4. **oxen**
5. **geese**
6. **mice**
7. **feet**

Directions: Look at the plural nouns you wrote above. Write the singular form of each noun on the line.

8. **child**
9. **man**
10. **woman**
11. **ox**
12. **goose**
13. **mouse**
14. **foot**

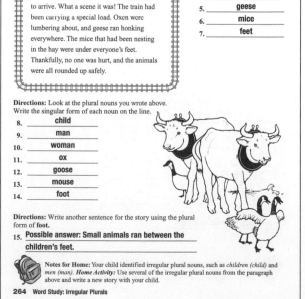

Directions: Write another sentence for the story using the plural form of **foot**.

15. **Possible answer: Small animals ran between the children's feet.**

Notes for Home: Your child identified irregular plural nouns, such as *children (child)* and *men (man)*. **Home Activity:** Use several of the irregular plural nouns from the paragraph above and write a new story with your child.

© Scott Foresman 5

Spelling: Irregular Plurals

Pretest Directions: Fold back the page along the dotted line. On the blanks, write the spelling words as they are dictated. When you have finished the test, unfold the page and check your words.

1.	radios	1.	Some **radios** run on batteries.
2.	videos	2.	The store rents **videos**.
3.	pianos	3.	**Pianos** are very heavy.
4.	patios	4.	Some houses have **patios**.
5.	banjos	5.	Bluegrass music uses **banjos**.
6.	heroes	6.	This book has stories of **heroes**.
7.	potatoes	7.	Baked **potatoes** are tasty.
8.	echoes	8.	The cave is full of **echoes**.
9.	tornadoes	9.	**Tornadoes** cause damage.
10.	tomatoes	10.	These **tomatoes** are not ripe yet
11.	cuffs	11.	The **cuffs** of his pants are dirty.
12.	cliffs	12.	**Cliffs** rise high above the river.
13.	beliefs	13.	We have the same **beliefs**.
14.	hoofs	14.	Animal **hoofs** are hard.
15.	roofs	15.	All the **roofs** were full of snow.
16.	themselves	16.	They talked among **themselves**.
17.	lives	17.	Paramedics save **lives**.
18.	leaves	18.	The **leaves** are turning red.
19.	loaves	19.	These **loaves** of bread are stale.
20.	halves	20.	They cut the fruit into **halves**.

Notes for Home: Your child took a pretest on words that are irregular plurals. **Home Activity:** Help your child learn misspelled words before the final test. Your child can underline the word parts that caused the problems and concentrate on those parts.

Spelling: Irregular Plurals **265**

Spelling: Irregular Plurals

Word List				
radios	banjos	tornadoes	beliefs	lives
videos	heroes	tomatoes	hoofs	leaves
pianos	potatoes	cuffs	roofs	loaves
patios	echoes	cliffs	themselves	halves

Directions: Choose the words from the box that are formed by adding **-es** to a base word. Write each word in the correct column. **Order may vary.**

f changes to v before -es is added

1. themselves
2. lives
3. leaves
4. loaves
5. halves

-es is added to words ending with o

6. heroes
7. potatoes
8. echoes
9. tornadoes
10. tomatoes

Directions: Add **-s** to each word in ( ) to form a word from the box and complete the sentence. Write the word on the line.

hoofs	11.	The horses' (hoof) loosened several rocks.
cliffs	12.	Rocks from the (cliff) fell onto the land below.
roofs	13.	Some rocks went through the (roof) of old buildings.
patios	14.	Other rocks crashed onto several (patio).
radios	15.	A rescue alert was heard on many (radio).
beliefs	16.	All differing customs and (belief) were set aside during the rescue.
pianos	17.	One musician was able to rescue her two (piano).
banjos	18.	But she wasn't able to save her damaged (banjo).
cuffs	19.	One man escaped with only minor tears to his shirt (cuff).
videos	20.	Newscasts showed home (video) of the damage shot by the homeowners.

Notes for Home: Your child spelled irregular plural nouns that have -s and -es added to them but that do not follow regular spelling patterns. **Home Activity:** Spell each spelling word aloud to your child. Have your child spell each word you say.

266 Spelling: Irregular Plurals

Spelling: Irregular Plurals

Directions: Proofread this news bulletin. Find five spelling mistakes. Use the proofreading marks to correct each mistake.

≡	Make a capital.
/	Make a small letter.
∧	Add something.
⌒	Take out something.
⊙	Add a period.
¶	Begin a new paragraph.

News Bulletin!

Alert! Several tornados have been spotted near the cliffs. The rooves of some homes have been damaged. No lifes have been lost, and many have been rescued. People should shut themselfs safely in their basements and stay off their patios. Do not try to take home videos. Stay tuned to your radios for updated reports.

Word List				
radios	banjos	tornadoes	beliefs	lives
videos	heroes	tomatoes	hoofs	leaves
pianos	potatoes	cuffs	roofs	loaves
patios	echoes	cliffs	themselves	halves

Write a News Report

Imagine you are a news correspondent reporting the results of a storm. On a separate sheet of paper, write your news report. Try to use at least five of your spelling words. **Answers will vary, but each report should include at least five spelling words.**

Spelling Tip
potatoes
How can you remember to spell **potatoes**, not **potatos**? Think of this hint: Po**tatoes** have both **eyes** and **toes**.

Notes for Home: Your child spelled irregular plural nouns that have -s and -es added to them but that do not follow regular spelling patterns. **Home Activity:** Make a list of the spelling words, but misspell several words. Have your child correct the list.

Spelling: Irregular Plurals **267**

Spelling: Irregular Plurals

REVIEW

Word List				
radios	banjos	tornadoes	beliefs	lives
videos	heroes	tomatoes	hoofs	leaves
pianos	potatoes	cuffs	roofs	loaves
patios	echoes	cliffs	themselves	halves

Directions: Choose the word from the box that best completes each statement. Write the word on the line to the left.

pianos	1.	*Strings* are to *violins* as *keys* are to ____.
hoofs	2.	*People* are to *feet* as *horses* are to ____.
roofs	3.	*Below* is to *basements* as *above* is to ____.
loaves	4.	*Corn* is to *ears* as *bread* is to ____.
heroes	5.	*Talent* is to *artists* as *bravery* is to ____.
leaves	6.	*Head* is to *hair* as *tree* is to ____.
themselves	7.	*We* is to *ourselves* as *they* is to ____.
tomatoes	8.	*Green* is to *lettuce* as *red* is to ____.
tornadoes	9.	*Shake* is to *earthquakes* as *swirl* is to ____.
banjos	10.	*Bang* is to *drums* as *strum* is to ____.
potatoes	11.	*Creamed* is to *spinach* as *mashed* is to ____.
cuffs	12.	*Arms* is to *hands* as *sleeves* is to ____.

Directions: Choose the word from the box that answers each question. Write the word on the line.

videos	13.	What might you rent for a double feature?	patios	17.	Where do people hold barbecues in the summer?
cliffs	14.	Where would you not want to walk if you were afraid of heights?	radios	18.	What do teenagers usually play too loud?
echoes	15.	What might you hear when you shout in the Grand Canyon?	halves	19.	Into what would you cut a pie for two very big eaters?
lives	16.	What would you learn about if you read biographies?	beliefs	20.	What do you call strong feelings or ideas?

Notes for Home: Your child spelled irregular plural nouns that have -s and -es added to them but that do not follow regular spelling patterns. **Home Activity:** Give your child clues about each spelling word. See if your child can identify and spell each word.

268 Spelling: Irregular Plurals

Atlas/Map

An **atlas** is a book of maps. A **map** is a drawing of a place. A **map key** shows what the symbols on a map mean. A **compass** shows the directions north, south, east, and west.

Directions: Use the map below to answer the questions on the next page.

MICHIGAN

Lake Erie

Toledo

PENNSYLVANIA

Cleveland

OHIO

Akron

Youngstown

INDIANA

Canton

Columbus

Dayton

Cincinnati

WEST VIRGINIA

Ohio River

KENTUCKY

0   25   50 Miles

0   25   50 Kilometers

Key

• State capital
• City or town
— River

N
W + E
S

Research and Study Skills: Atlas/Map   **269**

---

1. What five states border Ohio? **Michigan, Indiana, Kentucky, West Virginia, Pennsylvania**

2. Which state is on Ohio's western border? **Indiana**

3. If you measured that the distance between two cities was two inches on the map, how many actual miles is this distance? How do you know?
100 miles; The scale shows one inch equals 50 miles, so two inches equals 100 miles.

4. Approximately how many miles is it from Columbus to Dayton? **about 65 miles**

5. Approximately how many miles is it from Toledo to Dayton? **about 125 miles**

6. What body of water is located north of Cleveland? **Lake Erie**

7. What body of water runs along Ohio's southern border? **the Ohio River**

8. Which city in Ohio is the state capital? How do you know? **Columbus; It has a star next to it which is the symbol for the state capitol.**

9. If you flew from Toledo to Cincinnati, what other city would you fly over? **Dayton**

10. If you traveled west from Youngstown, what city would you come to first? **Akron**

11. If you went from Cincinnati to Cleveland, in which direction would you be traveling? **northeast**

12. Is the distance between Toledo and Columbus greater or less than the distance between Toledo and Akron?
The distance between Toledo and Columbus is greater than the distance between Toledo and Akron.

13. Why is it important for a map to have a compass? **Possible answer: A compass tells you the directions.**

14. Why is it important for a map to have a map key? **Possible answer: A map key explains what the symbols on a map mean.**

15. Describe a situation where you might use a map. **Possible answer: You might use a map to find the location of a place or to plan a trip.**

 Notes for Home: Your child read a map and answered questions about it. *Home Activity:* Look at any map you have at home. Have your child point out information on it, such as the location of places or the direction and distance from one place to another.

270 Research and Study Skills: Atlas/Map

Plot

- The important events that happen in a story make up the **plot**.
- A plot has several parts. **Conflict** is the story's main problem. During the **rising action** one event follows another. Each event adds interest or suspense to the conflict. The **climax** is the high point when the main character faces the problem directly. The **outcome** is the ending of the story.

Directions: Reread "Anything You Set Your Mind To." Then complete the plot map by identifying each important part of the story. **Possible answers given.**

Climax: When is Terry's problem finally solved?
4. **It is solved when suddenly he is swimming.**

Rising Action: What does Terry do to try to solve his problem?
2. **He keeps trying to swim.**
3. **He practices with a new teacher.**

Outcome: How does the story end?
5. **His dad says that Terry can do anything he sets his mind to. Terry says that for his next birthday, he wants to fly!**

Conflict: What problem does Terry have?
1. **He cannot learn to swim.**

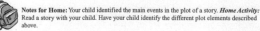 **Notes for Home:** Your child identified the main events in the plot of a story. *Home Activity:* Read a story with your child. Have your child identify the different plot elements described above.

Plot   **273**

Vocabulary

Directions: Choose the word from the box that best matches each clue. Write the word on the line.

Check the Words You Know
__ championship
__ opponent
__ strengthen
__ swollen
__ trophy

____**strengthen**____   1. Healthy foods do this to you.
____**championship**____   2. You might play in this.
____**trophy**____   3. You might win this.
____**opponent**____   4. It's someone to defeat.
____**swollen**____   5. A hurt finger might become this.

Directions: Write the word from the box that belongs in each group.

6. enemy, foe, ____**opponent**____
7. award, medal, ____**trophy**____
8. enlarged, puffy, ____**swollen**____
9. contest, competition, ____**championship**____
10. toughen, harden, ____**strengthen**____

Directions: Choose the word from the box that best completes each sentence. Write the word on the line.

____**championship**____   11. The big ____ wrestling match would be held this Saturday night.
____**opponent**____   12. My ____ was bigger than me, but I was faster.
____**strengthen**____   13. I had worked hard to ____ my upper body muscles.
____**swollen**____   14. Although my wrist is a little ____, I believe I can win the match.
____**trophy**____   15. I already know where I want to display the ____ in my room.

Write a Pep Talk

Imagine you are a sports coach. On a separate sheet of paper, write a pep talk to give to your players. Your pep talk should help make the team eager to win. Use as many vocabulary words as you can.
Students' pep talks should make correct use of vocabulary words. The tone of the pep talk should be motivational.

 Notes for Home: Your child identified and used vocabulary words from "The Marble Champ." *Home Activity:* Choose items in the room where you and your child are sitting. Describe each item. See if your child can guess what it is, based on the clues you offer.

274 Vocabulary

© Scott Foresman 5

Plot

- The important events that happen in a story make up the **plot**.
- These parts include the conflict that a character faces, the rising action, the climax, and resolution, or outcome.

Directions: Read the following plot summary of "The Marble Champ." Then answer the questions below.

> Lupe was a straight-A student who had won many awards and contests, but she wasn't good at sports. She wanted desperately to win some kind of sports contest. She chose marbles.
>
> For the next two weeks, Lupe practiced marbles so much that her thumb became swollen. She received tips from her brother on how to shoot.
>
> At the playground championship, Lupe beat all her female opponents in marbles and won a trophy. She then defeated the winner of the boys' division and won a second trophy.
>
> That night, Lupe went out with her family to celebrate. Later, she proudly placed the two trophies on her bedroom shelf. She felt good about finally winning a sports award.

1. Who is the main character of the story? How would you describe this character?
Lupe is the main character. She is a straight-A student, but not very athletic.

2. What conflict does Lupe face early in the story?
She wants desparately to win some kind of sports contest.

3. What is the rising action, the events that build to the climax?
Possible answer: She practices marbles for two weeks. She receives tips on shooting from her brother. Her thumb gets swollen.

4. What is the climax, or high point, of the story?
Possible answer: The climax is the day of the championship, when she defeats the final girl and then the final boy.

5. What is the resolution, or outcome, of the story? Write your answer on a separate sheet of paper.
Possible answer: Lupe celebrates with her family and then goes home with her trophies. She feels proud of her accomplishment.

 Notes for Home: Your child read a plot summary of a story read in class, and then answered questions about its plot, or important parts of the story. **Home Activity:** Read a story with your child. Then talk together to identify the most important parts of the story.

Selection Test

Directions: Choose the best answer to each item. Mark the letter for the answer you have chosen.

Part 1: Vocabulary

Find the answer choice that means about the same as the underlined word in each sentence.

1. Maria watched her opponent.
   A. person who helps a player
   B. person who judges a game
   C. person who writes about sports
   D. person one plays against in a game *(D circled)*

2. The championship is on Saturday.
   F. game to decide the first-place winner *(F circled)*
   G. important test
   H. party held to honor a special person
   J. practice time

3. Sarah put the trophy on her dresser.
   A. book signed by the author
   B. award in the form of a figure or cup *(B circled)*
   C. marble of three different colors
   D. woven string worn around the neck

4. I need to strengthen my legs.
   F. wash
   G. stretch
   H. make stronger *(H circled)*
   J. cool off

5. My hand was swollen.
   A. cut
   B. larger than normal *(B circled)*
   C. broken
   D. covered with spots

Part 2: Comprehension

Use what you know about the story to answer each item.

6. The beginning of this story is mostly about—
   F. what Lupe has done in the past. *(F circled)*
   G. how Lupe plans to become the marble champ.
   H. where Lupe Medrano comes from.
   J. when Lupe learned to ride a bike.

7. Lupe's main problem in this story is that she—
   A. doesn't get along with her family.
   B. never gets enough attention for her achievements.
   C. is doing poorly in school.
   D. wants to be good at sports, but she isn't. *(D circled)*

8. The first time Lupe tries to play marbles, what is her main problem?
   F. The marbles keep breaking.
   G. Her thumb is too weak. *(G circled)*
   H. Her aim is not accurate.
   J. Her brother takes his marbles back.

9. Which word best describes Lupe?
   A. lazy
   B. determined *(B circled)*
   C. complaining
   D. nervous

GO ON ➡

---

10. How do the members of Lupe's family react to her plans to become the marble champ?
    F. They tell her to focus on schoolwork and give up on other activities.
    G. They are positive that she will win.
    H. They are surprised, but they support her. *(H circled)*
    J. They pay no attention to her.

11. Lupe's hardest match is against—
    A. Rachel, her first opponent.
    B. Yolanda, her second opponent.
    C. the girl in the baseball cap. *(C circled)*
    D. Alfonso, a boy from her neighborhood.

12. During the rising action in this story, Lupe is—
    F. practicing. *(F circled)*
    G. beating the girls' champion.
    H. beating the boys' champion.
    J. receiving a trophy.

13. Why was Lupe's decision to play marbles a sensible one?
    A. She picked a sport that nobody else could play well.
    B. She picked a sport that fit her abilities. *(B circled)*
    C. She picked a sport in which winning is a matter of luck rather than skill.
    D. She picked a sport that would make her stronger and healthier.

14. The author's main purpose in this selection is to—
    F. tell an amusing story about Lupe. *(F circled)*
    G. explain how to play marbles.
    H. persuade kids to play marbles.
    J. describe the awards that Lupe has won before.

15. What does Lupe's treatment of the girls she defeats suggest about her?
    A. She wishes she had never won.
    B. She is a good sport. *(B circled)*
    C. She wants to embarrass them.
    D. She is a mean person.

STOP

Plot

- The important events that happen in a story make up the **plot**.
- These parts include the conflict that a character faces, the rising action, the climax, and the resolution, or outcome.

Directions: Read the story below.

> Dave wanted to win the school spelling bee badly. Both his older brothers had won when they were his age. Now Dave wanted to prove that he was just as good!
>
> A month before the contest, Dave began to prepare. He studied a long list of spelling words every day. His sister also read aloud words from the dictionary that Dave would then try to spell.
>
> On the day of the spelling bee, Dave was ready. His first words to spell were *separate, rhythm,* and *judgment.* Dave got each one right.
>
> In the final round, Dave faced only one other student. The word was *chrome.* The other student spelled it without the *h.* Now it was Dave's turn. He said, "Chrome. C-H-R-O-M-E." Dave won the contest! The crowd cheered.

Directions: Complete the diagram. Think about what happens in each part of the plot.

Climax
4. **Dave spells *chrome* correctly.**

Rising Action Events
3. **He spells dictionary words with his sister's help.**

2. **Dave studies word lists.**

Resolution
5. **Dave wins the spelling bee. The crowd cheers.**

Conflict
1. **Dave wants to win the school spelling bee.**

 Notes for Home: Your child read a story and identified the plot, or important parts of the story. **Home Activity:** Make up a story with your child about someone who faces and overcomes a problem. Then talk with your child about the different parts of the story.

Answers 743

Name _____

The Marble Champ

Theme

REVIEW

Directions: Read the story. Then read each question about the story. Choose the best answer to each question. Mark the letter for the answer you have chosen.

A Runner's Shortcut

Kevin really wanted to win the city runners' marathon. First prize was a hundred dollars in cash. Kevin needed the money badly. He had persuaded his brother to loan him money for a new stereo, and it was time to pay him back. His brother had already asked him twice about getting his money back.

Keven hadn't been running on a regular basis lately, but he really wanted a chance at the hundred dollars. He decided he would enter the race.

When the race began, Kevin ran hard. But he just couldn't keep up with the leaders. After two hours, his legs hurt and he was panting. He was also very far behind. He could see the hundred dollars slipping away, and he could hear his brother yelling at him about paying back the loan.

Then Kevin had a new thought. He decided to cheat. He remembered that the Number 10 bus came along the same route as the race. He left the running path and caught the bus. It drove him near the finish line where Kevin got off the bus and ran the rest of the race. He arrived feeling fresh and hardly out of breath. The judges awarded Kevin the cash prize.

Later, however, many people complained. They said they saw Kevin get on and off the bus. The judges had no choice but to take the prize away from Kevin. He felt embarrassed. He was sorry he had cheated and knew that no prize was worth his good name.

1. Kevin wanted to win the race because—
   A. he was a good runner.
   B. he was proud.
   C. he had won before.
   D. he needed money.

2. When Kevin saw he was behind, he decided to—
   F. ride the bus.
   G. quit the race.
   H. run faster.
   J. rest for a while.

3. In the end, Kevin—
   A. won the prize.
   B. lost the prize.
   C. split the prize with someone else.
   D. gave away the prize.

4. One theme of the story is that—
   F. cheaters sometimes win.
   G. cheaters never lose.
   H. cheating doesn't pay.
   J. cheating is okay.

5. Another theme of the story is that cheaters—
   A. should hide better.
   B. shouldn't need money.
   C. may end up embarrassed and sorry.
   D. may win big money.

 Notes for Home: Your child read a story and identified its underlying meaning, or theme. **Home Activity:** Watch a TV show or movie with your child. Later, discuss what the characters learned from their experiences, and what the story can teach you about real life.

Theme **279**

Writing Across Texts

Directions: Think about Lupe from "The Marble Champ" and Kate Shelley from *Kate Shelley: Bound for Legend.* Each girl succeeded against difficult odds. What enabled them to succeed? Use the web below to organize what you would like to learn about the girls. **Possible answers given.**

1. What made them do the things they decided to do?

2. What made them keep going?

How did they feel?

What I want to learn about Kate Shelley and Lupe

5. Which part was the most difficult?

3. What did they think about what they had done?

4. Would they have any advice for me?

Write Interview Questions

Think about the personalities of Lupe from "The Marble Champ" and Kate Shelley from *Kate Shelley: Bound for Legend.* Suppose you could interview each girl to find out more about her as a person. Make a list of interview questions that would help you get to know each girl better. **Questions will vary. Check that students ask questions that will help them understand the characters and why they did what they did. Check that students referenced specific examples from the stories in their questions.**

Notes for Home: Your child prepared interview questions for a fictional story character and a real-life person. **Home Activity:** As you read stories with your child, discuss what else you would like to know about each main character and whether the characters are like people you know.

280 Writing Across Texts

Name _____

The Marble Champ

Grammar: Subject-Verb Agreement

REVIEW

Directions: Circle the action verb in ( ) that agrees with the subject in each sentence.

1. Athletes always (practices/**practice**) their particular sports many hours a day.

2. Practice (**makes**/make) perfect!

3. Lots of things, however, (improves/**improve**) with practice.

4. My older sister, for example, (**bakes**/bake) chocolate chip cookies.

5. The cookies (tastes/**taste**) good now, but at the beginning she always burned them.

6. My dad really (**enjoys**/enjoy) the computer.

7. His fingers (moves/**move**) fast on the keyboard now, but he started with one finger at a time.

8. Even my dog (**gets**/get) better every time he catches a ball.

9. My younger brother, however, (**disproves**/disprove) this theory.

10. His singing voice never (**gets**/get) better!

Directions: Circle the linking verb in ( ) that agrees with the subject in each sentence.

11. Practice (**is**/are) even important in arithmetic.

12. The multiplication tables (was/**were**) hard for me to learn.

13. My younger sister (**has**/have) the same problem.

14. Flash cards (was/**were**) a big help to me.

15. The answers (is/**are**) much easier after many tries.

 Notes for Home: Your child identified verbs that agree with their subjects. **Home Activity:** Practice and oral repetition help children become familiar with the sound of correct agreement between subjects and verbs. Read aloud a short story with your child.

Grammar: Subject-Verb Agreement **281**

Name _____

The Marble Champ

Grammar: Verb Tenses: Present, Past, and Future

Verbs in the **present tense** show actions happening now. Remember that in a sentence about present time, the verb that agrees with a singular noun subject usually ends in **-s** or **-es**.

Karen <u>swings</u> the bat fast. Jan <u>catches</u> the ball expertly.

Present tense verbs that agree with plural subjects usually do not end in **-s** or **-es**.

Both girls <u>swing</u> at the ball swiftly. They also <u>catch</u> expertly.

Verbs in the **past tense** show actions that have already happened. Add **-ed** to most verbs to show the past tense. The spelling of some regular verbs changes when you add **-ed.**

- For verbs ending in e, drop the e and add **-ed: hoped, loved.**
- For verbs ending in a **consonant** and y, change the y to i and add **-ed: tried, hurried.**
- For one-syllable verbs ending in one vowel followed by one consonant, double the consonant and add **-ed: flipped, planned.**

Verbs that do not add **-ed** in the past tense are called **irregular verbs.** Irregular verbs do *not* follow a regular pattern: **sang, went, caught.**

A verb in the **future tense** shows an action that will happen. Verbs in the future tense include the helping verb *will.*

We <u>will play</u> marbles. I <u>will win</u> the championship!

Directions: Write the correct tense for each verb below. Use the verb form that agrees with a singular subject.

Verb	Present		Past		Future	
jump	1. jumps		6. jumped		11. will jump	
stop	2. stops		7. stopped		12. will stop	
carry	3. carries		8. carried		13. will carry	
bake	4. bakes		9. baked		14. will bake	
draw	5. draws		10. drew		15. will draw	

 Notes for Home: Your child wrote verbs in the present, past, and future tenses. **Home Activity:** Ask your child to describe a time when he or she excelled at something: sports, academics, music, and so on. Check that your child uses the correct verb tense when speaking.

282 Grammar: Verb Tenses: Present, Past, and Future

© Scott Foresman 5

---

744 Answers

Name _____

The Marble Champ

Grammar: Verb Tenses: Present, Past, and Future

Directions: Circle the verb in each sentence. Write **present, past,** or **future** to tell the tense of each verb.

present	1. Some people (succeed) mainly through hard work.
present	2. Others (demonstrate) natural talent.
present	3. Both types (develop) their skills through constant effort.
past	4. James Francis Thorpe (possessed) both talent and ambition.
present	5. Some sportswriters (call) Jim Thorpe the greatest American male athlete ever.
past	6. A Sac and Fox Native American, Jim Thorpe (lived) in Oklahoma as a child and as a teenager.
past	7. Jim Thorpe (began) his athletic career as a college football star.
future	8. If you know football history, you (will recognize) the name of Glenn "Pop" Warner, his first coach.
past	9. In 1912, Jim Thorpe (earned) two gold medals at the Olympic Games in Sweden.
past	10. Later, he (played) professional baseball and football.
present	11. Today's professional players (enjoy) salaries far higher than Jim Thorpe's.
future	12. Few athletes (will equal) this champion's record.
present	13. People (admire) great athletes like Jim Thorpe.
future	14. They (will remember) his accomplishments for a long time.
past	15. They even (made) a movie about his life.

Write a Recipe for Success
How can you become good at something? On a separate sheet of paper, write a recipe for success. Use all three verb tenses—present, past, and future—to explain how to succeed at sports, studying, or anything else worth doing.
Students should include all three tenses. Check to make sure that they have used the correct form for each verb.

 Notes for Home: Your child identified verb tenses: present, past, and future. *Home Activity:* Say a simple sentence in the present tense. Then invite your child to say the sentence in the past tense and then in the future tense.

Name _____

The Marble Champ

Grammar: Verb Tenses: Present, Past and Future

RETEACHING

The verb in each sentence is underlined. Draw a line to match each sentence with the word that tells when the action takes place.

1. The team practices in the gym. — past
2. They won a game last night. — present
3. The coach will discuss it with them. — future

The **tense** of a verb shows the time of the action. Add **-ed** to most verbs to show the past tense. Past-tense verbs that do not end in **-ed** are called **irregular verbs.** They do not follow a regular pattern. The future tense usually is formed with the helping verb **will.**

Directions: A verb in each sentence is underlined. Circle its tense.

1. The players tap the ball back and forth. (present) past
2. One player hits the ball too hard. (present) future
3. The coach will talk to her about it later. past (future)
4. I hope she learned from her mistake. (past) future
5. Someone loudly blows a whistle. future (present)
6. The two captains of the teams will shake hands. (future) present
7. She will toss a coin in the air. (future) present
8. The spectators in the stands cheer for their teams. (present) past
9. The long game ended with the score tied. (past) present

Directions: Rewrite each sentence. Use the tense shown in ( ) to help you change the underlined verb.

10. Ivan plays a new position. (future tense)
Ivan will play a new position.

11. The coach wants him at third base. (past tense)
The coach wanted him at third base.

12. He watches Ivan very carefully during the game. (future tense)
He will watch Ivan very carefully during the game.

 Notes for Home: Your child identified and wrote verbs in the present, past, and future tenses. *Home Activity:* Read aloud some poems with your child. Have your child point out verbs in the poems and tell whether each is in the present, past, or future tense.

Name _____

The Marble Champ

Grammar: Verb Tenses: Present, Past and Future

Directions: Rewrite the paragraph. Change each verb to the past tense and underline it.

The crew prepares the powerful car for the big race. One man rolls two new tires to another worker. They remove the old tires from the special wheels. Then they attach the new ones. Meanwhile, other crew members check the engine and brakes. A special team fills the large tank in the car with fuel. The crew chief times the car with a watch. He studies its movement. The car stops many laps later.

1.–9. The crew prepared the powerful car for the big race. One man rolled two new tires to another worker. They removed the old tires from the special wheels. Then they attached the new ones. Meanwhile, other crew members checked the engine and brakes. A special team filled the large tank in the car with fuel. The crew chief timed the car with a watch. He studied its movement. The car stopped many laps later.

Directions: Rewrite the paragraph in the future tense. Underline each verb.

10.–18. The crew will prepare the powerful car for the big race. One man will roll two new tires to another worker. They will remove the old tires from the special wheels. Then they will attach the new ones. Meanwhile other crew members will check the engine and brakes. A special team will fill the large tank in the car with fuel. The crew chief will time the car with a watch. He will study its movement. The car will stop many laps later.

Write a Sportscast
On a separate sheet of paper, write a broadcast of a sports competition. Describe what happens before, during, and after the event. Use verbs in the present, past, and future tenses.
Make sure students have used verbs in the correct tenses.

 Notes for Home: Your child identified present-tense verbs and rewrote them in the past tense. *Home Activity:* Have your child write three sentences in which he or she tells about the weather yesterday and today and predicts it for tomorrow. Remind him or her to use correct verb tenses.

Name _____

The Marble Champ

Word Study: Contractions

Directions: A **contraction** is a word made by putting two words together. An **apostrophe** (') replaces the letter or letters that are left out. Combine each word pair to form a contraction. Write the contraction on the line.

1. I will — **I'll**
2. that is — **that's**
3. was not — **wasn't**
4. he is — **he's**
5. should not — **shouldn't**
6. she will — **she'll**
7. is not — **isn't**
8. will not — **won't**
9. we have — **we've**
10. let us — **let's**
11. that is — **that's**
12. we would — **we'd**

Directions: Read the letter. Circle each contraction. Write the two words that make up each contraction on the line.

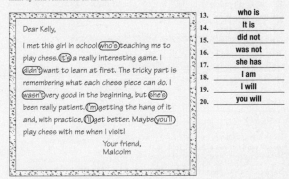

Dear Kelly,
I met this girl in school (who's) teaching me to play chess. (It's) a really interesting game. I (didn't) want to learn at first. The tricky part is remembering what each chess piece can do. I (wasn't) very good in the beginning, but (she's) been really patient. (I'm) getting the hang of it and, with practice, (I'll) get better. Maybe (you'll) play chess with me when I visit!

Your friend,
Malcolm

13. **who is**
14. **It is**
15. **did not**
16. **was not**
17. **she has**
18. **I am**
19. **I will**
20. **you will**

 Notes for Home: Your child formed contractions such as *I'd (I had)* and *haven't (have not)*. **Home Activity:** Watch a favorite television show with your child and listen for contractions in the dialogue or narration. See who can be the first to say the two words that the contraction represents.

Answers 745

Spelling Workbook 5.3, p. 49

Spelling: Contractions

Pretest Directions: Fold back the page along the dotted line. On the blanks, write the spelling words as they are dictated. When you have finished the test, unfold the page and check your words.

1. **can't**
2. **wouldn't**
3. **don't**
4. **weren't**
5. **I'm**
6. **I'll**
7. **let's**
8. **that's**
9. **there's**
10. **what's**
11. **she's**
12. **you're**
13. **they're**
14. **who's**
15. **we're**
16. **I've**
17. **you've**
18. **should've**
19. **could've**
20. **we've**

1. Carrie **can't** sing very well.
2. I **wouldn't** know.
3. **Don't** you live nearby?
4. They **weren't** happy with him.
5. **I'm** writing a letter to a friend.
6. **I'll** tell you about it later.
7. **Let's** go to the movies tonight.
8. **That's** not what I meant.
9. **There's** someone at the door.
10. **What's** your favorite color?
11. **She's** trying to pay attention.
12. **You're** not crying, are you?
13. **They're** waiting for a ride home.
14. **Who's** coming to the party?
15. **We're** having a picnic tomorrow.
16. **I've** finished reading my book.
17. **You've** helped me a lot.
18. We **should've** taken the bus.
19. Tammy **could've** fixed anything.
20. **We've** only just arrived.

 Notes for Home: Your child took a pretest on words that are contractions. *Home Activity:* Help your child learn misspelled words. Dictate the word and have your child spell the word aloud for you or write it on paper, making sure the apostrophe is in the correct place.

Spelling Workbook 5.3, p. 50

Spelling: Contractions

Word List			
can't	I'll	she's	I've
wouldn't	let's	you're	you've
don't	that's	they're	should've
weren't	there's	who's	could've
I'm	what's	we're	we've

Directions: Choose the words from the box that contain the pronouns **I, you, she, we, they,** and **us.** Write the words in alphabetical order.

1. **I'll**
2. **I'm**
3. **I've**
4. **let's**
5. **she's**
6. **they're**
7. **we're**
8. **we've**
9. **you're**
10. **you've**

Directions: Write the word from the box that matches each clue.

should've 11. It rhymes with *could've* and means "should have."
weren't 12. It rhymes with *burnt* and means "were not."
don't 13. It rhymes with *won't* and means "do not."
that's 14. It rhymes with *bats* and means "that is."
what's 15. It rhymes with *cuts* and means "what is."
who's 16. It rhymes with *shoes* and means "who is."
could've 17. It rhymes with *should've* and means "could have."
wouldn't 18. It rhymes with *shouldn't* and means "would not."
there's 19. It rhymes with *bears* and means "there is."
can't 20. It rhymes with *ant* and means "cannot."

 Notes for Home: Your child spelled contractions. *Home Activity:* Read a story with your child. Have your child identify the contractions and explain which two words have been combined to form each contraction.

Spelling Workbook 5.3, p. 51

Spelling: Contractions

Directions: Proofread this speech. Find five spelling mistakes. Use the proofreading marks to correct each mistake.

≡	Make a capital.
/	Make a small letter.
∧	Add something.
✗	Take out something.
⊙	Add a period.
¶	Begin a new paragraph.

As team captain, I'm telling you players that we've got to practice more if we're going to win games. We should've won yesterday, and we could've won. But we're making too many mistakes, and that's hurting us. We can't win if we don't practice. So let's work hard and show who's the best!

Word List			
can't	I'll	she's	I've
wouldn't	let's	you're	you've
don't	that's	they're	should've
weren't	there's	who's	could've
I'm	what's	we're	we've

Write a Pep Talk

Imagine you were coach of the team addressed above. On a separate sheet of paper, write a pep talk to give to team members. Try to use at least five of your spelling words. **Answers will vary, but each pep talk should include at least five spelling words.**

Spelling Tip
who's
Don't confuse **who's** with **whose.** Use **who's** when it takes the place of the words **who is.**

 Notes for Home: Your child spelled contractions—words made of two other words with an apostrophe representing the missing letters. *Home Activity:* Say the two words that each spelling word combines, such as *let us* for *let's.* Have your child spell the contraction.

Spelling Workbook 5.3, p. 52

Spelling: Contractions

REVIEW

Word List			
can't	I'll	she's	I've
wouldn't	let's	you're	you've
don't	that's	they're	should've
weren't	there's	who's	could've
I'm	what's	we're	we've

Directions: Choose the word from the box that can replace the underlined words in each sentence. Write the word on the line to the left.

there's 1. I hear <u>there is</u> band practice today.
don't 2. I <u>do not</u> know the exact time, however.
we're 3. I think <u>we are</u> practicing right after school.
I'll 4. <u>I will</u> check the exact time.
they're 5. Do you know where <u>they are</u> holding it?
I'm 6. <u>I am</u> pretty sure it is on the football field.
should've 7. They <u>should have</u> told us already.
who's 8. Do you know <u>who is</u> leading the practice?
she's 9. Ms. Davis told me that <u>she is</u> attending.
wouldn't 10. However, she <u>would not</u> say if she is leading it.
I've 11. <u>I have</u> got to be home by six o'clock.
Let's 12. <u>Let us</u> hope that practice is over by then.

Directions: Choose the word from the box that means the same as each word or words below. Write the word on the lines.

13. could have **could've**
14. what is **what's**
15. cannot **can't**
16. we have **we've**
17. you are **you're**
18. were not **weren't**
19. you have **you've**
20. that is **that's**

 Notes for Home: Your child spelled contractions—words made of two other words with an apostrophe representing the missing letters. *Home Activity:* Spell each spelling word aloud, without saying "apostrophe." See if your child can tell you where the apostrophe (') belongs.

Technology: Diagram/Scale Drawing

The Internet is a great place to find information. To find your topic, use a search engine to look for web pages. The computer screen for a search engine might look like this:

Search the Web

Search Tip: Type in more than one word and put AND between them. Enter your words, then click Find!

[Find!]

If you need help, click here.

If you wanted to find out about games played with marbles, you could enter "marbles AND games." Then you might get this list of web pages:

You Searched For: marbles AND games
Top 8 of 2145 matches
Playing with the Past
Games Kids Play
Marble Tournaments
Crazy Marbles
Traditional Games, History
Marbles, Collecting
Game Strategies
Rules for Games

Web pages often include diagrams or scale drawings. A **diagram** is a special drawing with labels that usually show how something is made or done. A **scale drawing** is a diagram that uses a mathematical scale, such as 1 inch on the drawing equals 1 foot in real life.

Research and Study Skills: Technology: Diagram/Scale Drawing **291**

Directions: The web page below explains how to play a game of marbles called Three Holes. It includes a diagram of the playing area. Use the instructions and the diagram to answer the questions that follow.

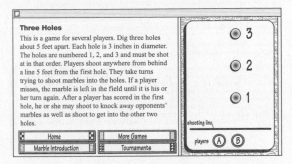

Three Holes

This is a game for several players. Dig three holes about 5 feet apart. Each hole is 3 inches in diameter. The holes are numbered 1, 2, and 3 and must be shot at in that order. Players shoot anywhere from behind a line 5 feet from the first hole. They take turns trying to shoot marbles into the holes. If a player misses, the marble is left in the field until it is his or her turn again. After a player has scored in the first hole, he or she may shoot to knock away opponents' marbles as well as shoot to get into the other two holes.

[Home] [More Games]
[Marble Introduction] [Tournaments]

1. What does the line represent in the diagram? **The line represents the shooting line.**

2. Is player B in a good position to shoot a marble into hole 3? Explain. **No, player B could shoot his or her marble into hole 1 by mistake.**

3. If the diagram were drawn using a scale of 1 inch equals 1 foot, how many inches apart should the holes be drawn? Explain. **The holes should be drawn 5 inches apart. The holes are supposed to be 5 feet apart, and the scale is 1 inch equals 1 foot.**

4. Why do you think the web page above included a diagram? **Possible answer: The diagram helps show how the game is set up and played. The diagram makes it easier to understand the instructions.**

5. If you wanted to find games that senior citizens might enjoy, what key words could you type to search the Internet for web pages? **Possible answer: games AND senior AND citizen**

Notes for Home: Your child read a diagram and answered questions about it. *Home Activity:* Help your child draw a scale drawing of the playing field for the marble game described above using a scale of 1 inch equals 1 foot.

292 Research and Study Skills: Technology: Diagram/Scale Drawing

---

Text Structure

- **Text structure** is the way a piece of writing is organized. There are two main kinds of writing—fiction and nonfiction.
- Fiction tells stories of made-up people and events. Fiction is often organized in chronological order.
- Nonfiction tells stories of real people and events or gives real information. It can be organized in chronological order, by main ideas with supporting details, or as relationships such as cause and effect, problem and solution, and compare and contrast.

Directions: Reread "Bee Bodies." Then complete the table. Give two supporting details for each main idea in the article. **Possible answers given.**

Main Ideas	Supporting Details
Body	1. The bee's honey stomach is in the abdomen.
	2. Fine hairs on the body carry pollen from flower to flower.
Eyes	3. There are three small eyes on top of its head and a large compound eye on each side.
	4. Bees' eyes cannot focus because the eyes have no pupils.
Mouth	5. A bee uses its tongue to suck water, nectar, and honey.
	6. The bee's tongue is on the outside of the head.
Wings	7. There are two thin wings on each side of the thorax.
	8. The wings can move up, down, forward, and backward.
Legs	9. There are three legs on each side of the thorax.
	10. Each leg has five main joints, plus tiny segments of the foot.

Notes for Home: Your child used a table to help show how information in an article has been organized. *Home Activity:* Read a newspaper or magazine article with your child. Have him or her identify the way the information is organized.

Text Structure **295**

Vocabulary

Directions: Choose the word from the box that best completes each sentence. Write the word on the line to the left.

__colony__ 1. Ants often live together in a _____.

__emerge__ 2. See how they _____ from their anthill.

__storage__ 3. At a picnic, keep all your spare food in _____.

__react__ 4. If food is left out, the ants _____ to it quickly.

__condition__ 5. What good _____ those ants are in! Watch them lift that cracker!

Check the Words You Know
__ colony
__ condition
__ emerge
__ nectar
__ producers
__ react
__ storage
__ venom

Directions: Choose the word from the box that best matches each clue. Write the letters of the word on the blanks. The boxed letters spell something that some ants in a colony might be.

6. sweet liquid — 6. n e c t a **r**

7. product makers — 7. p r o d **u** c e r s

8. poison — 8. v e **n** o m

9. state someone is in — 9. c o n d i **t** i o n

10. state of being stored — 10. **s** t o r a g e

What some ants in a colony might be: a u n t s

Write a Description

Imagine you are a scientist who has discovered a new creature. On a separate sheet of paper, describe the creature. Give vivid details that tell what the creature looks like, how it moves, what sounds it makes, and what it likes to eat. Use as many vocabulary words as you can. **Students' descriptions should make correct use of vocabulary words.**

Notes for Home: Your child identified and used vocabulary words from "From Bees to Honey." *Home Activity:* Find out more about an insect that interests your child. Create an encyclopedia entry of text and a picture that describes the insect.

296 Vocabulary

© Scott Foresman 5

Text Structure

- Text structure is the way a piece of writing is organized.
- Fiction tells stories of made-up people and events. Fiction is usually organized in chronological order. Nonfiction tells of real people and events. It can be organized in chronological order, by main idea and supporting details, or as relationships such as cause and effect, problem and solution, or compare and contrast.

Directions: Reread this passage from "From Bees to Honey" about the history of beekeeping. Then answer the questions below.

The relationship between humans and honeybees goes back thousands of years. In prehistoric times, people took honey from the hives of wild bees in hollow trees. About four thousand years ago, the Egyptians kept bees in cigar-shaped hives made of clay. During the Middle Ages, beekeepers used dome-shaped hives called skeps, which were woven of straw.

John Wetzler, like most modern beekeepers, uses hives made of wood. A hive consists of several boxes, or *hive bodies*, which are open at the top and bottom. Hanging inside each hive body are ten movable wooden *frames*. The frames hold sheets of wax called *foundation*, on which bees build the six-sided cells of their combs.

From A BEEKEEPER'S YEAR by Sylvia Johnson, Copyright © 1994 by Sylvia Johnson (Text); Illustrations © by E.M. Peterson Books. By permission of Little, Brown and Company.

1. What four time periods does the passage mention?
It mentions prehistoric times, 4,000 years ago, the Middle Ages, and modern times.

2. Which period is the earliest example of beekeeping?
The earliest example is prehistoric times.

3. Which period is the most recent example of beekeeping?
The most recent example is modern times.

4. Is this passage an example of fiction or nonfiction writing? Explain. Which kind or kinds of organization does the author use: chronological order, main idea and supporting details, cause and effect, problem and solution, or compare and contrast?
It is nonfiction because it tells of real people and events. The author uses chronological order, as well as compare and contrast.

5. What kinds of organization do you find in "From Bees to Honey"? Give examples. Write your answer on a separate sheet of paper. **Check that students support their answers with appropriate examples from the text.**

 Notes for Home: Your child read a passage and identified the ways that information was organized. *Home Activity:* Read a newspaper article together with your child. Invite him or her to describe how the information is organized.

Text Structure **297**

Selection Test

Directions: Choose the best answer to each item. Mark the letter for the answer you have chosen.

Part 1: Vocabulary
Find the answer choice that means about the same as the underlined word in each sentence.

1. The teacher told us about nectar.
   A. the main bee in a hive
   B. a sheet of wax made by bees
   C. a mixture of sugar and water
   (D) the sweet liquid found in flowers

2. When José teases you, don't react.
   F. listen carefully
   G. complain to someone
   (H) respond to something
   J. disappear

3. Those ants live in a colony.
   (A) group of living things
   B. barn for storing hay
   C. cage for birds
   D. underground cave

4. Scientists studied the venom.
   (F) poison from an insect or animal
   G. communication between animals
   H. home for bees
   J. sticky substance

5. What is the condition of the animal?
   A. diet
   (B) state
   C. age
   D. name

6. Who are the producers of that jelly?
   (F) people who make
   G. people who sell
   H. people who use
   J. people who like

7. The proper storage of food is important.
   A. cooking to kill germs
   B. preparing to mix flavors
   C. selecting for good quality
   (D) saving for a later date

8. When will the children emerge?
   F. stop playing
   G. pay attention
   (H) come out
   J. work together

Part 2: Comprehension
Use what you know about the selection to answer each item.

9. John Wetzler produces honey mainly because he likes to—
   A. make money.
   B. eat lots of sweet foods.
   (C) work with bees.
   D. hire his neighbors to work for him.

10. The information in this selection is presented as—
   F. a series of comparisons and contrasts.
   G. a series of causes and effects.
   H. problems and solutions.
   (J) events in chronological order.

GO ON

298 Selection Test

---

11. John uses a smoker when opening the hive because he—
   A. wants some of the bees to die.
   B. has to melt the bee glue.
   (C) does not want to be stung.
   D. wants to keep the bees warm.

12. What is the main difference between worker bees under 20 days old and worker bees over 20 days old?
   F. Young worker bees cannot lay eggs, but older ones can.
   (G) Young worker bees work inside the hive, and older worker bees collect nectar.
   H. Older worker bees mostly guard the hive from wasps, but younger ones don't.
   J. Young worker bees forage for nectar and pollen while older ones stay inside the hive.

13. What does John do just before placing a frame in the honey extractor?
   A. puts plastic bags over the hives
   B. removes impurities from the honey
   C. removes the supers from the hives
   (D) uncaps the frames

14. Which detail suggests that John is good at thinking of creative solutions to problems?
   (F) his use of the brick code
   G. his use of the bee tool
   H. his use of the honey extractor
   J. his use of hive bodies

15. The text structure helps you understand the content of this selection mainly by—
   A. illustrating the dangers of beekeeping.
   (B) describing the natural order of a beekeeper's activities.
   C. suggesting unusual solutions to problems.
   D. comparing wild bees and domesticated bees.

STOP

Selection Test **299**

Text Structure

- **Text structure** is the way a piece of writing is organized.
- Fiction tells stories of made-up people and events. Fiction is usually organized in chronological order. Nonfiction tells of real people and events. It can be organized in chronological order, or as relationships such as cause and effect, as problem and solution, and compare and contrast.

Directions: Read each passage.

1. A serious danger that all beekeepers face is getting stung. They protect themselves by wearing a special bee suit and a hat with a heavy veil.

2. First, the worker bees are born. For their first twenty days, they do indoor jobs such as cleaning cells. After that, they collect pollen in the field.

3. Most bees in a colony are worker bees, who are all females. There is one queen bee. She is the only one in the colony

who lays eggs. The male bees are drones, who mate with queens.

4. When bees take nectar from flowers, the enzymes in their bodies react to it. As a result, a sweet substance—honey— is produced.

5. The beekeeper places small boxes in the hive. The bees then start to fill up the boxes with honey. Later, the boxes are removed.

Directions: Complete the table. Think about the text structure in each passage. Write whether it uses chronological order, cause and effect, problem and solution, or compare and contrast. Explain your answers. **Possible explanations given.**

Passage	Text Structure	Explanation
1	problem and solution	describes how beekeepers protect themselves against stings
2	chronological order	describes the life of worker bees
3	compare and contrast	compares different types of bees
4	cause and effect	tells how honey is made from nectar
5	chronological order	describes the sequence of getting honey from hives

  Notes for Home: Your child read nonfiction passages and identified the way that each one was organized. *Home Activity:* Read a magazine article together with your child. Invite him or her to describe how the information is organized.

300 Text Structure

© Scott Foresman 5

Panel 1 (top-left)

Practice Book 5.3, p. 137

Name _____

From Bees to Honey

Steps in a Process

REVIEW

Directions: Read the passage. Then read each question about the passage. Choose the best answer to each question. Mark the letter for the answer you have chosen.

Baking a Honeycake

To bake a honeycake, you will need these ingredients: flour, baking powder, baking soda, cinnamon, brown sugar, eggs, honey, and oil. You will need two large bowls and a tube baking pan.

Start making the honeycake by mixing together these ingredients in a large bowl: $2\frac{1}{2}$ cups of flour, 2 teaspoons of baking powder, 1 teaspoon of baking soda, and 2 teaspoons of cinnamon.

Then in a second large bowl, mix $\frac{3}{4}$ cup of brown sugar with 3 eggs.

Next, add a cup of honey and $\frac{3}{4}$ cup of oil to the second bowl.

Pour the contents of the first bowl into the second. Mix until blended.

Pour the batter into a 10-inch tube pan.

Bake at 325°F for 1 hour. After an hour, remove the pan from the oven and let it cool. Then remove the cake from the pan.

1. The first step in the process of making a honeycake involves—
   A. sugar.
   B. eggs.
   C. oil.
   D. cinnamon. *(circled)*

2. Just before adding honey and oil, you—
   F. mix the batter.
   G. mix sugar and eggs. *(circled)*
   H. mix flour and cinnamon.
   J. pour the contents of one bowl into another.

3. Right after mixing the batter, you—
   A. add eggs and sugar.
   B. add oil and honey.
   C. pour it in a pan. *(circled)*
   D. bake at 325° F.

4. The contents of the two bowls are combined—
   F. before honey is used.
   G. after honey is used. *(circled)*
   H. before oil is used.
   J. while honey is being added.

5. The final step in the process is to—
   A. remove the cake from the pan. *(circled)*
   B. let cool for 20 minutes.
   C. add oil and honey.
   D. remove the cake from the oven.

 Notes for Home: Your child read an explanation of a process and identified the order of the steps. **Home Activity:** Read a set of directions, such as a cookbook recipe, with your child. Then have your child tell you the order of the steps.

Steps in a Process **301**

Panel 2 (top-right)

Name _____

From Bees to Honey

Writing Across Texts

Directions: Think about what you learned in "From Bees to Honey" and what you learned in other selections in this unit. Use the web below to organize your thoughts about the lessons you or the characters learned in these selections.

Possible answers given.

1. Even if you can't hear or are not good at sports, you may have other abilities that make you special.

2. You don't have to be an adult to help others.

Even experienced beekeepers like John Wetzler get stung sometimes.

Learning

3. Getting honey to market is a lot of work for both bees and beekeepers.

5. If you practice really hard, you can achieve your goals.

4. People who are not afraid of challenges and who keep trying can make a difference.

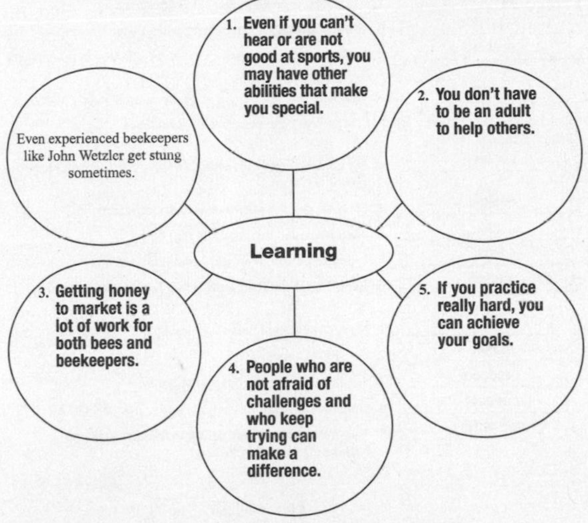

Write a Paragraph

The selection "From Bees to Honey" shows that there is a lot to learn about bees before you can become a beekeeper. The first four selections in this unit relate to the theme of learning and working. On a separate sheet of paper, write a summary of the kinds of things characters learned in these four stories as well as what you learned by reading these selections. **Paragraphs will vary. Check that students support their opinions with details from the selections.**

Notes for Home: Your child wrote a summary about the things that were learned in the four selections read so far in this unit. **Home Activity:** As you read stories with your child, discuss the lessons that the characters learn or the things that your child learns from the stories.

302 Writing Across Texts

Panel 3 (bottom-left)

Grammar Practice Book 5.3, p. 66

Name _____

From Bees to Honey

Grammar: Verb Tenses: Present, Past, and Future

REVIEW

Directions: Circle the verb in each sentence. Write **present, past,** or **future** on the line to name the tense of each verb.

future	1. After college, Jill (will train) as a veterinarian.
past	2. She (worked) part-time for a veterinarian last year in high school.
past	3. She once (helped) a woman with a pet snake!
present	4. Jill (likes) all kinds of animals.
present	5. She (goes) to a woman veterinarian with her two dogs.
present	6. This animal doctor (shows) love and concern for all her patients.
future	7. Jill (will follow) her example.
past	8. Jill's uncle (took) care of circus animals all of his life.
future	9. Jill (will spend) most of her time as a veterinarian with house pets.

Directions: Write a sentence using the verb and verb tense given. **Possible answers given.**

10. the present tense of *talk*
I talk on the phone with my friends every evening.

11. the past tense of *talk*
I talked to Karen for an hour last night.

12. the future tense of *talk*
I will talk with her again tonight.

13. the present tense of *play*
I play the piano.

14. the past tense of *play*
I played the piano in a recital last week.

15. the future tense of *play*
I will play the piano for the rest of my life.

 Notes for Home: Your child identified the three main tenses of a verb. **Home Activity:** Ask your child to create sentences for all three tenses of the following verbs: (1) give, gave, will give; (2) make, made, will make; (3) run, ran, will run.

Grammar: Verb Tenses: Present, Past, and Future **303**

Panel 4 (bottom-right)

Grammar Practice Book 5.3, p. 67

Name _____

From Bees to Honey

Grammar: Using Correct Verb Tenses

Use the correct verb tense to show action that is happening now **(present tense)**, action that happened in the past **(past tense)**, and action that will happen in the future **(future tense)**.

Present: Lara helps immigrant classmates with their English.

Past: Yesterday, Steven volunteered at the hospital.

Future: Next week, Reggie will start soccer practice.

Directions: Circle the correct verb form in ( ) to complete each sentence.

1. Last summer, Denise (visits/visited) her cousins in Minnesota for the first time.

2. Right away, she (noticed/will notice) several different crops on the cousins' farm.

3. For as long as she lives, Denise (remembers/will remember) the fun of hayrides and picnics.

4. On her very first day at the farm, she (will feed/fed) the chickens and milked a cow.

5. Denise was not afraid of bees, so she (helps/helped) workers gathering honey from the hives.

6. She was very careful, and she (will receive/received) no stings.

7. Every day during her visit, Denise and her cousins (swims/swam) in a pond.

8. On her last evening with her cousins, she (see/saw) a film with them at a drive-in movie theater.

9. Denise usually (cries/cried) a little when a pleasant vacation is over!

10. She writes to her cousins often, and she (visits/will visit) them again next summer.

 Notes for Home: Your child identified verb tenses to show action that takes place in the past, present, and future. **Home Activity:** Ask your child to describe a hobby he or she enjoys. Encourage your child to use present, past, and future tenses.

304 Grammar: Using Correct Verb Tenses

Scott Foresman 5

Answers 749

Grammar: Using Correct Verb Tenses

Directions: Circle the correct verb form in ( ) to complete each sentence. Write **present, past,** or **future** to tell the tense of the verb.

___future___ 1. If you want to listen, I (tell/(will tell)) you about my hobby.

___present___ 2. My hobby is archery, and I (liked/(like)) it a lot.

___past___ 3. I (learn/(earned)) about archery when I went to camp.

___present___ 4. In the mornings I practice, and in the afternoons I (took/(take)) a break.

___future___ 5. I am sure that I (love/(will love)) my unusual hobby always.

Directions: Use the correct form of the verb in ( ) to complete each sentence. Write the verb on the line.

___decided___ 6. My cousin's hobby is fishing, so last week I (decide) to go fishing with her.

___looked___ 7. First, we dug for worms and (look) for insects.

___sat___ 8. Then we baited the hook and (sit) down.

___was___ 9. It (be) so boring, I thought I would fall asleep.

___tasted___ 10. Even though the fish (taste) good, I will never go fishing again.

___is___ 11. Now, it (be) time to visit my Grandpa.

___makes___ 12. He (make) honey.

___produce___ 13. Actually, the bees (produce) the honey.

___collects___ 14. Grandpa regularly (collect) the honey from the bee hives.

___will write___ 15. Tomorrow, I (write) my cousin to tell her to take up beekeeping instead of fishing!

Write a Description

What hobby do you enjoy? On a separate sheet of paper, describe your hobby. (If you don't have a hobby yet, use your imagination and write as if you do have one.) Tell how you got started with that hobby and explain why it is fun. Be sure to use the correct tenses for your verbs.
Check that the verbs students used are in the correct tenses.

 Notes for Home: Your child used verb tenses (present, past, and future) to complete sentences. *Home Activity:* Invite your child to write an advertisement for his or her hobby. Encourage your child to make sure each verb uses the correct tense.

Grammar: Using Correct Verb Tenses **305**

Grammar: Using Correct Verb Tenses

RETEACHING

> Read each sentence. Underline the verb.
>
> **Present Tense:** Levi studies a book about Roman ruins.
>
> **Past Tense:** I finally completed the difficult assignment.
>
> **Future Tense:** They will grow vegetables in the summer.

> Verbs in the **present tense** tell about action that is happening now. Verbs in the **past tense** tell about action that already happened. Verbs in the **future tense** tell about action that will happen.

Directions: Read each sentence. Underline the verb. Write **present, past,** or **future** on the line to identify the tense of the verb.

___past___ 1. The clerk stayed busy all that time.

___past___ 2. Mr. Corm finally stopped here Tuesday.

___present___ 3. Two rivers flood their banks

___present___ 4. Deep puddles are everywhere.

___past___ 5. Schools and businesses closed.

___future___ 6. They will open again in a few days.

___future___ 7. Mrs. Allen will begin a new class in the fall.

Directions: Choose a verb that makes sense in each sentence and write it on the line. Make sure the verb you choose is in the correct tense. **Possible answers given. Verb tenses may vary.**

8. Last year, ten of us ___went___ on vacation.

9. We ___took___ so many pictures that we used all our film.

10. Today I ___arrange___ the pictures in an album.

11. I ___write___ a caption under each picture so I know who and what is in each one.

12. Later I ___will show___ the album to my family and friends.

13. I hope they ___will enjoy___ the pictures!

14. At the very least, the pictures ___will remind___ them of the fun time we had.

 Notes for Home: Your child labeled verb tenses and wrote verbs in the present, past, and future tenses in sentences. *Home Activity:* Ask your child to describe to you one of his or her favorite experiences from school this year. Remind your child to use verbs in the correct tenses.

306 Grammar: Using Correct Verb Tenses

Grammar: Using Correct Verb Tenses

Directions: Read all the sentences. Then use the correct form of the verb in ( ) to complete each sentence. Write the verb on the line.

___has___ 1. My family (have) a Saturday morning tradition.

___will tell___ 2. I (tell) you about why we have the tradition and when it started.

___began___ 3. It all (begin) two years ago when we lived in another city.

___sneaked; selected___ 4. My brother (sneak) into the kitchen and (select) the ingredients.

___joined___ 5. Then my father (join) him while my mother and I slept.

___made___ 6. The two of them (make) blueberry waffles with whipped cream.

___drifted___ 7. The delicious smell of the waffles (drift) down the hallway to my bedroom.

___smelled___ 8. My mother (smell) it too.

___found___ 9. We went into the kitchen and (find) breakfast was ready!

___prepare___ 10. Now my father and brother (prepare) breakfast every Saturday morning.

___talk___ 11. We (talk) about the tradition as if we have been doing it forever.

___will change___ 12. Soon our tradition (change).

___will have___ 13. My brother (have) marching band practice on Saturday mornings.

___will leave___ 14. He (leave) very early in the morning to get there on time.

___will begin___ 15. When that happens, I (begin) to help my father prepare Saturday breakfast.

___will have___ 16. Then my family (have) a new tradition!

Write a Family Story

Think about a funny or exciting experience you had with your family. What happened? Does your family still talk about it? On a separate sheet of paper, write a family story to tell about your experience. Remember to use verbs in the correct tenses.
Make sure students use correct verb tenses in their stories.

 Notes for Home: Your child wrote verbs in the correct tenses in sentences. *Home Activity:* Provide your child with three verbs, such as *to jump, to laugh,* and *to write,* and have him or her correctly use each verb in the present, past, and future tenses in sentences.

Grammar: Using Correct Verb Tenses **307**

Word Study: Possessives

Directions: Read the sentences below. Rewrite each underlined phrase using an apostrophe (') and s to show possession. For example, **the ball of the boy** can be written as **the boy's ball.** Write the new phrase on the line.

___the worker bee's job___ 1. It is the job of the worker bee to look for flower nectar.

___the beekeeper's hive___ 2. They visited the hive that belongs to the beekeeper.

___The beekeeper's wife___ 3. The wife of the beekeeper shows visitors the honey house.

___The hive's combs___ 4. The combs of the hive were filled with honey.

___the honey's flavor___ 5. Everyone enjoys the flavor of honey.

Directions: Read the phrases below. Rewrite each phrase using the possessive form. Write the new phrase on the line. Remember, for plural nouns that end in -s, add only an apostrophe, as in **the sisters' bikes.**

___the bees' job___ 6. the job of bees

___the beekeepers' honey___ 7. the honey of beekeepers

___the farmers' market___ 8. the market of farmers

___the families' enjoyment___ 9. the enjoyment of the families

___a hive's bees___ 10. the bees of a hive

___a flower's nectar___ 11. the nectar of a flower

___a farmer's responsibility___ 12. the responsibility of a farmer

___many seasons' harvests___ 13. the harvests of many seasons

___many farms' crops___ 14. the crops from many farms

___the queen bee's eggs___ 15. the eggs of the queen bee

 Notes for Home: Your child formed singular and plural possessives, such as *the boy's ball* and *the sisters' bikes. Home Activity:* Point out objects that belong to one person or more. Ask your child to use possessives to tell who owns them.

308 Word Study: Possessives

© Scott Foresman 5

Spelling: Capitalization

Pretest Directions: Fold back the page along the dotted line. On the blanks, write the spelling words as they are dictated. When you have finished the test, unfold the page and check your words.

1. **Houston**
2. **Alaska**
3. **Kentucky**
4. **Little Rock**
5. **Duluth**
6. **Arizona**
7. **Miami**
8. **Indiana**
9. **Alabama**
10. **South Carolina**
11. **Baltimore**
12. **Detroit**
13. **Los Angeles**
14. **Hawaii**
15. **Memphis**
16. **Virginia**
17. **Oregon**
18. **Pittsburgh**
19. **Texas**
20. **Florida**

1. Her sister went to **Houston**.
2. It gets very cold in **Alaska**.
3. I have never been to **Kentucky**.
4. We are going to **Little Rock**.
5. Where is **Duluth** on the map?
6. Much of **Arizona** is desert.
7. **Miami** is in Florida.
8. Hoosiers are from **Indiana**.
9. **Alabama** is in the south.
10. I live in **South Carolina**.
11. Have you been to **Baltimore**?
12. Cars are made in **Detroit**.
13. **Los Angeles** is near the ocean.
14. **Hawaii** is made up of islands.
15. I want to go back to **Memphis**.
16. Jefferson lived in **Virginia**.
17. Eugene is a city in **Oregon**.
18. **Pittsburgh** is my hometown.
19. **Texas** is a large state.
20. It is warm in **Florida**.

 Notes for Home: Your child took a pretest on capitalized words. *Home Activity:* Help your child learn misspelled words before the final test. Have your child divide misspelled words into parts (such as syllables) and concentrate on each part.

Spelling: Capitalization **309**

Spelling: Capitalization

Word List

Houston	Duluth	Alabama	Los Angeles	Oregon
Alaska	Arizona	South Carolina	Hawaii	Pittsburgh
Kentucky	Miami	Baltimore	Memphis	Texas
Little Rock	Indiana	Detroit	Virginia	Florida

Directions: Choose the words from the box that name U.S. states. Write the words in alphabetical order.

1. **Alabama**
2. **Alaska**
3. **Arizona**
4. **Florida**
5. **Hawaii**
6. **Indiana**
7. **Kentucky**
8. **Oregon**
9. **South Carolina**
10. **Texas**
11. **Virginia**

Directions: Choose the word from the box that answers each question. Write the word on the line.

Los Angeles 12. Which city has the word *angel* in it?
Memphis 13. Which city has the word *his* in it?
Pittsburgh 14. Which city has the word *pit* in it?
Duluth 15. Which city rhymes with *truth*?
Houston 16. Which city has *us* in the middle?
Little Rock 17. Which city means the same as *pebble*?
Detroit 18. Which city rhymes with *exploit*?
Baltimore 19. Which city has the word *more* in it?
Miami 20. Which city has the word *am* in the middle?

 Notes for Home: Your child spelled names of cities and states. *Home Activity:* Look at a map of the United States with your child. Together, try to find all the states and cities that are spelling words. Have your child identify the capital letter or letters in each name.

310 Spelling: Capitalization

Spelling: Capitalization

Directions: Proofread this article. Find five spelling mistakes. Use the proofreading marks to correct each mistake.

☰	Make a capital.
/	Make a small letter.
∧	Add something.
⟋	Take out something.
⊙	Add a period.
¶	Begin a new paragraph.

Many cities and states are famous for their products. In detroit, many people make cars. In Florida, thousands work on citrus farms. Lots of farmers have cotton fields in Alabama and South carolina, while others have tobacco fields in virginia. Oregon has lumberjacks, huseton has oil workers, and pitsburgh has many steel workers.

Spelling Tip
Hawaii
The end of the word **Hawaii** can be tricky to spell. Remember this hint: See **Hawaii** with your two eyes (ii).

Word List

Houston	Duluth	Alabama	Los Angeles	Oregon
Alaska	Arizona	South Carolina	Hawaii	Pittsburgh
Kentucky	Miami	Baltimore	Memphis	Texas
Little Rock	Indiana	Detroit	Virginia	Florida

Write a Report

Find out more about the different states and cities listed in the box. On a separate sheet of paper, write a report with your information. Try to use at least five cities or states. **Students will need time for research before writing. Answers will vary, but each report should include at least five spelling words.**

 Notes for Home: Your child spelled names of cities and states. *Home Activity:* Begin to spell each spelling word slowly, one letter at a time. When your child recognizes the word, have him or her complete its spelling.

Spelling: Capitalization **311**

Spelling: Capitalization

REVIEW

Word List

Houston	Duluth	Alabama	Los Angeles	Oregon
Alaska	Arizona	South Carolina	Hawaii	Pittsburgh
Kentucky	Miami	Baltimore	Memphis	Texas
Little Rock	Indiana	Detroit	Virginia	Florida

Directions: Choose the word from the box that best matches each clue. Use a map of the United States to help you. Write the word on the line.

Alaska 1. This state is between Canada and Russia.
Texas 2. This state is south of Oklahoma.
Arizona 3. This state is south of Utah.
Indiana 4. This state is between Ohio and Illinois.
Virginia 5. This state is east of West Virginia.
Kentucky 6. This state is just north of Tennessee.
Alabama 7. This state is between Mississippi and Georgia.
South Carolina 8. This state is just south of North Carolina.
Hawaii 9. This state is actually a group of islands.
Oregon 10. This state is south of Washington state.
Florida 11. This state is south of Georgia.

Directions: Choose the word from the box that names a city located in each state below. Use a map of the United States to help you. Write the word on the line.

Memphis 12. Tennessee
Little Rock 13. Arkansas
Pittsburgh 14. Pennsylvania
Houston 15. Texas
Detroit 16. Michigan
Miami 17. Florida
Los Angeles 18. California
Duluth 19. Minnesota
Baltimore 20. Maryland

 Notes for Home: Your child spelled names of cities and states. *Home Activity:* Say each spelling word aloud. See if your child can locate the state or city on a map of the United States. Then have your child close his or her eyes and spell the word.

312 Spelling: Capitalization

© Scott Foresman 5

Name _____

Outlining

An **outline** is a plan that shows how a story, article, report, or other text is organized. You can use an outline to better understand how a text is organized or as a way to organize your own thoughts before you write something of your own.

Directions: Read the following outline. Then answer the questions.

> **Occupations**
>
> I. Outdoor jobs
>   A. Forest ranger
>   1. Cut down dead trees
>   2. Watch for forest fires
>   3. Plant new trees
>   B. Landscaper
>   1. Plant gardens
>   2. Mow lawns
> II. Indoor jobs
>   A. Lab technician
>   1. Conduct experiments
>   2. Analyze results
>   B. School teacher
>   1. Instruct students
>   2. Evaluate students

1. What other main topic is shown in the outline besides outdoor jobs? **Indoor jobs**

2. What two subtopics are listed under the first main topic? **Forest ranger and Landscaper**

3. What subtopics are listed under the second main topic? **Lab technician and School teacher**

4. What details are listed under the subtopic "Lab technician"? **Conduct experiments; Analyze results**

5. Which subtopic has the most details? **Forest ranger**

Name _____

Directions: Read the following article. Then complete the outline below.

> **Where Would You Like to Work?**
>
> There are two main kinds of jobs you can have—outdoor jobs and indoor jobs. Working outdoors offers many benefits. For example, you get to enjoy fresh air. You also see pretty landscapes. In addition, you get to be more active. On the other hand, outdoor work can present disadvantages too. Sometimes you may have to work in the rain. Some days may be unbearably cold or hot.
>
> Working indoors has its benefits. For example, you may be in a climate-controlled environment, so you don't get too hot or too cold. Also, it is usually easy to get from place to place, without any rough roads or hills to climb. On the other hand, indoor work also has disadvantages. You may start to feel "cooped up" on long days. You may have to work in a room with poor air circulation.

Occupations

I. Outdoor jobs
  A. Benefits
    1. Enjoy fresh air
    2. **See pretty landscapes**
    3. **Be more active**
  B. **Disadvantages**
    1. Work in rain
    2. **Work when it's too hot or too cold**
II. Indoor jobs
  A. **Benefits**
    1. **Be in a climate-controlled environment**
    2. **Easy to get from place to place**
  B. Disadvantages
    1. **Feel "cooped up"**
    2. **Work in a room with poor air circulation**

Notes for Home: Your child practiced organizing information in an outline. **Home Activity:** Talk with your child about the different jobs that people in your family have. Then invite your child to create an outline that organizes the information you discussed together.

Name _____

Summarizing

- **Summarizing** means telling just the main ideas of an article or the plot of a story.
- A good summary is brief. It does not include unnecessary details, repeated words or thoughts, or unimportant ideas.

Directions: Reread "What Do Animals Say?" Then complete the table. Write one sentence to summarize each portion of the article indicated. Then write a summary of the entire article. **Possible answers given.**

Portion of Article	Summary
Paragraph 1	1. **According to one theory, people first spoke by imitating the sounds they heard.**
Paragraphs 2–4	2. **English and other languages have echoic words that echo the sounds they describe. Just as dogs have different barks, other languages use different words for animal sounds.**
Paragraph 5	3. **Different words are used for a pig's "oink" in Russian, Rumanian, Greek, and French.**
Paragraph 6	4. **Different words are used for a dog's bark in French, Italian, Rumanian, Vietnamese, and Turkish.**
Paragraph 7	5. **Different words are used for a rooster's sound in English, French, Arabic, and Russian.**

Notes for Home: Your child read an article and summarized each part of it. **Home Activity:** Read a story with your child. Stop at various points during the story and have your child summarize what happened in only a few sentences.

Name _____

Vocabulary

Directions: Match each word on the left with its definition on the right. Write the letter of the definition next to the word.

d	1. civil	a. without warning
c	2. instinct	b. having good judgment
e	3. raid	c. inborn way of acting
a	4. unexpected	d. polite
b	5. sensible	e. sudden attack

> **Check the Words You Know**
> __ chaos
> __ civil
> __ confusion
> __ instinct
> __ raid
> __ sensible
> __ unexpected

Directions: Read the news report. Choose the word from the box that best completes each sentence. Write the word on the matching numbered line below.

BIG STORM HITS PRAIRIE TOWN

The storm was entirely **6.** _____. At first, there was great **7.** _____. Everyone ran to a huge tree on the prairie for shelter. Then a **8.** _____ young girl said, "That's not safe. Lightning could strike you!" Her **9.** _____ was right. In spite of the **10.** _____, she led the people to safe shelter in a nearby barn.

6. **unexpected**
7. **chaos or confusion**
8. **sensible**
9. **instinct**
10. **confusion or chaos**

Write a Story

On a separate sheet of paper, write a story that tells about a war or battle that took place. Use as many vocabulary words as you can. **Students' stories should make correct use of vocabulary words.**

Notes for Home: Your child identified and used vocabulary words from "Babe to the Rescue." **Home Activity:** Think of a word. Say a word to your child that means the opposite. See if your child can guess your word. For example, the opposite of *foolish* is *sensible*.

© Scott Foresman 5

Name _____

Babe to the Rescue

Summarizing

- **Summarizing** means telling just the main ideas of an article or the plot of a story. A good summary is brief. It does not include unnecessary details, repeated words or thoughts, or unimportant ideas.

Directions: Read the following four summaries of the opening of "Babe to the Rescue." Then answer the questions below.

A. Fly and Babe went to the pond where the ducks swam. After the ducks came out of the water, Babe tried to round them up and bring them to Fly. His efforts failed.

B. Fly and Babe went to the pond where the ducks swam. The pond was soupy green. Babe tried to round up the ducks after they came out of the water. His efforts failed.

C. Fly and Babe went to the pond where the ducks swam. Fly was a sheepdog. She was also a collie. Babe tried to round up the ducks when they came out of the water.

D. Fly and Babe went to the pond where the ducks swam. After the ducks came out of the water, Babe tried to round them up. When Babe spoke with Fly, he said, "Yes, Mum."

1. Which of the four summaries is best? Explain why.
Summary A is best because it gives only the most important details.

2. What unnecessary detail is given in Summary B?
The color of the pond is an unnecessary detail.

3. What unnecessary detail is given in Summary C?
Mentioning that Fly is a sheepdog and a collie is not necessary.

4. What unnecessary detail is given in Summary D?
Saying that Babe says, "Yes, Mum" when he speaks with Fly is not necessary.

5. Summarize in a few sentences the part of the story about the sheep rustlers. Write your summary on a separate sheet of paper.
Possible answer: When Farmer Hogget and Fly leave the farm, rustlers try to steal the sheep. Babe attacks the men and their dogs, and the noise drives the thieves away.

 Notes for Home: Your child identified characteristics that make a good summary. *Home Activity:* Watch a TV show or movie with your child. Then ask your child to summarize the story. Discuss whether the summary included the most important parts of the story.

Summarizing **319**

Name _____

Babe to the Rescue

Selection Test

Directions: Choose the best answer to each item. Mark the letter for the answer you have chosen.

Part 1: Vocabulary
Find the answer choice that means about the same as the underlined word in each sentence.

1. Your telephone call was <u>unexpected</u>.
   A. too long
   B. made incorrectly
   C. not planned for
   D. not wanted

2. The cat followed its <u>instinct</u>.
   F. markings
   G. inborn way of acting
   H. owner
   J. sense of smell

3. The speaker stopped in <u>confusion</u>.
   A. state of being embarrassed
   B. state of feeling ill
   C. state of being frightened
   D. state of not knowing what to do

4. The salesperson was very <u>civil</u>.
   F. polite
   G. friendly
   H. eager
   J. cold

5. There was <u>chaos</u> on the field.
   A. joy
   B. lack of order
   C. sorrow
   D. movement

6. The <u>raid</u> was planned for Thursday.
   F. surprise party
   G. instructional gathering
   H. sudden attack
   J. formal test

7. Please try to be <u>sensible</u>.
   A. having good judgment
   B. being brave
   C. being generous
   D. having good taste

Part 2: Comprehension
Use what you know about the story to answer each item.

8. What does Babe first try to herd?
   F. puppies
   G. piglets
   H. ducks
   J. lambs

9. Unlike Fly, Babe tries to herd sheep by—
   A. shouting at them.
   B. standing in one place.
   C. speaking politely to them.
   D. nipping at their heels.

10. Why is Babe's style of herding different from a normal sheepdog's?
    F. Fly wants him to be different.
    G. Babe was not born with a sheepdog's instincts.
    H. Farmer Hoggett teaches Babe a new method of herding.
    J. Pigs are not intelligent animals.

11. Ma does not like sheepdogs because they—
    A. are rude to sheep.
    B. talk to sheep.
    C. try to herd sheep.
    D. are stupid.

 GO ON

320 Selection Test

Name _____

Babe to the Rescue

12. Which is the best summary of the first half of this story?
    F. Babe makes friends with Ma, an old ewe, by telling her she doesn't look old.
    G. Babe practices his herding skills with Fly's help and makes friends with Ma.
    H. Babe herds some ducks and talks with Fly.
    J. When Babe meets Ma, she tells him that she doesn't like sheepdogs, which she calls wolves.

13. Which is the best summary of the second half of this story?
    A. When Ma rejoins the flock and Mr. Hoggett goes away, Babe tries to steal the sheep.
    B. Mrs. Hoggett decides to keep Babe because he makes so much noise.
    C. Sheep rustlers come to the Hoggetts' farm one day while Mr. Hoggett and Fly are away.
    D. Babe saves the sheep from rustlers, and Mrs. Hoggett decides to keep him.

14. Which part of this story is fantasy?
    F. sheep stealers
    G. dogs that can herd sheep
    H. talking animals
    J. dogs that obey human commands

15. Based on her decision to keep Babe, you can tell that Mrs. Hoggett highly values—
    A. loyalty.
    B. money.
    C. an easy life.
    D. being meek and quiet.

STOP

Selection Test **321**

Scott Foresman 5

Name _____

Babe to the Rescue

Summarizing

- **Summarizing** means telling just the main ideas of an article or the plot of a story. A good summary is brief. It does not include unnecessary details, repeated words or thoughts, or unimportant ideas.

Directions: Read the following five summaries of the same story.

A. Once on a farm, a hen, a cow, and a bee were hungry. The cow gave milk and the bee made honey. The cow was white with brown spots. The hen laid eggs. They all ate custard!

B. Once on a farm, a hen, a cow, and a bee were hungry. The cow gave milk, the bee made honey, and the hen laid eggs. They mixed the foods together and had custard to eat!

C. Once on a farm, a hen, a cow, and a bee were hungry. The farm was a year old. The cow gave milk, the bee made honey, and the hen laid eggs. They mixed the foods and had custard!

D. Once on a farm, a hen, a cow, and a bee were hungry. The cow gave milk and the hen laid eggs. They mixed the foods together and had custard!

E. Once on a farm, a hen, a cow, and a bee were hungry. The cow gave milk, the bee made honey, and the hen laid eggs. They mixed the foods together and had custard! It all happened on a farm.

Directions: Complete the table. Think about the details in each summary. Explain why each summary is or is not a good summary. Tell which summary is the best.

Summary	Good Summary?
Summary A	1. **Summary A is not good because it includes this unnecessary detail: The cow was white with brown spots. It leaves out the information about mixing the foods together.**
Summary B	2. **Summary B is the best summary because it includes only important details.**
Summary C	3. **Summary C is not good because it includes this unnecessary detail: The farm was a year old.**
Summary D	4. **Summary D is not good because it leaves out this important detail: The bee made honey.**
Summary E	5. **Summary E is not good because it repeats a detail: It all happened on a farm.**

 Notes for Home: Your child identified characteristics of a good summary. *Home Activity:* Read a story with your child. Invite your child to summarize the most important details for you. Check that the summary contains only key story events.

322 Summarizing

Answers 753

Name _____

Babe to the Rescue

Compare and Contrast
REVIEW

Directions: Read the passage. Then read each question about the passage. Choose the best answer to each question. Mark the letter for the answer you have chosen.

Pigs and Sheep

Both pigs and sheep are common farm animals that are raised for the products they furnish to people. These animals provide food but also other things. Most pigs and sheep are raised in order for people to be able to have products made with their skin, hair, and meat.

Although pigs and sheep are never likely to be mistaken for one another, they actually share several qualities. That is, both of these animals are used by people for some of the same products.

First, both pigs and sheep provide people with meat. Sheep yield lamb chops and mutton, while pigs give ham, sausage, bacon, and pork chops. In addition, the fat and skin of both pigs and sheep are used to produce leather, soap, glue, and fertilizer.

Of course, you are aware of using the hair of sheep. It is the wool that is a common product for weaving into heavy warm clothing. You might not as quickly think of using the hair of pigs. In fact, you might not think of pigs as having much hair. Certainly, it is not as abundant as the wool of sheep. Although pigs do not grow wool, their hair is used as bristles for brushes. Pig hair is also used as stuffing for mattresses and for baseball gloves.

1. The article explains how pigs and sheep are—
   A. alike only.
   B. different only.
   (C.) alike and different.
   D. like other animals.

2. Both pigs and sheep are used to produce—
   F. mutton.
   G. ham.
   H. sausage.
   (J.) soap.

3. One difference between pigs and sheep is that—
   A. pigs live on farms.
   (B.) sheep grow wool.
   C. sheep supply meat.
   D. pigs supply meat.

4. One way that pigs and sheep are alike is that both—
   (F.) are used for leather.
   G. look the same.
   H. yield pork chops.
   J. yield bacon.

5. Bristles for brushes are a product supplied by—
   A. sheep only.
   (B.) pigs only.
   C. both pigs and sheep.
   D. neither pigs nor sheep.

 Notes for Home: Your child read an article and identified comparisons and contrasts that the writer made. **Home Activity:** Choose two separate items in your home. Talk with your child about ways that the two items are alike and different.

Compare and Contrast 323

Writing Across Texts

Directions: Think about the different ways Babe in "Babe to the Rescue" and the shepherd boy in "Cry Wolf" care for sheep. Think about what the effect is. Then fill in the following chart. **Possible answers given.**

	Babe	The Shepherd Boy
How did each character treat the sheep?	Treated them with respect	3. He put them in danger by constantly crying wolf.
How did each react to the threat of danger?	1. Babe jumped on the tailgate of the rustlers' truck and politely asked the sheep not to come any closer.	4. He cried wolf, and then kept crying wolf until no one believed him anymore.
How did others react to the way Babe and the shepherd boy cared for the sheep?	2. The farmer's wife was so pleased with the way Babe protected the sheep that she told Farmer Hogget not to butcher Babe.	5. They stopped believing his cries. When a wolf finally did come and ate the sheep, the villagers took away the shepherd boy's job.

Write a Letter

Imagine you are the shepherd boy in "Cry Wolf" and you want to convince the villagers to trust you again. Write a letter to them explaining why you cried wolf and how you will make it up to them. **Letters will vary. Check that students used words and phrases that persuade the villagers to trust the shepherd boy again.**

 Notes for Home: Your child compared and contrasted information from two texts. **Home Activity:** Read a story with your child about an animal character. Then discuss how the character is like or different from one of the characters in "Babe to the Rescue" or another animal story.

324 Writing Across Texts

Name _____

Babe to the Rescue

Grammar: Using Correct Verb Tenses
REVIEW

Directions: Use the correct form of the verb in ( ) to complete each sentence. Write the verb on the line.

started	1. Often a farmer's day hasn't (start) until he feeds the pigs.
finished	2. By the end of the day, the pigs have (finish) all their food.
keeping	3. That electric fence isn't (keep) other animals out.
causing	4. The fence is (cause) the piglets to stay together.
stay	5. The piglets always (stay) close to their mother.

Directions: Circle the correct verb form in ( ) to complete each sentence.

6. After a year, a pig has (growed/(grown)) to its adult size.
7. Pigs usually aren't (keeped/(kept)) as pets.
8. Pigs aren't (knowed/(known)) for their cleanliness, but they are very clean animals.
9. Farmers are always ((taking)/taken) fresh straw to the pigs' pen.
10. Pigs often are (lain/(lying)) in mud to keep cool, not because they are filthy!

Directions: Add a word or words to each verb to form a sentence. Write the complete sentence on the line. **Possible answers are given.**

11. eat
I eat an apple every day.

12. am eating
I am eating a delicious apple right now.

13. ate
I ate several delicious apples last week.

14. have eaten
I have eaten two apples for lunch on some days.

15. will eat
I will eat apple pie tomorrow.

 Notes for Home: Your child practiced using the correct tense of verbs. **Home Activity:** Have your child read aloud a simple story book. Then have him or her identify the tenses of the verbs.

Grammar: Using Correct Verb Tenses 325

Name _____

Babe to the Rescue

Grammar: Contractions

A **contraction** is a word made by combining two words. An **apostrophe (')** shows where letters have been left out.

Many contractions are formed by joining a verb and **not**. An apostrophe takes the place of **o** in **not**. There is only one contraction that includes a spelling change: **will not** becomes **won't**.

Do not worry.	She **will not** be gone long.
Don't worry.	She **won't** be gone long.

Other contractions are formed by joining a pronoun and a verb.

I am sure that **you are** right.
I'm sure that **you're** right.

Directions: Draw a line to match each word pair on the left with its contraction on the right.

1. they would   you've
2. she has   isn't
3. he is   he's
4. we have   she's
5. did not   didn't
6. I will   couldn't
7. you have   they'd
8. could not   I'll
9. it will   we've
10. is not   it'll

Directions: Write the two separate words that each underlined contraction combines.

I am	11. I'm proud of our flock of unusual types of hens.
It is	12. It's actually a special collection of my dad's.
does not	13. He doesn't mind paying the breeders to ship them here.
they will	14. Once every morning, suddenly, they'll all fly up in the air.
You have	15. You've got to see it to believe it.

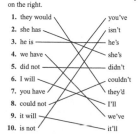 **Notes for Home:** Your child identified and formed contractions—short words formed by combining two words. **Home Activity:** Invite your child to discuss whether it is a good idea to have an unusual pet, such as an iguana or a ferret. Ask your child to use contractions.

326 Grammar: Contractions

© Scott Foresman 5

Name _____

Babe to the Rescue

Grammar: Contractions

Directions: Write a contraction to replace the underlined words in each sentence.

I'm	1. I am thinking of getting a pet rabbit.
haven't	2. We have not ever had a family pet.
aren't	3. Rabbits make good pets because they are not noisy.
It's	4. It is fun to hold a rabbit gently and pat its soft fur.
mustn't	5. I must not decide on a pet until I learn more about rabbits.
they're	6. Peacocks might be a good choice because they are beautiful.
We're	7. We are going to visit a peacock farm.
isn't	8. It is not very far from my home.
doesn't	9. At the farm, I learned that the female peacock does not have a beautiful tail.
She's	10. She is not colorful like the male bird.

Directions: Choose the contraction from the box that best completes each sentence. Write each contraction on the line to the left. Remember that verbs should agree with their subject.

he'd	don't	wasn't	they'll	weren't

he'd	11. A new hired hand decided that _____ save money for the farmer.
don't	12. "If we _____ buy food for the barn cats," he thought, "they will catch more mice!"
wasn't	13. Yet after a few weeks, the mouse population _____ smaller, but larger!
weren't	14. The farmer told him why the cats _____ catching more mice.
they'll	15. "To keep their supply of food," the farmer explained, "_____ leave more mice alive."

Write a Journal Entry

If you were a bird or an animal, which one would you be? On a separate sheet of paper, write a journal entry describing your life as a pet. You might be a watchdog, a peacock, or even an owl. Describe your activities, your friends, and what you eat. Use contractions in your journal entry. **Check to make sure that students have used apostrophes correctly in contractions and that their sentences show correct subject-verb agreement.**

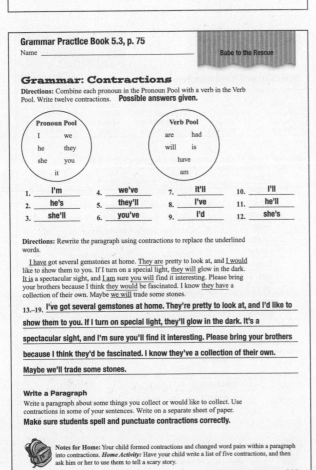

Notes for Home: Your child used apostrophes to write contractions. *Home Activity:* Play a game with contractions. Say a contraction, such as *it's*, and have your child give the two words it combines (*it is*). Switch roles after five contractions.

Grammar: Contractions 327

Name _____

Babe to the Rescue

RETEACHING

Grammar: Contractions

Draw a line under each contraction in the sentences below.

1. I am ready. I'm ready.
2. You are on time. You're on time.
3. They will join us later. They'll join us later.

The shorter sentences have contractions. The words **I'm, you're,** and **they'll** are contractions. These contractions were formed by combining pronouns with verbs.

I am = I'm   you are = you're   they will = they'll

A **contraction** is made by combining two words. Pronouns can be combined with verbs to form contractions. Use an apostrophe (') to show where a letter or letters have been left out.

Directions: Match the pairs of words on the left with the correct contraction on the right.

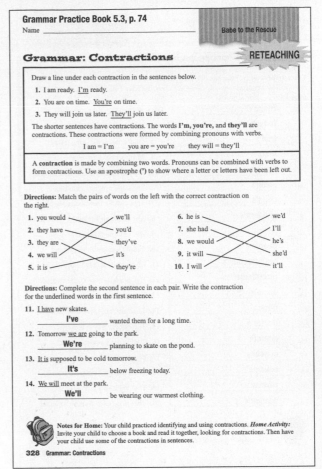

1. you would	we'll	
2. they have	you'd	
3. they are	they've	
4. we will	it's	
5. it is	they're	

6. he is	we'd	
7. she had	I'll	
8. we would	he's	
9. it will	she'd	
10. I will	it'll	

Directions: Complete the second sentence in each pair. Write the contraction for the underlined words in the first sentence.

11. I have new skates.
    I've _____ wanted them for a long time.

12. Tomorrow we are going to the park.
    We're _____ planning to skate on the pond.

13. It is supposed to be cold tomorrow.
    It's _____ below freezing today.

14. We will meet at the park.
    We'll _____ be wearing our warmest clothing.

Notes for Home: Your child practiced identifying and using contractions. *Home Activity:* Invite your child to choose a book and read it together, looking for contractions. Then have your child use some of the contractions in sentences.

328 Grammar: Contractions

Name _____

Babe to the Rescue

Grammar: Contractions

Directions: Combine each pronoun in the Pronoun Pool with a verb in the Verb Pool. Write twelve contractions. **Possible answers given.**

Pronoun Pool
I   we
he   they
she you
it

Verb Pool
are   had
will   is
have
am

1.	I'm	4.	we've	7.	it'll	10.	I'll
2.	he's	5.	they'll	8.	I've	11.	he'll
3.	she'll	6.	you've	9.	I'd	12.	she's

Directions: Rewrite the paragraph using contractions to replace the underlined words.

I have got several gemstones at home. They are pretty to look at, and I would like to show them to you. If I turn on a special light, they will glow in the dark. It is a spectacular sight, and I am sure you will find it interesting. Please bring your brothers because I think they would be fascinated. I know they have a collection of their own. Maybe we will trade some stones.

13.–19. **I've got several gemstones at home. They're pretty to look at, and I'd like to show them to you. If I turn on special light, they'll glow in the dark. It's a spectacular sight, and I'm sure you'll find it interesting. Please bring your brothers because I think they'd be fascinated. I know they've a collection of their own. Maybe we'll trade some stones.**

Write a Paragraph

Write a paragraph about some things you collect or would like to collect. Use contractions in some of your sentences. Write on a separate sheet of paper. **Make sure students spell and punctuate contractions correctly.**

Notes for Home: Your child formed contractions and changed word pairs within a paragraph into contractions. *Home Activity:* Have your child write a list of five contractions, and then ask him or her to use them to tell a scary story.

Grammar: Contractions 329

Name _____

Babe to the Rescue

Word Study: Unusual Possessives

Directions: Some plural nouns do not end in **-s.** To make them possessive, add an **apostrophe (')** and the letter **s.** Rewrite each phrase using the possessive form. Write the new phrase on the line.

the geese's honks	1. the honks of the geese
the children's laughter	2. the laughter of the children
the men's conversation	3. the conversation of the men
the women's voices	4. the voices of the women
the mice's squeaks	5. the squeaks of the mice

Directions: Some singular nouns end in **-s.** To make them possessive, add an **apostrophe (')** and the **s.** Rewrite each phrase using the possessive form. Write the new phrase on the line.

the boss's orders	6. the orders of the boss
the class's desks	7. the desks of the class
the chorus's singing	8. the singing of the chorus
the dress's color	9. the color of the dress
the glass's contents	10. the contents of the glass

Directions: Read each sentence. Circle the correct possessive form in ( ).

11. The animals heard the main (boss's/boss') words, and they started to make noise.
12. The farmer could hear the many (sheep's/sheep') cries.
13. Then he heard the (mens/men's) low voices.
14. He saw the two (thieves's/thieves') truck.
15. Quietly, he crept to the truck and let out all four of the (tires'/tire's) air.

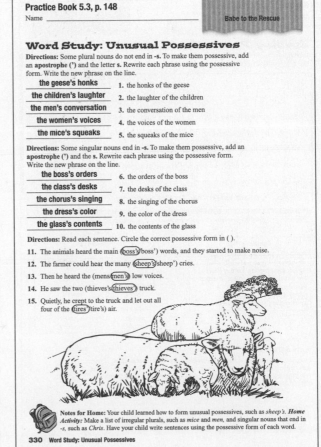

Notes for Home: Your child learned how to form unusual possessives, such as *sheep's*. *Home Activity:* Make a list of irregular plurals, such as *mice* and *men*, and singular nouns that end in *-s*, such as *Chris*. Have your child write sentences using the possessive form of each word.

330 Word Study: Unusual Possessives

© Scott Foresman 5

Name_____

Babe to the Rescue

Spelling: Possessives

Pretest Directions: Fold back the page along the dotted line. On the blanks, write the spelling words as they are dictated. When you have finished the test, unfold the page and check your words.

1. friend's
2. today's
3. Dad's
4. Mom's
5. sister's
6. sisters'
7. child's
8. children's
9. person's
10. people's
11. grandmother's
12. grandfather's
13. uncle's
14. uncles'
15. doctor's
16. doctors'
17. cousin's
18. cousins'
19. woman's
20. women's

1. These are my **friend's** toys.
2. Has **today's** mail arrived yet?
3. **Dad's** magazine came today.
4. **Mom's** books are on the shelf.
5. My little **sister's** doll was broken.
6. My **sisters'** dresses are blue.
7. That **child's** face needs washing.
8. The **children's** drawings are here.
9. Did you see that **person's** hat?
10. **People's** intentions are good.
11. My **grandmother's** cat is sick.
12. Her **grandfather's** car is outside.
13. Our **uncle's** name is Steven.
14. Their **uncles'** homes are old.
15. The **doctor's** coat is white.
16. That is the **doctors'** entrance.
17. My **cousin's** hair is red.
18. Their **cousins'** names are long.
19. That **woman's** coat is brown.
20. That store sells **women's** clothes.

 Notes for Home: Your child took a pretest on words that show ownership, or possessives. *Home Activity:* Help your child learn misspelled words before the final test, concentrating on whether one person or more than one person owns something.

Spelling: Possessives   **331**

Name_____

Babe to the Rescue

Spelling: Possessives

Word List			
friend's	sisters'	grandmother's	doctors'
today's	child's	grandfather's	cousin's
Dad's	children's	uncle's	cousins'
Mom's	person's	uncles'	woman's
sister's	people's	doctor's	women's

Directions: Choose the words from the box that name ownership by one person or thing. Write the words on the lines. **Order may vary.**

1. friend's
2. today's
3. Dad's
4. Mom's
5. sister's
6. child's
7. person's
8. grandmother's
9. grandfather's
10. uncle's
11. doctor's
12. cousin's
13. woman's

Directions: Choose the word from the box to complete each equation, using a plural possessive noun. Write your word on the line.

children's   14. the pets of the children = the _____ pets
doctors'   15. the offices of the doctors = the _____ offices
people's   16. the jobs of the people = the _____ jobs
cousins'   17. the farm of the cousins = the _____ farm
uncles'   18. the ducks of the uncles = the _____ ducks
women's   19. the votes of the women = the _____ votes
sisters'   20. the hogs of the sisters = the _____ hogs

 Notes for Home: Your child spelled possessive nouns—words that show ownership. *Home Activity:* Look at magazine pictures together. Invite your child to identify people and their possessions, such as *the farmer's hat,* and spell each possessive noun.

332   Spelling: Possessives

Name_____

Babe to the Rescue

Spelling: Possessives

Directions: Proofread this diary entry. Find five spelling mistakes. Use the proofreading marks to correct each mistake.

≡ Make a capital.
/ Make a small letter.
∧ Add something.
◞ Take out something.
⊙ Add a period.
¶ Begin a new paragraph.

Dear Diary,

Today's trip to our uncle's farm was fun! I rode my
grandmothers horse. Later, it was my two cousin's
turns. The horse licked my one cousin's face! Later we
took a childrens' tour of the farm. I saw Moms favorite
duck and Dad's favorite pig. My grandfather's favorite
is the old hen who lays an egg every day. I think farm
animals' lives are better than peoples lives!

Spelling Tip
sister's   sisters'
To form possessives of singular nouns, add an **apostrophe (')** and **s: sister's.** For plural nouns that end in **-s,** add an **apostrophe ('): sisters'.** For plural nouns that do not end in **-s,** add **apostrophe (')** and **s: children's.**

Word List	
friend's	grandmother's
today's	grandfather's
Dad's	uncle's
Mom's	uncles'
sister's	doctor's
sisters'	doctors'
child's	cousin's
children's	cousins'
person's	woman's
people's	women's

Write a Diary Entry

Imagine you are a farm animal who keeps a diary. On a separate sheet of paper, write a diary entry that describes a typical day on the farm. Try to use at least five of your spelling words. **Answers will vary, but each diary entry should include at least five spelling words.**

 Notes for Home: Your child spelled possessive nouns—words that show ownership. *Home Activity:* Have your child make a list of items or places around the house, using possessive nouns. For example: *Mom's favorite chair* or *my twin sisters' room.*

Spelling: Possessives   **333**

Name_____

Babe to the Rescue

Spelling: Possessives

REVIEW

Word List				
friend's	sister's	person's	uncle's	cousin's
today's	sisters'	people's	uncles'	cousins'
Dad's	child's	grandmother's	doctor's	woman's
Mom's	children's	grandfather's	doctors'	women's

Directions: Choose the word from the box that is the possessive form of the underlined word in each sentence. Write the possessive noun on the line.

children's   1. The vacation of the <u>children</u> was spent on a farm.
cousins'   2. They visited the farm of the <u>cousins</u> in Iowa.
person's   3. On the farm, the work of a <u>person</u> is important.
grandmother's   4. The job of the <u>grandmother</u> is to feed the chicks.
uncles'   5. The job of the <u>uncles</u> is to milk the cows.
women's   6. The job of the <u>women</u> is to collect chicken eggs.
child's   7. The job of one <u>child</u> is to feed hay to the horses.
Mom's   8. The suggestion of <u>Mom</u> was to help out with chores.
today's   9. Shearing the sheep was one chore of <u>today</u>.
Dad's   10. The children assisted with the help of <u>Dad</u>.
sister's   11. The task of the <u>sister</u> was to gather the wool.
doctor's   12. Later the animals received an exam of a <u>doctor</u>.

Directions: Choose the word from the box that is the possessive form of each word below. Write the word on the line.

13. friend   friend's
14. cousin   cousin's
15. grandfather   grandfather's
16. people   people's
17. sisters   sisters'
18. doctors   doctors'
19. uncle   uncle's
20. woman   woman's

 Notes for Home: Your child spelled possessive nouns—words that show ownership. *Home Activity:* Read a magazine article with your child. Together, identify possessive nouns that you find. Have your child tell whether each noun is singular or plural.

334   Spelling: Possessives

© Scott Foresman 5

Magazines/Periodicals/Almanacs

Periodicals are materials published at regular time periods, such as weekly, monthly, and so on. **Magazines** are a type of periodical that contain news articles, opinion columns, advertisements, cartoons, reports, and so on. The *Readers' Guide to Periodic Literature* is a good resource for locating magazine articles about specific topics.

Directions: Suppose you found the following articles in the *Readers' Guide.* Use these sample entries to answer the questions that follow.

ANIMALS, FARM
See also
Farming

A horses's life: just say neigh. N. Johansen.
Farming Mag Ap 4 '98 p 87–90
All vets are off: a shortage of animal doctors.
L. Landon. Time Mag D 13 '98 p 45
An udder disgrace: the milk strike continues.
J. Jackson. US News Report Ja '98 p 23–24
Chicks and ducks and geese better scurry: a
cold winter's coming. Weather Gazette.
N '98 p 12–13
Do pigs really eat like pigs? D. Taylor.
Farmer's Guide F 16 '98 p 90–94
Don't be a chicken with your chickens.
G. McMillan. Farming Mag Jl 16 '98
p 44–45

Ducks and swans: what's the difference?
B. Barello. Science Digest D 14 '98 p 34–35
Honk if you love geese! N. Michelson.
Agriculture and You. My '98 p 56–58
Is any animal really as stubborn as a mule? M.
Vicars. Science Digest F 12 '98 p 87–89
Never pull the wool over a sheep's eyes.
T. Albright. Newsweek Mag Jl 14 '98
p 29–32
New feed for a new age. G. O'Tooney.
Science Digest Mr 14 '98 p 99–101
New ways to shear sheep at the baa-baa shop.
P. Nelson. Farmer's Guide Ag '98 p 78–80
Should farmers clone sheep? J. Miller. Time
Mag Mr 10 '98 p 55–58
Why did the chicken cross the road? and
other farm animal jokes. F. Mock. Humor
Mag F '98 p 17

1. In which magazine does the article "Honk If You Love Geese!" appear?
Agriculture and You

2. What is the date of the *Farmer's Guide* that carries the article "Do Pigs Really Eat Like Pigs?"
February 16, 1998

3. Who wrote the article "New Ways to Shear Sheep at the Baa-Baa Shop"?
P. Nelson

4. On what page or pages does the article "Never Pull the Wool Over a Sheep's Eyes" appear?
pages 29–32

5. What other listing is given by the *Readers' Guide* for more information about farm animals?
Farming

Research and Study Skills: Magazines/Periodicals/Almanacs   335

An **almanac** is a book published each year that contains calendars, weather information, dates of holidays, and charts and tables of current information in many different subject areas.

Directions: Use the almanac index to answer the questions that follow.

Agriculture, U.S.	
Congressional committees	159
Corn blight	428
History	54
Income	498
Animals	
Endangered wildlife	330
Farm animal revenues	229
Sheep cloning	109
Use in research	24

6. For a report on farm animals, would you find more helpful information under "Agriculture, U.S." or under "Animals"?
Animals

7. On what page of the almanac would you find information on farm animal revenues?
page 229

8. Information about what topic appears on page 109 of the almanac? **Sheep cloning**

9. If you wanted to learn about problems farmers have had with corn crops, which page would you turn to?
page 428

10. When might an almanac be a more useful resource than a book? Explain.
Possible answer: If you needed current information, an almanac may give you more up-to-date information than a book.

 Notes for Home: Your child learned how to find information in magazines and an almanac. *Home Activity:* With your child, look through the table of contents of a magazine or almanac. Choose a specific topic, and see if your child can find it in the magazine or almanac.

336   Research and Study Skills: Magazines/Periodicals/Almanacs

---

Comparison/Contrast Chart

Comparison/contrast charts should be filled out completely.

Directions: Write the titles and main-character names from two stories, and identify the problem each character faces. Follow the directions in the first column to complete the chart.

List the story titles and characters.		
Describe each character's problem.		
List ways in which the characters' efforts to solve the problems are similar.		
List ways in which the characters' efforts to solve the problems are different.		
Tell how well you think each character solves the problem.		

Directions: Write a possible topic sentence.

 Notes for Home: Your child used this chart to compare and contrast two story characters' efforts to solve problems. *Home Activity:* Ask your child to explain how well each character dealt with the problem he or she faced.

Unit 3: Writing Process   337

Elaboration
Precise and Vivid Verbs

• You can make sentences clearer by replacing unclear verbs with **precise** verbs.
• You can make sentences more interesting by replacing **dull** verbs with **vivid** verbs.

Directions: For each sentence, pick a more precise or vivid verb from the box to replace the underlined verb. Rewrite each sentence, using the new verb. Make sure you select verbs that make sense in the sentences.

Verbs			
act	earns	stay	watches
draw	prefer	talk	whispers

1. Some story characters <u>are</u> with great courage.
Some story characters act with great courage.

2. Other characters <u>are</u> in one place for a long time.
Other characters stay in one place for a long time.

3. My friend <u>sees</u> mystery movies for every clue.
My friend watches mystery movies for every clue.

4. I <u>see</u> comedies over mysteries.
I prefer comedies over mysteries.

5. In some comedy stories, animals can say.
In some comedy stories, animals can talk.

6. It can be hard to hear a person who says.
It can be hard to hear a person who whispers.

7. It's fun to see cartoonists <u>make</u> characters.
It's fun to see cartoonists draw characters.

8. A successful artist <u>makes</u> a lot of money.
A successful artist earns a lot of money.

 Notes for Home: Your child has improved sentences by choosing verbs that express ideas clearly. *Home Activity:* With your child, read a newspaper or magazine article to find verbs that vividly describe action or express ideas.

338   Unit 3: Writing Process

Name _____

Self-Evaluation
Comparison/Contrast Paper

Directions: Think about the final draft of your comparison/contrast paper. Then answer each question in the chart. **Students' responses should show they have given careful thought to the papers they have written.**

	Yes	No	Not sure
1. Did I include similarities between the two characters' decisions or actions?			
2. Did I explain differences between the characters' decisions or actions?			
3. Are my important ideas expressed clearly?			
4. Did I use transition words or phrases well?			
5. Did I proofread and edit carefully to correct errors?			

6. What is the best part of my comparison/contrast paper?

_____

_____

_____

_____

7. Write one thing that you would change about this paper if you had the chance to write it again.

_____

_____

_____

_____

 Notes for Home: Your child has answered questions about preparing and writing a comparison/contrast paper. *Home Activity:* Ask your child what writing strategies he or she learned that may help in the writing of future papers.

Unit 3: Writing Process **339**

Name _____

The Yangs' First Thanksgiving

Compare and Contrast

- To **compare** is to tell how two or more things are alike. To **contrast** is to tell how two or more things are different.
- Authors sometimes use clue words such as *similar to, like,* or *as* to compare things. They may use clue words such as *different from, but,* or *unlike* to contrast things.

Directions: Reread "A Visitor from Japan." Then complete the diagram. Write what the story says and what you already know about people and places in Japan on the left. Write about the people and places in America on the right. Write things that both countries have in common in the middle. Some ideas have been given to help you get started. **Possible answers given.**

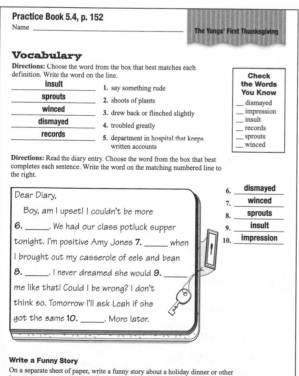

Japan — **Both Countries** — America

1. **eat with chopsticks**

speak Japanese

sit on straw mats

wear kimonos and clogs

2. **write haiku**

5. **wear jeans and suits**

big, modern, crowded cities

eat with forks, knives, and spoons

3. **speak mainly English**

4. **sit on chairs**

 Notes for Home: Your child read a story and learned how to compare and contrast. *Home Activity:* With your child, look at family photographs of two people, places, or things. Invite your child to describe how the people, places, or things in the photos are alike and different.

342 Compare and Contrast

Name _____

The Yangs' First Thanksgiving

Vocabulary

Directions: Choose the word from the box that best matches each definition. Write the word on the line.

insult	1. say something rude	
sprouts	2. shoots of plants	
winced	3. drew back or flinched slightly	
dismayed	4. troubled greatly	
records	5. department in hospital that keeps written accounts	

Check the Words You Know
__ dismayed
__ impression
__ insult
__ records
__ sprouts
__ winced

Directions: Read the diary entry. Choose the word from the box that best completes each sentence. Write the word on the matching numbered line to the right.

Dear Diary,

Boy, am I upset! I couldn't be more

6. _____. We had our class potluck supper

tonight. I'm positive Amy Jones 7. _____ when

I brought out my casserole of eels and bean

8. _____. I never dreamed she would 9. _____

me like that! Could I be wrong? I don't

think so. Tomorrow I'll ask Leah if she

got the same 10. _____. More later.

6. **dismayed**
7. **winced**
8. **sprouts**
9. **insult**
10. **impression**

Write a Funny Story

On a separate sheet of paper, write a funny story about a holiday dinner or other important event your family celebrates. Use as many vocabulary words as you can in your story. **Students' stories should be humorous and make correct use of vocabulary words.**

Notes for Home: Your child identified and used vocabulary words from "The Yangs' First Thanksgiving." *Home Activity:* Ask your child to make expressions that match the words *dismayed* and *winced.* Take turns doing the same for the other words about strong feelings.

Vocabulary **343**

Name _____

The Yangs' First Thanksgiving

Compare and Contrast

- To **compare** is to tell how two or more things are alike. To **contrast** is to tell how two or more things are different.
- Authors sometimes use clue words such as *similar to, like,* or *as* to compare things. They may use clue words such as *different from, but,* or *unlike* to contrast things.

Directions: Reread what happens in "The Yangs' First Thanksgiving" after Mrs. Conner tries to get Mrs. Hanson to take a piece of pie. Then answer the questions below.

Mother was staring at Mrs. Hanson and Mrs. Conner during this exchange. We Chinese think that being fat is good. It's a sign of good fortune. Thin people are considered unfortunate and miserable. But I knew here, being thin is supposed to be attractive. A lot of the girls in school are worried about their weight, and some of them even go on diets.

I saw Mother open her mouth. Don't say it, Mother, I wanted to shout. Don't say it! But she did. Radiating good will, Mother said, "Why you're not skinny at all, Mrs. Hanson. You're actually quite fat!"

From YANG THE THIRD AND HER IMPOSSIBLE FAMILY by Lensey Namioka. Copyright © 1995 by Lensey Namioka (Text); Illustrations © by Kees de Kiefte. By permission of Little, Brown and Company.

Possible answers given.

1. What is the author contrasting in this scene?
She's contrasting American and Chinese attitudes toward weight.

2. What clue word does the writer use to show contrast?
but

3. How is Mother different from Mrs. Hanson and Mrs. Conner?
Mother is Chinese. Mrs. Hanson and Mrs. Conner are American. They have different attitudes toward weight.

4. Tell why Mrs. Hanson will probably feel insulted by Mother's remark.
As an American woman, Mrs. Hanson probably feels that being fat means being unattractive, so being called fat is an insult.

5. In what other ways are the Yangs different from the Conners and their guests? On a separate sheet of paper, describe another example of contrast from the story.
Possible answer: Many Chinese people consider it an honor to be old and will often ask a person's age. However, many Americans do not like getting old and think it's rude to ask a person's age.

Notes for Home: Your child read a story and identified comparisons and contrasts. *Home Activity:* Work with your child to compare and contrast two people, places, or things.

344 Compare and Contrast

© Scott Foresman 5

Name _____

The Yangs' First Thanksgiving

Selection Test

Directions: Choose the best answer to each item. Mark the letter for the answer you have chosen.

Part 1: Vocabulary

Find the answer choice that means about the same as the underlined word in each sentence.

1. She made a good impression.
   A. sound
   B. effect on people
   C. statement of facts
   D. look on one's face

2. Stefanie winced when she heard the yell.
   F. cried out
   G. burst into laughter
   H. shrugged
   J. drew back suddenly

3. Mr. Jackson got a bag of sprouts.
   A. shoots of plants
   B. small twigs
   C. flower buds
   D. small bushes

4. She is in charge of the records department.
   F. where products are made
   G. having information about patients or workers
   H. where medicines are stored
   J. for very ill patients

5. Why are you so dismayed?
   A. very sneaky
   B. shy
   C. greatly troubled
   D. quiet

6. Did Mark mean to insult his guest?
   F. pay no attention to
   G. invite again
   H. talk louder than
   J. say something rude to

Part 2: Comprehension

Use what you know about the story to answer each item.

7. The Yang family lives in—
   A. Shanghai, China.
   B. Washington, D.C.
   C. Seattle.
   D. Hong Kong.

8. What do most of the kids at the Thanksgiving meal have in common?
   F. playing music
   G. playing baseball
   H. doing carpentry
   J. taking care of pets

9. Mrs. Yang is horrified by the idea of—
   A. cooking anything.
   B. her children making new friends.
   C. roasting a turkey.
   D. shaking hands.

10. The narrator of this story is looking forward to dinner at the Conners' because she wants to—
    F. talk with Holly Hanson.
    G. try cranberries for the first time.
    H. get to know Matthew.
    J. learn how to prepare a turkey.

GO ON →

Name _____

The Yangs' First Thanksgiving

11. Why are the Yangs horrified when Mr. Conner starts to scoop stuffing out of the turkey?
    A. They do not want to eat food that has been served by a man.
    B. They do not like the taste of onions.
    C. They think the turkey has not been prepared properly.
    D. They think a lot of meat has been wasted.

12. Unlike in America, most people in China think that—
    F. young people should be served first.
    G. the hosts should serve themselves before serving others.
    H. every family should have a pet.
    J. it is an honor to be old.

13. Why does Mrs. Hanson become upset during dinner?
    A. She feels insulted by Mother.
    B. Mary spills cranberries on her dress.
    C. She does not like turkey.
    D. Mary says she plays viola better than Holly.

14. Unlike in America, people in China think that it is—
    F. very rude to discuss money.
    G. rude to ask questions about a person's family.
    H. not proper for women to work outside the home.
    J. good to be fat.

15. What lesson does this story teach about meeting with people from other countries?
    A. Except for differences in language, people everywhere are the same.
    B. There may be misunderstandings between people who were raised to behave differently.
    C. It is impossible to learn what people from other countries believe.
    D. There is always one right way to behave, no matter where you were born and raised.

STOP

Name _____

The Yangs' First Thanksgiving

Compare and Contrast

- To **compare** is to tell how two or more things are alike. To **contrast** is to tell how two or more things are different.
- Authors sometimes use clue words such as *similar to, like,* or *as* to compare things. They may use clue words such as *different from, but,* or *unlike* to contrast things.

Directions: Read the story below.

I remember the first time we went to one of Vito's parties. It was unlike any party I had ever attended. First of all, it was at night. My parties were always in the afternoon. When we arrived, we saw a huge tent in the yard, covered with twinkling lights. I usually had my parties inside. The food was also a surprise. Instead of the cake and punch that I was used to, they had meatballs, spaghetti, and garlic bread. And what a crowd they had—more than 100 people! My parents never let me invite more than ten people to my parties. Boy, did we have a great time. I went home hoping to be invited to Vito's next party.

Directions: Complete the table. Give details about each party. Then write whether the author is comparing or contrasting and why.

Describe the . . .	Vito's Party	Writer's Parties
Place	tent in the backyard	inside
Time	night	1. **afternoon**
Food	2. **spaghetti, meatballs, garlic bread**	3. **cake and punch**
Size	4. **more than 100 people**	no more than ten guests

5. Conclusion: **Possible answer: The writer is contrasting his or her parties with Vito's because the details show how different the two types of parties are.**

 Notes for Home: Your child read a story and looked for comparisons and contrasts. *Home Activity:* Work with your child to compare and contrast two parties or celebrations you have attended. Make a list that shows how the two events are alike and different.

Name _____

The Yangs' First Thanksgiving

REVIEW

Summarizing

Directions: Read the passage. Then read each question about the passage. Choose the best answer to each question. Mark the letter for the answer you have chosen.

America's Patriotic Holidays

Two of our nation's most important patriotic holidays are Memorial Day and Independence Day. Memorial Day is observed on the last Monday in May, regardless of the date. It honors all those who died in our nation's wars. Independence Day always falls on the fourth of July, regardless of the day of the week. It celebrates the signing of the Declaration of Independence.

Most Americans feel that Memorial Day is a serious occasion. Many towns hold parades in which war veterans march. Ceremonies are held to remember the war dead. Often an important citizen will give a speech, and a firing of guns and the playing of taps bring the ceremony to a close.

Independence Day, by contrast, is a time for celebration. Towns and families hold afternoon picnics in which there frequently are games, contests, music, and plenty of food. The high point comes at nightfall. In towns across America on Independence Day, fireworks explode in brilliant shades of red, silver, and blue.

1. What is the main idea of the second paragraph?
   A. Memorial Day is a serious occasion.
   B. We should honor our war dead.
   C. Speeches should be kept short.
   D. Taps are an important custom.

2. What is the main idea of the third paragraph?
   F. Picnics are fun.
   G. Independence Day is a fun holiday.
   H. Fireworks are an important custom on Independence Day.
   J. Celebrations are an important American custom.

3. A summary of the details about Memorial Day should mention—
   A. taps.
   B. speeches.
   C. ceremonies.
   D. gun fire.

4. What would be the *least* important detail to include in a summary about Memorial Day?
   F. Memorial Day honors the many fallen soldiers.
   G. Memorial Day is a serious holiday.
   H. An important citizen may give a speech.
   J. Memorial Day is marked by parades and ceremonies.

5. Which would be the *most* important detail to include in a summary about Independence Day?
   A. food
   B. games
   C. contests
   D. fireworks

 Notes for Home: Your child read a nonfiction article and practiced summarizing. *Home Activity:* Read a story with your child. Then have him or her summarize it. Encourage your child to keep the summary brief and to include only the most important ideas or events.

Writing Across Texts

Directions: "The Yangs' First Thanksgiving" and "Harvest Moon" both take place during holidays: Thanksgiving and the Harvest Moon festival. These holidays are alike in some ways, but differ in others. Read the sentences below and write each one on the chart under the name of the holiday to which it applies. If the statement applies to both holidays, write it under both.

1. This holiday takes place in the fall.
2. People usually eat turkey.
3. It is a time when families and friends get together.
4. People often eat in the afternoon, so their food can digest.
5. The mooncakes may be in the shape of the animal that represents the current Chinese year.

6. People eat harvest mooncakes
7. It is a time of giving thanks.
8. People make good luck toasts to the harvest moon.
9. It is a time of feasting.
10. Pilgrims and Native Americans celebrated at the first of these.

Thanksgiving	The Harvest Moon Festival	Both
People usually eat turkey. Pilgrims and Native Americans celebrated at the first of these. People often eat in the afternoon, so their food can digest.	People eat harvest mooncakes. People make good luck toasts to the harvest moon. The mooncakes may be in the shape of the animal that represents the current Chinese year.	This holiday takes place in the fall. It is a time when families and friends get together. It is a time of giving thanks. It is a time of feasting.

Write a Comparison-Contrast Paragraph

Use the information in the chart above to write a paragraph comparing the two holidays of Thanksgiving and the Harvest Moon festival. Write your paragraph on a separate sheet of paper. **Paragraphs will vary. Check that students have included words and phrases that show both likenesses and differences.**

 Notes for Home: Your child used information from two different selections to compare and contrast holidays. *Home Activity:* Talk with your child about special holiday traditions in your family. Compare them with traditions of people you know.

Writing Across Texts **349**

Grammar: Complete Subjects

REVIEW

Directions: Underline the complete subject in each sentence.

1. Different people celebrate holidays in different ways.
2. My best friend walks with her family through the woods on Thanksgiving.
3. The natural beauty helps them appreciate the holiday more.
4. My favorite cousin serves Thanksgiving dinner at a shelter every year.
5. The pleasant, friendly faces make the holiday meaningful for her.
6. Several hours of hard work make her really hungry too.
7. A wonderful visit to Plymouth in Massachusetts is my family's custom.
8. The first Thanksgiving celebration took place there.
9. My home is only an hour away from that historic spot.
10. Our Thanksgiving meal is always a special event.

Directions: Add a complete subject to each predicate to create a sentence. Your subject should have at least three words. Write your sentence on the line. **Possible answers given.**

11. may be different this year
Our holiday celebration may be different this year.

12. will visit us at Thanksgiving
Old friends from Korea will visit us at Thanksgiving.

13. might be part of the meal
Delicious Korean food might be part of the meal.

14. can be interesting and fun
New and unusual food can be interesting and fun.

15. may enjoy a traditional American holiday
Our Korean visitors may enjoy a traditional American holiday.

 Notes for Home: Your child identified and used complete subjects in sentences. *Home Activity:* Have your child write some sentences about celebrations in your family. Then ask your child to underline the complete subject in each sentence.

350 Grammar: Complete Subjects

Grammar: Adjectives

An **adjective** describes the person, place, or thing that is named by a noun or identified by a pronoun. Many adjectives come before the words they describe. Adjectives can tell what kind, which one, or how many.

sweet relish (what kind)
this week (which one)
four hours (how many)

The words **a, an,** and **the** are called **articles.** They are used before nouns or before words that modify, or describe, nouns.

- Use **a** before singular words that begin with a consonant sound: a celebration; a lovely dinner.
- Use **an** before singular words that begin with a vowel sound or a silent **h:** an announcement; an hour.
- Use **the** before singular or plural words beginning with any letter: the song; the efforts.

Directions: Underline every article and every adjective in each sentence.

1. The Fourth of July is a loud and lively tradition in the USA.
2. Many people celebrate with festive parties.
3. Some parks offer brilliant displays of fireworks.
4. Colorful rockets explode in the smoky sky.
5. Happy families watch the spectacular sights.
6. Concerts of patriotic music often accompany these displays.
7. In a big city, famous singers and even Miss America appear on stage.
8. A concert in Washington, D.C., Boston, or Philadelphia may be televised to the entire country.
9. The audience at an outdoor concert may wear red, white, and blue T-shirts or caps.
10. When the bandleader announces traditional songs, the enthusiastic concert goers wave small flags and sing.

Directions: Read each sentence. For each underlined word, write whether the article or adjective tells **what kind, which one,** or **how many.**

_____what kind_____ 11. This holiday recalls an historic event.
_____how many_____ 12. The thirteen colonies declared independence.
_____which one_____ 13. Those colonies had been under England's rule.
_____which one_____ 14. The Declaration of Independence was signed on July 4, 1776.
_____what kind_____ 15. Every year we recall these brave patriots.

 Notes for Home: Your child identified adjectives, words that describe people, places, and things. *Home Activity:* Point out items in your home. Ask your child to describe the items by offering adjectives that tell what kind, which one, or how many.

Grammar: Adjectives **351**

Grammar: Adjectives

Directions: Read each sentence. Write the articles and adjectives on the line. For each article or adjective you find, write whether it tells **what kind, which one,** or **how many.**

1. Thanksgiving is an annual holiday.
an (which one); annual (what kind)

2. Large families often gather on this day.
Large (what kind); this (which one)

3. Some people take the time to offer sincere thanks.
Some (how many); the (which one); sincere (what kind)

4. The group may eat juicy turkey and tasty pie.
The (which one); juicy (what kind); tasty (what kind)

5. Americans look forward to this joyous event.
this (which one); joyous (what kind)

Directions: Write an adjective on the line to complete each sentence. **Possible answers given.**

_____festive_____ 6. Thanksgiving is a _____ occasion.
_____Many_____ 7. _____ people express their thankfulness.
_____different_____ 8. They find _____ ways to observe the day.
_____Some_____ 9. _____ individuals talk about the Pilgrims.
_____new_____ 10. The Pilgrims found a _____ home here.
_____hard_____ 11. At first their lives were _____.
_____friendly_____ 12. Then a _____ Native American helped them.
_____strong_____ 13. The Pilgrims and Native Americans began a _____ friendship.
_____large_____ 14. Together they held a _____ feast.
_____first_____ 15. This feast was the _____ Thanksgiving.

Write a Description

Invent a new holiday. On a separate sheet of paper, describe how the holiday should be celebrated. Use adjectives in your writing to make your sentences more interesting.
Check to be sure that students have used adjectives correctly.

 Notes for Home: Your child identified adjectives, words that describe people, places, and things. *Home Activity:* Read a story with your child. Have your child point out adjectives that appear in the sentences. Then ask him or her to tell what each adjective describes.

352 Grammar: Adjectives

© Scott Foresman 5

Grammar Practice Book 5.4, p. 79

Name _____

The Yangs' First Thanksgiving

Grammar: Adjectives

Look at the sneakers on the right. **Possible answers given.**
Write words that describe these sneakers.

four, old, new, white, dirty,

clean, laced, untied

Read the words you wrote that answer the question **what kind, which one,** or **how many**. These words are called **adjectives.**

An **adjective** describes the person, place, or thing that is named by a noun or identified by a pronoun. The words **a, an,** and **the** are called **articles.** They appear before nouns or before adjectives that are in front of nouns.

Directions: Circle the articles in each sentence. Then underline the noun that follows each article.

1. (An) elephant hid in (the) refrigerator.
2. We found (a) footprint in (the) pudding.
3. We saw (a) peanut on (the) shelf.
4. (An) embarrassed elephant fell out of (the) freezer.

Directions: Underline two adjectives and one article in each sentence. Then write each adjective and article in the correct space in the chart.

5. One breakfast was the tastiest meal I ever ate.
6. Some people drink a glass of fresh juice.
7. Many children eat a bowl of cold cereal.
8. Two eggs and toast make a delicious breakfast.

	How Many?	What Kind?	Article
5.	One	tastiest	the
6.	Some	fresh	a
7.	Many	cold	a
8.	Two	delicious	a

 Notes for Home: Your child used adjectives to describe a picture and identified articles (*a, an,* and *the*) and adjectives in sentences. *Home Activity:* Ask your child to write a list of at least five adjectives that tell more about a picture in a magazine.

Grammar: Adjectives **353**

Grammar Practice Book 5.4, p. 80

Name _____

The Yangs' First Thanksgiving

Grammar: Adjectives

Directions: Circle the adjectives that tell **What kind.** Underline the adjectives that tell **How Many.** Draw two lines under the adjectives that tell **Which one.** Put an X on the articles.

1. Many years ago there were (long) periods of (cold) temperatures in this area.
2. (Large)(frozen) rivers covered some parts of the (magnificent) planet.
3. Several (huge)(icy) sheets cut (wide) valleys in the (mountainous) areas.
4. X few glaciers dug (enormous) holes into that (soft)(brown) earth.
5. Some (large) holes became (deep) lakes.
6. Many lakes were formed by those (powerful) glaciers.
7. One lake made by an (ancient) glacier is Cayuga.

Directions: Unscramble each adjective and write it on the line. **Order may vary.**

ngetsra   gluy   everlsa

itwhe   tfory   aymn   wfe   riigdf

8.	white	12.	frigid
9.	forty	13.	ugly
10.	few	14.	several
11.	many	15.	strange

Write a Description

Write sentences that describe what the land looks like where you live. Use at least five adjectives. Write on a separate sheet of paper.

Make sure that students have used at least five adjectives.

 Notes for Home: Your child identified and unscrambled adjectives and used them in a paragraph. *Home Activity:* Write a list of five adjectives that describe something in your kitchen. Write the list again, but scramble the letters. Have your child unscramble the adjectives.

354 Grammar: Adjectives

Practice Book 5.4, p. 158

Name _____

The Yangs' First Thanksgiving

Word Study: Inflected Endings -ed, -ing

Directions: Two endings that are commonly added to verbs are **-ed** and **-ing.** If the verbs end in **e,** drop the **e** before adding **-ed** or **-ing.** Read the words in the table. Find the words that dropped the **e** before adding the ending. Write the base word on the lines.

1. relieve
2. illustrate
3. invite
4. hope
5. arrive

Base Word	Add -ed	Add -ing
relieve	relieved	relieving
cook	cooked	cooking
illustrate	illustrated	illustrating
invite	invited	inviting
hope	hoped	hoping
embarrass	embarrassed	embarrassing
arrive	arrived	arriving
help	helped	helping

Directions: Add **-ed** and **-ing** to each base word. Write the new word on the line.

Base Word		Add -ed		Add -ing
excite	6.	excited	16.	exciting
introduce	7.	introduced	17.	introducing
work	8.	worked	18.	working
interest	9.	interested	19.	interesting
slice	10.	sliced	20.	slicing
complain	11.	complained	21.	complaining
dine	12.	dined	22.	dining
wince	13.	winced	23.	wincing
start	14.	started	24.	starting
boil	15.	boiled	25.	boiling

 Notes for Home: Your child read and wrote words with the endings *-ed* and *-ing.* **Home Activity:** Read a magazine article with your child. List any words with *-ed* or *-ing* endings. Discuss whether the spelling of each verb was changed before *-ed* or *-ing* was added.

Word Study: Inflected Endings *-ed, -ing* **355**

Spelling Workbook 5.4, p. 61

Name _____

The Yangs' First Thanksgiving

Spelling: Homophones

Pretest Directions: Fold back the page along the dotted line. On the blanks, write the spelling words as they are dictated. When you have finished the test, unfold the page and check your words.

1. write		1.	Please **write** to me.
2. right		2.	You must do what is **right.**
3. buy		3.	Ted wants to **buy** a candy bar.
4. by		4.	The book is **by** a famous author.
5. to		5.	This letter is **to** your mother.
6. too		6.	There are **too** many choices.
7. bored		7.	Are you **bored** by this movie?
8. board		8.	I need some nails and a **board.**
9. it's		9.	**It's** easy to ride a bike.
10. its		10.	The bird spread **its** wings.
11. threw		11.	Jason **threw** the baseball to me.
12. through		12.	The kids ran **through** the yard.
13. knead		13.	You must **knead** the dough.
14. need		14.	I **need** to see you tomorrow.
15. main		15.	This is the library's **main** branch.
16. mane		16.	The lion shook his **mane.**
17. past		17.	I forget things about the **past.**
18. passed		18.	The truck **passed** the school bus.
19. allowed		19.	Are you **allowed** to go?
20. aloud		20.	She was reading **aloud.**

Notes for Home: Your child took a pretest on homophones, words that sound alike but are spelled differently and have different meanings. *Home Activity:* Help your child learn to connect the spelling of the word with its meaning.

356 Spelling: Homophones

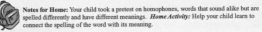

Spelling: Homophones

Word List

write	to	it's	knead	past
right	too	its	need	passed
buy	bored	threw	main	allowed
by	board	through	mane	aloud

Directions: Read each sentence. Then match each underlined word to its definition. Write the word on the line.

He <u>threw</u> the ball <u>through</u> the window.   You <u>need</u> to <u>knead</u> the dough to make bread.

tossed   from end to end   must   press together
1. **threw**   2. **through**   5. **need**   6. **knead**

Are you going <u>to</u> the ball game <u>too</u>?   We <u>buy</u> our milk <u>by</u> the gallon.

also   in the direction of   in the amount of   purchase
3. **too**   4. **to**   7. **by**   8. **buy**

Directions: Choose the word from the box that best completes each sentence. Write the word on the line to the left.

_____ **write** _____   9. Did you _____ the thank-you letter?
_____ **right** _____   10. Please do it _____ now.
_____ **main** _____   11. The lions were the _____ circus attraction,
_____ **mane** _____   12. The biggest lion had a magnificent _____.
_____ **board** _____   13. The _____ meeting went on for hours.
_____ **bored** _____   14. I was so _____ I nearly fell asleep.
_____ **passed** _____   15. Father _____ the potatoes to me.
_____ **past** _____   16. We finished eating at half _____ four.
_____ **it's** _____   17. I think _____ time for dessert.
_____ **its** _____   18. I gave the dog a piece of cake in _____ bowl.
_____ **allowed** _____   19. You're not _____ to talk loudly in the library.
_____ **aloud** _____   20. You also can't read _____ in the library.

 Notes for Home: Your child spelled homophones—words that sound the same but have different spellings and meanings. *Home Activity:* Make up short sentences using one spelling word in each sentence. Say each sentence and have your child spell the word you used.

Spelling: Homophones   **357**

Spelling: Homophones

Directions: Proofread the rules for how to behave at a special dinner. Find seven spelling mistakes. Use the proofreading marks to correct each mistake.

≡	Make a capital.
/	Make a small letter.
∧	Add something.
ℐ	Take out something.
⊙	Add a period.
¶	Begin a new paragraph.

Always place your napkin in your lap before eating.

Hold the fork in your left hand, and the knife in your ~~write~~. *right*

If you need to have a dish past, always ask politely. *sed*

Never sing or read aloud at the table, unless asked to~~o~~ do so.

Avoid yawning, even if you are bor~~d~~. *e*

When you are ~~thru~~ eating, wait for others to finish before *ough*

leaving the table.

Remember to thank your host b~~u~~y the time you leave.

Spelling Tip

it's   its

Homophones are words that sound alike but have different spellings and meanings. Don't confuse the homophones **its** and **it's**. **It's** means **it is**. **Its** is a possessive pronoun that means **belonging to it**. Remember: **It's** easy to remember **its** spelling: **i-t-s**.

Word List

write	threw
right	through
buy	knead
by	need
to	main
too	mane
bored	past
board	passed
it's	allowed
its	aloud

Write a Set of Rules

On a separate sheet of paper, write your own rules for another social situation, such as talking on the telephone or meeting new people. Try to use at least five of your spelling words.
Answers will vary, but each set of rules should contain at least five spelling words.

Notes for Home: Your child spelled homophones—words that sound exactly alike but have different spellings and meanings. *Home Activity:* Write each pair of homophones on index cards. Take turns choosing a card and writing a sentence that uses both words.

358   Spelling: Homophones

REVIEW

Spelling: Homophones

Word List

write	to	it's	knead	past
right	too	its	need	passed
buy	bored	threw	main	allowed
by	board	through	mane	aloud

Directions: Choose the word from the box that has the same or nearly the same meaning as each word or words below. Write the word on the line.

1. wooden plank   **board**   6. squeeze   **knead**
2. finished   **through**   7. hair   **mane**
3. purchase   **buy**   8. near   **by**
4. uninterested   **bored**   9. require   **need**
5. most important   **main**   10. pitched   **threw**

Directions: Choose a pair of homophones from the box to complete each sentence. Write the words on the lines to the left.

_____ **too** _____   11. It's _____ late _____ go to the parade.
_____ **to** _____   12.
_____ **passed** _____   13. We _____ the marchers when we drove _____ the bank.
_____ **past** _____   14.
_____ **write** _____   15. I should _____ myself a note _____ now before I forget.
_____ **right** _____   16.
_____ **it's** _____   17. When the cat meows, _____ time for _____ dinner.
_____ **its** _____   18.
_____ **allowed** _____   19. The teacher _____ the students to read _____ to one another.
_____ **aloud** _____   20.

 Notes for Home: Your child spelled homophones—words that sound alike but are spelled differently and have different meanings. *Home Activity:* Help your child write a short rhyming poem using several of the spelling words.

Spelling: Homophones   **359**

Research Process/Evaluate Reference Sources

There are many different resources you can use to find information, such as atlases, almanacs, CD-ROMs, and the Internet. When beginning a research project, follow these steps to make the best use of your time.

Research Process

1. Set a purpose.
2. Form and revise questions.
3. Evaluate and choose sources.
4. Collect, organize, and present information.

360   Research and Study Skills: Research Process/Evaluate Reference Sources

© Scott Foresman 5

Practice Book 5.4, p. 160

Name _____

The Yangs' First Thanksgiving

Directions: Suppose you wanted to do a research report about holidays. Think about the research process and the resources you might use. Then answer the questions below.

1. First, narrow down the topic for your report on holidays. What holiday or aspect of holidays are you most interested in? Write your topic on the line below.
Answers will vary.

2. What questions about your topic do you want to answer through your research? List at least two questions.
Possible answer: When was this holiday invented? Is this holiday celebrated in other countries?

_____

3. List two resources you might use to begin your research into the questions above and explain why these are good resources to use. Consider whether such resources are reliable, accurate, sufficient, and up-to-date.
Possible answer: An encyclopedia article might tell me about the history of the holiday. A nonfiction book about holidays around the world might tell me whether this holiday is celebrated in other countries.

_____

4. What might your finished report look and sound like? For example, could you use a diagram, a map, or a recording of a speech or music? Describe how you could organize and present your report.
Possible answer: A report on the holiday might be organized to discuss its history, its customs, and current celebrations. The presentation might include time line illustrations that show how traditions or customs have changed over time.

_____

5. How might the research process help you make the best use of your time? Explain.
Possible answer: The research process helps you to stay focused. You look for and use only the information that is related to your purpose.

_____

 Notes for Home: Your child wrote about the steps in the research process. *Home Activity:* Watch a news report on television with your child. Talk about the research the news team probably had to do before giving the report.

Research and Study Skills: Research Process/Evaluate Reference Sources **361**

Practice Book 5.4, p. 161

Name _____

The Jr. Iditarod Race

Main Idea and Supporting Details

- The **main idea** is the most important idea about the topic of a paragraph, article, or story. **Supporting details** tell more about the main idea.
- When the main idea is not directly stated, you will have to decide what is most important and put it in your own words.

Directions: Reread "Saving Nome." Then complete the table. Decide on the most important idea about the topic. Then list important supporting details that tell more about that idea. **Possible answers given.**

Topic
The diphtheria epidemic in Nome

Main Idea
1. Nome, Alaska, was in desperate need of serum because of a diphtheria epidemic.

Detail
Nome wasn't reachable by ship in winter.

Detail
2. To get serum to Nome by dogsled could take weeks.

Detail
3. Serum was sent by train to Nenana, but Nome was still 674 miles away.

Detail
4. Nineteen mushers volunteered for a dogsled relay.

Detail
5. To save time, each team would only travel to the next village.

 Notes for Home: Your child read a story, identified its main idea, and described important supporting details. *Home Activity:* With your child, read a small section of a simple magazine article. Ask your child to identify the main idea of the section and list some supporting details.

364 Main Idea and Supporting Details

Practice Book 5.4, p. 162

Name _____

The Jr. Iditarod Race

Vocabulary

Directions: Draw a line to connect each word on the left with its definition on the right.

1. skids — slides
2. obstacles — catches up and moves ahead
3. cargo — load of goods
4. injuries — damages
5. overtakes — things that get in the way or slow you down

Check the Words You Know
___ announcer
___ cargo
___ delays
___ injuries
___ obstacles
___ overtakes
___ skids
___ wilderness

Directions: Choose the word from the box that best completes each sentence. Write the word on the line to the left.

cargo 6. We awoke before dawn to load the _____ into the camper van.

wilderness 7. Our plan was to drive to the mountains and spend two weeks in the _____.

announcer 8. As we drove, we listened to the radio _____ give a traffic report.

delays 9. She said to expect long _____ on the mountain road.

obstacles 10. I hope we don't face any other _____ on our vacation.

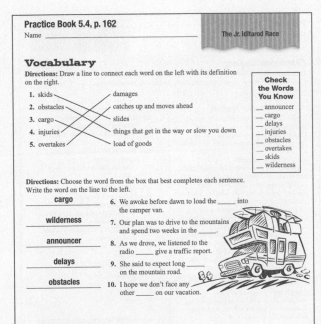

Write a Sports Announcement

Imagine you are a radio announcer covering a big sports event. How will you convey to your listeners what you see? Write your account of what happens, blow by blow. Use as many vocabulary words as you can.
Students' announcements may be whimsical. They should make correct use of vocabulary words.

Notes for Home: Your child identified and used new vocabulary words from "The Jr. Iditarod Race." *Home Activity:* With your child, write a postcard describing a real or imaginary trip to the wilderness. Encourage your child to use as many of the vocabulary words as possible.

Vocabulary **365**

Practice Book 5.4, p. 163

Name _____

The Jr. Iditarod Race

Main Idea and Supporting Details

- The **main idea** is the most important idea about the topic of a paragraph, article, or story. When the main idea is not stated, you have to figure it out and state it in your own words.
- **Supporting details** tell more about the main idea.

Directions: Reread what happens in "The Jr. Iditarod Race" as Dusty and his team enter the woods. Then answer the questions below.

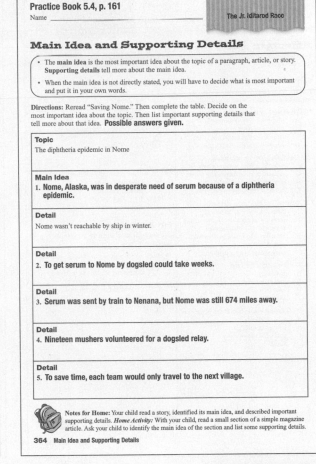

> They cross the lake safely, following the red plastic cones marking the route. But as they enter the woods, Dusty is on edge. He's never done this part of the trail, and it's crowded with obstacles. Snowmobiles roar along the same trail, and within ten miles he has to cross four roads. Sometimes the roads are so slick the dogs fall, or they get confused by the cars and spectators. Dusty knows he just needs to survive this part until he hits the main Iditarod trail.
>
> From IDITAROD DREAM. Copyright © 1996 by Ted Wood. Reprinted with permission from Walker and Company. All Rights Reserved.

Possible answers given.

1. In a few words, write the topic of this paragraph.
the Iditarod trail

2. State the main idea of the paragraph in your own words.
The part of the trail that goes through the woods is extremely difficult.

_____

3. List three supporting details for the main idea.
Dusty is on edge; it's crowded with obstacles; snowmobiles use the same trail; they have to cross four roads; the roads can be slick; the dogs get confused.

_____

4. Is the description of the red plastic cones marking the route a supporting detail? Why or why not?
No, it doesn't give information about the main idea.

_____

5. What are the topic and main idea of "The Jr. Iditarod Race"? On a separate sheet of paper, identify the topic, state the main idea, and list supporting details.
Topic: The Jr. Iditarod Race. Main idea: The Jr. Iditarod Race is extremely challenging. Check that supporting details are drawn from Dusty's experiences and that they relate to the main idea.

Notes for Home: Your child read a paragraph from a nonfiction text and identified the main idea and supporting details. *Home Activity:* With your child, read a newspaper article. Help him or her to identify its main idea and supporting details.

366 Main Idea and Supporting Details

Selection Test

Directions: Choose the best answer to each item. Mark the letter for the answer you have chosen.

Part 1: Vocabulary

Find the answer choice that means about the same as the underlined word in each sentence.

1. There were many <u>obstacles</u> in the street.
   A. people looking at something
   (B) things that stand in the way
   C. large holes that need to be filled
   D. booths where people sell things

2. Jenna hiked into the <u>wilderness</u>.
   (F) wild place with no people living in it
   G. piece of land surrounded by water
   H. area full of ancient buildings
   J. border separating two countries

3. What did the <u>announcer</u> just say?
   A. someone who acts on a stage
   (B) person who introduces a program or event and tells what happens
   C. someone who writes news articles
   D. person who represents the government of a foreign country

4. Workers carried the <u>cargo</u>.
   F. passengers
   G. broken machines
   H. sails on a ship
   (J) load of goods

5. What should you do if your car <u>skids</u>?
   A. stops suddenly
   B. catches on fire
   C. gets a flat tire
   (D) slides

6. The hiker had some <u>injuries</u>.
   (F) wounds; hurt body parts
   G. hot meals
   H. successes; wins
   J. favorite sights

7. My horse <u>overtakes</u> the leader.
   A. bumps into
   (B) moves ahead of
   C. loses to
   D. makes a noise at

8. There were many <u>delays</u> during the trip.
   F. surprising events
   G. pleasant meetings
   (H) stops along the way
   J. dangers to avoid

Part 2: Comprehension

Use what you know about the selection to answer each item.

9. Both the Iditarod and Jr. Iditarod races are held to honor—
   A. the coming of pioneers to Alaska.
   B. the earliest Eskimo mushers.
   (C) a dog team that carried medicine to Nome.
   D. Alaska's natural beauty.

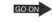 GO ON

Selection Test **367**

---

10. What is this selection mostly about?
    F. how Dusty Whittemore and his family became involved in mushing
    G. the fifteen young people who competed in the 1995 Jr. Iditarod
    H. how the Jr. Iditarod is different from the adults' race
    (J) the experiences of the boy who won the 1995 Jr. Iditarod

11. Which detail supports the idea that sled dogs love to run and pull sleds?
    A. "It's zero degrees, which is perfect for the dogs."
    B. "Dusty has to walk each dog from the truck."
    (C) "The dogs are so excited by the other teams it takes every hand to hold them in place."
    D. "QT and Blacky have splits in the webs between their toes."

12. What can you tell about Dusty from how he acts in the early part of the race?
    F. He doesn't realize that mushing can be a dangerous sport.
    (G) He stays clear-headed when faced with a problem.
    H. He panics when something unexpected occurs.
    J. He keeps imagining victory and forgets to pay attention to what is happening.

13. You can tell from this selection that sled dogs—
    A. are very calm and patient.
    B. are more powerful than a moose.
    C. need no training to mush correctly.
    (D) remember places they have been before.

14. Which sentence states an opinion?
    F. "The handlers step away and Dusty flies from the start."
    G. "Back on the trail, he uses his track brake to slow the dogs."
    (H) "The team is running perfectly now, strong and fast."
    J. "It takes him five minutes to straighten them out and get under way."

15. What part of the story shows that Dusty follows the spirit of the race?
    A. People think Dusty has mistreated his dogs.
    B. Dusty got lost in the race the year before.
    C. Snowmobilers almost run into Dusty's dogs.
    (D) Dusty helps the other racers build a fire.

 STOP

368 Selection Test

Main Idea and Supporting Details

- The **main idea** is the most important idea about the topic of a paragraph, article, or story. When the main idea is not stated, you have to figure it out and state it in your own words.
- **Supporting details** tell more about the main idea.

Directions: Read the story below.

This year Misty entered a 100K bicycle marathon. Because it was her first marathon, Misty was nervous. On the day before the race, she studied a map of the marathon's route, mentally preparing for its challenges. She checked and double-checked the brakes on her bike. She also measured the air pressure in her tires and made sure her bike helmet fit correctly. Misty was careful to fill out the emergency card that all racers must carry. It had the name of a person to call in case she was sick or injured during the race. On the day of the race, Misty felt confident that she was prepared for anything.

Directions: Complete the diagram. Describe the story's main idea and give details that support the main idea.

Main Idea

1. Possible answer: Misty was careful and thorough as she prepared for the marathon.

Supporting Details
She studied a map of the route.

2. She double-checked her brakes.

3. She checked the air pressure in her tires.

4. She checked the fit of her helmet.

5. She filled out her emergency card.

 Notes for Home: Your child read a nonfiction passage and identified its main idea and supporting details. **Home Activity:** With your child, read a section from a school textbook. Help him or her identify the main idea and supporting details of the section read.

Main Idea and Supporting Details **369**

Generalizing

REVIEW

Directions: Read the passage. Then read each question about the passage. Choose the best answer to each question. Mark the letter for the answer you have chosen.

Siberian Huskies

Siberian Huskies were originally bred as sled dogs. These dogs were bred by the Chukchi people of northeastern Asia. In general, the breed's compact size, quickness, and endurance make it perfect for pulling loads over long distances.

In 1909, the first team of Siberian Huskies was brought to Alaska to compete in the All Alaska Sweepstakes Race. Soon, many Alaskan dog breeders were breeding Siberian Huskies. The dogs became popular in Alaska for racing, and they also became popular in other parts of the United States as family pets.

If you are thinking about getting a Siberian Husky for a pet, there are three important things to know about them. First, all Siberian Huskies love to run. A fenced-in yard is important so that your dog has plenty of room to run. Second, Siberian Huskies shed. If dog hair bothers you or anyone in your family, this is probably not the dog for you. Finally, Siberian Huskies are friendly and love company. If you will have to leave your dog alone for long periods of time, consider a different breed of dog.

1. What clue words in the first paragraph signal a generalization?
   A. originally
   (B) in general
   C. perfect
   D. Siberian Huskies

2. Which generalization is valid based on information given in the passage?
   F. Siberian Huskies are loners.
   (G) Siberian Huskies make great sled dogs.
   H. Siberian Huskies are slow, but steady runners.
   J. Siberian Huskies are easy dogs to care for.

3. Why isn't the first sentence of the second paragraph a generalization?
   A. It tells a historical fact.
   B. It doesn't give enough information about the team.
   (C) It doesn't tell what most Huskies have in common.
   D. It doesn't say whether the team won the race.

4. What clue word in the third paragraph signals a generalization?
   (F) all
   G. second
   H. first
   J. finally

5. Which of the following generalizations is faulty based on information given in the passage?
   A. Siberian Huskies are compact in size.
   B. Siberian Huskies love to run.
   C. Siberian Huskies originated in Siberia.
   (D) Siberian Huskies are quick runners, but tire easily.

 Notes for Home: Your child read an article and identified generalizations in it. **Home Activity:** Use the following clue words to take turns making generalizations with your child: *many, all, most, never, always, often.* For example: *All my children have dark hair.*

370 Generalizing

© Scott Foresman 5

Writing Across Texts

Directions: Dusty in "The Jr. Iditarod Race" prepares himself and his dogsled team for an Alaskan tradition—the Iditarod race. Mary Yang, from "The Yangs' First Thanksgiving," may find many of these traditions unfamiliar but exciting. Some may be similar to things from her own traditions. In the table below, make a list of traditions that Dusty might explain to Mary and what Mary may think of them. **Possible answers given.**

Dusty's Traditions	Mary's Reactions
Sled dogs are working dogs, not pets.	In China, dogs are not kept as pets.
1. The Iditarod is a dogsled race that has been running for about 30 years.	2. Marathons and bicycle races are races held in China.
3. In Alaska, people use dogsleds and snowmobiles, as well as trucks and airplanes to travel distances.	4. In China, most people walk or use bicycles to get from place to place.
5. The number one position in the race is a place of honor.	6. In Chinese culture, elders and ancestors are honored.
7. Dusty's mother and father help him prepare for the race and wait for him at the finish line.	8. Families are very important to Chinese people.
9. Racers have to stay with their dogs outside at night.	10. In China, many families live in small apartments.

Write a Story

Through our experiences and traditions, we learn about who we are, where we come from, and what we think is important. Think about Mary, from the story "The Yangs' First Thanksgiving." Suppose Mary's family had moved to Alaska. Write a story about Mary meeting Dusty as he prepared for the Jr. Iditarod. Think about traditions that might be new or similar to traditions from Mary's own culture. Write your story on a separate sheet of paper. **Stories will vary. Check that students have used adjectives to elaborate their sentences.**

 Notes for Home: Your child used information from different sources to write a story. *Home Activity:* As you read a story or article with your child, discuss how its ideas connect to other reading your child has done.

Writing Across Texts **371**

Grammar: Adjectives

REVIEW

Directions: Underline each adjective. Draw a circle around each article.

1. In February 1978, Naomi Uemura began (an) amazing trip.
2. Mr. Uemura, with several dogs and (a) sled, would try to reach (the) faraway North Pole.
3. It would be (a) long and dangerous trip.
4. Mr. Uemura would have to deal with frigid weather and many difficult conditions.
5. (The) strong, speedy dogs needed constant, careful care.
6. Dogs with frozen paws or empty stomachs cannot pull (a) heavy sled.
7. One day Mr. Uemura was attacked by (an) enormous angry bear.
8. (The) brave team traveled six hundred miles over (the) frozen Arctic.
9. For fifty-four difficult days, Mr. Uemura and (the) loyal dogs moved over (the) ice.
10. On April 30, 1978, Mr. Uemura became (the) first person to reach (the) North Pole alone over land.

Directions: Complete each sentence with an article or with an adjective that tells how many or how much. More than one word may work in a sentence. Choose an article or an adjective from the box that makes sense. Write your new sentences on the lines. **Possible answers given. Accept all reasonable answers.**

| no   a *or* an   many   sixty   several |

11. There are _____ dogsled drivers who dream of racing in the Iditarod.
There are many (or several) dogsled drivers who dream of racing in the Iditarod. _____

12. About _____ "mushers" actually do compete each year.
About sixty "mushers" actually do compete each year. _____

13. Some enter the race even if they have _____ chance of winning.
Some enter the race even if they have no chance of winning. _____

14. Training for the race is not _____ easy task.
Training for the race is not an easy task. _____

15. Teams must win _____ shorter races before they can run the Iditarod.
Teams must win several (or many) shorter races before they can run the Iditarod.

 Notes for Home: Your child identified and used adjectives as well as the articles *a, an,* and *the* in sentences. *Home Activity:* Ask your child questions about persons, places, and things at school. Have your child write sentences, using adjectives and articles.

372 Grammar: Adjectives

Grammar: Using Adjectives to Improve Sentences

Adjectives describe persons, places, or things that nouns or pronouns identify. Adjectives tell what kind, which one, or how many. You can improve your sentences by using adjectives. They add vivid and precise details so that readers can picture what you are writing about.

Without Adjectives: Dogs run in yards.
With Adjectives Added: Five large dogs run in grassy yards.

Be careful not to use more adjectives than you need: Two large, long, tall, alert Dobermans sat in the kennel's waiting room.

Directions: Underline each adjective. Circle the noun or pronoun it modifies.

1. Dogs come in a wide (variety) of interesting (breeds).
2. Friendly (dogs) make wonderful (companions).
3. Intelligent (dogs) can perform amazing (tasks).
4. Expert (trainers) teach them important (skills).
5. Some fierce (dogs) guard homes and businesses.
6. Other (dogs) guide blind (people) on busy (sidewalks).
7. Special (dogs) herd stray (sheep) on big (farms).
8. Some large (dogs) rescue injured (climbers).
9. Dogs have a long (tradition) of good (deeds).

Directions: Add an adjective to make each sentence more vivid or more precise. Write the adjective on the line to the left. **Possible answers given.**

alert	10. Police rely on _____ dogs in their work.
special	11. These dogs receive _____ training.
dangerous	12. Some dogs search for _____ criminals.
important	13. Other dogs can accurately sniff out _____ clues.
missing	14. Rescue dogs search for _____ persons.
great	15. Dogs and police do _____ work together.

 Notes for Home: Your child identified and used adjectives in sentences. Adjectives describe people, places, and things. *Home Activity:* Look at pictures in a magazine together. Invite your child to name adjectives that describe the people, places, or things in each picture.

Grammar: Using Adjectives to Improve Sentences **373**

Grammar: Using Adjectives to Improve Sentences

Directions: Think of a different adjective to replace the one that is underlined. Write each new adjective on the line. **Possible responses:**

favorite	1. Football is a nice American tradition.
outstanding	2. Many good teams play on New Year's Day.
Noisy	3. Big crowds fill stadiums around the country.
great	4. The Rose Bowl is a fine football contest.
beautiful	5. Before the game a pretty parade is held.

Directions: Choose at least two adjectives to improve each sentence. Write each new sentence on the line. **Possible answers given.**

6. A band marches in the parade.
A talented band marches in the festive parade. _____

7. Floats of flowers travel on streets.
Floats of beautiful flowers travel on wide streets. _____

8. Spectators cheer with voices.
Excited spectators cheer with booming voices. _____

9. Music and laughter are heard.
Lively music and loud laughter are heard. _____

10. People in costumes take part in the celebration.
People in colorful costumes take part in the grand celebration. _____

Write a Description

Imagine you are at a football game or parade on New Year's Day. On a separate sheet of paper, describe the people, places, and things that you see. Use precise and vivid adjectives in your sentences. **Students' adjectives should tell what kind, which one, or how many. Check that students do not overuse adjectives.**

 Notes for Home: Your child used adjectives—words that describe people, places, and things—to improve sentences. *Home Activity:* Have your child think of an object and offer adjectives to describe it *(cold, white, big)*. See if you can guess the object *(refrigerator)*.

374 Grammar: Using Adjectives to Improve Sentences

Answers **765**

Grammar: Using Adjectives to Improve Sentences

Read the sentence. Write an adjective on each line in the second sentence to make the sentence more vivid. **Possible answers given.**

Children play games on the playground.

___**Many**___ children play ___**fun**___ games on the ___**busy**___ playground.

Adjectives describe persons, places, or things that nouns or pronouns identify. They can tell **what kind, which one,** or **how many.** Adjectives add details to sentences to help readers understand more clearly what the writing is about. Make sure you do not use too many adjectives in your writing.

Directions: Underline each adjective. Circle the noun or pronoun it modifies.

1. You must focus the new (camera) before you take a picture.
2. I'm sorry my little (brother) was rude.
3. After receiving her difficult (orders), the proud (soldier) left.
4. (Ginny) was nasty in her refusal to attend the party.
5. Don't let Luke fool you; he has a soft (heart.)
6. (Linda) is gloomy when it rains.
7. "A good (morning) to you," Miss Sprolls called in a bright (tone.)
8. Here comes another cheerful (person.)
9. (Holly) was thoughtful, and her long (silence) worried her mother.
10. The bright (ribbon) was wrapped around the large (box) and tied in a bow.

Directions: Add an adjective to make each sentence more vivid or precise. Write the adjective on the line to the left. **Possible answers given.**

___**toy**___ 11. My younger brother's _____ truck barreled down the street made of blocks.

___**pretend**___ 12. His _____ people had to be moved out of the way to avoid it.

___**little**___ 13. I asked my _____ brother why the truck was going so fast.

___**plastic**___ 14. He said, "Watch. Do you see this _____ man running down the street?"

___**big**___ 15. "He forgot to turn off the _____ truck when he got out!"

Notes for Home: Your child learned how to use adjectives to improve sentences. *Home Activity:* Say sentences describing your home. Have your child think of adjectives to make the sentences more vivid and interesting. Then have him or her say the sentences with adjectives.

Grammar: Using Adjectives to Improve Sentences

Directions: Think of some adjectives that could describe a favorite gift you've received, and write the name of the gift in the center circle. Then write one adjective in each oval. Picture the gift in your mind to help you think of words that tell how it looks, sounds, smells, feels, or tastes.

Answers will vary. Students should write one adjective in each oval.

Directions: Write three sentences describing the gift. Before you write, think about what quality or characteristic of the gift you want to describe, and decide how you might use adjectives in your sentences.

___**Answers will vary. Make sure students' sentences**___
___**include adjectives from the web above.**___
_____
_____
_____

Notes for Home: Your child wrote adjectives that described a favorite gift and used those adjectives in sentences. *Home Activity:* Together, write a list of at least eight adjectives that describe your child's favorite food.

Word Study: Inflected Endings -er, -est

Directions: The endings **-er** and **-est** are added to words to show comparisons. Read the base words below. Add **-er** and **-est** to each word. Write the new word on the line.

Base Word	Add -er		Add -est	
warm	1.	warmer	2.	warmest
high	3.	higher	4.	highest
short	5.	shorter	6.	shortest
new	7.	newer	8.	newest

Directions: Read each sentence. Circle the word that ends with either **-er** or **-est.** Write the base word on the line.

___quick___ 9. The goal of any race is to be (quicker) than the competition.

___high___ 10. In many sports, the team with the (highest) score wins.

___cool___ 11. In dogsled racing, the person with the (coolest) head often wins.

___cold___ 12. Dogsled races only occur in the north, where the weather is (colder.)

___low___ 13. (Lower) temperatures usually mean good track conditions.

___warm___ 14. (Warmer) temperatures and melting snow can slow down a team.

___slow___ 15. A (slower) pace will lose a race.

___soft___ 16. It is important to stay away from the (softer) patches of snow.

___hard___ 17. Some races may be (harder) to win than others!

___long___ 18. The last night of the race often seems like the (longest.)

___loud___ 19. It's always nice to get the (loudest) cheer at the finish line.

___fast___ 20. It feels great to know you have the (fastest) time among all the people racing.

Notes for Home: Your child identified words with the endings -er and -est. *Home Activity:* Make a list of words that have these endings. Have your child use them to make comparisons about two objects (use -er words) and more than two objects (use -est words).

Spelling: Including All the Letters

Pretest Directions: Fold back the page along the dotted line. On the blanks, write the spelling words as they are dictated. When you have finished the test, unfold the page and check your words.

1. answer
2. minute
3. happened
4. library
5. opened
6. length
7. getting
8. when
9. finished
10. maybe
11. mystery
12. dentist
13. actually
14. width
15. caramel
16. pumpkin
17. quarter
18. sandwich
19. grabbed
20. frightening

1. What is the **answer**?
2. Sixty seconds make a **minute**.
3. Something **happened** today.
4. Let's go to the **library**.
5. The store **opened** last week.
6. What is the **length** of the track?
7. I am **getting** a dog.
8. We leave **when** the bell rings.
9. I have **finished** my work.
10. **Maybe** they will come tomorrow.
11. His mom likes **mystery** novels.
12. It is time to go to the **dentist**.
13. I am not **actually** afraid.
14. The car is five feet in **width**.
15. My sundae has **caramel** topping.
16. Please pass the **pumpkin** pie.
17. I found a **quarter** on the stairs.
18. I ate a roast beef **sandwich**.
19. The monkey **grabbed** the banana.
20. Thunder can be **frightening**.

Notes for Home: Your child took a pretest on words that have difficult letter combinations. *Home Activity:* Help your child learn misspelled words before the final test. Your child can underline the word parts that caused the problems and concentrate on those parts.

Name _____

The Jr. Iditarod Race

Spelling: Including All the Letters

Word List

answer	opened	finished	actually	quarter
minute	length	maybe	width	sandwich
happened	getting	mystery	caramel	grabbed
library	when	dentist	pumpkin	frightening

Directions: Choose the word from the box that is formed by adding an ending to each base word. Write the word on the line.

1. open   **opened**
2. actual   **actually**
3. happen   **happened**
4. frighten   **frightening**
5. get   **getting**
6. grab   **grabbed**
7. finish   **finished**

Directions: Choose the word from the box that best matches each definition. Write the word on the line.

pumpkin	8. It's a fall vegetable.
library	9. It's a home for books.
sandwich	10. It's a popular luncheon food made with bread.
maybe	11. It means the same as "perhaps."
minute	12. It's the same as sixty seconds.
caramel	13. It's a sticky candy you put on apples.
length	14. It's the distance you measure from end to end.
answer	15. It's a reply.
width	16. It's the distance across.
dentist	17. It's a tooth doctor.
mystery	18. It's something that is hard to figure out, like a puzzle.
when	19. It's a word you use to ask about the time something begins.
quarter	20. It's the same as one-fourth.

 Notes for Home: Your child spelled words that have more letters than one might expect. *Home Activity:* Have a spelling bee with your child, taking turns spelling the words from the box. If one of you spells a word incorrectly, the other must try to spell it correctly.

Spelling: Including All the Letters   379

Name _____

The Jr. Iditarod Race

Spelling: Including All the Letters

Directions: Proofread the letter. Find five spelling mistakes. Use the proofreading marks to correct each mistake.

≡ Make a capital.
／ Make a small letter.
∧ Add something.
ℐ Take out something.
⊙ Add a period.
¶ Begin a new paragraph.

Dear Paul,

When I opend your letter, I had just finished feeding our new husky puppy. Then I saw the picture of your new puppy! Isn't it cool? We both have huskies! I got some books out of the library about dogsled racing. It actually sounds like a really fun sport. Maybe some day we'll compete in the Iditarod. Write back and tell me how your dog is getting along.

Love,

Keiko

Spelling Tip
Some words have more letters than you might think. When spelling these words, pronounce each syllable carefully. You'll be less likely to leave out letters.

Word List
answer
minute
happened
library
opened
length
getting
when
finished
maybe
mystery
dentist
actually
width
caramel
pumpkin
quarter
sandwich
grabbed
frightening

Write a Letter
On a separate sheet of paper, write a letter that Paul might send back to Keiko. Try to use at least five of your spelling words.
Answers will vary, but each letter should include at least five spelling words.

 Notes for Home: Your child spelled words that have more letters than one might expect. *Home Activity:* On a piece of paper, write the spelling words with the letters scrambled. Invite your child to unscramble the letters to spell each word.

380   Spelling: Including All the Letters

Name _____

The Jr. Iditarod Race

Spelling: Including All the Letters   REVIEW

Word List

answer	opened	finished	actually	quarter
minute	length	maybe	width	sandwich
happened	getting	mystery	caramel	grabbed
library	when	dentist	pumpkin	frightening

Directions: Write the word from the box that belongs in each group of words.

1. distance, long measure, **length**
2. squash, gourd, **pumpkin**
3. second, hour, **minute**
4. doctor, veterinarian, **dentist**
5. soup, salad, **sandwich**
6. gym, cafeteria, **library**
7. nickel, dime, **quarter**
8. folk tale, science fiction, **mystery**
9. fudge, butterscotch, **caramel**
10. wideness, measure side to side, **width**

Directions: Choose the word from the box that best completes each sentence in the paragraph. Write the word on the matching numbered lines to the right.

My Most Embarrassing Moment
It was my first dogsled race and I was 11. _____ quite nervous. Then, 12. _____ the race began, I 13. _____ the reins and told my dogs to "Mush!" The dogs' 14. _____ was to bark and take off. Then it 15. _____. A bag of supplies somehow 16. _____ and everything spilled out. I pulled hard on the reins, 17. _____ a bit too hard. It was 18. _____ how fast the sled flipped over. As I was 19. _____ up, I saw four other sleds pass us. I knew then I'd be lucky if I 20. _____ the race at all!

11. **actually**
12. **when**
13. **grabbed**
14. **answer**
15. **happened**
16. **opened**
17. **maybe**
18. **frightening**
19. **getting**
20. **finished**

 Notes for Home: Your child spelled words that have more letters than might be expected. *Home Activity:* Challenge your child to pronounce each spelling word carefully and then spell it. Talk about how sounding out each syllable makes it easier to spell these words.

Spelling: Including All the Letters   381

Name _____

The Jr. Iditarod Race

Graphs

Graphs present information visually. **Circle graphs** have a pie shape and show the division of something into parts or percentages. **Bar graphs** use vertical or horizontal bars to show amounts that you can compare easily. **Line graphs** use lines to represent information that shows how something changes over a period of time.

Directions: Use the three graphs to answer the questions on the next page.

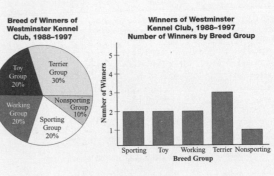

Breed of Winners of Westminster Kennel Club, 1988–1997

Winners of Westminster Kennel Club, 1988–1997 Number of Winners by Breed Group

Number of Cat Shows, January–June 1998

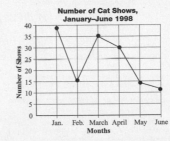

382   Research and Study Skills: Graphs

Answers   **767**

Practice Book 5.4, p. 170

Name _____

1. From 1988 to 1997, what percentage of Westminster Kennel Club winners were dogs in the Terrier Group?
30%

2. From 1988 to 1997, how many Westminster Kennel Club winners were from the Nonsporting Group?
one

3. Which dog breed groups had the same percentage of wins during the 10-year period? How do you know?
Sporting, Working, Toy groups all had 20 percent wins. Possible answer: The labels
show the percents are the same and the size of the wedges are the same.

4. Between which two months was there the greatest change in the number of cat shows? Between which two months was there the smallest change in the number of cat shows?
Greatest: January and February; Least: May and June

5. How many more cat shows were held in March 1998 than in February 1998? _____ **20**

6. Does the bar graph tell you which breed won in 1997? Explain. **No, the bar graph only**
shows the number of winners during 1988–1997.

7. Does the line graph tell you where the cat shows were held? Explain. **No, the line graph**
only shows the number of cat shows each month; it doesn't show where they took
place.

8. If the percentages were not shown on the circle graph, could you still tell which dog breed had the greatest percentage of wins? Explain.
Possible answer: Yes, the largest wedge represents the greatest percentage, so you
could still tell that the Terrier group had the greatest percentage of wins.

9. Suppose you had kept track of how much your dog weighed each month from birth until now. Which type of graph would best show how much your dog had grown? Explain.
Possible answer: A line graph would be the best because it shows how information
changes over a specific time period.

10. Do you find one type of graph easier to read and understand than another? Explain.
Answers will vary. Check that students support their answers with reasonable
explanations.

Notes for Home: Your child analyzed three types of graphs. *Home Activity:* Help your child keep a weather record for one week. Then work together to make a line graph showing high and low temperatures or a bar or circle graph showing the number of cloudy or sunny days.

Research and Study Skills: Graphs **383**

Practice Book 5.4, p. 171

Name _____

Predicting

• To **predict** is to give a statement about what you think might happen next in a story or come next in an article. The statement you give is a **prediction.**

• You make predictions based on what you already know and what has already happened in the story or article.

• After you predict something, continue reading to check your prediction. As you learn new information, you might need to change your prediction.

Directions: Follow the directions for making predictions as you reread "Why Bears Have Short Tails." As you read each section of the story, tell what logical prediction can be made based on what you have read up to that point in the story. Give a reason for each prediction you make. One prediction has been done for you. **Possible answers given.**

Paragraphs 1–5: Predict what will happen after Fox tells Bear how he caught the fish.
Prediction:
Bear will try what Fox told him.
1. Reason:
The story says he ran off toward the river.

Paragraphs 6–9: Predict what will happen after Bear's tail freezes off.
2. Prediction:
Bear will get angry and try to get back at Fox.
3. Reason:
I know that nobody likes to be tricked.

Paragraphs 10–13: Predict what will happen to Fox.
4. Prediction:
Bear will let Fox go.
5. Reason:
Fox says he will give Bear his fish if Bear lets him go.

Notes for Home: Your child read a legend and made predictions about what would happen next. *Home Activity:* Have your child read the first chapter of a book and predict what will happen next. Encourage your child to read the next chapter to see if his or her prediction was accurate.

386 Predicting

Practice Book 5.4, p. 172

Name _____

Vocabulary

Directions: Write the word from the box that belongs in each group.

1. careless, thoughtless, _____ **reckless**
2. bag, purse, _____ **pouch**
3. cabin, resort, _____ **lodge**
4. injured, damaged, _____ **bruised**
5. property, object owned, _____ **possession**

> **Check the Words You Know**
> __ bruised
> __ lodge
> __ possession
> __ pouch
> __ reckless

Directions: Choose the word from the box that best matches each clue. Write the letters of the word on the blanks. The boxed letters spell something that you might wear or carry.

6. thing owned   6. p o s s e s s i o n
7. dwelling   7. l o d g e
8. hurt   8. b r u i s e d
9. careless   9. r e c k l e s s
10. bag or sack   10. p o u c h

Something you might wear or carry: p o u c h

Directions: Choose a word from the box that best completes each sentence. Write the word on the line to the left.

_____ **lodge** 11. When we visited the Rocky Mountains we stayed in a _____.
_____ **pouch** 12. Hanging from the wall was a leather _____.
_____ **reckless** 13. My _____ little brother threw it across the room.
_____ **bruised** 14. It hit me hard and _____ my arm.
_____ **possession** 15. I told him it hurt and that he shouldn't just grab someone else's _____.

Write a Diary Entry
Imagine that you are spending the night alone in the woods. On a separate sheet of paper, write a diary entry that describes your adventure. Tell what you see and hear and how you feel. Use as many vocabulary words as you can.
Students' diary entries should make correct use of vocabulary words.

Notes for Home: Your child identified and used new vocabulary words from "The Night Alone." *Home Activity:* Help your child write a description of what it would be like to live in the woods. Encourage your child to use as many vocabulary words as possible.

Vocabulary **387**

Practice Book 5.4, p. 173

Name _____

Predicting

• To **predict** is to give a statement about what you think might happen next in a story or article, based on what has already happened and what you know.

• The statement you give is a **prediction.**

Directions: Reread what happens in "The Night Alone" when Ohkwa'ri returns from his first night alone in his own lodge. Then answer the questions below.

> As he walked down the rocky trail toward his canoe, which he had drawn up into the alders at the edge of the river, he wondered what food might be ready so early in the morning. His thoughts were divided between his hunger and his memory of Grabber's story. He began to walk faster as he thought of food. He no longer considered the possibility of danger. By the time Ohkwa'ri reached the place where the trail curved around a great stone to cross a rocky ledge, he was no longer watching where he put his feet.
>
> From CHILDREN OF THE LONGHOUSE by Joseph Bruchac. Copyright © 1996 by Joseph Bruchac. Used by permission of Dial Books for Young Readers, a division of Penguin Putnam Inc.

Possible answers given.

1. What clues help you predict what will happen next?
Clues include that he no longer thought about danger and that as he rounded a
curve he no longer watched where he put his feet.

2. What prediction would you make after reading this paragraph?
Ohkwa'ri is going to run into something dangerous, low on the ground near his feet.

3. How can you check your prediction?
You can check your prediction by reading on.

4. In the next paragraph, Ohkwa'ri almost steps on a rattlesnake. How does this event compare to your prediction? Explain.
The prediction was correct in that Ohkwa'ri encountered danger. The specific type
of danger was not predicted.

5. On a separate sheet of paper, describe some of the predictions you made while reading "The Night Alone." Were there any events that surprised you? Did you have to change any of your predictions?
Answers will vary. Check that students' answers demonstrate that they base
predictions on what they have read and that they check and change their
predictions as needed as they continue reading.

Notes for Home: Your child read a paragraph and predicted what would happen next. *Home Activity:* Watch a television show with your child. As you watch, take turns making predictions about what will happen next.

388 Predicting

Scott Foresman 5

Name _____

The Night Alone

Selection Test

Directions: Choose the best answer to each item. Mark the space for the answer you have chosen.

Part 1: Vocabulary
Find the answer choice that means about the same as the underlined word in the sentence.

1. Nick's arms were <u>bruised</u>.
   A. dirty
   Ⓑ hurt
   C. strong
   D. tired

2. You shouldn't be <u>reckless</u>.
   F. filled with fear
   G. selfish
   Ⓗ careless; ignoring danger
   J. lazy

3. The mover picked up each <u>possession</u> and placed it in a box.
   Ⓐ something owned by someone
   B. chair
   C. something that has been damaged
   D. book

4. That is a model of an Indian <u>lodge</u>.
   Ⓕ home
   G. weapon
   H. farming tool
   J. toy

5. Put the coins in that <u>pouch</u>.
   A. box
   Ⓑ bag
   C. drawer
   D. hole

Part 2: Comprehension
Use what you know about the story to answer each question.

6. What does Ohkwa'ri reach for twice during the night?
   F. a snack
   G. his mother's hand
   Ⓗ a special stone
   J. a deerskin robe

7. Ohkwa'ri wakes up many times during the night because—
   A. he is cold.
   B. he is hungry.
   C. bears are near his lodge.
   Ⓓ his lodge is too quiet.

8. Ohkwa'ri seems to feel that the moon and the sun are like—
   Ⓕ members of his family that keep him company.
   G. giant stars that care nothing for him.
   H. animals about to attack him.
   J. mighty gods who will protect him.

9. During his first night and morning alone, Ohkwa'ri thinks mostly about—
   A. the dangers he faces.
   B. the future.
   Ⓒ his family.
   D. his own achievements.

GO ON →

Name _____

The Night Alone

10. According to this selection, the people of Ohkwa'ri's tribe used which of the following to teach lessons to young people?
    F. hunting maps
    G. diagrams
    H. scientific experiments
    Ⓙ spoken stories

11. The author most likely included the story of "Grabber" to—
    Ⓐ make the reader laugh.
    B. scare the reader.
    C. make the reader sad.
    D. teach the reader about bears.

12. When the story says that Ohkwa'ri was "no longer watching where he put his feet," a reader is most likely to predict that he will—
    F. die in the wilderness.
    G. kill a bear for food.
    Ⓗ soon run into danger.
    J. return to his little lodge instead of to his family.

13. The stories of Grabber and the two young men of the Turtle Clan suggest that—
    A. most young men in Ohkwa'ri's tribe are as wise as adults.
    B. wild animals are not very intelligent.
    C. it is the men, not the women, who rule Ohkwa'ri's tribe.
    Ⓓ young men sometimes do foolish things.

14. How does Ohkwa'ri's experience with the rattlesnake show that he is gaining in good judgment?
    F. He jumps when he hears the snake rattle.
    Ⓖ He decides to be more careful in the future.
    H. He realizes that he has bruised his shoulder.
    J. He realizes that he has missed breakfast back at the lodge.

15. You can tell from this story that the "Little People" probably are—
    A. Ohkwa'ri's brothers and sisters.
    Ⓑ spirits of the forest.
    C. members of the Turtle Clan.
    D. wild birds and animals.

STOP

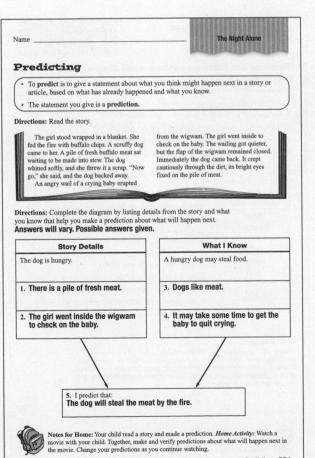

Name _____

The Night Alone

Predicting

- To **predict** is to give a statement about what you think might happen next in a story or article, based on what has already happened and what you know.
- The statement you give is a **prediction**.

Directions: Read the story.

> The girl stood wrapped in a blanket. She fed the fire with buffalo chips. A scruffy dog came to her. A pile of fresh buffalo meat sat waiting to be made into stew. The dog whined softly, and she threw it a scrap. "Now go," she said, and the dog backed away.
> An angry wail of a crying baby erupted from the wigwam. The girl went inside to check on the baby. The wailing got quieter, but the flap of the wigwam remained closed. Immediately the dog came back. It crept cautiously through the dirt, its bright eyes fixed on the pile of meat.

Directions: Complete the diagram by listing details from the story and what you know that help you make a prediction about what will happen next.
Answers will vary. Possible answers given.

Story Details	What I Know
The dog is hungry.	A hungry dog may steal food.
1. There is a pile of fresh meat.	3. Dogs like meat.
2. The girl went inside the wigwam to check on the baby.	4. It may take some time to get the baby to quit crying.

5. I predict that:
The dog will steal the meat by the fire.

Notes for Home: Your child read a story and made a prediction. **Home Activity:** Watch a movie with your child. Together, make and verify predictions about what will happen next in the movie. Change your predictions as you continue watching.

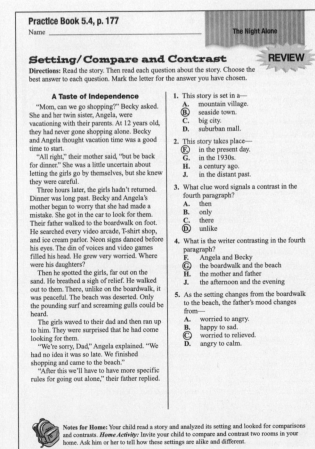

Name _____

The Night Alone

Setting/Compare and Contrast

REVIEW

Directions: Read the story. Then read each question about the story. Choose the best answer to each question. Mark the letter for the answer you have chosen.

A Taste of Independence

"Mom, can we go shopping?" Becky asked. She and her twin sister, Angela, were vacationing with their parents. At 12 years old, they had never gone shopping alone. Becky and Angela thought vacation time was a good time to start.

"All right," their mother said, "but be back for dinner." She was a little uncertain about letting the girls go by themselves, but she knew they were careful.

Three hours later, the girls hadn't returned. Dinner was long past. Becky and Angela's mother began to worry that she had made a mistake. She got in the car to look for them. Their father walked to the boardwalk on foot. He searched every video arcade, T-shirt shop, and ice cream parlor. Neon signs danced before his eyes. The din of voices and video games filled his head. He grew very worried. Where were his daughters?

Then he spotted the girls, far out on the sand. He breathed a sigh of relief. He walked out to them. There, unlike on the boardwalk, it was peaceful. The beach was deserted. Only the pounding surf and screaming gulls could be heard.

The girls waved to their dad and then ran up to him. They were surprised that he had come looking for them.

"We're sorry, Dad," Angela explained. "We had no idea it was so late. We finished shopping and came to the beach."

"After this we'll have to have more specific rules for going out alone," their father replied.

1. This story is set in a—
   A. mountain village.
   Ⓑ seaside town.
   C. big city.
   D. suburban mall.

2. This story takes place—
   Ⓕ in the present day.
   G. in the 1930s.
   H. a century ago.
   J. in the distant past.

3. What clue word signals a contrast in the fourth paragraph?
   A. then
   B. only
   C. there
   Ⓓ unlike

4. What is the writer contrasting in the fourth paragraph?
   F. Angela and Becky
   Ⓖ the boardwalk and the beach
   H. the mother and father
   J. the afternoon and the evening

5. As the setting changes from the boardwalk to the beach, the father's mood changes from—
   A. worried to angry.
   B. happy to sad.
   Ⓒ worried to relieved.
   D. angry to calm.

Notes for Home: Your child read a story and analyzed its setting and looked for comparisons and contrasts. **Home Activity:** Invite your child to compare and contrast two rooms in your home. Ask him or her to tell how these settings are alike and different.

© Scott Foresman 5

Answers 769

The Night Alone

Writing Across Texts

Directions: The story and illustrations in "The Night Alone" give details about many traditions of the Mohawk Indians. The selection "How the Sun Came" is a mythical explanation about how other traditions began. Complete the table by listing some of the traditions you read about. **Possible answers given.**

Mohawk Indian Traditions
Mohawk Indians respect all things in nature, such as the moon.
1. People only marry outside of their own clan.
2. Children belong to their mother's clan.
3. Husbands move in with the wife's clan after they get married.
4. Uncles help raise their nieces and nephews.
5. People adopt orphan forest animals and let the animals live in the lodges.
6. Many Mohawk families live together in a longhouse.
7. When they eat, Mohawk Indians leave bits of food to share with the Little People.
8. The moon is called "Grandmother" and is thanked for always being there.
9. The sun is called Elder Brother.
10. People explain events in nature with mythical stories.

Write a Caption

Look back at "The Night Alone" and "How the Sun Came." Think about the ways in which these stories connect to the theme "Traditions." Brainstorm a list of traditions that you read about in these stories. Then choose one tradition, illustrate it, and write a caption to go with it. Draw your illustration and write your caption on a separate sheet of paper. **Captions will vary. Check that students based their captions and illustrations on traditions from the two selections.**

 Notes for Home: Your child listed traditions based on a fiction story and a myth, illustrated a tradition, and wrote a caption to explain it. *Home Activity:* Talk with your child about traditions that are part of your culture. If you can, tell your child how each tradition began.

Writing Across Texts **393**

The Night Alone

Grammar: Using Adjectives to Improve Sentences

REVIEW

Directions: Add one or more adjectives to improve each sentence. Write your new sentence on the line. **Possible answers given.**

1. Leroy is standing in a line with skiers.
Leroy is standing in a long line with many other skiers.

2. He takes the ski lift to the top of a trail.
He takes the ski lift to the top of a challenging trail.

3. At the top, the skier looks at the view.
At the top, the young skier looks at the thrilling view.

4. He loves to see the snow on the mountains.
He loves to see the sparkling snow on the mountains.

5. He takes a breath of air.
He takes a deep breath of fresh, crisp air.

Directions: Take out any unneeded adjectives in each sentence below. Write your new sentence on the line. **Possible answers given.**

6. The high, steep slope is covered with fast, whooshing, graceful skiers.
The steep slope is covered with fast, graceful skiers.

7. This is the first and only time Leroy has stood at this scary and challenging spot alone.
This is the first time Leroy has stood at this challenging spot alone.

8. His father, a good, experienced, and careful skier, has always been with him before.
His father, an experienced skier, has always been with him before.

9. Leroy has worked for this big, special moment, but he feels scared, nervous, and shaky.
Leroy has worked for this special moment, but he feels scared and shaky.

10. Is he ready and able to ski down this steep, windy, difficult trail by himself?
Is he ready to ski down this difficult trail by himself?

 Notes for Home: Your child rewrote sentences, adding and taking away adjectives to make the sentences clearer. *Home Activity:* Ask your child to write a short description of a place he or she likes. Then help your child to add, take away, or change some of the adjectives.

394 Grammar: Using Adjectives to Improve Sentences

The Night Alone

Grammar: Comparative and Superlative Adjectives

Adjectives change form when they are used to make comparisons. Add the ending **-er** to the adjective when you are comparing two items. Add the ending **-est** to the adjective when you are comparing more than two items.

Joe is <u>tall</u>. Ed is <u>taller</u> than Joe. Al is <u>tallest</u> of all.

Sometimes you need to make spelling changes before adding **-er** or **-est**.

Dad felt <u>hungry</u>. Jay felt <u>hungrier</u>. I felt the <u>hungriest</u> of all.
Mia looks <u>slim</u>. Carol looks <u>slimmer</u>. Della looks the <u>slimmest</u> of all.

Longer adjectives use the words **more** or **most** to make comparisons. **More** is used to compare two things. **Most** is used to compare more than two. Do not use **more** or **most** with **-er** or **-est** endings.

Sue is <u>more</u> concerned than Bob. Kay is <u>most</u> concerned of all.

The adjectives **good** and **bad** have special comparative (two) and superlative (more than two) forms.

Walking is <u>good</u>. Skating is <u>better</u>. Swimming is <u>best</u> of all.
A cold is <u>bad</u>. The flu is <u>worse</u>. Pneumonia is <u>worst</u> of all.

Directions: Circle the correct adjective in ( ) to complete each sentence.

1. A cabin is (smaller/smallest) than a house.
2. A palace is the (larger/largest) home I have seen.
3. Many hotels are (bigger/biggest) than motels.
4. A tent is (better/best) than the cold, hard ground.
5. The purple and green house is the (worse/worst) looking house on the block.

Directions: Choose the correct form of the adjective in ( ) to complete each sentence. Write the adjective on the line.

oldest	6. A tepee is one of the (old) kinds of homes.
older	7. A cave may be (old) than a tepee.
best	8. Which is the (good) home of all?
better	9. Nothing is (good) than a snug log cabin!
worse	10. Is a leaky tent (bad) than no tent at all?

 Notes for Home: Your child used comparative and superlative adjectives to compare people and things. *Home Activity:* Ask your child to describe people, places, or things in your neighborhood, using adjectives that compare.

Grammar: Comparative and Superlative Adjectives **395**

The Night Alone

Grammar: Comparative and Superlative Adjectives

Directions: Circle the correct adjective in ( ) to complete each sentence.

1. Kim has the (most interesting/more interesting) type of home I have ever visited.
2. Her houseboat is much (neater/neatest) than any house on land.
3. Her view is the (more beautiful/most beautiful) I've ever seen.
4. A ride on a houseboat is not the (worse/worst) way to spend an afternoon.
5. In fact, it's the (nicer/nicest) ride I can imagine!

Directions: Use the correct form of the adjective in ( ) to complete each sentence. Write the adjective on the line.

best	6. What is the (good) home of all?
most pleasant	7. Is a cute little cottage by the sea the (pleasant)?
larger	8. A cottage is (large) than a boat.
better	9. Some people feel that a boat is still (good) than a house ashore.
darker	10. Kim's room is (dark) than mine.
warmer	11. My room is much (warm) than hers.
drier	12. When it rains, my room stays (dry) than hers.
nicer	13. Kim thinks water is (nice) to live on than land!
freshest	14. She says sea air is the (fresh) you will find.
coolest	15. We both agree that her houseboat is the (cool) place we know!

Write a Description

Imagine that you could design your own "dream house." On a separate sheet of paper, describe what your home would look like. Use adjectives that compare. **Students might compare features of their dream houses to features of other, more traditional, homes. Check to make sure that they use the correct forms of adjectives.**

 Notes for Home: Your child used special forms of adjectives to compare people and things. *Home Activity:* Choose two members of your family. Ask your child to talk about how the two people are different from each other. Have your child use adjectives that compare.

396 Grammar: Comparative and Superlative Adjectives

© Scott Foresman 5

Grammar: Comparative and Superlative Adjectives

Victor Mickey Lou

Underline the adjective in each sentence.

1. Mickey is <u>small</u>.

2. Lou is <u>smaller</u> than Mickey.

3. <u>Smallest</u> of all is Victor.

Did you notice that the adjective **smaller** compared two things? Did you notice that the adjective **smallest** compared three things?

Use the **-er** form of an adjective to compare two persons, places, or things. Use the **-est** form of an adjective to compare three or more persons, places, or things. The spelling of some adjectives changes before **-er** or **-est** is added.

Directions: Complete each sentence by writing the correct form of the adjective in ( ).

1. My dog is __friendlier__ than your dog. (friendlier/friendliest)

2. That is the __funniest__ joke in the world. (funnier/funniest)

3. Kansas is __flatter__ than Arizona. (flatter/flattest)

4. Jetliners are __bigger__ than helicopters. (bigger/biggest)

5. Whales are the __heaviest__ animals on earth. (heavier/heaviest)

6. Mercury is the __hottest__ planet. (hotter/hottest)

Directions: Write the correct form of the adjective in ( ).

7. Truth is sometimes _____ than fiction. (strange) — **stranger**

8. A hurricane is _____ than a blizzard. (rare) — **rarer**

9. June was the _____ month of the year. (hot) — **hottest**

10. Mount Everest is the _____ mountain in the world. (tall) — **tallest**

11. China is a _____ country than India. (large) — **larger**

12. Mars is the _____ of all the other planets. (near) — **nearest**

 Notes for Home: Your child used adjectives that compare, such as *bigger* and *tallest*. **Home Activity:** Have your child compare fifth grade to first grade by writing sentences, using adjectives that compare.

Grammar: Comparative and Superlative Adjectives **397**

Grammar: Comparative and Superlative Adjectives

Directions: Write the missing forms for each adjective below.

	Adjective	Comparing Two	Comparing Three or More
1.	fresh	fresher	freshest
2.	dry	drier	driest
3.	wonderful	more wonderful	most wonderful
4.	fat	fatter	fattest
5.	terrible	more terrible	most terrible
6.	slim	slimmer	slimmest
7.	nice	nicer	nicest
8.	bold	bolder	boldest
9.	intelligent	more intelligent	most intelligent
10.	low	lower	lowest
11.	trustworthy	more trustworthy	most trustworthy
12.	careful	more careful	most careful

Directions: Use the word in ( ) to write an adjective with **-er** or **-est** that completes each comparison.

13. In many places our air is __cleaner__ today than it was in the 1950s. (clean)

14. Is air __warmer__ in cities than it is on farms? (warm)

15. Power plants use the __largest__ air filters of all. (large)

16. The monorail is a __newer__ form of transportation than the train. (new)

17. Are today's laws to control air pollution the __strictest__ laws of all? (strict)

18. Which country produces the __highest__ level of air pollution? (high)

Write a Speech

On a separate sheet of paper, write a short speech about why it is important to keep our air and water clean. Use the **-er** and **-est** forms of adjectives in your sentences.

Check to make sure students have spelled adjectives correctly in their speeches.

 Notes for Home: Your child used the -er and -est forms of adjectives. **Home Activity:** With your child, take turns saying sentences with the -er and -est forms of adjectives. (For example: *A car is faster than a bicycle. An airplane is the fastest.*)

398 Grammar: Comparative and Superlative Adjectives

Word Study: Inflected Endings

When adding **-ed, -er,** or **-est** to words that end in a **consonant** and **y,** change the **y** to **i,** and then add **-ed.** For example, **fry** becomes **fried.**

When adding **-ed, -ing, -er,** or **-est** to words that end in a single consonant preceded by a single vowel, double the consonant and add the ending. For example, **hop** becomes **hopping. Thin** becomes **thinner.**

Directions: Add an ending to each word below. Write the new word on the line.

1. drop + -ing = **dropping**
2. grab + -ing = **grabbing**
3. flat + -er = **flatter**
4. big + -est = **biggest**
5. cry + -ed = **cried**
6. pat + -ed = **patted**

Directions: Read the journal entry. Circle each word that ends in **-ed, -ing, -er,** or **-est.** Then write the base word for each circled word on the line.

Day 1

It is my first night alone in the woods. I'm (worried.) I (tried) to sleep, but I heard the (strangest) noises. I (zipped) and (snapped) all the tent flaps shut and (buried) my head in my pillow. But I'm still awake. I couldn't imagine a (scarier) place! I ran through the woods most of the day, only (stopping) twice to take a drink from my canteen. I'll be much (happier) when daylight comes.

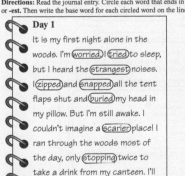

7. **worry**
8. **try**
9. **strange**
10. **zip**
11. **snap**
12. **bury**
13. **scary**
14. **stop**
15. **happy**

 Notes for Home: Your child practiced changing *y* to *i* and doubling the final consonant when adding *-ed* and *-ing.* **Home Activity:** Read a short story with your child and find words with these endings. He or she can write the words with and without the endings.

Word Study: Inflected Endings **399**

Spelling: Adding -ed and -ing, -er and -est

Pretest Directions: Fold back the page along the dotted line. On the blanks, write the spelling words as they are dictated. When you have finished the test, unfold the page and check your words.

1. **followed** — 1. We **followed** the rules.
2. **following** — 2. The chicks are **following** the hen.
3. **lighter** — 3. This bag is **lighter** than the other.
4. **lightest** — 4. You can carry the **lightest** box.
5. **tried** — 5. He **tried** to remain quiet.
6. **trying** — 6. I am **trying** to remember her.
7. **cuter** — 7. Which of the two cats is **cuter**?
8. **cutest** — 8. My neighbor had the **cutest** baby.
9. **excited** — 9. The children were very **excited**.
10. **exciting** — 10. Fireworks can be **exciting**.
11. **amused** — 11. The teacher was **amused**.
12. **amusing** — 12. The joke was very **amusing**.
13. **bigger** — 13. Melons are **bigger** than oranges.
14. **biggest** — 14. Sequoias are the **biggest** trees.
15. **wrapped** — 15. Are the presents all **wrapped**?
16. **wrapping** — 16. We need more **wrapping** paper.
17. **earlier** — 17. We should have left **earlier**.
18. **earliest** — 18. I need to catch the **earliest** flight.
19. **easier** — 19. Is math **easier** than science?
20. **easiest** — 20. Do not give me the **easiest** job.

 Notes for Home: Your child took a pretest on adding *-ed, -ing, -er,* and *-est* to words. **Home Activity:** Help your child learn misspelled words before the final test. Dictate the word and have your child spell the word aloud for you or write it on paper.

400 Spelling: Adding *-ed* and *-ing, -er* and *-est*

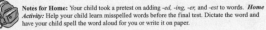

Name _____

The Night Alone

Spelling: Adding -ed and -ing, -er and -est

Word List				
followed	tried	excited	bigger	earlier
following	trying	exciting	biggest	earliest
lighter	cuter	amused	wrapped	easier
lightest	cutest	amusing	wrapping	easiest

Directions: Choose the word from the box that is formed by adding **-er** or **-est** to each base word. Write the word on the correct line.

Base Word	Add -er		Add -est	
big	1.	bigger	2.	biggest
cute	3.	cuter	4.	cutest
early	5.	earlier	6.	earliest
light	7.	lighter	8.	lightest
easy	9.	easier	10.	easiest

Directions: Add **-ed** or **-ing** to the word in ( ) to form a word from the box and to complete each sentence. Write the word on the line.

excited	11. Sarah is not very (excite) about tonight's sleepover.
tried	12. She (try) spending the night at a friend's once before.
exciting	13. She started out thinking it was (excite) to be there.
trying	14. An hour after the lights went out, Sarah was still (try) to sleep.
amused	15. She (amuse) herself by counting the teddy bears on the wallpaper.
following	16. She started (follow) the teddy bears in her imagination.
wrapped	17. She (wrap) herself tightly in her sleeping bag.
followed	18. She (follow) her mother's advice to think sleepy thoughts.
wrapping	19. Then she found herself (wrap) her arms around a big teddy bear.
amusing	20. Suddenly she woke up and knew she'd have an (amuse) story to tell about not sleeping!

 Notes for Home: Your child spelled words that have *-ed, -ing, -er,* or *-est* endings. **Home Activity:** Think of base words that are regular verbs *(jump, play)* or adjectives *(soft, tall)*. Have your child add *-ed* or *-ing* to the verbs and *-er* or *-est* to the adjectives to spell new words.

Spelling: Adding *-ed* and *-ing*, *-er* and *-est* **401**

Name _____

The Night Alone

Spelling: Adding -ed and -ing, -er and -est

Directions: Proofread the letter. Find seven spelling mistakes. Use the proofreading marks to correct each mistake.

≡	Make a capital.
/	Make a small letter.
∧	Add something.
⌿	Take out something.
⊙	Add a period.
¶	Begin a new paragraph.

Dear Lucy,

Yesterday I took my first airplane ride by myself. It was really exiting. I tryed to act very grown-up. Next to me was a lady with the cutest baby boy. The baby was all wraped up. I got to hold him. He felt lighter than a feather! Then he threw up on me. I pretended to be amuzed, but really it was gross. Folowing dinner was a movie. We arrived in Chicago half an hour earlier than expected. Flying is easyer than I thought!

Your friend,

Karen

Spelling Tip

Words that end in -y
If a base word ends in a **consonant** and y, change the y to i before adding **-ed, -er,** or **-est.** Keep the y when adding **-ing.** For example: **try, tried, trying.**

Write a Letter

On a separate sheet of paper, write a letter Lucy might write back to Karen telling how she achieved something all by herself. Try to use at least six of your spelling words.
Answers will vary, but each letter should contain at least six spelling words.

Word List	
followed	amused
following	amusing
lighter	bigger
lightest	biggest
tried	wrapped
trying	wrapping
cuter	earlier
cutest	earliest
excited	easier
exciting	easiest

 Notes for Home: Your child spelled words that end in *-ed, -ing, -er,* or *-est.* **Home Activity:** Look at video boxes, mail, or magazines to find words with these endings. Help figure out whether the spelling of the base word was changed before the ending was added.

402 Spelling: Adding *-ed* and *-ing*, *-er* and *-est*

Name _____

The Night Alone

Spelling: Adding -ed and -ing, -er and -est

REVIEW

Word List				
followed	tried	excited	bigger	earlier
following	trying	exciting	biggest	earliest
lighter	cuter	amused	wrapped	easier
lightest	cutest	amusing	wrapping	easiest

Directions: Choose the word from the box that is most opposite in meaning for each word below. Write the word on the line.

1. uglier	cuter		6. bored	excited	
2. later	earlier		7. led	followed	
3. smaller	bigger		8. harder	easier	
4. heavier	lighter		9. leading	following	
5. smallest	biggest		10. hardest	easiest	

Directions: Choose the word from the box that best completes each person's statement. Write the word on the line to the left.

wrapped	11. Fast Food Worker: "Our food comes hot, _____ in foil, and ready to go."
amusing	12. Comedian: "Most people find me _____."
cutest	13. Child Actor: "Everyone says I have the _____ baby face."
exciting	14. News Photographer: "My work often takes me to _____ places."
trying	15. Athlete: "I keep _____ to break records in my sport."
wrapping	16. Store Clerk: "I'm always _____ presents for people."
earliest	17. School Bus Driver: "I have to be the _____ person awake at my house."
lightest	18. Jockey: "The _____ jockey on the fastest horse usually wins the race."
tried	19. Politician: "I _____ my best to get elected."
amused	20. Clown: "Are you _____ by my funny costume?"

 Notes for Home: Your child spelled words that end in *-ed, -ing, -er,* or *-est.* **Home Activity:** Ask your child to explain why the base words of some spelling words were changed before an ending was added, such as *cute/cutest, big/bigger,* and *try/tried.*

Spelling: Adding *-ed* and *-ing*, *-er* and *-est* **403**

Name _____

The Night Alone

Technology: Encyclopedia

Encyclopedias can be purchased on CD-ROMs or found on the Internet. The computer lets you search the entire encyclopedia for your topic using letters or a few key words. The welcome screen for an online encyclopedia might look like this:

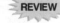

Welcome to the Encyclopedia

Choose a letter to browse the encyclopedia.
Or, type the key words to search.
A B C D E F G H I J K L M N O P Q R S T U V W X Y Z

Search the Encyclopedia for:
_____

Search for:
☐ Articles and Tables
☐ Pictures, Flags, Maps, Charts, Sounds
☐ Websites
☐ All of the Above

If you wanted an article about Native Americans, you could either type key words: Native AND Americans, or you could click on the letter *N.* Clicking on a letter will give you a list of articles about topics that begin with that letter.

nasturtium
Natchez
national parks
Native Americans
navigation
navy
Nebraska
Neptune
Try another letter:
A B C D E F G H I J K L M N O P Q R S T U V W X Y Z
Search the Encyclopedia for:
_____

404 Research and Study Skills: Technology: Encyclopedia

When you find an article about your topic, it will probably have links to other articles. The links will most likely be set in capital letters and underlined. Clicking on an underlined phrase will show you the other related articles.

Native American Art

The traditional arts of the indigenous native peoples of North America (see <u>NORTH AMERICA, INDIGENOUS PEOPLES OF</u>) were an important part of the everyday lives of Native Americans. Different arts were practiced in different regions. The cultures of the Eastern woodlands (see <u>IROQUOIS</u>) made pottery, baskets, beadwork, and <u>MASKS</u>. The Plains tribes (see <u>SIOUX</u>) used beads and quills to decorate hides. On the Northwest coast, native peoples used wood carving to make houses, large <u>CANOES</u>, and <u>TOTEM</u> poles. The <u>NAVAHO</u> of the Southwest had sophisticated techniques for making silver jewelry.

Directions: Use the sample computer screens to answer these questions.

1. What are two different ways to find an article about Native Americans using an online encyclopedia?
Type the key words Native AND Americans or click on N.

2. In the second computer screen, what will you get if you click on *Nebraska?*
You will get an encyclopedia article about the state of Nebraska.

3. In the first and second computer screens, what will you get if you click on the letter *B?*
You will get a list of articles about topics that start with the letter B.

4. In the third computer screen, which link would you choose to see a related article about Native Americans who lived in the Eastern woodlands?
IROQUOIS

5. Which links would you choose to find articles about the arts and crafts of the Northwest coast peoples?
CANOES and TOTEM

 Notes for Home: Your child learned how to use an online encyclopedia. *Home Activity:* Ask your child to list possible key words to use to search for articles about native peoples in Alaska.

Research and Study Skills: Technology: Encyclopedia **405**

Context Clues

- **Context clues** are words that can help you figure out a word that is unfamiliar to you.
- Look for specific clues by asking yourself questions like: "Does the sentence give a definition of the word or explain anything about it?"

Directions: Reread "Physical Fitness." Then complete the table. Use context clues to figure out the meaning of each word or phrase in the table. **Possible answers given.**

Word or Phrase	Meaning
skills fitness	1. the ability to perform well in activities that require special skills
agility	2. the ability to change body positions quickly and to control body movements
balance	3. the ability to keep upright while standing still or moving
coordination	4. the ability to use the senses with body parts and to use two or more body parts together
reaction time	5. the amount of time it takes to start moving once a signal is heard

 Notes for Home: Your child read an article and used context clues to figure out the meanings of unfamiliar words. *Home Activity:* Read a newspaper article with your child. Help your child use context clues to figure out the meanings of any unfamiliar words.

408 Context Clues

Vocabulary

Directions: Choose the word from the box that best matches each definition. Write the word on the line.

ankle	1. joint that connects foot with leg
confident	2. self-assured
overcame	3. conquered an obstacle
responsible	4. having the duty to take care of someone or something
sprint	5. run a short way at top speed

Check the Words You Know
__ ankle
__ athlete
__ confident
__ overcame
__ relay
__ responsible
__ sprint

Directions: Choose the word from the box that best matches each clue. Write the word on the line.

overcame	6. It's a compound word and you'll feel good if you've done it.
athlete	7. It's what you call a person who is good at sports.
responsible	8. It's the kind of person you would want to have baby-sit your little brother.
confident	9. It's how you feel when you know you can do something well.
sprint	10. It's something you can do for a short while, but not for too long.

Directions: Read the news story. Choose the word from the box that best completes each sentence. Write the word on the matching numbered line to the right.

RUNNER SWEEPS STATE MEET
The city has never seen a **11.** _____ like Aysha Morgan. At Thursday's track competition, this young unknown rose to stardom. Despite a sore **12.** _____, she was able to **13.** _____ the 100-meter event in record time. She also **14.** _____ an early setback to win the quarter mile. Later, she led her team to victory by running the fastest leg in the 400-meter **15.** _____. Sports fans, this is a young woman to watch. Congratulations, Aysha!

11. **athlete**
12. **ankle**
13. **sprint**
14. **overcame**
15. **relay**

Write a Description
Whom do you respect? On a separate sheet of paper, describe a person whom you respect and tell why you respect him or her. Use as many vocabulary words as you can in your description. **Students' descriptions should make correct use of vocabulary words.**

 Notes for Home: Your child identified and used vocabulary words from "The Heart of a Runner." *Home Activity:* With your child, write a story about an athlete your child admires. Encourage your child to use as many of the vocabulary words as possible.

Vocabulary **409**

Context Clues

- **Context clues** are words that can help you figure out a word that is unfamiliar to you.
- Look for specific types of clues as you read. Context clues include synonyms, antonyms, definitions and explanations, examples, and descriptions.

Directions: Reread what happens in "The Heart of a Runner" when E.R. writes about the relay race. Then answer the questions below.

I have to tell you what an anchor is. An anchor is the final leg of a relay, the fastest runner. The anchor has to overcome any slowness of the other three runners and power on to the end. The lead runner, or lead-off, is the first leg of a relay team. The runner has to be superfast, and confident, too.

The runners in a relay depend on one another to be fast and not make mistakes. Like dropping one of the batons. I'm not mentioning any names, but you know who I mean!

Excerpt from RUNNING GIRL: THE DIARY OF EBONEE ROSE, copyright © 1997 by Sharon Bell Mathis, reprinted by permission of Harcourt Brace & Company.

Possible answers given.

1. What is an *anchor?*
An anchor is the final leg of a relay, the fastest runner.

2. What kind of context clue helped you define *anchor?*
The sentence in the story gave a definition.

3. Give the meaning of *leg* in the first paragraph and tell what clues you used to figure it out.
A leg is used to mean one runner of a relay team, or one part of the relay race. Clues include the adjectives *final* and *first*.

4. Define *lead-off* and tell what type of context clue you used to define it.
The lead-off is the lead runner. The sentence uses *lead-off* as a synonym for lead runner.

5. Go back to the story and find the terms *baton-passing* and *field event*. Use context clues to figure out their meanings. On a separate sheet of paper, write the meanings and tell what clues you used. Then use a dictionary to see if your definitions were correct.
Baton-passing is the passing of the baton from one runner to the next. Clues include "like dropping one of the batons" and "she passes it perfectly." *Field event* means an event held on the field, as opposed to the track. Clues: E.R.'s dislike of the long jump as opposed to sprinting, and the sentence "This is a track-and-field meet, remember?"

 Notes for Home: Your child read a story and used context clues to define unfamiliar words. *Home Activity:* Read a challenging book with your child. Work together to use context clues to define words that are unfamiliar to your child.

410 Context Clues

© Scott Foresman 5

Name _____

The Heart of a Runner

Selection Test

Directions: *Choose the best answer to each item. Mark the letter for the answer you have chosen.*

Part 1: Vocabulary

Find the answer choice that means about the same as the underlined word in each sentence.

1. I hurt my <u>ankle</u>.
   A. bone in the knee
   B. part of the leg between the knee and hip
   C. bottom of the foot
   (D) joint that connects the foot and leg

2. The other team looked <u>confident</u>.
   F. unfriendly
   G. full of energy
   H. large
   (J) sure of themselves

3. Meghan is <u>responsible</u> for the picnic.
   A. signed up to attend
   (B) having the duty to do something
   C. trying to stop
   D. curious about the reason for something

4. We watched Jeremy <u>sprint</u> down the sidewalk.
   F. ride
   G. walk slowly
   (H) run at top speed
   J. hop

5. Alisha <u>overcame</u> her fears.
   A. talked about for a long time
   B. asked help for
   (C) got the better of; defeated
   D. was ashamed of

6. The first event in the meet is a <u>relay</u>.
   F. long jump
   (G) race in which each member of a team runs or swims for one part
   H. race in which a runner must leap over a series of gates
   J. event that involves throwing an object

7. My sister is a fine <u>athlete</u>.
   (A) person who is skilled in physical games
   B. person who attends school
   C. person who makes crafts
   D. person who organizes others to get things done

Part 2: Comprehension

Use what you know about the story to answer each item.

8. Ebonee Rose was upset when she twisted her ankle because she—
   F. knew her mother would be angry.
   G. would be kicked off the team for the year.
   (H) did not want to miss the All-City meet.
   J. was afraid to go to the hospital.

9. Which track star raced jackrabbits in the Mojave Desert as a child and won four medals in the 1988 Olympics?
   A. Evelyn Ashford
   B. Robin Campbell
   (C) Florence Griffith Joyner
   D. Wyomia Tyus

Name _____

The Heart of a Runner

10. The story says, "Our fans in the <u>bleachers</u> are going crazy." <u>Bleachers</u> are—
    F. long race tracks.
    (G) benches for people to sit on.
    H. school buses.
    J. large crowds of people.

11. In this story, Ebonee Rose seems to think of "Dee" as—
    A. an opponent.
    B. a pacer.
    C. her mother.
    (D) a friend.

12. The story says, "The name MAIN TRACK CLUB will be <u>inscribed</u> on the brass plate beneath the golden track shoe." <u>Inscribed</u> means—
    F. remembered.
    (G) written on stone or metal.
    H. borrowed.
    J. carried by the winners.

13. How do E.R.'s parents feel before the All-City Meet?
    (A) nervous but proud
    B. worried but calm
    C. bored and impatient
    D. happy and relaxed

14. The author most likely included information about African American track stars in this story to—
    (F) show how heroes and heroines inspire young people.
    G. make readers think that Ebonee Rose is a real person.
    H. prove that Ebonee Rose is the greatest runner ever.
    J. show that good athletes can also be good writers.

15. The author probably focuses more on E.R.'s experience in the relay instead of the long jump to show the importance of—
    A. kindness.
    (B) teamwork.
    C. independence.
    D. trying new sports.

STOP

Name _____

The Heart of a Runner

Context Clues

- **Context clues** are words that can help you figure out a word that is unfamiliar to you.
- Look for specific types of clues as you read. Context clues include synonyms, antonyms, definitions and explanations, examples, and descriptions.

Directions: Read the story below.

Dear Diary,
Today's the big day! My whole stomach feels like it's filled with butterflies! My coach says not to be <u>apprehensive</u>, but I can't help it. We're swimming against some really tough <u>opponents</u>. I hope the water isn't <u>frigid</u> the way it was last time. I don't swim as well in really cold water. We always get together before a meet, so we're going to <u>assemble</u> today at noon to go over strategy. If I <u>prevail</u> in my event, I'll go on to the finals. If I don't, I'll practice harder and try again next year. I hope I win!

Directions: Complete the table. Write a definition for each underlined word. Show how you arrived at the definition by filling in context clues from the story.

Unfamiliar Word	Definition	Context Clue
apprehensive	1. nervous	2. "stomach feels like it's filled with butterflies"
opponents	3. people you compete against	4. "swimming against some really tough opponents"
frigid	5. very cold	6. hopes it isn't frigid; doesn't do well in really cold water
assemble	7. get together	8. "We always get together...."
prevail	9. win	10. "If I prevail ..., I'll go to the finals...."

 Notes for Home: Your child read a story and used context clues to define unfamiliar words. *Home Activity:* Read a newspaper article with your child and work together to use context clues to define new words. Check your definitions in a dictionary.

Name _____

The Heart of a Runner

Author's Viewpoint

REVIEW

Directions: Read the passage. Then read each question about the passage. Choose the best answer to each question. Mark the letter for the answer you have chosen.

Run for Your Life

Couch potatoes of the world, listen carefully. There's a very good chance that you are ruining your health sitting right there on the couch. Throw down those television remote controls and lace up your sneakers! It's time to get moving!

As a whole, American children and young people are not getting nearly enough exercise. For American adults, the situation is even worse. Many Americans do not exercise on a regular basis. (Getting up to go to the refrigerator for a soda doesn't count!)

An inactive lifestyle is dangerous at any age. It puts a person at higher risk for serious health problems. Heart disease, diabetes, and other serious diseases become more likely for people who are not active.

How can you get on the road to good health? Start by getting some regular exercise. You might choose running, jogging, walking, bicycling, gardening, or aerobics. They are all good ways to get "heart smart"! You might actually find out that you enjoy getting healthier by exercising.

1. The first paragraph suggests the author will try to—
   A. describe.
   B. explain.
   C. tell a story.
   (D) persuade.

2. Which of the following words reveals how the author feels about the subject of this article?
   (F) couch potatoes
   G. remote controls
   H. children
   J. young people

3. The author's opening implies that—
   A. people should never watch television.
   B. people who watch television are more relaxed.
   (C) people who watch too much television don't exercise enough.
   D. couch potatoes have diabetes.

4. In this article the author—
   F. criticizes all Americans.
   (G) links exercise and health.
   H. describes aerobic exercises that are dangerous.
   J. recommends consulting a doctor as soon as possible.

5. The author is strongly—
   (A) in favor of regular exercise.
   B. in favor of lace-up sneakers.
   C. in favor of an inactive lifestyle.
   D. against exercise.

 Notes for Home: Your child read a passage and identified the author's viewpoint. *Home Activity:* Read an editorial or a letter to the editor with your child. Together, identify the author's viewpoint and look at how well the author's opinions are supported.

© Scott Foresman 5

Writing Across Texts

Directions: Think about Ebonee Rose from "The Heart of a Runner" and Carlie Huberman from "Finding a Way to Win." Both girls compete in sports they love. How do their sports compare? Fill in the chart below to compare and contrast the two sports.

	Track and Field	Orienteering
Skills Needed	1. **ability to run fast, determination, commitment**	2. **a good sense of direction, ability to read maps and a compass**
Tools Used	3. **track shoes, possibly a uniform**	4. **a compass and a map**
Steps Involved in a Race	5. **warm up your muscles, get on the blocks, wait for the signal to start, then run as fast as you can**	6. **bring a compass to the race, pick up a map, orient the map, then start running down the trail**
Possible Obstacles to Overcome	7. **injuries, teammates who drop the baton**	8. **bad weather, getting lost**
The Goal	9. **to win the race**	10. **to win the race**

Write a Compare and Contrast Paragraph

Use the information in the chart above to write a paragraph comparing and contrasting the sports of track and field and orienteering. Tell the one in which you would rather participate. Write your paragraph on a separate sheet of paper.
Paragraphs will vary. Check that students used details from the chart in their comparisons.

 Notes for Home: Your child compared and contrasted the information from two selections. *Home Activity:* As you read stories or articles with your child, discuss how the ideas are presented and how they compare with information obtained from other sources.

Grammar: Comparative and Superlative Adjectives

REVIEW

Directions: Complete the table below, using -er, -est, more, or most.

Adjective	Comparative Adjectives	Superlative Adjectives
friendly	1. **friendlier**	2. **friendliest**
safe	3. **safer**	4. **safest**
difficult	5. **more difficult**	6. **most difficult**
thin	7. **thinner**	8. **thinnest**
fresh	9. **fresher**	10. **freshest**

Directions: Use the correct form of the adjective in ( ) to complete each sentence. Write the comparative or superlative adjective on the line.

fastest 11. In 1960, Wilma Rudolph became the (fast) woman in the world.

more popular 12. No athlete in the 1960 Olympics was (popular) than this young runner.

oldest 13. Track, or foot racing, is the (old) Olympic sport.

easier 14. Most people have had (easy) lives than Wilma Rudolph.

skinniest 15. She was a sickly and poor child, perhaps the (skinny) child in Clarksville, Tennessee.

bigger 16. However, as she grew (big), she showed a great talent for running.

more experienced 17. At 16, she competed in the 1956 Olympics against (experienced) runners.

later 18. In a (late) Olympic competition, in 1960, she became a gold-medal champion.

most famous 19. After winning three gold medals, she was the (famous) Olympic star in the world.

most thrilling 20. One of her (thrilling) rewards was being invited to the White House to meet President John F. Kennedy.

 Notes for Home: Your child used special forms of adjectives to compare two or more people, places, and things. *Home Activity:* Challenge your child to find comparative and superlative adjectives in a book or magazine and explain why each form is used.

Grammar: Adverbs

Adverbs tell more about verbs. An adverb tells when, where, or how an action happens. Many adverbs that tell how end in **-ly**.

The runners ran <u>quickly</u>. (how)
The time <u>soon</u> passed. (when)
The race ended <u>there</u>. (where)

Like adjectives, adverbs change form when they are used to make comparisons.

Add **-er** to an adverb when the actions of two people are being compared. This is called the **comparative form** of the adverb.

Comparative: I found a good viewing spot <u>sooner</u> than one of my cousins did.

Add **-est** when the actions of three or more people are being compared. This is called the **superlative form** of the adverb.

Superlative: Which group in that crowd had waited there <u>longest</u>?

Use **more** or **most**, instead of **-er** or **-est**, with most adverbs that end in **-ly**. Don't use **more** or **most** with **-er** and **-est** endings.

Comparative: Tyrone ran more wearily than Reggie.

Superlative: Roger ran the most wearily as the four men crossed the finish line.

Directions: Underline the adverb or adverbs in each sentence.

1. Dave runs in the New York City Marathon <u>yearly</u>.
2. Runners wait <u>anxiously</u> on the Verrazano Narrows Bridge.
3. A starter's gun <u>loudly</u> sounds at the start of the race.
4. Runners move <u>hard</u> and <u>fast</u> along the road.
5. They race <u>steadily</u> for 26.2 miles.

Directions: Choose the correct form of the adverb in ( ) to complete each sentence. Write the adverb on the line.

most excitedly 6. Runners' relatives cheer (more excitedly/most excitedly) of all the onlookers.

faster 7. At the start, the inexperienced runners sometimes go (faster/fastest) than the experienced ones do.

more cheerfully 8. Some runners wave (more cheerfully/most cheerfully) than others to spectators along the way.

most successfully 9. Of all Dave's family members, his little niece took photos of the race (more successfully/most successfully).

more triumphantly 10. At the finish line, no runner grins (more triumphantly/most triumphantly) than Dave.

 Notes for Home: Your child identified adverbs—words that tell when, where, or how an action happens. *Home Activity:* Watch a show on television together. Ask your child to use adverbs to describe the action that he or she sees.

Grammar: Adverbs

Directions: Underline the adverb in each sentence. Write whether it tells **how**, **when**, or **where** on the line.

when 1. Many people jog <u>daily</u>.

how 2. They move <u>slowly</u> along a path.

how 3. They <u>hardly</u> notice the passing time.

where 4. Look at the joggers <u>there</u>.

when 5. They started jogging <u>early</u> this morning.

Directions: Write an adverb on the line to the left to complete each sentence. **Possible answers given.**

regularly 6. Joggers run _____ on the track.

gently 7. Their feet _____ hit the dirt.

often 8. Some joggers _____ wear headsets.

quietly 9. Music plays _____ in their ears.

pleasantly 10. The time passes _____ on the track.

Directions: Add -er, -est, more, or most to the adverb in ( ) to complete each sentence. Write the comparative or superlative form of the adverb on the line to the left.

longer 11. Certain older joggers exercise _____ than younger ones do. (long)

more quickly 12. Young joggers with high energy levels may run _____ than other joggers. (quickly)

fastest 13. College students with eight o'clock classes hurry away _____ of all. (fast)

more closely 14. Now that I'm learning to run, I watch all these joggers _____ than ever before. (closely)

more smoothly 15. Someday I hope to run _____ than I do now. (smoothly)

Write Instructions

Imagine that you are a gym teacher giving instructions on how to exercise. On a separate sheet of paper, write the instructions. Use at least four adverbs in your instructions.
Students' adverbs should tell how, when, or where an action happens.

Notes for Home: Your child identified adverbs, words that describe verbs. *Home Activity:* Look at sentences in a book or newspaper with your child. Ask him or her to point out the adverbs. Discuss whether an adverb tells how, when, or where an action happens.

Grammar: Adverbs

Directions: Read each pair of sentences. Circle the adverb that was added to the second sentence in each pair.

1. The reporter told us about a circus.

   The reporter (excitedly) told us about a circus.

2. The children waited.

   The children waited (more patiently) than their parents.

A word that tells more about a verb is an **adverb**. Each adverb modifies a verb by telling **how, when,** or **where.** Many adverbs end in **-ly.** Adverbs have forms that are used to compare actions. Use the **-er** and **-est** forms, or **more** and **most,** to compare actions. The adverbs **well** and **badly** have special forms that show comparison.

Directions: Each verb is underlined. Write the adverb that tells about the verb.

1. The lion roared fiercely.   **fiercely**
2. The circus vans arrived yesterday.   **yesterday**
3. The first jumper leaped higher than that one.   **higher**
4. The activity stopped suddenly.   **suddenly**
5. Maria started more quickly than Harry.   **more quickly**
6. Kim runs more gracefully than Kelly.   **more gracefully**
7. Workers ran rapidly toward the tent.   **rapidly**

Directions: Write an adverb from the box to complete each sentence. The word in ( ) is a clue to the adverb.

| often | carefully | most vigorously | more slowly | inside |

8. Jim exercises the **most vigorously** of all my friends. (How?)
9. Violet runs **more slowly** than Jim. (How?)
10. The lions snarled, growled, and roared **often** . (When?)
11. The lion tamer **carefully** moved among the six lions. (How?)

 Notes for Home: Your child identified and wrote adverbs in sentences. *Home Activity:* Talk with your child about a book he or she is reading. Discuss characters' choices and behaviors. Challenge your child to describe characters' actions in detail, using adverbs.

Grammar: Adverbs **419**

Grammar: Adverbs

Directions: Circle the adverb that tells more about the underlined verb.

1. The large white and orange kite flew (gracefully)
2. The wind blew (harder) than yesterday.
3. The family members (carefully) constructed the kite.
4. Kite builders (often) enter various contests.
5. Many curious and enthusiastic spectators come (here.)
6. Children watched the kites (most excitedly) of all.
7. The strong wind (soon) became a gentle breeze.

Directions: Rewrite each sentence below. Use the correct form of the word in ( ) to complete each sentence.

8. Most flowers grow (well) of all in full sun.
   Most flowers grow best of all in full sun.

9. Our new kite with the long tail flew (beautiful) through the sky.
   Our new kite with the long tail flew beautifully through the sky.

10. Two large kites crashed (wild) in this pond.
    Two large kites crashed wildly in this pond.

11. The wind damaged my flowers (bad) than the rain did.
    The wind damaged my flowers worse than the rain did.

Write Song Lyrics

Think about what it might feel like to be a kite flying through the air on a warm, breezy day. Write song lyrics from the point of view of a kite. Include at least four adverbs in your lyrics.

Students' lyrics should be written from the point of view of a kite and should include at least four adverbs.

 Notes for Home: Your child identified and wrote adverbs in sentences. *Home Activity:* Have your child create a comic strip to illustrate something he or she has seen or done today. Challenge him or her to use adverbs in captions in the comic strip.

420 Grammar: Adverbs

Phonics: Schwa Sound (Within Word)

Directions: The **schwa sound** is an indistinct vowel sound heard in unstressed syllables. For example, the **a** in **ago**, the **o** in **complete**, and the **e** in **agent** are all schwa sounds. Read each sentence. Say each underlined word aloud. Write each underlined word on the line and circle the syllable that has the **schwa sound.**

com(pete)	1. In most cultures, people compete in races.
to(day's)	2. For today's race, there are more runners than usual.
ex(er)cise	3. Before the race, runners stretch and exercise their legs.
stom(ach)	4. They know that it isn't wise to run on a full stomach.
ner(vous)	5. Many runners feel nervous before a big race.
hand(ker)chief	6. One athlete wiped her face with her lucky handkerchief.
vic(to)ry	7. She was hoping for a big victory.
o(ver)come	8. However, in order to win, she must overcome her fears.
dif(fi)cult	9. She knows she has a difficult race ahead of her.
iden(ti)fy	10. Many people identify with the runner's fears.

Directions: Each word below has two schwa sounds. Circle the schwa sounds in each word.

11. diff(e)r(e)nt
12. tol(e)r(a)nce
13. conf(i)d(e)nt
14. t(o)g(e)ther
15. respons(i)b(i)lity
16. emi(gr)(a)nt
17. ge(l)(a)tin
18. imi(t)(a)tion
19. lit(e)r(a)lly
20. ni(t)r(o)gen
21. orch(e)st(r)a
22. pass(a)b(l)e
23. pres(i)d(e)nt
24. consid(e)r
25. sing(u)l(a)r

 Notes for Home: Your child identified the schwa sound. *Home Activity:* Read an article with your child. Ask your child to write down words that might have the schwa sound. Check the words in a dictionary. The symbol for the schwa sound looks like an upside down *e*.

Phonics: Schwa Sound (Within Word) **421**

Spelling: Vowels with No Sound Clues

Pretest Directions: Fold back the page along the dotted line. On the blanks, write the spelling words as they are dictated. When you have finished the test, unfold the page and check your words.

1. **manager** — 1. The store's **manager** helped us.
2. **president** — 2. We will elect a class **president**.
3. **different** — 3. There is a **different** way.
4. **terrible** — 4. What a **terrible** storm!
5. **finally** — 5. I **finally** finished the book.
6. **really** — 6. This is **really** the place.
7. **supposed** — 7. Are you **supposed** to do that?
8. **probably** — 8. There will **probably** be more.
9. **California** — 9. **California** is a populous state.
10. **especially** — 10. She **especially** likes pears.
11. **balance** — 11. Don't lose your **balance**.
12. **constant** — 12. There was a **constant** noise.
13. **innocent** — 13. She proved herself **innocent**.
14. **realize** — 14. I did not **realize** it was so far.
15. **opportunity** — 15. This is a wonderful **opportunity**.
16. **pollute** — 16. Cars **pollute** the air.
17. **prisoner** — 17. The **prisoner** was in jail.
18. **celebrate** — 18. We will **celebrate** your birthday.
19. **grocery** — 19. We buy milk at the **grocery** store.
20. **elevator** — 20. The **elevator** does not work.

 Notes for Home: Your child took a pretest on words whose vowel sounds have no sound clues. *Home Activity:* Help your child learn misspelled words before the final test. Have your child divide misspelled words into parts (such as syllables) and concentrate on each part.

422 Spelling: Vowels with No Sound Clues

Spelling: Vowels with No Sound Clues

Word List

manager	finally	California	innocent	prisoner
president	really	especially	realize	celebrate
different	supposed	balance	opportunity	grocery
terrible	probably	constant	pollute	elevator

Directions: Choose the three-syllable words from the box. Write the words in in alphabetical order. Draw lines between syllables.

1. _____ cel/e/brate _____
2. _____ dif/fer/ent _____
3. _____ fi/nal/ly _____
4. _____ gro/cer/y _____
5. _____ in/no/cent _____
6. _____ man/ag/er _____
7. _____ pres/i/dent _____
8. _____ pris/on/er _____
9. _____ prob/a/bly _____
10. _____ re/al/ize _____
11. _____ re/al/ly _____
12. _____ ter/ri/ble _____

Directions: Choose the word from the box that best matches each clue. Write the word on the line.

_____ elevator _____ 13. You ride one of these to get to the top of a building.

_____ pollute _____ 14. You do this if you throw a piece of trash in the river.

_____ opportunity _____ 15. This means almost the same as "chance."

_____ constant _____ 16. This is something that stays the same without changing.

_____ balance _____ 17. A gymnast needs to have this if she doesn't want to fall.

_____ California _____ 18. This is a large state along the western coast of the United States.

_____ supposed _____ 19. This means almost the same as "expected" or "required."

_____ especially _____ 20. You might use this word instead of *very* to show that something is special.

Notes for Home: Your child spelled words with unstressed vowel sounds that give no clue to their spelling, such as *grocery*. **Home Activity:** On a sheet of paper, write the consonants of each spelling word and leave blanks for the vowels. Challenge your child to fill in the vowels.

Spelling: Vowels with No Sound Clues **423**

Spelling: Vowels with No Sound Clues

Directions: Prootread the student announcement. Find six misspelled words. Use the proofreading marks to correct each mistake.

≡ Make a capital.
╱ Make a small letter.
∧ Add something.
ᵧ Take out something.
⊙ Add a period.
¶ Begin a new paragraph.

Roosevelt High School will celebrat its new playing field with a special Track and Field Day on October 24. Students will have the oportunety to compete in many diferent events. Prizes will be given and refreshments served. It should be a really fun day. Rain date: October 25. (But only if the weather is especially terible.) Come and realize your potential on Track and Field Day!

Spelling Tip

Spelling schwa
Sometimes knowing a base word can help you remember how to spell the schwa sound, the unstressed vowel sound that gives no clue to its spelling. Example: Something that **differs** is **different**.

Word List

manager	really	balance	pollute
president	supposed	constant	prisoner
different	probably	innocent	celebrate
terrible	California	realize	grocery
finally	especially	opportunity	elevator

Write an Announcement

On a separate sheet of paper, write an announcement for a real or imaginary event. Try to use at least five of your spelling words. **Answers will vary, but each announcement should contain at least five spelling words.**

Notes for Home: Your child spelled words with unstressed vowel sounds that give no clue to their spelling, such as *grocery*. **Home Activity:** Write each spelling word in a list, misspelling several words. Have your child check and correct the list.

424 Spelling: Vowels with No Sound Clues

Spelling: Vowels with No Sound Clues

REVIEW

Word List

manager	finally	California	innocent	prisoner
president	really	especially	realize	celebrate
different	supposed	balance	opportunity	grocery
terrible	probably	constant	pollute	elevator

Directions: Choose the word from the box that best completes each statement. Write the word on the line to the left.

_____ California _____ 1. *City* is to *Los Angeles* as *state* is to _____.

_____ innocent _____ 2. *Hot* is to *cold* as *guilty* is to _____.

_____ president _____ 3. *Castle* is to *king* as *White House* is to _____.

_____ grocery _____ 4. *Automobile* is to *car* as *market* is to _____.

_____ different _____ 5. *Big* is to *little* as *same* is to _____.

_____ prisoner _____ 6. *Cage* is to *bird* as *jail* is to _____.

_____ manager _____ 7. *Child* is to *parent* as *worker* is to _____.

_____ celebrate _____ 8. *Sad* is to *mourn* as *happy* is to _____.

_____ pollute _____ 9. *Build* is to *destroy* as *clean* is to _____.

_____ terrible _____ 10. *Sure* is to *certain* as *awful* is to _____.

_____ balance _____ 11. *Unequal* is to *equal* as *imbalance* is to _____.

_____ finally _____ 12. *Usual* is to *usually* as *final* is to _____.

Directions: Choose the word from the box that best replaces the underlined word or words. Write the word on the line.

_____ supposed _____ 13. You are <u>required</u> to run every day when in training.

_____ constant _____ 14. If the weather is <u>always the same</u>, you can run outdoors daily.

_____ opportunity _____ 15. Dedicated runners take every <u>good chance</u> to run.

_____ elevator _____ 16. Skip riding the <u>mechanical car that lifts</u> and take the stairs.

_____ realize _____ 17. People don't <u>understand</u> how important proper nutrition is.

_____ really _____ 18. Eating right is <u>actually</u> just as important as working out.

_____ especially _____ 19. It is <u>particularly</u> important to avoid foods that are high in fat.

_____ probably _____ 20. If you eat right and train hard, you will <u>most likely</u> succeed.

Notes for Home: Your child spelled words with unstressed vowel sounds that give no clue to their spelling, such as *grocery*. **Home Activity:** Write each word on an index card. Draw a card, read it aloud, and have your child spell it. Switch roles and repeat.

Spelling: Vowels with No Sound Clues **425**

Organize and Present Information/Draw Conclusions

As you read, take notes about important information. You can use your notes to help you **organize information** for a report and to help you **present information** to others. You can also use your notes to help you **draw conclusions** about the information by telling what it means.

Directions: Suppose you were planning a research report. Use the notes shown to answer the questions on the next page.

Track and field events involve running, walking, jumping, and throwing.

Some athletes are good at other events but not at the track and field events. Other athletes excel in track and field as well as other sports.

Older outdoor tracks are dirt or cinders. Newer ones use a waterproof synthetic surface. Indoor tracks are a wooden or synthetic surface with banked turns.

Track and field events of the summer Olympic Games include: Men's—runs of 100, 200, 400, 800, 1500, 5000, and 10,000 meters; hurdles of 100 and 400 meters; relays of 400 and 1600 meters; 3000-meter steeplechase; walks of 20 and 50 meters; marathon; high, long, and triple jump; discus, hammer, and javelin throw; pole vault; 16-pound shot put; and decathlon. Women's—runs of 100, 200, 400, 800, 1500, 3000, 5000, and 10,000 meters; hurdles of 100 and 400 meters; relays of 400 and 1600 meters; 10-kilometer walk; marathon; high, long, and triple jump; discus and javelin throw; 8-pound, 13-ounce shot put; and heptathlon.

The Olympic records for men's track and field go back to 1896. The women's records are from 1928.

The first Olympic games in Greece took place in 776 B.C. The only event was a foot race—the first competitive track and field event.

426 Research and Study Skills: Organize and Present Information/Draw Conclusions

---

Practice Book 5.4, p. 190

Name _____

The first U.S. woman to win an Olympic track and field event was Elizabeth Robinson in 1928 (the first year of the records). In 1896, the first year of the men's records, there were six Olympic winners in track and field from the United States—Thomas Burke, Thomas Curtis, Ellery Clark, James Connolly, Robert Garrett, and William Hoyt.

In the decathlon, heptathlon, and pentathlon, the athletes compete in several different events over a period of time.

Jackie Joyner-Kersee holds the heptathlon record with 7,215 points, set in 1988.

Possible answers given.

1. The title of your report will give the main idea. What title will you give your report?

Olympic Runners and Jumpers

2. The information in the notes came from several different sources, but the notetaker made the mistake of not listing the sources. What reference sources could you use to verify the information in the notes and add to it?

encyclopedia, almanac, biographies of track and field athletes

3. If you wanted to present the information about the different Olympic track and field events for men and women, how might you organize this information so it is easier for readers to understand and compare?

You could create a table showing men's events in one column and women's events in another column. You could also use subheads to group types of events such as running, jumping, or throwing.

4. Think of things that might make your report interesting to hear and see, such as videotapes, audiotapes, graphic organizers, drawings, or posters. What might you use in your report?

The report might include a videotape of Olympic athletes in action, a chart of winners over the years, and posters.

5. Why will taking good notes as you read help you organize and present information and then draw conclusions about it? Will you use every note you wrote in your report? Explain.

The better notes you take as you read, the easier it will be to organize and present the information later and explain what it means. You probably won't use every note you take, but you can decide which notes are the most important and useful.

 Notes for Home: Your child described how information might be organized and presented for a report. **Home Activity:** Together with your child, make a poster using information from the notes shown.

Research and Study Skills: Organize and Present Information/Draw Conclusions **427**

Practice Book 5.4, p. 191

Name _____

Author's Purpose

- An **author's purpose** is the reason or reasons an author has for writing.
- Authors don't usually state a purpose so it helps to remember that the four common purposes for writing are to persuade, inform, entertain, and express.

Directions: Reread "Your Life Remembered." Then complete the web. Write the author's purpose or purposes in the middle. In the outer ovals, write words or phrases from the article that helped you identify the purpose or purposes.
Possible answers given.

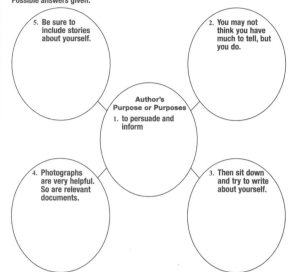

5. Be sure to include stories about yourself.

2. You may not think you have much to tell, but you do.

Author's Purpose or Purposes
1. to persuade and inform

4. Photographs are very helpful. So are relevant documents.

3. Then sit down and try to write about yourself.

 Notes for Home: Your child read an article and identified the author's purpose. **Home Activity:** Look through a magazine with your child. Invite your child to identify the author's purpose for various kinds of writing, such as editorials, poems, profiles, how-to articles, ads, or cartoons.

430 Author's Purpose

Practice Book 5.4, p. 192

Name _____

Vocabulary

Directions: Choose the word from the box that best completes each statement. Write the word on the line to the left.

Check the Words You Know
__ recall
__ reel
__ sheath
__ souvenirs
__ squished
__ traditions

_____squished_____ **1.** *Inflated* is to *blew up* as *flattened* is to _____.

_____souvenirs_____ **2.** *Journals* are to *diaries* as *keepsakes* are to _____.

_____recall_____ **3.** *Think* is to *act* as *forget* is to _____.

_____sheath_____ **4.** *Hand* is to *glove* as *knife* is to _____.

_____reel_____ **5.** *Throw* is to *catch* as *cast* is to _____.

Directions: Choose the word from the box that best matches each clue. Write the word in the puzzle.

Down
6. to draw in by winding
7. keepsakes
8. case or covering for a knife

Across
9. remember
10. beliefs and customs handed down from parents to children

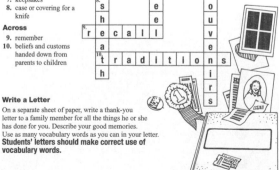

Write a Letter
On a separate sheet of paper, write a thank-you letter to a family member for all the things he or she has done for you. Describe your good memories. Use as many vocabulary words as you can in your letter.
Students' letters should make correct use of vocabulary words.

 Notes for Home: Your child identified and used vocabulary words in *The Memory Box*. **Home Activity:** Invite your child to draw a picture for at least three vocabulary words. Work together to write sentences under the pictures that use the vocabulary words.

Vocabulary **431**

Practice Book 5.4, p. 193

Name _____

Author's Purpose

- An **author's purpose** is the reason or reasons an author has for writing. Sometimes an author has more than one reason for writing.
- Four common purposes for writing are to persuade (convince), to inform (explain something), to entertain (amuse), or to express (describe something to help you see or feel a scene).

Directions: Reread what happens in *The Memory Box* after Zach's first dinner with Gramps and Gram. Then answer the questions below.

After dinner, we dragged our fish-full bellies to the porch to watch the sun slip into the lake. Crickets fiddled and owls hoo-ooted, but the rest of the world was quiet. All except Gram and Gramps and me in our rickety rockers on the wooden porch.

"Hmm-mmmm-m." Gramps was settling in, getting ready for another true tale. He's a great storyteller. I know, because she always puts down her cross-stitch when he begins.

THE MEMORY BOX by Mary Bahr. Text copyright © 1992 by Mary Bahr. Excerpt reprinted by permission of Albert Whitman & Company.

Possible answers given.

1. What is happening in this scene?
Zach, Gram, and Gramps are sitting on the porch, talking.

2. How do you think Zach feels when he and Gram and Gramps are on the porch?
relaxed, peaceful, warm

3. What are some of the unusual words and phrases the author uses in writing this part of the story?
fish-full bellies, hoo-ooted, Hmm-mmmm-m

4. What do you think is the author's purpose for writing this scene? Explain what makes you think so.
The author's purpose is to express. The passage uses vivid description to help you experience the characters' relaxed, peaceful feeling.

5. On a separate sheet of paper, tell what you think is the author's reason (or reasons) for writing *The Memory Box*. Support your answer with examples from the story.
She is writing mainly to express the love and caring between generations but also to inform people about Alzheimer's disease. Possible example: "'Your Mom's going to hurt,' Gramps said. 'When it gets bad, bring out our Memory Box. Show her what I remember.'"

 Notes for Home: Your child read a story and identified the author's purpose for writing. **Home Activity:** Discuss each of the four common purposes for writing described above. Name a favorite book, story, or article that is an example of each purpose.

432 Author's Purpose

© Scott Foresman 5

Name _____

The Memory Box

Selection Test

Directions: Choose the best answer to each item. Mark the letter for the answer you have chosen.

Part 1: Vocabulary

Find the answer choice that means about the same as the underlined word in each sentence.

1. Mariah put her <u>souvenirs</u> in a box.
   - A. rings meant to be worn
   - B. food for a light meal
   - Ⓒ things that bring back memories
   - D. important papers

2. I <u>recall</u> a trip to Niagara Falls.
   - Ⓕ remember
   - G. plan
   - H. photograph
   - J. describe

3. What <u>traditions</u> does your family have?
   - A. pets
   - B. silly names
   - C. valuable objects kept for a long time
   - Ⓓ beliefs and customs handed down through time

4. The baby happily <u>squished</u> the chocolate pudding.
   - Ⓕ pressed something soft and wet
   - G. licked something cold
   - H. pointed at something far away
   - J. grabbed something hard

5. It was difficult to <u>reel</u> in the kite.
   - Ⓐ draw in by winding
   - B. pack up
   - C. sew together
   - D. put in a certain order

6. Put it in the <u>sheath</u>.
   - F. drawer
   - Ⓖ case or covering
   - H. envelope
   - J. trash bag or can

Part 2: Comprehension

Use what you know about the story to answer each item.

7. What do Zach and Gramps do the first day of Zach's visit?
   - A. take a hike
   - Ⓑ go fishing
   - C. build a box
   - D. cook a meal together

8. From whose point of view is this story told?
   - Ⓕ Zach's
   - G. Gramps's
   - H. Gram's
   - J. Francie's

9. How does Zach react when Gramps says, "No matter what happens to the old person, the memories are saved forever"?
   - A. He is happy to know he will always have memories of Gramps.
   - B. He is bored that he will have to listen to more old stories.
   - C. He realizes that Gramps has Alzheimer's.
   - Ⓓ He is confused and worried that something is wrong.

GO ON

Selection Test **433**

Name _____

The Memory Box

10. Which of these events happens first?
    - F. Gramps gets lost.
    - G. Zach sees Gramps talking to someone who is not there.
    - Ⓗ Zach wonders why Gramps has not shaved.
    - J. Gramps gives Zach the special knife.

11. Why does Gramps think that Zach's mom is "going to hurt"?
    - A. Zach will not spend any more summers with Gram and Gramps.
    - B. She will not like how Zach has changed.
    - C. Zach has decided to live with Gram and Gramps instead of with his mom.
    - Ⓓ She will feel sad to see Gramps when his memory is gone.

12. The author's main purpose in this story is to—
    - F. entertain the reader with funny tales about a forgetful man.
    - G. persuade kids to spend summers with their grandparents.
    - Ⓗ express what it feels like for a family to deal with Alzheimer's.
    - J. inform people about the causes of memory loss.

13. When Zach finally gets the knife he wanted, he realizes that—
    - Ⓐ other things are more important than having a knife.
    - B. he would rather have a newer and more valuable knife.
    - C. he will have to return the knife to Gram.
    - D. he will never go fishing again.

14. A "memory-box day" is best described as something that—
    - F. happens when a person is alone.
    - Ⓖ two people want to remember sharing with each other.
    - H. happens when a man or woman gets very old.
    - J. causes worry for everyone in a family.

15. What does the ending of this story suggest about Zach's view of life?
    - Ⓐ He accepts things as they are.
    - B. He does not take responsibility for himself.
    - C. He always sees the worst in everything.
    - D. He is too hopeful most of the time.

STOP

434 Selection Test

Name _____

The Memory Box

Author's Purpose

- An **author's purpose** is the reason or reasons an author has for writing. Sometimes an author has more than one reason for writing.
- Four common purposes for writing are to persuade (convince), to inform (explain something), to entertain (amuse), or to express (describe something to help you see or feel a scene.)

Directions: Read each passage below.

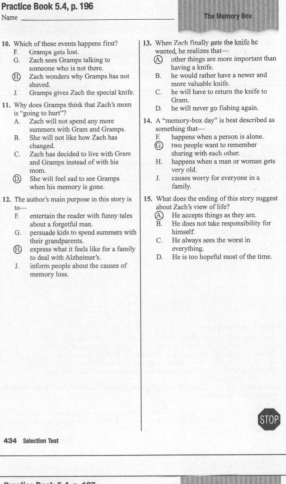

1. I remember staying in the water until my teeth chattered. Then my aunt would wrap me in a sun-warmed towel and give me an ice pop. I loved its cold, sweet taste on my tongue.

2. Finding a cure for Alzheimer's disease is the most important task facing modern medicine. The Alzheimer's Research Fund supports this great work. We need your generous contribution.

3. Memory is the storing of learned information and the ability to recall that

which has been stored information. There are two kinds of memory: short-term memory and long-term memory.

4. I remember everything that's ever happened to me, every single thing. Did I ever tell you about the time I, uh... I, uh... uh ... Wait a minute. Hold on. It'll come to me.

5. The word *memoir* is French for "memory." In literature, a memoir may take many forms. It can be a biography, an autobiography, or an account of important events.

Directions: Complete each box. Write whether the purpose of each passage is to persuade, inform, entertain, or express. Give an explanation for each answer.

Passage 1	Passage 2	Passage 3
Author's Purpose: **express**	Author's Purpose: **persuade**	Author's Purpose: **inform**
Explanation: **Author uses "sun-warmed," "cold," "sweet" to help readers see and feel the scene.**	Explanation: **Author uses "most important task," "great work," to try to convince readers to contribute.**	Explanation: **Author explains the meaning of memory and the two kinds of memory.**

Passage 4	Passage 5
Author's Purpose: **entertain**	Author's Purpose: **inform**
Explanation: **Author brags about a good memory, but then forgets the example.**	Explanation: **Author defines "memoir" and gives examples of literature related to memories.**

Notes for Home: Your child read several passages and identified the author's purpose for writing each one. *Home Activity:* With your child, skim newspaper articles, editorials, and comics and identify the author's purpose or purposes for writing each one.

Author's Purpose **435**

Name _____

The Memory Box

REVIEW

Plot and Theme

Directions: Read the story. Then read each question about the story. Choose the best answer to each question. Mark the letter for the answer you have chosen.

The Scrapbook

When Aunt Rose got sick and went to the hospital, Misha and his little sister Emily were both very upset. She was their favorite aunt. She often brought them books and entertained them with stories about when she was young.

Misha decided to make a scrapbook for Aunt Rose. Emily felt jealous of his idea. It seemed to her that Misha always thought of everything first and could do it better. She wanted to do something too, but her ideas didn't seem as interesting as Misha's. Misha offered to let her help, but she refused.

For the next few days, Misha worked on Aunt Rose's scrapbook. He wrote a poem, and he drew pictures. He chose favorite family snapshots. He put everything into the scrapbook. He decorated the pages with some of his favorite stickers.

Emily, meanwhile, spent a lot of time sulking. Whenever Misha tried to talk to her, she turned on her heel and walked away.

On the day they had planned to visit Aunt Rose, Misha stormed into the kitchen.

"Where's my scrapbook?" he said accusingly to Emily. She burst into tears.

"I took it," she sobbed. "I want it to be from me too."

Misha put his arm around Emily and hugged her. Emily said she was sorry. Misha told Emily to hurry and get ready to go so they could give Aunt Rose their scrapbook together.

1. What is the conflict, or problem, in this story?
   - A. Aunt Rose is in the hospital.
   - B. Misha and Emily are upset.
   - Ⓒ Emily is jealous of Misha.
   - D. Misha has to make a scrapbook.

2. The rising action of the story, where the action builds, is in—
   - F. the first two paragraphs.
   - Ⓖ the third and fourth paragraphs.
   - H. the fifth and sixth paragraphs.
   - J. the seventh and eighth paragraphs.

3. The climax, or the high point, of the story comes when—
   - Ⓐ Misha confronts Emily and she cries.
   - B. Emily turns on her heel and walks away.
   - C. Misha finishes the scrapbook.
   - D. Misha hugs Emily.

4. How is the conflict, or problem, resolved?
   - F. Emily has a good cry.
   - G. Misha finishes the scrapbook.
   - H. Misha apologizes to Emily.
   - Ⓙ Emily apologizes to Misha, who agrees to share the scrapbook.

5. Which of following best states a theme for this story?
   - A. Jealous feelings should always be kept hidden.
   - Ⓑ Jealousy is harmful.
   - C. Jealousy is not harmful if it's kept hidden.
   - D. Jealousy should be ignored.

Notes for Home: Your child read a story and identified elements of the plot and the theme. *Home Activity:* Watch a movie with your child. Then work with him or her to write a movie review, outlining the plot and identifying the theme.

436 Plot and Theme

Answers **779**

Writing Across Texts

Directions: Think about how Gramps in *The Memory Box* and Ebonee Rose in "The Heart of a Runner" prepared for big events in their lives. Add examples to the Venn diagram below to show how their preparations were the same and different. **Possible answers given.**

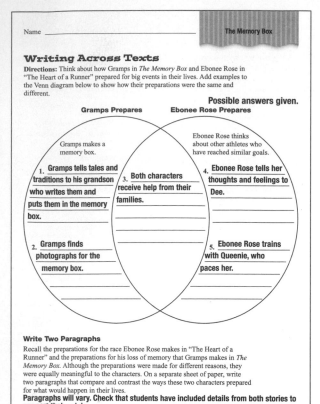

Gramps Prepares   Ebonee Rose Prepares

Gramps makes a memory box.

Ebonee Rose thinks about other athletes who have reached similar goals.

1. Gramps tells tales and traditions to his grandson who writes them and puts them in the memory box.

3. Both characters receive help from their families.

4. Ebonee Rose tells her thoughts and feelings to Dee.

2. Gramps finds photographs for the memory box.

5. Ebonee Rose trains with Queenie, who paces her.

Write Two Paragraphs

Recall the preparations for the race Ebonee Rose makes in "The Heart of a Runner" and the preparations for his loss of memory that Gramps makes in *The Memory Box*. Although the preparations were made for different reasons, they were equally meaningful to the characters. On a separate sheet of paper, write two paragraphs that compare and contrast the ways these two characters prepared for what would happen in their lives. **Paragraphs will vary. Check that students have included details from both stories to support their opinions.**

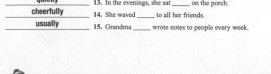 **Notes for Home:** Your child wrote two paragraphs comparing and contrasting characters from different stories. *Home Activity:* As you read stories or articles, discuss with your child how the ideas or characters are alike or different.

Grammar: Adverbs   REVIEW

Directions: Find the adverb in each sentence that tells about the underlined verb. Write the adverb on the line.

sleepily	1. Yesterday morning I <u>walked</u> to school sleepily.
Suddenly	2. Suddenly I <u>remembered</u> a dream I had had.
still	3. I <u>stood</u> still as I thought about it.
up	4. As I <u>looked</u> up at the sky, I pictured my grandfather in the dream.
again	5. I <u>saw</u> him again as he had looked when I was little.

Directions: Choose an adverb from the box to complete each sentence. More than one adverb may work in a sentence. Choose the adverb that makes sense. Write the adverb on the line to the left. **Possible answers given.**

before	clearly	nearby	often	softly

clearly	6. I remembered my grandfather _____.
often	7. In fact, I thought about him _____.
before	8. However, I don't think I had dreamed about him _____.
nearby	9. In my dream, he was sitting _____.
softly	10. He was speaking to me _____, telling funny stories.

Directions: Use the correct form of the adverb in ( ) to complete each sentence. Write the comparative or superlative adverb on the line.

more frequently	11. After my dream, I thought about my grandfather (frequently) than before.
earliest	12. When relatives visited, he always arrived (early) of all.
more often	13. He told jokes (often) than anyone else in my family.
highest	14. In the playground, he would swing me (high) of all.
more lovingly	15. There is no one I remember (lovingly) than my grandfather.

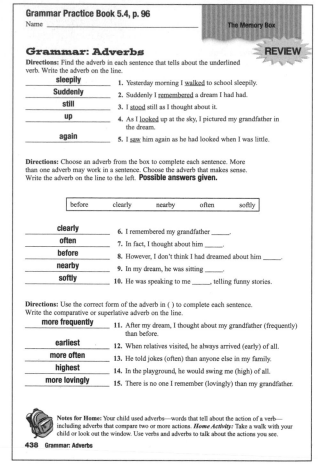 **Notes for Home:** Your child used adverbs—words that tell about the action of a verb— including adverbs that compare two or more actions. *Home Activity:* Take a walk with your child or look out the window. Use verbs and adverbs to talk about the actions you see.

Grammar: Using Adverbs to Improve Sentences

Adverbs tell more about verbs. They tell how, when, or where actions happen. You can improve your sentence by using adverbs. They add vivid details so that readers can picture the action in their minds.

Without Adverbs: Grandfather walked.
With Adverbs: Grandfather walked <u>slowly</u> and <u>carefully</u>.

Be careful not to use more adverbs than the sentence needs.

Grandfather walked <u>quietly</u>, <u>slowly</u>, <u>steadily</u>, and <u>carefully</u>.

Directions: Underline the adverb in each sentence. Circle the word it modifies.

1. The man (talked) happily about his childhood.
2. He clearly (recalled) many exciting moments.
3. The children (listened) closely to his stories.
4. Grandfather often (smiled) as he spoke.
5. The children (stayed) late at his house.

Directions: Add an adverb to make each sentence more vivid or precise. Write the adverb on the line to the left. **Possible answers given.**

lovingly	6. Grandma spoke _____ about her childhood.
far	7. She walked _____ to her country school.
frequently	8. She visited _____ with her neighbors.
happily	9. In the summer she played _____ in the yard.
often	10. Her playmates _____ joined her.
always	11. They _____ thought of games to play.
slowly	12. The summer days passed _____.
quietly	13. In the evenings, she sat _____ on the porch.
cheerfully	14. She waved _____ to all her friends.
usually	15. Grandma _____ wrote notes to people every week.

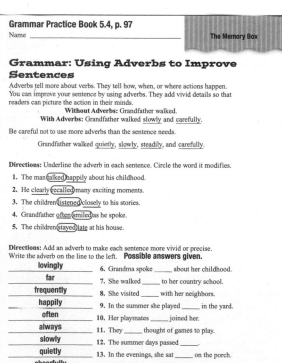 **Notes for Home:** Your child identified and wrote adverbs in sentences. An adverb can add details about actions. *Home Activity:* Watch a television show or movie together. Invite your child to name adverbs that describe the actions you see.

Grammar: Using Adverbs to Improve Sentences

Directions: Think of a different adverb to replace the one that is underlined. Write your new adverb on the line. **Possible answers given.**

sometimes	1. We <u>occasionally</u> hold family reunions.
frequently	2. Family members <u>often</u> meet at our home.
generously	3. Mom <u>always</u> serves a large meal to everyone.
Then	4. <u>Later</u>, relatives take turns telling stories.
truly	5. Relatives <u>fully</u> enjoy this festive occasion.

Directions: Add one or two adverbs to improve each sentence. Write the new sentence on the line. **Possible answers given.**

6. Uncle Joe tells jokes at each reunion.
Uncle Joe always tells jokes at each reunion.

7. Aunt Mary shares pictures.
Then Aunt Mary gladly shares pictures.

8. My cousins play in the backyard.
My cousins often play wildly in the backyard.

9. We all enjoy ourselves at our reunions.
We all enjoy ourselves greatly at our reunions.

10. I will tell you about it.
Soon I will tell you more about it.

Write a Description

Think about things your family likes to do. On a separate sheet of paper, describe your family's activities. Use precise and vivid adverbs in your sentences. **Students might write about their weekends or family get-togethers, for example. Adverbs should tell how, when, or where the activities happen. Check that students do not overuse adverbs.**

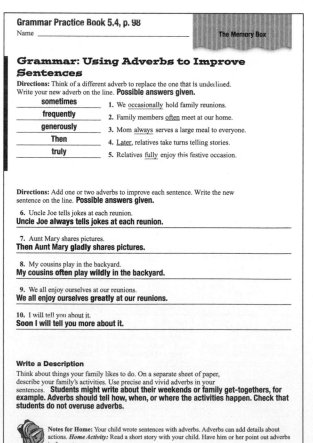 **Notes for Home:** Your child wrote sentences with adverbs. Adverbs can add details about actions. *Home Activity:* Read a short story with your child. Have him or her point out adverbs in the sentences.

© Scott Foresman 5

Grammar: Using Adverbs to Improve Sentences

RETEACHING

Write the underlined words.

1. Puppies are <u>wonderfully</u> cute. — **wonderfully**
2. Certain dogs learn <u>well</u>. — **well**
3. Others behave <u>badly</u>. — **badly**

Use **adverbs** to tell more about how, when, or where actions happen. The words **well** and **badly** often are used as adverbs.

Directions: Choose the word in ( ) that correctly completes each sentence. Write it on the line.

1. My dog eats _____ **quickly** . (quick/quickly)
2. Sometimes she barks _____ **noisily** . (noisy/noisily)
3. Her voice is very _____ **easily** heard. (easy/easily)
4. That dog is _____ **extremely** funny. (extreme/extremely)
5. The animals in the show performed _____ **happily** . (happy/happily)

Directions: Choose an adverb to complete each sentence. Write it on the line to the right. **Possible answers given.**

6. The trainer practices with his dogs _____. — **often**
7. Sometimes a dog performs _____. — **badly**
8. That small poodle walks _____ around the ring. — **daintily**
9. Most show dogs behave well _____. — **there**
10. The golden retriever wagged her tail _____ for the judges. — **wildly**
11. My collie scored _____ at today's show. — **well**

 Notes for Home: Your child added adverbs to sentences to make them more clear and interesting. **Home Activity:** Together, take a walk or look out the window. Have your child describe what he or she sees, using adverbs to present details more vividly.

Grammar: Using Adverbs to Improve Sentences **441**

Grammar: Using Adverbs to Improve Sentences

Directions: Choose an adverb to complete each sentence. Write it on the line.

1. The first swimmer _____ **slowly** warms up in the pool. **Possible answers given.**
2. We watch him _____ **there** .
3. Another swimmer joins him _____ **soon** .
4. The girl in the red suit dives _____ **beautifully** .
5. She swims _____ **amazingly** fast.
6. Her arms and legs move _____ **smoothly** .
7. She must have practiced _____ **thoroughly** .
8. That last dive was _____ **wonderfully** done.
9. Once she swam _____ **nervously** .
10. Now she performs _____ **confidently** .
11. She trains very _____ **carefully** .
12. She always breathes _____ **correctly** in the water.
13. I swim _____ **well** .
14. My school swim team has a whole group of _____ **extremely** talented swimmers.
15. Our coach tells us _____ **often** that he is proud of us.
16. Not one of us swims _____ **badly** .
17. Once we met _____ **briefly** at the community pool.
18. It was so nice, we said we would rather practice _____ **there** than anywhere else.

Write a Paragraph

On a separate sheet of paper, write a paragraph about what you like to do at a pool or a beach. Use adverbs in your sentences.

Check to make sure that students have used adverbs correctly.

Notes for Home: Your child chose adverbs to correctly complete sentences. **Home Activity:** Make a list of adverbs, such as *carefully, slowly,* and *confidently.* Have your child choose an adverb and make up a sentence, using that adverb.

442 Grammar: Using Adverbs to Improve Sentences

Phonics: Schwa Sound (Final Syllable)

Directions: The **schwa sound** is often found in a final, unstressed syllable. For example, the final syllables of **table, summer,** and **natural** have the schwa sound. Read the words in the box. Say each word to yourself. Sort the words by their final **schwa sounds.** Write each word in the correct column.
Order may vary.

freckle	soccer	tackle
professional	festival	flower
water	normal	circle

Sounds like *table*	Sounds like *summer*	Sounds like *natural*
1. **freckle**	4. **water**	7. **festival**
2. **tackle**	5. **soccer**	8. **professional**
3. **circle**	6. **flower**	9. **normal**

Directions: Read each sentence. Listen for the word that has the **schwa sound** in the final syllable. Circle the word and write it on the line.

remember	10. I (remember) taking trips to go fishing.
Uncle	11. (Uncle) Ted always caught the biggest fish.
album	12. We would take a photo of it for the photo (album).
dinner	13. Then the fresh fish was cooked for (dinner).
whistle	14. We ate, and then we would sit on the porch and (whistle) songs.
better	15. I could not think of anything I liked (better).

Notes for Home: Your child identified the schwa sound heard at the end of words, such as *table, summer,* and *natural.* **Home Activity:** In the car, read signs and billboards with your child. Take note of words with the schwa sound in the final syllables.

Phonics: Schwa Sound (Final Syllable) **443**

Spelling: Vowels in Final Syllables

Pretest Directions: Fold back the page along the dotted line. On the blanks, write the spelling words as they are dictated. When you have finished the test, unfold the page and check your words.

1. **either** — 1. I do not want **either** one.
2. **another** — 2. Read me **another** story.
3. **computer** — 3. Th school has a new **computer**.
4. **calendar** — 4. Hang the **calendar** on the wall.
5. **solar** — 5. I drew a map of the **solar** system.
6. **particular** — 6. Which place in **particular** is it?
7. **evil** — 7. Good is the opposite of **evil**.
8. **fossil** — 8. We found a **fossil** of a fern.
9. **civil** — 9. To be polite is to be **civil**.
10. **cancel** — 10. Please **cancel** my subscription.
11. **label** — 11. The **label** on the bottle is red.
12. **channel** — 12. May I change the **channel**?
13. **quarrel** — 13. The twins had a bad **quarrel**.
14. **eaten** — 14. Have you **eaten** yet?
15. **frozen** — 15. I do not like **frozen** vegetables.
16. **siren** — 16. The fire engine has a loud **siren**.
17. **curtain** — 17. She opened the **curtain**.
18. **captain** — 18. Who is the ship's **captain**?
19. **fountain** — 19. I threw coins in the **fountain**.
20. **bargain** — 20. His father always gets a **bargain**.

Notes for Home: Your child took a pretest on how to spell the vowel sound in final syllables. **Home Activity:** Help your child learn misspelled words before the final test. See if there are any similar errors and discuss a memory trick that could help.

444 Spelling: Vowels in Final Syllables

© Scott Foresman 5

Answers 781

Spelling Workbook 5.4, p. 78

Name _____

Spelling: Vowels in Final Syllables

Word List

either	particular	label	siren
another	evil	channel	curtain
computer	fossil	quarrel	captain
calendar	civil	eaten	fountain
solar	cancel	frozen	bargain

Directions: Choose the words from the box that have a final syllable that sounds like the final syllable in *open*. Write each word in the correct column. **Order may vary.**

Final syllable spelled -ain

1. curtain
2. captain
3. fountain
4. bargain

Final syllable spelled -en

5. eaten
6. frozen
7. siren

Directions: Each word below has a letter missing. Decide which vowel—**e, i,** or **a**—to add to each word to form a word from the box. Write the word on the line.

8. lab_l — label
9. anoth_r — another
10. sol_r — solar
11. civ_l — civil
12. quarr_l — quarrel
13. particul_r — particular
14. eith_r — either
15. ev_l — evil
16. comput_r — computer
17. chann_l — channel
18. foss_l — fossil
19. calend_r — calendar
20. canc_l — cancel

Notes for Home: Your child spelled words with indistinct vowel sounds in their final syllables that sound alike but are spelled differently, such as *solar* and *either*. **Home Activity:** Give your child clues about each spelling word. Have him or her guess and spell the word.

Spelling: Vowels in Final Syllables **445**

Spelling Workbook 5.4, p. 79

Name _____

Spelling: Vowels in Final Syllables

Directions: Proofread the book review. Find seven spelling mistakes. Use the proofreading marks to correct each mistake.

≡ Make a capital.
/ Make a small letter.
∧ Add something.
𝒫 Take out something.
⊙ Add a period.
¶ Begin a new paragraph.

BETWEEN A BOOK'S COVERS

Memories of My Travels, by Captain Ronald Tweet, is filled with tales of the famous explorer's adventures. In one chapter, he tells of his search for the fossel of a forgotten dinosaur. In another, he describes his quest for the fountin of youth in India, where he had a close call with death after he had eaten a two-month old sandwich! On an expedition to the frozin lands of the North Pole, Sir Ronald's ship almost sinks in a dangerous chanel. My particuler favorite is his foolish quarrell with a huge anaconda in the Amazon. If you like excitement, you'll love this book. It's a bargen at $11.95!

Spelling Tip
another
If you have trouble spelling **another,** remember that it's made up of three words:
a not her.

Word List
either
another
computer
calendar
solar
particular
evil
fossil
civil
cancel
label
channel
quarrel
eaten
frozen
siren
curtain
captain
fountain
bargain

Write a Review
On a separate sheet of paper, write a review of a book, movie, or television program you have recently read or watched. Try to use at least six of your spelling words. **Answers will vary, but each review should contain at least six spelling words.**

Notes for Home: Your child spelled words with indistinct vowel sounds in their final syllables that sound alike but are spelled differently. **Home Activity:** With your child, sort the spelling words into separate lists according to how their final syllables are spelled.

446 Spelling: Vowels in Final Syllables

Spelling Workbook 5.4, p. 80

Name _____

Spelling: Vowels in Final Syllables **REVIEW**

Word List

either	solar	civil	quarrel	curtain
another	particular	cancel	eaten	captain
computer	evil	label	frozen	fountain
calendar	fossil	channel	siren	bargain

Directions: Choose the word from the box that best matches each clue. Write the word on the line.

civil — 1. This refers to rights of citizens, such as the right to vote.
calendar — 2. It tells the date.
evil — 3. It's the opposite of *good.*
cancel — 4. You do this when you can't meet someone as planned.
either — 5. It can be one or the other.
fossil — 6. You might dig for one.
bargain — 7. You might find it at a yard sale.
computer — 8. It has a keyboard and a monitor attached to it.
solar — 9. This kind of power comes from the sun.
channel — 10. It's something you change on the television set.
label — 11. It appears on packaged foods.

Directions: Choose the word from the box that best completes each sentence. Write the word on the line to the left.

particular — 12. There was one day in _____ that I'll never forget.
eaten — 13. We had just _____ lunch.
frozen — 14. We ate _____ fish sticks that we had thawed and baked.
siren — 15. Suddenly we heard a loud police _____.
curtain — 16. We all ran to the window and pulled back the _____.
fountain — 17. The police were hauling a soaking wet man out of the _____.
Another — 18. _____ man had pushed him in the town's fountain.
quarrel — 19. They had apparently had a _____.
captain — 20. A police _____ took both men down to the station.

Notes for Home: Your child spelled words with indistinct vowel sounds in their final syllables that sound alike but are spelled differently, such as *solar* and *either*. **Home Activity:** Give your child clues to a spelling word. Have him or her guess the word and spell it.

Spelling: Vowels in Final Syllables **447**

Practice Book 5.4, p. 199

Name _____

Alphabetical Order

Resources such as encyclopedias, dictionaries, glossaries, indexes, and telephone directories list information in **alphabetical order** to make it easier for readers to find information quickly. Remember to use the first letter of the first word in each entry when you order alphabetically. If the first letters are the same, use the second letters. If the second letters are the same, use the third letters, and so on.

Directions: Suppose you wanted to find a particular photograph among the boxes of photographs below. The boxes are labeled, but they are not in any order. Someone has started to put them in alphabetical order on a shelf. On the next page, answer the questions about organizing the rest of the boxes in alphabetical order.

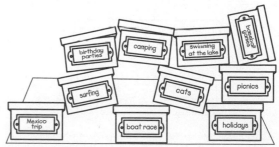

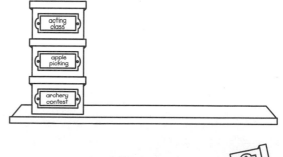

448 Research and Study Skills: Alphabetical Order

© Scott Foresman 5

Practice Book 5.4, p. 200

Name _____

Directions: Write the names of the photo boxes not on the shelf in alphabetical order.

1. baseball games
2. birthday parties
3. boat race
4. camping
5. cats
6. holidays
7. Mexico trip
8. picnics
9. surfing
10. swimming at the lake

11. For which boxes did you have to use the second letter of the words on the labels to alphabetize the boxes?
baseball games, birthday parties, and boat race; surfing and swimming at the lake

12. For which boxes did you have to use the third letter of the words on the labels to alphabetize the boxes?
camping and cats

13. Between which two boxes would you put a photo box labeled *school trips*?
between picnics and surfing

14. Between which two boxes would you put a box labeled *canoeing*? **between camping and cats**

15. Why might it be useful to sort and organize materials at school or at home by alphabetical order? Give an example of something in your class or at home that it would be helpful to organize by alphabetical order.
Possible answer: Using alphabetical order makes it easier to find things quickly. You could organize books in the classroom or at home in alphabetical order.

Notes for Home: Your child used alphabetical order to organize information. *Home Activity:* With your child, arrange the titles of some books in alphabetical order. Ignore the articles *a, the,* and *an* when alphabetizing book titles.

Research and Study Skills: Alphabetical Order **449**

Name _____

How-To Chart

The How-To Chart should be filled out completely.

Directions: Fill in the how-to chart with information about your project. **Students may not have complete ideas for the Introduction and Conclusion at this time. These sections can be completed later.**

Explain task _____

Materials _____

Introduction _____

Steps _____

Conclusion _____

Notes for Home: Your child has been preparing to write a how-to report. *Home Activity:* Think of everyday chores such as brushing teeth, making a bed, or cleaning a room. Ask your child to outline the steps in the process. Try it out. Are there any steps missing?

450 Unit 4: Writing Process

Name _____

Elaboration
Add Details

- When you write, you can elaborate by **adding interesting and specific details** that help readers easily understand your directions.
- You can provide interesting and specific details by telling how things look, sound, feel, taste, and smell.

Directions: Read each sentence below. Pick a few words from the box to tell more about the process. Write your new sentence using the details.

Responses will vary. Reasonable answers are given.

carefully	light	creative
sturdy	unique	thick
shallow	interesting	thin
fun	completely	unusual
arrange	colorful	special
great	scrap	bright

1. You need to find a box.
You need to find a shallow, sturdy box.

2. Some paint would add a nice touch.
Some colorful paint would add a nice touch.

3. You can cover your box with paper.
You can cover your box with interesting paper.

4. Poster board makes shelves.
Scrap poster board makes great shelves.

5. Put the shelves in the box.
Put the shelves in the box carefully.

6. Add your things to the box.
Add your special things to the box.

7. Is your box a work of art?
Is your box an unusual work of art?

8. Your Memory Box is a masterpiece!
Your Memory Box is a creative masterpiece!

Notes for Home: Your child recently expanded sentences by adding interesting and specific details. *Home Activity:* Ask your child to explain three steps in a how-to process. Take turns elaborating on these steps to make them as clear as possible. Encourage your child to be specific.

Unit 4: Writing Process **451**

Name _____

Self-Evaluation Guide
How-To Report

Directions: Think about the final draft of your how-to report. Then answer each question below. **Students' responses should show that they have given thought to the how-to reports they have written.**

	Yes	No	Not sure
1. Are there any steps missing?			
2. Are all the steps in the right order?			
3. Are the steps clearly written and easy to follow?			
4. Did I provide all of the necessary information?			
5. Did I use words such as *first* to indicate order?			
6. Did I proofread carefully for spelling, capitalization, and punctuation?			
7. Did I accomplish what I set out to accomplish?			

8. Did I learn anything new from this report?
_____

9. In what way would you improve your report if you rewrote it?
_____

Notes for Home: Your child completed a self-evaluation of a writing assignment. *Home Activity:* Discuss the form with your child. Ask: *What did you learn from the exercise? What would you do differently next time? Are there other areas where this experience is applicable?*

452 Unit 4: Writing Process

Setting

- The **setting** is the time and place in which a story happens.
- In some stories, the author tells you exactly when and where the story takes place. In other stories, the author tells about the setting through details and you have to figure out the time and place.

Directions: Reread "The Year of Mother Jones." Then complete the table. **Possible answers** Provide details from the story to support each statement about the setting. **given.**

Setting	How I Know (Supporting Details from the Story)
The story takes place in Philadelphia.	1. **The heading gives the name of the city.**
The story begins in November, 1903.	2. **The heading gives the date.**
The children work in a mill.	3. **This is stated in the first paragraph.**
The mill is dirty and dangerous.	4. **"Dirty" is stated in the first paragraph. James' mention of accidents suggests that the mill is dangerous.**
The strike takes place in the summer of 1903.	5. **The heading of the second part of the story gives the date "June, 1903" and the text says the event happened "last summer."**

Notes for Home: Your child read a story and identified details about its setting. *Home Activity:* Read a story with your child. Have him or her point out details that help identify when and where the story takes place. Talk about how important the setting is to the story.

Setting **455**

Vocabulary

Directions: Choose the word from the box that best completes each sentence. Write the word on the line.

	Check the Words You Know
	__ banners
	__ headlines
	__ parlor
	__ pavement
	__ splattered
	__ stockings
	__ trolley

___headlines___ 1. Kate stared at the _____ on the newspapers: FAIR WAGES NOW!

___trolley___ 2. Kate rode the _____ through town to the factory.

___banners___ 3. She saw striking workers marching along, carrying _____ and signs.

___splattered___ 4. Even when they began to be _____ by rain, they didn't quit.

___pavement___ 5. So much rain had fallen that the _____ was covered with deep puddles.

___stockings___ 6. A few striking workers complained that the rainwater had soaked their shoes and _____.

Directions: Choose the word from the box that best matches each clue. Write the word on the line.

___trolley___ 7. I am something you can ride in to travel throughout the city.

___parlor___ 8. I am a sitting room in which you entertain guests.

___pavement___ 9. I am a road or sidewalk covered with a hard surface.

___stockings___ 10. I am worn over your feet and under your shoes.

Write a Song

On a separate sheet of paper, write a political song that suffragists might sing at marches, parades, or demonstrations. Use as many vocabulary words as you can. **Students' songs should be about the right to vote and make correct use of vocabulary words.**

Notes for Home: Your child identified and used vocabulary words from the story "I Want to Vote!" *Home Activity:* If possible, show your child pictures of suffragists from the 1910s and 1920s. Invite your child to make up his or her own story about the fight for the right to vote.

456 Vocabulary

Setting

- The **setting** is the time and place in which a story happens. It may be directly identified or only described through details.
- In some stories, the setting is very important. It affects what happens and why it happens.

Directions: Reread the section of "I Want to Vote!" in which the parade begins. Then answer the questions below. Think about where and when the story takes place. **Possible answers given.**

> All at once, all the bands were playing and the columns of women began to move. Left, left, Lila was marching. Above her, the yellow banners streamed.
> Out of Washington Square they marched and onto Fifth Avenue. Before and behind came the sound of the drums, and the flags snapped in the breeze. Left, left. On they went up the street, marching in time to the music.
> From the curbs came the sound of whistles and cheers. Yellow streamers flew from the shop doors. White-gloved policemen held back the crowds as the bands and the marchers passed.
>
> From A LONG WAY TO GO by Zibby Oneal. Copyright © 1990 by Zibby Oneal. Used by permission of Viking Penguin, a division of Penguin Putnam Inc.

1. Where is the parade taking place?
The parade takes place outside of Washington Square along Fifth Avenue in New York City.

2. Is the setting directly identified or implied through details? Explain.
Washington Square and Fifth Avenue are directly identified; New York City is not directly stated.

3. Which details make the setting come alive for the reader?
the bands, the columns of marchers, the breeze, the yellow ribbons, the cheers and whistles

4. How does the setting affect the marchers?
They are probably happy about the cheers and excited by the music.

5. How important is the time period in which the story is set? Explain your answer on a separate sheet of paper. **The time period of the story is very important since the story is all about a specific moment in American history—women fighting for their right to vote.**

Notes for Home: Your child read a story and analyzed how the time and place affected the characters and events. *Home Activity:* Read a story with your child. Then talk about the way the setting (time and place) affects the characters and events.

Setting **457**

Selection Test

Directions: Choose the best answer to each item. Mark the letter for the answer you have chosen.

Part 1: Vocabulary

Find the answer choice that means about the same as the underlined word in each sentence.

1. Lou rode the <u>trolley</u>.
  A. station wagon
  B. bicycle
  C. horse-drawn carriage
  (D.) streetcar

2. The milk <u>splattered</u> everywhere.
  (F.) splashed
  G. grew wildly
  H. smelled
  J. froze

3. The marchers carried <u>banners</u>.
  A. protective coverings
  (B.) signs made of cloth
  C. musical instruments
  D. small children

4. Her <u>stockings</u> were dirty.
  F. coverings for the hand
  G. drawers in a cabinet
  H. glasses used to improve eyesight
  (J.) coverings for the foot or leg

5. George is in the <u>parlor</u>.
  A. park
  B. garage
  (C.) living room
  D. basement

6. We stood on the <u>pavement</u>.
  (F.) street or sidewalk
  G. upper floor of a theater
  H. long, wooden porch
  J. flat stretch of sand by the sea

7. These <u>headlines</u> are not very exciting.
  A. small wrinkles on a person's face
  B. coverings or decorations for the head
  C. long lines at the store
  (D.) lines printed at the top of newspaper articles

Part 2: Comprehension

Use what you know about the story to answer each item.

8. At the beginning of the story, Lila and Mike were—
  F. marching in a parade.
  (G.) selling newspapers.
  H. fighting a fire.
  J. printing newspapers.

9. Lila read about women in Washington who refused to eat because they—
  A. were angry at the cook.
  B. did not like the food they got in jail.
  C. could not afford to buy food.
  (D.) would rather starve than not have the right to vote.

10. How did things change for the women in the story because there was a war on?
  F. They were allowed to vote.
  G. They had the same rights as men.
  (H.) They were working in offices and factories.
  J. They were not allowed to make speeches.

GO ON →

458 Selection Test

© Scott Foresman 5

11. Where does this story take place?
  Ⓐ New York
  B. Washington, D.C.
  C. Georgia
  D. California

12. When does this story take place?
  F. at the time of the Civil War
  Ⓖ in the early 1900s
  H. after World War II
  J. in the 1960s

13. How did Lila's father react to her speech?
  A. He became angry.
  B. He pretended to be bored.
  C. He was annoyed.
  Ⓓ He was impressed.

14. This story supports the idea that—
  Ⓕ women deserve the same rights as men.
  G. boys are smarter than girls.
  H. women should not be allowed to vote.
  J. women don't need to know how to drive.

15. Lila's father was wrong in thinking that she—
  A. was not as smart as George.
  B. would grow into a beautiful lady.
  Ⓒ would prefer dances and parties to learning to drive.
  D. would make speeches when she was older.

STOP

Selection Test **459**

Setting

- The **setting** is the time and place in which a story happens. It may be directly identified or only described through details.
- In some stories, the setting is very important. It affects what happens and why it happens.

Directions: Read the story below.

"Penny for a shine! Penny for a shine!" Mike glanced down at his kit; polish, brushes, and soft flannel rags. He exchanged grins with Pat, who was selling newspapers across the gate.

Sunlight streamed in through the huge skylight in the roof of Pennsylvania Station. Many businessmen in dark hats, scarves, and heavy overcoats passed him, all on their way to their offices. Several of them stopped to buy papers, dropping their nickels in the box at Pat's feet.

The station was so huge it never seemed crowded or noisy, even on a busy morning. Mike wondered for a moment whether Grand Central Station was as large. Then his thoughts were interrupted as a man called to him for a shine. Time to stop daydreaming and earn his breakfast!

Directions: Complete the table. Think about details of time and place. **Possible answers given.**

Setting	How Do You Know?
Time of Year/Season	1. **Probably winter; the men are wearing scarves and heavy overcoats.**
Time of Day	2. **Morning; men are on their way to work and Mike hasn't had breakfast.**
Long Ago or Modern Time?	3. **Long ago; shoeshine costs a penny and newspaper costs a nickel.**
Location	4. **Pennsylvania Station; stated in the story**
Settings Effect on Character	Pat is happy because a busy station means many customers to buy his newspapers. 5. **Mike is impressed at station's size.**

Notes for Home: Your child read a story and identified the setting (time and place) and its effect on the characters and events. *Home Activity:* Watch a movie or TV show with your child. Then talk about ways in which the setting was important to the story.

460 Setting

Making Judgments

REVIEW

Directions: Read the story. Then read each question about the story. Choose the best answer to each question. Mark the letter for the answer you have chosen.

Forward March!

Jack and Paul were going all the way to Washington to march in the parade with their friends Sally and Roberto. They would travel down by train the day before. Jack had been thinking about it all week. He and Paul were good friends, and they would have a great time at the parade.

The night before, Jack and Paul got together to pack their bags. Paul noticed that Jack didn't pack an umbrella.

"Aren't you taking your umbrella, Jack? I read that it may rain tomorrow."

"I can't be bothered with an umbrella," objected Jack. "My pack is heavy enough already. Besides, why would it rain? The weather has been great all week."

Paul said nothing. He went back to his packing.

Jack watched as Paul stuffed a sweater into his pack. "Why are you taking that? Your pack will be so heavy you won't want to go anywhere! Besides, it's warm out."

"Sally travels on those trains all the time, and she says they're always cold," Paul explained. "They always have the air conditioning on full blast."

"Oh, what does she know?" scoffed Jack. "Sally always thinks it's cold. Bring that sweater if you want to, but I'm not taking one."

Paul grinned at his friend and zipped his full pack. "All set?" he asked. "We should get some sleep if we want to be awake in time for our train tomorrow!"

1. Jack thinks he won't need an umbrella because—
  A. it's too big to fit into his backpack.
  B. he has no room for it.
  Ⓒ he doesn't believe it will rain.
  D. Paul has an umbrella.

2. Jack should take an umbrella because—
  F. Paul tells him to.
  Ⓖ Paul read a forecast that predicted rain.
  H. they can sell it later.
  J. it will balance the weight of his pack.

3. Paul takes a sweater because—
  A. Sally told him it would snow.
  B. he likes to wear sweaters.
  C. he thinks it will amuse Jack.
  Ⓓ Sally told him the train would be cold.

4. Which character do you think is best prepared for whatever may happen?
  F. Jack
  Ⓖ Paul
  H. Sally
  J. Roberto

5. Which character do you think is least prepared for whatever may happen?
  Ⓐ Jack
  B. Paul
  C. Sally
  D. Roberto

Notes for Home: Your child read a story and made judgments about the characters and their actions. *Home Activity:* Talk with your child about some of the decisions he or she made recently. Together, discuss your opinion of each decision.

Making Judgments **461**

Writing Across Texts

Directions: Think about the character Lila and children's lives as described in "I Want to Vote!" and the article "Kids Voting USA." How is being a child today different from the way it was in 1917? How has the attitude toward voting changed? Fill in the following table to record some of the differences. **Possible answers:**

Changing Times	
Today	**In the Early 1900s**
Children are encouraged to learn about voting.	Lila was discouraged from attending a suffragist parade
1. **All children are invited to the polls and given preparation in voting technique.**	2. **Girls were told they would not be able to vote.**
3. **Children learn about elections on computers.**	4. **There were no computers.**
5. **All children are able to learn to drive when they reach the legal age.**	6. **Lila is told by her father that only her brother will learn to drive.**
7. **Teachers, schools, and volunteers work together to encourage children to get involved in elections.**	8. **Women and girls work to earn equal rights.**
9. **Over half the population was not allowed to vote as adults.**	10. **Kids Voting USA is trying to increase voter numbers.**

Write a Paragraph

Compare what you learned about children's lives from "I Want to Vote!" to ideas in "Kids Voting USA." On a separate sheet of paper, write a paragraph that describes some of the differences in most children's lives today compared with the lives of children in the early 1900s. **Paragraphs will vary. Check that students have a topic sentence and supporting details.**

Notes for Home: Your child wrote about how times have changed since the early 1900s. *Home Activity:* Show your child an old family photograph or some other photograph of another era. Together, discuss things in the photograph that show things that were different then.

462 Writing Across Texts

I Want to Vote!

Grammar: Contractions

REVIEW

Directions: Rewrite each contraction as two separate words.

1. he'll	**he will**	11. won't	**will not**
2. don't	**do not**	12. haven't	**have not**
3. it's	**it is**	13. let's	**let us**
4. I'm	**I am**	14. that's	**that is**
5. you're	**you are**	15. they've	**they have**
6. didn't	**did not**	16. she'll	**she will**
7. they're	**they are**	17. we've	**we have**
8. I've	**I have**	18. you've	**you have**
9. she's	**she is/she has**	19. they'll	**they will**
10. there's	**there is**	20. wouldn't	**would not**

Directions: Change the underlined words into a contraction. Then rewrite each sentence.

21. "<u>I am</u> going to the polls now!" declares my sister Lin.
"I'm going to the polls now!" declares my sister Lin.

22. "<u>They are</u> closing soon, so <u>you had</u> better hurry," says Mom.
"They're closing soon, so you'd better hurry," says Mom.

23. Lin <u>does not</u> say much, but <u>she is</u> proud to be voting.
Lin doesn't say much, but she's proud to be voting.

24. She just turned eighteen, so <u>it is</u> her first time to vote.
She just turned eighteen, so it's her first time to vote.

25. Lin knows that before 1920 women <u>could not</u> vote at all.
Lin knows that before 1920 women couldn't vote at all.

 Notes for Home: Your child wrote contractions—word combinations such as *don't, we'll, you're*. **Home Activity:** Take a walk with your child, and try to spot contractions on neighborhood signs and posters. Name the words each contraction represents.

Grammar: Contractions **463**

I Want to Vote!

Grammar: Pronouns

Pronouns are words that take the place of nouns or noun phrases. Like nouns, pronouns have singular and plural forms. A singular pronoun replaces a singular noun. A plural pronoun replaces a plural noun.

<u>Lucy Stone</u> was an early suffragist. <u>She</u> argued for women's right to vote.

<u>Elizabeth Cady Stanton</u> and <u>Susan B. Anthony</u> were early suffragists too.

<u>They</u> wanted new laws about women's rights.

Pronouns
Singular: I, me, you, she, her, he, him, it   **Plural:** we, us, you, they, them

Possessive pronouns are pronouns that show ownership. One form of possessive pronouns is used before nouns. The other form stands alone without a noun following it.

<u>Their</u> struggle for justice is part of history. Honor and respect are now <u>theirs</u>.

Possessive Pronouns
Before a Noun: my, your, her, his, its, our, their
By Itself: mine, yours, hers, his, ours, theirs

Directions: Underline the pronoun or pronouns in each sentence. Be sure to underline possessive pronouns too.

1. <u>We</u> talked about <u>our</u> favorite candidates.
2. Carmen and <u>I</u> listened to <u>their</u> speeches.
3. <u>She</u> waved at <u>her</u> relatives outside the polling place.
4. <u>They</u> smiled at <u>us</u> and held up signs.
5. Any right means responsibilities, so <u>we</u> are learning about <u>ours</u>.

Directions: Choose a pronoun or possessive pronoun in ( ) to replace the underlined words. Write the pronoun or possessive pronoun on the line.

it	6. Carmen's mom did campaign work and liked <u>campaign work</u>. (it/she)
his	7. Her dad made a speech in <u>her dad's</u> strong, deep voice. (his/their)
her	8. The candidate offered him <u>the candidate's</u> thanks afterward. (her/our)
our	9. Carmen and I met her, and she shook <u>Carmen's and my</u> hands. (her/our)
we	10. When Carmen and I are old enough, <u>Carmen and I</u> will vote in every election! (they/we)

 Notes for Home: Your child identified and wrote pronouns (words that take the place of nouns). **Home Activity:** Read a short magazine or newspaper article together. Invite your child to identify all the pronouns he or she recognizes.

464 Grammar: Pronouns

I Want to Vote!

Grammar: Pronouns

Directions: Underline the pronoun or pronouns in each sentence. Underline the possessive pronouns too.

1. Herman said <u>he</u> had a question for <u>our</u> teacher.
2. Would <u>she</u> give <u>us</u> <u>her</u> permission to have a student government?
3. <u>It</u> would give <u>us</u> practice in voting and in citizenship.
4. With <u>our</u> classmates, <u>we</u> would elect a student governor.
5. Then <u>we</u> could decide what <u>his</u> or <u>her</u> duties would be.
6. <u>Our</u> classmates listened, and Herman explained <u>his</u> idea to <u>them</u>.
7. <u>He</u> asked Amelia, "Did <u>your</u> last school have a student government?"
8. "Yes," <u>she</u> told <u>him</u>. "Each grade had <u>its</u> own representatives."
9. Next, two of <u>my</u> classmates nominated <u>me</u> for governor.
10. Other students named <u>their</u> choices for student governor.

Directions: Choose a pronoun or possessive pronoun to replace the underlined word or words. Write the pronoun or possessive pronoun on the line.

she	11. Layla said that <u>Layla</u> had been a class treasurer the year before. (it/she)
his	12. Dan decided to give Layla <u>Dan's</u> vote for treasurer. (their/his)
her	13. Herman thanked the teacher for <u>the teacher's</u> interest and help. (her/their)
their	14. Our teacher praised the students for the <u>students'</u> interest in government. (its/their)
it	15. She added, "We will have the election next week, and I hope students will support <u>the election</u> by voting." (it/us)

Write a Letter

Think about a class project or activity you enjoyed with your classmates. On a separate sheet of paper, write a letter that describes that project or activity. Tell what different people did. Use pronouns and possessive pronouns in your letter. **Check whether students have used singular pronouns to replace singular nouns, plural pronouns to replace plural nouns, and the correct forms of possessive pronouns.**

 Notes for Home: Your child identified and wrote pronouns in sentences. Pronouns are words that take the place of nouns. **Home Activity:** Write the pronouns *I, you, he, she, it, we,* and *they* on slips of paper. Take turns drawing a slip and using the pronoun in a sentence.

Grammar: Pronouns **465**

I Want to Vote!

Grammar: Pronouns

RETEACHING

Read each pair of sentences. Write the pronoun that replaces the circled word.

1. a. (Sam) has a pet snail.
   b. He has a pet snail.   **He**
2. a. Sam gave the snail to (Sandra.)
   b. Sam gave the snail to her.   **her**

Pronouns take the place of nouns or noun phrases. A pronoun can be singular or plural.

Directions: Circle the pronoun in each sentence. Write it on the line.

1. (My) team had never won a championship.	**My**
2. (I) was the last batter up.	**I**
3. (My) friends cheered loudly from the sidelines.	**My**
4. Would the winning run be (mine?)	**mine**
5. Cheering teammates surrounded (me) at home base.	**me**
6. Victory was (ours.)	**ours**
7. The coach congratulated (us.)	**us**
8. (We) shook hands with the other team.	**We**
9. The players were good sports about (their) loss.	**their**

Directions: Write a pronoun for the underlined word or words.

10. <u>Rosa</u> won the Most Valuable Player award.	**She**
11. The trophies in the bookcase are <u>Rosa's</u>.	**hers**
12. Not all of <u>the trophies</u> are for sports.	**them**
13. Music interests <u>Rosa</u> too.	**her**
14. <u>Rosa</u> plays the violin in the school orchestra.	**She**
15. Rosa's favorite trophy has a violin on <u>the trophy</u>.	**it**

 Notes for Home: Your child identified pronouns in sentences and replaced proper nouns with pronouns. **Home Activity:** Have your child write sentences about people he or she knows, replacing proper nouns with pronouns.

466 Grammar: Pronouns

© Scott Foresman 5

I Want to Vote!

Grammar: Pronouns

Directions: Circle the pronoun in each sentence.

1. (I) like the beach.
2. Usually (my) friend Janice brings along a radio.
3. Sometimes Janice brings (her) umbrella for some shade.
4. Not even an umbrella gives complete protection from the sun and (its) rays.
5. (We) use sunscreen for added protection.
6. Sometimes the sand sticks to (our) skin.
7. (It) gets on towels and clothes.
8. (Their) towels feel gritty.
9. The sand does not bother (us) too much.
10. The ocean waves splash on (his) towel.

Directions: Replace the underlined word or words in each sentence with a pronoun. Then rewrite the sentence.

11. Janice dropped a piece of bread on the sand.
    She dropped a piece of bread on the sand.

12. The bread attracted nearby gulls.
    It attracted nearby gulls.

13. The gulls swooped down toward the food.
    They swooped down toward the food.

14. The small piece of bread was not enough for all of the birds.
    The small piece of bread was not enough for all of them.

Write Sentences

Write sentences that tell how you keep cool on hot days. Use pronouns in your sentences. Write on a separate sheet of paper.

Make sure students have used pronouns correctly.

 Notes for Home: Your child identified pronouns in sentences and wrote new sentences with pronouns. *Home Activity:* Together, make a list of pronouns your child knows. Then make a list of proper nouns and have your child identify which pronouns match them.

I Want to Vote!

Phonics: Complex Spelling Patterns

Directions: In some words, the sound /sh/ is spelled **ci, sci,** or **ti.** Read the list of words. Say each word to yourself. Underline the letters that represent the sound /sh/.

1. official
2. special
3. commotion
4. spacious
5. occupation
6. imagination
7. dictionary
8. conscious
9. delicious
10. caution
11. conscience
12. luscious
13. socially
14. artificial
15. motion

Directions: Read the diary entry. Circle the words with the sound /sh/. Write the words on the lines.

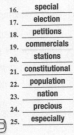

May 29
Dear Diary,
    Today was a (special) day for our family. It was (election) day, and Mom just got elected to the city council! We worked very hard on her campaign. We passed out flyers and asked people to sign (petitions) saying they would vote for Mom. We ran (commercials) on the local radio and television (stations). We reminded everyone we talked to that it was their (constitutional) right to vote. Mom told me that not so long ago women did not have the right to vote. Can you imagine that such a large percent of our (population) had no say in how the (nation) was run? It made me realize how (precious) our rights are, (especially) the right to vote. Now I can't wait till I turn 18 and can cast my own vote!

16. __special__
17. __election__
18. __petitions__
19. __commercials__
20. __stations__
21. __constitutional__
22. __population__
23. __nation__
24. __precious__
25. __especially__

 Notes for Home: Your child identified words with the sound /sh/ spelled **ci,** **sci,** and **ti.** *Home Activity:* Make a list of words with your child that end in *-tion* and have the sound /sh/. Make up rhymes with these words.

I Want to Vote!

Spelling: Words with *ng, nk, th*

Pretest Directions: Fold back the page along the dotted line. On the blanks, write the spelling words as they are dictated. When you have finished the test, unfold the page and check your words.

1. strong
2. nothing
3. everything
4. clothing
5. among
6. sting
7. hanger
8. lightning
9. blank
10. trunk
11. Thanksgiving
12. chipmunk
13. shrink
14. they
15. then
16. north
17. there
18. without
19. though
20. thought

1. The weightlifter is **strong**.
2. I brought **nothing** to the party.
3. **Everything** happened at once.
4. This **clothing** is expensive.
5. You are **among** friends.
6. Wasps might **sting** a dog.
7. Put your coat on a **hanger**.
8. The **lightning** was very bright.
9. Fill in the **blank**.
10. Open the **trunk** of the car.
11. We ate a lot on **Thanksgiving**.
12. The **chipmunk** buries a nut.
13. The sweater will **shrink**.
14. **They** talked for a long time.
15. There were no cars **then**.
16. We drove **north**.
17. I lost my watch **there**.
18. Do not come **without** her.
19. I walked **though** I was tired.
20. She **thought** it was hers.

 Notes for Home: Your child took a pretest on words that include *ng, nk,* or *th.* *Home Activity:* Help your child learn misspelled words before the final test. Your child should look at the word, say it, spell it aloud, and then spell it with eyes shut.

I Want to Vote!

Spelling: Words with *ng, nk, th*

Word List				
strong	among	blank	shrink	there
nothing	sting	trunk	they	without
everything	hanger	Thanksgiving	then	though
clothing	lightning	chipmunk	north	thought

Directions: Choose the one-syllable words from the box. Write each word in the correct column. **Order may vary.**

Contains ng
1. strong
2. sting

Contains nk
3. blank
4. trunk
5. shrink

Contains th
6. they
7. then
8. north
9. there
10. though
11. thought

Directions: Write the word from the box that is associated with each word or words.

12. thunder — lightning
13. squirrel — chipmunk
14. zero — nothing
15. fashion — clothing
16. hook — hanger
17. lacking — without
18. one of — among
19. turkey — Thanksgiving
20. all — everything

 Notes for Home: Your child spelled words that have *ng, nk,* or *th.* *Home Activity:* Challenge your child to identify the four spelling words that are compound words and use each in a sentence.

© Scott Foresman 5

Name _____

I Want to Vote!

Spelling: Words with *ng, nk, th*

Directions: Proofread this description. Find six spelling mistakes. Use the proofreading marks to correct each mistake.

≡	Make a capital.
/	Make a small letter.
∧	Add something.
⌿	Take out something.
⊙	Add a period.
¶	Begin a new paragraph.

Next week my Grandmother is taking me to the city to see a parade celebrating Independence Day. Nothin~g~ is better than visiting the big city. Everything the~ir~ is so exciting and fast paced. I ~t~ought that I should wear red, white, and blue for the parade. In an old trun~c~k in the attic of my house, I found the perfect costume. Finally the big day arrived. As the parade began, a bolt of ligh~n~ting lit up the sky. I was worried that the parade might be canceled, but the storm passed and the parade continued. I truly enjoyed my day in the city.

Word List

strong	among	blank	shrink	there
nothing	sting	trunk	they	without
everything	hanger	Thanksgiving	then	though
clothing	lightning	chipmunk	north	thought

Write a Description

On a separate sheet of paper, write a description of something mysterious or strange. It might be a tree, a house, or an animal. You can write from experience or use your imagination. Try to use at least five of your spelling words. **Answers will vary, but each description should contain at least five spelling words.**

Spelling Tip
there
People often mix up **there** and **their**. Remember the **here** in **there**. Both **here** and **there** refer to **where**.

Notes for Home: Your child practiced writing spelling words that contain the consonants *ng, nk,* or *th*. **Home Activity:** Help your child think of additional words that begin or end with the letters *th*. Make a list of these words.

Spelling: Words with *ng, nk, th* **471**

Name _____

I Want to Vote!

Spelling: Words with *ng, nk, th*

REVIEW

Word List

strong	among	blank	shrink	there
nothing	sting	trunk	they	without
everything	hanger	Thanksgiving	then	though
clothing	lightning	chipmunk	north	thought

Directions: Choose the word from the box that begins and ends with the same letter as each word below. Write the word on the line.

1. entering   **everything**
2. workout   **without**
3. listening   **lightning**
4. napping   **nothing**
5. today   **they**
6. thorough   **though**
7. aging   **among**
8. tease   **there**

Directions: Choose the word from the box that best completes each person's statement. Write the word on the line.

hanger   9. Mother: "Put your coat on this _____."

clothing   10. Department Store Clerk: "Take a look at our new line of _____."

sting   11. Beekeeper: "Sometimes I'm not careful and I get a bee _____."

chipmunk   12. Forest Ranger: "I have a pet _____ that I feed daily."

strong   13. Wrestler: "You have to be _____ in my line of work."

trunk   14. Elephant: "I feed myself with my _____."

north   15. Trail Guide: "I don't need a compass to find _____."

thought   16. Writer: "I just _____ of a great idea for my next book."

blank   17. Artist: "I love filling up a _____ canvas."

shrink   18. Dry Cleaner: "I have to be careful not to _____ my customers' clothes."

then   19. Storyteller: "And _____ they lived happily ever after."

Thanksgiving   20. Turkey Farmer: "My favorite holiday is _____."

Notes for Home: Your child spelled words with *ng, nk,* and *th*. **Home Activity:** With your child, take turns making up tongue twisters using words that contain *th*. (Example: *Theo threw the third throw through the window.*)

472 Spelling: Words with *ng, nk, th*

Name _____

I Want to Vote!

Technology: Electronic Media

Electronic media includes audiotapes, videotapes, films, and computers. You can use computers to locate information on CD-ROMs and to search the Internet. To find a topic on the Internet, use a search engine and type in your key words.

Directions: Suppose you type "voting AND registration" in a search engine. You might get the following list that links you to related web pages. Use the list to answer the questions on the next page.

You Searched For:

voting AND registration	Top 6 of 3789 matches.

CENSUS - Voting and Registration Data Information about who votes and is registered to vote according to characteristics such as age, gender, race, amount of money earned, and so on.

Programs — Voting Rights Voting for Everyone is a group that works to eliminate any discriminatory obstacles that might prevent Asian Pacific Americans from participating in the voting process. This includes working to enforce the protections of the Voting Rights Act, encouraging voter registration through enforcement of the National Voter Registration Act, and providing data about Asian Pacific American participation.

Voting Information for Minnesota To vote, you must be: A U.S. citizen, at least 18 years old, a Minnesota resident for at least 20 days on election day, and properly registered. Election Dates and Absentee Ballot Application provided here.

Voting in Oregon Casting a ballot is as easy as mailing a letter in Oregon. Vote by mail started in 1981 when the Legislature authorized it for special district elections. Since then, it has become extremely popular and common for many elections.

League of Women Voters: Austin, Texas Qualifications for Voting: You must be a citizen of the United States. You must be at least 18 years old on the day of the election. You must be registered to vote. You may register to vote at any time.

Voting Information in Delaware, Maryland Voting Information: To be eligible to vote, one must be eighteen (18) years of age by the day after the election.

Research and Study Skills: Technology: Electronic Media **473**

Name _____

I Want to Vote!

1. Which web page has information about eliminating discrimination?
Programs — Voting Rights

2. How long must you live in Minnesota to be able to vote in that state?
for at least 20 days before election day

3. In which state listed can you vote by mail? **Oregon**

4. Which web page would you go to for data about how different groups of people voted in past elections?
CENSUS — Voting and Registration Data

5. What is the difference between the voting age requirement in Texas and the voting age requirement in Maryland?
In Texas, you must be 18 on the day of the election. In Maryland, you must be 18 by the day after the election.

6. What key words could you use to find out about voting in Ohio on the Internet?
Enter the key words "voting AND Ohio" in a search engine.

7. What key words could you use to find out about the history of voting rights for women?
Enter key words such as "voting AND rights AND women AND history".

8. Suppose your library has an audiotape of interviews of older women describing their struggles to win the right to vote. How might you use a resource like this in a report on the history of women's voting rights?
Possible answer: You could quote or paraphrase information given by the women interviewed. You could also play part of an audiotape interview during a presentation of your report.

9. Suppose your library had a videotape that showed how to use a voting booth. For what kind of report might this resource be useful?
Possible answer: The videotape may give you useful information if you were writing a report describing the voting process.

10. What are the advantages of searching the Internet for information? **Possible answer: You can search a lot of sources on the Internet very quickly to find information you need. The Internet may contain more up-to-date information than printed sources.**

Notes for Home: Your child analyzed the results of a web page search on the Internet. **Home Activity:** Work with your child to find the requirements for voting in your area. Help your child use a telephone directory or online resources to find the voting requirements.

474 Research and Study Skills: Technology: Electronic Media

© Scott Foresman 5

Practice Book 5.5, p. 211

Name _____

Paraphrasing

- **Paraphrasing** is explaining something in your own words.
- After you read a sentence or paragraph, think about what the author is trying to say. Then put the sentence or paragraph into your own words without changing the meaning or adding your own opinion.

Directions: Reread "A Dream of Equal Rights." Then complete the table.
Paraphrase each original statement in your own words. (The beginning words of each sentence will help you find the sentence to paraphrase.) **Possible answers given.**

Original Statement	My Paraphrase
Paragraph 1, Sentence 1 "Movements are born. . . ."	1. **Movements start when many individuals recognize together that change is needed.**
Paragraph 1, Sentence 3 "Often, it takes. . . ."	2. **Frequently, one individual is required to show the world what is possible.**
Paragraph 2, Sentence 2 "People around the nation. . . ."	3. **From coast to coast, people recognized that some Americans were not getting equal treatment.**
Paragraph 3, Sentence 3 "Many people had. . . ."	4. **Lots of citizens had different plans for gaining those rights.**
Paragraph 3, Sentence 6 "His dream was. . . ."	5. **Achieving peace, justice, and equality was a goal he shared with the entire civil rights movement.**

Notes for Home: Your child read an article and restated its ideas in his or her own words. *Home Activity:* Read a newspaper article with your child. Have your child restate sentences or paragraphs in his or her own words.

Paraphrasing **477**

Practice Book 5.5, p. 212

Name _____

Vocabulary

Directions: Draw a line to connect each word on the left with its definition on the right.

1. liberty — freedom
2. slavery — holding people against their will
3. vow — a solemn promise
4. plantation — a large farm or estate
5. runaway — fugitive

Check the Words You Know
__ liberty
__ plantation
__ quickened
__ runaway
__ slavery
__ unconscious
__ vow

Directions: Choose a word from the box that is the most opposite in meaning for each word or words below. Write the word on the line.

liberty	6. captivity
vow	7. broken promise
quickened	8. slowed
unconscious	9. conscious
slavery	10. freedom

Directions: Choose the word from the box that best completes each sentence. Write the word on the line on the left.

Slavery	11. _____ was a way of life for Annie and her family for as long as Annie could remember.
plantation	12. The master's _____ had more than fifty slaves working in the fields and the house.
vow	13. Annie made a _____ to herself that she would not die a slave.
runaway	14. The punishment for a _____ slave who was caught was severe.
liberty	15. However, for Annie, the chance for true _____ was worth any risk.

Write a Speech
On a separate sheet of paper, write a speech that a person in the 1850s might have delivered in the fight against slavery. Use as many vocabulary words as you can. **Students' speeches should make correct use of vocabulary words.**

Notes for Home: Your child identified and used vocabulary words from "The Long Path to Freedom." *Home Activity:* Talk with your child about what kind of life a slave had. Use the vocabulary words in the conversation.

478 Vocabulary

Practice Book 5.5, p. 213

Name _____

Paraphrasing

- **Paraphrasing** is explaining something in your own words.
- A paraphrase should include only the author's ideas and opinions. When paraphrasing, don't change the meaning or add your own opinions.

Directions: Reread what happened in "The Long Path to Freedom" when Harriet ran away with her brothers. Then answer the questions below.

> That night Harriet waited until her husband, John, fell asleep. Then she slid silently out of their cabin. She met her brothers, and they started off through the woods. Harriet took the lead. She knew the woods. They did not. Every owl that hooted, every frog that croaked startled them. They did not move very fast. And to Harriet they seemed to stomp and crash like a herd of cattle.
> Harriet kept encouraging them on. But at last her brothers stopped. They were frightened. They were going back. Harriet began to protest. They must go on!
>
> From THE STORY OF HARRIET TUBMAN by Kate McMullan. Copyright © 1991 by Parachute Press, Inc. Used by permission of Dell Books, a division of Bantam Doubleday Dell Publishing Group, Inc.

Possible answers given.

1. How might you paraphrase the first two sentences as a single sentence?
After Harriet's husband fell asleep, she quietly left the cabin.

2. How might you paraphrase the last sentence in the first paragraph?
Harriet thought they made a lot of noise walking.

3. How might you paraphrase the second paragraph as a single sentence?
Despite Harriet's urging, her scared brothers refused to go on.

4. How might you paraphrase the final two sentences as a single sentence?
Harriet insisted that they continue.

5. When you paraphrase, why is it important to use your own words and not the author's exact words? Explain your thinking on a separate sheet of paper.
It is wrong to copy an author's words exactly, unless you intend to quote the person.

Notes for Home: Your child read a story and then retold parts of it in his or her own words. *Home Activity:* Read a newspaper article with your child. Challenge your child to restate individual sentences in his or her own words.

Paraphrasing **479**

Practice Book 5.5, p. 215

Name _____

Selection Test

Directions: Choose the best answer to each item. Mark the letter for the answer you have chosen.

Part 1: Vocabulary
Find the answer choice that means about the same as the underlined word in each sentence.

1. Patrick fights for <u>liberty</u>.
   - Ⓐ freedom
   - B. life
   - C. food
   - D. shelter

2. Mercy lived on a <u>plantation</u>.
   - F. boat
   - Ⓖ large farm
   - H. busy road
   - J. government-owned housing

3. Ben told us about his <u>vow</u>.
   - A. experience
   - Ⓑ promise
   - C. secret
   - D. project

4. When we found the child, he was <u>unconscious</u>.
   - F. chilled
   - G. very hungry
   - H. happy
   - Ⓙ not able to think or feel

5. <u>Slavery</u> existed in ancient Greece.
   - Ⓐ a system in which one person can own another
   - B. type of building with columns
   - C. the study of the universe
   - D. a system of measurement

6. The hikers <u>quickened</u> the pace.
   - F. took a rest
   - G. felt better
   - H. cleaned up
   - Ⓙ speeded up

7. The <u>runaway</u> asked for help.
   - A. person with no money
   - B. person who is sick
   - C. person who is from another country
   - Ⓓ person who has left somewhere secretly

Part 2: Comprehension
Use what you know about the selection to answer each item.

8. According to this selection, Harriet's master was—
   - Ⓕ Dr. Thompson.
   - G. John Tubman.
   - H. Mr. Trent.
   - J. Ezekiel Hunn.

9. When Harriet Tubman realized that her mother had been tricked into remaining a slave, she knew that she—
   - A. had to hire a lawyer to become free herself.
   - B. would never be free.
   - Ⓒ would have to go outside the legal system to become free.
   - D. had to go to a judge to free her mother.

10. Harriet trusted the Quaker woman who approached her one morning because—
   - F. the stranger was a female.
   - Ⓖ Quakers did not believe in slavery.
   - H. the woman asked Harriet's name.
   - J. the woman lived near Dr. Thompson's plantation.

GO ON ➡

480 Selection Test

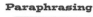
11. How were Harriet's brothers different from her?
  A. They did not mind being slaves.
  B. They wanted to be sold South.
  C. They were not as brave as she was.
  D. They were not as physically strong as she was.

12. Just before Harriet reached the Hunns' house, she—
  F. got a pair of new shoes from Thomas Garrett.
  G. heard slave hunters talking about a runaway girl.
  H. sold her quilt.
  J. put on elegant clothes to wear to the Pennsylvania border.

13. "She wanted to repay her kindness. She had no money, but she had one thing she valued." Which is the best paraphrase of these sentences?
  A. She wanted to show she was thankful. Although she had no money, she did own one valuable item.
  B. She wanted to get something back for being so kind. She didn't care about money, but she loved nice things.
  C. She decided that the only way to repay the woman was with kindness, since she had no money.
  D. She didn't want to have to pay the woman, since she had no money and only one valuable possession.

14. Harriet knows that she has found the right man in the cemetery when he—
  F. tips his hat toward her.
  G. says he has a ticket for the railroad.
  H. gives her a pair of shoes.
  J. tells her that he is a Quaker.

15. Ezekiel Hunn and Thomas Garrett would likely agree that—
  A. slaves are property and should be returned to their owners.
  B. a runaway slave is worth about the same as a bale of cotton.
  C. Harriet Tubman did a foolish thing when she tried to escape.
  D. no one has the right to own another human being.

STOP

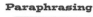
Paraphrasing

- **Paraphrasing** is explaining something in your own words.
- A paraphrase should include only the author's ideas and opinions. When paraphrasing, don't change the meaning or add your own opinions.

Directions: Read the passage below. Each sentence is numbered.

(1) In the 1600s, slavery spread quickly in the South, where laborers toiled on large plantations that grew cotton, tobacco, and other crops. (2) But in the North, where small farms and businesses existed, there were fewer slaves. (3) During the 1700s, many American leaders began to speak out against slavery, which nonetheless continued to grow. (4) By 1860, the Southern states had about four million slaves. (5) In fact, slaves made up almost a third of the population in the region at that time.

Directions: Complete the table. Rewrite the numbered sentences in your own words. **Possible answers given.**

Sentences	Paraphrases
1	1. **Slavery spread rapidly on Southern plantations in the 1600s.**
2	2. **Fewer slaves were needed in small Northern farms and businesses.**
3	3. **In the 1700s, many people started protesting slavery, which kept spreading.**
4	4. **There were about 4 million Southern slaves by 1860.**
5	5. **Slaves were nearly a third of the Southern population at the time.**

 Notes for Home: Your child read a passage and then retold parts of it in his or her own words. *Home Activity:* Read a magazine article together with your child. Let your child restate individual sentences in his or her own words.

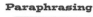
Main Idea and Supporting Details/Summarizing

REVIEW

Directions: Read the passage. Then read each question about the passage. Choose the best answer to each question. Mark the letter for the answer you have chosen.

Slavery

The practice of human slavery is something we would like to think had a short history that has long since ceased to be. It is hard to imagine how any group of people could think they could own another group of people.

It is a sad truth, however, that slavery has a long history. There is evidence that slavery was first practiced in prehistoric times. It became widespread in Greece and in the Roman Empire. During the 1500s and 1600s, slavery was established in the New World as Europeans established colonies in the Americas. They brought slaves from Africa to work on sugar plantations in the West Indies and South America. Later, slavery spread to North America.

Eventually, changing attitudes about human rights brought an end to slavery in most parts of the world. But slavery is still practiced today in parts of Africa, Asia, and South America. While the number of people living in slavery is unknown, most slaves are believed to be captives of war or persons sold into slavery to pay debts.

People who are enslaved are almost always restricted in many ways. Often they cannot legally marry or have a family. They cannot testify in court, vote, or own property. They are forced to work hard for little or no pay.

1. The main idea in the second paragraph is that—
  A. Greece had slaves.
  B. Slavery ended in places.
  C. Asia still has slavery.
  D. The practice of slavery is very old.

2. A detail that supports the main idea of the second paragraph is that—
  F. slaves are restricted.
  G. there was slavery in prehistoric times.
  H. slavery is very old.
  J. slaves can't vote.

3. The main idea in the fourth paragraph is that—
  A. slaves are restricted.
  B. slaves can't testify in court.
  C. Africa has slavery.
  D. attitudes have changed.

4. A detail that supports the main idea of the fourth paragraph is that—
  F. the New World had slavery.
  G. slavery is historic.
  H. attitudes have changed.
  J. slaves can't testify in court.

5. Which statement best summarizes the article?
  A. Slavery is everywhere.
  B. Slavery is an old and inhumane practice.
  C. Slavery has now ended.
  D. Slavery means hard work.

 Notes for Home: Your child identified the main ideas and supporting details of an article and summarized it. *Home Activity:* Read a newspaper article with your child. Together, identify its main ideas and supporting details. Then have your child summarize the article.

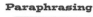
Writing Across Texts

Directions: Think about how "The Long Path to Freedom" and "How the Underground Railroad Got Its Name" help describe the escape system for slaves known as the Underground Railroad. What might slaves have wanted to know about the Underground Railroad before they risked their lives and made the trip? Complete the following table by listing questions slaves may have had. **Possible answers given.**

Questions About the Underground Railroad
What are the risks?
1. **What are the possible routes?**
2. **Where will I stop along the way?**
3. **How long will the trip take?**
4. **What will happen when I get there?**
5. **What items will I need to bring and wear?**

Write a Brochure

Use questions from your table, details from both selections, and information from any other sources to write and illustrate a secret brochure designed for Underground Railroad conductors to help them help slaves understand and prepare for their journeys to freedom. **Brochures will vary. Check that the brochures give accurate information about the Underground Railroad and answer students' questions.**

 Notes for Home: Your child designed a brochure about the Underground Railroad. *Home Activity:* Help your child write a poem about what it might have been like to be hiding, or hiding someone, on the Underground Railroad.

© Scott Foresman   5

Name _____

The Long Path to Freedom

Grammar: Pronouns

REVIEW

Directions: Replace each phrase with a pronoun. Write the letter of the pronoun of the line.

b	1. Harriet Tubman	a. he
c	2. my friend and I	b. she
e	3. the runaway slaves	c. we
d	4. the Underground Railroad	d. it
a	5. Abraham Lincoln	e. they

Directions: Choose the correct pronoun in ( ) to complete the sentence. Write the pronoun on the line.

We	6. (We/Us) were walking near the State House in Boston.
I	7. (I/Me) was the one who noticed the statue.
me	8. What I learned about the statue impressed (I/me).
us	9. The name Colonel Robert Gould Shaw puzzled (we/us).
we	10. Then (we/us) read that Colonel Shaw had led a regiment of African American soldiers in the Civil War.
we	11. As (we/us) discovered, this Massachusetts regiment had fought bravely.
me	12. It saddened (I/me), though, that almost half of the regiment had been killed in a single battle.
us	13. A passerby told (we/us) that one soldier had been given the Medal of Honor.
me	14. That really impressed (I/me).
we	15. Would (we/us) learn other interesting facts on our trip to Boston?

Directions: Replace the underlined pronoun and verb with a contraction. Write the contraction on the line.

I'll	16. <u>I will</u> tell you about one man's remarkable rise from slavery.
You've	17. <u>You have</u> heard of Frederick Douglass, haven't you?
he'd	18. Although <u>he had</u> been a slave, he learned to read and write.
It's	19. <u>It is</u> amazing that a few years after escaping he wrote a book.
he's	20. Today <u>he is</u> still a much-quoted historical figure.

Notes for Home: Your child identified pronouns, used *I, me, we,* and *us* in sentences, and wrote contractions. *Home Activity:* Read sentences aloud, leaving out the pronoun. Ask your child which pronoun makes sense in each sentence.

Grammar: Pronouns   485

Name _____

The Long Path to Freedom

Grammar: Subject and Object Pronouns

Pronouns used as the subjects of sentences are called **subject pronouns.**
<u>He</u> traveled with friends.
<u>They</u> cared about his safety.

Singular Subject Pronouns: I, you, he, she, it
Plural Subject Pronouns: we, you, they

When you use a person's name and a pronoun in a compound subject, be sure to use a subject pronoun. When *I* is used with another noun, *I* comes last.
Aunt Kate and <u>I</u> went on the journey too.
<u>She</u> and <u>I</u> had wanted to join the group.

Pronouns that follow action verbs are called **object pronouns.**
We joined <u>him</u> near the train station.

Singular Object Pronouns: me, you, him, her, it
Plural Object Pronouns: us, you, them

Directions: Underline each subject pronoun once. Underline each object pronoun twice.

1. <u>We</u> accompanied <u>them</u> on the road.
2. <u>He</u> and <u>they</u> helped <u>us</u> along the way.
3. Later <u>we</u> met two more friends and asked <u>them</u> for help.
4. <u>They</u> led <u>us</u> to a restaurant owner.
5. <u>He</u> and the cook gave <u>us</u> a meal inside.

Directions: Circle the correct pronoun in ( ) to complete each sentence.

6. The two men offered (we/(us)) plenty of food.
7. ((They)/them) asked about our trip on the road.
8. They gave Aunt Kate and (I/(me)) travel directions.
9. Soon ((she)/her) said it was time to go.
10. We had extra rolls, so we took (they/(them)) in a paper bag.

Notes for Home: Your child identified subject and object pronouns. *Home Activity:* Look at magazine pictures or photographs together. Ask your child to use subject pronouns and object pronouns to describe the people and actions in each picture.

486   Grammar: Subject and Object Pronouns

Name _____

The Long Path to Freedom

Grammar: Subject and Object Pronouns

Directions: Underline the pronoun in each sentence. Write S on the line if the pronoun is a subject pronoun. Write O if it is an object pronoun.

S	1. <u>We</u> read about a slave named Kunta Kinte.
S	2. <u>He</u> traveled from Africa to America by ship, long ago.
O	3. The voyage was a terrible ordeal, yet Kinte survived <u>it</u>.
O	4. Traders in slavery had captured <u>him</u> in Africa.
O	5. The slave trade made <u>them</u> wealthy at the cost of human rights and human lives.
O	6. Alex Haley gave <u>us</u> Kinte's true story in a book called *Roots*.
S	7. <u>He</u> had heard about the young African boy from older members of the Haley family.
O	8. The capture of Kunta Kinte moved <u>him</u> greatly.
S	9. <u>I</u> thought the story was fascinating.
O	10. My grandparents bought <u>me</u> the TV film version of *Roots*.

Directions: Circle the correct pronoun in ( ) to complete each sentence.

11. (Us/(We)) wanted information about the TV film.
12. We admired Kunta Kinte and wondered who had played ((him)/he).
13. A classmate and (me/(I)) tried several searches on the computer catalog.
14. A librarian supplied (we/(us)) with printouts of reviews.
15. Your library can help ((you)/it) learn more about Alex Haley, Kunta Kinte, *Roots*, and slavery.

Write a Journal

Think of a person from the past that you learned about from your family or from a book or TV show. Imagine you are that person. What is your life like? What difficulties have you had to face? On a separate sheet of paper, write several entries for a journal. Tell what things you might see or have experienced. Use subject and object pronouns. **Students' subject pronouns should serve as subjects in the sentences, and their object pronouns should serve as direct and indirect objects of verbs.**

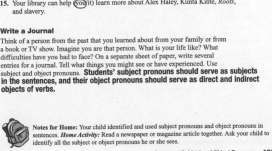

Notes for Home: Your child identified and used subject pronouns and object pronouns in sentences. *Home Activity:* Read a newspaper or magazine article together. Ask your child to identify all the subject or object pronouns he or she sees.

Grammar: Subject and Object Pronouns   487

Name _____

The Long Path to Freedom

Grammar: Subject and Object Pronouns

RETEACHING

The action verb in each sentence below is underlined. Circle the pronoun or pronouns in each sentence.

1. ((I)) <u>bought</u> a parakeet from a friend last week.
2. Dad <u>thanked</u> ((her.))
3. ((He)) and ((I)) <u>left</u> with the new bird.

Notice that in sentences 1 and 3, the pronouns are the subjects of the sentences. These are **subject pronouns.** In sentence 2, the pronoun comes after the action verb. It is an **object pronoun.**

Use a **subject pronoun** as the subject of a sentence. Use an **object pronoun** after an action verb. When you use *I* or *me* and another pronoun or someone else's name, use *I* or *me* last.

Directions: Write each sentence with the correct word or words in ( ).

1. Judy and (I/me) read books about birds.
   Judy and I read books about birds.

2. Mom and Dad gave (me and Judy/Judy and me) some information.
   Mom and Dad gave Judy and me some information.

3. Dad and (I/me) taught the bird how to talk.
   Dad and I taught the bird how to talk.

Directions: Write each sentence with the correct pronoun in ( ). Circle **subject** if the pronoun is in the subject. Circle **object** if the pronoun is in the predicate.

4. Hilda and (her/she) own a parrot.
   Hilda and she own a parrot.   ((subject))   object

5. Fernando and (I/me) are raising pigeons.
   Fernando and I are raising pigeons.   ((subject))   object

6. Our parents help Fernando and (I/me).
   Our parents help Fernando and me.   subject   ((object))

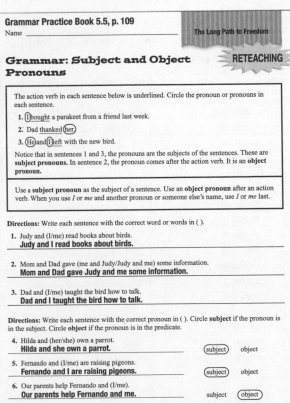

Notes for Home: Your child chose subject and object pronouns to complete sentences. *Home Activity:* Talk about what your family has been doing recently. Have your child write sentences about family activities, using subject and object pronouns. *(he, she, they; him, her, them)*

488   Grammar: Subject and Object Pronouns

© Scott Foresman 5

Name _____

The Long Path to Freedom

Grammar: Subject and Object Pronouns

Directions: Circle the pronouns in each sentence below. Write each pronoun under the correct heading on the chart.

1. Tena and (I) made that clay sculpture of a cat.
2. (It) and the other sculptures are on the table.
3. The art instructors helped (her) and (me.)
4. A famous artist once spoke to (us.)
5. (She) and (they) worked with the students.
6. (We) and the other students learned a great deal.
7. (You) and (he) should visit the art class sometime.
8. Tena will show (you) two and (him) what to do.

Subject Pronouns		Object Pronouns	
I	it	she	her	me	us
they	we	you	you	him
he			

Directions: Complete each sentence by writing a name from the name box and the correct pronoun from the pronoun box. **Possible answers given.**

| Bill | Emilio | Kim | Lucy | | I | me |

9. _____ **Bill** _____ and _____ **I** _____ bought a book.
10. The store owner led **Emilio** and **me** to it.
11. My father drove **Kim** and **me** to the store.

Write a Paragraph

On a separate sheet of paper, write a paragraph about a project you might do. Tell how you and a friend would work together to complete the project. Use subject and object pronouns.

Check to make sure that students have used subject and object pronouns correctly.

Notes for Home: Your child identified subject and object pronouns in sentences. *Home Activity:* Sit around a table with a group. Play a passing game. Pass objects as fast as possible, saying a sentence with two pronouns, such as, "I pass this _____ to him" as you pass the object.

Grammar: Subject and Object Pronouns **489**

Name _____

The Long Path to Freedom

Word Study: Suffixes

Directions: Letters added to the ends of words are called **suffixes**. Suffixes can change the meaning of the base word. Add a suffix to each word below to make a new word. Write each new word on the line.

	Base Word		Suffix		New Word
1.	free	+	-dom	=	freedom
2.	legal	+	-ly	=	legally
3.	own	+	-er	=	owner
4.	grate	+	-ful	=	grateful
5.	joy	+	-ous	=	joyous
6.	risk	+	-y	=	risky

Directions: Read the diary entry below. Find nine words that have the suffix -ly, -er, -ful, -ous, or -y. Circle the words. Then write the base word and the suffix on the line connected by a + sign. For example, for **slowly,** you would write **slow + ly.**

June 9, 1863

On a dark and (rainy) night, I packed my things into a bundle. (Silently,) I slipped from the cabin and (quickly) disappeared into the woods. The journey was (dangerous) and (lonely.) Each day I feared that a slave (tracker) was following me. But when I crossed the state line, my heart set up a (thunderous) beat. A (joyful) feeling came over me. I was on my own! I was free! And it felt (wonderful!)

7. _____ rain + y
8. _____ silent + ly
9. _____ quick + ly
10. _____ danger + ous
11. _____ lone + ly
12. _____ track + er
13. _____ thunder + ous
14. _____ joy + ful
15. _____ wonder + ful

Notes for Home: Your child added suffixes to base words to make new words, such as *slow + ly = slowly.* *Home Activity:* Read an advertisement with your child. Help your child notice words with suffixes. Ask your child to write down the words and circle the suffixes.

490 Word Study: Suffixes

Name _____

The Long Path to Freedom

Spelling: Suffixes -able, -ible, -ant, -ent

Pretest Directions: Fold back the page along the dotted line. On the blanks, write the spelling words as they are dictated. When you have finished the test, unfold the page and check your words.

1. comfortable
2. reasonable
3. washable
4. agreeable
5. valuable
6. responsible
7. convertible
8. flexible
9. sensible
10. reversible
11. contestant
12. defiant
13. observant
14. servant
15. occupant
16. student
17. urgent
18. confident
19. resident
20. opponent

1. This is a **comfortable** chair.
2. That is a **reasonable** question.
3. His shirt is hand **washable**.
4. Are you **agreeable** to the plan?
5. She owns a **valuable** painting.
6. Who is **responsible** for you?
7. I saw a **convertible** car go by.
8. The hose is **flexible**.
9. Jane is a very **sensible** person.
10. He bought a **reversible** jacket.
11. That **contestant** won the game.
12. Are you **defiant** of my orders?
13. A detective must be **observant**.
14. Their **servant** has her own car.
15. The house has a new **occupant**.
16. The **student** won an award.
17. I received an **urgent** letter.
18. We are **confident** we will win.
19. He is a **resident** of San Antonio.
20. My **opponent** played well.

Notes for Home: Your child took a pretest on words that have the suffixes *-able, -ible, -ant,* and *-ent.* *Home Activity:* Help your child learn misspelled words before the final test. Your child can underline the word parts that caused the problems and concentrate on those parts.

Spelling: Suffixes *-able, -ible, -ant, -ent* **491**

Name _____

The Long Path to Freedom

Spelling: Suffixes -able, -ible, -ant, -ent

		Word List		
comfortable	valuable	sensible	observant	urgent
reasonable	responsible	reversible	servant	confident
washable	convertible	contestant	occupant	resident
agreeable	flexible	defiant	student	opponent

Directions: Choose the words from the box that have the suffixes **-able** and **-ible.** Write each word in the correct column. **Order may vary.**

Words with -able
1. comfortable
2. reasonable
3. washable
4. agreeable
5. valuable

Words with -ible
6. responsible
7. convertible
8. flexible
9. sensible
10. reversible

Directions: Choose the word from the box that best matches each clue. Write the word on the line.

11. someone who enters a contest — **contestant**
12. a person who occupies a place — **occupant**
13. someone who serves — **servant**
14. a person who studies — **student**
15. watchful, quick to notice — **observant**
16. the person who resides in a place — **resident**
17. something that needs immediate attention — **urgent**
18. disobedient — **defiant**
19. a person or group on the opposite side in a game or debate — **opponent**
20. very sure of yourself — **confident**

Notes for Home: Your child spelled words that end with *-able, -ible, -ant,* and *-ent.* *Home Activity:* Start to spell each word slowly, one letter at a time. When your child recognizes the word, have him or her say the whole word and then spell it.

492 Spelling: Suffixes *-able, -ible, -ant, -ent*

© Scott Foresman 5

Spelling: Suffixes -able, -ible, -ant, -ent

Directions: Proofread this speech. Find five spelling mistakes.
Use the proofreading marks to correct each mistake.

≡	Make a capital.
/	Make a small letter.
∧	Add something.
ℐ	Take out something.
⊙	Add a period.
¶	Begin a new paragraph.

*Ladies and gentlemen, I am an oppon**e**nt of slavery
who brings you an urgent message today. No serv**a**nt can
be comfortable as a forced resident or occup**a**nt in a home
that is not agreeable. As respons**i**ble and sensible people, we
must admit that slavery is not reason**a**ble nor humane. Free
all slaves, because freedom is valuable to all people!*

Spelling Tip

For base words that end in
e, drop the **e** before adding
the suffixes **-able, -ible,
-ant,** and **-ent.** For most
words that end in **y**, change
the **y** to an **i** and then add
the suffix.

Word List

comfortable	responsible	contestant
reasonable	convertible	defiant
washable	flexible	observant
agreeable	sensible	servant
valuable	reversible	occupant
		student
		urgent
		confident
		resident
		opponent

Write a Speech

Imagine you were asked to give a speech about a
subject you feel strongly about. On a separate sheet of
paper, write the speech you would deliver. Try to use
at least five of your spelling words. **Answers will
vary, but each speech should include at least
five spelling words.**

Notes for Home: Your child spelled words that end with *-able, -ible, -ant,* and *-ent.* **Home
Activity:** Spell each spelling word for your child, but purposely make one or more letters
wrong. See if your child can recognize each error and spell the word correctly.

Spelling: Suffixes -able, -ible, -ant, -ent

Word List

comfortable	valuable	sensible	observant	urgent
reasonable	responsible	reversible	servant	confident
washable	convertible	contestant	occupant	resident
agreeable	flexible	defiant	student	opponent

Directions: Complete each equation to spell a word from the box. Write each
word on the line.

1. serve – e + ant = **servant**
2. observe – e + ant = **observant**
3. urge – e + ent = **urgent**
4. study – y + ent = **student**
5. defy – y + i + ant = **defiant**
6. confide – e + ent = **confident**
7. occupy – y + ant = **occupant**
8. reside – e + ent = **resident**
9. contest + ant = **contestant**
10. flex + ible = **flexible**

Directions: Choose the word from the box that best completes each sentence.
Write the word on the line to the left.

reasonable 11. Car Salesperson: You can buy this car at a very _____ price.

responsible 12. Home Owner: I'll find out who's _____ for this broken window!

reversible 13. Clothing Store Clerk: You'll love this _____ jacket. It's green on one side and purple on the other.

comfortable 14. Grandmother: Do you need another blanket, dear, or are you _____ now?

agreeable 15. Team Captain: If it's _____ to everyone, we'll meet for practice at 10:00 A.M.

valuable 16. Detective: Someone has stolen a very _____ diamond necklace!

sensible 17. Scout Leader: If you get lost, the _____ thing to do is to follow the creek.

washable 18. Baby Sitter: Oh, no! I thought the walls were all _____.

convertible 19. Driver: Let's put down the top on the _____ and drive it.

opponent 20. Chess player: My _____ must make the next move.

Notes for Home: Your child spelled words that end with *-able, -ible, -ant,* and *-ent.* **Home
Activity:** Read a newspaper article with your child. Together, see how many words you can
find that have the ending *-able, -ible, -ant,* or *-ent.*

Time Line

A **time line** is a line divided into years or other periods of time. The line is labeled
with events that show when events happened or will happen in time order.

Directions: The time line below shows when slavery was abolished, or outlawed,
in various parts of the world. Use it to answer the questions on the next page.

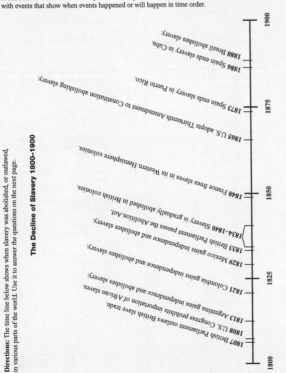

The Decline of Slavery 1800–1900

1900
1888 Brazil abolishes slavery.
1886 Spain ends slavery in Cuba.
1875
1873 Spain ends slavery in Puerto Rico.
1865 U.S. adopts Thirteenth Amendment to Constitution abolishing slavery.
1850
1848 France frees slaves in its Western Hemisphere colonies.
1834–1840 Slavery is gradually abolished in British colonies.
1833 British Parliament passes the Abolition Act.
1829 Mexico gains independence and abolishes slavery.
1825
1821 Colombia gains independence and abolishes slavery.
1813 Argentina gains independence and abolishes slavery.
1808 U.S. Congress prohibits importation of African slaves.
1807 British Parliament outlaws British slave trade.
1800

---

1. How many years does the time line show? **100 years**
2. How many years does each of the four sections of the time line represent? **25 years**
3. When did it become illegal to import slaves into the United States? **1808**
4. When was slavery abolished in Brazil? **1888**
5. What happened in 1865? **The Thirteenth Amendment to the Constitution was adopted, abolishing slavery.**
6. When did the British Parliament pass the Abolition Act? **1833**
7. When did France end slavery in its Western Hemisphere colonies? **1848**
8. What happened between 1834 and 1840? **Slavery was gradually abolished in British colonies.**
9. Who ended its slave trade first, Great Britain or the United States? **Great Britain**
10. How many years passed between the abolition of slave importation and the abolition of slavery in the United States? **57 years**
11. Which nation—Britain, Spain, or France—was the last to end slavery in its colonies? **Spain**
12. Summarize the events that took place between 1810 and 1830. **Three Latin American nations—Argentina, Colombia, and Mexico—gained independence and abolished slavery.**
13. President Lincoln signed the Emancipation Proclamation in January 1863. This document freed all slaves in the Confederate states. Between which two events would you place this event on the time line? **between France freeing slaves in 1848 and the United States abolishing slavery in 1865**
14. Do you think a time line is a useful way to present this information about slavery? Explain. **Yes, the time line helps show at a glance when slavery ended in different parts of the world.**
15. If you were to make a time line showing five upcoming events in your future, what would they be? Give a date and list each event in time order. **Events will vary. Check that students list events in chronological order.**

Notes for Home: Your child read and interpreted a time line showing when slavery ended in
various countries. **Home Activity:** With your child, list several important events in your child's
life and include the years. Then help your child create a time line of the events.

Visualizing

- **Visualizing** is creating a picture in your mind as you read.
- An author may help you visualize by using imagery. This happens when an author uses words that give you a strong mental picture or image. *Enormous billowing clouds* is an example of imagery.
- Another way an author may help you become part of what you are reading is through sensory details. Authors use words that describe how something looks, sounds, smells, tastes, or feels to do this.

Directions: Reread "Little Billy's Swan Rides." Then complete the table. List **Possible** examples of words and phrases from the story that appeal to one of the five senses. **answers given.**

Example	Sense
house was quiet	hearing
curtains were drawn back	1. **sight**
2. **window was open wide**	3. **sight**
4. **great white bird**	5. **sight**
6. **magical world of silence**	7. **hearing**
8. **pale golden light**	9. **sight**
10. **huge gaping hole**	11. **sight**
12. **brightness like sunlight**	13. **sight**
14. **vast lake of water, gloriously blue**	15. **sight**

Notes for Home: Your child read a story and identified words and phrases that helped create a mental picture of story events. *Home Activity:* Choose a familiar place. Give clues about how this place looks, smells, and sounds. Have your child guess the place.

Visualizing 499

Vocabulary

Directions: Read the following paragraph. Choose the word from the box that best completes each sentence. Write the word on the matching numbered line to the right.

Tom Cat's whiskers acted as 1. _____ to help him find his way in the dark. Suddenly, a shadow came swooping down and swept him up in the air! As Tom Cat rose into the air, the very strong winds felt like a 2. _____ against his face. 3. _____ to whatever had snatched him, Tom yelled for help. Then he heard a deep chuckle and tilted his head back to see Harry Hawk! "Doesn't it give you a 4. _____ to fly on exciting 5. _____ such as these?" asked Harry innocently.

1. **feelers**
2. **gale**
3. **Clinging**
4. **thrill**
5. **excursions**

Check the Words You Know

__ clinging
__ excursions
__ feelers
__ gale
__ thrill

Directions: Choose the word from the box that has the same or nearly the same meaning as each word or phrase below. Write the word on the line.

6. clutching   **clinging**
7. high wind   **gale**
8. trips   **excursions**

9. excitement   **thrill**
10. an animal's sensors   **feelers**

Write a Travel Log

Where do your journeys take you? On a separate sheet of paper, write an entry in a travel log describing a real or imaginary journey. Describe the people you meet, the animals you see, and the adventures you have. Use as many vocabulary words as you can in your travel log. **Student's log should describe a journey and make correct use of vocabulary words.**

Notes for Home: Your child identified and used vocabulary words from *Chester Cricket's Pigeon Ride*. *Home Activity:* Invite your child to draw a cartoon describing an adventure on a first flight. Help him or her use as many vocabulary words as possible in the speech balloons.

500   Vocabulary

Visualizing

- **Visualizing** is creating a picture in your mind as you read.
- Authors may help you visualize by using imagery. These are words that give you a strong mental picture, or image.
- Another way an author may help you visualize is through sensory details. These are words that describe how something looks, sounds, smells, tastes, or feels.

Directions: Reread what happens in *Chester Cricket's Pigeon Ride* when Lulu takes Chester to Central Park. Then answer the questions below. Think about how the author uses imagery and sensory details to help you visualize.

"Here's Central Park," Lulu screeched against the wind.

And now Chester had another thrill. For there weren't only sycamore trees in the park. The cricket could smell birches, beeches, and maples—elms, oaks—almost as many kinds of trees as Connecticut itself had to offer. And there was the moon!—the crescent moon—reflected in a little lake. Sounds, too, rose up to him: the shooshing of leaves, the nighttime countryside whispering of insects and little animals, and—best of all—a brook that was arguing with itself, as it splashed over rocks. The miracle of Central Park, a sheltered wilderness in the midst of the city, pierced Chester's heart with joy.

From CHESTER CRICKET'S PIGEON RIDE by George Selden pictures by Garth Williams. Text copyright © 1981 by George Selden Thompson. Illustrations copyright © 1981 by Garth Williams. Reprinted by permission of Farrar, Straus, & Giroux, Inc.

Possible answers given.

1. Which details in the passage help you visualize what the park smells like?
Chester smells many different kinds of trees.

2. Which details in the passage help you visualize what the park sounds like?
Lulu screeched; leaves shooshing, insects and animals whispering, brook splashing

3. Which details help you visualize what the park looks like?
the reflection of the crescent moon in the little lake, and the many trees

4. What sound reminds Chester of an argument?
the water of the brook splashing over rocks

5. How does the author help you visualize the view from the top of the Empire State Building? On a separate sheet of paper, list the sensory details and imagery he uses.
The author describes a strong wind, people looking as small as bugs, miniature taxis and buses, and Chester's dizziness. These details help the reader feel and see the building's great height.

Notes for Home: Your child read a story and pictured the scene in his or her mind. *Home Activity:* Have your child listen as you describe how an object looks, sounds, smells, feels, or tastes. See if your child can guess what it is. Then switch roles and repeat.

Visualizing   501

Selection Test

Directions: Choose the best answer to each item. Mark the letter for the answer you have chosen.

Part 1: Vocabulary

Find the answer choice that means about the same as the underlined word in each sentence.

1. This is such a <u>thrill</u>!
   A. scary movie
   Ⓑ exciting feeling
   C. grand performance
   D. sudden storm

2. He was <u>clinging</u> to his mother.
   F. speaking in a soft voice
   G. singing words over and over again
   H. sitting next to
   Ⓙ holding on tightly

3. They flew into the <u>gale</u>.
   A. side of a mountain
   B. tall building in a city
   Ⓒ very strong wind
   D. large storm cloud

4. Margo has taken many <u>excursions</u>.
   F. photographs
   G. tests
   H. helpings
   Ⓙ trips

5. A cricket has several <u>feelers</u>.
   A. close friends
   Ⓑ parts of an insect's body used for sensing
   C. family members
   D. strong emotions

Part 2: Comprehension

Use what you know about the story to answer each item.

6. Chester's friend Lulu is a—
   Ⓕ pigeon.
   G. cricket.
   H. mouse.
   J. cat.

7. How did Chester get from Connecticut to the city?
   A. He crossed the Atlantic on a sailing vessel.
   Ⓑ He was carried there inside a picnic basket.
   C. He took an airplane ride.
   D. He flew there on a pigeon's back.

8. Lulu gives Chester a—
   F. ride on the subway.
   G. free trip to Connecticut.
   H. place to stay in Bryant Park.
   Ⓙ tour of New York.

9. Which phrase best helps you see in your mind what Central Park looks like?
   A. "Big beautiful Central Park!"
   B. "coasted down through the air"
   Ⓒ "a sheltered wilderness in the midst of the city"
   D. "the best place in the city"

10. How does Chester feel about flying?
    F. completely terrified
    G. extremely bored
    Ⓗ a little afraid, but excited
    J. somewhat embarrassed

11. While flying down into Central Park, Lulu probably looks most like a—
    Ⓐ paper airplane.
    B. hunting bird.
    C. hot-air balloon.
    D. speeding bullet.

502   Selection Test

GO ON

© Scott Foresman   5

---

794   Answers

12. How can you tell that Chester is very happy in Central Park?
   F. He jumps up and down.
   G. He dances around with Lulu.
   H. He holds on to Lulu's claw.
   Ⓙ. He chirps to his heart's content.

13. Which sentence from the story gives an opinion?
   A. "Lulu gripped the pinnacle of the TV antenna with both her claws."
   B. "They reached the Battery, . . . part of lower New York."
   Ⓒ. "The finest shops in all the world are on Fifth Avenue."
   D. "Her right hand was holding something up."

14. After being blown off the Empire State Building, Chester most likely wants to return to the drainpipe because he—
   F. is angry at Lulu for putting his life in danger.
   Ⓖ. needs to feel safe again.
   H. wants to tell everyone about his adventure.
   J. wants to pack up and leave New York.

15. Which part of this story is fantasy?
   Ⓐ. A cricket talks to a pigeon.
   B. A pigeon flies over New York.
   C. A cricket chirps in Central Park.
   D. A pigeon looks at the Statue of Liberty.

STOP

Visualizing

- **Visualizing** is creating a picture in your mind as you read.
- Authors may help you visualize by using imagery. These are words that give you a strong mental picture.
- Another way an author may help you visualize is through sensory details. These are words that describe how something looks, sounds, smells, tastes, or feels.

Directions: Read the story below.

Their first trip to Yankee Stadium! Josh and Tom were excited. The view from their seats, high up in the stadium, was marvelous. The huge field was brilliantly green. The Yankees' white uniforms gleamed in the sunshine. The sound of the stadium organ mingled with the vendors' cries of "Ice cream!" "Popcorn!" and "Hot dogs!" The smells of the hot food made Tom's mouth water. He bought a steaming hot dog. Josh thirstily gulped a tart lemonade.

Then the voice of the announcer boomed, "Good afternoon, ladies and gentlemen. Welcome to Yankee Stadium." Josh and Tom exchanged wide grins as they settled back to enjoy the game. The seats were a bit hard, and there wasn't much room to stretch their legs, but who cared? Today was a dream come true!

Directions: Complete the web. Visualize the story details in your mind. What do you see? hear? feel? taste? smell? **Possible answers given.**

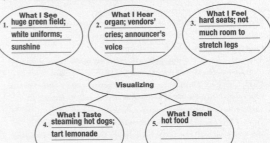

1. **What I See** huge green field; white uniforms; sunshine
2. **What I Hear** organ; vendors' cries; announcer's voice
3. **What I Feel** hard seats; not much room to stretch legs

Visualizing

4. **What I Taste** steaming hot dogs; tart lemonade
5. **What I Smell** hot food

 Notes for Home: Your child read a story and visualized, or pictured, the story details in his or her mind. *Home Activity:* Ask your child to describe his or her favorite place. Encourage your child to describe what can be seen, heard, smelled, felt, and tasted in that place.

Paraphrasing

REVIEW

Directions: Read the story. Then read each question about the story. Choose the best answer to each question. Mark the letter for the answer you have chosen.

Strange Planet

Maria, the nation's newest astronaut, journeyed to the planet Backwards. No one had ever explored the territory before. Maria was overwhelmed by what she found there.

On this planet, everything appeared upside down and backwards from the way it appeared on Earth. The planet had a ground of clouds and a sky of grass. The trees grew with their leaves down and their roots up. When it rained, the rain actually traveled upward.

The people of Backwards had their faces on the backs of their heads. They greeted Maria with a "good-bye." And when they were ready to leave, they said "hello."

"This planet certainly deserves its name," Maria said to herself. She couldn't wait to get back to Earth, where everything and everyone was right side up and forward!

1. Which of the following best paraphrases the first two sentences in the first paragraph?
   A. Astronaut Maria wasn't sure she wanted to go to Backwards.
   B. Astronaut Maria was sent to the planet Backwards.
   Ⓒ. Astronaut Maria was the first to explore the planet Backwards.
   D. Maria, the nation's newest astronaut, journeyed to the planet Backwards.

2. Which of the following best paraphrases the second and third sentences in the second paragraph?
   Ⓕ. Clouds and grass were reversed, and trees grew upside down.
   G. The sky was grass, and the ground was clouds.

   H. Leaves grew down, and roots grew up on trees.
   J. The trees had no roots, and the leaves grew underground.

3. Which of the following best paraphrases the third paragraph?
   A. People had backward heads, feet, and arms.
   Ⓑ. People had backward heads and said "good-bye" first and "hello" last.
   C. The people of Backwards had their faces on the backs of their heads.
   D. People had backward heads and said "hello" last.

4. Which of the following best paraphrases the last paragraph?
   F. Maria was frightened by the planet Backwards.
   G. Maria couldn't wait to get back to Earth and return to a normal life.
   H. Maria was ready to leave Backwards and return to Earth.
   Ⓙ. Maria found Backwards deserving of its name and was eager to return to a right side up and forward Earth.

5. Which of the following best paraphrases the whole story?
   A. Maria traveled to Backwards and never returned to Earth.
   B. Maria loved being an astronaut.
   C. The people of Backwards do everything in reverse.
   Ⓓ. Astronaut Maria explored Backwards, a planet where everything is backwards or upside down.

 Notes for Home: Your child identified statements that best paraphrase a story. *Home Activity:* Say a pair of sentences to your child, such as *It would be fun to take a vacation. We could go camping.* Challenge your child to restate the same idea in a single sentence.

Writing Across Texts

Directions: Think about how Chester the cricket traveled in the excerpt from *Chester Cricket's Pigeon Ride.* The animals in "Easy Riders" also ride on other animals. Complete the web with reasons explaining why these animals travel that way. **Possible answers given.**

1. **Chester the Cricket** Chester rides on Lulu's claw for a sightseeing tour of New York City.

2. **Remora** Remora ride on other sea animals to get food.

3. **Crocodiles** Crocodile mothers carry their new babies from land (where they are born) to the safety of nearby water.

Why Animals Hitch a Ride on Other Animals

4. **Poison Frogs** Poison frogs carry their tadpoles to a nearby pool of water.

5. **Anemones** Some anemones hitch rides on the shells of hermit crabs. They get food while the crab is eating a meal.

Write a Conversation

Use the ideas from your web to write a conversation between the animals on the web above. Write on a separate sheet of paper. **Conversations will vary. Check that the dialogues use details from the web.**

 Notes for Home: Your child wrote a conversation between animals who are in selections they read. *Home Activity:* With your child, read a story about an animal who depends on others. Ask your child how the animal in the story is like a person.

Answers 795

Grammar: Subject and Object Pronouns

REVIEW

Directions: Circle the correct pronoun in ( ) to complete each sentence. Then write S or O on the line to tell whether it is a subject pronoun or an object pronoun.

S **1.** Gloria just read *Around the World in Eighty Days*, and (she/her) cannot stop talking about the book.

S **2.** (It/him) was written by Jules Verne in 1873.

O **3.** Phileas Fogg and his servant do not look for adventure, but adventure finds (they/them).

S **4.** To win a wager, (they/them) take a journey around the world.

O **5.** A detective mistakes Phileas Fogg for a bank robber and follows (he/him).

S **6.** Since there are no airplanes yet, (they/them) travel by train, ship, elephant, and sailboat.

S **7.** On Phileas Fogg's incredible journey, (he/him) collects other companions.

O **8.** The lovely Madame Aouda, for example, is a recent widow when Mr. Fogg meets (she/her).

O **9.** Amazingly, Mr. Fogg and his group return to London on time, where friends welcome (they/them) home.

O **10.** Gloria loved the book, and she is recommending (her/it) to everyone.

Directions: Circle the words in ( ) that complete each sentence.

11. (Gloria and I/Gloria and me) both loved Jules Verne's book *Around the World in Eighty Days*.

12. Yesterday (Anthony and I/Anthony and me) decided to go to the library.

13. Gloria met (Anthony and I/Anthony and me) there.

14. Anthony saw a friend, but (Gloria and I/Gloria and me) went right to the computers.

15. Gloria knew what books would please (Anthony and I/Anthony and me).

16. (Gloria, Anthony, and I/Gloria, Anthony, and me) were looking for other books by Jules Verne.

17. (Gloria and I/Gloria and me) found the listings on the computer at the library.

18. *Journey to the Center of the Earth* tempted (Anthony and I/Anthony and me).

19. The title *20,000 Leagues Under the Sea* attracted (Gloria and I/Gloria and me).

20. Jules Verne would soon be taking (my friends and I/my friends and me) on some exciting journeys.

 Notes for Home: Your child used the subject pronouns *I, we, you, he, she, it, they* and the object pronouns *me, us, you, him, her, it, them*. **Home Activity:** Write subject and object pronouns on cards. Then take turns choosing a card and using the pronoun in a sentence.

Grammar: Subject and Object Pronouns **507**

Grammar: Pronouns and Their Referents

Pronouns get most of their meaning from the nouns they replace. The noun or noun phrase that a pronoun replaces is called its **referent**. A referent names the person, place, or thing to which the pronoun refers. In the following sentences, the referents are underlined once, and the pronouns are underlined twice.

<blockquote>

Lisa boarded the boat. Then she handed in her ticket.

Dwayne loves airplanes, so he flies in them often.

</blockquote>

Pronouns and their referents must agree. In the example sentences above, the singular subject pronoun *she* agrees with its referent, *Lisa*. The plural object pronoun *them* agrees with its referent, *airplanes*.

Directions: Underline the referent or referents once and the pronoun twice in the sentences. Hint: Some pronouns are possessive pronouns

1. Tom and Keisha had no money for a vacation. They planned a fantasy trip instead.

2. Keisha wrote three travel brochures, and Tom read them.

3. Tom praised the ideas in the brochures, and Keisha smiled at him.

4. Tom chose the "Antarctica by Air" trip. He would see dark blue seas, gleaming icebergs, ice streams, and glaciers.

5. Keisha felt pleased. Then she proposed a route to Antarctica.

6. On their imaginary trip, the brother and sister traveled by ship to the tip of South America.

7. There, Tom and Keisha hired a private plane, and it flew over the ocean to the continent of Antarctica.

8. From the aircraft, Tom took the best photos of his life.

9. A helicopter pilot said he would show Tom and Keisha some wildlife.

10. The best part of her journey, Keisha said, was the sight of penguins in a natural habitat.

 Notes for Home: Your child identified pronouns and referents. **Home Activity:** Invite your child to write a postcard describing an imaginary journey the family might have taken. Ask your child to use pronouns in the postcard. Then ask him or her to identify the referents.

508 Grammar: Pronouns and Their Referents

Grammar: Pronouns and Their Referents

Directions: Use the correct pronoun to complete each sentence. Write the pronoun on the line below. Then, beside the pronoun, write its referent.

1. Sarah liked her host family members in Mexico because _____ were kind.

they; members

2. Sarah's parents let _____ live with her Mexican hosts for a month.

her; Sarah

3. She had been studying Spanish at her American school and was good at _____.

it; Spanish

4. The Mexican hosts told Sarah they would speak only Spanish to _____.

her; Sarah

5. Whenever she made a mistake, they carefully explained why _____ was an error.

it; mistake

6. She soon felt at home in Mexico, and when _____ grows up, Sarah wants to live there!

she; Sarah

7. When two Mexican children come to live with her family next summer, Sarah will help _____ feel at home.

them; children

8. If they don't understand an American word, she will explain _____ to them.

it; word

9. When American words have Spanish roots, the Mexican children will learn _____ quickly.

them; words

10. Sarah says _____ hopes to practice her Spanish with these Mexican guests.

she; Sarah

Write a Get-Help Letter

Imagine that you have voyaged to a strange new world, but now you need to escape from it! On a separate sheet of paper, write a letter you could send in a bottle to get help. Describe your trip, and tell why you are unable to leave. Don't forget to give your location! Use pronouns and referents in your letter.

Students should describe the trip to the place from which they need to escape, and they should tell why they need help. Students should use pronouns and their referents correctly.

 Notes for Home: Your child wrote pronouns and their referents (the nouns to which pronouns refer). **Home Activity:** Make up sentence pairs that use a noun in the first sentence and a pronoun in the second. Ask your child to identify the referent.

Grammar: Pronouns and Their Referents **509**

Grammar: Pronouns and Their Referents

RETEACHING

In each sentence or pair of sentences, the pronoun is underlined. Circle the referent to which it refers.

1. (Mrs. Grady) agreed to walk our dog. She was going to do it for a week.

2. (Dan and Mack) were delighted because Mr. Lawrence chose them to speak first.

Pronouns get most of their meaning from the nouns they replace. The noun or noun phrase that a pronoun replaces is called its **referent**. Pronouns and their referents must agree. In the example sentences above, the singular subject pronoun *she* agrees with its referent, *Mrs. Grady*. The plural object pronoun *them* agrees with its referent *Dan and Mack*.

Directions: Underline each pronoun, and circle each referent in the sentences.

1. (Mr. Thomas's students) visited a radio station last month. They met the (manager) in her office.

2. Then the (manager) gave the class a tour of the building. She was very helpful.

3. Next the class went to see the studio's (collection) of CDs. It was huge!

4. The next person Mr. Thomas's class met was (June Moon), a producer. She gave a short talk about what she did every day.

5. Later a (program manager) came to speak to the group. He talked about different programs the radio show put on the air.

6. The information the (students) learned was very valuable to them.

7. Finally, the class reached the studio of the great (Deejay Spin). He gave out autographs.

8. (Mr. Thomas) said he was Deejay Spin's biggest fan!

9. Deejay Spin was glad to talk with the (students) because they were so excited to learn about what types of things deejays do.

10. After the field trip, the (students) organized their own radio station!

11. The class did lots of (work), but it was worth the time and effort.

12. The first (broadcast) of the new radio station was yesterday. It was a huge success!

 Notes for Home: Your child identified pronouns and their referents—nouns or noun phrases that pronouns replace. **Home Activity:** Listen to a radio program. Have your child write some dialogue from the program. Then have your child identify pronouns and referents in what he or she wrote.

510 Grammar: Pronouns and Their Referents

© Scott Foresman 5

Top Left Quadrant

from Chester Cricket's Pigeon Ride

Grammar: Pronouns and Their Referents

Directions: Use the correct pronoun to complete each sentence. Write the pronoun on the line below. Then beside each pronoun, write its referent.

1. Maggie played a guitar in a recital last weekend. _____ was very nervous.
she/Maggie

2. Other guitar students had practiced for many hours, and _____ performed well.
they/students

3. Maggie was concerned that her guitar was not in tune. _____ sounded strange when she was warming up.
it/guitar

4. Maggie asked Luke if _____ would tune the guitar.
he/Luke

5. Luke said to Maggie that the guitar sounded fine to _____. _____ told _____ not to be nervous.
him/Luke; He/Luke; her/Maggie

6. When it was Maggie's turn to perform, _____ felt ready.
she/Maggie

7. Maggie's parents were very proud of the performance. _____ thought _____ played beautifully.
They/parents; she/Maggie

Directions: Use the referents provided to write sentences with pronouns. Make sure the pronouns and their referents agree.   **Possible answers given.**

8. the whole team
The whole team cheered when it won.

9. one player
One player thought she played the best game ever.

10. the coaches
The coaches were so proud they bought everyone lunch.

11. Sheri
Sheri was so hungry she ate three hamburgers!

Notes for Home: Your child identified and wrote pronouns and referents. *Home Activity:* Look at newspaper articles with your child. Have him or her circle pronouns and referents in six sentences. Then have him or her use two of the pronouns and their referents in new sentences.

Grammar: Pronouns and Their Referents **511**

Top Right Quadrant

from Chester Cricket's Pigeon Ride

Word Study: Suffixes

Directions: Sometimes the spelling of a base word changes when a suffix is added. In most words, when the base word ends in -e, drop the -e and add the suffix. In most words, when the base word ends in -y, change the -y to -i and add the suffix. Read each sentence. Combine the base word and suffix in ( ) to make one word. Write the new word on the line.

pleasure	1. Traveling with my cousin is always a (please + ure).
usually	2. Something fantastic (usual + ly) happens on our trips.
conversation	3. Our adventures make for a very interesting (converse + ation).
fortunately	4. (Fortunate + ly), we have plenty of time for traveling.
remarkable	5. On our last trip, we saw some (remark + able) ruins in the jungle.
passage	6. A hidden (pass + age) led us to an amazing treasure room.
plentiful	7. We were thrilled to find the (plenty + ful) riches.
respectable	8. Finding treasure is a (respect + able) way to get rich!
excitement	9. For us, the (excite + ment) of traveling never wears off.

Directions: Read the words below. Write each base word and the suffix in the correct column.

	Base word		Suffix
10. lazily	lazy	+	ly
11. direction	direct	+	ion
12. sorrowful	sorrow	+	ful
13. sleepy	sleep	+	y
14. possibly	possible	+	ly
15. disappointment	disappoint	+	ment
16. dizziness	dizzy	+	ness
17. beautiful	beauty	+	ful
18. imaginable	imagine	+	able
19. famous	fame	+	ous
20. musician	music	+	ian

Notes for Home: Your child made new words by adding suffixes to base words, such as *please + ure = pleasure*. *Home Activity:* Read a newspaper article with your child. Ask your child to find words with suffixes. Have your child break each word into the base word and suffix.

512 Word Study: Suffixes

Bottom Left Quadrant

from Chester Cricket's Pigeon Ride

Spelling: Suffixes -ous, -ion, -ation

Pretest Directions: Fold back the page along the dotted line. On the blanks, write the spelling words as they are dictated. When you have finished the test, unfold the page and check your words.

1. **famous**
2. **nervous**
3. **joyous**
4. **marvelous**
5. **humorous**
6. **mysterious**
7. **dangerous**
8. **selection**
9. **instruction**
10. **attraction**
11. **rejection**
12. **education**
13. **inflation**
14. **decoration**
15. **information**
16. **organization**
17. **conversation**
18. **imagination**
19. **admiration**
20. **preparation**

1. He is a **famous** writer.
2. Barking dogs make him **nervous**.
3. They sang a **joyous** song.
4. What a **marvelous** idea!
5. That was a **humorous** joke.
6. A **mysterious** man entered.
7. The boat is not **dangerous**.
8. There is a **selection** of pens.
9. She is taking speech **instruction**.
10. He has an **attraction** to parks.
11. Everyone hates **rejection**.
12. A good **education** is valuable.
13. It costs more due to **inflation**.
14. I made a **decoration**.
15. The police took our **information**.
16. This project needs **organization**.
17. They had a nice **conversation**.
18. You have a vivid **imagination**.
19. He has our **admiration**.
20. The plan takes **preparation**.

Notes for Home: Your child took a pretest on words that have the suffixes *-ous*, *-ion*, and *-ation*. *Home Activity:* Help your child learn misspelled words before the final test. Have your child divide misspelled words into parts (such as syllables) and concentrate on each part.

Spelling: Suffixes *-ous, -ion, -ation* **513**

Bottom Right Quadrant

from Chester Cricket's Pigeon Ride

Spelling: Suffixes -ous, -ion, -ation

Word List				
famous	humorous	instruction	inflation	conversation
nervous	mysterious	attraction	decoration	imagination
joyous	dangerous	rejection	information	admiration
marvelous	selection	education	organization	preparation

Directions: Add the suffix -ion or -ation to form a word from the box. Write the word on the line. Remember to drop the silent e when necessary.

Add -ion
1. instruct — **instruction**
2. select — **selection**
3. reject — **rejection**
4. attract — **attraction**
5. decorate — **decoration**
6. educate — **education**
7. inflate — **inflation**

Add -ation
8. inform — **information**
9. converse — **conversation**
10. imagine — **imagination**
11. admire — **admiration**
12. prepare — **preparation**
13. organize — **organization**

Directions: Add the suffix -ous to each base word to form a word from the box. Write the letters of each word in the blanks. The boxed letters spell one of the words you wrote, a word that tells how you might feel if you were flying for the first time. Hint: Three words will change spelling before adding -ous.

14. danger   14. d a n g e r o u s
15. mystery   15. m y s t e r i o u s
16. marvel   16. m a r v e l o u s
17. nerve   17. n e r v o u s
18. fame   18. f a m o u s
19. humor   19. h u m o r o u s
20. joy   20. j o y o u s

How might you feel on your first flight?
n e r v o u s

Notes for Home: Your child spelled words that end in *-ous*, *-ion*, and *-ation*. *Home Activity:* Read a newspaper article with your child. See how many words he or she can recognize that end in *-ous*, *-ion*, or *-ation*.

514 Spelling: Suffixes *-ous, -ion, -ation*

Spelling: Suffixes -ous, -ion, -ation

Directions: Proofread this story. Find five spelling mistakes. Use the proofreading marks to correct each mistake.

Proofreading Marks
☰ Make a capital.
/ Make a small letter.
∧ Add something.
ℐ Take out something.
⊙ Add a period.
⊞ Begin a new paragraph.

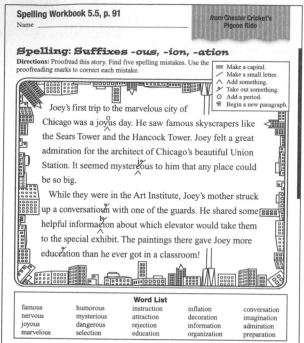

Joey's first trip to the marvelous city of Chicago was a joyus day. He saw famous skyscrapers like the Sears Tower and the Hancock Tower. Joey felt a great admiration for the architect of Chicago's beautiful Union Station. It seemed mystereous to him that any place could be so big.

While they were in the Art Institute, Joey's mother struck up a conversatiom with one of the guards. He shared some helpful informaeion about which elevator would take them to the special exhibit. The paintings there gave Joey more educaion than he ever got in a classroom!

Word List				
famous	humorous	instruction	inflation	conversation
nervous	mysterious	attraction	decoration	imagination
joyous	dangerous	rejection	information	admiration
marvelous	selection	education	organization	preparation

Write a Story

On a separate sheet of paper, write a paragraph describing things you saw on a trip to the city. Try to use at least five of your spelling words. **Answers will vary, but each story should include at least five spelling words.**

Spelling Tip
marvelous
How can you remember that **marvelous** has an o before the u? Think of this hint: Oh, **you** (**o-u**) look **marvelous**!

 Notes for Home: Your child spelled words that end in *-ous*, *-ion*, and *-ation*. *Home Activity:* Say each spelling word to your child. Have him or her identify whether it ends in *-ous*, *-ion*, or *-ation*. Then have your child spell the word.

Spelling: Suffixes -ous, -ion, -ation   REVIEW

Word List				
famous	humorous	instruction	inflation	conversation
nervous	mysterious	attraction	decoration	imagination
joyous	dangerous	rejection	information	admiration
marvelous	selection	education	organization	preparation

Directions: Choose the word from the box that best matches each clue. Write the word on the line.

1. **conversation** It's a talk between two or more people.
2. **organization** It's a group of people who work together.
3. **imagination** It's what you use to create interesting make-believe stories.
4. **preparation** It's what you do to get ready.
5. **rejection** It's being turned down or turned away.
6. **attraction** It's what happens when a magnet is near metal.
7. **decoration** It's often seen on top of a cake.
8. **inflation** It's what happens to a balloon that's blown up.
9. **selection** It's a choice that you make.
10. **admiration** It's what a person feels for a hero or idol.
11. **information** It's what you find in any encyclopedia article.
12. **education** It's what you get from going to school.

Directions: Choose the word from the box that has the same or nearly the same meaning as each word below. Write the word on the line.

13. directions   **instruction**
14. strange   **mysterious**
15. funny   **humorous**
16. unsafe   **dangerous**
17. well-known   **famous**
18. happy   **joyous (marvelous)**
19. worried   **nervous**
20. wonderful   **marvelous (joyous)**

 Notes for Home: Your child spelled words that end in *-ous*, *-ion*, and *-ation*. *Home Activity:* Say each spelling word without the suffix. Have your child add the proper suffix and spell the word.

Following Directions

Following directions involves reading or listening and then doing or making something.

Directions: Follow these directions to complete the Unusual Journey puzzle. Read all the directions before you begin. Follow each step closely. Some letters have been filled in for you.

1. What is the name for a book of maps? Write the word in both columns marked **1.** (The first letter in each column is written for you.)
2. What is the name of a book of facts that is published each year? Write the word in both columns marked **2.**
3. What is the name of a book you use to learn about a subject in school? Write the word in both columns marked **3.**
4. What is the name of a book that has words and their definitions? Write the word in both columns marked **4.**
5. What is the name for a set of books that has information about many different subjects? Write the word in both columns marked **5.**
6. Use a colored pencil or crayon to shade the space marked **6.**
7. Use different colored pencils or crayons to shade the spaces marked **7a** and **7b.**
8. Write your name in the box marked **8.**
9. Find all the letters that are set inside a diamond. Write the word the letters make after **Hot** in the box marked **9.**
10. Find all the letters that are circled. Write the word the letters make in the box marked **10.**
11. Use a pencil or crayon to color in all the empty boxes.

Directions: Use the completed puzzle to answer the questions below.

12. What type of unusual flying machine does the complete puzzle show?
a hot air balloon

13. Where would you travel to have an unusual journey?
Answers will vary. Students may name a real or imaginary place.

14. Why is it important to read all the directions before you begin?
Possible answer: You will get a better sense of the entire task if you read all the directions before you begin.

15. Why is it important to follow directions in the order they are given?
Possible answer: If you don't follow the directions in the order they are given, you might not get the correct result.

Unusual Journey

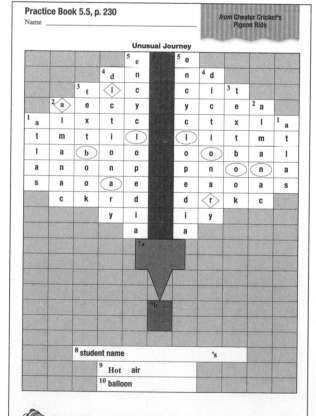

 Notes for Home: Your child followed detailed directions to fill in a puzzle. *Home Activity:* With your child, make several lists of numbered directions to follow for writing words on a page. For example: *1. Write your name. 2. Cross out every other letter. 3. Write the letters that are left.*

© Scott Foresman 5

Context Clues

- **Context clues** are words that help explain an unfamiliar word.
- Context clues can appear just before or after an unfamiliar word. But sometimes they are in a different part of the story or article, far from the unfamiliar word.
- Look for specific context clues such as definitions, explanations, examples, and descriptions.

Directions: Reread "Butterfly Memorial." Then complete the table. Write the meaning of each word in the table. Tell what context clue helped you figure out the meaning and where you found it.

Possible answers given.

Word	Meaning	Context Clues
ghetto	1. **a walled-off, isolated area**	The definition appears just before the word in the first paragraph.
Holocaust	2. **the murder of Jews by Germany's Nazi Party from 1938 to 1945**	3. **The definition appears just before the word in the third paragraph.**
remembrance	4. **the act of remembering**	5. **The final paragraph says, "We should remember what happened. . . ." which helps explain the word's meaning.**

 Notes for Home: Your child read an article and figured out the meanings of unfamiliar words by using context clues. **Home Activity:** Read a magazine article with your child. When you come to a word your child doesn't know, use context clues to figure out its meaning.

Context Clues **521**

Vocabulary

Directions: Choose a word from the box that best completes each sentence. Write the word on the line to the left.

	Check the Words You Know
	__ agreement
	__ cable
	__ disobey
	__ issue
	__ permission
	__ representatives
	__ superiors
	__ translated

representatives 1. We elected _____ to speak for the rest of us.

issue 2. They approached an official who had the power to _____ passports to our group.

permission 3. We needed this official's _____ to leave the island.

disobey 4. He was worried we might _____ his orders.

agreement 5. After much discussion, we finally reached an _____.

Directions: Choose the word from the box that best matches each clue. Write the letters of the word on the blanks. The boxed letters spell something that a happy child does.

6. consent — 6. **p e r m i s s i o n**

7. insulated bundle of wires for carrying electric current — 7. **c a b l e**

8. changed from one language to another — 8. **t r a n s l a t e d**

9. refuse to obey — 9. **d i s o b e y**

10. people who are higher in rank — 10. **s u p e r i o r s**

Something a happy child does: **p l a y s**

Write an Award Citation

Imagine that one of your classmates has won an award for helping others. On a separate sheet of paper, write a paragraph to go with the award. Describe what the person did and the result of his or her actions. Try to use as many vocabulary words as you can. **Students' award citations should make correct use of vocabulary words.**

 Notes for Home: Your child identified and used vocabulary words from *Passage to Freedom: The Sugihara Story.* **Home Activity:** With your child, take turns telling a story using the vocabulary words. At each turn, the teller may choose any unused word.

522 Vocabulary

Context Clues

- **Context clues** are words that help explain an unfamiliar word. Context clues can appear just before or after an unfamiliar word. Sometimes, they are in a different part of the story or article.
- Context clues include synonyms, antonyms, definitions and explanations, examples, and descriptions.

Directions: Reread what happened in *Passage to Freedom: The Sugihara Story* when a crowd gathered outside the Sugiharas' home. Then answer the questions below.

I couldn't help but stare out the window and watch the crowd, while downstairs, for two hours, my father listened to frightening stories. These people were refugees—people who ran away from their homes because, if they stayed, they would be killed. They were Jews from Poland, escaping from the Nazi soldiers who had taken over their country.

The five men had heard my father could give them visas—official written permission to travel through another country. The hundreds of Jewish refugees outside hoped to travel east through the Soviet Union and end up in Japan. Once in Japan, they could go to another country. Was it true? the men asked. Could my father issue these visas?

Text copyright © 1997 Ken Mochizuki. Excerpt from PASSAGE TO FREEDOM: THE SUGIHARA STORY. Reprinted by arrangement with Lee & Low Books, Inc.

1. What does the word *refugees* mean?
Refugees are people who flee their homes because they would be killed if they stayed.

2. What type of context clue did you use to determine the meaning of *refugees*?
definition or explanation

3. What does the word *visas* mean?
Visas are official written permissions to travel through another country.

4. What type of context clue did you use to determine the meaning of *visas*?
definition or explanation

5. How can you be sure if you have determined the correct meaning of a word after using context clues? **Possible answers: You could see if your definition makes sense in the sentence; you could look up the word in a dictionary.**

 Notes for Home: Your child used clues within a story to figure out the meanings of unfamiliar words. **Home Activity:** Read a story with your child. Help your child try to figure out the meaning of an unfamiliar word by looking at words surrounding it.

Context Clues **523**

Selection Test

Directions: Choose the best answer to each item. Mark the letter for the answer you have chosen.

Part 1: Vocabulary

Find the answer choice that means about the same as the underlined word in each sentence.

1. Mr. Park <u>translated</u> for me.
   - A. wrote out by hand
   - B. read carefully
   - C. changed into a different language ●
   - D. learned by heart

2. The leaders were in <u>agreement</u>.
   - F. official stopping of work by a group of employees
   - G. loud protest
   - H. sudden rise in banking costs
   - J. understanding between two or more parties ●

3. Did the government <u>issue</u> those uniforms?
   - A. take back
   - B. design
   - C. forbid
   - D. give out ●

4. Captain Jones reported to his <u>superiors</u>.
   - F. bosses ●
   - G. people who buy goods
   - H. friends
   - J. people who are related

5. The <u>cable</u> was damaged in the storm.
   - A. tall tower
   - B. wooden structure in a body of water
   - C. bundle of wires for sending messages electronically ●
   - D. power station

6. Did you <u>disobey</u> the orders?
   - F. refuse to go along with ●
   - G. hear
   - H. misunderstand
   - J. give

7. Several <u>representatives</u> of the company spoke at the meeting.
   - A. people who dislike something
   - B. people appointed or elected to speak or act for others ●
   - C. people who refuse to take charge
   - D. people who have just paid money

8. Dad gave his <u>permission</u>.
   - F. money
   - G. help
   - H. decision to allow something ●
   - J. words of advice

Part 2: Comprehension

Use what you know about the selection to answer each item.

9. The major events in this story take place in—
   - A. Israel.
   - B. Germany.
   - C. Poland.
   - D. Lithuania. ●

10. This story is told from the point of view of—
    - F. a Japanese diplomat.
    - G. a Jewish refugee.
    - H. the diplomat's son. ●
    - J. the diplomat's wife.

11. Why do all the refugees come to talk to the diplomat?
    - A. They want visas so they can leave the country. ●
    - B. They want someone to speak out against the Germans.
    - C. They want his help in returning to the homes they have left.
    - D. They want him to hide them from the German army.

GO ON ▶

524 Selection Test

© Scott Foresman 5

Answers 799

12. The selection says, "Grown-ups <u>embraced</u> each other, and some reached to the sky." <u>Embraced</u> means—
    F. hugged.
    G. yelled at.
    H. struck.
    J. cheered for.

13. The selection says, ". . . and when we finally returned to Japan, my father was asked to <u>resign</u> from diplomatic service." <u>Resign</u> means—
    A. join.
    B. return.
    C. quit.
    D. change.

14. The most important thing to Mr. Sugihara was to—
    F. protect his family.
    G. obey his government.
    H. save people's lives.
    J. make money.

15. The author's main purpose in this selection is to—
    A. honor a brave act.
    B. explain the causes of the war.
    C. describe what it was like to be a refugee.
    D. entertain readers.

STOP

Selection Test **525**

Context Clues

- **Context clues** are words that help explain an unfamiliar word. Context clues can appear just before or after an unfamiliar word. Sometimes, they are in a different part of the story or article.
- Context clues include synonyms, antonyms, definitions and explanations, examples, and descriptions.

Directions: Read the passage below.

World War II was the most catastrophic war ever, taking more lives and destroying more property than any other war. It is nearly impossible to <u>calculate</u> the number of people killed, wounded, and missing during the war's six years, although history experts guess that it totals about 16 million.

The war began when Germany attacked Poland on September 1, 1939. The successful test of its blitzkrieg, or lightning war, methods led Germany to take control of six more countries—Denmark, Norway, Belgium, Luxembourg, The Netherlands, and France—in only three months in 1940.

Directions: Complete the table. Tell the meaning of each word in the table and explain what context clues you used to figure out the meaning.

Word	Word's Meaning	Context Clues
catastrophic	1. **causing terrible disaster**	2. **mention of more lost lives and property damage than in any other war**
calculate	3. **to figure out or guess by using math**	4. **mention of a total number being guessed**
blitzkrieg	5. **lightning war**	Meaning is given after the word.

Notes for Home: Your child read a story and used context clues within the story to figure out the meanings of unfamiliar words. *Home Activity:* Use a challenging word in a sentence. Have your child use context clues to explain its meaning.

526 Context Clues

Main Idea and Supporting Details/Generalizing

REVIEW

Directions: Read the passage. Then read each question about the passage. Choose the best answer to each question. Mark the letter for the answer you have chosen.

D-Day

The D-Day invasion was an important event during World War II that made a big difference in the outcome of the war. That event occurred on June 6, 1944. On that day the Allied forces crossed the English Channel and attacked the German forces on the northern coast of France. The forces made this surprise landing on open beaches in the French region of Normandy.

The D-Day invasion required great planning. England, Canada, and the United States brought together some 3 million soldiers and 16 million tons of supplies in Great Britain. The Allies had 5,000 large ships, 4,000 small craft, and over 11,000 airplanes.

Months before the D-Day invasion, Allied planes bombed the Normandy coast to prevent Germans from taking over in the area. Allied soldiers cut rail lines, blew up bridges, and took control of landing strips to prepare for the invasion.

During the night of June 5, troops, jeeps, and even small tanks were brought in on gliders and warships. Beginning at 6:30 A.M. on June 6, German groups of soldiers on the coast were attacked by shells from Allied warships. All was ready for the largest land invasion in recent history—D-Day.

1. The main idea of the article is that—
   A. 3 million men fought.
   B. the D-Day invasion took planning.
   C. bridges were blown up.
   D. the D-Day invasion was June 6, 1944.

2. A detail that supports the main idea is that—
   F. 11,000 planes were used.
   G. Germans built up their forces.
   H. Britain was attacked.
   J. it happened in Normandy.

3. A detail that does **not** support the main idea is that—
   A. rail lines were cut.
   B. 5,000 ships were used.
   C. bridges were blown up.
   D. Normandy is in France.

4. A valid generalization you could make about the last paragraph is that—
   F. few warships were needed.
   G. all the troops, jeeps, and tanks were loaded on the morning of June 6.
   H. gliders and warships were important to the D-Day invasion.
   J. the D-Day invasion occurred on June 6, 1944.

5. A generalization you could make about the D-Day invasion is that—
   A. Germany was the enemy.
   B. Canada was in the war.
   C. many people took part in the invasion.
   D. the invasion was in June.

Notes for Home: Your child identified a main idea, supporting details, and general statements about an article. *Home Activity:* Read an article with your child. Invite him or her to tell you the main idea and supporting details. Look for generalizations.

Main Idea and Supporting Details/Generalizing **527**

Writing Across Texts

Directions: Think about the Jewish refugees described in *Passage to Freedom: The Sugihara Story* and other events in Europe near that time. Compare that to what was happening in the United States then. Use information from "1939" to compare events in the two areas of the world.

Possible answers given.

The United States in 1939–40	Europe in 1939–40
The movie *Gone With the Wind* was released.	Jewish refugees were trying to get away from the Nazis.
1. **The Glenn Miller band had a huge hit.**	6. **Hitler's troops invaded Poland.**
2. **Birds Eye introduced precooked frozen meals**	7. **British children were evacuated from large cities.**
3. **The movie *The Wizard of Oz* premiered in Hollywood.**	8. **Britain declared war against Hitler.**
4. **Nylon stockings went on sale for the first time.**	9. **Stained-glass windows were removed from Notre Dame Cathedral for fear of air raids.**
5. **The first televised football game was broadcast from Randall's Island, New York.**	10. **Hitler narrowly escaped a bomb explosion in Munich, Germany.**

Write a Letter

Imagine you are a Jewish refugee child described in the story. On a separate sheet of paper, write a letter to an American friend explaining what you learned and how you changed throughout this ordeal. Then write a reply from the American friend who is becoming aware of what is happening in Europe.
Letters will vary. Check that one letter is written from a refugee's point of view and the other from an American child's point of view. Both letters should contain information that relates to what students learned from the selection.

Notes for Home: Your child wrote two letters from other people's points of view. *Home Activity:* Together, write a letter to a special family member or friend. Encourage your child to include a description of something he or she has learned and how this has changed him or her.

528 Writing Across Texts

© Scott Foresman 5

Grammar: Pronouns and Referents REVIEW

Directions: Underline the pronoun in each sentence or pair of sentences. Draw a circle around its referent.

1. (Leo), what do you know about D-Day?

2. On June 6, 1944, Allied (troops) landed in France. They began the invasion of northern Europe in World War II.

3. (General Eisenhower) commanded the troops. Later the American people elected him president.

4. (Doreen) knows an interesting story about the invasion. Is she here?

5. (Doreen) isn't here, but John can tell the story instead of her.

6. A Nazi (spy) stole the plans for the invasion, and he gave the information to the German generals.

7. The generals who saw the (plans), however, didn't think much of them.

8. These leaders believed the real (invasion) would be elsewhere. The German army began to prepare for it.

9. Of course, the German (generals) were wrong, and because of them, the D-Day invasion was a success.

10. That's interesting, (John) You told the story well.

Directions: Cross out the incorrect pronoun in each sentence. Then rewrite the sentence, using the correct pronoun.

11. Did you give the book about World War II to ~~she~~?
Did you give the book about World War II to her?

12. The librarian will reserve the book for ~~we~~.
The librarian will reserve the book for us.

13. I want to know more about General Patton, and the book tells about ~~he~~.
I want to know more about General Patton, and the book tells about him.

14. Can you tell ~~I~~ anything about General Patton?
Can you tell me anything about General Patton?

15. ~~Him~~ was a very skilled general in World War II.
He was a very skilled general in World War II.

 Notes for Home: Your child identified pronouns and their referents—the nouns that they replace. *Home Activity:* Have your child write a paragraph about something that happened at school, and identify the referent of each pronoun that she or he uses.

Grammar: Pronouns and Referents **529**

Grammar: Prepositions and Prepositional Phrases

A **preposition** begins a group of words called a **prepositional phrase**. The noun or pronoun that follows the preposition is the **object of the preposition**. Prepositional phrases can be used to tell more about the words they accompany.

The runaway horse galloped <u>toward a red house</u>.
The runaway horse galloped <u>around a red house</u>.
The runaway horse galloped <u>behind a red house</u>.

Notice how the prepositional phrases in the sentences above give a more vivid and clear picture about the runaway horse.

Common Prepositions
above, across, after, around, at, before, behind, by, down, for, from, in, into, near, of, on, to, toward, under, with

Directions: Underline the prepositional phrase in each sentence once. Draw a second line under the preposition.

1. The ship moved <u>with the tide</u>.

2. The immigrants were standing <u>by the rail</u>.

3. <u>Among the passengers</u> was my father.

4. He stood <u>between my two grandparents</u>.

5. He watched the ship sail <u>into the harbor</u>.

6. It docked <u>beside a small ferryboat</u>.

7. The immigrants clustered <u>around the railing</u>.

8. Then they walked <u>down the gangplank</u>.

9. There was a bus <u>on the dock</u>.

10. It would take them <u>to a federal building</u>.

11. The dock felt wonderfully steady <u>under their feet</u>.

12. <u>On the ship</u>, they had felt seasick sometimes.

13. Salty ocean breezes blew <u>around them</u>.

14. My father gazed <u>at the American trucks</u> nearby.

15. His father held him <u>by the hand</u>, and the family boarded the bus.

 Notes for Home: Your child identified prepositions such as *into* and *under* and prepositional phrases such as *by the rail* and *around then*. *Home Activity:* Make up a two-word sentence. Have your child add a prepositional phrase, (for example: *I ran. I ran to the milk truck.*)

530 Grammar: Prepositions and Prepositional Phrases

Grammar: Prepositions and Prepositional Phrases

Directions: Add a prepositional phrase to each sentence using the preposition in ( ). Write the new sentence on the line. **Possible answers given.**

1. The immigrants saw the Statue of Liberty. (through)
The immigrants saw the Statue of Liberty through the fog.

2. People cheered. (on)
People on the docks cheered.

3. The immigrants had planned the voyage. (for)
The immigrants had planned the voyage for many years.

4. Anya finally smiled. (with)
Anya finally smiled with happiness.

5. She felt welcome. (in)
She felt welcome in America.

Directions: Add a prepositional phrase to each sentence to make it more vivid and clear. Write the new sentence on the line. **Possible answers given.**

6. Anya walked.
Anya walked around the unfamiliar city.

7. She found a library.
She found a library on a side street.

8. She sat.
She sat among the books.

9. The silence was soothing.
The silence was soothing after the excitement of the arrival.

10. She fell asleep.
She fell asleep in her chair.

Write a Biographical Sketch Students should use prepositions and prepositional phrases to write about someone who immigrated to America.
On a separate sheet of paper, write a biographical sketch of someone who immigrated to America. Describe why the person came to America, the journey, and the person's new life here. Use prepositional phrases to write vivid and clear sentences.

 Notes for Home: Your child used prepositional phrases, such as *on a street. Home Activity:* Say a preposition, such as *under, around, to,* or *on.* Have your child use it first in a prepositional phrase and then in a sentence. Switch roles and repeat.

Grammar: Prepositions and Prepositional Phrases **531**

Grammar: Prepositions and Prepositional Phrases RETEACHING

Prepositional Phrases		
Preposition	Words Between	Object
by	the	hill
beside	an old	oak
down	a winding	lane

Complete each sentence. Write words from each column. **Possible answers given.**

1. The ball bounced **down the hill**.
2. The child rode a bicycle **by an old oak**.

A **prepositional phrase** includes the preposition, the object of the preposition, and all the words that come between them. Every prepositional phrase starts with a preposition and ends with its object.

Directions: Write a prepositional phrase from the box below to complete each sentence. **Possible answers given.**

with her fingertips	from its fur	behind a box of books
beside her pillow	in the closet	

1. Jenny found her old teddy bear **in the closet**
2. It was lying **behind a box of books**
3. She could reach it **with her fingertips**
4. She brushed the dust **from its fur**
5. She put it gently **beside her pillow**

Directions: Underline the prepositional phrase. Then write 1 above the preposition and 2 above its object.

6. Chin caught a fish <u>in the lake</u>.
7. Marcie rowed the boat <u>to the shore</u>.
8. Raoul waited <u>on the dock</u>.
9. The three friends went <u>inside the cabin</u>.
10. They talked happily <u>beside the fireplace</u>.

 Notes for Home: Your child wrote prepositional phrases and identified parts of prepositional phrases in sentences. *Home Activity:* Make a list of prepositions your child knows, and have him or her use five of them in phrases in sentences about animals.

532 Grammar: Prepositions and Prepositional Phrases

Name _____

Passage to Freedom:
The Sugihara Story

Grammar: Prepositions and Prepositional Phrases

Directions: Read the paragraph. Underline the seven prepositional phrases and write them below.

The skeleton contains the bones <u>of the body</u>. Soft material is <u>inside the bones</u>. Red blood cells are made <u>in the bones</u>. The bones <u>of children</u> <u>under the age of one year</u> are soft. Bones are held together <u>by strong bands</u>. Calcium helps keep the cells <u>of the bones</u> strong. Your bones should last a lifetime. **Order may vary.**

1. of the body
2. inside the bones
3. in the bones
4. of children
5. under the age of one year
6. by strong bands
7. of the bones

Directions: Choose a word from each box to use in a prepositional phrase. Write each phrase. Below the phrase, write a sentence with the phrase in it. **Possible answers given.**

Prepositions	Words Between	Objects
in under	the a	bones skeleton
between of	your	skull body

8. between the bones
   There are strong bands between the bones.

9. in your body
   In your body are hundreds of bones.

10. of a skull
   The back of a skull is hard.

Write Sentences

On a separate sheet of paper, write sentences about insects that you have seen. Use prepositional phrases in each sentence.

Make sure students have used prepositional phrases correctly.

Notes for Home: Your child identified and wrote prepositional phrases. *Home Activity:* Have your child write directions to school, using prepositional phrases. *(First walk over the bridge. Next go down the hill.)*

Grammar: Prepositions and Prepositional Phrases **533**

Name _____

Passage to Freedom:
The Sugihara Story

Word Study: Syllabication, Common Syllable Patterns

Directions: A **syllable** is an individual part of a word that you say or hear. When a word is a compound word, it is usually divided between the two words that make up the compound word: **base • ball.** When two consonants come between two vowels (VCCV), the word is divided between the two consonants (**num • ber**). Separate each word into its syllables, using a dot (**base • ball**).

1. office — of • fice
2. poster — pos • ter
3. downstairs — down • stairs
4. issue — is • sue
5. outside — out • side
6. written — writ • ten
7. cannot — can • not
8. window — win • dow

Directions: Read the words in the box. Separate each word into its syllables, using a dot (**base • ball**). Write each divided word in the correct column.

something	winter	curtains	suitcase	almost	tractor
indoors	danger	basket	flashbulb	daylight	nowhere
doctor	mittens	uptown	common	popcorn	

Compound Words

9. some • thing
10. in • doors
11. suit • case
12. flash • bulb
13. day • light
14. no • where
15. up • town
16. pop • corn

VCCV

17. win • ter
18. dan • ger
19. cur • tains
20. bas • ket
21. al • most
22. trac • tor
23. doc • tor
24. mit • tens
25. com • mon

Notes for Home: Your child separated words into their syllable parts, such as *baseball* (*base • ball*). *Home Activity:* Read recipes, food packages, and game notes. Look for two-syllable words. Say each word aloud and clap to show its syllables.

534 Word Study: Syllabication, Common Syllable Patterns

Name _____

Passage to Freedom: The Sugihara Story

Spelling: Compound Words 2

Pretest Directions: Fold back the page along the dotted line. On the blanks, write the spelling words as they are dictated. When you have finished the test, unfold the page and check your words.

1. bookshelf
2. someone
3. everybody
4. nowhere
5. cupcake
6. wristwatch
7. everyone
8. blindfold
9. typewriter
10. grandparent
11. home run
12. each other
13. hot dog
14. all right
15. high school
16. pen pal
17. living room
18. peanut butter
19. no one
20. first aid

1. My **bookshelf** is full.
2. **Someone** ate the apples.
3. **Everybody** came to the party.
4. She is **nowhere** to be found.
5. She wants a chocolate **cupcake**.
6. Eleanor has a new **wristwatch**.
7. **Everyone** is here.
8. We **blindfold** the player.
9. My dad found a **typewriter**.
10. She is my only **grandparent**.
11. The girl hit a **home run**.
12. We are talking to **each other**.
13. I want ketchup on my **hot dog**.
14. Is a window seat **all right**?
15. My sister goes to **high school**.
16. Her **pen pal** lives in Tobago.
17. The stereo is in the **living room**.
18. **Peanut butter** is sticky.
19. **No one** was home when I called.
20. I got **first aid** for my injury.

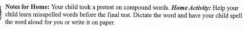

Notes for Home: Your child took a pretest on compound words. *Home Activity:* Help your child learn misspelled words before the final test. Dictate the word and have your child spell the word aloud for you or write it on paper.

Spelling: Compound Words 2 **535**

Name _____

Passage to Freedom:
The Sugihara Story

Spelling: Compound Words 2

Word List

bookshelf	cupcake	typewriter	hot dog	living room
someone	wristwatch	grandparent	all right	peanut butter
everybody	everyone	home run	high school	no one
nowhere	blindfold	each other	pen pal	first aid

Directions: Choose the compound words from the box that are written as one word. Write the words in alphabetical order on the lines.

1. blindfold
2. bookshelf
3. cupcake
4. everybody
5. everyone
6. grandparent
7. nowhere
8. someone
9. typewriter
10. wristwatch

Directions: Choose the compound word from the box that best completes each sentence. Write the word on the line to the left. Hint: Each compound word is spelled as two words, and one word of the compound word is the same as the underlined word in the sentence.

high school — 11. The <u>school</u> that I will attend next is _____.
hot dog — 12. It is too <u>hot</u> to eat a _____.
home run — 13. <u>Run</u> around all the bases after hitting a _____.
pen pal — 14. I bought a new <u>pen</u> to write to my _____.
first aid — 15. Let's <u>first</u> pack a _____ kit for the camping trip.
each other — 16. <u>Each</u> day we find ways to help _____.
no one — 17. I need <u>one</u> helper, but _____ is here right now.
peanut butter — 18. One food made from the <u>peanut</u> is _____.
living room — 19. The <u>room</u> where we watch television is the _____.
all right — 20. I have confidence that <u>all</u> of us will be _____.

Notes for Home: Your child spelled compound words. *Home Activity:* Say one of the words in each compound: for example, say *type* for *typewriter*. Have your child tell you the entire word and spell it.

536 Spelling: Compound Words 2

© Scott Foresman 5

Spelling: Compound Words 2

Directions: Proofread this paragraph. Find five spelling mistakes.
Use the proofreading marks to correct each mistake.

Every grand/parent of mine helped out in
World War II in some way. Grandpa Joe was
a doctor who gave first aid to every/body in
the hospital. Grandpa Gus was a soldier that
no one
~~noone~~ could beat! Grandma Jane worked in
a war office with her new typewriter.
Grandma Gail became a nurse right after
high/school and made sure wounded
all right
soldiers were ~~allright~~.

Proofreading Marks
☰ Make a capital.
/ Make a small letter.
∧ Add something.
✐ Take out something.
⊙ Add a period.
¶ Begin a new paragraph.

Spelling Tip

How can you
remember that **all**
right is not spelled
allright? Remember:
There is a space to the
right of **all** in **all**
right.

Word List

bookshelf	cupcake	typewriter	hot dog	living room
someone	wristwatch	grandparent	all right	peanut butter
everybody	everyone	home run	high school	no one
nowhere	blindfold	each other	pen pal	first aid

Write a Paragraph

Imagine that you or someone you know served in World War II. On a separate
sheet of paper, write a paragraph describing what you or the other person did in
the war. Try to use at least five of your spelling words.
Answers will vary, but each description should include at least five
spelling words.

 Notes for Home: Your child spelled compound words. *Home Activity:* Write each spelling
word with the letters scrambled. See if your child can unscramble each word and spell it
correctly.

Spelling: Compound Words 2

Word List

bookshelf	cupcake	typewriter	hot dog	living room
someone	wristwatch	grandparent	all right	peanut butter
everybody	everyone	home run	high school	no one
nowhere	blindfold	each other	pen pal	first aid

Directions: Choose the word from the box that best completes each statement.
Write the word on the line to the left.

home run	1. *Football* is to *touchdown* as *baseball* is to _____.
blindfold	2. *Ears* are to *earplugs* as *eyes* are to _____.
living room	3. *School* is to *gymnasium* as *house* is to _____.
wristwatch	4. *Temperature* is to *thermometer* as *time* is to _____.
hot dog	5. *Picnic* is to *sandwich* as *ballgame* is to _____.
typewriter	6. *Artist* is to *paintbrush* as *author* is to _____.
bookshelf	7. *Food* is to *cupboard* as *book* is to _____.
peanut butter	8. *Salt* is to *pepper* as *jelly* is to _____.
grandparent	9. *Mother* is to *parent* as *grandmother* is to _____.
high school	10. *Doctor* is to *hospital* as *teacher* is to _____.
pen pal	11. *Play* is to *teammate* as *write* is to _____.
cupcake	12. *Main course* is to *stew* as *dessert* is to _____.

Directions: Unscramble the letters to find a word from the box. Write the word
on the line. (Be careful with compounds that are written as two words.)

13. on neo	**no one**		17. ache herot	**each other**	
14. bevedyory	**everybody**		18. lal thrig	**all right**	
15. nevereoy	**everyone**		19. emoneos	**someone**	
16. stirf dai	**first aid**		20. onhewer	**nowhere**	

 Notes for Home: Your child spelled compound words. *Home Activity:* See how many more
compound words your child can list that contain words found in each spelling word. For
example, from *bookshelf* you could get *bookstore, bookmark, bookbag.*

Schedule

A **schedule** is a special chart that lists events and tells when they
take place, such as the arrival and departure times
of planes, trains, and buses.

Directions: The schedules below show airline
flights and times between Boston, Massachusetts,
and St. Louis, Missouri. Use these schedules to
answer the questions on the next page.

To St. Louis, Missouri

Flight Number	Leave Boston	Arrive St. Louis	Frequency
123	5:50 A.M.	8:06 A.M.	Daily
321	8:15 A.M.	10:21 A.M.	Daily
557	11:20 A.M.	1:24 P.M.	Daily
55	2:00 P.M.	4:10 P.M.	Daily
287	5:20 P.M.	7:40 P.M.	Daily
727	7:35 P.M.	9:46 P.M.	Daily Ex. Sat.

To Boston, Massachusetts

Flight Number	Leave St. Louis	Arrive Boston	Frequency
222	7:54 A.M.	11:35 A.M.	Daily
354	10:23 A.M.	2:04 P.M.	Daily
408	12:50 P.M.	4:26 P.M.	Daily
292	4:20 P.M.	7:45 P.M.	Daily
156	6:55 P.M.	10:40 P.M.	Daily
166	9:30 P.M.	1:04 A.M.	Daily Ex. Sat.

---

1. Sara has been visiting her brother in St. Louis for the weekend. She needs to be back in
Boston by noon on Monday. What is the latest flight she can take on Monday morning?
What time will she arrive in Boston?
She can take flight 222, which arrives at 11:35 A.M.

2. Gary is attending a meeting in Boston. His meeting ends at 5:00 P.M. on Friday. It takes one
hour to get to the airport. Will he be able to get home to St. Louis on Friday night, or will he
have to wait until Saturday? Explain.
He can get home Friday night by taking flight 727, leaving Boston at 7:35 P.M. and
arriving in St. Louis at 9:46 P.M.

3. Flights that arrive at their destinations between midnight and 5:00 A.M. are less expensive
than other flights. What flight would qualify for the less expensive rate? Explain.
Flight 166 to Boston from St. Louis would qualify since it doesn't arrive until
1:04 A.M.

4. Gayle likes to travel between 10:00 A.M. and 4:30 P.M. She wants to fly from St. Louis to
Boston on Monday. She wants to return to St. Louis on Saturday. What flights could she take
to make this trip during the hours she prefers?
She should take flight 354 or 408 from St. Louis to Boston on Monday, and return via
flight 557 or 55 from Boston to St. Louis on Saturday.

5. Henry lives and works in St. Louis. On Wednesday at 10:00 A.M., Henry received a call at
work from a family member in Boston. He has to fly to Boston as soon as possible. It will
take him an hour and a half to go home, pack, and get to the airport. What is the earliest he
can arrive in Boston? Explain how you figured out the answer.
He won't get to the St. Louis airport until 11:30 A.M. The next available flight leaves
St. Louis at 12:50 P.M. Therefore, the earliest he could arrive in Boston would be
4:26 P.M.

 Notes for Home: Your child has read and interpreted an airline schedule. *Home Activity:* Find
a schedule of television programs. Read the schedule with your child. Take turns saying what
each line means. For example: The news is on today at 5:00 P.M. and at 10:00 P.M.

Paraphrasing

- **Paraphrasing** is explaining something in your own words.
- When you paraphrase, you restate ideas without changing their original meaning or adding your own opinion.

Directions: Reread "Samuel Adams." Then complete the table. Paraphrase each original statement in your own words. (The beginning words of each sentence will help you find the sentence to paraphrase.)

Possible answers given.

Original Statement	My Paraphrase
Introduction, Paragraph 1, Sentence 1 "Samuel Adams didn't want. . . ."	**1. Samuel Adams opposed British soldiers ruling the new American colonies.**
Paragraph 3, Sentence 1 "On April 18 the redcoats. . . ."	**2. On April 18, British soldiers left Boston for Concord in search of a hidden cannon.**
Paragraph 3, Sentence 3 "The more trouble there was. . . ."	**3. More clashes with British soldiers would motivate Americans to declare themselves free.**
Paragraph 6, Sentence 1 "Samuel jumped out. . . ."	**4. Samuel arose from bed quickly and was ready to escape.**
Paragraph 6, Sentence 3 "John also jumped out. . . ."	**5. John also leapt from bed, but he wanted to fight instead of run.**

Notes for Home: Your child read an article and restated its ideas in his or her own words.
Home Activity: Challenge your child to listen to part of a family conversation and then paraphrase what each speaker said.

Vocabulary

Directions: Match each word on the left with its definition on the right. Write the letter of the definition next to the word.

b	1. lingers	a. destiny
e	2. magnified	b. delays in starting
d	3. tread	c. faint, unsteady light
a	4. fate	d. walk
f	5. somber	e. caused to look larger
c	6. glimmer	f. gloomy

Check the Words You Know
___ fate
___ fearless
___ glimmer
___ lingers
___ magnified
___ somber
___ steed
___ tread

Directions: Read the help-wanted advertisement. Choose the word from the box that best completes each sentence. Write the word on the matching numbered line to the right.

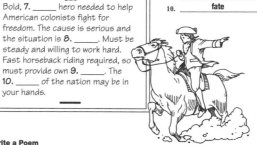

HERO WANTED

Bold, **7.** _____ hero needed to help American colonists fight for freedom. The cause is serious and the situation is **8.** _____. Must be steady and willing to work hard. Fast horseback riding required, so must provide own **9.** _____. The **10.** _____ of the nation may be in your hands.

7. **fearless**
8. **somber**
9. **steed**
10. **fate**

Write a Poem

On a separate sheet of paper, write a poem that alerts people to an important problem, such as the destruction of the rain forests. Describe the problem and some possible solutions. Use as many vocabulary words as you can.
Students' poems should make correct use of vocabulary words.

Notes for Home: Your child identified and used vocabulary words from *Paul Revere's Ride.*
Home Activity: Have your child write a telegram announcing a heroic act by a friend, family member, or public figure.

Paraphrasing

- **Paraphrasing** is explaining something in your own words.
- When you paraphrase, include only the author's ideas and opinions and do not change the author's meaning.

Directions: Reread what happened in *Paul Revere's Ride* when Paul watched for the tower signal. Then answer the questions below.

But mostly he watched with eager search
The belfry tower of the Old North Church,
As it rose above the graves on the hill,
Lonely and spectral and somber and still.
And lo! as he looks, on the belfry's height
A glimmer, and then a gleam of light!
He springs to the saddle, the bridle he turns,
But lingers and gazes, till full on his sight
A second lamp in the belfry burns!

From "Paul Revere's Ride" from TALES OF THE WAYSIDE INN by Henry Wadsworth Longfellow, 1863.

Possible answers given.

1. How might you paraphrase lines 1 and 2 as a single sentence?
He watched the North Church's belfry tower closely.

2. How might you paraphrase lines 5 and 6 as a single sentence?
Suddenly he sees a light shine in the tower.

3. How might you paraphrase line 7 as a single sentence?
He jumps on his horse and turns the bridle.

4. How might you paraphrase lines 8 and 9 as a single sentence?
But he waits until he sees a second light in the tower.

5. When you paraphrase, why is it important not to change the author's ideas and opinions?
If you change the author's ideas and opinions, the information in your paraphrase will not be accurate.

Notes for Home: Your child read a poem and then retold parts of it in his or her own words.
Home Activity: Read a story with your child. Have him pick out sentences and restate the same ideas in his or her own words.

Selection Test

Directions: Choose the best answer to each item. Mark the letter for the answer you have chosen.

Part 1: Vocabulary

Find the answer choice that means about the same as the underlined word in each sentence.

1. Sarah is completely <u>fearless</u>.
   A. making others afraid
   Ⓑ without fear
   C. very clever
   D. acting in a frightened way

2. The window <u>magnified</u> the tree outside.
   F. caused to look darker
   G. hid
   H. showed
   Ⓙ caused to look larger

3. Philip saw a <u>glimmer</u> in the woods.
   Ⓐ faint light
   B. dark shape
   C. tall tree
   D. red bird

4. The building looked very <u>somber</u>.
   F. wealthy
   G. elegant
   H. proper
   Ⓙ gloomy

5. The soldier wondered what his <u>fate</u> would be.
   A. position in the army
   Ⓑ what happens in the future
   C. meal
   D. punishment

6. The last guest <u>lingers</u>.
   Ⓕ delays in starting
   G. leaves
   H. travels
   J. is repaired

7. I heard the man's <u>tread</u> on the stairs.
   Ⓐ footstep
   B. loud crash
   C. squeaking noise
   D. ringing bell

8. The prince called for his <u>steed</u>.
   F. protective clothing for battle
   G. helper
   H. old-fashioned weapon
   Ⓙ horse

Part 2: Comprehension

Use what you know about the poem to answer each item.

9. Where did Paul Revere wait for the signal?
   A. in the belfry of the North Church
   B. on a farm in Lexington
   C. on the bridge in Concord
   Ⓓ across the water from the North Church

10. Revere's friend in the North Church belfry noticed that the British were—
    F. marching toward Connecticut.
    G. returning quietly to their camps.
    Ⓗ heading to Concord by boat.
    J. heading toward Paul Revere's hiding place.

© Scott Foresman 5

Name _____

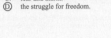

Paul Revere's Ride

11. "He heard the bleating of the flock, / And the twitter of birds among the trees." Which is the best paraphrase of these lines?
A. He scared the flock of sheep as he rode by.
B. The bleating of sheep made him keep riding.
C. He heard the sounds made by sheep and birds.
D. Birds and a flock of sheep waved to him.

12. "And one was safe and asleep in his bed / Who at the bridge would be first to fall." Which is the best paraphrase of these lines?
F. The man who would die first that day was still sleeping.
G. The bridge was still safe, but it fell that day.
H. While everyone else was sleeping, a man fell off the bridge.
J. A man dreamed that he would be the first to die.

13. What can you conclude from the information in this poem?
A. The British wanted the patriots to know they were coming.
B. Paul Revere's friend discovered the British troops by accident.
C. The patriots in Concord and Lexington were waiting for the British.
D. Paul Revere was secretly working for the British.

14. The speaker in this poem often mentions shadows, silence, and graveyards to—
F. show that Revere was a gloomy fellow.
G. remind the reader that war and death were coming soon.
H. suggest that Paul Revere's ride was all a bad dream.
J. give the poem a peaceful, happy mood.

15. The end of this poem suggests that Paul Revere's ride stands for—
A. the horror of war.
B. cleverness and secrecy.
C. fear and alarm.
D. the struggle for freedom.

STOP

Selection Test **547**

Name _____

Paul Revere's Ride

Paraphrasing

- **Paraphrasing** is explaining something in your own words.
- When you paraphrase, include only the author's ideas and opinions and do not change the author's meaning.

Directions: Read the passage below. Each sentence is numbered.

(1) The Revolutionary War led the way for the 13 British colonies in America to win their independence and become the United States of America. (2) On April 19, 1775, the war began when American colonists battled British soldiers at Lexington, Massachusetts. (3) The war ended in 1783, eight years later.

(4) Not all Americans had been in favor of challenging the British, whom they saw as more powerful than themselves. (5) Some colonists believed that to fight against England was an act of disloyalty, even though they admitted that life in the colonies was less than perfect at the time.

Directions: Complete the diagram. Rewrite the numbered sentences in your own words.
Possible answers given.

Sentence 1: The Revolutionary War made it possible for the 13 British colonies to become an independent United States.

Sentence 2: Colonists first fought the British on April 19, 1775, at Lexington, Massachusetts.

Sentence 3: The war lasted eight years, from 1775 until 1783.

Sentence 4: Some Americans opposed fighting the powerful British.

Sentence 5: Some colonists felt that, despite their hardships, it was disloyal to fight against England.

Notes for Home: Your child read an article and then retold each sentence in his or her own words. *Home Activity:* Read a newspaper article with your child. Have him pick out sentences and restate the same ideas in his or her own words.

548 Paraphrasing

Name _____

Paul Revere's Ride

Visualizing

REVIEW

Directions: Read the story. Then read each question about the story. Choose the best answer to each question. Mark the letter for the answer you have chosen.

The Battle of Bunker Hill

Johnny was only eighteen years old, yet he was doing a man's job. He stood on Breed's Hill, next to Bunker Hill, overlooking the city of Boston. Other armed patriots stood all around him. They watched silently as the British prepared to attack.

Time stood still as Johnny waited with the others. Finally a long line of redcoats began marching up the steep hill. To Johnny, the long line of enemy soldiers looked like one huge, red monster. A drummer beat a steady rhythm as the British troops came toward him.

As the soldiers drew near, Johnny took aim with his rough, heavy rifle. It felt uncomfortable in his hands. On the captain's order, a tremendous blast of gunfire erupted. It sounded like an explosion.

Smoke from the muskets filled the air and Johnny's lungs. His mouth went dry suddenly, as if he had been chewing on cotton. Johnny reloaded his musket and prepared to fire again.

Twice, the British charged up the hill and both times the patriots drove them back. At the third charge, Johnny found he was out of gunpowder. He left the battle field, along with most of the other Americans. It didn't matter. They had won what would come to be called the Battle of Bunker Hill.

1. The image "a long line of enemy began marching" appeals to the sense of—
A. hearing
B. sight
C. touch
D. taste

2. The image "a drummer beat a steady rhythm" appeals to the sense of—
F. hearing
G. sight
H. touch
J. smell

3. The image "rough, heavy rifle" appeals to the sense of —
A. hearing
B. sight
C. touch
D. taste

4. The image "smoke from the muskets filled the air and Johnny's lungs" appeals to the sense of—
F. hearing
G. sight
H. touch
J. smell

5. The image "chewing on cotton" appeals to the sense of—
A. hearing
B. sight
C. touch
D. taste

Notes for Home: Your child read a story and used its sensory details to picture the story in his or her mind. **Home Activity:** Read a poem with descriptive details. Have your child describe what he or she sees, hears, tastes, feels, or smells, based on the details.

Visualizing **549**

Name _____

Paul Revere's Ride

Writing Across Texts

Directions: How was the heroism displayed by Paul Revere in *Paul Revere's Ride* similar to Mr. Sugihara's heroism in *Passage to Freedom: The Sugihara Story*? How were these experiences alike? Complete the following table to organize your ideas. **Possible answers given.**

How the Experiences of Paul Revere and Chiune Sugihara Were Alike
Both Paul Revere and Mr. Sugihara saved lives through their efforts.
1. Both Paul Revere and Mr. Sugihara placed the lives of others before their own.
2. War caused Paul Revere and Mr. Sugihara to act.
3. Both had the help of others to complete their mission.
4. Both went against their government's rules.
5. Both Paul Revere and Mr. Sugihara trusted their own beliefs and values over the orders of a government.

Write a Conversation Starter and Follow-Up Questions

Imagine meeting Paul Revere or Chiune Sugihara. What question could you ask that would be an appropriate conversation starter? What questions would help you learn about their heroism and the obstacles they faced? **Conversation starters and follow-up questions will vary. Check that students' questions elicit information that reflects heroism and a discussion of the obstacles the heroes faced.**

Notes for Home: Your child compared characters from two different selections. *Home Activity:* Read aloud to your child two true stories about heroes. Help your child list the similarities between the heroes in both stories.

550 Writing Across Texts

© Scott Foresman 5

Grammar: Compound and Complex Sentences REVIEW

Directions: Write **compound** or **complex** to tell what kind of sentence each of the following sentences is.

compound   1. The U. S. flag is called the Stars and Stripes, but it is also known as Old Glory.

compound   2. Did Betsy Ross sew the first American flag, or is that just a legend?

complex   3. Although it has never been proved, Betsy Ross's grandson told the following story.

compound   4. It is said that George Washington visited her in 1776, and he asked her to make a flag for the new nation.

compound   5. He gave her a rough sketch, and she added ideas of her own.

complex   6. When the design was settled, she made the flag in her home.

compound   7. The story is a popular one, but no one can prove it.

Directions: Combine each pair of sentences. Add a connecting word to make the kind of sentence shown in ( ). Write your new sentences on the lines. **Possible answers given.**

8. The Revolutionary War began. An American flag was raised near Boston. (complex)
After the Revolutionary War began, an American flag was raised near Boston.

9. It had red and white stripes. It had a British symbol in the corner instead of stars. (compound)
It had red and white stripes, but it had a British symbol in the corner instead of stars.

10. The Continental Congress met in 1777. It approved a flag with stars and stripes. (complex)
When the Continental Congress met in 1777, it approved a flag with stars and stripes.

 Notes for Home: Your child identified and wrote compound and complex sentences. **Home Activity:** With your child, make a list of simple sentences on a specific topic. Then add words to make each sentence first a compound and then a complex sentence.

Grammar: Compound and Complex Sentences   551

Grammar: Conjunctions

Conjunctions such as *and*, *but*, or *or* can connect individual words, groups of words, or entire sentences. Conjunctions are used to make compound subjects, compound predicates, and compound sentences.

For compound sentences, you usually add a comma before the conjunction. The conjunction you use depends on your purpose.

Conjunction	Purpose
and	joins related ideas
but	joins different ideas
or	suggests a choice between ideas

Compound Subject: British troops <u>and</u> American minutemen confronted each other in many battles.
Compound Predicate: They exchanged shots on Lexington Green <u>and</u> fought again at Concord Bridge.
Compound Sentence: British troops and American minutemen exchanged shots on Lexington Green, <u>and</u> they fought again at Concord Bridge.

Directions: Underline the conjunction in each sentence.

1. American patriots fought the British <u>and</u> won independence.

2. The colonists objected to unfair laws <u>and</u> rebelled at paying taxes to the Crown.

3. They were angry, <u>but</u> they were determined to resist.

4. Either the king <u>or</u> the colonists would have to give in.

5. The British marched into Lexington <u>and</u> ordered the rebels to go home.

Directions: Choose a conjunction in ( ) to complete each sentence. Be sure to choose the conjunction that makes the most sense. Write the conjunction on the line.

but   6. Some Americans were killed, (but/or) others kept fighting.

and   7. The British soldiers turned (and/but) fled.

and   8. They retreated (and/or) hoped to escape death.

and   9. Soldiers (and/but) officers waited anxiously for help to arrive.

or   10. Either General Washington (or/but) General Ward would lead the army.

 Notes for Home: Your child used the conjunctions *and*, *but*, or *or* to connect ideas. **Home Activity:** Have your child use *and*, *but*, or *or* in sentences that describe the day's events. For example: *We played soccer, but the team didn't win.*

552   Grammar: Conjunctions

Grammar: Conjunctions

Directions: Circle the conjunction in each sentence.

1. George Washington organized (and) trained an army.

2. His troops were willing (but) poorly trained.

3. General Washington (and) his men lacked the enemy's resources.

4. His officers wanted to attack, (but) he decided to hold off.

5. Then the British attacked, (and) General Washington's troops were beaten back.

Directions: Choose a conjunction in ( ) to combine each pair of sentences. Write the new sentence on the line.

6. The Americans retreated. The British troops followed. (and/or)
The Americans retreated, and the British troops followed.

7. The British thought they had won. They were wrong. (or/but)
The British thought they had won, but they were wrong.

8. General Washington led a surprise attack on the British. It was successful. (but/and)
General Washington led a surprise attack on the British, and it was successful.

9. The Americans were happy. They were starving. (or/but)
The Americans were happy, but they were starving.

10. The colonists needed to get fresh supplies of food. They would starve. (and/or)
The colonists needed to get fresh supplies of food, or they would starve.

Write a Description
On a separate sheet of paper, write a description of what your life might be like if the British had won the Revolutionary War. Describe the language, food, and customs. Use conjunctions to connect ideas. **Students may need to do some research before writing their descriptions. Check whether students have joined related ideas logically, using conjunctions.**

 Notes for Home: Your child used conjunctions to connect ideas. **Home Activity:** Invite your child to make sentences using the conjunctions *and*, *but*, or *or*. Challenge your child to make the sentences tell a story about the Revolutionary War.

Grammar: Conjunctions   553

Grammar: Conjunctions RETEACHING

The conjunction *and* joins related ideas in a sentence. Underline the conjunction in the sentence.

1. Reggie washed the dishes, <u>and</u> Dave dried them.

The conjunction *but* joins contrasting ideas in a sentence. Underline the conjunction in the sentence.

2. The boys were finished with the dishes, <u>but</u> they hadn't cleaned their bedroom.

The conjunction *or* suggests a choice between ideas. Underline the conjunction in the sentence.

3. Their mother wanted them to make their beds <u>or</u> do their laundry first.

Conjunctions such as *and*, *but*, and *or* can connect individual words, groups of words, or entire sentences. They are used to make compound subjects, compound predicates, and compound sentences.

Directions: Read each sentence. Write a conjunction—*and*, *but*, or *or*—that makes sense in the sentence.

1. Friendships are difficult, **but** they are worth it.

2. Deanna **and** I have been best friends since first grade.

3. We like to do many of the same things, such as swimming **and/or** singing.

4. On the weekends, we usually go to a movie **or/and** we rent one.

5. Our favorite thing to do is bake chocolate chip cookies **and** eat them.

6. We argue sometimes, **but** we always manage to settle our differences.

7. I listen to her side, **and/or** she listens to mine.

8. Then we talk about our thoughts **and** feelings.

9. Sometimes an adult **or** my older sister helps us.

10. Most of the time she **and** I get along.

11. This afternoon we are going to have lunch **and/or** go to the park!

 Notes for Home: Your child wrote conjunctions—connecting words, such as *and*, *but*, and *or*—in sentences. **Home Activity:** Talk about what each of you did today. Encourage your child to use conjunctions correctly.

554   Grammar: Conjunctions

Grammar: Conjunctions

Directions: Circle the conjunction in ( ) that best fits each sentence.

1. When my family (but/**and**) I went camping last summer, I had a wonderful time.
2. At first I didn't want to go, (or/**but**) eventually I changed my mind.
3. We packed the car with food, gear, (or/**and**) clothes.
4. My dad made us choose between bringing a raft (but/**or**) inner tubes.
5. We brought the raft, (or/**but**) my sister was not happy about it.
6. She wanted to bring the raft (**and**/but) the inner tubes.
7. My mom said that if we brought both, my sister (but/**or**) I would have to stay home.
8. There would be no room in the car for both water toys (but/**and**) both of us!
9. My sister laughed (but/**and**) said, "I don't want to stay home!"
10. When we got to the camp site, we saw beautiful trees (**and**/but) flowers.
11. There were also paths through the woods (**and**/but) to a lake.
12. My sister and I couldn't decide if we would either hike in the woods (and/**or**) go swimming.
13. My mother said we could go exploring, (**but**/or) she didn't want to yet.
14. We went hiking, (or/**but**) later we went swimming.
15. When we got back, we had to wash lots of laundry (**and**/but) scrub our camp dishes.

Directions: Read each group of words. Add more information and the conjunction in ( ) to create a complete sentence. Write it on the line. **Possible answers given.**

16. go camping again next summer (and)
I would like to go camping again next summer, but I don't know if my parents do.

17. My sister and I will make lots of plans (and)
My sister and I will make lots of plans, and we will compromise.

18. go to a new place (or)
We might go to a new place, or we will go to the same one we went to last year.

19. take many photos (and)
Next time we take a trip, I will take many photos and put them in an album.

 Notes for Home: Your child used conjunctions correctly in sentences. *Home Activity:* Ask your child to talk about what he or she can do now that wasn't possible at a younger age. Help your child recognize conjunctions in his or her sentences.

Grammar: Conjunctions **555**

Word Study: Word Building

Directions: Say each pair of related words to yourself. Listen for the syllable that is stressed in each word. Write **same** if the same word part is stressed in each pair. Write **different** if different word parts are stressed in each pair.

different	1. real	reality
different	2. oppose	opposite
same	3. sorrow	sorrowful
different	4. history	historical
same	5. office	officer

Directions: When you add a suffix to a word, you have built a new word. Most of the time, the base word still sounds the same. But sometimes when you add a suffix, you change the way the base word sounds. Read the paragraph below. Say each underlined word to yourself. Write each word in the correct column.

The patriot's <u>curiosity</u> was aroused by a strange ship moored on the <u>opposite</u> shore. He sent a <u>respectful</u> <u>inquiry</u> to the ship's captain to ask its purpose. No one responded. <u>Plainly</u>, he thought, the newcomers are up to no good. He feared that they were <u>dangerous</u>. He leaped onto his horse. This journey would not be a <u>pleasure</u>. By riding hard under the cover of <u>darkness</u>, he could get a <u>signal</u> to his compatriots. The <u>sooner</u> they learned the news, the better.

Base Word Sound Unchanged	Base Word Sound Changed
6. **respectful**	11. **curiosity**
7. **plainly**	12. **opposite**
8. **dangerous**	13. **inquiry**
9. **darkness**	14. **pleasure**
10. **sooner**	15. **signal**

Notes for Home: Your child recognized sound changes when building new words by adding suffixes to base words. *Home Activity:* Read a magazine article with your child. Look for words with suffixes, and ask your child to identify which base words sound different with the suffix added.

556 Word Study: Word Building

Spelling: Related Words

Pretest Directions: Fold back the page along the dotted line. On the blanks, write the spelling words as they are dictated. When you have finished the test, unfold the page and check your words.

1. **please**
2. **pleasant**
3. **cloth**
4. **clothes**
5. **sign**
6. **signature**
7. **dream**
8. **dreamt**
9. **part**
10. **partial**
11. **moist**
12. **moisten**
13. **breathe**
14. **breath**
15. **create**
16. **creature**
17. **elect**
18. **election**
19. **practice**
20. **practical**

1. **Please** pass the stuffing.
2. We had a very **pleasant** day.
3. My scarf is made of soft **cloth**.
4. Dirty **clothes** go in the hamper.
5. The **sign** pointed north.
6. She has a lovely **signature**.
7. I had a strange **dream** last night.
8. She **dreamt** she was dancing.
9. My bicycle needs a new **part**.
10. This is only a **partial** list.
11. The cake was rich and **moist**.
12. We **moisten** the stamps.
13. Smoke makes it hard to **breathe**.
14. Take a deep **breath**.
15. His stories **create** new worlds.
16. A toad is an odd **creature**.
17. We will **elect** a new governor.
18. The **election** is tomorrow.
19. You must **practice** every day.
20. Paper shoes are not **practical**.

Notes for Home: Your child took a pretest on pairs of words that have parts spelled the same but pronounced differently. *Home Activity:* Help your child learn misspelled words before the final test by underlining the parts that are different in each pair and concentrating on those.

Spelling: Related Words **557**

Spelling: Related Words

	Word List			
please	sign	part	breathe	elect
pleasant	signature	partial	breath	election
cloth	dream	moist	create	practice
clothes	dreamt	moisten	creature	practical

Directions: Choose the words from the box that have one syllable. Write each word on a line. **Order may vary.**

1. **please**
2. **cloth**
3. **clothes**
4. **sign**
5. **dream**
6. **dreamt**
7. **part**
8. **moist**
9. **breathe**
10. **breath**

Directions: Complete each equation to form a word from the box. Write the word on the line.

11. practice – e + al = **practical**
12. assign – as + ature = **signature**
13. moisture – ure + en = **moisten**
14. depart – de + ial = **partial**
15. please – e + ant = **pleasant**
16. select – s + ion = **election**
17. create – e + ure = **creature**
18. practical – al + e = **practice**
19. creation – ion + e = **create**
20. election – ion = **elect**

 Notes for Home: Your child spelled pairs of words that have parts that are spelled the same but pronounced differently. *Home Activity:* Say a spelling word aloud. Have your child say the related word and spell it for you. Repeat for other pairs of related words.

558 Spelling: Related Words

Spelling: Related Words

Directions: Proofread this diary entry. Find five spelling mistakes. Use the proofreading marks to correct each mistake.

Proofreading Marks
≡ Make a capital.
/ Make a small letter.
∧ Add something.
⌿ Take out something.
⊙ Add a period.
¶ Begin a new paragraph.

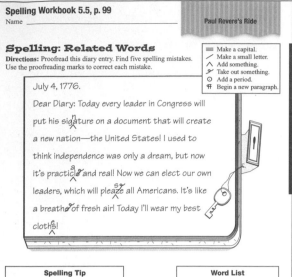

July 4, 1776.

Dear Diary: Today every leader in Congress will put his signature on a document that will create a new nation—the United States! I used to think independence was only a dream, but now it's practicl and real! Now we can elect our own leaders, which will pleaze all Americans. It's like a breath of fresh air! Today I'll wear my best cloths!

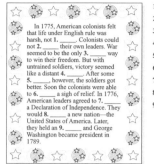

Spelling Tip

breath	breathe

How can you remember the difference between **breath** and **breathe**? Think of this hint: You **breathe** **the** air.

Word List

please	moist
pleasant	moisten
cloth	breathe
clothes	breath
sign	create
signature	creature
dream	elect
dreamt	election
part	practice
partial	practical

Write a Diary Entry

Imagine you were an American colonist at the time of the Revolutionary War. Write a diary entry that describes your experiences or your feelings about the war. Try to use at least five of your spelling words.
Answers will vary, but each diary entry should include at least five spelling words.

 Notes for Home: Your child spelled pairs of words that have parts that are spelled the same but pronounced differently. **Home Activity:** Write one word for each pair of related spelling words. Have your child show how the word can be changed to spell a related word.

Spelling: Related Words **559**

Spelling: Related Words   REVIEW

Word List

please	sign	part	breathe	elect
pleasant	signature	partial	breath	election
cloth	dream	moist	create	practice
clothes	dreamt	moisten	creature	practical

Directions: Choose the word from the box that best completes each sentence. Write the word on the line to the right.

In 1775, American colonists felt that life under English rule was harsh, not 1. _____. Colonists could not 2. _____ their own leaders. War seemed to be the only 3. _____ way to win their freedom. But with untrained soldiers, victory seemed like a distant 4. _____. After some 5. _____, however, the soldiers got better. Soon the colonists were able to 6. _____ a sigh of relief. In 1776, American leaders agreed to 7. _____ a Declaration of Independence. They would 8. _____ a new nation—the United States of America. Later, they held an 9. _____ and George Washington became president in 1789.

1. **pleasant**
2. **elect**
3. **practical**
4. **dream**
5. **practice**
6. **breathe**
7. **sign**
8. **create**
9. **election**

Directions: Choose the word from the box that belongs in each group of words. Write the word on the line.

10. gasp, sigh, **breath**
11. fantasized, imagined, **dreamt**
12. piece, portion, **part**
13. thank you, excuse me, **please**
14. animal, beast, **creature**
15. dampen, rinse, **moisten**
16. autograph, written name, **signature**
17. humid, damp, **moist**
18. incomplete, unfinished, **partial**
19. shoes, hats, **clothes**
20. leather, plastic, **cloth**

 Notes for Home: Your child spelled pairs of words that have parts that are spelled the same but pronounced differently. **Home Activity:** Together, see if you and your child can name more words that are related to each pair. For example, *create* and *creature* are also related to *creation*.

560 Spelling: Related Words

Study Strategies

Learning and using different **study strategies** can help you better understand what you read and help you focus on the most important information.

Directions: Three different study strategies are described on the index cards below. Each one is a little different. Read about them and then answer the questions that follow.

Skim and Scan

When you skim, you glance through a piece of writing quickly to get a general idea of what it is about. When you scan, you read quickly to locate specific information, key words or ideas, or to answer a specific question.

SQ2R

SQ2R stands for Survey, Question, Read, and Recite. First you survey a new work by looking at its title, author, chapter titles, headings, picture captions, and so on. Then think of questions you want to find out about that you think might be answered in the reading. Then, as you read, look for answers to the questions. Finally, recite by telling what you learned.

K-W-L

"K-W-L" stands for "What I Know," "What I Want to Know," and "What I Learned." The letters go at the top of a chart. Before reading, list what you already know in the K column. Write questions you still have in the W column. As you read, write answers to your questions in the L column. Also write in the L column additional interesting information you discovered.

K What I Know	W What I Want to Know	L What I Learned

Possible answers given. Be sure students support their answers.

1. Which strategy would you use if you wanted to find major battles with their dates in an encyclopedia article about the Revolution? Explain.
skim/scan; You can scan to find the specific information about battles and dates.

2. Which strategy would you use for reading an article from *American History Magazine* about the winter of 1777 at Valley Forge? Explain.
K-W-L; You can use a K-W-L chart to help you focus on the article's most important information.

Research and Study Skills: Study Strategies **561**

---

3. Which strategy would you use for reading a new biography of Paul Revere? Explain.
SQ2R; You can use this strategy with a longer text and survey chapter titles, pictures, captions, and so on.

4. Which strategy would you use to review a chapter of your textbook for a test on the American Revolution? Explain.
skim/scan; To study for a test, you can skim and scan to recall what the chapter is about and to find specific information.

5. Which strategy would you use to decide whether to read a historical novel about Abigail Adams? Explain.
skim/scan; You can skim the novel to get a general idea of what it is about.

6. Which strategy would you use for reading a nonfiction book about the role Native Americans played in the American Revolution? Explain.
K-W-L or SQ2R; Either a K-W-L chart or SQ2R will help you organize information found in a nonfiction book.

7. Which strategy would you use to decide whether a historical atlas would be a useful resource for your Revolutionary War research? Explain.
skim/scan; You can skim and scan the atlas to see if it has the specific information you need for your research.

8. Which strategy would you use for reading an illustrated history of the American Revolution? Explain.
SQ2R; You can use SQ2R and carefully survey the pictures and captions in an illustrated history text.

9. Which strategy would you use for reading a collection of letters and diaries by American colonists during the Revolution? Explain.
K-W-L or SQ2R; You could use a K-W-L chart or SQ2R to help you organize the information in the collection.

10. Suppose you were reading a nonfiction text about Paul Revere's ride. What are some questions you might ask yourself that you could then use with one of the study strategies to help you find the answers?
Questions will vary but should reflect some information already learned from reading the poem *Paul Revere's Ride*.

 Notes for Home: Your child made decisions about which of three study strategies works best with different kinds of texts. **Home Activity:** Discuss with your child a subject you would like to know more about. Make and complete a K-W-L chart like the one shown.

562 Research and Study Skills: Study Strategies

© Scott Foresman 5

Name _____

Time Line

Time lines should be filled out completely, during the research process.

Directions: Write your topic. Between the slanted lines, write notes about the person. Below the bold line, write the dates. Identify your information sources.

Topic: _____

Information Sources: _____

Date or time: _____

Notes for Home: Your child made a time line to organize information for a research report. *Home Activity:* Think of a person of the past who did something brave or admirable. Tell your child about this person's deed and ask how the facts could be organized on a time line.

Unit 5: Writing Process **563**

Name _____

Elaboration
Prepositional Phrases

- You can add information to sentences or make sentences clearer by using **prepositional phrases**.
- Prepositional phrases begin with **prepositions**—words such as *across, at, for, in, of, on, until,* and *with.*

Directions: Complete each sentence by picking a prepositional phrase from the box that tells more about the topic. Rewrite the sentence with the prepositional phrase in place of the blank. More than one phrase may fit a sentence. Choose one that makes sense.

Prepositional Phrases	
about new taxes	of England
across the ocean	to the presidency
by General Washington	until 1776
for many years	with battles

Responses will vary. Reasonable answers are given.

1. The first thirteen United States were ruled by England ____.
The first thirteen United States were ruled by England until 1776.

2. King George ____ never visited those American colonies.
King George of England never visited those American colonies.

3. Americans felt that a government ____ was too far away.
Americans felt that a government across the ocean was too far away.

4. Many people in the colonies became upset ____.
Many people in the colonies became upset about new taxes.

5. In the Revolutionary War, the army was led ____.
In the Revolutionary War, the army was led by General Washington.

6. War lasted ____ before the United States became free.
War lasted for many years before the United States became free.

7. Soldiers on both sides were happy to be finished ____.
Soldiers on both sides were happy to be finished with battles.

8. Finally George Washington was elected ____.
Finally George Washington was elected to the presidency.

Notes for Home: Your child added information to sentences by using prepositional phrases, such as *across the ocean. Home Activity:* Ask your child to make up three sentences telling about an event in history. Have your child identify any prepositional phrases in the sentences.

564 Unit 5: Writing Process

Name _____

Self-Evaluation
Research Report

Students' responses should show that they have given thought to the research reports they have prepared and written.

Directions: Think about the final draft of your research report. Then answer each question in the chart.

	Yes	No	Not sure
1. Did I find interesting information about a person and event?			
2. Did I present the information from my research clearly?			
3. Did I keep my purpose and audience in mind?			
4. Did I identify sources of special information?			
5. Did I proofread and edit carefully to correct errors?			

6. What is the best part of my research report?

_____

_____

_____

7. Write one thing that you would change about this research report if you had the chance to research or write it again.

_____

_____

_____

Notes for Home: Your child has answered questions about writing a research report. *Home Activity:* Ask your child what sources provided useful information. Ask your child whether it was difficult to find information about the person and event he or she chose to research.

Unit 5: Writing Process **565**

Practice Book 5.6, p. 251

Name _____

The Baker's Neighbor

Theme

- **Theme** is an underlying meaning or message of a story. Themes can be statements, lessons, or generalizations that stand on their own, such as: *Life is what you make of it.*
- Sometimes the author states the theme directly. Sometimes readers have to figure out a theme on their own by asking, "What did I learn from reading this story?"

Directions: Reread "King Midas." Then complete the table. Answer the questions in order to determine the story's theme. **Possible answers given.**

Questions	Answers
What did King Midas wish for?	1. He wished that everything he touched would turn to gold.
Why did King Midas make the wish that he did?	2. He loved gold and thought a person could never have enough.
Why was Bacchus disappointed by King Midas' wish?	3. He knew that King Midas already had enough gold.
What ultimately happened to King Midas?	4. He was unable to eat because his food turned to gold.
What lesson does this story teach you?	5. Be careful what you wish for. Being too greedy can lead to disaster.

Notes for Home: Your child read a story and identified its theme, or message. *Home Activity:* Read a story with your child. Later, talk about the lesson that it teaches. Discuss what the main characters learn from their experiences in the story.

568 Theme

© Scott Foresman 5

Vocabulary

Directions: Choose the word from the box that best matches each clue. Write the word on the line.

scowling	**1.** A grumpy person is always doing it.	
trial	**2.** This decides if a person is guilty or not guilty.	
pastries	**3.** Don't eat too many of these sweet treats.	
inspects	**4.** It's what an inspector does.	
fragrance	**5.** It appeals to the sense of smell.	

Check the Words You Know
___ fragrance
___ inspects
___ pastries
___ pleasures
___ privilege
___ scowling
___ trial

Directions: Choose the word from the box that best completes each sentence. Write the word on the line to the left.

inspects	**6.** A good baker _____ his ingredients before he starts to bake.
pastries	**7.** He uses only the finest flour, sugar, and butter to make _____.
fragrance	**8.** A delicious _____ wafts from the bakery.
privilege	**9.** His neighbors feel it is a _____ to live next door.
pleasures	**10.** There are so many _____ to being a baker's good friend!

Write a Recipe
What is your favorite dish? On a separate sheet of paper, write a recipe for it. List the ingredients and steps in the preparation. Don't forget to tell how good the food tastes and smells! Use as many vocabulary words as you can in your recipe.
Students' recipes should make correct use of vocabulary words.

Notes for Home: Your child identified and used vocabulary words from "The Baker's Neighbor." *Home Activity:* Act out with your child a conversation between a baker and a customer. Use as many listed vocabulary words as you can.

Theme

- **Theme** is an underlying meaning or message of a story. Themes can be statements, lessons, or generalizations that stand on their own, such as: *Life is what you make of it.*
- Sometimes the author states the theme directly. Sometimes readers have to figure out a theme on their own by asking, "What did I learn from reading this story?"

Directions: Reread what happens in "The Baker's Neighbor" when the judge makes his ruling. Then answer the questions below.

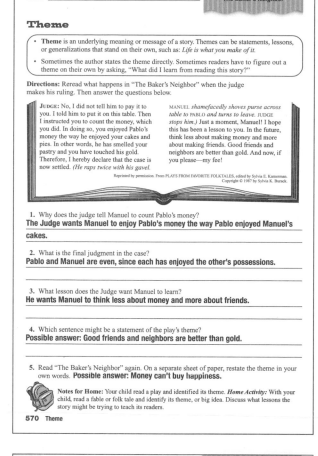

JUDGE: No, I did not tell him to pay it to you. I told him to put it on this table. Then I instructed you to count the money, which you did. In doing so, you enjoyed Pablo's money the way you enjoyed your cakes and pies. In other words, he has smelled your pastry and you have touched his gold. Therefore, I hereby declare that the case is now settled. (*He raps twice with his gavel.*

MANUEL *shamefacedly shoves purse across table to* PABLO *and turns to leave.* JUDGE *stops him.*) Just a moment, Manuel! I hope this has been a lesson to you. In the future, think less about making money and more about making friends. Good friends and neighbors are better than gold. And now, if you please—my fee!

Reprinted by permission. From PLAYS FROM FAVORITE FOLKTALES, edited by Sylvia E. Kamerman. Copyright © 1987 by Sylvia K. Burack.

1. Why does the judge tell Manuel to count Pablo's money?
The Judge wants Manuel to enjoy Pablo's money the way Pablo enjoyed Manuel's cakes.

2. What is the final judgment in the case?
Pablo and Manuel are even, since each has enjoyed the other's possessions.

3. What lesson does the Judge want Manuel to learn?
He wants Manuel to think less about money and more about friends.

4. Which sentence might be a statement of the play's theme?
Possible answer: Good friends and neighbors are better than gold.

5. Read "The Baker's Neighbor" again. On a separate sheet of paper, restate the theme in your own words. **Possible answer: Money can't buy happiness.**

Notes for Home: Your child read a play and identified its theme. *Home Activity:* With your child, read a fable or folk tale and identify its theme, or big idea. Discuss what lessons the story might be trying to teach its readers.

Selection Test

Directions: Choose the best answer to each item. Mark the letter for the answer you have chosen.

Part 1: Vocabulary

Find the answer choice that means about the same as the underlined word in each sentence.

1. The traveler inspects the hotel.
A. enters
B. describes in words
C. visits again
(D) looks at closely

2. Aunt Melanie brought pastries to the party.
F. gifts
(G) bakery goods
H. things for decorating
J. guests

3. What is that wonderful fragrance?
(A) smell
B. music
C. color
D. flavor

4. Jasper was scowling throughout the game.
F. clapping loudly
G. yelling
(H) looking angry
J. whispering

5. Niki acts as if she has some special privilege.
A. gift
B. information
(C) right
D. skill

6. The trial was covered in the newspaper.
F. big party
G. recount of votes in an election
H. championship game
(J) deciding of a case of law

7. Mom wrote us a letter describing the pleasures of her trip.
A. problems
(B) things that are enjoyed
C. places where one stops
D. reasons for doing something

Part 2: Comprehension

Use what you know about the play to answer each item.

8. After Manuel sets his pies out in the morning, he—
F. lies down to rest.
G. travels from door to door selling his pies.
H. invites the neighborhood children to sample his pies.
(J) counts his money.

9. At the beginning of the play, why is Manuel angry with Pablo?
A. Pablo does not think Manuel's pies are very good.
B. Pablo makes more money than Manuel.
(C) Pablo enjoys Manuel's pies without paying for them.
D. Pablo sends children to Manuel's to beg for free pies.

10. What is Pablo's attitude about work?
(F) He works when he has to.
G. He thinks work is the most important thing in life.
H. A man should have his children support him.
J. He would like to work part time for Manuel.

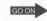

---

11. When the children ask what sound Pablo would like to be, he says that—
(A) he would like to be a song.
B. he would like to be gold coins jingling.
C. the question is a foolish waste of time.
D. only children could think up such a question.

12. Which best states a theme of this play?
F. People need to work hard to get ahead in life.
G. When people grow up, they should stop acting like children.
(H) Some of life's simple pleasures don't have a price.
J. It is just as bad to be greedy for food as to be greedy for money.

13. Which sentences from the story best help support the theme?
A. "It has not yet been proved that Pablo is a thief. First he must have a fair trial."
B. "Every night I mix the flour and knead the dough and slave over a hot oven while that shiftless, good-for-nothing Pablo sleeps."
(C) "I am a man of simple pleasures. Just the smell of a bakery makes me happy!"
D. "I must make sure I haven't been cheated. How kind of you to remind me!"

14. The Judge decided the case the way he did because he wanted to—
F. show everyone that stealing is punished severely.
G. have people make fun of Manuel.
H. scare Pablo so that he would stop smelling the pies.
(J) make Manuel truly understand why Pablo was innocent.

15. The writer probably ends the play with the Judge and Pablo eating the same pie in order to—
(A) have it end in a funny way.
B. show that the Judge is just as greedy as Manuel.
C. add an air of excitement.
D. prove that the pies really taste good.

© Scott Foresman 5

Theme

- **Theme** is an underlying meaning or message of a story. Themes can be statements, lessons, or generalizations that stand on their own, such as: *Life is what you make of it.*

Directions: Read the play below.

CHARACTERS: HENRY and LEWIS, neighbors; MARTHA, Henry's wife.

HENRY *(mowing his lawn and muttering):* I've had it with these rotten apples from Lewis's tree. *(shouts)* Hey, Lewis! I'm going to have that tree cut down. I don't care if we've been friends for years. I don't care if my daughter is engaged to marry your son.

LEWIS: You can't have my tree cut down, you obnoxious loud-mouth! If you—

MARTHA *(runs out of the house in a panic):* Henry! Lewis! Listen—Pete and Susie have been in a car accident! They are both at the hospital.

LEWIS and HENRY *(talking at once):* What fools we are to fight about apples. Our children might have been killed! Come on, friend. Let's go to our children.

Directions: Complete the table. Use the questions to help you think about the story's big idea. Answer each question and then write the story's theme.
Possible answers given.

Ask Yourself . . .	Answer
What comes between Henry and Lewis's friendship?	1. **Rotten apples fell from Lewis's tree into Henry's yard.**
What other bond do the two friends share?	2. **Their children are engaged.**
What happens to make them forget their fighting?	3. **Their children are in a car accident.**
What effect does this event have on them?	4. **It brings them together again.**

5. Theme: **Family and friends are what matter most.**

Notes for Home: Your child read a passage from a play and identified its theme, or big idea. *Home Activity:* Read a story with your child. Together, identify the theme by talking about the characters and what happens to them. Think about what lessons were learned from the story.

Theme **573**

Compare and Contrast

REVIEW

Directions: Read the story. Then read each question about the story. Choose the best answer to each question. Mark the letter for the answer you have chosen.

Resolving Conflict

Maggie and Beth both tend to have many conflicts with their friends. They handle these conflicts differently, however. Maggie tries to resolve problems by sitting down and talking with her friends. Beth, on the other hand, tends to dwell on the misunderstandings.

When Maggie has a disagreement with her friends, she listens to them and they listen to her. They come to understand each other's point of view and work out a resolution to their problem. Maggie's friendships don't seem to suffer from the fact that there are conflicts.

Beth refuses to sit down and talk out the differences honestly with the person with whom she disagrees. As a result, the conflicts between Beth and her friends never get resolved. The fights go on and on.

When the girls have conflicts with their parents, they use the same approaches as they do with their friends. Last week, for instance, both girls had trouble with their parents over their math grades.

Maggie agreed to sit down with her parents and talk about her math grade. She explained that she just didn't understand the new material and was too embarrassed to ask her teacher for extra help. Then she let her parents talk.

Beth, however, simply got angry when her parents brought up the subject of her math grade. She threw her math book on the floor, stormed out of the kitchen, slammed the door of her room, and sulked.

1. From the first paragraph, we learn that Maggie and Beth both—
   A. settle conflicts by talking.
   B. dwell on conflicts.
   C. tend to argue with friends.
   D. have a lot of friends.

2. In the first paragraph, the author shows contrast with the clue words—
   F. however, on the other hand.
   G. both, conflicts.
   H. resolve, dwell.
   J. sitting down, talking.

3. In the fourth paragraph, the author shows comparison with the clue word—
   A. for instance.
   B. both.
   C. when.
   D. conflicts.

4. In the fourth and fifth paragraphs, the author contrasts—
   F. the girls' grades in math.
   G. how the girls deal with their parents.
   H. the reactions of the girls' parents.
   J. the difficulty of growing up.

5. Overall, the girls are—
   A. exactly alike.
   B. completely different.
   C. alike in the way they handle conflicts.
   D. different in the way they handle conflicts.

Notes for Home: Your child read a story and identified comparisons and contrasts in the text. *Home Activity:* Have your child compare and contrast the ways that different family members or friends settle conflicts.

574 Compare and Contrast

Writing Across Texts

Directions: Think about items and services that have been used for money or barter as shown in "All Kinds of Money." What might the characters in "The Baker's Neighbor" use for barter? Consider what special skills each has and fill in the table below with your ideas. **Possible answers:**

Character	Skill to Be Used as Barter
Pablo	1. **Pablo could barter with his ability to entertain others.**
Manuel	2. **Manuel could barter with his baked goods.**
Carlos	3. **Carlos could work in the garden, as he did for his father.**
The Three Women	4. **The three women could work as companions.**
The Judge	5. **The judge could offer legal services as barter.**

Write a Paragraph

Write a paragraph about a time you or someone you know has bartered with someone else. You may have done a chore for a trip to a favorite restaurant or traded one toy for another. Use a separate sheet of paper for your paragraph.
Paragraphs will vary. Check that students support topic sentences with details.

Notes for Home: Your child applied information from a selection to his or her own life. *Home Activity:* As you read stories and articles with your child, talk about how the ideas in this reading material connect to his or her own experiences.

Writing Across Texts **575**

Grammar: Conjunctions

REVIEW

Directions: Choose the conjunction *and, but,* or *to* to complete each sentence. Write the complete sentence on the line.

1. Brittany _____ Rose went to the bakery together.
Brittany and Rose went to the bakery together.

2. I did not go, _____ Dan went with them.
I did not go, but Dan went with them.

3. Will you call me _____ stop by my house later?
Will you call me and/or stop by my house later?

4. I have some questions about tomorrow's test, _____ we should talk about our group project.
I have some questions about tomorrow's test, and we should talk about our group project.

5. We have to decide whether Brittany _____ Rose will be the presenter.
We have to decide whether Brittany or Rose will be the presenter.

Directions: Choose the conjunction *and, but,* or *or* to combine each pair of sentences. Write your new sentence on the line.

6. Brittany agreed to come to my house. Rose couldn't make it.
Brittany agreed to come to my house, but Rose couldn't make it.

7. Dan, Brittany, and I met. Dan took notes for Rose.
Dan, Brittany, and I met, and Dan took notes for Rose.

8. We know we need to work hard. We will not get a good grade.
We know we need to work hard, or we will not get a good grade.

9. I think we should use drawings. Dan thinks a videotape would be more interesting.
I think we should use drawings, but Dan thinks a videotape would be more interesting.

10. We want to show how bread is made at a bakery. We want to show how bread is sold.
We want to show how bread is made and sold at a bakery.

Notes for Home: Your child used the conjunctions *and, but,* or *or* to complete sentences and to join two simple sentences. *Home Activity:* Look in a book or magazine for sentences with *and, but,* or *or.* Decide what sentence parts or simple sentences these conjunctions join.

576 Grammar: Conjunctions

© Scott Foresman 5

Grammar Practice Book 5.6, p. 127

Name _____

The Baker's Neighbor

Grammar: Review of Sentences

A **sentence** is a group of words that makes a statement, a question, a command, a request, or an exclamation. It begins with a capital letter and ends with a punctuation mark. You can tell whether a group of words is a sentence by checking to see whether it makes a complete statement.

A **declarative sentence** makes a statement. It ends with a period.
  The two neighbors got into an argument about how to make apple pie.

An **interrogative sentence** asks a question. It ends with a question mark.
  Which one puts cinnamon into her pies?

An **imperative sentence** gives a command or makes a request. It ends with a period.
  Please, teach me how to make apple pie.

An **exclamatory sentence** shows strong feeling. It ends with an exclamation mark.
  I just love a good homemade pie!

Directions: Read each sentence. Determine whether the sentence is declarative, interrogative, imperative, or exclamatory. Write your answer on the line.

declarative	1. The peach pies are cooling in the oven.
imperative	2. Take them out after you've finished cleaning the counter.
interrogative	3. Do you think any of the pies are ready yet?
declarative	4. Sometimes the pies have to cook for a little longer than you think.
exclamatory	5. What a great smell those pies have!

Directions: Add the correct end punctuation to complete each sentence.

6. Oh no, the apple pies are burning __!__

7. Are they ruined __?__

8. Get more apples from the farmers' market __.__

9. Do we have enough money to buy some more apples __?__

10. We need at least twenty pies for the bakery __.__

11. Do you know what time the bakery opens __?__

12. Please, be there at 7 A.M. __.__

13. People count on our bakery opening on time __.__

14. What great customers we have __!__

15. It's important that we keep them happy __.__

Notes for Home: Your child wrote sentences that make statements, questions, commands or requests, and exclamations. *Home Activity:* Have your child create examples of all four types of sentences by writing greeting cards to friends and family.

Grammar: Review of Sentences **577**

Grammar Practice Book 5.6, p. 128

Name _____

The Baker's Neighbor

Grammar: Review of Sentences

Directions: Add the correct end punctuation to complete each sentence.

1. Don't you think that my bread is the best in town __?__

2. No, I think mine is better __.__

3. Try my cinnamon raisin bread __.__

4. Why should I when I have my own __?__

5. I'm just trying to be helpful __.__

6. What a good friend you are __!__

7. Do you like to eat bread when it's toasted __?__

8. I prefer my bread freshly baked __.__

9. Please, help me prepare my new recipe __.__

10. What a great idea that is __!__

Directions: Add words, capital letters, and punctuation marks to make each group of words a complete sentence. Write the type of sentence shown in ( ). Write your sentence on the line. **Possible answers given.**

11. makes bread at the bakery (declarative)
The baker makes bread at the bakery.

12. delicious pies (exclamatory)
What delicious pies he makes!

13. when will the pies (interrogative)
When will the pies be ready?

14. the bakery in my neighborhood (declarative)
The bakery in my neighborhood sells them.

15. some bread for me (imperative)
Buy some bread for me.

Write a Recipe

What foods do you like best? On a separate sheet of paper, write a recipe for your favorite food. Give clear steps in the directions. Use different types of sentences. List the different types of sentences you used.
Students will likely use imperative and declarative sentences in their recipes. Check that all sentences express complete thoughts, begin with capital letters, and end with appropriate punctuation marks.

Notes for Home: Your child wrote sentences that make statements, questions, commands, and exclamations. *Home Activity:* Together, write sentences on index cards but leave off the end punctuation. Take turns identifying the type of sentence and adding correct punctuation marks.

578 Grammar: Review of Sentences

Grammar Practice Book 5.6, p. 129

Name _____

The Baker's Neighbor

Grammar: Review of Sentences

RETEACHING

Underline the declarative sentence. Circle the interrogative sentence. Put a check mark by the imperative sentence. Circle the punctuation mark at the end of the exclamatory sentence.

1. How often do you go to the movies?

2. I go to the movies at least once a month.

3. There sure are a lot to choose from!

4. Please bring me the newspaper. ✓

A **sentence** is a group of words that makes a statement, a question, a command or a request, or an exclamation. It begins with a capital letter and ends with a punctuation mark.

Directions: Read each sentence. Write *declarative*, *interrogative*, *imperative*, or *exclamatory* on the line to the left.

imperative	1. Listen to the wind blowing through the orchard.
interrogative	2. Can you hear the soft sound?
declarative	3. I think it sounds like someone is whistling.
exclamatory	4. How beautiful it is!

Directions: Think about an exciting adventure you have had, or an event you have attended. Write a declarative sentence, an interrogative sentence, an imperative sentence, and an exclamatory sentence about your experience. Then label each one *declarative, interrogative, imperative,* or *exclamatory*. **Possible answers given.**

5. declarative
We went to the amusement park last Saturday.

6. imperative
Get in the roller coaster line as soon as possible.

7. exclamatory
How fast the largest roller coaster moves!

8. interrogative
Will there be new rides when we go back next year?

Notes for Home: Your child identified and wrote four kinds of sentences. *Home Activity:* Have your child find examples of declarative, interrogative, imperative, and exclamatory sentences in books. Then have him or her explain the differences between sentence types.

Grammar: Review of Sentences **579**

Grammar Practice Book 5.6, p. 130

Name _____

The Baker's Neighbor

Grammar: Review of Sentences

Directions: Add the correct punctuation to complete each sentence.

1. Many interesting things happen in the sky at night __.__

2. Please look up there __.__

3. Did you see that __?__

4. It was a shooting star __.__

5. How bright it was __!__

6. What is a shooting star __?__

7. It is a burning meteor traveling through the air __.__

8. It leaves a glowing trail behind it __.__

9. Here, look through my telescope __.__

10. It certainly is exciting to watch the sky __!__

Directions: Add words, capital letters, and punctuation marks to make each group of words a complete sentence. Write the type of sentence shown in ( ). Write your sentence on the line. **Possible answers given.**

11. at my poor angelfish (imperative)
Look at my poor angelfish.

12. is hiding under a piece of seaweed (declarative)
It is hiding under a piece of seaweed.

13. scared it is (exclamatory)
How scared it is!

14. bought it yesterday (declarative)
I bought it yesterday from Mr. Smith at the pet store.

15. nice of him (interrogative)
Wasn't it nice of him to include the fish food?

16. give it a little food (your choice)
Please give it a little food.

Notes for Home: Your child punctuated and wrote four types of sentences. *Home Activity:* Have your child write a short scene for a play. Encourage him or her to include declarative, interrogative, imperative, and exclamatory sentences as lines for the characters in the scene.

580 Grammar: Review of Sentences

© Scott Foresman 5

The Baker's Neighbor

Phonics: Vowel Digraphs

Directions: Read the words in the box. Each word contains the vowel combination **ea,** but the words have different vowel sounds. Write each word in the correct column.

steal	please	pleasure
tread	treat	break
great	steak	instead

Long e Sound
1. steal
2. please
3. treat

Short e Sound
4. tread
5. pleasure
6. instead

Long a Sound
7. great
8. steak
9. break

Directions: Read the words in the box. Even though some words have the same vowel combination, the vowels have different vowel sounds. Write each word in the correct column.

pies	tough	belief	dough	tries
enough	pieces	ties	though	thief

Long o Sound
10. dough
11. though

Short u Sound
15. tough
16. enough

Long e Sound
12. pieces
13. belief
14. thief

Long i Sound
17. pies
18. tries
19. ties

Directions: Write six words that have the **long a** sound spelled **ay** as in **way** on the lines below. **Possible answers given.**

20. display
21. trays
22. paying

23. may
24. day
25. stay

 Notes for Home: Your child distinguished between different vowel sounds for words with *ea, ou, ie,* and *ay.* **Home Activity:** With your child, write words with these vowel combinations on slips of paper. Say each word aloud and group the words that have the same vowel sounds and spellings.

Phonics: Vowel Digraphs **581**

The Baker's Neighbor

Spelling: Easily Confused Words

Pretest Directions: Fold back the page along the dotted line. On the blanks, write the spelling words as they are dictated. When you have finished the test, unfold the page and check your words.

1. of
2. off
3. except
4. accept
5. which
6. witch
7. where
8. were
9. weather
10. whether
11. plant
12. planet
13. bounds
14. bounce
15. desert
16. dessert
17. rise
18. raise
19. dinner
20. diner

1. This is the last **of** the oranges.
2. Please turn **off** the lamp.
3. I like all fruit **except** bananas.
4. I didn't **accept** the invitation.
5. **Which** is the way to town?
6. She was a **witch** for Halloween.
7. **Where** is the grocery store?
8. We **were** lost in the hills.
9. The **weather** was stormy.
10. Tell me **whether** you will come.
11. He has a **plant** with red flowers.
12. They saw a new **planet.**
13. The ball went out of **bounds.**
14. The girls **bounce** the ball.
15. Camels live in the **desert.**
16. We will have cake for **dessert.**
17. The sun will **rise** soon.
18. They **raise** the flags up high.
19. What is for **dinner**?
20. This **diner** serves malts.

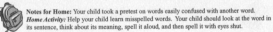 **Notes for Home:** Your child took a pretest on words easily confused with another word. **Home Activity:** Help your child learn misspelled words. Your child should look at the word in its sentence, think about its meaning, spell it aloud, and then spell it with eyes shut.

582 Spelling: Easily Confused Words

The Baker's Neighbor

Spelling: Easily Confused Words

Word List				
of	which	weather	bounds	rise
off	witch	whether	bounce	raise
except	where	plant	desert	dinner
accept	were	planet	dessert	diner

Directions: Choose the word from the box that is easily confused with the word given. Write the word on the line.

1. off — of
2. except — accept
3. which — witch
4. where — were
5. weather — whether

6. plant — planet
7. bounds — bounce
8. dessert — desert
9. rise — raise
10. dinner — diner

Directions: Write the word from the box that belongs in each group of words.

11. leaps, jumps, — bounds
12. flower, bush, — plant
13. under, over, on, — off
14. breakfast, lunch, — dinner
15. here, there, — where
16. what, who, — which
17. swell, lift, — rise
18. exclude, omit, — except
19. snow, rain, — weather
20. pie, cake, — dessert

 Notes for Home: Your child spelled words that are easily confused, such as *off* and *of.* **Home Activity:** Help your child think of other pairs of easily confused words, such as *conscience/conscious, adapt/adopt,* and *wreck/wreak.* Invite him or her to spell both words.

Spelling: Easily Confused Words **583**

The Baker's Neighbor

Spelling: Easily Confused Words

Directions: Proofread this letter of apology. Find five spelling mistakes. Use the proofreading marks to correct each mistake.

≡	Make a capital.
/	Make a small letter.
∧	Add something.
⌓	Take out something.
⊙	Add a period.
¶	Begin a new paragraph.

Dear Rita,

I'm sorry that I yelled at you yesterday. You were right, and I was out of bounds. Please accept my apology, which is sincere. We could plant some flowers if the whether is nice or go out to diner. I will buy you a nice desert, anything except strawberry shortcake because I know you don't like it.

Your friend,

Carlos

Spelling Tip

Remember the number of s's in **dessert** and **desert** this way: **Desserts** are **so sweet,** but a **desert** is only **sandy.**

Word List	
of	plant
off	planet
except	bounds
accept	bounce
which	desert
witch	dessert
where	rise
were	raise
weather	dinner
whether	diner

Write a Letter

On a separate sheet of paper, write a note to a friend in which you settle a conflict or other problem between you. Try to use at least five of your spelling words.
Answers will vary, but each letter should include at least five spelling words.

 Notes for Home: Your child spelled words that are easily confused, such as *off* and *of.* **Home Activity:** Spell each word aloud, pausing between each letter. As soon as your child recognizes the word, have him or her say the word and tell its meaning.

584 Spelling: Easily Confused Words

Name _____

The Baker's Neighbor

Spelling: Easily Confused Words — REVIEW

Word List

of	which	weather	bounds	rise
off	witch	whether	bounce	raise
except	where	plant	desert	dinner
accept	were	planet	dessert	diner

Directions: Choose the word from the box that best matches each clue. Write the letters of the word on the blanks. The boxed letters answer the riddle: What do you do to place *it* and *run* in alphabetical order?

1. a very dry place — 1. d e **s** e r t
2. a foul ball is out of — 2. b o u **n** d s
3. rubber balls do this — 3. b o u **n** c e
4. atmospheric conditions — 4. w e **a** t h e r
5. pledge _____ allegiance — 5. o **f**
6. Mars, for example — 6. p l a n e **t**
7. sweet item served at the end of a meal — 7. d **e** s s e r t
8. a place to eat — 8. d i n e **r**
9. an important meal — 9. d **i** n n e r
10. an ivy, for example — 10. p l a n **t**

What would you do to place *it* and *run* in alphabetical order?

r u n a f t e r i t

Directions: Unscramble the letters to find a word from the box. Write the word on the line.

11. fof — **off**
12. rheew — **where**
13. rewe — **were**
14. itwch — **witch**
15. xetecp — **except**
16. seira — **raise**
17. wreheth — **whether**
18. pctace — **accept**
19. chiwh — **which**
20. ires — **rise**

Notes for Home: Your child spelled words that are easily confused, such as *off* and *of*. **Home Activity:** Challenge your child to write a sentence that uses each pair of words together in a single sentence.

Name _____

The Baker's Neighbor

Advertisement/Order Form

An **advertisement** is an announcement that tries to persuade readers, viewers, or listeners to do something, buy something, or feel a particular way about something. An **order form** is a chart that allows a person to respond to an advertisement or catalog.

Directions: Read the advertisement and order form below. Then answer the questions on the next page.

Momma's Marvelous Muffins Can't seem to wake up? One taste of Momma's Marvelous Muffins will wake you up and make you smile!

Just ask the basketball star, Harriet Hoopster. She eats Momma's Muffins every single morning, and her team has not lost a game all year.

Momma's Marvelous Muffins come in six delicious flavors: outrageous orange, raisin razzmatazz, strawberry surprise, peanut butter perfection, lemon zip, and blueberry bonanza.

Every bite is loaded with great flavor.

Order your muffins by phone, fax, mail, or in person.

Call 1-888-555-2020 today, or use the handy order form below.

Visit our web site at www.marvmuffins.com. for more information.

1. Ship to:
   Name _____
   Address _____
   _____
   Phone Number _____

2. Method of payment
   ___ check
   ___ credit card
   Card number: _____

3. Muffins ordered (order in boxes of six each)

ITEM	Quantity	Price per box	Cost
Outrageous Orange	2	$12.00	$24.00
Raisin Razzmatazz		$12.00	
Strawberry Surprise	1	$12.00	$12.00
Peanut Butter Perfection		$10.00	
Lemon Zip		$10.00	
Blueberry Bonanza	3	$14.00	$42.00

Mail to Momma's Marvelous Muffins, 15390 Delicious Drive, Bakerville, MD 20888.

Or fax your completed order form to 1-888-555-2025.

Subtotal	$78.00
Add shipping and handling	
$10–$24 $1.50	
$25–$49 $2.50	
over $50 $3.50	3.50
Subtotal, shipping and handling	
TOTAL	**$81.50**

Name _____

The Baker's Neighbor

1. What information in this advertisement consists of statements of fact? **The statement that lists the muffin flavors is a statement of fact. So are the statements that Harriet Hoopster eats them every day and that her team has not lost a game all year.**

2. What information in this advertisement consists of statements of opinion? **The statements that the muffins will wake you up and make you smile, that everyone is talking about them, and that each bite is loaded with flavor are all statements of opinion.**

3. What exaggerated claim does this advertisement make? **Possible answer: The claim that the muffins will wake you up and make you smile.**

4. What conclusion does the advertiser want you to draw about Harriet Hoopster's team's winning record? **The advertiser wants you to think that the team hasn't lost a game because Harriet has been eating the muffins.**

5. If you order muffins by mail, how can you pay for them? **You can pay by check or credit card.**

6. How many muffins come in a box? **six**

7. What is the price of a box of Lemon Zip muffins? **$10.00**

8. What would the shipping and handling costs be on an order worth $34.00? How do you know? **$2.50; $34.00 is between $25–$49, so the shipping and handling costs will be $2.50.**

9. How can you send the order form to the company? **You can mail or fax it.**

10. Suppose your class decided to order two boxes of Outrageous Orange, one box of Strawberry Surprise, and three boxes of Blueberry Bonanza muffins. Fill out the order form. Then write the total amount you must pay on the line below. **$81.50; Check that students have completed the order form correctly.**

Notes for Home: Your child read and interpreted an advertisement and filled out an order form. **Home Activity:** Look through magazines with your child. Talk about the ways the advertisers try to sell their merchandise. Then study an order form together and help your child fill it out.

Name _____

Andy's Secret Ingredient

Steps in a Process

- **Steps in a process** are the actions you take to reach a goal or to make something.
- Sometimes steps in a process are shown by numbers or clue words (*first, next, then,* and *last*). If there are no clues, use common sense to picture the steps.

First → Next → Last

Directions: Reread "Beetle Research." Then write the following steps in the order that they should be performed. The first step is done for you.

Steps
Compare beetles caught at different times of the day.
Cover the cup with the stones and the wood.
Gather a jar or plastic cup, four stones, and a small piece of wood.
Remove the trap when you have finished.
Bury the cup level with the surface.
Put food in the cup to see what attracts certain species.

Making a Pitfall Trap

Gather a jar or plastic cup, four stones, and a small piece of wood.
↓
1. Bury the cup level with the surface.
↓
2. Cover the cup with the stones and the wood.
↓
3. Compare beetles caught at different times of the day.
↓
4. Put food in the cup to see what attracts certain species.
↓
5. Remove the trap when you have finished.

Notes for Home: Your child read about a process and then identified its steps in order. **Home Activity:** Choose a job that your child performs, such as doing the laundry or setting the dinner table. Work together to list all the steps of the process in order.

© Scott Foresman 5

Vocabulary

Directions: Draw a line to connect each word on the left with its definition on the right.

1. essay — written composition
2. flyer — of early times
3. primitive — seeing similarities and differences
4. comparing — coarsely ground dried corn
5. cornmeal — written composition

Directions: Read the recipe. Choose the word from the box that best completes each sentence. Write the word on the matching numbered line to the right.

Fried Worms

This old family recipe dates all the way back to **6. _____** times. I **7. _____** my teeth when I first tried them, but I love them now. **8. _____** the taste to chicken, I'd say worms are sweeter and less chewy.

Step 1: Dip one dozen fat, juicy earthworms in a beaten egg.

Step 2: Roll the worms in 1 cup of **9. _____** or flour.

Step 3: Melt 2 tablespoons butter or **10. _____** in a skillet.

Step 4: Fry the worms in the hot fat for 2–3 minutes, or until brown and crispy. Drain on a paper towel. Enjoy!

6. **primitive**
7. **clenched**
8. **Comparing**
9. **cornmeal**
10. **grease**

Write Contest Rules

Imagine you are in charge of a creative cooking contest. On a separate sheet of paper, write the contest rules. Explain the type of contest, who can enter, and the prizes. Use as many vocabulary words as you can. **Students' contest rules should make correct use of vocabulary words.**

Notes for Home: Your child identified and used vocabulary words from "Andy's Secret Ingredient." *Home Activity:* Have your child write a story about the strangest food he or she has ever tasted. Guide your child to use as many vocabulary words as possible.

Steps in a Process

- **Steps in a process** are the actions you take to reach a goal or to make something.
- Sometimes steps in a process are shown by numbers or clue words (*first, next, then,* and *last*). If there are no clues, use common sense to picture the steps.

Directions: Reread what happens in "Andy's Secret Ingredient" when Andy makes his special brownies. Then answer the questions below.

> The batter was dark and moist. When the flour and eggs and sugar had been mixed, Andy put in a quarter of a cup of chopped walnuts and then, his teeth clenched, a quarter of a cup of chopped beetle.
>
> All the time the brownies were baking, Andy wondered if he could smell the beetles.
>
> When the brownies were done, he took them out, cooled them for twenty minutes, then cut them into squares and piled them onto a platter. He was just washing out the bowl and spoon in the sink when Wendell came into the kitchen, a screwdriver hanging out of one pocket.
>
> Reprinted with the permission of Atheneum Books for Young Readers, an imprint of Simon & Schuster Children's Publishing Division from BEETLES, LIGHTLY TOASTED by Phyllis Reynolds Naylor. Copyright © 1987 by Phyllis Reynolds Naylor.

1. What is the first step in the process described here?
The first step is mixing flour, eggs, and sugar.

2. What are the second and third steps in the process?
Second, he adds a quarter-cup chopped walnuts. Third, he adds a quarter-cup chopped beetle.

3. What steps does Andy take when the brownies are done?
He takes them out, cools them for twenty minutes, cuts them into squares, and piles the squares on a platter.

4. What is the last thing Andy does?
He cleans up.

5. On a separate sheet of paper, tell how Andy prepares the beetles he has found for baking. List the steps in order. **Possible division of steps: 1. puts beetles in cage; 2. puts in cornmeal; 3. feeds them and cleans cage for three days; 4. puts beetles in container; 5. puts container in freezer; 6. when frozen, peels off wings and legs; 7. chops up bodies in small pieces; 8. toasts chopped beetles in oven for five minutes; 9. stores in jar.**

Notes for Home: Your child read a story and identified the order of steps in a process. *Home Activity:* Using a simple recipe, bake cookies or brownies with your child. Check to make sure he or she follows the recipe steps in the correct order.

Selection Test

Directions: Choose the best answer to each item. Mark the letter for the answer you have chosen.

Part 1: Vocabulary

Find the answer choice that means about the same as the underlined word in each sentence.

1. Marisol <u>clenched</u> her fists.
   A. cleaned
   B. looked at carefully
   C. closed tightly ●
   D. raised

2. Jan studies how <u>primitive</u> people lived.
   F. simple, as in early times ●
   G. from a different country
   H. very smart
   J. of the forest

3. Grandma bought some <u>cornmeal</u>.
   A. corn kernels
   B. pancakes made from corn
   C. coarsely ground dried corn ●
   D. corn syrup

4. She placed the fish in the hot <u>grease</u>.
   F. oil ●
   G. salt
   H. spice
   J. oven

5. Our teacher was <u>comparing</u> two countries.
   A. traveling to
   B. seeing how things are alike in ●
   C. discussing the history of
   D. listing all the things wrong with

6. A woman handed me a <u>flyer</u>.
   F. free sample of food
   G. young turkey
   H. ticket for an airplane flight
   J. paper handed out for advertising ●

7. Kala finished her <u>essay</u>.
   A. daily chore
   B. speech read aloud
   C. physical exercise
   D. written composition ●

Part 2: Comprehension

Use what you know about the story to answer each item.

8. In what kind of project is Andy involved?
   F. an essay contest ●
   G. a cooking contest
   H. an animal-raising project
   J. a project to raise money

9. What is Andy's attitude toward his cousin Jack?
   A. Andy feels sorry for Jack and wants to help him.
   B. Andy feels that he and Jack make a great team.
   C. Andy feels that he and Jack are always in a competition. ●
   D. Andy doesn't want to do anything that Jack does.

10. Andy begins planning for his essay by—
   F. running away from the turkey.
   G. writing a letter to the university. ●
   H. deciding that he does not like catfish.
   J. letting Wendell eat a brownie.

11. What is the first step Andy takes in preparing the beetles?
   A. He puts them in the freezer.
   B. He washes them.
   C. He puts them in a cookie tin with a tight lid.
   D. He feeds them cornmeal. ●

12. Just before Andy chops the beetles into pieces, he—
   F. rolls them in cornmeal.
   G. freezes them.
   H. peels off the wings and legs. ●
   J. toasts them.

---

13. Through his experiment with the beetles, Andy wants to show that—
   A. beetles can live in a freezer.
   B. people don't care what is in their food as long as it tastes good.
   C. he can bake as well as his mother can.
   D. people can eat bugs. ●

14. What will Andy probably do when he takes his brownies to school?
   F. decide that he cannot continue with his experiment
   G. let his classmates eat the brownies before he tells them about the beetles ●
   H. write an essay about eating soul food
   J. make a flyer to help sell his beetle brownies

15. Andy's approach to writing his essay is a good example of how to—
   A. get along better with people.
   B. solve problems in creative ways. ●
   C. impress a girl who is a good cook.
   D. get by without much money.

Steps in a Process

- **Steps in a process** are the actions you take to reach a goal or to make something.
- Sometimes steps in a process are shown by numbers or clue words (*first, next, then,* and *last*). If there are no clues, use common sense to picture the steps.

Directions: Read the story.

"I wonder how I would look if I put on some makeup just like Mommy wears," four-year-old Jillian said to herself as she woke up early from her nap. "I think I'll try it while Mommy is downstairs."

First Jillian scrubbed her face. Then she applied a thick layer of powder all over her face. Next she colored her eyelids blue,

green, and gold. She drew over her eyebrows with eyebrow pencil. After that she smeared her lips with bright pink lipstick. She studied her face in the mirror. "I think I need some red stuff on my cheeks too," she said. So she dusted on a thick coat of blush. "Won't Mommy be surprised," Jillian thought as she made her way downstairs.

Directions: Complete the flowchart. Fill in the steps that Jillian took to make up her face.

Jillian scrubbed her face.

↓

1. She applied powder.

↓

2. She colored her eyelids.

↓

3. She drew over her eyebrows.

↓

4. She put on pink lipstick.

↓

5. She dusted on blush.

Notes for Home: Your child read a story and identified the order of steps in a process. *Home Activity:* Work with your child to create a flowchart showing the order of steps in an activity you both enjoy.

Steps in a Process   **595**

Fact and Opinion/Author's Viewpoint

REVIEW

Directions: Read the passage. Then read each question about the passage. Choose the best answer to each question. Mark the letter for the answer you have chosen.

Insects as Food

You probably think that you would never eat an insect, even if you were starving. Insects are ugly and disgusting, right?

But chances are you do eat them, or at least you use products that come from insects. Beeswax, for example, is used in lip balms. Honeycomb is sold in most American supermarkets.

Around the world, insects have long been an important food source. Insects were once a major food for Australian aborigines. In some countries, grasshoppers and large palm weevil grubs are still eaten. In South Africa, some people snack on roasted termites as if they were popcorn. In the Sinai Desert, some people eat the dry, scaly parts of certain bugs. In Mexico, a popular cake is made with the eggs of a water insect. In the United States, chocolate-covered ants are a delicacy sold in many food stores.

As someone who has eaten dishes made from insects, let me tell you that they are delicious. They are very nutritious, too, because insects are an excellent source of protein. It is simply prejudice that keeps most people from enjoying these delicacies. As with any new food, you have to give it a chance. You might be surprised at just how tasty insects can be!

1. In the first paragraph, the author assumes that most people—
   A. like insects.
   Ⓑ hate insects.
   C. have eaten insects.
   D. think insects are useful.

2. In the second and third paragraphs, the author supports his or her viewpoint by—
   F. quoting an expert.
   G. providing a variety of opinions.
   H. repeating the main idea.
   Ⓙ giving facts.

3. Which of the following is a statement of opinion?
   A. Insects have long been an important food source.
   B. Australian aborigines ate bugs.
   Ⓒ Insects are delicious.
   D. Beeswax is used in lip balms.

4. Which statement best sums up the author's viewpoint?
   Ⓕ Insects are unfairly rejected as a food source.
   G. Insects are better than most foods.
   H. Insects have no place in a modern diet.
   J. Insects are the food of the future.

5. This article is best described as—
   Ⓐ balanced.
   B. unbalanced.
   C. emotional.
   D. inaccurate.

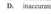
Notes for Home: Your child read an article and identified statements of fact and opinion, as well as the author's viewpoint. *Home Activity:* Read a newspaper editorial with your child. Have him or her identify the facts, opinions, and author's viewpoint.

596   Fact and Opinion/Author's Viewpoint

Writing Across Texts

Directions: Consider what you learned about eating bugs in "Andy's Secret Ingredient" and "Bug-a-licious!" Complete the table to answer the Central Issue question. Include both pro and con ideas and your conclusion.   **Possible answers given.**

Central Issue:
Would I try a dish that has insects as one of the ingredients?

Pros:	Cons:
Many people around the world eat bugs safely.	Some bugs are poisonous.
1. Insects are a very good source of protein.	3. Insects are ugly to look at.
2. There are lots of insects in the world.	4. No one I know eats insects.

Conclusion:
5. I might try eating an insect if it were nonpoisonous and disguised in a recipe, like the insects in Andy's brownies. Insects are another food source in nature.

Write an Essay

Both "Andy's Secret Ingredient" and "Bug-a-licious!" present surprising information about bugs you can eat. Each story contains additional facts or ideas not found in the other. After reading these stories, would you try a dish that has bugs as one of the ingredients? On a separate sheet of paper, write an essay in which you explain the pros and cons of eating insects and then give your own opinion.
Essays will vary but should reflect the understanding that people cook and eat insects as a creative solution to different problems.

Notes for Home: Your child used information from different sources to write an essay. *Home Activity:* As you read stories and articles with your child, discuss ways the characters in the stories, as well as people in your own lives, solve problems creatively.

Writing Across Texts   **597**

Grammar: Proper Nouns and Proper Adjectives

REVIEW

Directions: Rewrite each sentence correctly. Capitalize each proper noun.

1. My friend edward rabitoy lives on middle street.
My friend Edward Rabitoy lives on Middle Street.

2. He goes to diamond middle school instead of to king middle school.
He goes to Diamond Middle School instead of to King Middle School.

3. His science teacher, ms. garza, has assigned edward an interesting experiment.
His science teacher, Ms. Garza, has assigned Edward an interesting experiment.

4. I am meeting edward and his friend jonah in washington park.
I am meeting Edward and his friend Jonah in Washington Park.

5. Then we will all go to the herman museum of science.
Then we will all go to the Herman Museum of Science.

Directions: Rewrite each sentence correctly. Capitalize each proper adjective and proper noun.

6. The museum on third avenue was named after a german scientist.
The museum on Third Avenue was named after a German scientist.

7. He left germany to study at yale university and became an american citizen.
He left Germany to study at Yale University and became an American citizen.

8. At the herman museum, we learned about the swiss scientist, daniel bernoulli.
At the Herman Museum, we learned about the Swiss scientist, Daniel Bernoulli.

9. He discovered the bernoulli principle, which states that the faster air or liquid moves, the less pressure it has.
He discovered the Bernoulli principle, which states that the faster air or liquid moves, the less pressure it has.

10. edward, who is french, was testing the bernoulli principle in his science experiment.
Edward, who is French, was testing the Bernoulli principle in his science experiment.

Notes for Home: Your child capitalized proper nouns and proper adjectives. *Home Activity:* Ask your child to write some sentences about what he or she learned in school this week. Encourage your child to use proper nouns and proper adjectives in the sentences.

598   Grammar: Proper Nouns and Proper Adjectives

© Scott Foresman 5

Name _____

Andy's Secret Ingredient

Grammar: Capitalization

Capitalize the first word of a sentence.
A telescope was necessary for her space experiment, but she didn't have one.

Capitalize the first and every important word of a proper noun. Proper nouns name particular persons, places, or things.

Annie Johnson	Wednesday, December 21
Johnson Space Center	Independence Day
250 Park Place	*Journey to the Stars*

Capitalize the first letter of an abbreviation for parts of addresses. An abbreviation is a shortened form of a word. It usually ends with a period. When abbreviating state names in addresses, use two capital letters and no periods.

1558 Brummel St.
Evanston, IL 60202

Capitalize titles before people's names. Some titles may also be abbreviations.
Dr. Jacob Abboud was an expert on stars.
He liked to visit the home of Major Roger Nelson.
With the help of Ms. Rita Miller, they would spend hours observing the stars.

Directions: Rewrite the sentences using proper capitalization.

1. president matthew turner wanted an experiment to test the new telescope.
President Matthew Turner wanted an experiment to test the new telescope.

2. he asked his team of scientists to start working on friday, august 25.
He asked his team of scientists to start working on Friday, August 25.

3. the experiment would have to be finished by new year's day.
The experiment would have to be finished by New Year's Day.

4. the leader of the team was capt. julie mora, who was an experienced astronomer.
The leader of the team was Capt. Julie Mora, who was an experienced astronomer.

5. capt. mora had taught astronomy at the university of texas in austin.
Capt. Mora had taught astronomy at the University of Texas in Austin.

Notes for Home: Your child capitalized words in sentences, proper nouns, addresses, and titles. *Home Activity:* Have your child make a list of his or her five favorite holidays, five favorite books, and five favorite friends, capitalizing all proper nouns.

Grammar: Capitalization **599**

Name _____

Andy's Secret Ingredient

Grammar: Capitalization

Directions: Write C on the line if words are correctly capitalized in the sentences. Write NC on the line if words are not correctly capitalized. Circle each word that should be capitalized but isn't.

C	1.	Ms. Julia Rose came to visit her friend Rico.
NC	2.	(rico) was in the middle of an experiment.
NC	3.	He was doing the experiment at 16 Phillips (rd).
NC	4.	Rico lived with his parents, (dr) Troy Rose and (major) Phyllis Rose.
C	5.	They had just moved to Nashua, New Hampshire, from Salt Lake City, Utah.
NC	6.	Julia had an idea for an experiment that her teacher, (mr. mills) had told her.
NC	7.	Rico had a different idea that he'd learned from a friend in (newark, new jersey).
C	8.	Julia and Rico combined their ideas to create an experiment of their own.
NC	9.	One experiment was called *Freezing Water* and the other was called (look) at the (stars).
C	10.	They called their new experiment *Freezing the Stars*.

Directions: Add a proper noun to complete each sentence. Use the kind of proper noun in ( ). Write the proper noun on the line. Remember to capitalize proper nouns. **Possible answers given.**

Jane White	11. Mia liked to conduct experiments with her friend _____. (person's name)
Jonesville Middle School	12. They worked in the lab at _____. (name of school)
19 Weston Road	13. The school's address is _____. (street address)
Memorial Day	14. Tomorrow school would be closed for _____. (holiday)
Experiments and You	15. Mia and her friend will read their book of science experiments called _____. (book title)

Write a List

On a separate sheet of paper, write your "Top Ten" list of books, movies, TV shows, and magazines. Be sure to capitalize each title correctly. Then write a review of your #1 favorite, using complete sentences and proper nouns.
Students should correctly capitalize all words in their lists and reviews.

Notes for Home: Your child capitalized words in sentences, proper nouns, addresses, and titles. *Home Activity:* Write a postcard to a family member or friend. Have your child address the postcard and write the sentences you create together, using proper capitalization.

600 Grammar: Capitalization

Name _____

Andy's Secret Ingredient

Grammar: Capitalization

RETEACHING

Circle mistakes in capitalization.
1. (my) dog, (rex) is a (saint bernard)   2. My address is 1222 Rosamond (st).

Capitalize the first word of a sentence, the first and every important word of a proper noun, the first letter of an abbreviation for parts of addresses, and titles before people's names.

Directions: Read each sentence. Rewrite the sentences, adding capital letters where they belong.

1. my friend goes to franklin school.
My friend goes to Franklin School.

2. Her class took a trip on friday.
Her class took a trip on Friday.

3. they walked down morgan avenue and turned onto eagle drive.
They walked down Morgan Avenue and turned onto Eagle Drive.

4. The students visited the sears tower.
The students visited the Sears Tower.

5. amy, paul, and susie went into the gift shop.
Amy, Paul, and Susie went into the gift shop.

6. We could see lake michigan from the top floor of the building!
We could see Lake Michigan from the top floor of the building!

7. Then I went back home to 1534 durand st.
Then I went back home to 1534 Durand St.

8. I told my aunt donna about my trip.
I told my Aunt Donna about my trip.

9. she was very excited about it.
She was very excited about it.

10. She told me she walked past the building on her way to see dr. Philips, the dentist.
She told me she walked past the building on her way to see Dr. Philips, the dentist.

Notes for Home: Your child used capital letters correctly in sentences. *Home Activity:* Write a letter to your child, leaving out capital letters. Have him or her circle the words that need capital letters.

Grammar: Capitalization **601**

Name _____

Andy's Secret Ingredient

Grammar: Capitalization

Directions: Write each sentence below with the correct capitalization.

1. i wonder what Roaches and Grasshoppers would taste like.
I wonder what roaches and grasshoppers would taste like.

2. do You think they would know at Iowa state university.
Do you think they would know at Iowa State University?

3. i wonder if aunt Wanda would make a big Bug stew.
I wonder if Aunt Wanda would make a big bug stew.

4. andy was afraid of the moller's big tom turkey.
Andy was afraid of the Moller's big tom turkey.

5. aunt bernie always compared andy to jack.
Aunt Bernie always compared Andy to Jack.

6. andy wrote a letter asking about how to prepare bugs, and he addressed it to the department of bugs.
Andy wrote a letter asking about how to prepare bugs, and he addressed it to the Department of Bugs.

7. john burrows, entomologist, wrote a letter to andy.
John Burrows, entomologist, wrote a letter to Andy.

8. andy received the letter on may 1.
Andy received the letter on May 1.

Directions: For each sentence, underline the word or words that need a capital letter. Then write the word or words correctly on the line.

9. Uncle Delmar took care of his car on saturday.   **Saturday**

10. The soul food kitchen and carry-out was in a small building.
Soul Food Kitchen and Carry-Out

11. The restaurant was on North street.   **Street**

12. we really enjoyed our meal.   **We**

13. Now I'm going to write a letter to uncle delmar at his brother's house at 1345 martin st.
Uncle Delmar   **Martin St.**

Notes for Home: Your child capitalized words in sentences correctly. *Home Activity:* Have your child write a letter to a character in *Andy's Secret Ingredient.* Help him or her use capital letters correctly.

602 Grammar: Capitalization

© Scott Foresman 5

Name _____

Andy's Secret Ingredient

Phonics: Diphthongs and Vowel Digraphs

Directions: Read the words in the box. Each word has the letters **ow**, but the letters stand for different vowel sounds. Say each word to yourself. Listen for the words with the same vowel sound as **cow** and those with the same vowel sound as **low**. Write each word in the correct column.

brownies
bowl
swallow
down
showing
however

Vowel sound in *cow*
1. brownies
2. down
3. however

Vowel sound in *low*
4. bowl
5. shallow
6. showing

Directions: Read each sentence below. One word in each sentence has a word with the vowel sound heard at the beginning of **author**. Write the word on the line. Circle the letters that stand for that vowel sound.

A(u)gust
7. August is a good time to catch beetles.

bec(au)se
8. The cook needed beetles because he is making a special dessert.

s(au)cer
9. He placed the beetles on a saucer, then stored them in the freezer.

f(au)cet
10. He rinsed them under the faucet in the sink.

Directions: Read the announcement below. Listen for words that have a vowel sound like **boy** or **oil**. Circle the words and write them on the lines.

Everyone! (Join) in!
Make your (choice)
Sign up for the school science fair!
Don't (boycott) it this year!
You're sure to (enjoy) it!
You won't be (disappointed)
See Mr. Keller for more details.

11. Join
12. choice
13. boycott
14. enjoy
15. disappointed

Notes for Home: Your child worked with the vowel sounds represented by *oi* as in *join*, *oy* as in *boy*, *ow* as in *brownies* or *low*, and *au* as in *author*. **Home Activity:** As you read with your child, look and listen for these spellings and vowel sounds.

Phonics: Diphthongs and Vowel Digraphs   603

Name _____

Andy's Secret Ingredient

Spelling: Using Just Enough Letters

Pretest Directions: Fold back the page along the dotted line. On the blanks, write the spelling words as they are dictated. When you have finished the test, unfold the page and check your words.

1. until
2. went
3. enough
4. TV
5. one
6. didn't
7. a lot
8. want
9. doesn't
10. always
11. necklace
12. exact
13. burglar
14. equipment
15. chimney
16. exist
17. rumbling
18. upon
19. athlete
20. examine

1. Wait **until** tomorrow.
2. We **went** to the skating rink.
3. Is that **enough** food for you?
4. Do you watch too much **TV**?
5. I have **one** quarter left.
6. The cat **didn't** like water.
7. That is **a lot** of ice cream.
8. The boys **want** to play ball.
9. The librarian **doesn't** like noise.
10. The sun **always** sets at night.
11. Her **necklace** has a diamond.
12. What is the **exact** time?
13. The **burglar** wore a mask.
14. We need the right **equipment**.
15. The **chimney** is very dirty.
16. I thought it did not **exist**.
17. There was a **rumbling** below us.
18. I painted a cat **upon** the canvas.
19. She is a great **athlete**.
20. The doctor will **examine** your cut.

Notes for Home: Your child took a pretest on words that have difficult letter combinations. *Home Activity:* Help your child learn misspelled words before the final test. Your child can underline the word parts that caused the problems and concentrate on those parts.

604   Spelling: Using Just Enough Letters

Name _____

Andy's Secret Ingredient

Spelling: Using Just Enough Letters

Word List

until	one	doesn't	burglar	rumbling
went	didn't	always	equipment	upon
enough	a lot	necklace	chimney	athlete
TV	want	exact	exist	examine

Directions: Choose the words from the box that begin with a vowel. Sort them according to which vowel they start with. Write the words in the correct column. **Order may vary.**

Begins with a
1. a lot
2. always
3. athlete

Begins with u
4. until
5. upon

Begins with e
6. enough
7. exact
8. equipment
9. exist
10. examine

Begins with o
11. one

Directions: Choose the word from the box that best replaces the underlined word or words. Write the word on the line.

didn't — 12. Lauren <u>did not</u> have anything to do.
TV — 13. She decided to watch a science show on <u>television</u>.
went — 14. When the show was over, Lauren <u>left</u> from the room.
want — 15. "I <u>would like</u> to try an experiment!" she said.
doesn't — 16. "It <u>does not</u> look hard," she thought.
necklace — 17. Lauren put chemicals on an old <u>piece of jewelry worn around the neck</u>.
chimney — 18. Smoke from the chemicals drifted up the <u>smokestack over the fireplace</u>.
rumbling — 19. The experiment started <u>making a deep, rolling sound</u> like thunder.
burglar — 20. "Well, I guess a <u>robber</u> won't steal *this* experiment!" she laughed.

Notes for Home: Your child spelled words using just enough letters to spell them correctly. *Home Activity:* With your child, practice spelling the words by first pronouncing each word carefully and correctly, syllable by syllable.

Spelling: Using Just Enough Letters   605

Name _____

Andy's Secret Ingredient

Spelling: Using Just Enough Letters

Directions: Proofread this recipe. Find six spelling mistakes. Use the proofreading marks to correct each mistake.

☰	Make a capital.
/	Make a small letter.
∧	Add something.
℘	Take out something.
⊙	Add a period.
¶	Begin a new paragraph.

Salad Surprise

Eqipment: Cutting board, sharp knife, salad bowl

Ingredients: Enuf fresh lettuce to fill bowl; at least three "surprise" ingredients such as mini-crackers, raisins, nuts, or marshmallows; one-half cup bottled dressing.

• Always wash lettuce thoroughly. Examine it closely for bugs.

• Rip lettuce into alot of small pieces. Place in bowl.

• Add other ingredients, or at a time.

• Add dressing and toss until salad is evenly coated.

Spelling Tip

When you shorten **did not** and **does not** to **didn't** and **doesn't**, you must use apostrophes.

Write a Recipe

On a separate sheet of paper, write a recipe for a dish you have created—or one that you have always dreamed of making! Give it a surprise ingredient or two. Try to use at least five of your spelling words. **Answers will vary, but each recipe should include at least five spelling words.**

Word List

until	necklace
went	exact
enough	burglar
TV	equipment
one	chimney
didn't	exist
a lot	rumbling
want	upon
doesn't	athlete
always	examine

Notes for Home: Your child spelled words using just enough letters to spell them correctly. *Home Activity:* Spell each word for your child, but misspell several words. See if he or she can catch each mistake and spell the word correctly.

606   Spelling: Using Just Enough Letters

© Scott Foresman 5

818   Answers

Spelling Workbook 5.6, p. 108

Name _____

Spelling: Using Just Enough Letters REVIEW

Word List

until	one	doesn't	burglar	rumbling
went	didn't	always	equipment	upon
enough	a lot	necklace	chimney	athlete
TV	want	exact	exist	examine

Directions: Choose the word from the box that best completes each statement. Write the word on the line to the left.

equipment	1. *Knight* is to *armor* as *scuba diver* is to *diving* _____.
a lot	2. *Few* is to *many* as *a little* is to _____.
examine	3. *Inspector* is to *inspect* as *examiner* is to _____.
enough	4. *Satisfactory* is to *acceptable* as *sufficient* is to _____.
exact	5. *Vague* is to *precise* as *inexact* is to _____.
want	6. *Knowing* is to *know* as *wanting* is to _____.
always	7. *No* is to *yes* as *never* is to _____.
doesn't	8. *Is not* is to *isn't* as *does not* is to _____.
upon	9. *Below* is to *under* as *on* is to _____.
necklace	10. *Wrist* is to *bracelet* as *neck* is to _____.

Directions: Write the word from the box that belongs in each group.

11. sportscaster, coach, **athlete**
12. roaring, crackling, **rumbling**
13. radio, video, **TV**
14. be, live, **exist**
15. wouldn't, hadn't, **didn't**

16. three, two, **one**
17. now, after, **until**
18. thief, robber, **burglar**
19. came, saw, **went**
20. door, roof, **chimney**

Practice Book 5.6, p. 269

Name _____

Recipe

A **recipe** is a set of directions for preparing something to eat.

Directions: Use the recipe below to answer the questions on the next page.

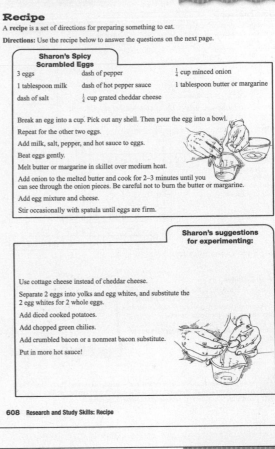

Sharon's Spicy Scrambled Eggs

3 eggs	dash of pepper	$\frac{1}{4}$ cup minced onion
1 tablespoon milk	dash of hot pepper sauce	1 tablespoon butter or margarine
dash of salt	$\frac{1}{4}$ cup grated cheddar cheese	

Break an egg into a cup. Pick out any shell. Then pour the egg into a bowl.

Repeat for the other two eggs.

Add milk, salt, pepper, and hot sauce to eggs.

Beat eggs gently.

Melt butter or margarine in skillet over medium heat.

Add onion to the melted butter and cook for 2–3 minutes until you can see through the onion pieces. Be careful not to burn the butter or margarine.

Add egg mixture and cheese.

Stir occasionally with spatula until eggs are firm.

Sharon's suggestions for experimenting:

Use cottage cheese instead of cheddar cheese.

Separate 2 eggs into yolks and egg whites, and substitute the 2 egg whites for 2 whole eggs.

Add diced cooked potatoes.

Add chopped green chilies.

Add crumbled bacon or a nonmeat bacon substitute.

Put in more hot sauce!

Practice Book 5.6, p. 270

Name _____

1. What is the first step in preparing this recipe? **Break each egg into a cup. Pick out shell. Then pour into bowl.**

2. Why does the recipe say to break each egg into a cup before pouring it into a bowl? **Possible answer: It prevents you from accidentally getting egg shell in the bowl.**

3. Which ingredients do you add before beating the eggs? **milk, salt, pepper, hot sauce**

4. What do you do after beating the eggs gently? **Melt butter or margarine in a skillet.**

5. What does the second illustration show? **It shows how to separate an egg.**

6. What "experimental" ingredients do you think you would like in this recipe? Explain why. **Answers will vary.**

7. Write your own suggestion for experimenting with this recipe. **Answers will vary.**

8. What are the advantages to watching a cooking show on television? What are the disadvantages? **Possible answer: Advantages: You can see how each step should be done and you get more information from the chef than from a recipe alone. Disadvantages: It's easier to follow steps when you can read them in a printed recipe than it is to hear them on television.**

9. Why is it important to follow a recipe's directions in the order that they are given? **Possible answer: If you don't follow the steps in the order that they are given, the food you are preparing may not turn out correctly.**

10. Are illustrations or photographs helpful in a recipe? Explain. **Possible answer: Yes, pictures help show how to do a specific step or what something should look like.**

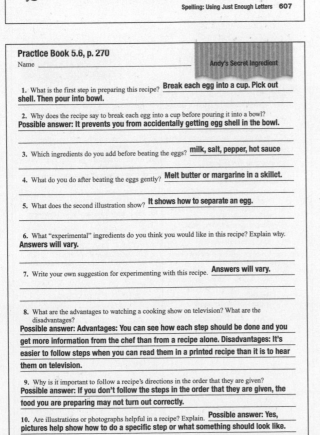

Practice Book 5.6, p. 271

Name _____

Plot

- A **plot** includes the important events that happen in a story.
- A plot usually has a conflict or problem, rising action, a climax, and the resolution, or outcome.

Directions: Reread "The Brahman and the Banker." Then identify each important part of the plot in the story map. **Possible answers given.**

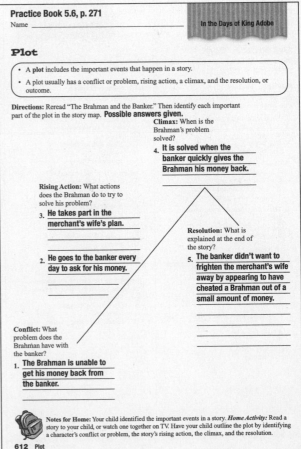

Climax: When is the Brahman's problem solved?
4. **It is solved when the banker quickly gives the Brahman his money back.**

Rising Action: What actions does the Brahman do to try to solve his problem?
3. **He takes part in the merchant's wife's plan.**

2. **He goes to the banker every day to ask for his money.**

Resolution: What is explained at the end of the story?
5. **The banker didn't want to frighten the merchant's wife away by appearing to have cheated a Brahman out of a small amount of money.**

Conflict: What problem does the Brahman have with the banker?
1. **The Brahman is unable to get his money back from the banker.**

Vocabulary

Directions: Choose the word from the box that has the same or nearly the same meaning as each word or words below. Write the word on the line.

__rascals__	1. scoundrels
__seldom__	2. rarely
__generous__	3. plentiful
__fascinated__	4. enchanted
__foolishness__	5. silliness

Check the Words You Know
___ fascinated
___ foolishness
___ generous
___ rascals
___ seldom

Directions: Choose the word from the box that best matches each clue. Write the word in the puzzle.

Down
6. mischievous persons
7. large; plentiful

Across
8. highly interested
9. not often
10. behavior that shows lack of judgment

Crossword puzzle:
- 6. Down: r a c a l s
- 7. Down: g e n e r o u
- 8. Across: f a s c i n a t e d
- 9. Across: s e l d o m
- 10. Across: f o o l i s h n e s s

Write an Epilogue

Ever wonder what happens to the characters *after* a story ends? Pick a story you like very much. On a separate sheet of paper, tell what happens after the end of the story. You may set your epilogue weeks, months, or years in the future! Use as many vocabulary words as you can.
Students' epilogues should make correct use of vocabulary words.

Notes for Home: Your child identified and used vocabulary words from "In the Days of King Adobe." *Home Activity:* Work with your child to make a puzzle that uses all these vocabulary words. The puzzle can be a word search or crossword, for example.

Vocabulary **613**

Plot

- A story's **plot** is the important events that happen in a story. These parts include the conflict or problem, the rising action, the climax, and the resolution, or outcome.

Directions: Read the plot summary of "In the Days of King Adobe." Then answer the questions below.

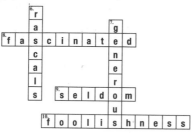

There once was a poor but thrifty old woman who had a fine ham. One evening two young men on a journey came to her door. She gave them lodging and ham for dinner. When they saw the ham, they decided to steal it.

That night, thinking the old woman was asleep, they took the ham and put it in their traveling bag. But the old woman, suspecting them, had watched them. After they were asleep, she took out the ham and put an adobe brick in its place.

The next day at breakfast the two young rascals told her a made-up dream about Hambone the First, king of a land called Travelibag. She responded with her own dream, in which King Hambone was usurped by Adobe the Great.

The young men went on their way. Later, upon opening the bag, they saw that the old woman had fooled them. The two hungry thieves never tricked another old woman.

1. Who are the main characters in the story?
The main characters are an old woman and two travelers.

2. What is the problem in this story?
The men want to steal the old woman's ham.

3. Describe the rising action of the story where the problem leads to other events.
The two men steal the ham; she takes it back. They try to fool her with a dream; she responds with her own dream.

4. What is the climax, or high point, of the story?
The men open the bag and realize they were the fools.

5. What is the resolution, or outcome, of the story? Write your answer on a separate piece of paper.
Possible answer: The young men continue their travels and don't play any more tricks on old women.

Notes for Home: Your child read a story summary and identified different elements of the story's plot. *Home Activity:* Watch a television show or movie with your child. Discuss the important parts of the story, the main problem characters face, and how it is resolved.

614 Plot

Selection Test

Directions: Choose the best answer to each item. Mark the letter for the answer you have chosen.

Part 1: Vocabulary

Find the answer choice that means about the same as the underlined word in each sentence.

1. Kayla <u>seldom</u> asks questions in class.
   A. every day
   D. often
   C. never
   (D). not often

2. Those boys are <u>rascals</u>.
   F. people who are related to each other
   (G). persons who cause mischief
   H. people who work together
   J. hard-working persons

3. Throughout the play, Jonas looked <u>fascinated</u>.
   (A). very interested
   B. upset
   C. very sleepy
   D. proud

4. Everyone commented on the <u>foolishness</u> of the plan.
   F. danger
   (G). lack of sense
   H. success
   J. difficulty

5. My grandmother served a <u>generous</u> bowl of soup.
   A. steaming hot
   B. tasty
   (C). large
   D. leftover

Part 2: Comprehension

Use what you know about the story to answer each item.

6. At the beginning of this story, we know only that the old woman was—
   (F). very poor.
   G. living with her family.
   H. very rich.
   J. going on a journey.

7. Where does the old woman live?
   A. in the marketplace of a town
   B. in a hotel where she works as a servant
   C. in the middle of a wilderness
   (D). at the edge of a village

8. The old woman gets the ham by—
   (F). saving a penny a day.
   G. stealing it.
   H. selling bricks.
   J. tricking the young men.

9. What can you conclude about the old woman based on the way she acts when the young men first come to her house?
   (A). She is lonely.
   B. She is very suspicious.
   C. She is lazy.
   D. She dislikes young people.

 GO ON

Selection Test **615**

---

10. The main problem in this story is between the—
    F. woman's wish to eat the ham and her wish to share it.
    G. men wanting to steal the ham and their wish to respect the woman.
    H. men's wish to travel and their wish to stay with the woman.
    (J). men wanting to steal the ham and the woman's wish to keep it.

11. Which of these events is part of the rising action in this story?
    A. The old woman sells most of her vegetables in the market.
    B. The young men decide not to trick the next person they stay with.
    C. The old woman buys the ham.
    (D). The young man tells about his dream of King Hambone the First.

12. The old woman shows that she has a sense of humor when she—
    (F). describes her dream of King Adobe.
    G. takes the ham from the traveling bag.
    H. notices the rascally look in the men's eyes.
    J. prepares the ham for supper.

13. The climax of this story occurs when the—
    A. young men steal the ham.
    (B). men open the bag and find the brick.
    C. woman puts the brick in place of the ham.
    D. woman asks the men about their dreams.

14. Which fact makes it hardest to forgive the young men's behavior to the old woman?
    (F). She was very generous to them.
    G. They were very hungry.
    H. She tricked them too.
    J. They had a long way to travel.

15. The author's main purpose in this story is to—
    A. explain how to cook a ham.
    B. describe the travels of two young men.
    (C). teach a lesson.
    D. convince readers to help travelers in need.

 STOP

616 Selection Test

© Scott Foresman 5

---

820 Answers

Plot

- A story's **plot** is the important events that happen in a story. These parts include the conflict or problem, the rising action, the climax, and the resolution, or outcome.

Directions: Read the folk tale.

There was once a young woman who was rich and beautiful, but she was never satisfied.

One day she took a walk on the beach. She sighed sadly and said, "I wish I were more beautiful." A fish leaped out of the surf and said, "I will grant your wish." The woman became the most beautiful woman in the world. Still she was unhappy.

A week later she went to the water's edge. "Fish," she cried, "I wish I had more money."

The fish said, "I will grant your wish." All the gold in the world became hers. Still she was not happy.

A week later, she went to the ocean. "Fish," she cried, "I need more beauty and riches." The fish said, "There is no pleasing you." With that, the woman became plain and poor. She married a fisherman and learned to live happily ever after.

Directions: Complete the plot map by describing the different parts of the plot. Describe two events for the rising action.

Climax
4. **The third time, the fish refuses her wish and takes away all her beauty and riches.**

Rising Action
3. **A fish grants her first two wishes.**

2. **She wishes three times for riches and beauty.**

Resolution or Outcome
5. **She marries a poor fisherman and is happy.**

Conflict or Problem
1. **She is never satisfied and always wants more.**

 Notes for Home: Your child read a story and identified its important story events. *Home Activity:* Read a folk tale, fable, or myth with your child. Work together to identify the different parts of the plot. Ask yourselves what problem the characters face and how they solve it.

Plot **617**

Context Clues

Directions: Read the story. Then read each question about the story. Choose the best answer to each question. Mark the letter for the answer you have chosen.

Now You See It, Now You Don't

Rudy is a master of legerdemain. He can make scarves fly from his ears and mouth. He can make birds vanish and pull rabbits out of hats. He can make nickels and dimes appear out of his assistant's nose and ears. Children gasp to see these acts. Adults shake their heads in wonder.

Rudy's hands are so nimble that no matter how carefully you watch, you cannot tell how he does it. He rarely rests, either—his act continues for hours without a hiatus. The only time he pauses in his act is when the audience applauds. Rudy is so good that the audience always applauds long and enthusiastically as Rudy bows and smiles.

There is another way in which Rudy is amazing. He is a stellar student, ranking first in his class despite the fact that he needs so much time to prepare for his tricks. How he finds the time to study and practice his magic is a mystery to everyone. It seems to be just one more way in which Rudy can seem to perform magic.

Today, Rudy wants to work out a new trick for the upcoming school talent show. He's starting with some ersatz gold—it looks real, but it isn't. Then he adds a pile of feathers and sets to work. It's the most difficult trick Rudy has attempted. He's having a hard time making it work the way he wants. You can bet that Rudy will be practicing his new trick long into the night. This, of course, will be after he has finished his school work.

1. In this story, the word legerdemain means—
   A. sewing.
   B. thievery.
   C. magic tricks.
   D. silliness.

2. In this story, the word nimble means—
   F. invisible.
   G. quick.
   H. strong.
   J. dirty.

3. In this story, the word hiatus means—
   A. break.
   B. mistake.
   C. blunder.
   D. accident.

4. In this story, the word stellar means—
   F. pointed.
   G. good.
   H. dull.
   J. outstanding.

5. The best synonym for ersatz is—
   A. artificial.
   B. real.
   C. expensive.
   D. fancy.

 Notes for Home: Your child used context clues to figure out the meaning of unfamiliar words. *Home Activity:* Encourage your child to make a list of unfamiliar words he or she finds while reading. Discuss how context clues can be used to figure out a word's meaning.

618 Context Clues

Writing Across Texts

Directions: Complete the tables with important events from "In the Days of King Adobe" and another folk tale you have read, such as "The Baker's Neighbor." Write *humor, trickery,* or *repetition* to show which literary element, or elements the event demonstrates. **Possible answers given.**

In the Days of King Adobe	The Baker's Neighbor
Event/Literary Element	**Event/Literary Element**
Two rascals steal a ham from a woman who has fed them and put the ham in their bag. (trickery)	6. **Each day Pablo comes to smell delicious baked goods, but doesn't buy anything. (repetition)**
1. **The woman watches the rascals steal the ham. She steals it back and replaces it with an adobe brick. (repetition, trickery)**	7. **The baker, Manuel, tries to charge Pablo for smelling his baked goods. (trickery)**
2. **The men make up a story about a dream. (trickery)**	8. **The baker goes to a judge to get Pablo to pay for smelling the bakery smells. (humor)**
3. **The woman tells about her dream. (trickery, repetition)**	9. **The neighbors joke about Manuel's plan. (humor)**
4. **The men go on their way and discover that their bag holds a brick, not a ham. (humor)**	10. **A wise judge lets the baker handle Pablo's gold and tells him that the pleasure he got from touching the money is payment for Pablo enjoying the smell of the baked goods. (trickery, humor)**
5. **Another old woman feeds the men. (repetition)**	

Write Two Paragraphs

Folk tales commonly rely on humor, trickery, or repetition of actions or events. On a separate sheet of paper, write two paragraphs that compare and contrast one or more of these elements in "In the Days of King Adobe" with another folk tale you have read, such as "The Baker's Neighbor." Use the information in the table you completed above. **Paragraphs will vary, but they should compare and contrast the use of literary elements of humor, repetition, and trickery throughout "In the Days of King Adobe" with another folk tale, such as "The Baker's Neighbor."**

Notes for Home: Your child wrote two paragraphs comparing and contrasting information from different folk tales. *Home Activity:* As you read stories and articles with your child, discuss ways the ideas, events, or characters connect to other literature your child has read.

Writing Across Texts **619**

Grammar: Compound Subjects and Objects

Directions: Combine each set of sentences by using a compound subject. Write your new sentences on the lines. (Remember to make each verb agree with its subject.) **Possible answers given.**

1. Stories about tricksters are found in many cultures. Myths about tricksters are also found.
Stories and myths about tricksters are found in many cultures.

2. The fox appears as the trickster in various stories. The coyote and the raven also appear as the trickster in various stories.
The fox, the coyote, and the raven appear as the trickster in various stories.

3. An animal may be the victim of the wily trickster. A human might be the victim also. Even an insect can be the trickster's victim.
An animal, a human, or even an insect may be the victim of the wily trickster.

Directions: Combine each set of sentences by using a compound object. Write your new sentences on the lines.

4. Some societies have used real-life jesters for entertainment. Sometimes, they have also used musicians.
Some societies have used real-life jesters or musicians for entertainment.

5. Jesters entertained Egyptian pharaohs. Similar figures entertained the Aztecs of Mexico. Jesters kept the nobles of Europe entertained too.
Jesters entertained Egyptian pharaohs, the Aztecs of Mexico, and the nobles of Europe.

Notes for Home: Your child used compound subjects and compound objects to combine sentences. *Home Activity:* Look through a book, a magazine, or a newspaper with your child. List all the sentences with compound subjects and objects that you find.

620 Grammar: Compound Subjects and Objects

Name _____

In the Days of King Adobe

Grammar: Commas

A **series** is a list of three or more items. Items may be words (such as nouns, adjectives, or verbs) or phrases (such as prepositional phrases). Use commas to separate the items in a sentence. A comma is used after each item in the series except the last.

> We ate beans, tortillas, and tacos.
> All the food was spicy, delicious, and plentiful.
> After dinner we cleaned up, talked for a while, and then walked home.
> We walked through the tunnel, across the road, and over the bridge.

A comma is also used to set off the names of people who are **directly addressed**. Use two commas if the name comes in the middle of a sentence.

> Maria, is dinner ready?
> Do you know, Hal, what time it is?
> You should go home now, Ali.

Directions: Write **C** on the line if commas are used correctly in each sentence. Write **NC** if they are not used correctly.

C 1. Nick and Sam, welcome to our new restaurant.

C 2. Tonight we will celebrate with food, music, and dancing.

NC 3. Would you like to help us prepare the chicken salad pasta and watermelon?

C 4. We'll move the hot plates from the oven, to the waiter's trays, and then onto the tables in the dining room.

NC 5. I'm really glad you could come celebrate with us Nick and Sam.

Directions: Rewrite each sentence, adding commas to set off items in a series and names directly addressed.

6. Nick thanks for helping out.
Nick, thanks for helping out.

7. It's a fun worthwhile and helpful thing to do.
It's a fun, worthwhile, and helpful thing to do.

8. I think Sam that you should clear the table now.
I think, Sam, that you should clear the table now.

9. Then you can serve dessert thank the customers and eat the leftovers.
Then you can serve dessert, thank the customers, and eat the leftovers.

10. It's been great working with you two as volunteers Nick and Sam.
It's been great working with you two as volunteers, Nick and Sam.

 Notes for Home: Your child used commas in a series and in direct address. *Home Activity:* Have your child create lists of favorite things in groups of three or more. Together, write a sentence about each group, using commas to separate the list of items as shown above.

Grammar: Commas **621**

Name _____

In the Days of King Adobe

Grammar: Commas

Directions: Add commas to punctuate each sentence correctly. Rewrite each sentence on the line.

1. Harold what do you know about your heritage?
Harold, what do you know about your heritage?

2. We can learn about a culture from its folk tales Nicole.
We can learn about a culture from its folk tales, Nicole.

3. The Middle East has folk tales that are scary funny or sad.
The Middle East has folk tales that are scary, funny, or sad.

4. Greg do you know any Chinese folk tales about the Monkey King?
Greg, do you know any Chinese folk tales about the Monkey King?

5. Many cultures have trickster tales with coyotes rabbits and spiders.
Many cultures have trickster tales with coyotes, rabbits, and spiders.

6. Anansi the Spider is a character from African trickster tales Ashley.
Anansi the Spider is a character from African trickster tales, Ashley.

7. Tricksters often hide behind rocks beneath bushes and in the branches of trees.
Tricksters often hide behind rocks, beneath bushes, and in the branches of trees.

8. The Native Americans George have trickster tales of their own.
The Native Americans, George, have trickster tales of their own.

9. We tell trickster tales at home in school and around a campfire at summer camp.
We tell trickster tales at home, in school, and at summer camp around a campfire.

10. I especially like the coyote stories Leah!
I especially like the coyote stories, Leah!

Write a Story

On a separate piece of paper, write a story describing how a trickster played a trick on someone else. Use commas to set off items in a series or the name of anyone directly addressed. **Students should correctly use commas in their story, both in direct address and in a series.**

 Notes for Home: Your child used commas to separate items in a series and to set off the names of people directly addressed. *Home Activity:* With your child, list names on slips of paper. Take turns using each name as a form of direct address in a sentence.

622 Grammar: Commas

Name _____

In the Days of King Adobe

Grammar: Commas

RETEACHING

> Add commas where they belong.
> 1. Lilly, please hand me that glass.
> 2. Do you really think, George, that that is a good idea?
> 3. I have to do my homework, shop for books, and go to hockey practice.
> 4. Please pick up eggs, milk, butter, and cereal on your way home.
>
> Use **commas** to separate items in a series. Each item may be one or more words. Also use a comma to set off the name of a person who is directly addressed. Use two commas if the name comes in the middle of the sentence.

Directions: Add commas where they belong. Rewrite the sentence correctly.

1. Lions elephants and tigers live in the game reserve.
Lions, elephants, and tigers live in the game reserve.

2. The jungle was dark damp hot and mysterious.
The jungle was dark, damp, hot, and mysterious.

3. John did you see how that road ran up the hill?
John, did you see how that road ran up the hill?

4. The mosquitoes were huge noisy and annoying.
The mosquitoes were huge, noisy, and annoying.

5. The guide carried a map Sonja and led us in the right direction.
The guide carried a map, Sonja, and led us in the right direction.

6. Our vehicle was fast Dave.
Our vehicle was fast, Dave.

7. The boat went across the lake up the river and into the harbor.
The boat went across the lake, up the river, and into the harbor.

8. The lake looked cool refreshing and inviting.
The lake looked cool, refreshing, and inviting.

9. Marta you should have seen those hippopotamuses!
Marta, you should have seen those hippopotamuses!

 Notes for Home: Your child added commas in sentences. *Home Activity:* Have your child write a letter to a younger person, telling that child what he or she needs to know about fifth grade. Help your child to use commas correctly in series and in direct address.

Grammar: Commas **623**

Name _____

In the Days of King Adobe

Grammar: Commas

Directions: Write **C** on the line if commas are used correctly in each sentence. Write **NC** if they are not used correctly.

NC 1. The plain was dry dusty and treeless.

NC 2. A buffalo and a mustang ran across the field Sheila.

C 3. Over the hill, around the lake, and into the forest ran the doe.

C 4. The guide raced down the hill, over the ditch, and into the heavy underbrush.

NC 5. The guide was experienced Terry.

Directions: Rewrite each sentence, adding commas to set off items in a series and names directly addressed.

6. I like ships trains and planes.
I like ships, trains, and planes.

7. Travel is fun Elizabeth if you know where to go.
Travel is fun, Elizabeth, if you know where to go.

8. Europe Asia and Africa are my favorite continents.
Europe, Asia, and Africa are my favorite continents.

9. Australia is a large distant and beautiful land.
Australia is a large, distant, and beautiful land.

10. Anne would you like to go there one day?
Anne, would you like to go there one day?

11. Kangaroos bandicoots dingos and wombats are some unusual Australian animals.
Kangaroos, bandicoots, dingos, and wombats are some unusual Australian animals.

12. I would like to see what a bandicoot looks like Tina.
I would like to see what a bandicoot looks like, Tina.

13. Australians live in large cities in small towns and on vast ranches.
Australians live in large cities, in small towns, and on vast ranches.

Write a Travel Journal

Imagine you have just gotten back home from an amazing journey to an exotic place. Write about your adventures. Include details about the people, places, animals, sights, sounds, and smells. Use a separate sheet of paper. **Make sure that students include details about their experiences and use commas appropriately.**

 Notes for Home: Your child identified and rewrote sentences with correct placement of commas. *Home Activity:* Talk with your child about what your family will do this weekend or on a vacation. Have your child write sentences listing items to remember.

624 Grammar: Commas

© Scott Foresman 5

Phonics: r-Controlled Vowels

Directions: Read the words in the box. Listen for the vowel sounds heard in **star, for, deer,** and **dirt.** Sort the words according to their vowel sounds. Write each word in the correct column. **Order may vary.**

beard	cornmeal	guitar	peer	serious	worked
burn	farthest	large	purple	steer	world
circle	fear	morning	series	tortilla	worthy

Sounds like *star*
1. farthest
2. guitar
3. large

Sounds like *deer*
4. beard
5. fear
6. peer
7. series
8. serious
9. steer

Sounds like *for*
10. cornmeal
11. morning
12. tortilla

Sounds like *dirt*
13. burn
14. circle
15. purple
16. worked
17. world
18. worthy

Directions: Read each sentence below. Listen for words that have the vowel sound in **dirt.** The sound may be spelled **or, ir,** or **ur.** Write each word on the line.

bursting — 19. The large dinner left them bursting at the seams.

shirt — 20. Their bellies were so full that their shirt buttons nearly popped!

first — 21. It was the first good meal they had had in days.

work — 22. To thank their hostess, they promised to do work in payment for the meal.

worth — 23. They felt a little labor was worth the good meal.

hurt — 24. It also wouldn't hurt them to do some physical activity.

assured — 25. But the hostess assured them that there was no reason for them to leave their chairs.

 Notes for Home: Your child identified words with vowels combined with the letter *r,* such as *star, for, deer,* and *dirt.* **Home Activity:** Read a story with your child. Help your child listen and look for words with these sounds. Say the words together to hear the sounds.

Phonics: *r*-Controlled Vowels **625**

Spelling: More Vowels with *r*

Pretest Directions: Fold back the page along the dotted line. On the blanks, write the spelling words as they are dictated. When you have finished the test, unfold the page and check your words.

1. aware — 1. They became **aware** of a sound.
2. prepare — 2. We have to **prepare** for our trip.
3. share — 3. It is nice of you to **share.**
4. declare — 4. **Declare** your allegiance!
5. spare — 5. The **spare** tire is flat.
6. beware — 6. **Beware** of the dog.
7. dairy — 7. Cheese is a **dairy** food.
8. stairway — 8. The **stairway** was dimly lit.
9. prairie — 9. Many bison lived on the **prairie.**
10. repair — 10. The mechanics **repair** the car.
11. dear — 11. This book is very **dear** to me.
12. beard — 12. Their father grew a **beard.**
13. appear — 13. Lights **appear** in the distance.
14. weary — 14. The workers were **weary.**
15. smear — 15. I **smear** the paint on the paper.
16. volunteer — 16. The **volunteer** firefighters came.
17. career — 17. To be a doctor is a good **career.**
18. cheery — 18. The room looked **cheery.**
19. pioneer — 19. He was a true **pioneer.**
20. reindeer — 20. **Reindeer** live in Scandinavia.

 Notes for Home: Your child took a pretest on words that have vowel sounds with the letter *r.* **Home Activity:** Help your child learn misspelled words before the final test. Dictate the word and have your child spell the word aloud for you or write it on paper.

626 Spelling: More Vowels with *r*

Spelling: More Vowels with *r*

Word List

aware	spare	prairie	appear	career
prepare	beware	repair	weary	cheery
share	dairy	dear	smear	pioneer
declare	stairway	beard	volunteer	reindeer

Directions: Choose the words from the box that have the vowel sound with **r** that you hear in **steer.** Sort them according to how the vowel sound is spelled. Write each word in the correct column. **Order may vary.**

Vowel-r spelled *ear*
1. dear
2. beard
3. appear
4. weary
5. smear

Vowel-r spelled *eer*
6. volunteer
7. career
8. cheery
9. pioneer
10. reindeer

Directions: Choose the word from the box that best matches each clue. Write the word on the line.

prepare — 11. When you get ready, you do this.
repair — 12. When you fix something, you do this.
aware — 13. A person who knows something is this.
dairy — 14. This is a type of farm that produces milk and cheese.
share — 15. When you give someone part of what you have, you do this.
stairway — 16. It's what you call the steps to go upstairs and downstairs.
declare — 17. When you're sure of yourself, you say things this way.
beware — 18. This word signals a warning.
spare — 19. It's something extra, such as a tire in a car.
prairie — 20. It's the place where the land is flat.

 Notes for Home: Your child spelled words where the letter *r* changes a word's vowel sound, as in *aware* and *cheery.* **Home Activity:** As you read with your child, look for words that have the vowel sound with *r* you hear in *spare* and *dear.*

Spelling: More Vowels with *r* **627**

Spelling: More Vowels with *r*

Directions: Proofread this radio announcement. Find seven spelling mistakes. Use the proofreading marks to correct each mistake.

≡	Make a capital.
/	Make a small letter.
∧	Add something.
✗	Take out something.
⊙	Add a period.
¶	Begin a new paragraph.

Beware! A man with a beard is playing tricks on people. He can appear anywhere. His usual approach is to offer to repare something, such as a broken stairway or window. Then he will smear paint on it and disappear. He makes a carere out of destructive practical jokes, so stay awear. He is friendly and cheary, but don't be fooled!

Spelling Tip

Watch out for words that have the same vowel sound but different spellings, such as **aware** and **repair,** or **smear** and **career.**

Word List

aware	dear
prepare	beard
share	appear
declare	weary
spare	smear
beware	volunteer
dairy	career
stairway	cheery
prairie	pioneer
repair	reindeer

Write Interview Questions

Imagine you are a reporter. On a separate sheet of paper, write some questions you could ask the man who plays tricks on people. Try to use at least five of your spelling words.
Answers will vary, but each set of questions should include at least five spelling words.

 Notes for Home: Your child spelled words where the letter *r* changes a word's vowel sound, as in *aware* and *cheery.* **Home Activity:** Write the spelling words, but leave blanks for the vowel-*r* combinations (are, air, ear, eer). Invite your child to fill in the blanks.

628 Spelling: More Vowels with *r*

Name _____

In the Days of King Adobe

Spelling: More Vowels with *r* REVIEW

Word List				
aware	spare	prairie	appear	career
prepare	beware	repair	weary	cheery
share	dairy	dear	smear	pioneer
declare	stairway	beard	volunteer	reindeer

Directions: Choose the word from the box that best replaces the underlined word. Write the word on the line.

pioneer	1. My grandmother was an early <u>settler</u> in this region.
prairie	2. Her journey across the <u>plains</u> was long and difficult.
weary	3. At the end of each day's travel she was <u>tired</u>.
appear	4. She never did <u>seem</u> to be discouraged, however.
cheery	5. She was always <u>happy</u> and ready to push on.
repair	6. Once a wheel broke and she was unable to <u>fix</u> it.
spare	7. Luckily another family had an <u>extra</u> to give her.
share	8. In those times, families would always <u>give</u> whatever they had.
aware	9. They were <u>conscious</u> of the dangers of their journey.
prepare	10. They tried to <u>be ready</u> themselves for anything.

Directions: Choose the word from the box that best matches each clue. Write the word on the line.

reindeer	11. These animals pull a holiday sled.
dairy	12. These food products include milk and cheese.
beard	13. It's what grows on a man's face.
career	14. It's what a person does for a living.
volunteer	15. It's what you do when you offer your time and help.
beware	16. It's what a warning sign may say.
smear	17. It's what babies often do with their food.
dear	18. It's how you start a friendly letter.
stairway	19. It's what you climb to get to a second floor.
declare	20. It means almost the same as *say*.

 Notes for Home: Your child spelled words where the letter *r* changes a word's vowel sound, as in *aware* and *cheery*. **Home Activity:** Together, write short rhymes using the spelling words. Include other words with the same vowel sounds and spellings.

Spelling: More Vowels with *r* **629**

Name _____

In the Days of King Adobe

Questions for Inquiry

A good way to begin a research project is by **asking yourself questions** about your topic. These questions will help guide you as you research information to find answers for your questions. As you research and read, revise your questions as needed.

Directions: Suppose you are doing research on tricksters. Many cultures have folk tales about tricksters—characters who use tricks to show a special trait. Some are animals and some are people. Sometimes the tricks are to teach a hard lesson, and sometimes they are just pranks. Choose one of the tricksters described below as a topic for a research report. Then answer the questions on the next page.

Coyote is a clever and sometimes naughty character in Native American folk tales. He sometimes doesn't play fair, but there is always a point to his antics.

Reynard the Fox is sly. He knows the weaknesses of those he plays tricks on. Often his tricks let people know that they need to think more of others than of themselves.

Till Eulenspiegel is a German character. He uses his abilities as a trickster to help the townsfolk and sometimes the whole country.

Anansi is a spider in African and Caribbean folk tales. He often shows his cleverness by getting the better of the larger animals and teaching them that size isn't everything.

630 Research and Study Skills: Questions for Inquiry

Name _____

In the Days of King Adobe

1. Which trickster will your report be about? **Answers will be one of four characters.**

2. What would you like to know about your topic? Think of at least three questions that you could use to guide you as you start your research.
Possible questions: When did this character first enter the folklore of this culture? What are some examples of his tricks? What is the point or lesson of the tricks? How is the character usually depicted in folk tales? Does the culture have any customs or traditions associated with this character?

Directions: Which of the following resources do you think might be helpful in finding answers to your questions? Explain why. **Possible answers given.**

3. *The Times of London World Atlas* **No, a book of maps won't tell me more about folk tale characters.**

4. *Famous Folk Tales from Around the World* **Yes, this book may include a folk tale about my trickster character.**

5. *Encyclopedia of Myth and Folklore* **Yes, this encyclopedia may give factual information about the character.**

6. *A Celebration of African Folk Tales* **Answers will vary depending on which character students have chosen.**

7. "Why Germans Love Till Eulenspiegel" (article) **Answers will vary depending on which character students have chosen.**

8. *The Illustrated Guide to Native American Mythology* **Answers will vary depending on which character students have chosen.**

9. "Fox Meets Coyote: A Comparison of Two Popular Folk Tale Characters" (article)
Answers will vary depending on which character students have chosen.

10. Why might you revise your questions during the research process? **You may need to revise your questions after reading new information to focus on something specific that you've read or if you can't find answers to the questions you asked.**

 Notes for Home: Your child formed questions for research and considered how to find the answers. **Home Activity:** Together with your child, write two or three questions about a topic you would like to know more about. Discuss how to find the answers.

Research and Study Skills: Questions for Inquiry **631**

Name _____

Just Telling the Truth

Making Judgments

- **Making judgments** means forming opinions about someone or something.
- Characters make judgments about situations and other characters. Authors make judgments on the subject of their writing. Readers make judgments about characters, authors, and ideas. A reader's judgment should be supported by evidence in the story or article.

Directions: Reread "Can You Change Your School Lunch?" Then complete the table. Give supporting evidence for each judgment. Then make your own judgment about the author's ideas. **Possible answers given.**

Judgments (Opinions)	Supporting Evidence
Justin's opinion: The school lunches needed to be improved.	1. He formed a youth advisory council and took a student survey.
Justin's opinion: The school lunches did improve.	2. Old foods were replaced with new ones.
Author's opinion: You can change your own school's lunches.	3. The author explains how other schools changed their lunch menus.
Your opinion of the author's ideas: 4. **The author's ideas are good.**	5. The author gives many examples and details about how to change lunches.

 Notes for Home: Your child identified supporting evidence for opinions in the article and made judgments about the author's ideas. **Home Activity:** Help your child write a letter about something he or she thinks should be changed.

634 Making Judgments

© Scott Foresman 5

Vocabulary

Directions: Choose the word from the box that best completes each sentence. Write the word on the matching numbered line to the right.

Check the Words You Know
__ career
__ critical
__ efficient
__ maneuvered
__ opinion
__ resolved
__ shattered
__ survey

★★★★★★★★★★★★★★★★★★★
A SURE FIRE HIT

"My New 1. _____" is a moving story about a fearless young woman's job search. Jean is a warm-hearted but extremely 2. _____ person. She gets her dream job because she is an 3. _____ worker, but then she gets fired for arguing with her boss. The conflict is 4. _____ when Jean learns to accept people. People then learn to accept her. In my 5. _____, this film has "Oscar" written all over it.

1.	Career
2.	critical
3.	efficient
4.	resolved
5.	opinion

Directions: Choose the word from the box that best matches each clue. Write the word on the line.

maneuvered	6. It's what the chess champion did.
career	7. A college degree will help you start this.
survey	8. It's what surveyors do.
opinion	9. You have a right to yours.
shattered	10. It's what the china plate did after falling.

Write a List

What *really* bothers you—barking dogs, smelly feet, annoying siblings? On a separate sheet of paper, list ten things that bother you a lot. Next to each entry, explain why it annoys you. Use as many vocabulary words as you can in your list.
Students' lists should make correct use of vocabulary words.

Notes for Home: Your child identified and used vocabulary words from "Just Telling the Truth." *Home Activity:* With your child, write a review of a book, television show, or movie like the one shown above. Guide your child to use as many vocabulary words as possible.

Vocabulary 635

Making Judgments

- **Making judgments** means forming opinions about someone or something. Characters, authors, and readers all make judgments.

Directions: Reread what happens in "Just Telling the Truth" when Felicia tells her mother she doesn't know why her friends were mad at her. Then answer the questions below.

> Her mother looked at her for a long time. "Are you sure," she said finally, "you don't know why? You haven't even got an idea?"
> "Well," Felicia hesitated, "I told the truth. Maybe they didn't like that."
> "Felicia," her mother said gently, "there's a difference between truth and opinion. The truth is facts. Opinion is what you think. You told them what you thought."
> "And they didn't like that. Shouldn't I say what I think?"
> Her mother frowned. "Look, if you have a great idea for something and someone comes along and says, 'Boy, what a dumb idea, this is wrong and this is wrong,' wouldn't you feel bad?"

Copyright © 1973 by Ellen Conford. From FELICIA THE CRITIC published by Little, Brown and Company. Reprinted by permission of McIntosh and Otis, Inc.

Possible answers given.
1. Do you agree that "the truth is facts"? Why or why not?
No, an honest opinion can be truthful too.

2. How would you answer Felicia when she says, "Shouldn't I say what I think?"
You should say what you think if you can do it without being mean.

3. What point is Felicia's mother trying to make?
It's important to be sensitive to other people's feelings.

4. What is your opinion of Felicia's mother? Explain.
She's a good mother because she's trying to help Felicia understand why her friends are upset.

5. What lesson does Felicia learn in "Just Telling the Truth"? On a separate sheet of paper, tell what Felicia learned and whether you think it was a worthwhile lesson for people to learn. **Felicia learned to be constructive in her criticism. This is a valuable lesson because it helps people get along better.**

Notes for Home: Your child read a story and made judgments about its characters and ideas. *Home Activity:* Read a newspaper editorial with your child. Ask him or her to make judgments about the ideas expressed.

636 Making Judgments

Selection Test

Directions: Choose the best answer to each item. Mark the letter for the answer you have chosen.

Part 1: Vocabulary

Find the answer choice that means about the same as the underlined word in each sentence.

1. Aunt Jessie told us about her new career.
   - Ⓐ job or occupation
   - B. apartment
   - C. hobby or activity
   - D. goal

2. Mr. Marlow maneuvered the car.
   - F. bought
   - G. fixed quickly
   - H. started
   - Ⓙ moved skillfully

3. My brother explained his opinion.
   - A. dream
   - Ⓑ what one believes
   - C. experience
   - D. what one plans

4. Why is Laura so critical?
   - F. forgetful
   - G. often sad
   - H. tending to be shy
   - Ⓙ quick to find fault

5. The vase was shattered.
   - A. painted
   - B. washed
   - Ⓒ broken
   - D. put away

6. Try to develop more efficient habits.
   - F. thoughtful of others
   - Ⓖ working in an effective way
   - H. tending to save money
   - J. careful

7. Nell told us what she had resolved.
   - A. completed
   - B. ruined
   - C. heard
   - Ⓓ decided

8. Mom came in to survey the damage.
   - Ⓕ look at
   - G. repair
   - H. blame someone for
   - J. clean up

Part 2: Comprehension

Use what you know about the story to answer each item.

9. Felicia's friends don't like her attitude about—
   - Ⓐ what a club should be.
   - B. walking to school alone.
   - C. Cheryl's mother.
   - D. her sister Marilyn.

10. When Felicia first comes home from school, she—
    - F. paints her nails.
    - Ⓖ makes a snack.
    - H. cleans the floor.
    - J. starts a building project.

11. Marilyn is partly responsible for the broken jar because she—
    - A. was the first to use the peanut butter.
    - B. left it on the table.
    - Ⓒ startled Felicia, causing Felicia's arm to hit it.
    - D. screamed when Felicia was picking up the jar.

12. You can tell from Felicia's problems at school that she—
    - F. tries to be cruel to others.
    - G. does not have any friends.
    - H. doesn't care what other people think.
    - Ⓙ doesn't understand the effect she has on others.

GO ON ➡

Selection Test 637

---

13. Felicia decides to change the broom closet because she wants to—
    - A. keep her mother from becoming angry about the broken jar.
    - B. get more attention from Marilyn.
    - Ⓒ practice being constructive.
    - D. put off doing her homework.

14. Telling Felicia to become a constructive critic is good advice because it—
    - F. fools Felicia into thinking everyone likes her.
    - G. gives Felicia a way to go out and get a job right away.
    - H. makes Felicia see that there's nothing wrong with how she acts.
    - Ⓙ gives Felicia a way to get along with others while still being herself.

15. How does Felicia show that she has understood her mother's advice about becoming a constructive critic?
    - A. She interrupts her mother when her mother is trying to cook.
    - B. She doesn't understand why her mother won't return the roast.
    - Ⓒ She asks her mother if she would mind hearing suggestions about the broom closet.
    - D. She yells at Marilyn to come look at what she has done with the closet.

STOP

638 Selection Test

Answers 825

Making Judgments

- **Making judgments** means forming opinions about someone or something. Characters, authors, and readers all make judgments.

Directions: Read the story below.

Richard walked into the cafeteria wearing his new athletic shoes.

"Wow! Look at those awesome shoes!" cried Mark.

"Awesomely expensive, I bet," said Paul. "How much did you pay for them, Richard?"

"Only $95," said Richard proudly. "They were on sale."

"I've got to get a pair of those myself," said Mark. "Then I'll be one cool dude!"

"You're crazy," replied Paul. "You can get a pair just as good for half that money

without the fancy designer label."

"You have to have the label," replied Richard. "They're the best. Just like the basketball player on the commercial says."

"You believe everything you hear on TV?" asked Paul.

Before Richard could reply, Paul had left the table with his empty tray.

"What's the matter with him?" asked Mark.

"Oh, he's just jealous, that's all," said Richard.

Directions: Complete the table. Make a judgment about the characters' actions and ideas. **Possible answers given.**

What do you think of . . .	Judgments
1. Mark's response to Richard's shoes?	1. **Mark is impressed with the shoes and seems superficial.**
2. Paul's response?	2. **Paul isn't impressed and is more thoughtful.**
3. Paul's judgment of Richard's shoes?	3. **He thinks they're a waste of money and is probably right.**
4. Richard's judgment of Paul?	4. **Richard misjudges Paul when he says he is jealous.**

5. Do you agree with Paul's judgment of the shoes? Explain your thinking.
Yes, many "designer" products are not worth all the money you pay for them.

Notes for Home: Your child read a story and made judgments about the actions and ideas of its characters. *Home Activity:* Discuss with your child some favorite fictional characters from books or movies. Ask your child to make a judgment about the characters' actions and ideas.

Making Judgments **639**

Character

REVIEW

Directions: Read the story. Then read each question about the story. Choose the best answer to each question. Mark the letter for the answer you have chosen.

The Lonely Critic

Anne and Teresa smiled and laughed as they left the movie theater. Joe walked close behind them. He had a serious expression as he rushed to keep up with Anne, Teresa, and their other friends.

"I really liked it," said Anne to the others as they walked outside.

"So did I," added Teresa. "It was so funny and entertaining."

"Didn't you love it when the dog got into the driver's seat?" commented another friend. One or two others in the group nodded their heads in agreement.

"Well," Joe said loudly, "I can't believe any of you liked it. The script was an absolute embarrassment. The acting was awful. The camera work was terrible, and the director doesn't know the first thing about filmmaking."

The others looked at each other and rolled their eyes.

"Joe thinks he knows everything," Anne whispered to Teresa.

"I'll say," Teresa whispered back.

"Who wants to grab some pizza and talk about the movie?" Joe asked. "There are a lot more things I could tell you about filmmaking."

"No thanks, we've got to get home," said Anne and Teresa at the same time. "It's getting late." One by one the others said they had to be up early in the morning.

Joe shrugged. "Suit yourselves," he said.

1. From what he says, Joe seems to—
   - Ⓐ value his own opinion highly.
   - B. value his friends' opinions.
   - C. want to learn about movies.
   - D. want to talk about himself.

2. You can tell from what Anne and Teresa say about Joe that he is—
   - F. well liked.
   - G. a film expert.
   - H. good company.
   - Ⓙ a know-it-all.

3. Which is **not** a clue to Joe's character?
   - A. His friends roll their eyes.
   - B. His friends turn down his invitation.
   - Ⓒ His friends liked the movie.
   - D. His friends whisper about him.

4. Joe might best be described as—
   - F. good-natured.
   - Ⓖ critical.
   - H. emotional.
   - J. kind.

5. What is missing from the story that would help you know more about Joe?
   - A. his actions.
   - B. his friends' actions.
   - Ⓒ his thoughts.
   - D. his words.

Notes for Home: Your child read a story and drew conclusions about the characters. *Home Activity:* Take turns describing people you know by what they say and do, as well as by what others say about them. Then, take turns trying to guess who is being described.

640 Character

Writing Across Texts

Directions: Consider the problems facing Andy and Felicia in the stories "Andy's Secret Ingredient" and "Just Telling the Truth." For each problem they encountered, they found a solution. Use information from the stories to complete the problem and solution diagrams below. **Possible answers given.**

Andy's Problems	Andy's Solutions
Andy needed to find out what bugs could be eaten safely.	1. **Andy wrote a letter to Iowa State University, asking for information.**
2. **Andy needed to prepare bugs to be eaten.**	3. **Andy collected beetles, kept them in a cage, fed them cornmeal, and froze them.**
4. **Andy wanted to know if the beetles tasted okay, but he did not want to eat them himself.**	5. **Andy baked beetle brownies and gave them to Wendell to eat.**

Felicia's Problems	Felicia's Solutions
At lunch, Phyllis scowled at Felicia and said, "Eat your corn chips, Felicia."	6. **Felicia spoke with her mother about the situation and learned about constructive criticism.**
7. **Felicia's family had difficulty finding things in the broom closet.**	8. **Felicia studied the picture of the "cleaning closet" and reorganized the family broom closet.**
9. **Felicia had a critical comment about everyone she met.**	10. **Felicia decided to use her critical nature in a positive way by helping people with her ideas.**

Write a Comparison/Contrast Paragraph

Both Andy, from "Andy's Secret Ingredient," and Felicia, from "Just Telling the Truth," creatively solved their problems. Use information from the stories to write a paragraph in which you compare and contrast the creative ways Andy and Felicia solved their problems. Write your paragraph on a separate sheet of paper.
Paragraphs will vary. Check that students have supported their statements with information from both stories.

Notes for Home: Your child combined and used information from two stories to write a comparison/contrast paragraph. *Home Activity:* As you read other stories and articles together, encourage your child to compare and contrast them.

Writing Across Texts **641**

Grammar: Sentence Capitals and End Punctuation

REVIEW

Directions: Rewrite each sentence correctly. Add the correct capitalization and end punctuation.

1. do you always read the reviews before you see a movie.
Do you always read the reviews before you see a movie?

2. What a ridiculous question that is?
What a ridiculous question that is!

3. make up your own mind about the movies you see?
Make up your own mind about the movies you see.

4. I Do think it's nice to have some guidance, don't you!
I do think it's nice to have some guidance, don't you?

5. good reviewers know how to criticize without being unkind?
Good reviewers know how to criticize without being unkind.

Directions: Write a sentence in response to each sentence given. Include at least one declarative, interrogative, imperative, and exclamatory sentence. **Possible answers given.**

6. Give your opinion of the last movie you saw.
What a wonderful movie that was!

7. Write a question you might ask a movie critic.
How do you review a bad movie without insulting people?

8. Write a sentence you might use in a movie review.
The performances made the movie come alive.

9. Write a piece of advice you might give to a movie goer.
Relax and enjoy the movie.

10. Write a question or comment about movie reviews.
Without reviews, how would I know which movies to avoid?

Notes for Home: Your child wrote sentences that began with a capital letter and ended with a period, a question mark, or an exclamation mark. *Home Activity:* Have your child write a note to a friend. Include examples of declarative, interrogative, imperative, and exclamatory sentences.

642 Grammar: Sentence Capitals and End Punctuation

© Scott Foresman 5

Grammar Practice Book 5.6, p. 142

Name _____

Grammar: Quotations and Quotation Marks

A person's exact words are a **direct quotation**. Direct quotations begin with capital letters and end with proper punctuation marks. To show you are using someone else's words and not your own, enclose a quotation in **quotation marks.**
"Critics review books and movies," my mother said.
My father added, "You can find reviews in the newspaper."

Use a comma to separate a quotation from the words that tell who is speaking. Put commas and end marks inside the last quotation mark. Sometimes words that tell who is speaking may interrupt a direct quotation. Then two sets of quotation marks are used. The words that tell who is talking may be followed by a comma or end punctuation. Use a comma if the second part of the quotation does not begin a new sentence. Use end punctuation and a capital letter if it does.
"Have you read the review?" she asked.
"I haven't," I said, "but I want to."
"The critic liked the book," Ann said. "He thought it was fascinating."

Directions: Write **C** if quotation marks are used correctly in each sentence. Write **NC** if the quotation marks are not used correctly.

NC 1. "Let's see a movie, Tim said."
NC 2. "Which one"? I asked.
C 3. "Well," he hesitated, "I really don't know."
C 4. I said, "Let's see what the critics thought."
C 5. "Do we have a newspaper?" he asked.
NC 6. "I think so I answered.

Directions: Add quotation marks and other punctuation marks to complete each sentence.

7. "Here's the newspaper," Mom said.
8. "Do you know," I asked, "where the movie reviews are?"
9. Tim answered, "They're on this page."
10. "Give me a minute to read these," said Tim.
11. Then he said, "The critics liked this movie."
12. "I want to see it," I said. "What time is it playing?"
13. "What is the rating?" my mother asked.
14. "It's rated G," Tim said.
15. I stood up and said, "Let's get going!"

 Notes for Home: Your child used quotation marks to show a speaker's exact words. *Home Activity:* Say aloud a brief series of sentences and have your child write them down, using quotation marks to show your exact words and words to tell who is talking.

Grammar: Quotations and Quotation Marks **643**

Grammar Practice Book 5.6, p. 143

Name _____

Grammar: Quotations and Quotation Marks

Directions: Add quotation marks, commas, end marks, and capital letters to complete each sentence. Write the new sentence on the line.

1. do you want to see a movie Amy asked
"Do you want to see a movie?" Amy asked.

2. I don't think so I answered movies aren't fun
"I don't think so," I answered. "Movies aren't fun."

3. how about playing a game she asked
"How about playing a game?" she asked.

4. I doubt it I said games are boring
"I doubt it," I said. "Games are boring."

5. let's go skating Amy urged
"Let's go skating," Amy urged.

6. skating is really boring I complained
"Skating is really boring," I complained.

7. then she asked do you want to visit David
Then she asked, "Do you want to visit David?"

8. why would I want to do that I shrieked he lives so far away
"Why would I want to do that?" I shrieked. "He lives so far away!"

9. it's not his fault Amy shouted
"It's not his fault!" Amy shouted.

10. you're right I answered let's go visit him
"You're right," I answered. "Let's go visit him."

Write a Conversation

Think of a movie, book, or TV show you have recently discussed with friends or family. Write what different people said about it. Use quotation marks to show the speaker's exact words. Be sure to tell who each speaker is.
Students should correctly apply the rules for using quotation marks and punctuating quotations to record each speaker's exact words.

 Notes for Home: Your child practiced punctuating quotations, a speaker's exact words. *Home Activity:* With your child, read some stories. Have your child point out the dialogue and explain the use of the quotation marks.

644 Grammar: Quotations and Quotation Marks

Grammar Practice Book 5.6, p. 144

Name _____

Grammar: Quotations and Quotation Marks

RETEACHING

Quotation marks help identify and set off the exact words of a speaker. Circle the speaker's exact words in each sentence below.

1. Wai remarked, "This is an interesting book."
2. "Can you find one like it for me?" asked Lin.
3. "Yes," said the librarian, "I think I can."
4. "Wow!" cried Lin. "Thank you very much."

Use quotation marks to show the exact words of a speaker. Don't overuse the word **said.** Vary the verbs that tell who spoke.

Directions: Write each sentence correctly. Add the necessary punctuation. Use capital letters where needed.

1. Mr. Part said "the new computers have arrived"
Mr. Part said, "The new computers have arrived."

2. can we begin using them today asked Lee
"Can we begin using them today?" asked Lee.

3. Mr. Part replied "first we must connect them and test them"
Mr. Part replied, "First we must connect them and test them."

4. maybe he said "some of you can help me"
"Maybe," he said, "some of you can help me."

5. "I will open the boxes" Josie said "I am good at that"
"I will open the boxes," Josie said. "I am good at that."

6. be sure that you do not drop anything warned Mr. Part
"Be sure that you do not drop anything," warned Mr. Part.

7. Lee asked should I read the instruction booklet
Lee asked, "Should I read the instruction booklet?"

8. "I think" replied Mr. Part "that is an excellent idea"
"I think," replied Mr. Part, "that is an excellent idea."

 Notes for Home: Your child capitalized and punctuated quotations correctly. *Home Activity:* Have your child eavesdrop on a conversation between you and another family member. Have him or her write some of the dialogue, punctuating sentences correctly.

Grammar: Quotations and Quotation Marks **645**

Grammar Practice Book 5.6, p. 145

Name _____

Grammar: Quotations and Quotation Marks

Directions: Write each sentence. Add the necessary punctuation.

1. Did you bring your new camera? asked Judy.
"Did you bring your new camera?" asked Judy.

2. I brought the camera, Olga replied, and two rolls of film.
"I brought the camera," Olga replied, "and two rolls of film."

3. They also sell film at the museum store, commented Judy.
"They also sell film at the museum store," commented Judy.

4. We can put the pictures on the bulletin board, suggested Ramon.
"We can put the pictures on the bulletin board," suggested Ramon.

5. That is an excellent idea for a project, Olga remarked.
"That is an excellent idea for a project," Olga remarked.

Directions: Unscramble each set of words to write a sentence with quotations. Add punctuation marks and capital letters where needed. **Possible answers given.**

6. asked class a our going is Raphael on trip
Raphael asked, "Is our class going on a trip?"

7. will Ms. Smith yes be replied the museum going to we
"Yes," Ms. Smith replied. "We will be going to the museum."

8. many the see Jane there at interesting museum things commented to are
"There are many interesting things to see at the museum," commented Jane.

9. cried boy great sounds this a like trip Raphael
"Boy, a trip like this sounds great!" cried Raphael.

10. Amy wish could I we now right leave said
Amy said, "I wish we could leave right now."

 Notes for Home: Your child wrote quotations with correct capitalization and punctuation. *Home Activity:* Watch a TV program with your child. Have him or her write part of the dialogue between two TV show characters, punctuating sentences correctly.

646 Grammar: Quotations and Quotation Marks

© Scott Foresman 5

Name _____

Just Telling the Truth

Phonics: Complex Spelling Patterns

Directions: Looking at spelling patterns can help you figure out how to pronounce a word. Some words have simple spelling patterns such as **cat** or **lake**. These spelling patterns can be written as CVC (consonant-vowel-consonant) or CVCe (consonant-vowel-consonant-*e*). But many words have more complex spelling patterns. Carefully read each word in the box. Sort the words according to their spelling patterns by following the instructions below.

Order may vary.

accident	curiously	gorgeous
actually	definite	grumbling
appreciated	disinterest	hesitated
constructive	dubiously	maneuvered
criticism	efficient	uncertainly

Write the words that have three vowels in a row—VVV.

1. **dubiously**   2. **gorgeous**   3. **curiously**

Write the words that have three consonants in a row—CCC.

4. **grumbling**   5. **appreciated**

Write the word that has four consonants in a row—CCCC.

6. **constructive**

Write the words that start with the pattern VCCV.

7. **actually**   8. **efficient**   9. **accident**

Write the words that alternate consonants and vowels.

10. **definite**   11. **hesitated**

Write the words that don't seem to follow a pattern.

12. **criticism**   14. **uncertainly**
13. **maneuvered**   15. **disinterest**

 Notes for Home: Your child recognized words with complex spelling patterns, such as *efficient* and *gorgeous*. **Home Activity:** Read a newspaper article with your child. Have your child look for consonant and vowel patterns in longer words.

Phonics: Complex Spelling Patterns **647**

Name _____

Just Telling the Truth

Spelling: Getting Letters in Correct Order

Pretest Directions: Fold back the page along the dotted line. On the blanks, write the spelling words as they are dictated. When you have finished the test, unfold the page and check your words.

1. **lonely** — 1. He is **lonely** without his friends.
2. **hundred** — 2. She owns one **hundred** books.
3. **friend** — 3. He is my best **friend**.
4. **built** — 4. The settlers **built** a cabin.
5. **beautiful** — 5. This is a **beautiful** vase.
6. **heard** — 6. Have you **heard** the news?
7. **radio** — 7. I heard the news on the **radio**.
8. **their** — 8. **Their** feet were getting cold.
9. **caught** — 9. Who **caught** the most fish?
10. **bored** — 10. I am **bored** with this program.
11. **guard** — 11. The **guard** fell asleep.
12. **pierce** — 12. Many people **pierce** their ears.
13. **shrieked** — 13. Someone **shrieked** outside.
14. **receive** — 14. Who will **receive** first prize?
15. **horrible** — 15. What a **horrible** noise!
16. **jewelry** — 16. They make **jewelry** for a living.
17. **tumble** — 17. Rocks **tumble** down the hill.
18. **northern** — 18. We walked to the **northern** cliff.
19. **acre** — 19. The field is only half an **acre**.
20. **museum** — 20. The **museum** is open late.

 Notes for Home: Your child took a pretest on words with difficult letter combinations. *Home Activity:* Help your child learn misspelled words before the final test. Have your child underline the word parts that caused the problem and concentrate on those parts.

648 Spelling: Getting Letters in Correct Order

Name _____

Just Telling the Truth

Spelling: Getting Letters in Correct Order

Word List

lonely	beautiful	caught	shrieked	tumble
hundred	heard	bored	receive	northern
friend	radio	guard	horrible	acre
built	their	pierce	jewelry	museum

Directions: Choose the words from the box that contain two or more vowels in a row. Sort them according to their vowel pattern. Write each word in the correct column.

Spelled ea or eau
1. **beautiful**
2. **heard**

Spelled ua
3. **guard**

Spelled io
4. **radio**

Spelled ei
5. **their**
6. **receive**

Spelled eu
7. **museum**

Spelled au
8. **caught**

Spelled ui
9. **built**

Spelled ie
10. **friend**
11. **pierce**
12. **shrieked**

Directions: Choose the word from the box that best completes each sentence. Write the word on the line to the left.

acre 13. My aunt lives on an _____ of land in Maine.
northern 14. In that _____ state, the winters are long and cold.
jewelry 15. My aunt makes beautiful _____ out of sea glass and sells it to tourists in the summer.
tumble 16. She picks which pieces to use by letting the glass gently _____ out of her basket.
hundred 17. She charges as much as one _____ dollars for some pieces.
lonely 18. Some people think that because my aunt works by herself she might be _____.
bored 19. She loves her work, though, and never gets _____ even when she does the same thing over and over.
horrible 20. Personally, I think it would be _____ to be so isolated, but she likes it.

 Notes for Home: Your child spelled words with letter combinations that are often mixed up. *Home Activity:* Write down the spelling words with the letters scrambled. Challenge your child to unscramble the letters to spell each word correctly.

Spelling: Getting Letters in Correct Order **649**

Name _____

Just Telling the Truth

Spelling: Getting Letters in Correct Order

Directions: Read this e-mail message. Find six spelling mistakes. Use the proofreading marks to correct each mistake.

≡ Make a capital.
／ Make a small letter.
∧ Add something.
∌ Take out something.
⊙ Add a period.
¶ Begin a new paragraph.

To All Museum Staff:

It has come to my attention that some of you are listening to the radio during work hours. The gaurd cuaght two people when thier radio made a horrible squawking noise. We have one hundred people working here. They all herd the music peirce the quiet. From now on, please be considerate and do not play the radio during work hours.

The Management

Spelling Tip
jewelry
Many people misspell **jewelry** by mixing up its letters. Remember: there is a **jewel** in **jewe**lry.

Word List

lonely	guard
hundred	pierce
friend	shrieked
built	receive
beautiful	horrible
heard	jewelry
radio	tumble
their	northern
caught	acre
bored	museum

Write an E-Mail Message
On a separate sheet of paper, write an e-mail message in which you criticize someone's bad behavior and suggest an alternative. Be constructive, not insulting. Try to use at least four spelling words.
Answers will vary, but each e-mail message should include at least four spelling words.

Notes for Home: Your child spelled words with letter combinations that are often mixed up. *Home Activity:* Have a spelling bee with your child. Take turns saying words from the list for the other person to spell and use in a sentence.

650 Spelling: Getting Letters in Correct Order

© Scott Foresman 5

Name _____

Just Telling the Truth

Spelling: Getting Letters in Correct Order

REVIEW

Word List

lonely	beautiful	caught	shrieked	tumble
hundred	heard	bored	receive	northern
friend	radio	guard	horrible	acre
built	their	pierce	jewelry	museum

Directions: Choose the word from the box that best completes each tongue twister. Write the word on the line to the left. Hint: The answer will start with the same letter as the first word in each sentence.

receive	1. Rita would rather _____ a rose from Ralph than Ronald.
pierce	2. Patty plans to _____ the paper with a pointed pen.
friend	3. Fred, a family _____, fried fish for folks at the fair.
guard	4. Greg greeted the gabby _____ at the gate.
their	5. Theda and Thelma took _____ three tan tank tops to Tahiti.
museum	6. Marcia and Mark managed a _____ of miniature models.
acre	7. An _____ offers a lot after all.
radio	8. Return the _____ to Rachel for repair.
hundred	9. Happy Hal has half a _____ hobbies.
tumble	10. Ten tip-top clowns _____ to tunes together.

Directions: Choose the word from the box that is associated with each word below. Write the word on the line.

11. shriek	shrieked	16. horror	horrible
12. beauty	beautiful	17. build	built
13. bore	bored	18. north	northern
14. catch	caught	19. jewel	jewelry
15. hear	heard	20. lone	lonely

 Notes for Home: Your child spelled words with letter combinations that are often mixed up. **Home Activity:** Help your child create a set of flash cards with these words. Use the cards to help your child practice spelling the words.

Spelling: Getting Letters in Correct Order **651**

Name _____

Just Telling the Truth

Textbook/Trade Book

A **textbook** is a book you use in school to learn about a subject. You can use the chapters, headings, subheadings, captions, and index to locate information in a textbook. A **trade book** is any book that is not a textbook, a periodical, or a reference book.

Directions: Use the sample pages from a textbook and a trade book below to answer the questions on the next page.

Chapter 4: American Artists of 19th and 20th Centuries

Artists in the United States used many painting styles. In this chapter you will read about women and men who created their own styles as well as adapted the styles of other painters.

Lesson 1

Mary Cassatt (1844–1926)

Mary Cassatt was born in the United States but lived and painted in France for much of her life.

Many of her best known oil paintings are of mothers and children. She became **associated** with the art school known as **Impressionism.**

Check Your Understanding

1. With what style of art did Mary Cassatt become linked?
2. Where did Mary Cassatt live most of her life?

associated connected (with)
Impressionism (See glossary and Chapter 2.)

Mary Cassatt, a Woman for Her Time and Ours

This American artist, associated with the French Impressionist movement, was born in Pittsburgh, Pennsylvania, in 1844. We often think of her paintings as sincere renderings of the power of the bond between mothers and children.

In 1866, after completing her study at the Pennsylvania Academy of Fine Arts with Thomas Eakins, Mary Cassatt moved to France. She spent the rest of her life in France, where she died in 1926.

In France, Mary Cassatt had the good fortune to become a close friend of Edgar Degas and other Impressionist painters of the time. Her style adds a welcome sensitivity, which many other of her contemporaries did not attain.

Mary Cassatt, a Woman for Her Time and Ours

652 Research and Study Skills: Textbook/Trade Book

Name _____

Just Telling the Truth

1. What chapter is shown in the textbook? What is the title of the chapter? **Chapter 4; American Artists of the 19th and 20th Centuries**

2. For what kind of class might you use this textbook? Explain. **Possible answer: You would probably use this textbook for a class that teaches about the history of art.**

3. What is the title of the trade book? What do you think this book would be about? **Mary Cassatt: A Woman for Her Time and Ours; The book will be about the life and work of the painter Mary Cassatt.**

4. Why might someone want to read this trade book? **Possible answer: if you needed information about Mary Cassatt or if you were interested in art and women artists**

5. How are the textbook and trade book sample pages alike? How are they different? **Possible answer: Both the textbook and the trade book provide information about Mary Cassatt. The textbook organizes its information by chapter and lesson, includes questions for the reader, and defines vocabulary. The trade book gives more detailed information about the artist and is written in a more narrative style.**

6. Which book would contain detailed information about the artist's childhood? Explain. **Possible answer: Since the trade book focuses only on Mary Cassatt, it would probably give the most detailed information about her childhood.**

7. Why are the words *associated* and *Impressionism* boldfaced in the textbook? **These words are boldfaced because they are defined at the bottom of the text.**

8. Why do you think the textbook includes questions? **Possible answer: Textbooks are used to help students learn. The questions help you check your understanding of what you have read.**

9. What subjects do you think Mary Cassatt painted most often? Explain. **Possible answer: Both the textbook and the trade book mention her paintings of mothers and children so these are probably the subjects she painted most often.**

10. Explain how you could use both a textbook and trade books for a research report. **Possible answer: The textbook would be useful for finding and learning basic facts. Trade books would provide detailed information about the subject.**

 Notes for Home: Your child compared a sample textbook and trade book. **Home Activity:** Ask your child to show you a textbook from school and explain to you how it is organized and what kind of information it has. Then do the same with a trade book from home or the library.

Research and Study Skills: Textbook/Trade Book **653**

Name _____

Is It Real?

Visualizing

- **Visualizing** is creating a picture in your mind as you read.
- Pay attention to description, imagery, and sensory words that help you imagine what you are reading. Also think about what you already know about the places, people, and things being described.

Directions: Reread "Mrs. Middlesome-Merry's Art Studio." Then complete the table. Tell what story details you used to help you visualize different parts of the story. **Possible answers given.**

I Visualized	Using These Story Details
Mrs. Middlesome-Merry	1. small, chubby woman with yellow-going-gray hair and bluebell-blue eyes
Mrs. Middlesome-Merry's apron	2. a big apron splodged with paint colors and soup colors
Mrs. Middlesome-Merry's apron pocket	3. full of paintbrushes and soup ladles
Mrs. Middlesome-Merry's stairs	4. ivy that went on and on, in and out of the banister rails in great loops and swirls, knots and jungle tangles
Mrs. Middlesome-Merry's studio	5. hyacinths in bowls, sweet peas in jugs, dog daisies in old milk bottles, lilies in a jam jar, poppies in a yogurt pot

 Notes for Home: Your child read a story and identified vivid images that helped him or her visualize the details. **Home Activity:** Describe a place, such as your kitchen. Give clues about things a person might see, hear, feel, taste, or smell there. Have your child guess the place.

656 Visualizing

Vocabulary

Directions: Choose the word from the box that best completes each statement. Write the word on the line to the left.

artistic	1. *Literature* is to *literary* as *art* is to _____.
deceive	2. *Depend* is to *trust* as *mislead* is to _____.
sculpture	3. *Paint* is to *painting* as *stone* is to _____.
realistic	4. *False* is to *real* as *fake* is to _____.
viewer	5. *Food* is to *taster* as *picture* is to _____.

Check the Words You Know
— artistic
— deceive
— realistic
— represent
— sculpture
— style
— viewer

Directions: Choose the word from the box that best completes each sentence. Write the word on the line to the left.

realistic	6. The paintings we saw at the museum were as _____ as photographs.
sculpture	7. We also visited the _____ exhibit and saw many different statues carved out of marble.
represent	8. The statues _____ the artists' ideas.
style	9. Some were done in a very modern _____.
viewer	10. One _____ sat for a long time just staring at an especially interesting piece.

Write an Essay

On a separate sheet of paper, write an essay about an art style or art work you especially like. Look at the paintings and sculpture in an art book for ideas. Use as many vocabulary words as you can in your essay.
Students should make correct use of vocabulary words.

Notes for Home: Your child identified and used vocabulary words from "Is It Real?" *Home Activity:* Have your child make an art project and then describe the process on an index card. Encourage your child to use as many vocabulary words as possible in the description.

Visualizing

- **Visualizing** is creating a picture in your mind as you read.
- Authors may help you visualize by using imagery. These are words that give you a strong mental picture, or image.
- Another way an author may help you visualize is through sensory details. These are words that describe how something looks, sounds, smells, tastes, or feels.

Directions: Reread the passage below from "Is It Real?" about the time when Marilyn Levine had difficulty finishing her sculpture on time. Then answer the questions below.

> Worried that the teacher would think she was too slow, she quickly molded two disks like the rubber tips on a pair of crutches. She placed these on both sides of her single ceramic shoe, so it looked like someone with an injured foot had hobbled to the party on crutches. The teacher was as impressed with Marilyn's quick-thinking as he was by her skill in creating a realistic shoe.
>
> Later, a friend gave Levine a pair of worn-out work boots. Scuffed, scratched, and battered, the boots had a strange appeal. They told a story.
>
> From ARTISTIC TRICKERY: THE TRADITION OF TROMPE L'OEIL by Michael Capek. Copyright © 1995 Lerner Publications. Reprinted by permission.

1. To which of the five senses does the phrase "molded two disks" appeal: touch, taste, sight, smell, hearing?
touch and sight

2. What image does the author use to help you visualize the sculpture?
". . . it looked like someone with an injured foot had hobbled to the party on crutches."

3. What do you see when you visualize Marilyn's finished sculpture?
Possible answer: A shoe with the tips of a crutch on each side of it.

4. What words help you visualize the work boots in the second paragraph?
worn out, scuffed, scratched, battered

5. Close your eyes and visualize Marilyn Levine's *Black Gloves*. Then, on a separate sheet of paper, describe what you see in your own words. **Possible answer: I picture big black leather gloves, that are worn, smelly, cracked, and caked with dirt.**

Notes for Home: Your child read an article and visualized images from it. *Home Activity:* Close your eyes while your child describes an object or a room in your home. Guess what is being described by the details your child uses.

Selection Test

Directions: Choose the best answer to each item. Mark the letter for the answer you have chosen.

Part 1: Vocabulary

Find the answer choice that means about the same as the underlined word in each sentence.

1. Max likes to <u>deceive</u> people.
   A. ignore
   B. refuse to help
   (C.) fool
   D. steal from

2. He has an interesting <u>style</u> of painting.
   F. place to work
   (G.) manner
   H. name
   J. amount of work

3. The <u>viewer</u> enjoyed the movie.
   A. actor
   (B.) someone who looks at something
   C. owner
   D. someone who makes something

4. What was she trying to <u>represent</u> in her picture?
   (F.) show
   G. explain
   H. buy
   J. fix

5. That painting is so <u>realistic</u>.
   (A.) like the actual thing
   B. expensive
   C. dark and ugly
   D. looking as if done by a child

6. We bought a <u>sculpture</u> for the garden.
   F. fountain
   (G.) art object that is usually carved or molded
   H. small bush
   J. tall wooden frame for vines to grow on

7. She has so many <u>artistic</u> interests.
   A. painted
   B. of money
   C. different
   (D.) related to art

Part 2: Comprehension

Use what you know about the story to answer each item.

8. In "trompe l'oeil," the artist tries mainly to—
   (F.) fool the eye.
   G. ask a riddle.
   H. show life as it should be.
   J. make people laugh.

9. Trompe l'oeil is an art form that—
   A. was recently invented.
   B. involves only one or two artistic techniques.
   C. is very hard to produce successfully.
   (D.) has been around for centuries.

10. Marilyn Levine's *Black Gloves* shows—
    F. a painting of the gloves.
    G. a life-size figure of a man wearing the gloves.
    H. leather gloves that look like ceramic.
    (J.) ceramic gloves that look like leather.

11. Which of these stories from the selection best proves how trompe l'oeil can fool people?
    A. Duane Hanson's *Traveler* portrays a person who looks tired.
    B. Some artists make floors look as if they are covered with litter.
    (C.) People said they smelled peanuts while looking at *Fresh Roasted*.
    D. The Greeks appreciated trompe l'oeil before the Romans did.

---

12. Which would be another good title for this selection?
    F. "Why Audrey Flack Painted *Strawberry Tart Supreme*"
    G. "When *Fresh Roasted* Was Painted"
    (H.) "How Artists Trick the Viewer"
    J. "Where to See Trompe l'oeil"

13. Which sentence best helps the reader visualize what is being discussed?
    (A.) ". . . looking like they were sliced just minutes ago, the apples and oranges seem to spill right out of the picture."
    B. "And the more familiar you become with the game, the more fun it is."
    C. "Throughout history, dozens of artistic movements and fads have come and gone."
    D. "Many different artistic styles and techniques have been used to create trompe l'oeil."

14. Which would be the best evidence that trompe l'oeil can fool people?
    F. A woman admires a mural on a bathroom wall.
    G. A child laughs at a painting of a clown.
    (H.) A man tries to open the door on a mural of a house.
    J. A teacher studies a painting of a pair of shoes.

15. Which of these best fits the definition of trompe l'oeil art?
    (A.) a ceramic frog made to look like a real frog that sits in a real pond
    B. a drawing of a historical figure wearing the clothes of that time
    C. a painting of flowers in which each blossom is a blot of color
    D. a life-size photograph of a real person

STOP

30 Answers

Visualizing

- **Visualizing** is creating a picture in your mind as you read.
- Authors may help you visualize by using imagery. These are words that give you a strong mental picture, or image.
- Another way an author may help you visualize is through sensory details. These are words that describe how something looks, sounds, smells, tastes, or feels.

Directions: Read the passage.

Optical illusions fascinate people. Flat images on paper take on new life when you look at them carefully. There's even a kind of modern art that uses optical illusions to trick the eye. It's called "Op Art" for *optical art*. Some Op Artists use colors and patterns to create the illusion of movement. For example, a painter might swirl a pattern of wavy stripes on a large canvas. By using hues of vivid purple and yellow, the stripes might appear to be vibrating.

Op Art paintings also create the illusion of three dimensions. If you run your hand over these paintings, you'll feel a flat, smooth surface. To the eye, however, they appear to have bumps and holes. It's almost impossible to see them as they really are. If you haven't seen any Op Art before, it is definitely worth a look, or two, or three . . .

Directions: Complete each box. Tell what details in the passage appeal to the senses of sight and touch that help you visualize the descriptions of different types of Op Art paintings.

Sight	Touch
1. wavy stripes	4. flat, smooth
2. vivid purple and yellow	5. bumps and holes
3. vibrating	

Notes for Home: Your child read a passage and visualized what it describes. **Home Activity:** Read a short poem or descriptive paragraph with your child. Share the mental pictures formed while you each read.

Visualizing **661**

REVIEW

Fact and Opinion

Directions: Read the passage. Then read each question about the passage. Choose the best answer to each question. Mark the letter for the answer you have chosen.

The Eyes Have It

The use of optical illusions in art has a long history. The ancient Greeks used trompe l'oeil techniques thousands of years ago. The painter Zeuxis, for example, reportedly painted such realistic grapes that the birds tried to eat them! Much later, the Italian painter Caravaggio painted insects in his pictures of fruit bowls to make them look more real.

I like optical illusion in art. It's fun to feel that your eyes are telling you one thing while your brain tells you something else.

In real life, however, it is always unpleasant when our eyes get fooled. On a hot summer's day, you might think you see water on a hot highway—but it's an optical illusion. Mirages in the desert are another type of optical illusion. They can be even more upsetting, especially if you're thirsty.

Why are some optical illusions upsetting? It's a matter of survival. To function each day, we need our eyes and brains to work together. We're uncomfortable when they don't. In art, optical illusions are a kind of game. But life is never a game. Life is serious business.

1. Which of the following is **not** a statement of fact?
   A. The use of optical illusions in art has a long history.
   B. The ancient Greeks used trompe l'oeil techniques thousands of years ago.
   C. Later, the Italian painter Caravaggio painted insects in his pictures of fruit bowls to make them look more real.
   (D.) I like optical illusions in art.

2. "In real life, however, it is always unpleasant when our eyes get fooled" is—
   F. a statement of fact.
   (G.) a statement of opinion.
   H. a combination of fact and opinion.
   J. a question.

3. "Mirages in the desert are another type of optical illusion" is—
   (A.) a statement of fact.
   B. a statement of opinion.
   C. both a statement of fact and opinion.
   D. a question.

4. Which of the following is a statement of fact?
   (F.) To function each day, we need our eyes and brains to work together.
   G. We're always uncomfortable when they don't.
   H. But life is never a game.
   J. Life is serious business.

5. This passage contains—
   A. only facts.
   B. only opinions.
   (C.) a mixture of facts and opinions.
   D. only one opinion.

Notes for Home: Your child read a passage and identified statements of fact and opinion. **Home Activity:** Work with your child to list statements of fact and opinion about a favorite food, such as *Oranges contain Vitamin C. I think they taste great!*

662 Fact and Opinion

Writing Across Texts

Directions: Consider what you learned about the eye and its functions in the feature "See the Picture!" Complete the table by listing the names and functions of important parts of the eye used for sight. Then list the jobs your eyes do.

Possible answers given.

Parts of the Eye and Their Functions	Jobs the Eyes Do
cornea: bends light rays as they near the eye	7. see motion
1. pupil: lets in light	8. observe objects around you
2. iris: makes pupils larger or smaller to let in more or less light	9. see colors
3. lens: bends light rays and reverses them as they travel to the retina	10. adjust to different amounts of light
4. retina: carries rods and cones that convert light rays into signals	
5. optic nerve: carries signals from the retina to the brain	Paragraphs should include an explanation of the parts of the eye and their functions, as well as the general elements of sight. Students should recognize that the eye and brain must sort out objects that are viewed and recognize what is real and what is trompe l'oeil.
6. brain: interprets signals to identify what is seen	

Write an Explanation

Use the information in "Is It Real?" and "See the Picture!" to explain how your eyes help you see and understand a work of art such as a trompe l'oeil painting or sculpture. Include information from the table above in your writing. Write your explanation on a separate sheet of paper.

Notes for Home: Your child used information from different sources to write an explanation. **Home Activity:** As you read stories and articles with your child, talk about how the ideas in this reading material connect to other reading he or she has done.

Writing Across Texts **663**

REVIEW

Grammar: Correcting Sentence Fragments and Run-Ons

Directions: Read each item. On the line at the left, write **S** if it is a sentence or pair of sentences. Write **F** if it contains a fragment. Write **R** if it is a run-on. Then, correct each fragment or run-on. Write the corrected sentence or sentences on the lines.

Possible answers given.

S 1. When a picture plays a trick on your eyes, it is called an optical illusion.

F 2. Not only humans are tricked by optical illusions. Birds and fish too.
Not only humans are tricked by optical illusions. Birds and fish are tricked too.

R 3. Look down a long, straight road it seems to grow narrower.
Look down a long, straight road, and it seems to grow narrower.

F 4. Trees along the road seem to get smaller. As they get farther away.
Trees along the road seem to get smaller as they get farther away.

S 5. The road and trees stay the same size, of course. The change is an optical illusion.

F 6. Compare a white house with a dark house. Of the same size.
Compare a white house with a dark house of the same size.

F 7. Although they are the same size. The white house will look larger.
Although they are the same size, the white house will look larger.

R 8. These are real examples, optical illusions can also be created.
These are real examples, but optical illusions can also be created.

S 9. Draw a faraway object the same size as a nearer one, and the faraway object will look bigger.

R 10. Sometimes an illusion fools the eye, other times it fools the brain.
While sometimes an illusion fools the eye, other times it fools the brain.

Notes for Home: Your child corrected sentence fragments and run-on sentences. **Home Activity:** Together with your child, write a paragraph or two about a family incident. Correct any fragments or run-ons.

664 Grammar: Correcting Sentence Fragments and Run-Ons

© Scott Foresman 5

Grammar: Review of Compound and Complex Sentences

You can make your writing more interesting by varying your sentences. A **simple sentence** contains one complete subject and one complete predicate. A **compound sentence** is like two simple sentences with related ideas joined with a comma and a conjunction such as *and, but,* or *or.*

    Simple Sentences: The artist is a genius. The mural is beautiful!
    Compound Sentence: The artist is a genius, and the mural is beautiful!

A **complex sentence** is a simple sentence combined with a sentence part that cannot stand on its own. The sentence part has a subject and predicate. It is joined to the sentence with a word such as *if, because,* or *when.*

    Complex Sentence: When the blue paint is gone, I'll paint the sky pink.
               sentence part   **simple sentence**

Directions: Write whether each sentence is **compound** or **complex.**

    compound   1. Water colors are nice, but they can fade.
    compound   2. Some artists paint, and others sculpt.
    complex   3. If materials are not available, an artist can't work.
    compound   4. Sculptors carve rock, or they mold clay.
    complex   5. Because they are artists, painters are creative.
    compound   6. They work hard, and they like to be praised.

Directions: Write a compound sentence by joining the two simple sentences with *and, but,* or *or* and a comma. Write the compound sentence on the line.

7. Tricia took an art class. She liked it a lot.
Tricia took an art class, and she liked it a lot.

8. She learned how to paint. She enjoyed working with clay.
She learned how to paint, and she enjoyed working with clay.

9. Tricia could paint a watercolor. She could sculpt a figure from clay.
Tricia could paint a watercolor, and/or she could sculpt a figure from clay.

10. Tricia usually paints every day. She took last Sunday off.
Tricia usually paints every day, but she took last Sunday off.

 Notes for Home: Your child identified compound and complex sentences, and then combined simple sentences to form compound sentences. **Home Activity:** Invite your child to read a comic strip and combine the simple sentences to create compound sentences.

Grammar: Review of Compound and Complex Sentences   **665**

Grammar: Review of Compound and Complex Sentences

Directions: Write a compound sentence by joining the two simple sentences with a conjunction in ( ) and a comma. Write the compound sentence on the line.

1. We went to an art museum. It was closed. (or/but)
We went to an art museum, but it was closed.

2. Sally went home. I took a walk. (but/or)
Sally went home, but I took a walk.

3. I arrived at the park. I saw some artists at work. (and/but)
I arrived at the park, and I saw some artists at work.

4. They seemed young. Their work was great. (but/or)
They seemed young, but their work was great.

5. I watched them paint. Then I went home. (or/and)
I watched them paint, and then I went home.

Directions: Make a complex sentence by adding a simple sentence to the end of each sentence part. **Possible answers given.**

6. Because he loved painting optical illusions, **Leon painted one after another.**

7. When he ran out of paint, **he would run down to the store to get some more.**

8. If the store didn't have any more paint, **he would borrow some from his friend Janice.**

9. When he had finished painting the optical illusion, **Leon entered it in a competition.**

10. If the painting confused people, **Leon would try to explain the optical illusion to them.**

Write a Description

On a separate sheet of paper, write a description of your favorite art work. It can be a famous work of art, a not-so-famous work of art, or even art you created yourself. Use compound and complex sentences in your descriptions.
Check that students have formed compound and complex sentences correctly.

 Notes for Home: Your child wrote compound and complex sentences. **Home Activity:** With your child, take turns saying two simple sentences and having the other person combine them with *or, and,* or *but.*

666   Grammar: Review of Compound and Complex Sentences

Grammar: Review of Compound and Complex Sentences

RETEACHING

Circle the simple sentences in the compound sentence.
1. (My brother likes spaghetti) and (I like lasagna.)

Circle the simple sentence and underline the other sentence part in the complex sentence.
2. (We were unable to go to the party) because the weather was nasty.

A **simple sentence** contains one complete subject and one complete predicate. A **compound sentence** is like two simple sentences with related ideas joined with a comma and a conjunction such as *and, but,* or *or.* A **complex sentence** is a simple sentence combined with another part that cannot stand on its own as a separate sentence.

Directions: Write a compound sentence by joining the two simple sentences with a comma and a conjunction. Write the compound sentence on the line.
Possible answers given.

1. Ballet looks easy. The dancers must work hard.
Ballet looks easy, but the dancers must work hard.

2. They go to classes regularly. They never stop practicing.
They go to classes regularly, and they never stop practicing.

3. Dancers learn movements. They practice them over and over.
Dancers learn movements, and they practice them over and over.

Directions: Write a complex sentence by combining the simple sentence with a word such as *when, because, although,* or *if* and the other sentence part. Add capital letters and punctuation where needed. Write each new sentence on the line.

4. professional dancers are very good at what they do   they have practiced for a long time
Professional dancers are very good at what they do because they have practiced for a long time.

5. young girls are good enough and have practiced   they can learn to dance with toe shoes.
If young girls are good enough and have practiced, they can learn to dance with toe shoes.

 Notes for Home: Your child wrote compound and complex sentences. **Home Activity:** Talk with your child about how compound and complex sentences are formed. Have him or her show you examples on this page.

Grammar: Review of Compound and Complex Sentences   **667**

Grammar: Review of Compound and Complex Sentences

Directions: Make a complex sentence by adding a simple sentence to the end of each sentence part. **Possible answers given.**

1. When we got home from school, **we made a snack.**

2. Since it was so late, **we didn't have time to go to the movie.**

3. If I hadn't packed extra T-shirts, **I would have had to go to the laundromat.**

4. When Martin talked to Brian, **he asked what time the football game started.**

5. Although he never told anyone, **he liked to create comic strips.**

Directions: Read each sentence. Write *compound* or *complex* on the line.

    complex   6. When I saw the frightening dog, I crossed the street.
    compound   7. The dog was big, and it had a long tail.
    complex   8. I stayed away from it because I was scared.
    complex   9. When I heard it yelp, I had to laugh.
    compound   10. Its bark was high and quiet, and it wagged its tail happily.

Write an Animal Adventure Story

Think about an adventure an animal might have. What would the animal see? Where would it go? How would it react to different situations? On a separate sheet of paper, write an animal adventure story, using compound and complex sentences.
Check to make sure students have used correct punctuation in their compound and complex sentences.

 Notes for Home: Your child identified and wrote compound and complex sentences. **Home Activity:** Have your child find compound and complex sentences in a book or newspaper. Then have him or her point out the two separate parts of five of the sentences.

668   Grammar: Review of Compound and Complex Sentences

© Scott Foresman 5

Name _____

Is It Real?

Phonics: Word Building

Directions: Sometimes when you add a prefix or a suffix to a word, the sound of the base word doesn't change. For example, when **-ness** is added to **dark**, the result is **darkness**. The sound of **dark** does not change. Other times, when you add a prefix or a suffix to a word, the sound of the base word changes. Add a suffix to each base word to make a new word. Write the new word on the line. Then tell whether the sound of the base word changes.

	Base Word		Suffix		New Word	Change or No Change?
1.	art	+	-ist	=	artist	no change
2.	remark	+	-able	=	remarkable	no change
3.	locate	+	-ion	=	location	change
4.	assign	+	-ment	=	assignment	no change
5.	sign	+	-al	=	signal	change

Directions: Sometimes when you add a prefix or suffix, the stressed syllable changes. Read the word pairs below. Underline the stressed syllable in each word, for example: **imitate** and **imitation**.

6. <u>art</u>ist   ar<u>tis</u>tic
7. re<u>al</u>ity   <u>re</u>alism
8. pre<u>fer</u>   <u>pref</u>erence
9. ex<u>hib</u>it   exhi<u>bi</u>tion
10. repre<u>sent</u>   represen<u>ta</u>tion

11. <u>nor</u>mal   nor<u>mal</u>ity
12. e<u>con</u>omy   eco<u>nom</u>ical
13. <u>his</u>tory   his<u>tor</u>ical
14. <u>proc</u>ess   pro<u>ces</u>sion
15. <u>ed</u>it   e<u>di</u>tion

Directions: Read the paragraph below. Five words with suffixes are underlined. Write the base word for each underlined word on the line.

The art <u>exhibition</u> was not a huge success. It had a strong <u>representation</u> of the modern art world, and the <u>artistic</u> level of the paintings was high. However, most images were too abstract. Viewers expressed a <u>preference</u> for realism, for pictures of the familiar, everyday world.

16. exhibit
17. present
18. art
19. prefer
20. real

Notes for Home: Your child examined how the sounds of words change when a suffix is added, such as *artist* and *artistic*. **Home Activity:** Point out words in a story that have suffixes. Have your child compare each word to its base word to see if the sounds change.

Phonics: Word Building   669

Name _____

Is It Real?

Spelling: Related Words

Pretest Directions: Fold back the page along the dotted line. On the blanks, write the spelling words as they are dictated. When you have finished the test, unfold the page and check your words.

1. column
2. columnist
3. face
4. facial
5. voice
6. vocal
7. limb
8. limber
9. fast
10. fasten
11. wise
12. wisdom
13. cycle
14. bicycle
15. human
16. humane
17. stable
18. stability
19. final
20. finality

1. He writes a newspaper **column**.
2. My brother is a **columnist**.
3. My **face** is sunburned.
4. Watch her **facial** expressions.
5. My sister has a beautiful **voice**.
6. Her **vocal** cords are sore.
7. The tree **limb** fell in the storm.
8. Athletes keep themselves **limber**.
9. He walks too **fast**.
10. Please **fasten** your seat belt.
11. Grandmother is very **wise**.
12. **Wisdom** comes with experience.
13. The machine finished its **cycle**.
14. My **bicycle** needs a new pedal.
15. We are all **human** beings.
16. Your behavior is quite **humane**.
17. The bridge is not **stable**.
18. **Stability** is difficult to achieve.
19. This is your **final** warning.
20. She spoke with great **finality**.

Notes for Home: Your child took a pretest on pairs of words that are related to one another. **Home Activity:** Help your child learn misspelled words before the final test. Your child can underline the parts that are different in each pair and concentrate on those parts.

670   Spelling: Related Words

Name _____

Is It Real?

Spelling: Related Words

Word List

column	voice	fast	cycle	stable
columnist	vocal	fasten	bicycle	stability
face	limb	wise	human	final
facial	limber	wisdom	humane	finality

Directions: Choose the word pairs from the box in which **all** of the letters of one word are contained in the longer related word. Write each word in the correct column. **Order may vary.**

	Shorter Word		Longer Related Word
1.	column	2.	columnist
3.	limb	4.	limber
5.	fast	6.	fasten
7.	cycle	8.	bicycle
9.	human	10.	humane
11.	final	12.	finality

Directions: Choose a pair of words from the box to complete each sentence. Write the words on the lines to the left.

face
facial
13. The skin on my _____ felt better after the _____ treatment.
14.

stable
stability
15. A structure won't be very _____ if its foundation lacks _____.
16.

vocal
voice
17. Before I sing, I do _____ exercises to warm up my _____.
18.

wise
wisdom
19. It's not _____ to question the _____ of your elders.
20.

Notes for Home: Your child spelled pairs of words that have parts that are spelled the same but pronounced differently. **Home Activity:** Say one word from the list and have your child say the related word. Then ask him or her to spell both words.

Spelling: Related Words   671

Name _____

Is It Real?

Spelling: Related Words

Directions: Proofread this flyer. Find six spelling mistakes. Use the proofreading marks to correct each mistake.

≡ Make a capital.
/ Make a small letter.
∧ Add something.
∘゜ Take out something.
⊙ Add a period.
¶ Begin a new paragraph.

Mandrake the Magician

—All New Illusions!

Come one, come all! He's fast, wize, and limber! In his finl show in the area, Mandrake will perform illusions with his face, hands, and voice. He'll have you spinning, so fastn your seatbelts. Show includes the famous "Human Bicycle" trick and the "Tower of Wisedom" illusion. You won't believe your eyes!

Spelling Tip
bicycle
Many people have trouble spelling **bicycle**. Remember this tip: **I** know **why** it's spelled **B-I-C-Y-C-L-E.**

Word List

column	wise
columnist	wisdom
face	cycle
facial	bicycle
voice	human
vocal	humane
limb	stable
limber	stability
fast	final
fasten	finality

Write a Poster
Imagine that you are a master of optical illusions. On a separate sheet of paper, create a poster advertising your latest show. Try to use at least five of your spelling words. **Answers will vary, but each poster should include at least five spelling words.**

Notes for Home: Your child spelled pairs of words that have parts that are spelled the same but pronounced differently. **Home Activity:** Write each word on a slip of paper. Take turns picking a word and writing a sentence for each word.

672   Spelling: Related Words

© Scott Foresman 5

Answers 833

Name _____

Is It Real?

Spelling: Related Words

REVIEW

Word List

column	voice	fast	cycle	stable
columnist	vocal	fasten	bicycle	stability
face	limb	wise	human	final
facial	limber	wisdom	humane	finality

Directions: Choose the word from the box that best matches each clue. Then write the word from the box that is related to it.

Clue		Matching Word		Related Word
coming at the end	1.	**final**	2.	**finality**
scholarly	3.	**wise**	4.	**wisdom**
arm or leg	5.	**limb**	6.	**limber**
solid as a rock	7.	**stable**	8.	**stability**
the front of the head	9.	**face**	10.	**facial**

Directions: Choose the word from the box that best completes each statement. Write the word on the line to the left.

fast	11. *Late* is to *early* as *slow* is to _____.
cycle	12. *Seasonal* is to *season* as *cyclical* is to _____.
humane	13. *Mean* is to *cruel* as *kind* is to _____.
column	14. *Author* is to *book* as *columnist* is to _____.
vocal	15. *Locate* is to *local* as *voice* is to _____.
bicycle	16. *Three* is to *tricycle* as *two* is to _____.
fasten	17. *Shoe* is to *tie* as *seatbelt* is to _____.
human	18. *Monkey* is to *animal* as *person* is to _____.
columnist	19. *Book* is to *author* as *column* is to _____.
voice	20. *Seeing* is to *eyes* as *singing* is to _____.

 Notes for Home: Your child spelled pairs of words that have parts that are spelled the same but pronounced differently. **Home Activity:** Work with your child to think of other pairs of related words, such as *oppose* and *opposite* or *history* and *historical*.

Spelling: Related Words **673**

Name _____

Is It Real?

Technology: Pictures and Captions

Most CD-ROM encyclopedias include **pictures with captions.** If you use an online encyclopedia, it may provide a special search function just for pictures. The welcome screen for an online encyclopedia might look like this:

Welcome to the Encyclopedia

Choose a letter to browse the encyclopedia.
Or, type the key words to search. Use AND between key words.
A B C D E F G H I J K L M N O P Q R S T U V W X Y Z

Search the Encyclopedia for:

_____

Search for:
☐ Articles
☐ Pictures, Flags, Maps, Charts, Sounds
☐ Web Sites
☐ All of the Above

If you need help, click here.

If you want both articles and pictures, then check the first two boxes. If you just want pictures, check only the second box.

Directions: Use the computer screen above to answer these questions.

1. Explain how to get just pictures of optical illusions. **Type the key words "optical AND illusions." Then click on the second box to search for pictures.**

_____

_____

_____

2. Explain how to find both articles and pictures about American oil painters. **Type the key words "American AND oil AND painters." Then click on the first two boxes for articles and pictures.**

_____

_____

_____

674 Research and Study Skills: Technology: Pictures and Captions

---

Name _____

Is It Real?

Online reference sources and web pages often include pictures with captions. You can usually click on either the picture or the caption to get more information. For example, a page about optical illusions might look like the one below. To get more information, you can click on any of the three pictures, any of the three underlined captions, or any of the four underlined links at the bottom of the page.

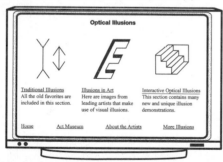

Optical Illusions

Traditional Illusions
All the old favorites are included in this section.

Illusions in Art
Here are images from leading artists that make use of visual illusions.

Interactive Optical Illusions
This section contains many new and unique illusion demonstrations.

Home   Art Museum   About the Artists   More Illusions

Directions: Use the web page above to answer these questions.

3. Where could you click to find a demonstration of an interactive optical illusion? **Click on the picture or the caption Interactive Optical Illusions.**

4. Where could you click to find a biography of the artist Scott Kim? **Click on the link About the Artists at the bottom of the screen.**

5. How are captions in an online encyclopedia similar to captions in a print encyclopedia? How are they different? **Possible answer: Captions in an online encyclopedia and a print encyclopedia both contain useful information. You can click on a caption in an online encyclopedia to find more information on the topic or a related topic.**

 Notes for Home: Your child learned how to access and interpret pictures and captions that might be found on a CD-ROM or web page. **Home Activity:** Use a book, magazine, or newspaper to discuss with your child the information shown in a picture and its caption.

Research and Study Skills: Technology: Pictures and Captions **675**

Name _____

Persuasive Argument Organizer

Directions: Complete the entire organizer. In each box, write a reason that supports the arguing statement. Next to each box, write three sentences that explain the reason. **Persuasion Chart should be filled out completely.**

Title: _____

Arguing Statement: _____

Concluding Statement: _____

Notes for Home: Your child recently completed a persuasive argument organizer. **Home Activity:** Ask your child how he or she chose the topic for the persuasive argument. Have your child give you convincing reasons why he or she chose the topic.

676 Unit 6: Writing Process

Name _____

Elaboration
Adding Persuasive Words

- When you write a persuasive argument, remember to elaborate by **adding persuasive words,** in order to sound more convincing.

Directions: Elaborate each sentence by adding persuasive words. Use the words in parentheses to help you. Here is an example.

Do your homework so you will learn more. (it's important)

It's important to do your homework so you will learn more.

Responses will vary. Reasonable answers are given.

1. Do not eat too many sweets. (it's much healthier)
It's much healthier not to eat too many sweets.

2. Bring a raincoat on your camping trip. (you'll be so glad)
You'll be so glad that you brought a raincoat on your camping trip.

3. Keep your room neat and clean. (you'll feel better)
You'll feel better if you keep your room neat and clean.

4. Save some of your allowance. (you'll be much better off)
You'll be much better off if you save some of your allowance.

5. Be a good sport. (your friends will respect you more)
Your friends will respect you more if you're a good sport.

6. Get your chores done first. (you'll worry less)
You'll worry less if you get your chores done first.

7. Kids need time to relax. (of course)
Of course, kids need time to relax.

8. Fifth graders shouldn't be treated like babies. (it's obvious)
It's obvious that fifth graders shouldn't be treated like babies.

Notes for Home: Your child elaborated sentences by adding persuasive phrases. *Home Activity:* Ask your child to listen for persuasive phrases in commercials, the next time he or she watches television or listens to the radio.

Unit 6: Writing Process **677**

Name _____

Self-Evaluation Guide
Persuasive Argument

Directions: Think about the final draft of your persuasive argument. Then answer each question below. **Accept all reasonable responses.**

	Yes	No	Not sure
1. Did I use the correct form for a five-paragraph essay?			
2. Did I use good reasons that will persuade my reader?			
3. Are my reasons organized in order of importance?			
4. Did I use persuasive words in my argument?			
5. Did I proofread and edit carefully to avoid errors?			

6. What is the best reason you used in your persuasive argument?

_____

_____

_____

7. How would you change this argument if your audience were your classmates? Explain.

_____

_____

_____

Notes for Home: Your child wrote and evaluated a five-paragraph persuasive argument . *Home Activity:* Ask your child to explain one new writing skill that he or she learned during this project.

678 Unit 6: Writing Process

Answers 835